Solar Energy Applications for the Home

A Collection of United States Patents

Kenneth E. Woodward, Ph.D.

Solar Energy Applications for the Home

A Collection of United States Patents

Kenneth E. Woodward, Ph.D.

Information Retrieval Inc.,
1911 Jefferson Davis Highway
Arlington, Va, 22202, USA.

Notice

United States patents give the owner the right to prevent all others from making, using or selling the patented device, method or process.

Nothing contained in this collection of United States patents shall be construed to constitute permission or recommendation to practice any associated invention without a license from the patent owners. Furthermore, neither the publisher nor the author assumes any liability with respect to the use of, or for damages resulting from the use of, any information, apparatus, method or process described in this patent collection. Again, portions of the included patents have been deleted for editorial and publishing purposes.

Copies of described patents may be obtained from the United States Patent and Trademark Office for $0.50 each prepaid.

Address orders to Commissioner of Patents
U. S. Patent & Trademark Office
Washington, D. C. 20231

ISBN 0-917000-02-1 Library of Congress Catalog Card No. 77-084457
Printed in England by Information Printing Ltd. Eynsham

Introduction

The energy crisis of the early 1970's dramatically emphasized the importance of energy in our lives. Modern uses of energy brighten, warm and cool the environment in which we live. It shortens distances, opens job and holiday opportunities never before possible and permits communication over vast distances in seconds. And the future promises that the need for energy will increase not only because more people will be permitted to benefit, but more applications will be found.

The early energy consuming inventions were those which could use available and less expensive energy resources. The steam engine, for example, could have the fire for its boilers provided by coal, wood or other available trackside combustibles. But such sources were hardly practical to power the automobile. Oil had more virtues, but oil was also more expensive. Now the end of the oil era is being forecast shortly. And new energy substitutes must be found.

Solar energy is one obvious substitute. Solar energy has not been developed to the levels of other energy resources because of the general availability of yet more attractive alternative sources. Nevertheless a substantial solar energy technology has developed over the years to a degree that would surprise many. Moreover, this technology has achieved relatively high definition through patents.

This book contains a majority of United States patents which have issued through the middle 1970's relating to home applications for solar energy. The early publishing date for many of these patents illustrates that inventors have not been oblivious to the potential of solar energy as an energy source. And the number of published patents emphasizes the general level of development. But the increasing frequency and sophistication of patents issuing in recent periods suggests the rising pressure being applied to the development of this energy resource to bring it to a point of every day usefulness. One can not now be called visionary who someday anticipates large numbers of homes heated and cooled by solar energy. The day of solar energy is just now beginning to dawn.

Foreword

This book consists entirely of United States Patents relating to solar energy inventions for home applications. These have been logically arranged according to basic divisions visible in the body of the technology and cover a period of 98 years. The first patent included was issued in 1877, emphasizing the fact that attempts to utilize the enormous amounts of available solar energy are not unique to recent energy crises.

In publishing this book it was believed that several useful purposes would be served. First, a comprehensive, foundational assessment of the existing technology would be achieved utilizing fundamental building blocks - patents. Second, it would serve as a source of ideas for those interested in solar energy inventions. Hopefully, its contents will not discourage the fledgling inventor who might find his invention patented years ago. And third, it would introduce the uninitiated to an invaluable and largely unexplored technical resource — patent literature.

It should be recognized that patents provide the most immediate published definition of an emerging technology. This results from the urgency to publish to satisfy legal requirements and to capitalize on the novelty of invention. In spite of this rush to patent, the information contained in patents is unusually accurate since disclosures are subject to the immediate scrutiny of accomplished legal and technical minds and the continuing challenge of those who would invalidate later.

Patents, too, contain a degree of detail offered by no other kind of technical literature. For example, technical books and journals do not laboriously identify and define structure and function of some machine or circuit. Even for the finely trained technical mind it would make boring reading. But such detail is occasionally essential. And these occasions are in view in preparing this book.

Patents included have been modified by eliminating claims, caveats and references to other solar energy patents and applications not included in this book. Deleted material in the patents has been indicated by asterisks. No attempt has been made to analyze or summarize the information contained in the patents included or to judge their technical merits. To do so would negate the purpose of the book. Each patent is a monument to the creativity of its inventor, and this book will not destroy that.

Publisher's note

In many cases the original copies of patent extracts included in this book are old library copies, much thumbed and somewhat dog-eared. In order to maintain legibility whilst still preserving the character of the original print some paragraphs have been re-set in the style of the original, but others where the sense is not obscured have been reproduced photographically.

Contents

Chapter 1

Solar Energy Collectors - Fluid

continued

Chapter 2

Solar Energy Collectors - Air

continued

Chapter 3

Solar Collectors with Heat Storage/Exchange Units

Chapter 4

House Heating Systems

continued

Chapter 5

House Cooling Systems -

Chapter 6

House Heating and Cooling Systems

continued

Chapter 7

Swimming Pool Heaters

Chapter 8

Solar Activated Dehumidifier

U.S. Patent Index

Inventor Index

Chapter 1

Solar Energy Collectors – Fluid

June 7, 1966 H. E. THOMASON 3,254,643

SOLAR HEAT APPARATUS

*

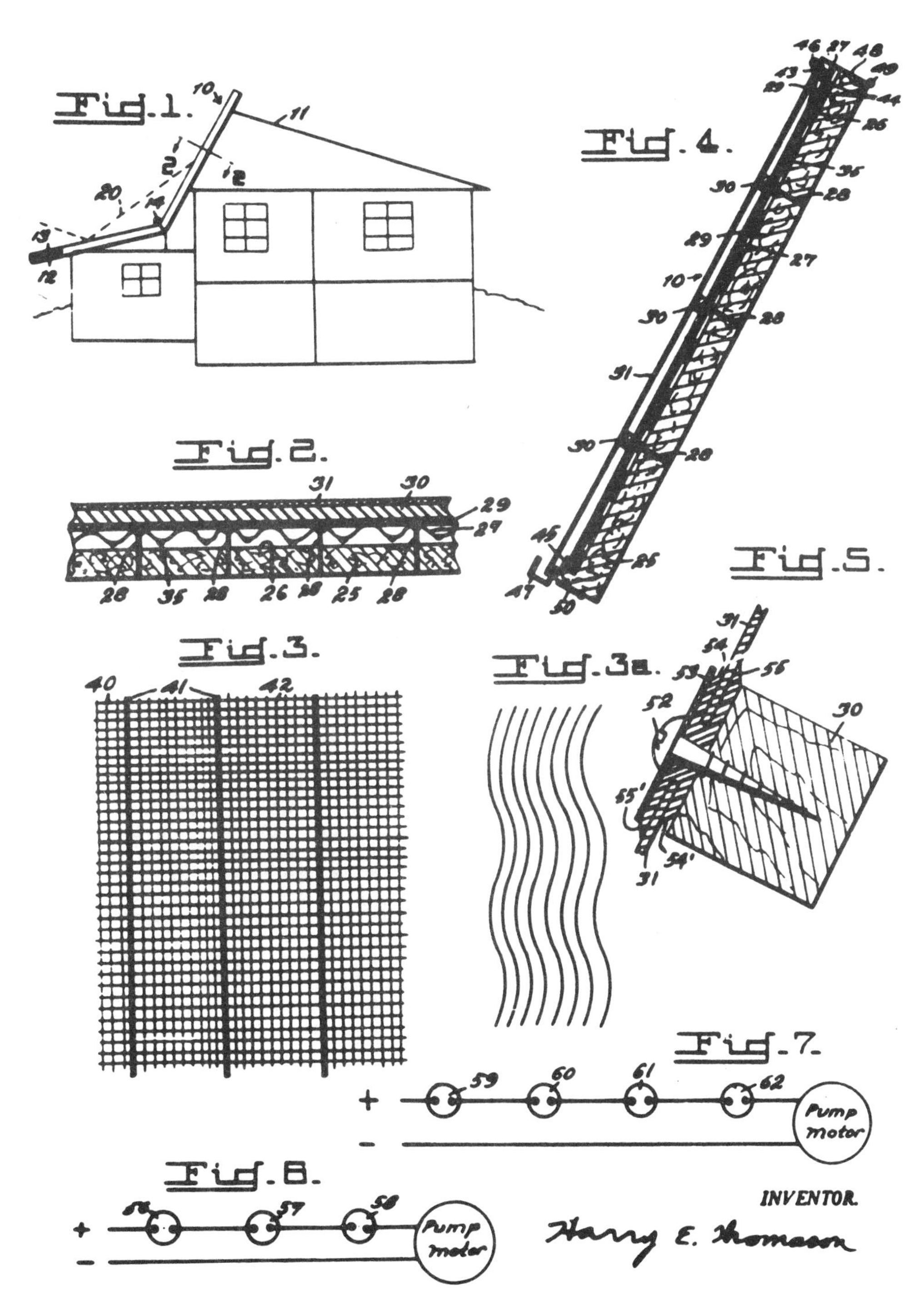

INVENTOR.

Harry E. Thomason

3,254,643
SOLAR HEAT APPARATUS
Harry E. Thomason, 7354 Walker Mill Road SE.,
Washington, D.C.

*

The present invention relates to solar heat collectors for converting incoming solar rays into heat and for trapping such heat for various purposes and uses. Although not limited to such uses, the present invention is usable to heat gases or liquids, which in turn can be used for space heating, domestic water heating, heating of swimming pools, heating of greenhouses, and for many other purposes.

Referring more particularly to the drawing:

FIG. 1 is an end elevation of a building showing an example of a construction embodying the present invention.

FIG. 2 is a view along line 2—2 of FIG. 1 illustrating one form of heat collector.

FIG. 3 is a plan view of a portion of another form of the heat collector.

FIG. 3a is a plan view of another modification.

FIG. 4 is a detailed side view of the collector of FIG. 1 showing other details of the invention.

FIG. 5 is a view through a spacer member illustrating a preferred construction for securing the upper transparency thereto.

FIG. 6 is a diagram of a circuit for operating the pump motor to circulate a fluid through the collector.

FIG. 7 is a diagram of a circuit for operating the pump motor to circulate liquid over the heat dissipator for summertime use.

As an example of how and where the present invention may be used, it has been illustrated in FIG. 1 in conjunction with a building such as a split level home, or a home with a garage attached thereto. The solar heat trap is illustrated at 10 with a roof section 11.

The section of roof at 12 has a reflective cover section at 13 which is pivoted at 14. During the colder months the reflective cover is in its lowermost position as illustrated. Sunshine falling on this area is reflected toward the heat collector by the upper surface of reflector 13 as illustrated at 20. Thus, the intensity of available solar energy on collector 10 is greatly increased by use of relatively inexpensive cover 13, and more energy is available per unit of area of heat collector.

In some sections of the world severe hailstorms are a menace to a transparency such as glass which may be used on the heat collector. Also, the summertime heat build-up in a heat collector is damaging to the materials and shortens the life of the materials. In addition, even though the collector insulation is good, it is not perfect and some of the heat gets through into the attic or other portions of the home. Reflective cover 13 is adapted to be positioned over collector 10 when desired, such as by swinging it about pivot 14. Said cover may be used during hot weather when hailstorms occur, or may be used during hurricanes or during blizzard conditions in the event that sheer weight of snow and ice would tend to damage the collector. However, the collector of the present invention is readily cleared of snow under most conditions, as will be explained later. During the hot months cover 13 protects against hail damage, and also reflects unwanted heat away from the collector by the reflective surface on the side of the reflector opposite that used during the colder months to help prolong the life of collector material and to help keep the home cooler.

Generally it is desirable to have some heat collection, even during the summer, for domestic water heating and such. Thus, if desired, the cover 13 may be designed not to cover the entire collector and to thereby leave part of it exposed for supplying the smaller heat load. Further, although the deflective cover 13 is shown as covering a garage or part of the home, obviously such reflective unit may itself be merely a wintertime carport roof or may be added above a carport roof or other. Although illustrated as hinged to the structure at 14, it is obvious that the protective reflector may be attached otherwise, or may be detachably secured to be stored away when not needed. Means to hold the cover 13 in its raised or lowered position may be provided if desired.

As to the heat collector construction illustrated in FIG. 2, such collector comprises insulation 25 and a material such as heat conductive corrugated sheet metal 27. Preferably a vapor or liquid barrier is employed at 26, and supports 28 maintain the sheet 27 spaced above barrier 26. One or more transparencies are employed, for example, a plastic transparency at 29 and a glass-like transparency 31 spaced thereabove by spacers 30.

In the modification of FIG. 2 a fluid is circulated below the corrugated sheet 27. If the fluid is air, it is preferably introduced at the bottom and brought out at the top. If the fluid to be heated is a liquid such as water, it is introduced near the top of the collector. In FIG. 4, one method for getting the liquid onto the undersides of the valleys is illustrated. A distributor manifold 43 is used to introduce a small stream of liquid into each valley. Just below the manifold a hole is placed in each valley as at 44 so that the liquid may run through the hole to the underside of the valley and will cling to the lower side of the valley as at 35 and will run down the incline. The small streams of hot water are collected in collector manifold 45 and are returned to a place of storage or use.

It is obvious that other apparatus may be used to get the liquid onto the undersides of the valleys such as by spraying the liquid thereagainst, by using an individual tube to project a small stream onto each valley or by other expedients.

Instead of using corrugated heat collecting metal as in FIG. 2, it has been found that a mesh-like material as illustrated in FIG. 3 yields good results. Such mesh may, for example, be screen wire, plastic or other material, preferably treated to make it black. A small stream of liquid to be heated is introduced at spaced intervals adjacent the upper edge of the mesh. Although ordinary screen wire is reasonably satisfactory, it has been found that the liquid sometimes ends to skew sidewise as it travels down the mesh. The mesh 40 is preferably provided at 41, 42 with means to prevent such side skewing. This preventive means may take any one of many forms. As examples, enlarged strands may be used at 41 which will tend to prevent crossover of the liquid while adding strength to the mesh if woven therein, or which will provide support for the mesh if stretced therebeneath. Or, a material with a high degree of molecular attraction for the liquid may be used at 42 so that the liquid tends to "wet" areas 42 thoroughly but does not tend to cross over the area or strand 41. Alternatively, a liquid repellent material may be at 41 so that the liquid will not readily cross thereover. Or, two or more of these expedients may be used jointly.

Liquid flowing down the mesh acts as a good heat collecting medium. However, a gas such as air may be passed through the collector whereby heat transfer to the gas is good due to the large surface contact between the mesh and gas as it flows under and over and through the mesh.

The mesh-like material may be physically separated from the insulation and a vapor-liquid barrier such as at 26 in FIG. 2 may be interposed between the insulation and the mesh. Certain advantages can be obtained by placing the mesh in contact with the vapor-liquid barrier, or in close proximity thereto, especially when the fluid to be heated is liquid. In such construction, the barrier prevents the liquid from dripping from the mesh, even if the heat collector is set at a more-or-less horizontal incline.

Examples of materials usable in such construction are; screen wire mesh, which is dark itself or is treated to make it black to absorb solar heat, whereas the barrier therebeneath may be made of material such as plastic, sheet metal, or such. If the mesh is metallic or heat conducting, it will readily transfer the heat to the liquid or gas flowing thereover or therethrough. If the mesh is not highly conductive of heat, a good rate of heat transfer the fluid will still be achieved due to the tremendous areas of contact between the fluid and the solar heated mesh. If the barrier itself is dark and heat absorbing it will tend to be heated when some of the sun rays get through the mesh and will tend to intensify the heat in the collector, and will also tend to heat any gas or liquid coming in contact therewith. On the other hand, if the barrier is reflective it will tend to "bounce" heat rays back against the mesh from beneath when the sun is substantially at right angles to the collector at which time some of the rays get through the mesh. Thus the mesh is bombarded from above by direct solar rays and is bombarded from beneath by reflected or secondary rays. Of course when the sun is many degrees past, or ahead of, a position at right angles to the collector then the strands of the mesh will intercept substantially all sun rays directly. Also, as the seasons change and the sun is higher or lower in the sky the mesh will intercept most of the rays directly when the rays do not strike the collector at right angles thereto.

The transparent material above the heat collector mesh may be in contact or substantially in contact with the mesh, or may be spaced thereabove if desired. It is apparent that the mesh material may be sandwiched between the transparency 29 and the barrier 26 and that, if the spacing is not great, the mesh will tend to spread the small streams of liquid entering the collector into a sheet of liquid of thin dimensions so as to have a maximum of exposure of the liquid to solar rays plus a maximum of exposure of the liquid to the heat collecting mesh. As FIG. 3a illustrates the blackened heat absorbing strands may take forms other than mesh-like illustrated in FIG. 3. If the strands are zig-zagged for example there will be a retardation of fluid flow through the collector, whether liquid or gas, plus more positive contact between the fluid and strands as the fluid flows a tortious path through the collector. In this modification the strands are preferably either in contact with the transparency thereabove and the barrier therebeneath, or are in close proximity thereto. As a practical manner of manufacture the strands may be secured to either the transparency, or to the barrier, or to both. Of course liquid repellent strands, or spaced enlarged strands, or liquid attracting strands may be used if desired, as taught in relation to FIG. 3. If desired, the fluid itself may be black to enhance heat collection inasmuch as much of the solar rays will be converted directly into heat within the sheet of liquid itself. Efficiency of the heat collectors described is high whether solar energy comes in by direct rays or by reflected and diffused sky radiation.

FIG. 4 illustrates a heat collector having a second distributor manifold at 46 and a second collector trough at 47. For wintertime use, water may be introduced onto the top of transparency 31 to dislodge or wash snow or ice from the collector in the event it does not skid off due to gravity. Also, trough 47 may be connected with the liquid reservoir if desired to provide makeup water from rain as needed. During the sumertime, water is circulated over the top of transparency 31 at night to give up its heat to the atmosphere due to radiation, evaporation, and cooling by the cool night air.

During the summertime the daytime temperatures inside the collector rise to a high degree, especially if apparatus such as that at 13 in FIG. 1 is not used. To permit such heat to escape more readily, damper 48 may be hinged at 49 to be opened and let the hot air out at the top. A damper may be provided at 50 to let cool air in at the bottom. Thus, overheating may be minimized or avodied by natural air circulation.

In FIG. 5 a preferred means for fastening the outer transparency 31 to spacer 30 is illustrated. Such means comprises screws 52, washers 53 and generally H-shaped gasket 54. Said gasket is not only H-shaped to secure two transparencies 31 therein, but also preferably has an upwardly projecting lip 55 to assure that no rain can get up around projection 55 even if it could get down between transparency 31 and gasket 54. The lower edge of the gasket is preferably formed somewat reversely of the upper edge with a downwardly projecting lip 55' lower than lip 54'. Thus, the same type of gasket may be used between the vertical joints of the transparencies and such may project upwardly to meet shortened lip 54' whereby rainwater will be diverted over the joint by overhanging lip 55'.

FIG. 6 illustrates a circuit for operating the pump motor for the solar heat collector and thereby controlling flow of fluid through the collector whether it be liquid or gas. Such circuit includes a photoelectric cell or "electric eye" 56 to determine whether the weather is sunny or cloudy, a time switch 57 which will cut on daily from say 8:30 to 4:00 and a temperature switch 58, which is preferably located where the heat is stored and which will cut off when the storage temperature reaches a desired level. These switches are in series. Thus, if the sun comes up on a cold morning, bright enough to actuate the electric eye, but is not yet intense enough to yield useful heating, the electric eye switch turns on but the time switch keeps the circulating pump cut off until say 8:30 when solar energy received is intense enough to be useful. At this pre-selected time the time switch will cut on and if the level of heat in the storage apparatus is low and needs to be increased, the temperature switch will be closed and the pump will operate to circulate fluid through the collector to collect solar heat. Then, suppose it becomes cloudy, the electric eye cuts the pump off and the gas or liquid heat transfer medium is no longer circulated through the collector. Suppose the sun comes back out, and stays out, the electric eye switch cuts back on and the pump operates until the time switch cuts off at say 4:00, or until the storage temperature level is as high as desired, at which time the temperature responsive switch cuts off. In any event, as soon as the collector pump is cut off the liquid in the system, if liquid is used, drains from the collector imediately and cannot freeze up and burst the collector.

During some days clouds and sunshine come intermittently and will start and stop the pump unnecessarily frequently. In such instance, a time delay device may be used to prevent immediate cut on or cut off when the "electric eye" 56 is actuated. While it is possible to substitute a reverse acting thermostatic switch for the electric eye, to turn the pump motor on when solar heat is available and to turn it off when no heat is available, the electric eye has certain advantages.

FIG. 7 illustrates a circuit and switches preferred for operating the summertime cooling apparatus to supply liquid to distributor manifold 46. Such circuit includes a "humidostat" switch 59, a time switch 60 and a temperature responsive switch 61. Time switch 60 will turn on nightly during the hot summer from say 10:00 p.m. to 6.00 a.m. If the night is fairly dry then "humidostat" 59 will be closed and the liquid will be circulated through manifold 46, over transparency 31, to collector trough 47 and back to the "cold" storage apparatus. Cooling takes place due to evaporation and radiation as the fluid flows over transparency 31. However, if the humidity is extremely high so that evaporative cooling is only nominal, the "humidostat" 59 will prevent the apparatus from operating. Temperature responsive switch 61 may be used to sense outside temperatures so that the dissipator will not come on early during an extremely hot night when heat dissipation may be low. However, if desired, both the "humidostat" 59 and the outdoor temperature sensing switch 61 may be omitted so that the heat dissipator will operate every summer night from say 10:00 p.m. to 6:00 a.m. if the "cold" storage apparatus needs chilling. If desired, a temperature responsive switch 62 may be provided to sense the "cold" storage apparatus temperature. If this temperature is low enough, switch 62 will cut out so that the pump will not operate again until further cooling is needed. *

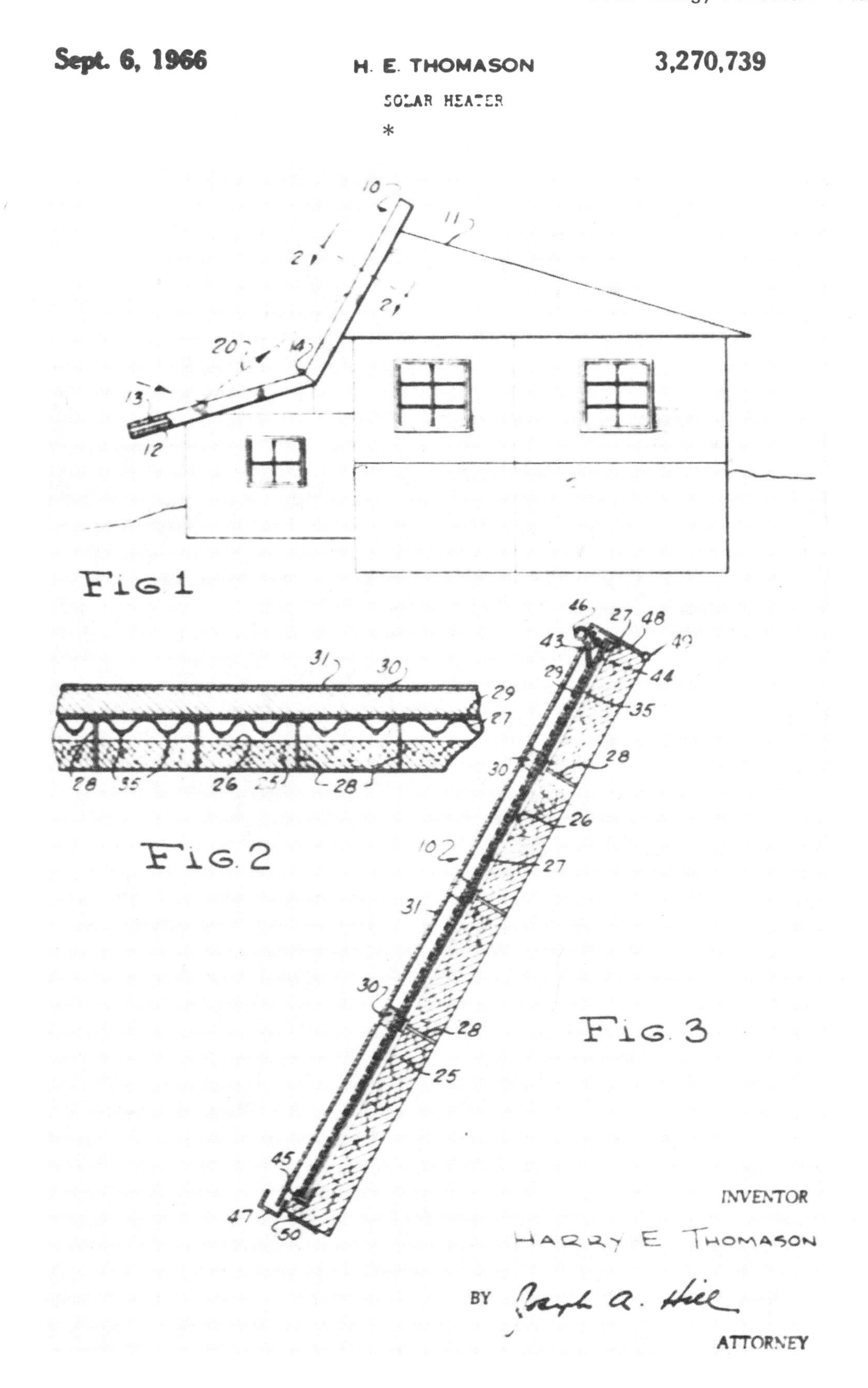
Sept. 6, 1966
H. E. THOMASON
3,270,739
SOLAR HEATER
Fig 1
Fig 2
Fig 3
INVENTOR
HARRY E THOMASON
BY
ATTORNEY

3,270,739
SOLAR HEATER
Harry E. Thomason, District Heights, Md.
(7354 Walker Mill Road SE., Washington, D.C. 20027)

*

The invention described herein may be manufactured and used by or for the Government for governmental purposes without the payment to me of any royalty thereon. *

The invention relates to an open-flow solar heat collector comprising an insulating base, an irregularly shaped, solar energy absorbing metal heat collecting sheet which is positioned above the base, and a transparent or translucent cover above the collecting sheet. This type collector is highly efficient in collecting solar energy and is very simple and inexpensive to construct. The collector unit is described more fully in my above-mentioned applications. The present invention is an improvement of this type collector.

In recent years much progress has been reported by Harry Tabor and others in the use of "selective" surfaces for solar heat collector sheets which receive solar energy and convert a high percentage of it into heat. As the temperature of the sheet rises, to temperatures of 150–200° F. for example, a selective surface will re-radiate much less heat than a typical blackened sheet (black body). Thus, the net heat gain is considerably higher for a collector sheet with a selective surface than for a sheet with a black surface.

To obtain better efficiency over a long period of time the selective surface should be kept free of corrosion and dirt. One way of minimizing corrosion on the outer surface exposed to incoming solar radiations is to introduce the heat transfer liquid in small streams near the upper edge of the inner surface of the inclined collector sheet. The liquid then clings to the inner surface (underside) of the sheet by molecular attraction as it gravitates down the sheet. The outer surface exposed to solar radiations thus remains dry and is less subject to corrosion. Further, if a black coating is applied to the outer surface of a collector sheet and collecting fluid is passed over the outer surface of the sheet, the coating reduces heat transfer from the sheet to the collecting fluid. If the fluid flows along the inner surface of the collector sheet, however, the fluid is in direct contact with the metal of the collector sheet and, consequently, heat is more easily transferred to the fluid.

An object of this invention is to provide a selective surface solar heat collecting sheet so constructed that the heat collecting fluid gravitates along the inner surface of the sheet, leaving the outer, selective surface dry and free from fluid corrosion and dirt accumulation.

Another object is to provide a selective surface heat collecting sheet so constructed that the heat collecting fluid gravitates along the inner surface of the sheet in direct contact with the metal of the sheet, thereby providing a better heat transfer between sheet and fluid than would be obtained if the fluid flowed along the selective outer surface.

The collector sheet may be corrugated, as illustrated in FIG. 2, or it may be V-crimped, embossed, or otherwise configured, as illustrated in Patent No. 3,145,707, for example.

FIG. 1 is an end elevation of a building showing an example of a construction embodying this invention.

FIG. 2 is a lateral cross sectional view taken along line 2—2 of FIG. 1.

FIG. 3 is a longitudinal center cross sectional view of the heat collector shown in FIG. 2.

Referring to FIG. 1, the solar heat trap is illustrated at **10** with a roof section **11**. The section of roof at **12** can have a reflective cover at **13**, pivoted at **14**, which can be lowered during colder months to reflect sunshine toward the collector as illustrated at **20**.

Referring to FIG. 2, the heat collector comprises an insulating material **25** and a heat conductive material such as corrugated sheet metal **27**. Preferably a vapor or liquid barrier is employed at **26**, and supports **28** maintain sheet **27** spaced above barrier **26**. One or more transparencies are employed, for example, a plastic transparency **29** and a glass-like transparency **31** spaced above sheet **29** by spacers **30**.

In the construction of FIG. 2 a fluid is circulated below the corrugated sheet **27**. If the fluid is air, it is preferably introduced at the bottom and brought out at the top. If the fluid to be heated is a liquid such as water, it is introduced near the top of the collector. In FIG. 3, one method for getting the liquid onto the undersides of the valleys of sheet **27** is illustrated. A distributor manifold **43** is used to introduce a small stream of liquid into each valley. Just below the manifold, a hole is placed in each valley as at **44** so that the liquid may run through the hole to the underside of the valley where it will cling to the lower side of the valley as at **35** and will run down the incline. The small streams of heated water are collected in collector manifold **45** and are returned to a place of storage or use.

It is obvious that other apparatus may be used to get the liquid onto the undersides of the valleys such as by spraying the liquid thereagainst, by using an individual tube to project a small stream onto each valley, or by other expedients.

A second distributor manifold can be added at **46** and a second collector trough at **47**. In winter, water may be flushed along transparency **31** to dislodge snow or ice from the collector. Also, trough **47** may be connected with the liquid reservoir of the heating system, if desired, to provide makeup water from rain. In summer, water can be circulated along transparency **31** at night to give up heat to the atmosphere. Damper **48**, hinged at **49** may be opened to let hot air escape. Damper **50** can be used to let cool air into the collector. *

Feb. 20, 1968 H. E. THOMASON **3,369,539**

SOLAR HEAT TRAP

*

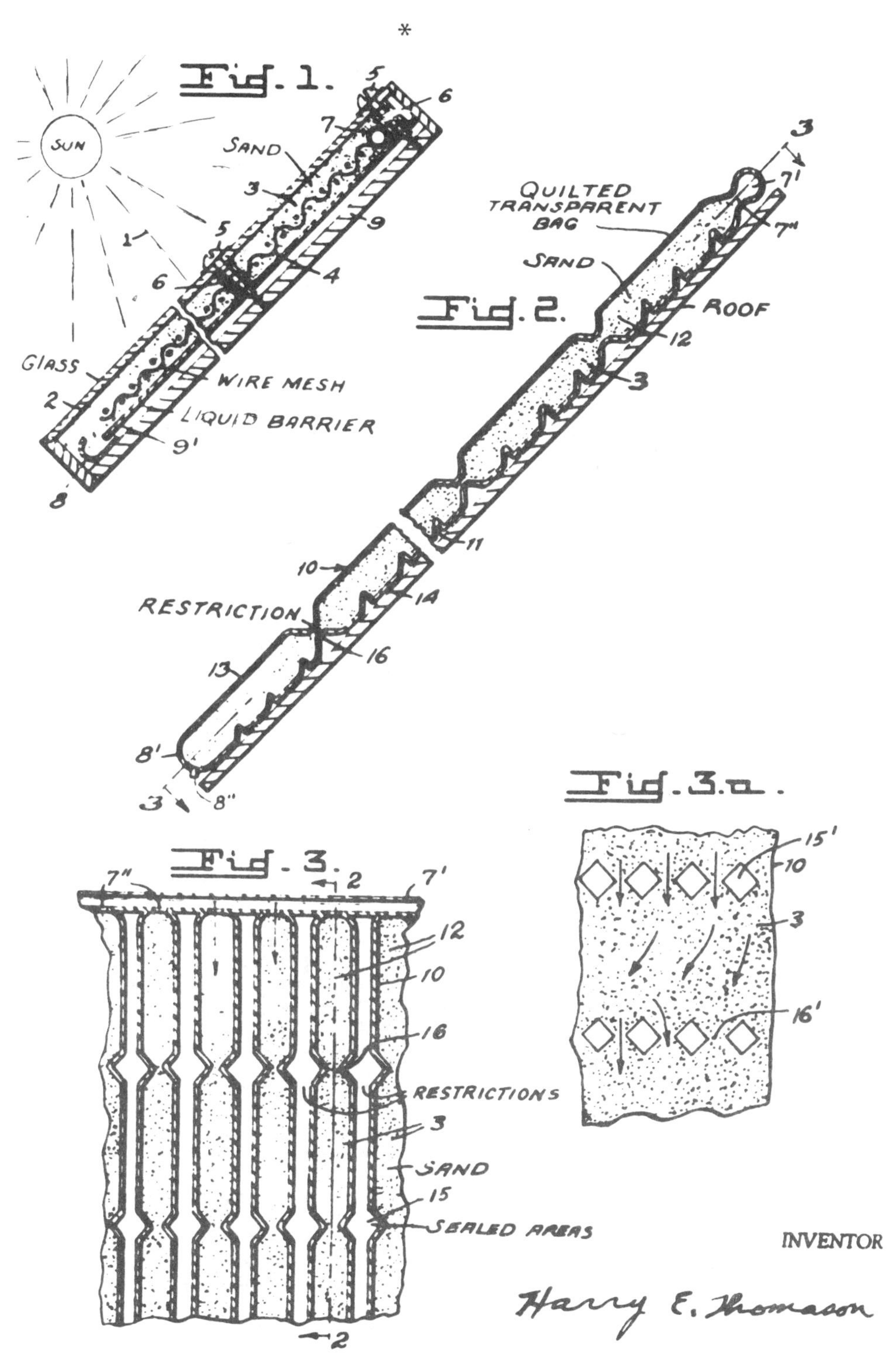

INVENTOR

Harry E. Thomason

3,369,539
SOLAR HEAT TRAP

Harry E. Thomason, District Heights, Md.
(6802 Walker Mill Road SE., Washington, D.C. 20027)

*

The present invention relates to an improved solar heat collector which is simple and low cost in construction, highly efficient in operation and which has a long life.

In the drawing:

FIG. 1 is a cross section through one form of the invention.

FIG. 2 is a cross section through a quilted solar heat collecting "bag" along line 2—2 of FIG. 3.

FIG. 3 is a view along line 3—3 of FIG. 2.

FIG. 3A is a view of a modified pattern of quilting.

In this invention solar rays 1 enter the solar heat trap or collector through substantially transparent or translucent cover transparency 2 and strike a heat collecting layer of bits of material, or dark sand or similar granular material 3. Other material such as bluestone chips may be used if desired. Either may be used with or without asphalt, coal tar or similar blackening binder.

The granular material, with or without the binder, has a tendency to slide or creep and flow toward the bottom of the collector if the incline is steep, for example, 30–90° commonly used for solar house heat collectors. This problem can be overcome by using mesh or such, as that illustrated at 4, to prevent sliding or creeping of the material. Water may be flowed through the trap to remove heat. If the mesh is wire, or other heat conducting material, it aids in transferring heat to the water from the heat collecting material.

If the incline of the collector is not too steep the wire mesh 4 is sufficient to prevent sliding or creeping. If the incline is very steep then the transparent member 2 itself together with securing screws 5 and spacer members 6, e.g. tubular bars, rectangular in cross-section, may be used to assist in reducing sliding and creeping. Liquid to be heated may be brought in at 7 and heated liquid may drain off through trough 8 and an outlet pipe (not shown) similar to 8" in FIG. 2. Screws, bolts or such at 5 may be anchored to base 9, which may be insulating in nature.

In the modification of FIG. 2 the invention is reduced to a very simple form. Dark sand 3 is placed in a transparent bag 10. Liquid is introduced at 7' to flow through passages 7" down the incline to bottom 8' and out at 8". For some uses this apparatus can be laid out on a common roof of a building and the water warmed thereby piped to a point of use or storage, for swimming pool, or house, or domestic water heating, and so on. Even highly chlorinated swimming pool water does not attack the heat absorbing sand or the bag material. And, the "sand bag" secures itself to the roof without expensive anchoring means.

For collecting heat when the sun is high in the sky the heat collector operates efficiently even when placed on a near-level roof with no incline or only a slight incline. For such usage heavy dark granular material tends to remain in place, especially when the rate of liquid flow through the collector is moderate. If the collector is to be operated on a steeper incline, or with a high rate of liquid flow, means must be provided to keep the granular material from washing down to the lower edge of the bag. This may be accomplished by use of one or more of the following. As illustrated at 11, the inner surface of the bag may be roughened, or corrugated or serrated, somewhat at right angles to the direction of flow of the liquid therethrough. Mesh 4, as illustrated in FIG. 1, may be used. The bag may be quilted to provide a large number of individual smaller compartments or cells, each having dark granular or bits of material therein, with each cell having an inlet to admit liquid to be heated and an outlet for the heated liquid.

Two quilted patterns are illustrated in FIGS. 2, 3 and 3A. Liquid flow channels or cells 12 are formed by securing the top substantially transparent or translucent layer of material 13 to the bottom layer of material 14 at areas 15. Restricted areas 16 in channels or cells 12 permit liquid to flow therethrough but restrict flow, sliding or creeping of granular material 3. The sealed areas 15 also resist pressure of granular material 3 and prevent separation of materials 13 and 14.

FIG. 3A illustrates a second of the many possible patterns of quilting the bag and securing top material 13 to bottom material 14. Securing means 15' leave restricted passages 16' for retention of granular material 3 but permit flow of liquid past the securing means.

Although FIGS. 2, 3 and 3A are described hereinabove as illustrating a quilted bag heat collector, with or without wire mesh 4, the collector "bag" need not necessarily be made of one material only. As examples, the upper transparency 13 may be substantially clear plastic sealed, at areas 15 or 15', to opaque, or black or reflectively coated plastic 14. Or, material 14 may be a metallic sheet, or some other watertight material. Or, transparent material 13 may be rigid, such as sheet plastic or glass, with material 14 secured thereto at areas 15 or 15' and leaving passageways or cells as at 12 in FIGS. 2 and 3. Other variations may be made to simplify and facilitate manufacture, packaging, shipping, storage and so on.

The bag-type solar heat collector and sand-like material are fast and easy to install, on existing roofs for example, and resist deterioration. If desired, insulation may be provided beneath the bag, e.g., foam insulation or insulation beneath the roof. Also, another transparency may be provided above the bag if desired.

This type of trickle-flow collector avoids pressure build-up inside the apparatus as would occur in a closed collector. As an example, a closed collector, filled with water under static conditions, with a vertical distance of fifteen feet between the bottom and the water level at the top, would have a pressure of approximately one thousand pounds per square foot at the bottom, tending to burst the collector transparency, seals, and so on. No such bursting pressure occurs in the present apparatus.

However, it would be possible to produce liquid-tight apparatus and bring the liquid in at the bottom, to flow to the top as it is heated.

It would be possible to use the present invention where a gas, such as air, is heated, instead of a liquid. The gas to be heated would preferably be brought in near the bottom and the heated gas would be taken out near the top to take advantage of the natural tendency of the heated gas to rise.

This apparatus is exceptionally simple and low cost to manufacture. The granular material may be dark sand, for example, which has advantages such as low cost, permanency and resistance to rusting, corrosion or other deterioration. There is no chemical reaction between sand and the common transparent materials such as plastic films, glass, and so on. There is no chemical reaction between sand and most known heat transfer liquids or gases. Dark sand is a good collector of heat and transfers heat readily to liquid flowing therethrough. Sand is heavy in weight which, in many cases, avoids the necessity of using any other anchoring means to secure the collector to a roof or other flat or inclined support. The plumbing connections to the collector apparatus are exceptionally simple and low-cost to make because no pressure fittings or connections are necessary. Even the perforated pipe at the top and the collector gutter trough at the bottom may be dispensed with by forming the material 13, 14 to serve these functions as at 7', 8'

The invention can be mass produced at very low cost by various techniques. As exemplary material 14 may be drawn from a roll while a hopper feeds thin parallel stripes of sand onto the upper surface. Simultaneously material 13 is drawn from a roll and is continuously sealed or attached to material 14 as at 15 or 15' (If desired, wire mesh may be drawn from a third roll, sandwiched between 13 and 14, and attached to either or both, or neither, as desired.) The lower end of 13, 14 is closed except for one or more outlet holes 8''. The upper end of 13, 14 is sealed to form header tube 7' with restricted outlets 7''. An inlet pipe, not shown, is connected to header tube 7'. *

Aug. 25, 1964 H. E. THOMASON **3,145,707**

SOLAR HEAT COLLECTOR

*

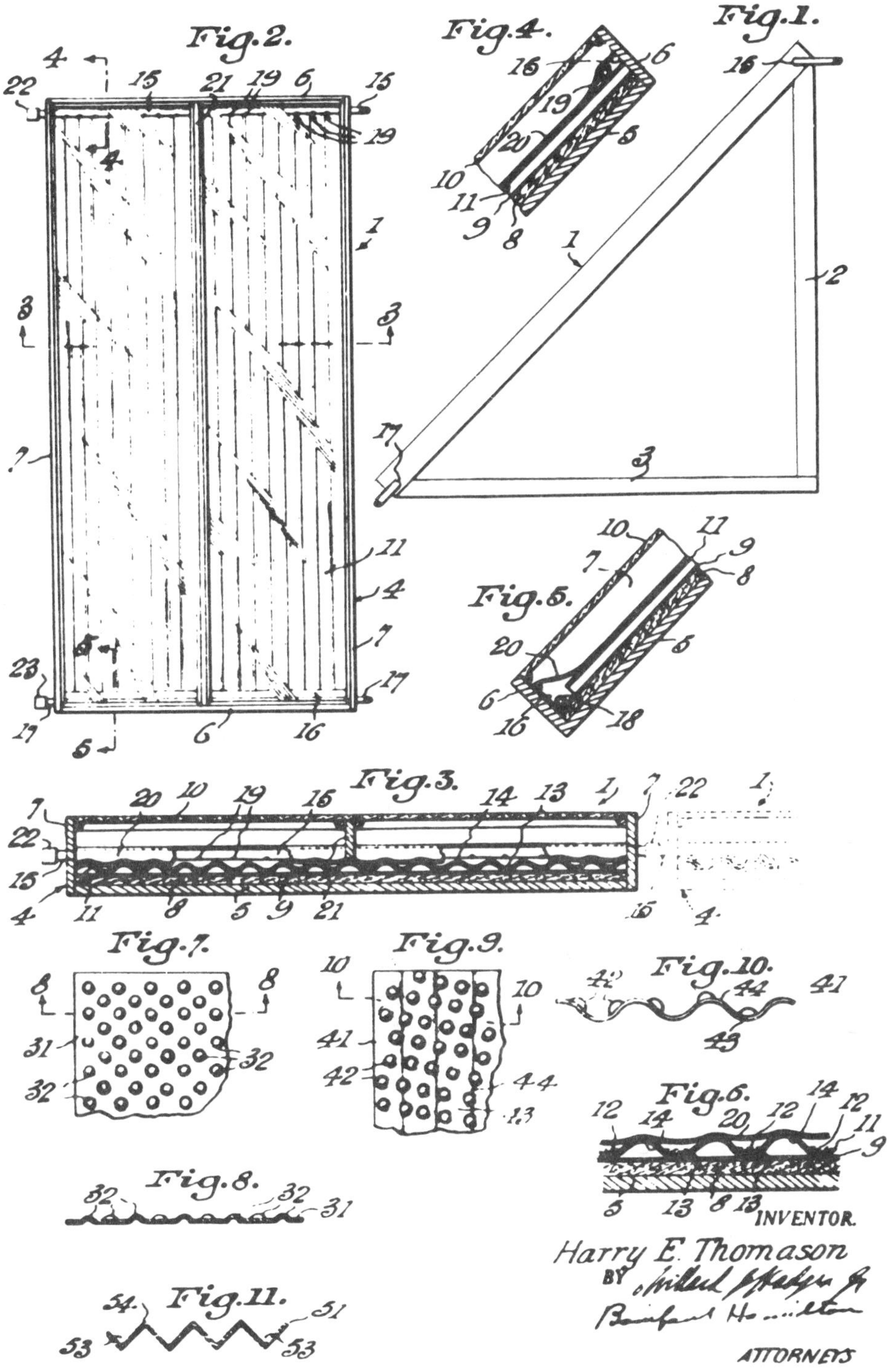

Fig. 2. Fig. 4. Fig. 1. Fig. 5. Fig. 3. Fig. 7. Fig. 9. Fig. 10. Fig. 6. Fig. 8. Fig. 11.

INVENTOR.

Harry E. Thomason

BY

ATTORNEYS

3,145,707
SOLAR HEAT COLLECTOR
Harry E. Thomason, 6911 Walker Mill Road SE., Washington 27, D.C.
(Granted under Title 35, U.S. Code (1952), sec. 266)
*

The invention described herein may be manufactured and used by or for the Government for governmental purposes without the payment of any royalty.

The present invention relates to improvements in solar heat collectors, and particularly the type that may be used both for collecting heat from solar radiation and for dissipating heat when not receiving solar heat, such as at night, or by turning the heat collector (dissipator) away from the sun.

Among the various known heat collectors are structures employing a black insulating base, a glass cover spaced an inch or so thereabove, and black fluid-carrying piping between the glass and the black base, which are used effectively in southern areas of the United States for heating water. These devices are sometimes constructed with the fluid-carrying piping zig-zagging in convolutions in a plane requiring many flow-restricting elbows and many lineal feet of piping per hundred square feet of collector surface, and resulting in very expensive construction as a result of both the cost of the piping and the labor cost. Inefficiencies also result from excessive spacing of the convolutions which permits radiation of much of the solar heat back to the atmosphere. Alternatively, these devices are sometimes constructed in saidwich fashion with the heat collecting fluid running between spaced metal sheets which may be parallel or crimped in imitation of tubing, but still require excessive amounts of copper and labor and still have a high ratio of fluid to heat absorbing metal.

Other existing solar heaters employ light and heat condensing lenses or reflectors to concentrate and localize the sun's light and heat, but such lenses or reflectors are extremely expensive, especially when it is desired to collect solar heat from an area of several hundreds of square feet.

A further type of existing solar heater has the heat conducting fluid contained directly between the insulated base and the transparent cover, or between a black metal heat collector and the transparent cover, in such a way that the transparent cover also constitutes one wall to a fluid container. This construction is not only expensive but lends itself readily to trouble because a broken or loose transparent cover, usually glass, permits the heat conducting fluid to be leaked or spilled, rendering the device inoperative. Therefore, this type device requires expensive and troublesome liquid sealing for the base, sides, and edges, and for the transparent top. Since areas of hundreds of square inches are involved, the glass used must be sufficiently thick and free of flaws and the glass retaining means must be sufficiently strong to withstand contained pressures of two to ten pounds per square inch over fairly large panes.

Many other types of solar heating devices are known, but with limitations and disadvantages so as to render them impractical except for very limited and specialized applications. Most of the solar heaters are very ineffective and practically worthless for dissipating heat, and are therefore not reversible in operation.

The present invention, directed to obviating many of the limitations of the solar heaters described, simplifies and lowers the cost of construction, raises efficiency and is substantially trouble-free in use and operation. Additionally, the present device is readily adaptable to use as a heat-dissipating device to permit service where it is desirable to alternately collect heat and dissipate heat.

Another object of the invention is to provide an improved solar heat collector having a low ratio of heat-absorbing fluid to area of surface exposed to solar radiation so as to obtain a maximum temperature rise. However, if a great quantity of heat is desired with a low rise in temperature, adjustment may be made merely by flowing a larger quantity of heat absorbing fluid through the heat collector.

Other objects and advantages of the invention will be apparent as the description proceeds and the features of novelty will be pointed out in particularity in the appended claims.

Briefly, in accordance with this invention, there is provided a solar heat collector including solar heat collector units which may be used singly or in multiples. The units may be mounted on any movable support as, for example, one designed to permit tracking of the sun, or may be mounted on a fixed structure or built into the roof of a building. When the present invention is constructed into a roof, it becomes the roof, is permanent in character, and saves the cost of providing conventional roofing. The heat collector roof also provides insulation for the building, saving part of the insulation costs of the building. Generally, the units include a box with a transparent protecting cover, a layer of insulation on the interior bottom of the box covered by a layer of reflecting foil and a heat collecting metallic sheet having an irregular and blackened upper surface supported by the foil. The heat collecting sheet is preferably covered by a second transparent cover intermediate the sheet and protecting cover, the intermediate cover preferably being flexible and installed so as to droop against the heat collecting sheet. The device is also provided with a fluid system including a distribution pipe at one end of the box having small ports regularly spaced along its length and a fluid trough parallel to the pipe at the other end of the box so that fluid may be introduced through the pipe to be discharged to run in small quantities along many paths across the heat collecting sheet under the intermediate flexible transparent cover and into the trough. This arrangement provides for a low ratio of volume of fluid to area of heat collecting sheet and for an even distribution of the fluid volume to unit area of heat collecting sheet. The invention also provides modified heat collecting sheets providing various means of controlling the paths of the heat absorbing fluid to provide for the best absorption of heat from the collecting sheet.

In the accompanying drawings, illustrating preferred embodiments of the improvements comprising the invention—

FIG. 1 is an end elevation showing the general configuration of a complete solar heat collector;

FIG. 2 is a front or face view of a heat collector unit included in FIG. 1 embodying the improvements of the instant invention.

FIG. 3 is a transverse section along the line 3—3 of FIG. 2 showing internal details of the collector unit;

FIG. 4 is a partial vertical section taken on line 4—4 of FIG. 2;

FIG. 5 is a partial vertical section taken on the line 5—5 of FIG. 2;

FIG. 6 is an enlarged fragmentary transverse section of a solar heat collector unit showing the details of features appearing in FIG. 3;

FIG. 7 is a fragmentary plan view of a modified heat collecting sheet;

FIG. 8 is a section of the heat collecting sheet substantially on the line 8—8 of FIG. 7;

FIG. 9 is a fragmentary plan view of a further modification of the heat collecting sheet;

FIG. 10 is a section of the heat collecting sheet taken substantially on line 10—10 of FIG. 9; and

FIG. 11 is a fragmentary section of a still further modification of the heat collecting sheet.

Referring more specifically to the drawings, a complete, self-supporting solar heat collector is illustrated in end elevation in FIG. 1 wherein the heat collector unit **1** is supported by frame members **2** and **3** at an inclination of approximately 45°, an attitude adapted to, but not necessarily the most efficacious for, the receipt of solar radiation. The unit **1** is also adaptable to mounting on a pedestal or other mount having mechanism, either hand operated or power driven, for tracking the sun to gain the maximum solar radiation or to turn the unit away from the sun when the unit is used as a radiator.

The structural details of the solar heat collector unit **1** are best illustrated in FIGS. 1 through 6. The unit **1** proper is contained by box **4** having bottom or base **5**, end walls **6** and side walls **7** but no top. The interior of the bottom of the box is covered by a bed of insulation **8** to prevent loss of heat through the bottom. Insulation **8** in turn is preferably, but not necessarily, covered by a sheet of reflecting foil **9** for the purpose of reflecting upwards a maximum amount of the heat reaching it. Box **4** is provided with a transparent cover **10** which will admit solar radiation but minimize heat loss during collection operation not only by its insulating quality of poor heat conduction but also by stopping convection currents and long wave heat radiation from the heated black surface. Although cover **10** is illustrated as glass, any transparent material, preferably one transmitting the full range of the solar spectrum, may be used. Similarly, in some applications of the invention it may be desirable to double the exterior transparent cover or, in other applications, to make the cover removable to enhance radiation when the unit is used to dissipate heat.

The collection of heat in the device is accomplished by a sheet of heat conducting material **11** which has the ability to absorb light energy and convert that energy to heat and the ability to transfer heat so collected to an absorbing fluid medium. If the heat absorbing fluid is a gas, the heat conduction properties of collecting sheet **11** become less significant. The collecting sheet **11** is superimposed on foil **9**, or insulation **8** if no foil is used and is preferably polished on its underside, i.e. the side toward the foil, to limit the escape of heat from that underside. The upper surface of heat conducting sheet **11** is preferably treated by any process, as for example painting, to produce a dull black finish or may be treated with a special solar receiving paint which absorbs the sun's rays and converts that radiation to heat while limiting the radiation back to the atmosphere. According to experts in the art, dull black paint will absorb as much as 95 percent of the solar radiation incident upon the surface. A very thin coat of such paint will permit the conducting sheet to readily receive heat for transfer to a fluid heat absorbing medium for ultimate transfer to, and use in, a heat exchanger or other consuming means as, for example, radiators in a building.

In the embodiment of the invention illustrated in FIGS. 2 through 6, conducting sheet **11** is corrugated or otherwise distorted from planar form to a wavelike configuration with curved surfaced hills and valleys running the length of the unit, i.e. from one end wall to the other and parallel to side walls **7**. This configuration is particularly efficacious when a liquid is used as the fluid heat absorbing and transferring medium because it permits the liquid to be trickled down the valleys of an inclined sheet **11** in controllable minute quantities with an even distribution of fluid over the area of the collecting sheet. By this controlled means a small quantity of fluid can steadily absorb heat from a large surface of collecting sheet to gain a maximum temperature increase, i.e. to absorb a maximum amount of heat per unit volume. As specifically illustrated in FIG. 6, liquid **12** running in valleys **13** between hills **14** of sheet **11** will absorb heat from the valleys **13** and because of the high heat conductivity of the material of sheet **11**, heat will flow from hills **14** to valleys **13** within the conducting sheet. As is obvious from FIG. 6, considerably less fluid is required than would be necessary to provide a constant, although thin, film of liquid over a planar conducting sheet. The canalization of the liquid by the corrugations as it gravitates across the conducting sheet is the most simple method of obtaining a constant predetermined low liquid to area ratio and prevents lateral or crosswise flow which, in the case of a planar configuration, could cause large areas of a heated collecting sheet to escape visit of the liquid thereby reducing the quantity of heat transferred.

As illustrated in FIGS. 2 through 5, the heat absorbing liquid is provided to the unit by a fluid distribution system including distribution pipe **15** at its upper end and trough **16** at the lower end wall **6** which directs the liquid to discharge pipe **17** which protrudes through side wall **7** at **18** to provide for conveyance of heated liquid from the unit. Distribution pipe **15** is provided with a plurality of ports **19** spaced so as to locate one port, or a constant number of ports, at each valley of corrugated conducting sheet **11**. Rate of flow and distribution of the liquid may be controlled by adjustment of the size of pipe **15**, size of ports **19**, number of ports, valving in pipe **15** and by any pressure or pump arrangement used with a completed solar heating system. Since solar heaters operate only when heat is available from the sun, the pump or other pressure apparatus supplying fluid to the distribution pipe may be actuated thermostatically to cut on when heat is available and to cut off when sunshine fails due to sundown or clouds.

Preferably an interior or inner transparent sheet or cover **20** is used intermediate the heat collecting sheet **11** and the cover **10** to reduce uncontrolled reradiation and convection currents and to decrease the undesired effects of vaporization of the liquid used. This inner cover **20** may be of rigid or flexible material resistant to heat and vapor of the fluid, supported in the same manner as cover **10**, but it is preferred that inner cover **20** be flexible and loosely secured to the inner portion of walls **6** over the pipe **15** and above trough **16** as illustrated in FIGS. 4 and 5 so as to droop onto the raised portions of collecting sheet **11**. This preferred installation of the inner cover **20** reduces the volume of the atmosphere adjacent the collecting sheet **11** limiting the amount of water vapor that can exist in that atmosphere and thereby establishing a maximum quantity of heat that can be lost or suspended by vaporization of the heat absorbing liquid. The cover **20** may, however, be stretched and secured to the raised portions of collecting sheet **11** by an adhesive or by heat sealing to prevent bulging or flapping.

If it is desired to use a gas as the heat absorbing fluid, the fluid distribution and collection systems are reversed to be in accord with the physical fact that a heated gas will travel upwards.

As illustrated in FIGS. 2 and 3, a central supporting member or spacer **21** is used to give additional support to transparent cover **10**. In the embodiment using a drooping flexible inner cover **20** as illustrated, spacer **21**, by being placed on top of the inner cover **20** and supported by a ridge **14** of the corrugated collecting sheet, also serves to keep the inner cover **20** close to the sheet **11**. The existence or frequency of use of spacers **21** obviously depends on the dimensions and material in a particular embodiment of the invention. If the invention were to be used in a non-portable or non-tracking form, such as for the roof of a building the most simple construction might consist of one very broad unit including several spacers **21** as needed for support of cover **10**. However, spacers

21 may be omitted completely to avoid shading in early morning and late afternoon, or horizontal spacers may be used to support transparent cover 10 if the shading is critical, since horizontal spacers will shade less of the collector surface. However, smaller units may be made for plurality use to facilitate prefabrication and transportation to installation location. For this reason, the embodiment of FIGS. 2 and 3 are provided for interconnecting fluid supply components enabling units to be "plugged together" as illustrated by the additional dotted line unit of FIG. 3. Distribution pipe 15 is provided with a female connector 22 on one side while the return system is provided with an additional pipe 17 and a female connector 23.

A first modification of the heat collecting sheet is illustrated in FIGS. 7 and 8. Here collecting sheet 31 which has the same requirements as sheet 11 as to characteristics of light absorption, heat collection and heat conduction, accomplishes the liquid distribution objective of the invention by use of a different surface configuration. Sheet 31 is basically planar but is embossed so as to provide bosses 32, illustrated as, but not necessarily, regularly spaced constituting hills separated by interconnecting valleys. In this modification, the bosses 32 provide the "dry area" used to reduce the liquid volume to surface area ratio forming an important object of the invention. Flow of the liquid along the tortuous path dictated by the bosses causes a retardation of flow providing for a higher temperature increase of the liquid. As described with reference to FIG. 3, one or more transparencies may be used. If two transparencies are used, the bosses may support the inner transparent cover 20 slightly raised above the main heat-collecting sheet. The bosses inherently help to keep the fluid flowing in small streams and distributed in the valleys, rather than permitting them to congregate into large streams at some areas with no water flowing over other areas. As can be seen in FIG. 7, these valleys constitute a larger percentage of the collecting sheet than do the valleys of the modification of FIG. 3. In this modification thin passageways are held open between the heat-collecting sheet 31 and the transparent cover 20 so that liquid, or gas, to be heated can flow through these passageways. Thus, if water is used as a heat transfer fluid, it can readily drain out with its "load of heat" when the apparatus stops for the night, rather than remain entrapped in the collector to get cold or to freeze and cause damage.

When the embossed projections are of only slight extent it is obvious that the transparent cover resting on the tops of the projections is spaced only slightly from the valleys of the collecting sheet. Thus, the gas or liquid flowing between the collecting sheet and transparent cover inherently is held to very small dimensions. If the bosses are high, and if the fluid flowing therebeneath is liquid, the liquid does not contact the transparent cover, but the bosses still help to retard the flow and to distribute the liquid more uniformly in the valleys of the heat-collecting sheet.

Further, since the bosses help keep the cover 20 from direct total contact with the valley parts of the collecting sheet, they help minimize damage to the cover due to extremely high temperatures of the collecting sheet when the collector is not operating, such as on a hot summer day. As described with respect to FIG. 3, the inner cover may be rigid or flexible. If it is a flexible transparency, the embossing helps keep it from sticking to the valley parts of the heat-collecting sheet and thus assures free passage of the fluid. Furthermore, the embossing increases the strength of the collecting sheet itself and thus makes it possible to use a lighter weight, less expensive heat-collecting sheet while retaining the desired strength. Additionally the embossing makes it possible for the sheet to expand and contract within itself as the temperature rises and falls, thus minimizing the tendency for the sheet to buckle and warp. From the economic point of view, commercially available embossed sheet metal generally costs the same price as the flat sheet, even if the thickness is the same; and it is less expensive if the sheet is thinner. Thus, the embossed form provides many advantages.

Another modification is illustrated in FIGS. 9 and 10 wherein sheet 41, of the same characteristics with regard to heat as sheets 11 and 31, is both corrugated and embossed, having bosses 42, valleys 43, and ridges 44. Again, for the purposes of illustration, the bosses are arranged in regular pattern but may be located at random. In this arrangement a tortuous path within each valley is provided for the liquid gaining both advantages viz: canalization and impediment of flow.

Still another modification is illustrated in FIG. 11 where sheet 51 is ararnged in a plurality of angularly disposed valleys 53 and ridges 54 by a crimped configuration. This modification has the capability of presenting planar surfaces to the solar radiation and thereby decreasing, on the average, the angles of incidence of the radiation; or as the angle of incidence increases, the configuration provides for the reflection of any deflected portion of the ray onto the opposing side of the valley rather than back to the atmosphere.

With the use of structure according to this invention, approximately 95 percent of the sun's rays reaching the collector are converted to heat, and a very large percentage of this heat is transferred to the fluid and immediately taken to the point of use or storage. If higher temperatures of the water are desired, it is merely necessary to increase the length of travel of the liquid through the valleys, i.e. to increase the length of the unit from top to bottom, to decrease the rate of flow, or to introduce the fluid intermittently, e.g. to cause the fluid to flow for a few minutes and not to flow for a few minutes.

In certain instances the insulating material may be dispensed with or minimized, for example, if the solar heater unit is constructed as a portion of the roof of a building, the insulation of the roof may serve a dual function.

The unit will dissipate heat readily when operated at night or turned away from the sun, and is particularly effective when any transparent covers are removed from above the heat collecting sheet. Heat dissipation is great in this use because of evaporation of water flowing down the collecting sheet utilizing the principle that heat of vaporization absorbs tremendous quantities of heat.

The present invention has numerous advantages such as simplicity of construction, low cost, and high efficiency. It is substantially trouble-free in operation. The liquid automatically drains from the heater as soon as it is turned off and thereby avoids freezing in cold weather. No liquid-tight joints are necessary among the frame members. A wavelike, corrugated, embossed, or raised projection heat conductor material is very inexpensive to manufacture and light-weight to transport. The sun's rays usually strike substantial portions of the corrugated surface at small angles of incidence, even if the sun is to the left or right of a line normal to the surface. Thus, even a stationarily mounted unit is very efficient in absorbing light.

Since no part of the heat-collecting surface is very far from the heat-collecting fluid flowing down the valleys or between bosses, very little heat is radiated back to the atmosphere and the efficiency is extremely high. Even if one outlet of the distribution pipe should become clogged, the others continue to function and efficiency is only insignificantly impaired.

The present structure is also very effective when used

to heat a gas since the corrugated surface has more square inches of exposed surface than a flat member providing greater metal-to-gas contact and therefore greater heat transfer.

In some installations the wavelike formation may be more pronounced, as channeled or crimped. Such form is particularly advantageous in adjustable collectors since the deep valleys or crimping keep the liquid flowing in closely spaced paths, even if the collector is tilted sidewise.

The present construction substantially eliminates the problem of condensation of liquid on the transparent material, experienced in many heat collectors. In addition to the action of inner cover **20**, the higher temperatures remain at the lower end of the collector (when a liquid is used) and this high temperature keeps the glass or other transparent material warm enough to prevent condensation. At the upper end, where the liquid flowing in is colder, there is less evaporation, and the transparent material is warm enough that very little condensation is experienced. In some forms of the invention the condensation is more pronounced. However, this condensation usually forms small droplets of liquid which act as tiny magnifying lenses and "bend" the light rays as they pass through the droplets. A high percentage of the sunlight is thus transmitted to the heat-collecting sheet and the amount of reflection away due to condensation is not nearly as great as had been anticipated by some authorities. Whether one, two, or more layers of transparent material are used, condensation and reflection due to condensation is at a minimum. *

Nov. 2, 1965 H. E. THOMASON **3,215,134**

SOLAR HEAT COLLECTOR

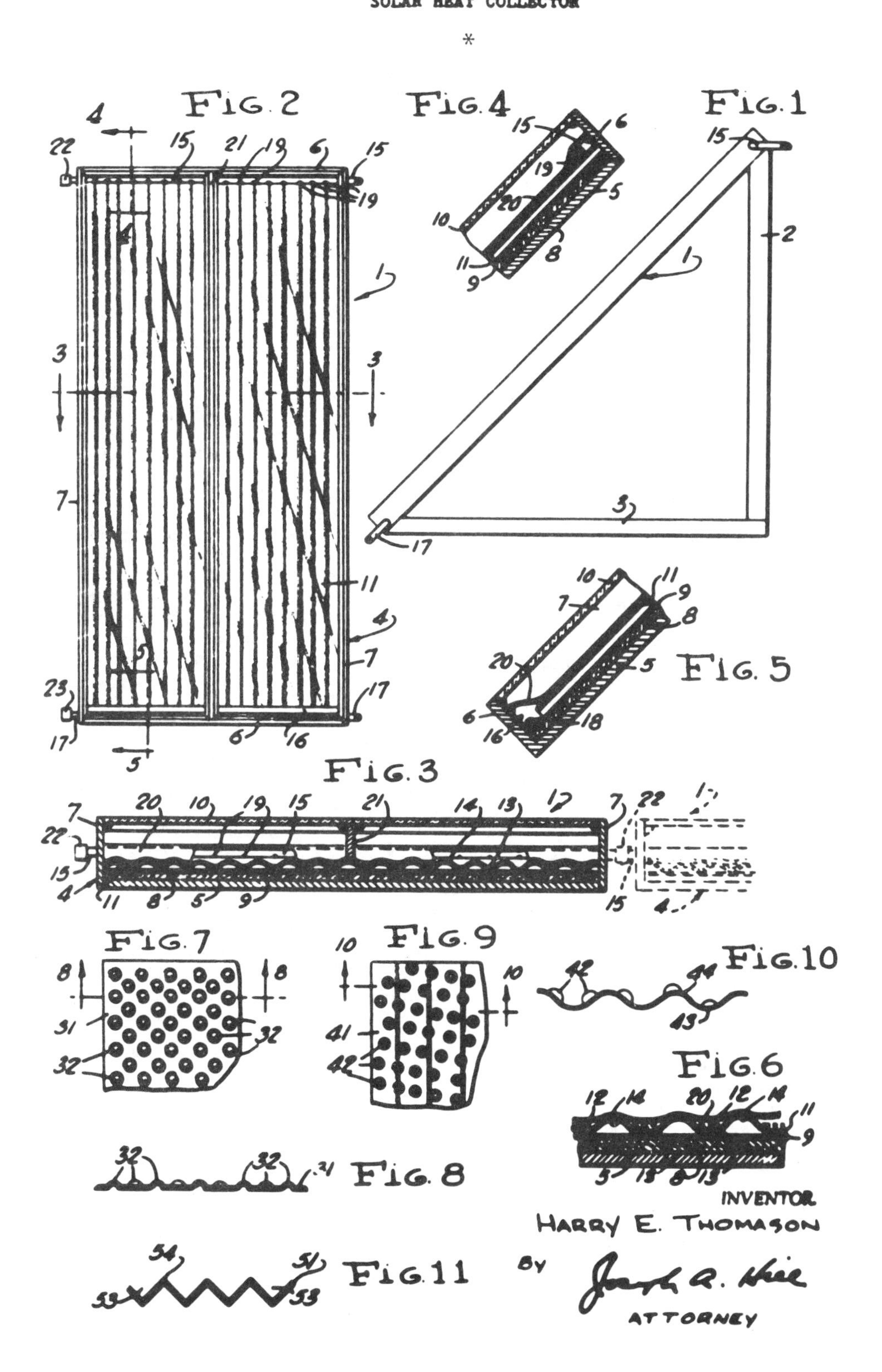

3,215,134
SOLAR HEAT COLLECTOR
Harry E. Thomason, 7354 Walker Mill Road SE., District Heights, Md.

*

The invention described herein may be manufactured and used by or for the Government for governmental purposes without the payment to me of any royalty thereon. *

The present invention relates to improvements in solar heat collectors, and particularly the type that may be used both for collecting heat from solar radiation and for dissipating heat when not receiving solar heat, such as at night, or by turning the heat collector (dissipator) away from the sun.

Among the various known heat collectors are structures employing a black insulating base, a glass cover spaced an inch or so thereabove, and black fluid-carrying piping between the glass and the black base, which are used effectively in southern areas of the United States for heating water. These devices are sometimes constructed with the fluid-carrying piping zig-zagging in convolutions in a plane requiring many flow-restricting elbows and many lineal feet of piping her hundred square feet of collector surface, and resulting in very expensive construction as a result of both the cost of the piping and the labor cost. Inefficiencies also result from excessive spacing of the convolutions which permits radiation of much of the solar heat back to the atmosphere. Alternatively, these devices are sometimes constructed in sandwich fashion with the heat collecting fluid running between spaced metal sheets which may be parallel or crimped in imitation of tubing, but still require excessive amounts of copper and labor and still have a high ratio of fluid to heat absorbing metal.

Other existing solar heaters employ light and heat condensing lenses or reflectors to concentrate and localize the sun's light and heat, but such lenses or reflectors are extremely expensive, especially when it is desired to collect solar heat from an area of several hundreds of square feet.

A further type of existing solar heater has the heat conducting fluid contained directly between the insulated base and the transparent cover, or between a black metal collector and the transparent cover, in such a way that the transparent cover also constitutes one wall to a fluid container. This construction is not only expensive but lends itself readily to trouble because a broken or loose transparent cover, usually glass, permits the heat conducting fluid to be leaked or spilled, rendering the device inoperative. Therefore, this type device requires expensive and troublesome liquid sealing for the base, sides, and edges and for the transparent top. Since areas of hundreds of square inches are involved, the glass used must be sufficiently thick and free of flaws and the glass retaining means must be sufficiently strong to withstand contained pressures of two or three pounds per square inch over fairly large panes.

Many other types of solar heating devices are known, but with limitations and disadvantages so as to render them impractical except for very limited and specialized application. Most of the solar heaters are very ineffective and practically worthless for dissipating heat, and are therefore not reversible in operation.

The present invention, directed to obviating many of the limitations of the solar heaters described, simplifies and lowers the cost of construction, raises efficiency and is substantially trouble-free in use and operation. Additionally, the present device is readily adaptable to use as a heat-dissipating device to permit service where it is desirable to alternately collect heat and dissipate heat.

Another object of the invention is to provide an improved solar heat collector having a low ratio of heat-absorbing fluid to area of surface exposed to solar radiation so as to obtain a maximum heat accumulation per unit volume of fluid used.

Other objects and advantages of the invention will be apparent as the description proceeds and the features of novelty will be pointed out in particularity in the appended claims.

Briefly, in accordance with this invention, there is provided a solar heat collector including solar heat collector units which which may be used singly or in multiples. The units may be mounted on any movable support as, for example, one designed to permit tracking of the sun, or may be mounted on a fixed structure or built into the roof of a building. Generally, the units include a box with a transparent protecting cover, a layer of insulation on the interior bottom of the box covered by a layer of reflecting foil and a heat collecting metallic sheet having an irregular and blackened upper surface supported by a second transparent cover intermediate the sheet and protecting cover, the intermediate cover preferably being flexible and installed so as to droop against the heat collecting sheet. The device is also provided with a fluid system including a distribution pipe at one end of the box having small ports regularly spaced along its length and a fluid trough parallel to the pipe at the other end of the box so that fluid may be introduced through the pipe to be discharged to run in small quantities along many paths across the heat collecting sheet under the intermediate flexible transparent cover and into the trough. This arrangement provides for a low ratio of volume of fluid to area of heat collecting sheet and for an even distribution of the fluid volume to unit area of heat collecting sheet. The invention also provides modified heat collecting sheets providing various means of controlling the paths of the heat absorbing fluid to provide for the best absorption of heat from the collecting sheet.

In the accompanying drawings, illustrating preferred embodiments of the improvements comprising the invention—

FIG. 1 is an end elevation showing the general configuration of a complete solar heat collector;

FIG. 2 is a front or face view of a heat collector unit included in FIG. 1 embodying the improvements of the instant invention;

FIG. 3 is a transverse section along the line 3—3 of FIG. 2 showing internal details of the collector unit;

FIG. 4 is a partial vertical section taken on line 4—4 of FIG. 2;

FIG. 5 is a partial vertical section taken on the line 5—5 of FIG. 2;

FIG. 6 is an enlarged fragmentary traverse sectoin of a solar heat collector unit showing the details of features appearing in FIG. 3;

FIG. 7 is a fragmentary plan view of a modified heat collecting sheet;

FIG. 8 is a section of the heat collecting sheet substantially on the line 8—8 of FIG. 7;

FIG. 9 is a fragmentary plan view of a further modification of the heat collecting sheet;

FIG. 10 is a section of the heat collecting sheet taken substantially on line 10—10 of FIG. 9; and

FIG. 11 is a fragmentary section of a still further modification of the heat collecting sheet.

Referring more specifically to the drawings, a complete, self-supporting solar heat collector is illustrated in end elevation in FIG. 1 wherein the heat collector unit 1 is supported by frame members 2 and 3 at an inclination of approximately 45°, an attitude adapted to, but not necessarily the most efficacious for, the receipt of solar radiation. The unit 1 is also adaptable to mounting on a pedestal or other mount having mechanism, either hand operated or power driven, for tracking the sun to gain the maximum solar radiation or to turn the unit away from the sun when the unit is used as a radiator.

The structural details of the solar heat collector unit 1 are best illustrated in FIGS. 1 through 6. The unit 1 proper is contained by box 4 having bottom or base 5, end walls 6 and side walls 7 but no top. The interior of the bottom of the box is covered by a bed of insulation 8 to prevent loss of heat through the bottom. Insulation 8 in turn is preferably, but not necessarily, covered by a sheet of reflecting foil 9 for the purpose of reflecting upwards a maximum amount of the heat reaching it. Box 4 is provided with a transparent cover 10 which will admit solar radiation but minimize heat loss during collection operation not only by its insulating quality of poor heat conduction but also by stopping convection currents. Although cover 10 is illustrated as glass, any transparent material, preferably one transmitting the full range of the solar spectrum, may be used. Similarly, in some applications of the invention it may be desirable to double the exterior transparent cover or, in other applications, to make the cover removable to enhance radiation when the unit is used to dissipate heat.

The collection of heat in the device is accomplished by a sheet of heat conducting material 11 which has the ability to absorb light energy and convert that energy to heat and the ability to transfer heat so collected to an absorbing fluid medium. If the heat absorbing fluid is a gas, the heat conduction properties of collecting sheet 11 become less significant. The collecting sheet 11 is superimposed on foil 9, or insulation 8 if no foil is used and is preferably polished on its underside, i.e. the side toward the foil, to limit the escape of heat from that underside. The upper surface of heat conducting sheet 11 is preferably treated by any process, as for example painting, to produce a dull black finish or may be treated with a special solar receiving paint which absorbs the sun's rays readily while limiting the radiation of heat back to the atmosphere. According to experts in the art, dull black paint will absorb as much as 95 percent of the solar radiation incident upon the surface. A very thin coat of such paint will permit the conducting sheet to readily receive heat for transfer to a fluid heat absorbing medium for ultimate transfer to, and use in, a heat exchanger or other consuming means as, for example, radiators in a building.

In the embodiment of the invention illustrated in FIGS. 2 through 6, conducting sheet 11 is corrugated or otherwise distorted from planar form to a wavelike configuration with curved surfaced hills and valleys running the length of the unit, i.e. from one end wall to the other and parallel to side walls 7. This configuration is particularly efficacious when a liquid is used as the fluid heat absorbing and transferring medium because it permits the liquid to be trickled down the valleys of an inclined sheet 11 in controllable minute quantities with an even distribution of fluid over the area of the collecting sheet. By this controlled means a small quantity of fluid can steadily absorb heat from a large surface of collecting sheet to gain a maximum heat increase, i.e. to absorb a maximum amount of heat per unit volume. As specifically illustrated in FIG. 6, liquid 12 running in valleys 13 between hills 14 of sheet 11 will absorb heat from the valleys 13 and because of the high heat conductivity of the material of sheet 11, heat will flow from hills 14 to valleys 13 within the conducting sheet. As is obvious from FIG. 6, considerably less fluid is required than would be necessary to provide a constant, although thin, film of liquid over a planar conducting sheet. The canalization of the liquid by the corrugations as it gravitates across the conducting sheet is the most simple method of obtaining a constant predetermined low liquid to area ratio and prevents lateral or crosswise flow which, in the case of a planar configuration, could cause large areas of a heated collecting sheet to escape visit of the liquid reducing the quantity of heat transferred.

As illustrated in FIGS. 2 through 5, the heat absorbing liquid is provided to the unit by a fluid distribution system including distribution pipe 15 at its upper end and trough 16 at the lower end wall 6 which directs the liquid to discharge pipe 17 which protrudes through side wall 7 at 18 to provide for conveyance of heated liquid from the unit. Distribution pipe 15 is provided with a plurality of ports 19 spaced so as to locate one port, or a constant number of ports, at each valley of corrugated conducting sheet 11. Rate of flow and distribution of the liquid may be controlled by adjustment of the size of pipe 15, size of ports 19, number of ports, valving in pipe 15 and by any pressure or pump arrangement used with a completed solar heating system.

Preferably an interior or inner transparent sheet or cover 20 is used intermediate the heat collecting sheet 11 and the cover 10 to reduce uncontrolled reradiation and convection currents and to decrease the undesired effects of vaporization of the liquid used. This inner cover 20 may be of rigid or flexible material resistant to heat and vapor of the fluid, supported in the same manner as cover 10, but it is preferred that inner cover 20 be flexible and loosely secured to the inner portion of walls 6 over the pipe 15 and above trough 16 as illustrated in FIGS. 4 and 5 so as to droop onto the raised portions of collecting sheet 11. This preferred installation of the inner cover 20 reduces the volume of the atmosphere adjacent the collecting sheet 11 limiting the amount of water vapor that can exist in that atmosphere and thereby establishing a maximum quantity of heat that can be lost or suspended by vaporization of the heat absorbing liquid.

If it is desired to use a gas as the heat absorbing fluid, the fluid distribution and collection systems are reversed to be in accord with the physical fact that a heated gas will travel upwards.

As illustrated in FIGS. 2 and 3, a central supporting member or spacer 21 is used to give additional support to transparent cover 10. In the embodiment using a drooping flexible inner cover 20 as illustrated, spacer 21, by being placed on top of the inner cover 20 and supported by a ridge 14 of the corrugated collecting sheet, also serves to keep the inner cover 20 close to the sheet 11. The existence or frequency of use of spacers 21 obviously depends on the dimensions and materials in a particular embodiment of the invention. If the invention were to be used in a non-portable or non-tracking form, the most simple construction might consist of one very broad unit including several spacers 21 as needed for support of cover 10. However, smaller units may be made for plurality use to facilitate prefabrication and transportation to installation location. For this reason, the embodiment of FIGS. 2 and 3 is provided for interconnecting fluid supply components enabling units to be "plugged together" as illustrated by the additional dotted line unit of FIG. 3. Distribution pipe 15 is provided with a female connector 22 on one side while the return system is provided with an additional pipe 17 and a female connector 23.

A first modification of the heat collecting sheet is illustrated in FIGS. 7 and 8. Here collecting sheet 31 which has the same requirements as sheet 11 as to characteristics of light absorption, heat collection and heat conduction, accomplishes the liquid distribution objective of the invention by use of a different surface configuration. Sheet 31 is basically planar but is embossed so as to provide bosses 32, illustrated as, but not necessarily, regularly spaced constituting hills separated by interconnecting valleys. In this modification, the bosses 32 provide the "dry area" used to reduce the liquid volume to surface area ratio forming an important object of the invention.

Flow of the liquid along the tortuous path dictated by the bosses causes a retardation of flow providing for a higher heat increase of the liquid.

Another modification is illustrated in FIGS. 9 and 10 wherein sheet 41, of the same characteristics with regard to heat as sheets 11 and 31, is both corrugated and embossed, having bosses 42, valleys 43, and ridges 44. Again, for the purposes of illustration, the bosses are arranged in regular pattern but may be located at random. In this arrangement a tortuous path within each valley is provided for the liquid gaining both advantages viz: canalization and impediment of flow.

Still another modification is illustrated in FIG. 11 where sheet 51 is arranged in a plurality of angularly disposed valleys 53 and ridges 54 by a crimped configuration. This modification has the capability of presenting planar surfaces to the solar radiation and thereby decreasing, on the average, the angles of incidence of the radiation; or as the angle of incidence increases, the configuration provides for the reflection of any reflected portion of the ray onto the opposing side of the valley rather than back to the atmosphere.

With the use of structure according to this invention, approximately 95 percent of the sun's rays are converted to heat, and a very large percentage of this heat is transferred to the fluid and immediately taken to the point of use or storage. If higher temperatures of the water are desired, it is merely necessary to increase the length of travel of the liquid through the valleys, i.e. to increase the length of the unit from top to bottom, or to decrease the rate of flow.

In certain instances the insulating material may be dispensed with or minimized, for example, if the solar heater unit is constructed as a portion of the roof of a building, the insulation of the roof may serve a dual function.

The unit will dissipate heat readily when operated at night or turned away from the sun, and is particularly effective when any transparent covers are removed from above the heat collecting sheet. Heat dissipation is great in this use because of evaporation of water flowing down the collecting sheet utilizing the principle that heat of vaporization absorbs tremendous quantities of heat.

The present invention has numerous advantages such as simplicity of construction, low cost, and high efficiency. It is substantially trouble-free in operation. The liquid automatically drains from the heater as soon as it is turned off and thereby avoids freezing in cold weather. No liquid-tight joints are necessary among the frame members. A wavelike, corrugated, embossed, or raised projection heat conductor material is very inexpensive to manufacture and light-weight to transport. The sun's rays usually strike substantial portions of the corrugated surface at small angles of incidence, even if the sun is to the left or right of a line normal to the surface. Thus, even a stationarily mounted unit is very efficient in absorbing light.

Since no part of the heat-collecting surface is very far from the heat-collecting fluid flowing down the valleys or between bosses, very little heat is radiated back to the atmosphere and the efficiency is extremely high. Even if one outlet of the distribution pipe should become clogged, the others continue to function and efficiency is only insignificantly impaired.

The present structure is also very effective when used to heat a gas since the corrugated surface has more square inches of exposed surface than a flat member providing greater metal-to-gas contact and therefore greater heat transfer.

In some installations the wavelike formation may be more pronounced, as channeled or crimped. Such form is particularly advantageous in adjustable collectors since the deep valleys or crimping keep the liquid flowing in closely spaced paths, even when the collector is tilted sidewise.

The present construction substantially eliminates the problem of condensation of liquid on the transparent material, experienced in many heat collectors. In addition to the action of inner cover 20, the higher temperatures remain at the lower end of the collector (when a liquid is used) and this high temperature keeps the glass or other transparent material warm enough to prevent condensation. At the upper end, where the liquid flowing in is colder, there is less evaporation, and the transparent material is warm enough that very little condensation is experienced. Whether one, two, or more layers of transparent material are used, condensation is at a minimum.

It is to be understood that the embodiment of the invention with its modification as illustrated and described is a preferred example and that various changes may be resorted to, or incorporation of many features old in the art may be resorted to, without departing from the spirit of the invention or the scope of the appended claims.

I claim:

1. A device for collection of heat from solar radiation and for radiation of heat comprising an insulated base; a heat collecting sheet comprising planar portions of substantial area superposed on said base; frame means at the perimeter of and inclosing said base and heat collecting sheet; a transparent cover substantially covering and in close proximity with said heat collecting sheet, the intervening spaces therebetween being further inclosed by said frame means; fluid distributing means for introducing a fluid at predetermined spaced intervals along said heat collecting sheet for transfer of heat between said fluid and said heat collecting sheet; means forming a part of said heat collecting sheet for controlling the course of flow of heat transferring fluid over said heat collecting sheet, said means comprising an irregular surface including a series of raised portions closely and uniformly spaced over said heat collecting sheet from frame to frame, said raised portions defining a plurality of narrow valleys forming a multiplicity of paths along which the fluid flows beneath said transparent cover; means for retrieving said fluid after it has flowed along and contacted said heat collecting sheet; and support means for said heat collecting sheet, said insulated base, and said transparent cover.

2. The apparatus of claim 1 wherein said planar portions comprise a flat sheet and wherein said raised portions comprise uniformly spaced bosses on said flat sheet, said bosses defining tortuous paths of flow for the fluid crossing said flat sheet.

3. The apparatus of claim 1 wherein said irregular surface comprises a plurality of angularly disposed intersecting planes disposed so that a substantial portion of solar radiation reflected from one of said planes is reflected onto another of said planes, the lines of intersection of said planes being substantially parallel and extending from the end of said sheet adjacent to said fluid distributing means to the end of said sheet adjacent to said fluid retrieving means.

June 7, 1966 H. E. THOMASON 3,254,701

COMBINATION SOLAR HEAT TRAP AND HEAT DISSIPATOR

*

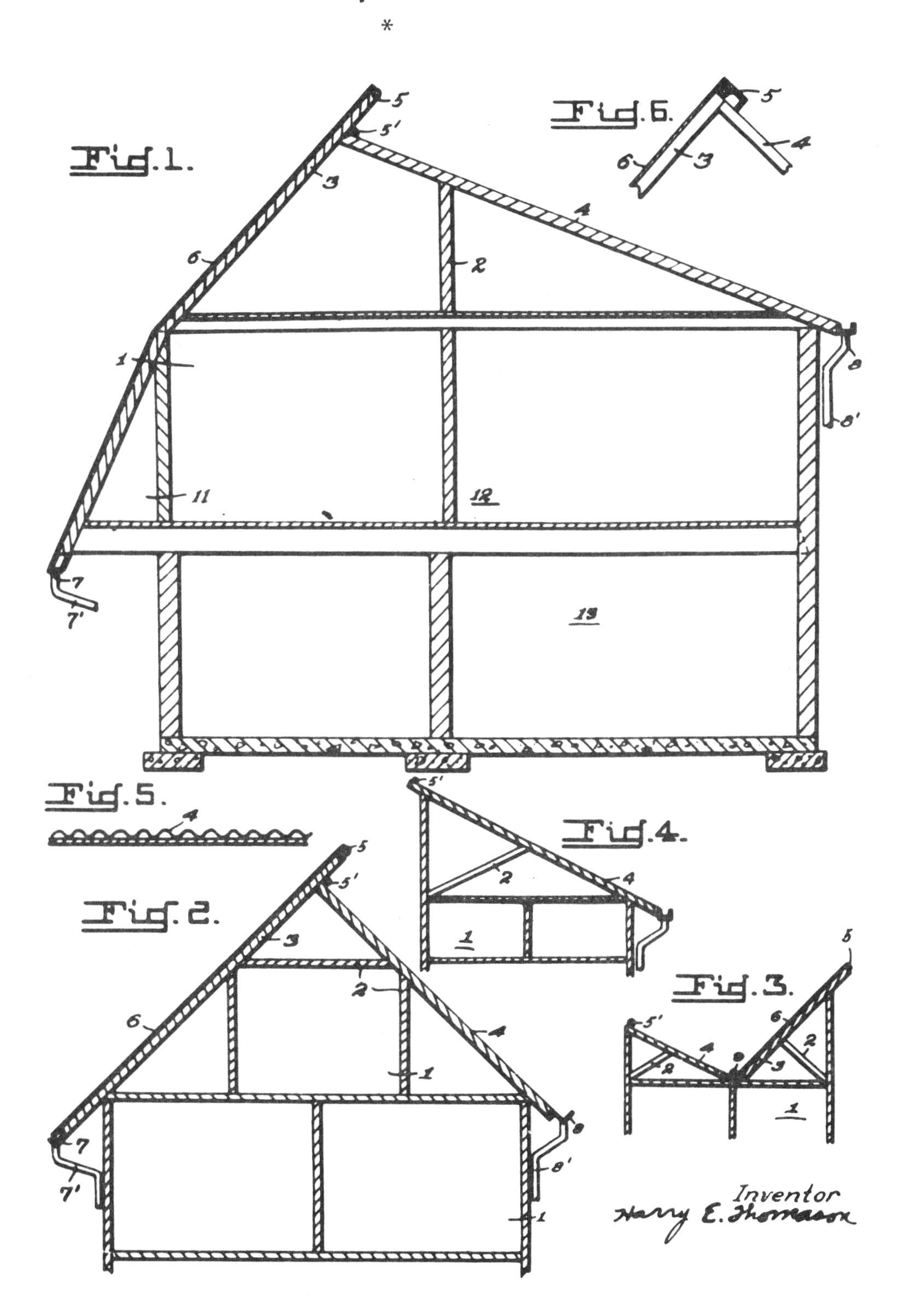

3,254,701
COMBINATION SOLAR HEAT TRAP AND HEAT DISSIPATOR

Harry E. Thomason, 6911 Walker Mill Road SE., Washington, D.C.

*

The present invention relates to a combination solar heat trap and heat dissipator.

In modern industry, homes, public buildings, private office buildings, and in numerous other places, there is a need for collecting free solar heat, and also for dissipating large quantities of heat, such as for refrigeration, air conditioning, cooling steam condenser water, and such. Obviously it is highly desirable that this heat be dissipated with the most simple and trouble-free apparatus possible, with little attention and maintenance being required. Also, it is highly desirable that the apparatus operate with the lowest amount of power possible.

It is an object of this invention to provide heat dissipating apparatus which is simple and trouble-free in operation.

It is another object to provide heat dissipating apparatus which is inexpensive to construct, yet substantially permanent and requiring practically no attention or maintenance.

It is another object to provide heat dissipating apparatus which will discharge tremendous quantities of heat to the atmosphere with an expenditure of power which is practically nil.

It is another object to provide heat dissipating apparatus which is usable in conjunction with a solar heat collector, if desired, such as the solar heat collector de- *scribed in Patent Number 3,145,707 granted Aug. 25, 1964. When the present invention is used with such heat collector, there are additional advantages to be described later.

The heat may be dissipated and the resulting "coolness" may be stored and used to air condition the build- *ing

Referring now to the drawings:

FIGURE 1 illustrates a building having a roof which comprises a solar heat collector and a heat dissipator in accordance with the present invention.

FIGURE 2 illustrates a modified roof construction embodying the present invention.

FIGURE 3 illustrates another modification embodying both a solar heat collector and a heat dissipator.

FIGURE 4 illustrates a modification wherein the entire roof may be used as a heat dissipator.

FIGURE 5 illustrates one type of roofing material usable as he heat-dissipator surface.

FIGURE 6 illustrates an embodiment wherein only one distributor manifold is required.

Refrring now specifically to FIG. 1, I have illustrated a building having living space at 1 and 12, and having a somewhat A-shaped roof with internal bracing 2. Closet space is provided at 11 and basement space at 13. On the southward exposed section of the roof, a solar heat collector 3 may be provided, the north-faced roof section being illustrated at 4, this section being utilized to dissipate heat to the atmosphere when desired.

The solar heat collector 3 may be constructed in accordance with teachings embodied in said Patent Number 3,145,707, and may include a liquid distributing pipe 5 through which liquid to be heated is introduced into the heat collector. The heat collector contains insulation, a blackened heat-collecting surface, and a transparent covering 6, (preferably two sheets of transparent material spaced apart) above the heat-collecting surface. Liquid from distributing pipe 5 flows down over the heat-collecting surface, thus becoming heated, and is collected in collector trough 7. The heated liquid flows from trough 7, via conduit 7' to a point of storage or use.

The heat dissipator 4 comprises a simple heat dissipating roofing material. One example of a suitable roofing is illustrated in FIG. 5. The heat dissipator has a distributor manifold 5' similar to manifold 5 of the heat collector. This manifold has small liquid outlet holes therein, for example, one hole for each valley, if corrugated sheet metal is used. The liquid flows down the valleys in small streams and is collected in collector trough 8. The cooled liquid flows from trough 8 via conduit 8' to a point of use or storage. Other types of conventional roofing material may be used, but corrugated aluminum is particularly good.

The construction illustrated in FIG. 2 is very similar to that of FIG. 1, except for the different roof style illustrated. Living space 1 is provided on both the first floor and on the second floor. The present heat dissipator, and the solar heat collector described and claimed in said copending application, lend themselves readily to various roof designs, at low-cost, only a few of which are illustrated.

FIG. 3 illustrates a "butterfly" roof design incorporating a heat dissipator 4, bracing 2 and inlet manifold 5'. The solar heat collector 3 has an inlet manifold 5, a transparent covering 6 and insulation, a blackened heat-collecting surface, etc. In this modification, a single collector trough 9 may be provided if the heat collector and heat dissipator are not to be operated simultaneously. In most installations these devices will be operated alternately, such as summertime use for the heat dissipator and wintertime for the solar heat collector or nighttime use for the dissipator and daytime use for the heat collector. However, where concurrent operation is desired, separate collector troughs may be provided.

FIG. 4 illustrates a building wherein the entire roof is used as a heat dissipator. For many purposes, such a large expanse of heat dissipator is not needed. However, such construction may be used in an installation such as where a stationary diesel power plant is operated in a building and excess heat must be liberated from the engine. The present heat dissipator may be used as a low-cost substitute for the "radiator." Also, where a steam boiler and turbine are used, excess heat from the condenser water may be dissipated from the roof of the building to produce the cooling necessary for high-vacuum on the final stage of the turbine.

As illustrated in FIG. 6, the upward extension of the solar heat collector may be omitted and a single distributor manifold 5 may be used. It may be turned to feed liquid to the heat collector during the winter and turned to feed the liquid to the heat dissipator during the hot months.

The present invention has many advantages over other forms of heat dissipating devices, and is particularly adaptable for use with a solar heat collector so that a building may be cooled and air-conditioned in the summertime, as well as heated by solar energy in the wintertime. (Exemplary apparatus for utilizing the heat, the "cool," or both, which is obtained by this apparatus, forms the subject matter of another Patent No. 3,254,702, filed Aug. 25, 1959, and is not disclosed herein.) Another example of use for both the solar heat collector and heat dissipator is a stationary power plant wherein solar heat is used to preheat boiler water, and the heat dissipator is used to cool the condenser water for a high-vacuum on the final stage of the steam engine, or turbine.

Among the salient features of the present invention are low-cost construction and simplicity of operation. The heat dissipator requires little more than a conventional roof of low-cost permanent roofing, which can be applied to the building with a minimum of labor. Although the solar heat collector disclosed in said prior patent application is simple, the present heat dissipator is even more simple, no glass, Mylar, insulation or black surface being required. (However, in some installations, insulation, or a darkened surface, or both, may be used.) Further, when the two units are utilized in the same installation, the same circulating pump and motor may be used to circulate liquid for heating or for cooling. Also, a single heat or "cool" storage apparatus may be used.

By extending the solar heat collector above the roof apex, as illustrated in FIGS. 1 and 2, the heat dissipator is shaded and kept cooler, so as to be more effective, while the solar heat collector is of greater capacity. Thus, this combination of features yields dual desirable results. If the utmost of cooling is not required, then the cooling apparatus need not be operated in the daytime, and more heat per hour may be liberated from, say midnight to 6:00 a.m. However, due to the heat collector extension keeping the heat dissipator cooler during the daytime, the heat dissipator can be used earlier than midnight if desired, or in the daytime under many conditions.

Heat dissipation is particularly great with this apparatus for several reasons. One reason is that, due to the upward extension of the solar heat collector, the sun does not shine on the roof and hence it is kept cooler. Another reason is that the heat dissipator surface is extremely large, thus being capable of dissipating large quantities of heat by radiation to the atmosphere. In addition, to radiation, the liquid (such as water) flows in thousands of feet of small streams, and hence there is much heat dissipation due to evaporation. Further, inasmuch as the top of the heat dissipator is not as high as the top of the heat collector, it is less steep and the water flows more slowly, thus liberating more heat.

Thus, due to the above factors, where the "coolness" can be stored from night, to be used to air-condition a building the following day, the apparatus need be operated for a short time only. Inasmuch as a small circulating pump is all that is required to run the liquid through the heat dissipator, very little power is required to "get rid of the heat." There is no necessity for a cooling tower, a river of cooling water, heat dissipating wells, heat dissipating coils, fans, or such.

This cooling apparatus may be used with or without the solar heat collector described in Patent No. 3,145,707. I have disclosed apparatus in Patent No. 3,254,702 which is usable with said solar heater and the present heat dissipator to store heat, or to store "coolness." Other apparatus disclosed in said latter application can extract the heat or cool from said storage apparatus and deliver it to living quarters of a home, can filter the air in the home, and can provide standby auxiliary heating means, all with simple, inexpensive equipment. *

Feb. 14, 1967 H. E. THOMASON **3,303,838**

SOLAR HEAT COLLECTOR

*

Fig. 1.

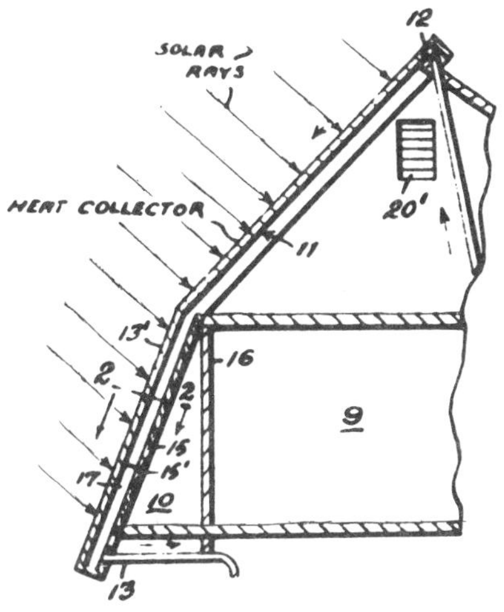

Fig. 2.

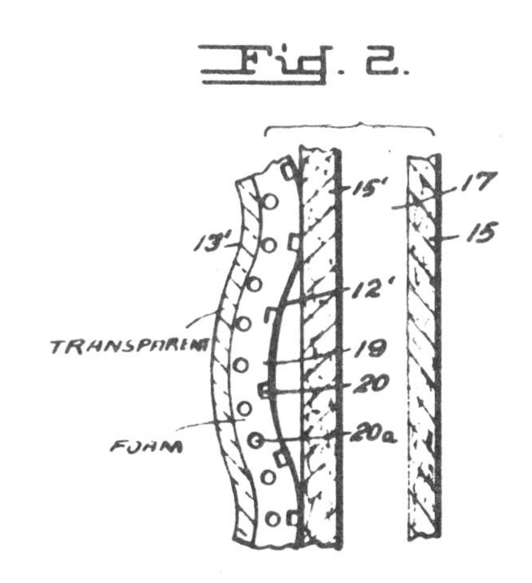

INVENTOR

Harry E. Thomason

3,303,838
SOLAR HEAT COLLECTOR
Harry E. Thomason, District Heights, Md.
(7354 Walker Mill Road SE., Washington, D.C. 20027)

*

The present invention relates to a solar heat collector and more particularly to insulating glazing material therefor with means to remove the heat so collected.

FIG. 1 is a diagrammatic cross section through a solar heat collector installed on a house embodying the present invention.

FIG. 2 is an enlarged view on line 2—2 of FIG. 1.

As illustrated in FIG. 1 the solar house may have living quarters **9**, closet area **10** and a solar heat collector **11**. The closet area has walls **15**, **16**, with both preferably being insulated. A louver **20'** permits escape of heated air from the attic.

The heat collector **11** preferably has a base sheet **12'** adjacent to insulation **15'**. "Chimneys" **17**, between insulation **15'** and **15**, remove excessive heat from the heat collector thus avoiding overheating of adjacent living or closet area **9**, **10** on hot sunny days.

Water is pumped to the top of solar heat collector **11**, is distributed by sparge pipe **12**, and is heated as it flows to the bottom, and out at **13**.

The specific form of the invention illustrated in detail in FIG. 2 has a layer **19** which may be a heat collecting porous layer of material having perforations or passages **20**, **20a**. Layer **19** is preferably attached to an inner base layer of material **12'** which is substantially impervious to a fluid being circulated through the collector and preferably has an external layer of material **13'** which is transparent or reasonably transparent to admit solar energy to or through the material **19**. Material **19** may be darkened to absorb solar energy and to thereby heat fluid passing thereinto or therethrough via perforations or passages **20** or **20a**. However the material may be transparent or translucent to let solar energy penetrate to inner layer **12'** where it heats said inner layer and fluid coming in contact therewith. The porous material may be of a desired thickness of a suitable material such as a porous metallic foam-like material, or plastic, or such, or may be one or more layers of a mesh-like material. Such material may be treated with dyes or other substances within the porous material itself or may be provided with coatings to render the material dark and more heat-arsorbing. Alternatively, the material may be semi-darkened so as to become heated itself or may be transparent or translucent to admit solar energy to the inner surface **12'**, which inner surface may be darkened to collect solar energy to heat a fluid being circulated through the heat collector. Fluid passages **20** are preferably adjacent the heat collecting surface **12'** such as by being embedded in the material **19**. Some materials are porous enough for fluid flow therethrough without additional passages. Fluid may be circulated through passages **20** only, or through passages **20a** only, or through both. Passages similar to those at **20a** are found at random in some foam-like preparations. Although the foam-like and transparent layers are illustrated as being applied to a corrugated base **12'** the base may take other forms or shapes as desired, including planar.

*

June 11, 1968 H. E. THOMASON **3,387,602**

SOLAR HEATER

*

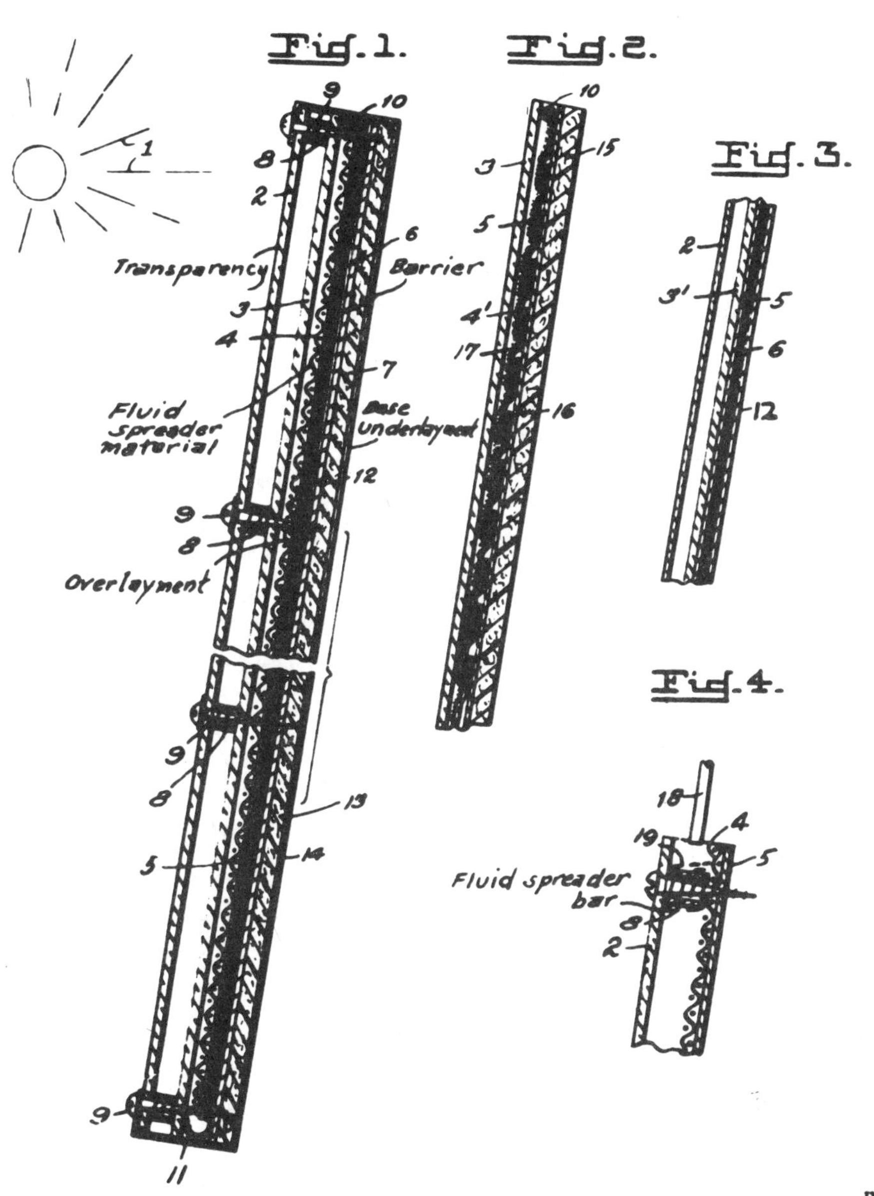

INVENTOR

Harry E. Thomason

3,387,602
SOLAR HEATER
Harry E. Thomason, District Heights, Md. (6802 Walker Mill Road SE., Washington, D.C. 20027)
*

The present invention relates to an improved solar heat collector which is simple and low cost in construction, highly efficient in operation and which has a long life. *

In the drawing:

FIG. 1 is a cross sectional view through one form of the invention;

FIG. 2 is a cross sectional view through a modified form of the invention;

FIG. 3 is a cross sectional view showing a detail of a further modification;

FIG. 4 is a modification of the fluid introducing and spreading apparatus.

Solar energy rays 1 enter the collector through one or more substantially transparent covers. One such cover is illustrated at 2. A solar heat collecting overlayment 5 has fluid spreader-heat collector material 4 closely adjacent thereto and a second substantially transparent cover 3 spaced closely adjacent to material 4. The overlayment 5, of glass fiber, asbestos, paper, wood, pulp, rag or the like, is impregnated with a fluid, as asphalt, coal tar pitch or such. A sand-asphalt, sand-coal tar mixture, or such may be used under certain conditions. The surface turned toward the sun is preferably dark or black and is capable of absorbing solar energy and converting it to heat. A barrier 6 and a base material 7 are preferably provided under overlayment 5, the base being insulating in character. Barrier 6, aluminum foil for example, minimizes passage of oils or fluids out of overlayment 5 and entrance of oxidizing air into this overlayment. Members 8, 9 secure the parts in assembled relationship.

The present invention may be used to heat various fluids. Water, for example, may be used as a fluid to transfer heat from the collector to a point of use or storage. Cold water may be introduced by distributor 10 to trickle and flow down between cover 3 and solar heat collecting overlayment 5 through solar heat absorber-fluid spreader 4, down to trough 11. The solar heat absorber-fluid spreader 4 may be wire mesh, rigid, non-fluid granular material such as sand, or such. Liquid attracting or liquid repelling agents may be used on fluid spreader 4 if desired to help keep the liquid in channels as it descends along the wire mesh or granular material. These agents may be used in parallel strips, ridges, or such, extending from top-to-bottom, to minimize side-skewing of the liquid. It has been found that a wetting agent, added to water, assists in spreading water over black sand-coated asphalt shingles as in FIG. 2, for example.

Underlayment base 7 may comprise, for example, wood sheeting 12, glass fiber or mineral wool 13 and aluminum heat reflective vapor barrier 14 to minimize reversed heat passage back through the collector at night. Barrier 14 also prevents moisture from entering the collector, and condensing on barrier 6.

In FIG. 3, instead of passing the heat transfer fluid to be heated between the overlayment 5 and transparency 3, as in FIG. 1, such fluid may be passed over transparency 3' between transparencies 3' and 2. Fluid flow channeling means, wetting agents or such may be used to obtain uniform wetting of transparency 3'. With this type of construction and operation the fluid spreader material 4 may be used or eliminated as desired. If material 4 is eliminated, inner transparency 3' may be placed directly in contact with overlayment 5, with no air or liquid passage space, to further reduce oxidation and loss of oils and fluids from the upper surface of the heat collecting overlayment.

The following discussion will lead to a better understanding of the principles involved and the value of the present combination of parts.

Numerous problems are encountered because of unusual conditions present in solar heating systems. In a solar heat collector, temperature extremes and temperature cycling deteriorate materials and much more rapidly than they would deteriorate under normal conditions. As examples, one researcher has written that screws used to hold collector parts together were pulled loose during temperature cycling because the collector expanded while collecting heat and contracted during the cool nighttime. Consequent pushing and pulling on the parts soon loosened the screws. The chief scientist of a paint company advises that most ordinary paints would soon crack and peel off from metal solar heat collector sheets due to high temperatures, and repeated temperature cycling, with expansion and contraction of the paint at a rate different from that of the collector sheet. One researcher reported shattering of substantially all of the glass covering soon after his large solar heat collectors for a house-heating system were constructed. Another reported that window glazing compounds, which would last more than twenty years in ordinary building construction, dried and cracked within a few years when used as solar heat collector glazing. Another report showed that a tough plastic film which would last five years or longer as a greenhouse covering material would fail quicker when used as an inner glazing material, "protected" by an outer glass covering, in a solar heat collector.

Products containing oils, asphalt, tar or such would appear useful in solar heat collectors. They are black and solar heat absorptive in character. They are not as subject to corrosion as some materials. They can be used to preserve certain materials. They are plastic when applied at moderate temperatures and are thereby capable of expanding and contracting with temperature changes. However, such materials have not been found satisfactory for use as solar heat collector sheets or as coatings for metal heat collector sheets. When the collector gets cold, asphalt or tar base coatings get hard, brittle, and tend to crack. As the collector gets hot the asphalt or tar base coatings tend to creep down the inclined sheet and drip from or pile up at the bottom. As the coatings age some of the oils oxidize and volatilize out leaving the coatings increasingly drier, brittle and "lifeless." The aging, oxidizing, drying process is accelerated by the high temperature baking in a solar heat collector, sometimes exceeding 250 degrees Fahrenheit.

In a preferred form of the present invention, a sheet of fibrous material is impregnated with asphalt, tar, oils or other fluids to help preserve the fibrous materials and keep them long-lived. The fibrous material, in turn, helps keep the preservative fluids from creeping and cracking. Difficulties arise, nevertheless, because the preservative fluids tend to oxidize, volatilize away and leave the fibrous material dry, brittle and subject to cracking and deterioration. Also, such sheets do not conduct heat readily, and tend to repel water. It is difficult to get heat collecting water to flow evenly over, fully contact, and collect the solar produced heat from such sheets. Thus, it would seem that a disadvantage offsets each advantage as we attempt to use products containing oils, asphalt, tar, etc.

The present invention discloses examples of certain combinations of parts and materials which render such fluid containing fibrous materials usable and long lived to collect solar heat and transfer it to a heat-transfer fluid, even in the extremely rough environmental conditions in solar heat collectors which have shattered glass, deteriorated tough plastic films, ruined paints and glazing compounds and torn screws from their anchorings.

Referring again to the drawing, if water is to be passed through the collector from distributor **10** to trough **11**, and if the rigid or semi-rigid base underlayment **7** comprises a material at **12**, such as plywood for example, it should be protected from water, water vapor or steam which is present between the transparency **3** and the solar heat collecting overlayment **5**. The overlayment **5** itself preferably contains oils or other preservative softening fluids which render the overlayment long-lived and resistant to leakage of water, water vapor or steam. Vapor barrier **6** keeps oxidizing air from getting to overlayment **5**. Barrier **6** may also be resistant to water vapor, in which event it gives added protection against water vapor damage to wood or such at **12**. In addition, vapor barrier **6** should be resistant to oils, oil vapors and such coming from overlayment **5**. Thus, barrier **6**, which may be reflective metal foil, for example, minimizes oxidation in and escape of oils and volatilizable fluids from overlayment **5**. This minimizes drying out and cracking of the overlayment, thereby adding greatly to the life of the overlayment.

High temperature baking and solar energy rays **1** accelerate oxidization and drive off the oils and volatilizable fluids from the upper surface also of overlayment **5**. Substantially transparent cover **3** is provided to admit solar energy rays **1** and to minimize oxidization and escape of such oils and fluids from the upper surface. This cover is preferably very closely spaced above the overlayment to minimize the amount of air, convection currents, etc. and drying effects thereof, between the overlayment and transparent cover. The close spacing between the cover and overlayment also helps keep the fluid spread evenly over the solar warmed surfaces of the overlayment inside of the transparent cover.

The present invention departs from recommendations of the experts. The transparent cover **3** is placed in very close proximity to the overlayment collector sheet **5**, instead of an inch or so above as is customary. This minimizes movement of the air and oxidization or drying of the collector sheet. Fluid spreader material **4** also helps reduce air convection currents. In the modification of FIG. 3 the transparency is preferably in contact with the collector sheet, thereby substantially eliminating contact of the hot oxidizing drying air with the overlayment collector sheet and prolonging the life of the overlayment.

A further benefit is realized from use of fluid spreader material **4**, which is also a solar heat absorbing material. Such fluid spreader-heat collector material provides shade for much of the surface of overlayment **5** to thereby reduce the deteriorating effects of direct sunshine. In some instances fluid does not flow perfectly and absolutely uniformly over an entire solar heat collecting sheet or overlayment. A heat conducting mesh at **4** assures that the heat can flow through the mesh from areas of heat collection but poor or no fluid flow, to areas of good fluid flow.

The inner transparency **3**, of plastic, glass or other, may be clamped under spreader-supports **8** if desired. The degree of tightness of the clamping of such spreader-support will squeeze the spreader material **4** more or less tightly against or into overlayment **5**. This results in an adjustable valve action whereby the degree of spreading of the fluid may be adjusted. If desired spreader-supports **8** may be supported directly by fluid spreader material **4**, and transparency **3** may extend between one member **8** and the next without extending beneath spreader supports **8**. In this type of construction also, members **8** serve to spread the fluid as it passes thereunder.

FIG. 4 illustrates that spreader-supports, as at **8**, may be used for the initial spreading of the liquid as it is brought onto the heat collector overlayment **5**. Thus, instead of using a distributor pipe with holes in it, as shown at the top of the collector in Patent Number 3,145,707, the liquid can be pumped onto the heat collecting overlayment directly, as at **18**, in one or more main streams. The liquid, illustrated at **19**, must then spread out into many small streams to pass under spreader-bar **8**. Thus, we can eliminate a part, as distributor pipe **10**, in FIG. 1, and yet retain the function, thereby simplifying the apparatus and lowering construction costs. If desired, the spreader **8** may be inclined slightly to aid in causing the fluid **19** to spread from the inlet pipe **18** toward the side or sides of the collector.

The spreader-supports, in this combination, yield an additional very important function in solar seat collectors which are vertical, or near vertical. In a construction as in Patent No. 3,145,707, wherein the heat collector sheet is corrugated, V-crimped, or similarly distorted, the "hills-and-valleys" become quite ineffective to channel the flow of liquid in parallel paths from top-to-bottom if the collector is stood vertically on end. If a corrugated sheet is stood vertically on end, there are no hills-and-valleys, only ins-and-outs. Therefore, fluid channeling ordinarily is not effective.

The construction described herein makes it feasible to operate the collector in a more nearly or completely vertical position and yet obtain good spreading characteristics of the fluid flow, and good contact between the fluid and the heat collecting overlayment, for reasons to follow. Cold liquid to be heated is introduced onto overlayment **5** by distributor **10**, or by spreader-distributor **8** as described above. It clings to overlayment **5** and fluid spreader **4** by molecular attraction as it descends. However, molecular attraction within the liquid itself also tends to gather the liquid into streams. If such streams form, they are sometimes deviated from their normal downward path as they follow paths of least resistance, or of greatest molecular attraction or repulsion. If these streams traveled 10, 20, 30, 40, 50 feet or further down the collector overlayment, without being re-spread, this could leave large areas of heat collecting overlayment unvisited by the heat transfer liquid. However, the successive spreader-supports **8** keep re-spreading and redistributing the liquid as it descends the overlayment, thereby increasing contact between the liquid and the heat collecting materials at **4**, **5**, thereby increasing heat collection ability of the collector.

Barrier **14** is preferably both reflective of heat, and resistant to passage of vapor. The solar heat collector may be used as a wall of an enclosed area such as a swimming pool, a home or other building, where the air inside is warmed and has fairly large quantities of water vapor therein. Infrared heat rays are reflected back into the enclosed area if barrier **14** is reflective. Also, moisture within the area is prevented from entering the insulation **13** and condensing or freezing in the insulation or on vapor varrier **6** during cold nights or at other periods when solar energy input is low and barrier **6** is cool.

FIG. 2 illustrates a modification. One or more transparent covers may be used. A rigid or semi-rigid insulating material, such as foamed glass, foamed plastic, or such, is used at **15**.

FIG. 2 also illustrates a detail as to how the heat collecting overlayment may be constructed. It has been found that, in solar heat collectors, some forms of overlayment containing asphalt or tar or other oil bearing or fluid containing materials, will expand and contract and thereby buckle and stretch as temperatures fluctuate widely, and as liquids, vapors, and humidity conditions adjacent to the overlayment fluctuate or are varied. This tends to shorten the life of the overlayment material and to disrupt and unbalance the flow of fluid over such overlayment. The overlayment here comprises a series of small sheets, preferably but not necessarily overlapped like shingles. Transparency 3, bearing directly on the overlayment, helps to overcome these problems by keeping the overlayment flat. If the transparency is fairly heavy and the collector is inclined, or flat, the weight of the transparency may be sufficient to keep the overlayment held firmly in place and to hold the flow of fluid to thin proportions. If the transparency is light in weight, or if the collector is mounted substantially vertically, spreader-support members 8 may be used as in FIG. 1 to clamp the transparency closely adjacent to the overlayment, spaced by fluid-spreader material 4', which may be screen wire, as illustrated in FIG. 1, non-volatilizable granules, or such.

The overlayment may be constructed as follows to further minimize the tendency to buckle and stretch. An under-overlayment member 16 may comprise one or more large sheets of material which have a minimum of joints per solar heat collector unit. If desired, these under-overlayment sheets may contain oils or other fluids to keep them from deteriorating and to keep them pliable, expandable and compressible. They may be overlapped or constructed as plies, with successive layers running at right angles to one another, or with wide overlaps of the plies, or with both features. Then, an outer-overlayment member 17, of smaller pieces of material, may be added, and the entire assembly secured to the rigid insulating base 15, or to a rigid underlayment as illustrated at 12 in FIG. 1. In such case a barrier may be added as at 6 in FIG. 1 and another barrier may be used between members 17 and 16. Such barriers may be aluminum foil, for example, which are simple and inexpensive and give further protection against transfer of water, steam, vapor or heat from heat-collecting overlayment 17 to the rigid underlayment 12 (FIG. 1) or 15 (FIG. 2).

Referring again to FIG. 3, overlayment 5 has a substantially transparent covering 3', preferably directly in contact with the upper surface of the overlayment. Thus, ambient air is precluded from coming into contact with the upper surface of the overlayment and oxidation and volatilization of the fluids in the overlayment are held to a minimum. Solar produced heat generated at the overlayment may be removed in one or more ways. As examples, the heat from the overlayment may be conducted to barrier 6 and picked up by a heat transfer fluid contacting the barrier. Alternatively, the heat from the overlayment may be conducted to transparency 3' (which also converts a portion of the solar energy into heat due to impurities in the transparency). The heat may be picked up by a heat transfer fluid contacting this transparency. One or more outer transparencies, as at 2, may be used adjacent to transparency 3' with heat transfer fluid being passed between transparency 3' and such outer transparency.

The present invention represents a further step forward in simplifying large solar heat collector construction and in cutting the cost. In the low temperature range especially, as used for some solar home heating systems, domestic water heating, swimming pool heating and such, the present invention is highly efficient in collecting solar heat. *

U.S. Patent Oct. 7, 1975 H.E. THOMASON H.J.L. THOMASON, Jr. 3,910,253

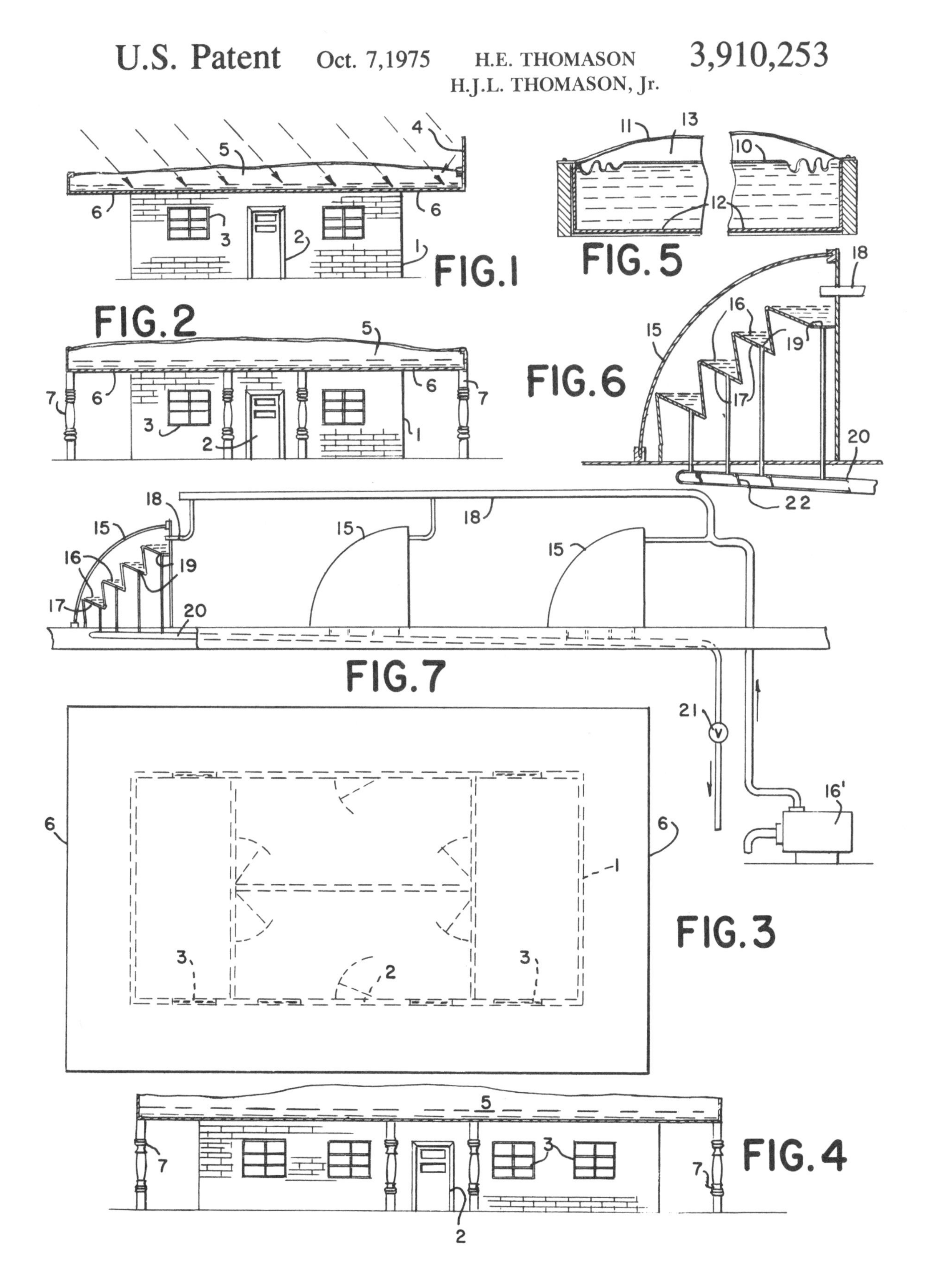

FLAT ROOF SOLAR HEATED BUILDING
*

INTRODUCTION

For rather cold climates where many cloudy days occur during the winter a flat-plate type of solar heat collector is generally set at a fairly steep angle (about 45° to 60° as in U.S. Pat. No. 3,145,707, granted to Harry E. Thomason. The heat is collected and stored in a heat storage bin in a basement area as in U.S. Pat. No. 3,254,702, granted to Harry E. Thomason. That combination of collector and storage has provided near 95% of the heat requirements for a three-bedroom home in the area of Washington, D. C. where the temperature drops below the freezing mark often, where near half of the days are cloudy, and where snow, ice and cold rain are common, (see Solar Energy Journal, Vol. X, No. 1, Jan. 1966, pages 17–22).

For areas where heating of buildings by solar energy is not as difficult the "Sunny South" model has been developed, described in the book "Solar Houses and Solar House Models," Second Edition, page 15, by Harry E. Thomason, published by Edmund Scientific Company, 605 Edscorp Building, Barrington N.J. 08007, Library of Congress Catalog Card No. 72-25084. A shallow pond of water on the roof, preferably covered by a transparent member, warms the water daily. The water flows to "pancake" heat storage space under the floors to warm the floors and building.

If a shallow pond of water were constructed on a roof in a conventional manner, the supporting members would have to be fairly strong to minimize bending. That would increase the cost of the building. Also, if the roof-pond were only as large as the building itself, it would intercept only the amount of solar energy falling on the limited roof area. Therefore, the amount of heat would not be adequate for some of the cold nights and cloudy days. By providing an overhanging heat collector, as taught in the present application, with or without supporting columns, the collector area may be increased significantly without heavy roof timbers.

If no protective cover were provided, cold rain falling on a solar heat collecting pond would have to be heated to be useful for solar heating of the building. Evaporation of a part of such water, and evaporation of water from the pond, would waste much valuable solar-produced heat. In the present invention cover means reduce such heat loss. Also, if the small ponds are stair-stepped they collect more solar heat, per gallon of water being warmed, during the winter when the sun is low in the sky.

The present invention helps solve the problems discussed above, and provides other benefits as will become apparent to those skilled in the art.

BRIEF SUMMARY

The present invention provides a solar heated building, with a substantially flat roof, with an overhanging area for a solar heat collector or collectors of the pond type. The heat collecting area may have many ponds, and reflectors if desired.

By using the roof overhang and rooftop pond approach of the present invention at least six advantages are obtained.

1. The heat collecting area is increased, to provide more free solar heat.

2. The roof area is cantilevered to support the weight of the pond of water with less bending of the roof beams and a minimum sagging of the ceiling inside. The larger pond area does not need to be as deep.

3. The roof-pond overhand protects the sides of the building from the weather.

4. The roof-pond overhang shade during the hot summer months.

5. The overhang provides a covered walkway area around the building and protects the area from the rain, snow, sleet and so on.

6. The architectural appearance of the building is improved. Colonial style columns may be provided, if desired, to enhance the beauty, or to help support the overhanging area, or both.

By covering the pond with an air supported or a dome-like covering, cold rain does not enter the solar heat collecting pond. And, the warm air trapped above the pond reduces heat losses from the pond on cold days.

IN THE DRAWINGS

FIG. 1 is a side elevational view of one embodiment, partly in cross section;

FIG. 2 is a view illustrating a modification;

FIG. 3 is a floor plan;

FIG. 4 is a side elevational view illustrating a larger building;

FIG. 5 is a detail of a heat collecting pond and covers;

FIG. 6 is a cross section of modified small heat collecting ponds;

FIG. 7 is a diagrammatic illustration of a series of groups of small ponds on a flat roof building.

The solar heated building illustrated at 1 may be a home, factory, warehouse, or other, and may have conventional doors 2 and windows 3. If desired a reflector 4 may be provided along the north edge of the building to intercept sunlight that would normally pass over the top of the building and reflect it down into the rooftop heat collecting pond 5.

The rooftop heat collecting area extends beyond the periphery of the building as illustrated at 6. The overhanging area may extend outwardly in cantilever fashion as illustrated in FIG. 1. Or, the overhanging area may be supported, or partially supported by columns 7, as in FIGS. 2 and 4. Columns 7 may be utilized to beautify the building, in Colonial styling, even if they are not used to support the overhanging area 6. In that event the columns may by "dummy" columns, more-or-less free standing without actually supporting the overhanging area. That would leave the overhanging area, and the weight of the water in the pond thereabove, to counterbalance a portion of the pond area above the building area. Or, the overhanging area may be made larger, in which event the columns support the additional weight without the necessity of extra-heavy, roof-supporting members.

To illustrate the value of the overhang, in terms of solar heat collecting area, let us assume the building to be a more-or-less standard 24 by 42 foot size house. Assume the overhang to be six feet. The building will cover 1,008 square feet while the heat collecting area covers 1,944 square feet. That substantially doubles the solar heat collecting area and the solar energy received by the collector. From another viewpoint, the water in the pond can be about half as deep and yet have the same number of gallons. Therefore, the water will become warmer, and the roof timbers may be much lighter and less expensive, due to the shallower pond supported thereabove. This is all-the-more true due to the cantilever feature, with the weight over the overhanging area partially counterbalancing the weight over the building. Indeed, by proper design, a substantially perfect counterbalance can be achieved.

The overhang also helps protect the building from weathering and provides a walkway area around the building protected from rain, snow, etc. in the winter. It also helps protect from the hot sun in the summer. This helps keep the building cool. And, the larger pond area provides far more cooling of the water on the rooftop at night, as taught in U.S. Pat. No. 3,295,591, by Harry E. Thomason.

The rooftop pond area itself may be a single pond or a series of smaller ponds as disclosed in Ser. No. 153,339. During the winter, cold rain, wind, etc. on the pond area could waste away heat from the rooftop. If cold rain were allowed to remain on or in the rooftop pond or ponds, much solar heat would be wasted in warming it. Or, cold wind would waste away much of the heat if it were allowed to blow directly onto the pond surface, or if it were allowed to blow directly onto a transparent or opaque cover in contact with the top of the water in the pond. To reduce such losses, preferably one or two transparent films or members are placed above the pond, as described more particularly hereafter.

FIG. 5 illustrates details of a type of rooftop pond usable on a flat roof building. One is illustrated at 10 and another at 11. The pond liner 12 is preferably substantially black, to absorb solar energy passing through the clear water to heat the water. The inner transparency 10 may be a plastic film, a clear film of oil or other liquid lighter than water, or a thin layer of clear insulating foam as in U.S. Pat. No. 3,303,838, by Harry E. Thomason, or even black as explained hereinafter. The outer transparency 11 may be a rigid transparent bubble of glass or plastic, or such. Or, it may be a plastic film, supported in bubble-like fashion, by air trapped in space 13. Or it may be a film, or glass, supported by conventional struts. If desired, transparency 10 may be eliminated, or it also may be supported above the water by air trapped between the transparency and the water. The bubble-supporting air may be simply trapped under the transparency or transparencies, or it may be blown in by a small low-pressure blower, or by funneling wind into the space under the transparency through a simple low-pressure check valve damper.

Although element 10 is described as transparent, it may be black, in which case it will become warm, as it intercepts solar energy, and will warm the water therebeneath.

A pipe, or pipes, may be used to introduce water to be heated and to extract heat water from the pond area, as described in application Ser. No. 153,339.

FIG. 6 illustrates a small pond type device adaptable for factory production and usable on the flat roof design buildings of FIGS. 1, 2, 3 and 4. FIG. 7 illustrates several of these ponds on a flat roof building. The transparent bubble 15 may be rigid and self supporting, or air supported, or strut supported as described with regard to FIG. 5. Water 16 may be pumped, by pump 16', into small ponds 17 through large inlet pipe 18 each morning. After the uppermost pond is filled it overflows and the others are filled successively. The water may drain from each pond back to storage by way of outlets 19 and pipes connected to return pipe 20. Valve 21 may be opened at the end of the day to permit flow back to the place for storage and use for the night. Check valves 22 prevent flow to a lower pond from a higher pond. Or, outlets 19 may be very small to permit slow drainage, calculated to empty each small pond within several hours. As one example, the ponds may be filled at 9:00 A.M. and drain empty by 4:00 P.M. As the hours go by a portion of the warmed water returns to storage each hour to help keep the building warm. And, that remaining in the ponds and returning latter in the day becomes warmer and warmer. As another example, the ponds may be filled at 9:00 A.M. and drain empty by about noon. Then they may be filled again to drain empty a second time by about 4:00 P.M.

The drawing does not illustrate overflow of one small pond to fill the one therebelow. It will be understood that overflow is the normal process of spilling over a lip of a pond, or spilling over a fluted edge or spillway of a lip, or overflowing through a pipe or trough adjacent to the top, or other well-known overflow arrangements.

From the foregoing it will be apparent that a numer of features in the improved "Sunny South Model" are combined to increase heat collection, to reduce construction costs, to reduce roof beam bending, to beautify the structure, to protect the exterior of the building, to provide a protected walk area, and so on. *

ABSTRACT

A solar heated building has a substantially flat roof with a substantially horizontal solar heat collector on top. The solar heat collector is of a type known as a shallow pond, or a plurality of shallow ponds, preferably covered by a transparency. The pond-type solar heat collector area is extended out beyond the area of the building itself in an overhanging fashion.

A transparent cover over the pond may be air supported, or may have a dome shape or such, to discharge cold rain and increase efficiency for solar heat collection.

A plurality of shallow ponds may be arranged in stair-step fashion to increase solar heat collection in winter when the sun is lower in the sky.

7 Drawing Figures

March 12, 1968 S. SHACHAR 3,372,691

METHOD AND SYSTEM FOR MAINTAINING A VERTICALLY VARYING CONCENTRATION IN A LIQUID SOLUTION AND FOR CONVERTING BODIES OF WATER INTO EFFICIENT SOLAR COLLECTORS

* *

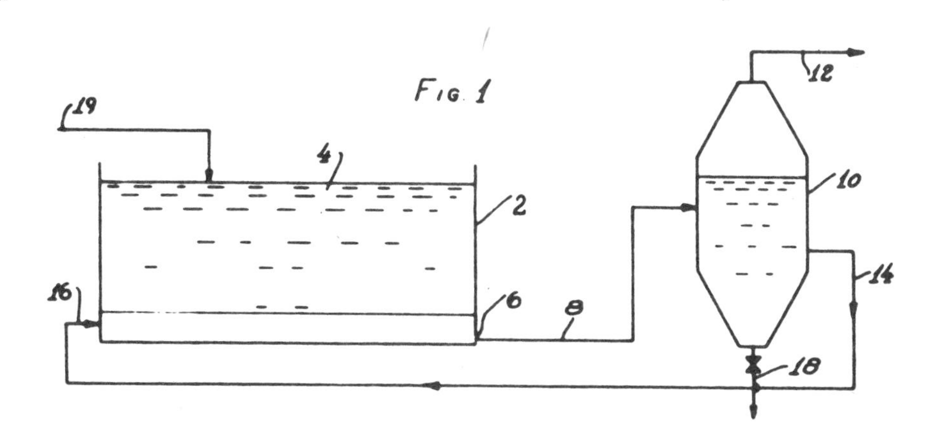

Fig. 1

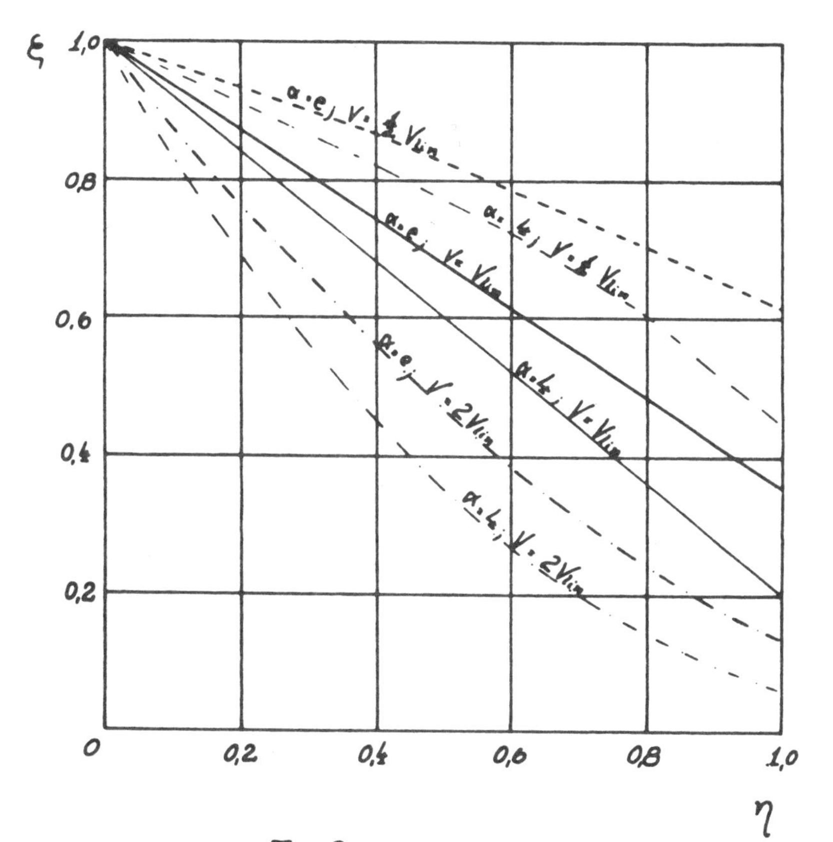

Fig. 2

INVENTOR

SPRAYA SHACHAR

BY Benjamin J. Barish

ATTORNEY

March 12, 1968 S. SHACHAR **3,372,691**

METHOD AND SYSTEM FOR MAINTAINING A VERTICALLY VARYING CONCENTRATION IN A LIQUID SOLUTION AND FOR CONVERTING BODIES OF WATER INTO EFFICIENT SOLAR COLLECTORS

* *

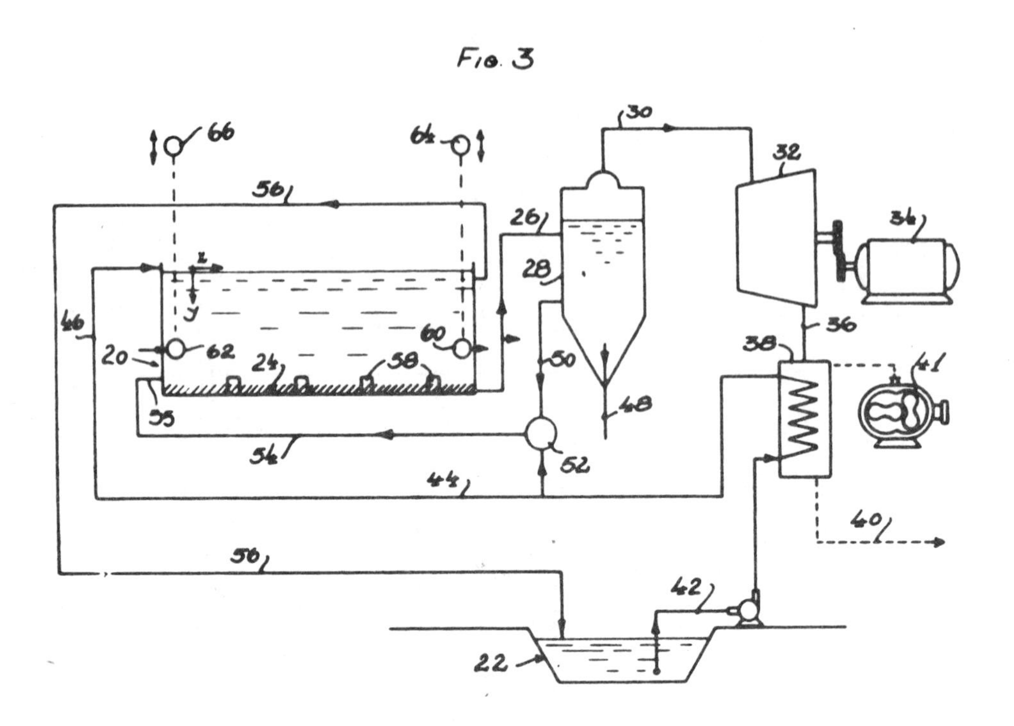

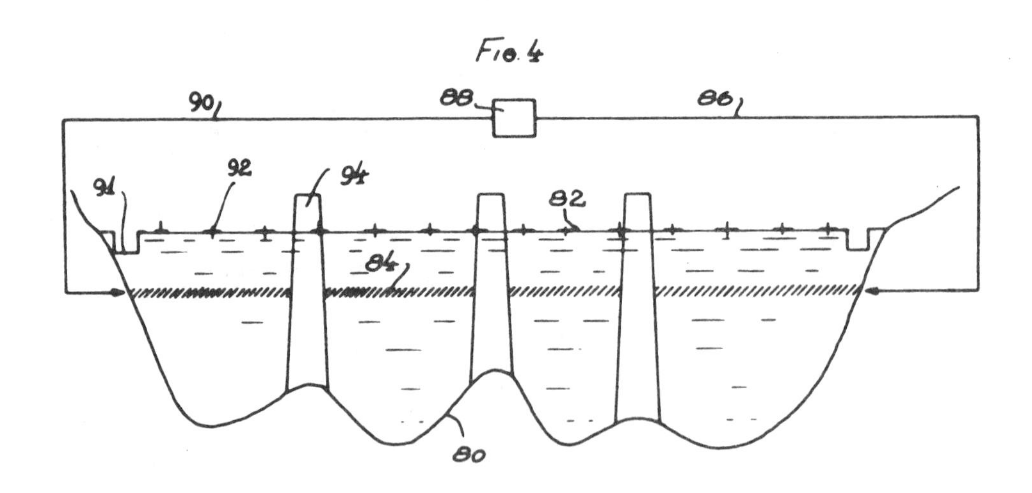

INVENTOR

SPRAYA SHACHAR

BY

ATTORNEY

3,372,691
METHOD AND SYSTEM FOR MAINTAINING A VERTICALLY VARYING CONCENTRATION IN A LIQUID SOLUTION AND FOR CONVERTING BODIES OF WATER INTO EFFICIENT SOLAR COLLECTORS
Sprays Shachar, 15 Sderot Ben-Zion, Tel Aviv, Israel
*

ABSTRACT OF THE DISCLOSURE

A method and system are described for maintaining an inverse temperature gradient between an upper and a lower level in a liquid column, for example, a solar pond of saline water in which the pond has a dark layer to absorb radiations from the sun applied through the upper layer. A vertically varying concentration of the salt in the solar pond sufficient to support the inverse temperature gradient is maintained by inducing a downward flow of the saline water counter to the diffusion flux of the salt. This counter flow is induced by extracting, from the lower level, water having a smaller concentration of salt then at the upper level, both being regulated at rates so as to maintain the vertically varying concentration while avoiding excessive mixing.

The present invention relates to a method and system for maintaining a vertically varying concentration in a liquid solution and for converting bodies of water into efficient solar collectors. The invention is hereafter described particularly with respect to the latter application, i.e. solar collectors or solar ponds, as this application represents the one which at the present time appears to have the greatest potential commercial importance.

Generally, there is no difficulty in creating and maintaining a considerable temperature gradient in liquids when they are being heated at the surface. The heated upper layer expands and its density is reduced so that it remains at the top. In the absence of mixing, the heat-transfer to the lower layers is therefore by means of conduction only. In a liquid of low conduction, a considerable temperature gradient can thus be created.

However, if the liquid is heated from below, the lower layer will expand and, because of its reduced density, will rise to the top starting the well-known convection currents. As a result, the temperature throughout the liquid will be substantially equalized. Ordinarily, therefore, an inverse temperature gradient (i.e. a temperature increasing with depth) cannot be created in a liquid column because of convection.

If a liquid solution is used where the solute is heavier than the solvent so that its concentration decreases continuously from the bottom toward the top, the density of the solution will also decrease from the bottom toward the top. If this solution is now heated from below, an inverse temperature gradient will be created and maintained so long as the reduction in density caused by the higher temperature of the bottom layer is not greater than the increase in density due to the higher concentration; or, more acurately, so long as the resulting density gradient does not reach the point required for the initiation of convection at any level. With a sufficiently large difference in concentration between the top and the bottom of the solution, the obtainable difference in temperature can be large enough for utilization in industrial processes. For example, in an experiment with an aqueous solution of magnesium chloride 100 cm. in depth, nearly saturated at the bottom (the density being 1.3 at 27° C.) and the concentration decreasing linearly down to zero at the top (density 1.0), there has been attained, after heating slowly from below, a temperature above 90° C. at the bottom decreasing to 30° C. at the top.

Although there is no difficulty in filling a container with a solution in which the concentration decreases from bottom to top as required, the maintenance of this varying concentration over a long period of time presents a very serious problem. As a result of molecular diffusion, the difference in concentration between the top and the bottom layers will decrease continuously with time. Thin convective layers will form at both ends, and their thickness will grow, until the whole column of liquid becomes convective and both concentration and temperature are practically the same at all depths. If the concentration gradient is used for maintaining an inverse temperature gradient in a large expanse of water, the situation is much worse, since in addition to the molecular diffusion, there will also be mixing caused by the wind, waves, evaporation, and other factors, all of which will combine in speeding up the destruction of the density gradient and causing the solution to become homogeneous.

The use of a concentration gradient for supporting an inverse temperature gradient in liquids can therefore be of practical significance only if the concentration gradient can be maintained substantially stable for a long period of time. One method proposed for accomplishing this is described in Israel Patent No. 12,561 of May 25, 1959, which deals with the conversion of shallow ponds into large collectors of solar energy known as "solar" ponds. As described there, the gradient is maintained by the continuous or periodic addition of solid solute or concentrated solution to the bottom region of the solar pond and the continuous or periodic addition of fresh water or dilute solution to the surface region of the pond, and draining by overflow some liquid from the surface region of the pond. In other words, this method is characterized by the addition of salt to the bottom of the pond and the washing of salt out at the top with fresh water.

An object of the present invention is to provide a new method and system for maintaining a relatively varying concentration of a solute in a liquid solution, which method and system do not necessarily require the continuous addition of either salt or fresh water.

A further object of the invention is to provide a new method and system for maintaining an inverse temperature gradient between an upper and a lower level in a liquid solution, particularly in a solar pond or solar collector.

A still further object of the invention is to provide a new method for producing a solar pond from a lake or other depression in land which is naturally filled, or which may be artifically filled, with water.

In practicing the invention, there is first prepared in any suitable manner a vertically varying concentration of a solute in a liquid column with the concentration of the solute greatest at one level of the solution and decreasing continuously toward a second level, so that the resulting density of the solution decreases continuously from the lower to the upper of the said two levels. According to the invention, this vertically varying concentration is maintained by inducing a vertical flow of the liquid column counter to the diffusion flux of the solute, the counterflow being induced by extracting from the said one level a solvent having a smaller concentration of solute than at said second level and adding at said second level solvent having a smaller concentration of solute than at said second level. The rates of the mentioned extraction and addition are regulated such as to maintain the required vertically varying concentration while avoiding excessive mixing tending to destroy the same.

It will be understood, with respect to the terminology

used above and as it may also be used hereinafter, that the solvent extracted from said one level could have a "zero" concentration of solute, i.e. it could be pure solvent. This also applies with respect to the solvent added at said second level. It will also be understood that the extraction step could be effected in many different manners involving one or more steps, so long as the final and net effect is that as set forth. For example, according to a preferred embodiment the solvent is extracted by withdrawing solution from the said one level, extracting the solvent from the withdrawn solution by evaporation, and returning the remaining solution (which may be mixed with fresh solution) back to the same level. It is also conceivable that the extraction of the solvent from the said one level could be done in some cases by vaporizing solvent at that level and passing it through the solution itself in the form of vapor bubbles to condense at the second level where the addition step is to be performed. Further, where levels are mentioned, this is intended to include not only exactly at, but also in the vicinity of, the mentioned level. Also, where a salt or solute is mentioned, it is of course contemplated that this could include a plurality of salts or solutes.

Preferably, the liquid solution is such that the concentration of the solute also decreases continuously from the lower to the upper of the said two levels. In this application, the counterflow is induced by extracting from the lower level solvent having a smaller concentration of solvent than at the upper level, and adding at the upper level solvent having a smaller concentration of solute than at the upper level.

According to a preferred embodiment of the invention, this method and system are used for maintaining an inverse temperature gradient between an upper and a lower level in a solar pond of saline water in which the solar pond has a dark layer to absorb radiations from the sun applied through the upper level of the pond. In this case, the counterflow is induced by extracting from the lower level water having a smaller concentration of salt than at the upper level, and adding at the upper level water having a smaller concentration of salt than at the upper level. The rates of the extraction and addition are regulated such as to maintain a substantially stable vertically varying concentration while avoiding excessive mixing tending to destroy same. The vertically varying concentration should be sufficient to maintain a substantially stable vertically varying density decreasing continuously from the lower level to the upper level, thus preventing convection currents and maintaining the inverse temperature gradient.

According to a further feature of the invention, there is provided a method of producing a solar pond from a lake or other natural depression in land filled with salt water, comprising establishing a vertically varying concentration of salt in the pond decreasing continuously from the bottom upwardly and introducing a darkened layer at a predetermined depth to constitute a false bottom in the pond, the vertically varying concentration between the darkened layer and the top of the pond being sufficient to support the required inverse temperature gradient between the darkened layer and the top of the pond. The vertically varying concentration is then maintained in the manner described above.

Further features and advantages of the invention will be apparent from the description below.

The invention may take a number of forms, but is herein described below with respect to the accompanying drawings which illustrate, by way of example only, three embodiments of the invention.

In the drawings:

FIG. 1 is a schematic diagram of a simple system constructed in accordance with the invention;

FIG. 2 is a chart helpful in understanding the basic principles of the invention;

FIG. 3 is a schematic diagram of another system constructed in accordance with the invention to show its use for the production of power, desalinated water, and salt; and

FIG. 4 is a schematic diagram of a further embodiment of the invention showing the utilization of natural depressions or existing lakes as solar ponds.

The invention will be better understood by first referring to FIG. 1 which is a simplified schematic diagram illustrating the main principles of the invention.

In FIG. 1, a container 2 is filled with a solution 4 the concentration of which increases with depth as required. The solution is heated slowly from below until the desired temperature of the bottom layer is reached. This temperature is usually referred to as the "operating temperature." For practical uses it should be at least 20° C. higher than the temperature of the upper layer, but in most cases the difference will be considerably greater.

When the operating temperature is reached, the bottom layer is circulated in the following manner: Solution from the bottom layer is withdrawn through outlet 6 at one end of the container near the bottom, and is pumped through a pipe 8 into a flash evaporator 10. Here, a small part of the solvent is evaporated and withdrawn through pipe 12. The remaining solution is cooled and concentrated thereby, and is returned through pipe 14 to an inlet 16 at the bottom of the opposite end of the container. The separated water vapor passing through pipe 12 may be used for power purposes and/or may be condensed and used as desalinated water. Crystallized salt accumulating in the flash evaporator 10 may be removed through duct 18.

This circulation of the bottom layer through outlet 6, evaporator 10, and return inlet 16, produces a slow and steady flow of the bottom layer from the end of inlet 16 toward the end of outlet 6. During this flow over the heated bottom of the container, the temperature of the flowing solution will rise. This circulation with a continuous evaporation of liquid in the flash evaporator 10 will cause the surface level of the solution in the container to fall at the velocity "u," which is equal to the quantity of liquid evaporated in the evaporator (Qe) divided by the horizontal cross section (A) of the container (thus $u=Qe/A$).

For a closed-cycle system, the surface level of the solution in the container could be kept constant by condensing the steam produced in the evaporator 10 with a surface condenser and adding the distilled liquid through pipe 19 to the top of the solution 4 in container 2. Disregarding for the moment possible losses, the surface level of the solution will thus be kept constant, and in addition to the flux of solute from the bottom toward the top of the solution caused by diffusion, there will be produced the steady counterflow, from the top downwardly, of the whole solution in the container. This counterflow will be at the velocity u.

Under these conditions, the change in concentration as a function of depth is fixed by the diffusion equation. The condition for steady state in the concentration-depth curve is that the total flux of solute through any horizontal plane be zero, and therefore the diffusion equation will have the form:

$$-uc=Ddc/dx \qquad \text{(Equation 1)}$$

where c is the concentration and D is the molecular diffusion coefficient of the solute at any height x above the bottom of the container. In the method described for purposes of the example, the concentration at the bottom is kept approximately constant (for $x=o, c=c_o$).

For the solution of this equation, we have to know the diffusion coefficient D. This coefficient is not constant as it depends on the concentration and temperature. It will therefore also vary with x and will generally be greater at the bottom of the solution where the concentration and temperature are higher, and decrease gradually towards the top as the concentration and temperature are reduced.

From the solution of the foregoing equation, when D is constant and also when D varies linearly with x as explained, it may be concluded as follows:

First, the described method (hereinafter sometimes referred to as the "counterflow stabilization" or "CFS" method) enables the constant existence of a varying concentration decreasing from bottom to top as required:

Secondly, the shape of the steady-state concentration-depth curve depends on the velocity u, and can be varied to become convex, linear, or concave by a suitable adjustment of u.

Thirdly, the method also enables the maintenance in the solution of an inverse temperature gradient the maximum value of which is fixed by the condition that the resultant density gradient at any level will not reach the point where convection is initiated. The maximum allowable inverse temperature gradient is therefore dependent on the concentration at the bottom of the container and the shape of the concentration curve, which in turn depends on the velocity u, both of which can be selected within certain fixed limits. By changing the velocity u during operation, the concentration curve can be modified or corrected, for example when desired to change somewhat the operating characteristics of the solution or to correct deviations caused by external factors.

FIG. 2 illustrates a group of steady-state concentration-depth curves resulting from the solution of the diffusion equation when the diffusion coefficient varies linearly with depth according to the equation:

$$D=D_h\left(1+\alpha-\frac{\alpha x}{h}\right) \quad \text{(Equation 2)}$$

where:

$$\alpha=\frac{D_o-D_h}{D_h}$$

In the foregoing, D_h is the diffusion coefficient at the surface; D_o is the diffusion coefficient at the bottom; and h is the height of the solution surface above the bottom.

The six curves in FIG. 2 are plotted for the following non-dimensional coordinates:

$$V=\frac{u.h}{D};\ \eta=\frac{x}{h};\ \xi=\frac{c}{C_o}$$

Each curve represents the steady-state concentration-depth distribution of the solute for the values of α and V indicated on the curve. The values of α are given numerically while the values of V are given in terms of V_{lin}, the latter being the non-dimensional counterflow velocity for which the concentration depth distribution is described by a straight line. The chosen values of α: $\alpha=e(e=2.7)$ and $\alpha=4$, are estimated to cover the variations of α to be expected in the actual operation of a solar pond filled with suitably concentrated sea water, while the chosen values of V show how the variation of the counter-flow velocity affects the shape of the concentration-depth curve as explained previously.

The rate of heat withdrawal from the container into the evaporator is equal to the rate of flow multiplied by the temperature drop in the evaporator. From the utilization point of view, the temperature drop should in most cases be as small as possible. On the other hand, the reduction of the temperature drop will be limited by economic considerations in view of the consequent increase in the rate of flow necessary for transferring the required amount of heat. An excessive temperature difference between the entry and exit end of the container should also be avoided as it is bound to affect the flow pattern of the bottom layer which may be difficult to control.

The quantity of liquid evaporated in the evaporator depends on the rate of heat withdrawal only, while the required counterflow velocity (u), and therefore also the quantity of liquid to be added to the top of the solution, is determined by considerations of concentration curve stability. When the required velocity is smaller than that resulting from condensing all the evaporated liquid and adding it to the top of the solution, it can be achieved by feeding part of the condensed liquid back into the bottom layer on its return from the evaporator. On the other hand, when the required velocity is greater than that made possible by the evaporation in the evaporator, the required velocity can be achieved by drawing off some solution from the circulating bottom layer. In this case, the addition of some solute may be required to keep the concentration of the bottom layer constant.

It is clear, therefore, that this method for maintaining stabilization by inducing a counterflow, can be adjusted as dictated by stability considerations without necessarily being influenced by the heat withdrawal rate. The velocity can also be made negative, if solution is added to the bottom layer. However, it should be clear that the counterflow velocity, ensuring a steady concentration curve when there exists in the solution an inverse temperature gradient, may vary in most cases only within a very limited range. The possibility for an extensive change in this velocity is therefore important only as a temporary measure for correcting harmful deviations in the planned concentration curve.

If the solution contains more than one solute, the correlation between the counterflow velocity and the steady-state distribution of the various solutes becomes much more complicated and may be quite difficult to calculate. However, it can always be determined experimentally. The counterflow velocity should be chosen so that the resulting steady-state vertical variation of the density would give maximum stability consistent with the relevant operational and economical considerations.

Since the liquid separated in the evaporator is usually valuable, it would normally not be circulated back to the top of the liquid solution. Instead, there may be added to the top additional solution which is less concentrated than the solution normally at the top. This is particularly advantageous in solar ponds where it may be desired to produce, in addition to or in lieu of power, desalinated water and/or salt. The steady state distribution in this case will be similar to that explained previously except that the concentration at all levels will now be greater by the concentration of the new solution added (C_s), provided that the total amount of solute in the solution remains constant by the continuous withdrawal, at the bottom, of the same amount of solute which is being added with the dilute solution at the top (or at any other level, as to be later described). This is achieved automatically if the concentration (C_o) at the bottom is permitted to rise until it reaches saturation and the solute starts precipitating in the evaporator. In the special case when it is preferred not to let the bottom solution reach saturation, surplus solute may be removed by withdrawing small quantities of solution from the circulating bottom layer.

The foregoing features of the invention, as well as other features to be later described, may be used in a solar pond for the production of power, and/or desalinated water, and/or salt. A system for producing all three is schematically illustrated in FIG. 3.

In FIG. 3, a solar pond 20 is supplied from a source of saline or sea water 22. The pond is darkened at the bottom 24 to absorb radiations from the sun. The pond is filled with salty water such that the concentration of salts, and therefore the density of the solution, decrease from the bottom upwardly, supporting thereby an inverse temperature gradient, the temperature decreasing from the bottom toward the top.

The hot bottom layer is continuously withdrawn from one end of the pond and passes through pipe 26 into flash evaporator 28. A part of the water is evaporated there and passes, in the form of steam, through pipe 30 to a turbine 32 to drive a generator 34 and thereby to produce electric power. From turbine 32, the steam passes through pipe 36 into a condenser 38 where it condenses and exits through pipe 40 as usable distilled water, vacuum pump 41 maintaining the vacuum in condenser 38. In condenser 38, the condensing steam is being cooled by sea water supplied from the sea 22 through pipe 42, which water then passes through pipes 44 and 46 to the top of the solar pond 20. Usable salts may be extracted from the evaporator-crystallizer 28 through pipe 48.

The water remaining in evaporator 28 following the evaporation of part of it (which remaining water is now at a lower temperature than the water introduced into the evaporator) passes through pipe 50 into a mixer 52 where it is mixed with a controlled amount of additional saline water from pipe 44. It is then passed through pipe 54 into the inlet 55 at the bottom end of the pond opposite to exit pipe 26 and at substantially the same level as the exit pipe. The controlled amount of new saline water supplied through pipe 44 is such as to obtain the required velocity of the counterflow, in accordance with the previously discussed considerations.

The mixer 52 may also be used when required for adjustment of the bottom layer concentration. Where the solution contains more than one salt (as in sea water), the mixer may also be used for controlling the bottom layer salt composition.

The withdrawal of hot solution from one end of the pond and the reintroduction of the cooled solution at the opposite end (the outlet and inlet both extending intermittently or continuously along the full width of the pond) will cause the solution in the bottom layer to flow slowly and continuously from the inlet side towards the outlet side and to thus be reheated by the solar radiations absorbed in the dark bottom. Theoretical analysis, as well as laboratory and field experiments, have shown that the required stratified flow of the bottom layer can be obtained as described without undue mixing if the values of the relevant characteristic flow parameters (the Reinolds & Fraud numbers) are kept within certain predetermined limits.

It may be desirable at certain times or in certain applications, to be discussed below, to "wash" the surface of the pond in order to reduce the salt concentration at the surface. This is provided in FIG. 3 by allowing additional quantities of the new saline water from duct 46 to flow horizontally at surface level from one end of the pond to the opposite end, where it is removed through duct 56 and returned back to the sea 22. Surface washing can also be carried out by spraying the dilute solution (e.g. new sea water) over the surface of the pond and drawing off the surplus in overflow troughs.

As in the case of the bottom layer flow it has been shown that stratified flow of a thin upper layer is also possible, and that such a flow does reduce the surface concentration. This might be desirable at certain times or in certain applications, as the difference in temperature between the hot bottom layer and the cool surface which can be allowed when the surface is washed is considerably greater than when the surface is not washed. Also, where there is a high rate of surface evaporation, particularly where sea water is used to replenish the pond rather than relatively pure water, the high rate of evaporation will cause a gradual increase in surface concentration and eventual mixing of the whole pond, which can be avoided by washing the surface to prevent the rise of surface concentration.

In some cases, it may be desirable to subject the solar pond to controlled vertical mixing of the various layers and thus also to increase the counterflow velocity necessary for maintaining the required vertical distribution. As indicated earlier, the counterflow velocity may be regulated to adapt the shape of the concentration curve to the specific requirements of the application. If it is desired that the curve be more concave, this can be quickly accomplished by temporary speeding up the counterflow velocity. But if the required shape is more convex, the rate of change depends on the rate of diffusion, and with only molecular diffusion to effect the change, its rate is going to be very slow. Speeding up the diffusion by controlled mixing will insure a more immediate response of the concentration curves shape to the control.

Controlled mixing may also be used in periods of high evaporation from the surface of the pond as an additional alternative means for preventing an excessive rise in surface concentration. This is particularly desirable when the pond is used for salt production where the reduction of surface concentration by the previously mentioned method of "surface washing" entails loss of salt and therefore loss of efficiency.

Controlled mixing is accomplished in FIG. 3 by means of air-bubbling, the air being introduced through small pipes 58 located toward the bottom of the pond. This arrangement enables mixing to be effected in a very simple, easily controlled, and inexpensive manner.

The need for effective control of the concentration distribution and quick response to corrective measures is important mainly in large ponds, where external mixing factors (winds, waves, etc.) may cause undesirable changes in the concentration curve which must be corrected without delay. Correction of the concentration curve by controlled mixing can be carried out selectively only at the specific depth where it is required.

It has also been found that the heat transfer from the bottom to the surface caused by controlled mixing is comparatively small, which is important in view of the fact that in most cases the main purpose of the system is to allow the absorption of heat in the bottom layer and minimize losses upwardly.

The correction of harmful deviations in the concentration curve can also be accomplished by controlled stratified flow of intermediate layers, so that a layer wherein the concentration of the solute is too high may be withdrawn through suitable outlets along one end of the pond and be replaced by the more dilute solution of the layer above it; while a layer wherein the concentration of solute is too low is normally displaced upwardly by the introduction, through inlets along the opposite end, of a more concentrated solution, excess solution and solute being washed away through overflow troughs. The complete replacement of a mixed upper layer may also be accomplished by this stratified flow technique, this being often required in a large pond after a storm.

The change in the concentration-depth curve resulting from the introduction and withdrawal of intermediate layers depends on their concentration, levels, the rates of flow, etc. The required adjustment of all these factors for effecting a required change in the said curve should be determined experimentally during operation, in view of the available solutions, and by observation of the gradual modification of the curve resulting from each of the various adjustments.

The possibility of controlling the shape of the concentration curve by this method has ben demonstrated in field trials.

In FIG. 3, solution may be withdrawn from any desired level by means of the horizontal perforated pipe 60 along one wall of the pond, and it can be introduced at any level by means of a similar pipe 62 along the opposite wall. The level of each of these two pipes may be adjusted by means of suitable lifting and lowering mechanisms, represented schematically in the drawings by hoists 64 and 66, respectively.

The darkened layer 24 is usually provided at the bottom of the pond by any suitable means, such as by the use of dark clay, coal dust, or other suitable darkening material. It may be desirable in some cases to make the darkened layer in the form of a floating layer constituting a false bottom of the pond. For example, two organic liquids of different densities may be mixed such that the resulting density of the mixture causes the mixture to float at a predetermined level, or the solution itself at said level may be darkened by the addition of suitably grained coal dust. The false bottom also may be made of solid dark sheets suspended at the required level.

The use of such a false bottom enables existing valleys and lakes to be converted into solar ponds.

FIG. 4 illustrates how a solar pond may thus be created. The natural depression shown in FIG. 4 is filled with salt water, the concentration of salts decreasing continuously from the bottom 80 toward the surface 82. The concentration gradient should be comparatively small between the bottom 80 and a level just below the predetermined level of the contemplated false bottom, and should be much larger from this level upwardly. The false bottom is then formed by introducing the dark floating liquid layer 84 of the appropriate density to float at the predetermined level.

Provided there is no seepage of solution through the actual bottom 80, the pond so formed can be used as a solar pond, the solar radiations being absorbed in the dark layer 84 and the heat being carried away by the circulation of the dark layer itself, or a layer of solution immediately over it. The required concentration gradient from the dark layer upwardly would be maintained in accordance with the CFS method described previously. The concentration gradient initially established in the lower section of the pond, from the false bottom 84 to the actual bottom 80, is required only for the heating up period. The continuous decrease of the temperature from the false bottom downwardly, obtained after some time, will ensure the stagnation of the lower section and thus also will minimize heat losses from the dark layer downwardly to the ground. Solution lost by seepage will have to be replenished by the addition of cold concentrated solution at the actual bottom, preferably at its lowest point.

If the false bottom is made of solid sheets suitably suspended at the required level, the initial concentration gradient in the lower section, between layer 84 and the actual bottom 80, is not required.

Besides enabling existing depressions in the land or existing lakes to be used as solar ponds, the use of the false bottom technique avoids the need for extensive levelling operations which would normally be required where a natural bottom pond is used. Moreover, a false bottom pond tends to reduce the rate of heat losses to the ground.

In constructing and using solar ponds, there is an optimum depth for which the collection efficiency is maximum. This depth depends on the radiation intensity, the operating temperature, the clarity of the solution, and other factors. Under conditions in Israel, a solar pond with average expected transmissivity would have a theoretical optimum depth, for a fully unconvective pond, varying from approximately 60 cm. for a working temperature of 20° C. above ambient to 130 cm. when the working temperature is 90° C. above ambient. (Assuming the ambient temperature to be 30° C. and the boiling temperature of the bottom solution to be 120° C., then 90° C. is the maximum possible difference in an uncovered pond.) Since, in open ponds, a thin mixed upper layer is unavoidable and so is the flowing bottom layer, the actual optimum depth will be greater, and will vary from about 90 to 200 cm.

Means could be provided for varying the depth of the pond, for example, for purposes of producing a "Tidal pond" which reduces seasonal differences in output. In this type of pond, the depth is not constant but varies continuously, increasing from spring to autumn and decreasing back again from autumn to spring, thus providing an annual tidal cycle.

The depth of the pond may be easily varied by providing overflow troughs, such as troughs 91 in FIG. 4, which can be positioned at varying heights to determine the top of the pond. Such an arrangement could of course also be provided in the systems illustrated in FIGS. 1 and 3. Alternatively, depth varying means may be provided in a false bottom type pond by changing the density of the darkened floating layer 84 so that it will float at the required level, or by changing the level of suspension, in the case of a darkened bottom in the form of suspended plates. Where a darkened floating layer is used, correcting device 88 in the system of pipes 86 and 90 for the darkened floating layer 84 may be used to change the density of the floating darkened layer.

In some types of heat utilization cycles, greater temperature drop in the evaporator may be preferred than may be allowed between the entry and the exit ends of the pond. In this case, raising the bottom layer temperature may be obtained in a number of ponds in series, so that the temperature difference between the end of any one pond is not greater than specified. Since the average bottom layer temperature is stepped up in each pond, and since the optimum depth of any pond increases with bottom temperature, the depth of the pond should also be varied accordingly.

In addition to the better control of bottom layer flow, the combined efficiency of such a series of ponds is obviously better than that of one pond with a constant depth operating at the same end temperature. The use of one pond with a sloping bottom would also appear to be possible.

Depending upon the size of the pond and the conditions under which it operates, it may be desirable to subdivide the pond by surface partitions or surface baffles, for shielding the water surface from the wind and suppressing the formation of waves. FIG. 4 illustrates surface baffles at 92. Such baffles could also be applied to the systems illustrated in FIGS. 1 and 3. The baffles should extend from about 10 cm. below the surface of the pond to about 20 cm. above it, and they should be installed perpendicularly to the direction of the prevailing winds. In large size ponds, it may be desirable to include deep baffles or partitions, such those shown at 94 in FIG. 4. Such deep partitions extend from the bottom of the pond (or from the ground where the pond has a false bottom) to a distance substantially above the top of the pond, that is, above the top of the surface baffles.

The pond should also preferably include a filtration system for filtering the solution as the pond is initially filled and for filtering the solution returned to the pond to the various ducts.

The heat energy collected by the solar pond in the form of a hot solution at a temperature which may reach 100° C. or more can be utilized for many types of industrial processes. The most important uses, however, are the production of electric power, the distillation of sea water, and the precipitation of salts from sea water or salt lakes. FIG. 3 illustrates a system in which all three are produced, primarily to demonstrate the possibility for producing each of the products and not as an indication that such simultaneous production is necessarily recommended. The optimal working conditions and the equipment most suitable for producing each of these products are different, and the economic advisability of simultaneous production of two or more products depends on many factors including local conditions.

When the main product required is distilled water, the evaporator (28 in FIG. 3 or 10 in FIG. 1) would probably be in the form of a multi-stage distillation plant, whereas if the main product is one or more salts, the evaporator would be in the form of a multi-stage crystallization plant.

One further important advantage in producing salts by the use of solar ponds, as compared to their production in evaporation pans, is that solar ponds can also be utilized in the humid zones where evaporation pans, due to excessive humidity and rainfall, are completely useless.

It has been calculated that under conditions in Israel a solar pond of 1 sq. km. may be designed and operated to produce the following annual output: 3.38×10^6 cu. meters of fresh water in a six stage distillation plant; 33×10^3 tons of sodium chloride from sea water in a one stage plant; and 38.5×10^3 tons of potassium chloride from Dead Sea water in a four stage plane. This is to be compared to the annual average output of 10,000 tons per sq. km. of sodium chloride in conventional evaporation pans for sea water, and approximately 5,000–7,000 tons of potassium chloride per sq. km. at the present Dead Sea evaporation pans.

The choice of product also affects the choice of the method for operating the pond. When the pond is utilized for the production of electric power or fresh water it would probably be necessary or desirable in most cases to include surface washing in order to prevent the rise of surface concentration due to evaporation and also to prevent undue mixing of the upper layer by wind and waves. When the pond is utilized for salt production, it would be advantageous to avoid the surface washing so that the natural evaporation from the surface of the pond is also utilized for concentrating the solution. The controlled mixing feature would probably be desirable for salt production. *

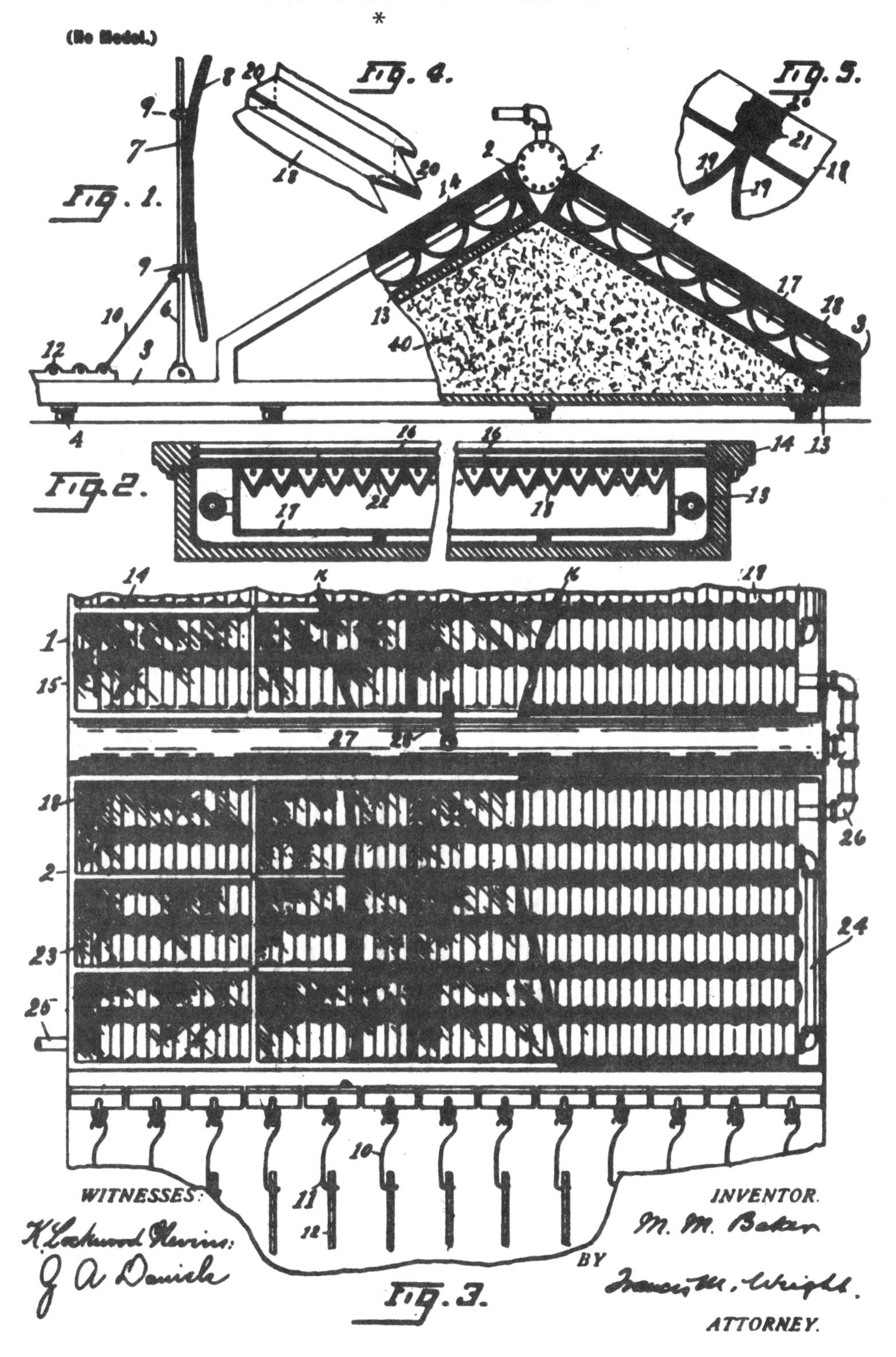
No. 679,451.
Patented July 30, 1901.
M. M. BAKER.
SOLAR WATER HEATER AND STEAM GENERATOR.
(No Model.)
Fig. 1.
Fig. 2.
Fig. 3.
Fig. 4.
Fig. 5.
WITNESSES:
INVENTOR.
M. M. Baker
BY
ATTORNEY.

UNITED STATES PATENT OFFICE.

MILTON M. BAKER, OF SAN FRANCISCO, CALIFORNIA.

SOLAR WATER-HEATER AND STEAM-GENERATOR.

SPECIFICATION forming part of Letters Patent No. 679,451, dated July 30, 1901.

*

* My invention relates to improvements in solar water-heaters and steam-generators, the object of my invention being to provide an apparatus of a simple and inexpensive construction by means of which water may be heated and steam generated by the direct action of the rays of the sun.

My invention therefore resides in the novel construction, combination, and arrangement of parts for the above ends, hereinafter fully specified, and particularly pointed out in the claims.

In the accompanying drawings, Figure 1 is an end elevation of my improved apparatus, certain parts being shown in sections. Fig. 2 is a broken longitudinal section of the heater proper on an enlarged scale. Fig. 3 is a broken plan view of the same, certain parts of the heater proper being broken away to show the interior construction. Fig. 4 is a perspective of a portion of the blank from which the top of the steam-generating tube is formed before the ends are bent up, and Fig. 5 is an enlarged view of two adjoining portions of the adjacent tubes.

Referring to the drawings, 1 2 represent boxes containing heaters, said boxes being mounted on a frame 3, movable on rollers 4. The boxes are set at an angle on said frame sloping in opposite directions, and the space below said boxes is filled with non-conducting material, as 4. Upon the frame 3 are pivotally supported a number of standards 6, which carry mirror-frames 7 and mirrors 8, said frames 7 being pivotally secured by eyes 9 upon said standards, and said standards being secured at any desired inclination to the vertical by means of rods 10, having hooks 11 engaging eyes 12. The box 1 is intended to receive the direct solar rays, while the box 2 is arranged opposite to the mirrors 8 to receive the indirect rays reflected therefrom. By mounting the whole apparatus on rollers it can be turned to advantageously receive the morning or evening sun, as desired.

Each of the boxes 1 2 has a lining of felted wool 13 and a cover 14, said cover comprising a frame 15 and two thicknesses of glass 16, with an air-space therebetween. Air is a bad conductor of heat, and the above construction of cover prevents the heat from escaping by conduction. In said box are arranged a series of tubes 17, each tube being of a general semicylindrical form, and its top 18 having corrugations in a direction transverse to the tube. Each tube consists of a sheet of metal 19, bent into the half of a cylinder, and the upper edges of said sheet of metal are riveted to extensions or ears 20 of the top 18. Said top consists of a sheet of metal V-crimped in form and having between adjacent edges thereof, at each end, the extensions or ears 20, which when bent up overlap each other and lie against the upper edge of the semicylindrical sheet 19. A rivet 21 is driven through the two overlapping ears 20, then through the edges of two adjacent semicylindrical sheets 19, and then through the overlapping ears 20 of the top of the next tube. The ears 20 may be conveniently formed out of a blank, as shown in Fig. 4, and then bent up at right angles to the corrugations of the top, as shown in Fig. 5. The edges of the semicylindrical sheets 19 are perforated, as at 22, immediately beneath the ridges of the tubes to permit the hot water to flow from each tube to the next tube above it. In this way only the hottest water in each tube is carried onto the next tube above. To compensate for the flow of water upward through the perforations 22, there are provided return-pipes 23 24, the pipe 23 leading from the bottom of the uppermost tube at one end of the heater to the bottom of the lowest tube and the tube 24 leading from the tube next to the uppermost at the other end of the heater to the lowest tube. The inlet-pipes 25 enter the lowest tube of each box at one end, and the outlet-pipes 26 for the steam lead from a point near to the top of the uppermost tube at the other end into the steam-cylinder 27, from which the steam may be drawn off to the engine by the pipe 28.

The device may be used either for heating water or generating steam. *

D. A. HARRISON.

SOLAR HEATER.

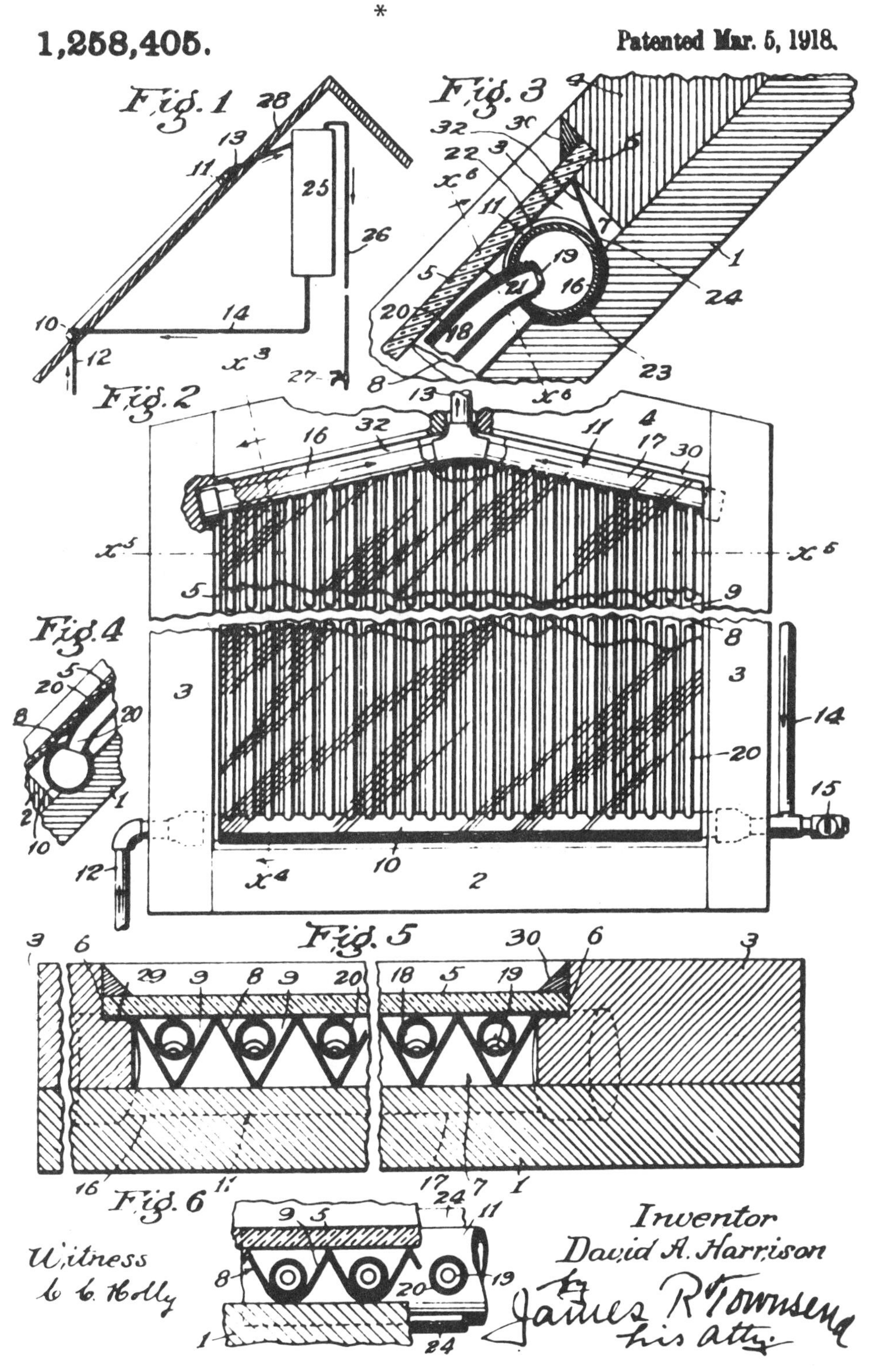

UNITED STATES PATENT OFFICE.

DAVID A. HARRISON, OF LOS ANGELES, CALIFORNIA.

SOLAR HEATER.

1,258,405. Specification of Letters Patent. Patented Mar. 5, 1918.

*

* This invention relates more particularly to a heater for heating water, by the rays of the sun, for domestic use; but is also applicable for heating rooms or apartments in buildings through the medium of air or other fluid heated by caloric rays from the sun or from sources of heat where waste would otherwise occur, as from furnace rooms and the like.

Objects of the invention are to provide at low cost a highly efficient heater adapted to apply caloric rays to a heat-conducting medium to heat the same and to conduct said medium away from the heater for use as desired.

An object of the invention is to make provision for rapidly heating a supply of water by the sun's rays.

Another object is to provide for removing sedimentary deposits from the interior of the heater.

An object of the invention is to provide a cheap and simple form of construction whereby the heater is at one and the same time cheapened and increased in efficiency. This object is attained by providing a corrugated reflecting sheet of metal, the corrugations of which are adapted to form grooves in which thin tubes may be mounted so as to be subject to the caloric rays; insulating said sheet and isolating the tube-containing grooves so that heat rays reaching the grooves of the corrugated sheet will be directed to heat the water in the thin tubes.

The accompanying drawing illustrates the invention as applied in a solar water heater installed on the roof of a building.

Figure 1 is an elevation of a diagrammatic character showing the invention installed on the roof of a house and connected with a storage reservoir located in the house and provided with circulating and service pipes.

Fig. 2 is a front elevation of the heater shown in Fig. 1 on a somewhat larger scale.

Fig. 3 is a full size fragmental sectional elevation on line x^3, Fig. 2.

Fig. 4 is a sectional detail on line indicated at x^4, Fig. 2.

Fig. 5 is a full size fragmental section on line x^5, Fig. 2 showing one form of reflector.

Fig. 6 is a fragmental sectional detail on line indicated at x^6, Fig. 3 showing another form of reflector.

A heat receiving and insulating frame is shown comprising a heat insulating back 1 and surrounding walls 2, 3 and 4 at the ends and sides of said backing and a transparent panel 5 mounted in said walls that are recessed at 6 to receive the same, and forming therewith a chamber 7 into which heat rays may be directed through the transparent side or panel 5 that may be a sheet of glass or other material transparent to caloric rays. Inside said chamber there is provided a grooved reflector 8 having parallel longitudinal grooves 9 formed therein; said reflector being preferably constructed of a bright crimped or corrugated sheet of copper or other suitable reflecting material having a burnished or bright reflecting face presented toward the transparent panel 5.

At the ends of the parallel grooves in said reflector, headers 10, 11 are provided; said headers being of comparatively large diameter and having connections as at 12, 13 and 14 for receiving and discharging fluid and for allowing a circulation of water in case the fluid supplied is water.

A blow-out cock 15 is also provided at the end of the bottom or inlet header 10.

The top or discharging header 11 is constructed with two upwardly slanting limbs 16, 17 which are arranged obliquely to the thin tubes 20 leading upward away from the receiving header 10 to the discharge connection 13 so that the fluid flowing into the discharging header will pass freely to the outlet connection 13 with minimized friction at the change of direction.

One end of each of the tubes is contracted for the purpose of affording a comparatively large chamber at 18 within the tubes between the headers as compared with an orifice as at 19 through which the fluid has to pass in order that it may flow through the tube.

The purpose of the reduced orifice is to prevent short-circuiting of fluid when a discharge through 13 occurs.

In practical construction the tubes 20 will be made of thin copper tubing and the diameter of said tubes will preferably be about one quarter of an inch and that of the orifices 19 about one eighth of an inch, said tubes being about six feet long and there being about 24 such tubes, more or less, for a water heater adapted to supply hot water for ordinary family use.

The contracted orifice may be at either or

both ends of the tube but it is preferred that the upper ends of the tube be provided with contracted orifices as shown in Fig. 3 and the lower ends of the tubes be fully open as shown in Fig. 4 so that in case water to be heated therein contains sedimentary material, the same may settle down and pass freely down through the lower ends of the tubes into the lower header 10.

The upper ends of the tubes may also be bent as indicated at 21 and entered into one side of the limbs of the upper header so that an adjacent side of said header as at 22 can be brought close to the transparent panel 5 and the parallel main bodies of the tubes be brought close to the inner surface of said transparent panel. The insulating backing 1 may be provided with a channel 23 to receive a bent sheet 24 in the bend of which, the upper header 11 is seated thus allowing said header to be subject to caloric rays passing through the panel.

The connections 13, 14 are in the form of pipes connected with a domestic tank or reservoir 25 from which a service pipe 26 leads for connection with the water faucets 27 of the house.

The heater proper is shown installed aslant on the sloping side of the roof 28 but it is understood that it may be otherwise installed.

The grooves formed in the reflecting sheet may be either V-shaped grooves as shown in Fig. 5, or U-shaped grooves as shown in Fig. 6 and the bodies of said tubes are brought close to the tops of the grooves but are not in contact with the walls thereof so that they are air insulated from the reflectors but receive radiant heat therefrom.

In practical operation the contracted ends of the tubes cause the fluid to be held back within the tubes so that when a faucet 27 is opened the flow will be distributed through all the tubes. The heat expanded peripheral skin of water in the tubes tends to rise to the upper ends of the tubes and collects in the bent limbs 21 thereof that are bent so that the orifices 19 are practically lateral draw off outlets to which the hot water of the tubes will be supplied while the colder water at the axes of the tubes may settle to the lower sides of the tubes to receive the reflected heat, and large capacity for heating liquid is secured by providing a large number of these thin tubes. The numerous tubes can be readily installed because of the small diameter in which I make the tubes; it being a very easy matter and comparatively inexpensive to construct a heater with numerous tubes of ¼ inch diameter inserted into two one-inch headers and since the contracted passage at 19 which controls the flow is of a still smaller diameter than the tube, the amount of liquid delivered from the tubes respectively will be equalized and the likelihood of short-circuiting when a service cock 27 is open, is thereby minimized.

To construct the heater the tubes 20 may be screwed or otherwise inserted and fixed into the headers 10, 11 while the tubes are straight, and then the bends 21, 29 may be made by heating the tubes close to the headers sufficiently to allow the metal to be bent without opening the joints.

When sediment is deposited in the lower header 10 the same may be blown out by opening the blow-out cock 15.

The thin heat conducting tubes 20 are proportionally spaced apart so that the inter-tube spaces are about equal in width to the diameters of the tubes, and said tubes are located as close to the transparent panel 5 as is practical without actual contact between the plate and the tubes; and the outer edges of the reflecting surfaces 8 practically contact with the transparent panel 5 and with the insulating backing 1; but are spaced apart slightly from the tubes; the whole construction thus being made compact and the tubes being isolated in separate chambers formed by the respective grooves and the sheet 5, and air insulated to prevent the escape of heat by conduction through the reflectors or the panel 5 when the external air is comparatively cold, or when the caloric rays are not active to heat the liquid.

The panel 5 that is transparent to the heat rays is arranged as shown extending over and closing the grooves 9; and the insulating backing and walls are connected with said panel for inclosing said tubes and the reflector, so that each of the tubes is isolated within a chamber having reflecting walls and a transparent face, and the reflector and tubes are inclosed within a common chamber constructed to retain the heat. Each tube is therefore confined by itself to conserve the heat rays it receives irrespective of the other tubes.

The copper sheet that is corrugated to receive the tubes is bent along its edges to form wings 29 to fit in recesses 6 under the edges of the transparent panel which may be secured by putty 30 that extends over the wings 29 on the shoulders formed by the recesses 6 in the side walls 3.

The contracted orifices 19 for the tubes are readily formed by the swaging that results from the process of cutting the copper tubes which are sufficiently ductile to be spun in at the ends by the same pipe-cutting tool that is used for cutting the tube.

The tubes are at right angles to the lower or supply header 10 from which the cold water is supplied to the tubes under pressure and the water thus readily flows directly through the tubes but as the water issues from the contracted portions 19 of the tubes in a heated condition it enters the oblique header and changes its direction gradually to flow to the outlet 13 thus avoiding friction that might tend to short-circuit the flow.

An oblique reflector 32 is provided above and extending along the upper header behind the transparent panel 5 so that said upper header is not only heated by the direct rays passing through the panel 5, but also by rays reflected from the reflector 32.

It is understood that the reflectors may be made of mirrors of any material but the most convenient and simple construction is secured by making the reflectors of the bright metal sheets as at 8 and 32.

By making the reflector of a single corrugated sheet of bright metal it is simply necessary to crimp or corrugate the sheet and apply it in the chamber 7 prepared therefor, and then to place the tubular structure comprising the headers 10, 11 and the tubes 20 in desired position, and then lay the transparent pane of glass 5 in place and secure with putty 30. It is thus seen that I have made very cheap and simple provision for applying to the contents of the tubes a maximum amount of caloric from the sun's rays.

By making the reflectors of corrugated sheet metal, the corrugations of which accommodate the tubes respectively with but small or slight clearance, it is a simple and inexpensive matter to construct the heater in a light, compact and effective form, the corrugations making excellent reflectors as well as forming the side walls for the chambers in which the thin tubes extend, said chambers and walls being made by corrugations of such a character that the sheet from side to side need not be in thickness, twice the diameter of the tubes they contain and all of the reflectors are formed by a single sheet that is easily placed in position in the insulating box ready to receive the tubes and the transparent sheet. *

April 19, 1949. W. J. FREUND **2,467,885**

SOLAR HEATER FOR HEATING LIQUIDS

*

FIG. 1

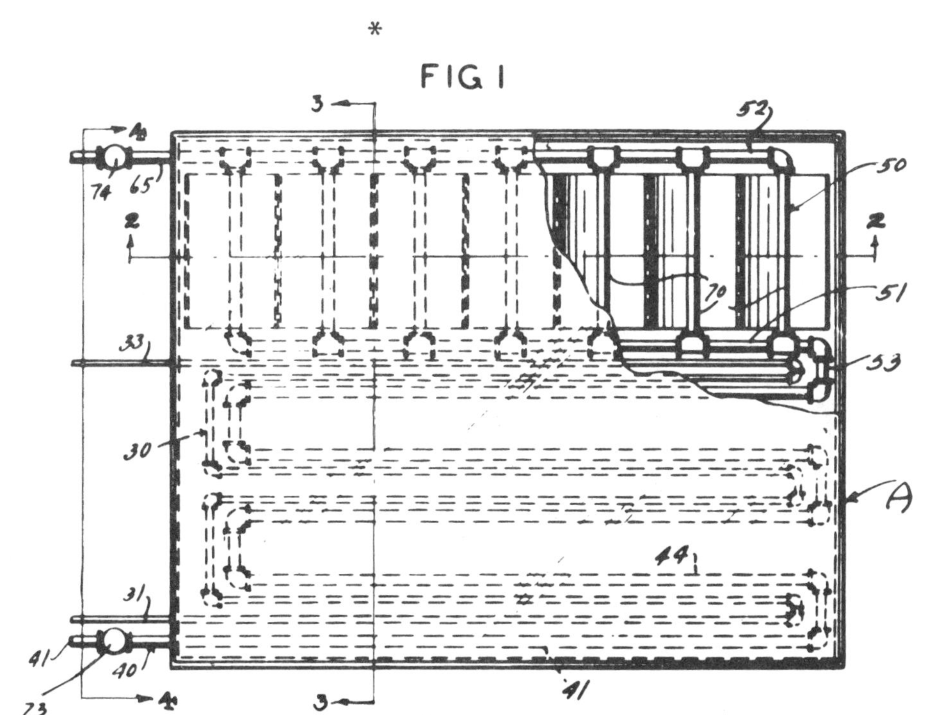

FIG. 2

FIG. 3

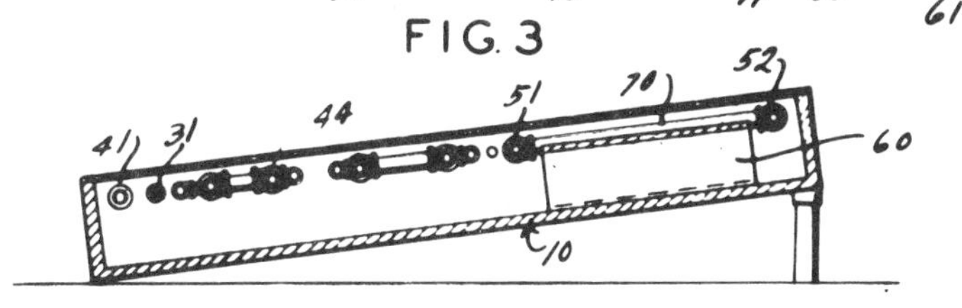

FIG. 4

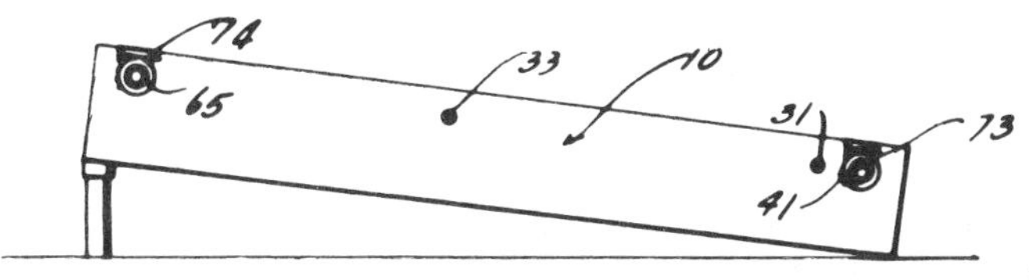

INVENTOR
WILLIAM J. FREUND

BY Lancaster, Allwine and Rommel
ATTORNEYS

UNITED STATES PATENT OFFICE

2,467,885

SOLAR HEATER FOR HEATING LIQUIDS

William J. Freund, Miami, Fla., assignor of forty-four one-hundredths to Walter J. Kelly, Miami, Fla.

*

This invention relates to improvements in solar heaters.

The primary object of this invention is the provision of an improved solar heater which is relatively simple in construction and which will efficiently produce hot water for domestic use, as well as for other purposes.

A further object of this invention is the provision of a solar heater having means for heating water for domestic supply purposes and which includes means for additionally heating a fluid of less volatile nature than water for the operation of other units such as coolers, refrigerators, air conditioning systems, etc.

Other objects and advantages of this invention will be apparent during the course of the following detailed description.

In the accompanying drawing, forming a part of this specification, and wherein similar reference characters designate corresponding parts thruout the several views,

Figure 1 is a plan view of one form of improved solar heater.

Figures 2, 3 and 4 are cross sectional views taken substantially on their respective lines in Figure 1 of the drawing.

In the drawing, wherein for the purpose of illustration is shown a preferred form of the invention, the letter A may generally designate the solar heater.

In the solar heater A, I prefer to provide a casing 10 including a bottom 11 and upstanding border walls 12. If desired, I may enclose a compartment 14 of this casing by means of a transparent wall 15, of glass or other materials which will not appreciably affect the efficiency of the sun's rays playing upon the tubes in the heater.

* I contemplate the operation of cooling units, refrigeration apparatus and air conditioning systems thru the utilization of hot water heated in the solar heater. To that end I provide means for the accommodation of a suitable volatile fluid utilized in connection with the operation of such apparatus and I also provide means for heating a domestic water supply in a simple and accessible assembly of parts.

The improved solar heater A includes a hot water heating coil 30 for domestic supply of water. This includes a cold water intake conduit or tube 31 which extends into the side wall of the casing and in the compartment 14 and therein is coiled back and forth for about one-half of the area of the compartment, and it has a hot water outlet conduit 32 leading from the casing to the hot water supply tank.

The means 40 for heating a suitable liquid adapted to be used in connection with operating cooling and refrigeration units, etc., includes an intake conduit 41 extending into the compartment 14 where it is coiled, providing the coil 44, in nesting relation with the coil of the domestic hot water tube and preferably located in the same plane therewith. The inner end of the coil 44, does not extend exteriorly of the casing, but continues to provide a booster unit 50. This booster unit preferably consists of intake and outlet headers 51 and 52; the former connecting at 53 with the end of the coil 44 to receive fluid therethru. The booster unit 50 preferably includes a plurality of concavo-convex reflectors 60 having mirrored surfaces 61. These concavo-convex reflectors are arranged with their axes transverse to the length of the coils of the domestic hot water tube and the heating coils. The concavo-convex reflectors 60 are arranged in parallelism and on the respective axes or focal points thereof the headers 51 and 52 are joined by heater tubes 70. The header 52 has an outlet end 65.

Inasmuch as the heating means 40 for receiving the fluid which will operate refrigeration and other units is adapted to elevate the pressure in the tubes of this system, I prefer to provide pressure regulating check valves 73 and 74 on the inlet and outlet tubes 41 and 65, preferably exteriorly of the casing 10.

This solar unit may be placed upon an incline, so as to better take advantage of the rays of the sun.

It is quite apparent that the coiled portion 44 forms a heater for preliminary heating of the volatile fluid and the booster unit 50 increases the temperature and pressure of the fluid as it passes into the outlet header 52. Of course the rays of light will be concentrated upon the connecting tubes 70.

The solar heater fluid should be non-inflammable and as freely flowing as water. Approximately this fluid has a boiling point of 340° F. and a freezing point of −60° F. The two fluids I may use are the following:

(*a*) ethylene glycol $HOCH_2CH_2OH$

(*b*) diethylene glycol 2,2′-oxydiethanol; Di-2 hydroxyethyl ether; $HOCH_2CH_2OCH_2CH_2OH$ *

Jan. 4, 1966 S. GODEL ETAL 3,227,153

SOLAR COLLECTOR

* 3 Sheets-Sheet 1

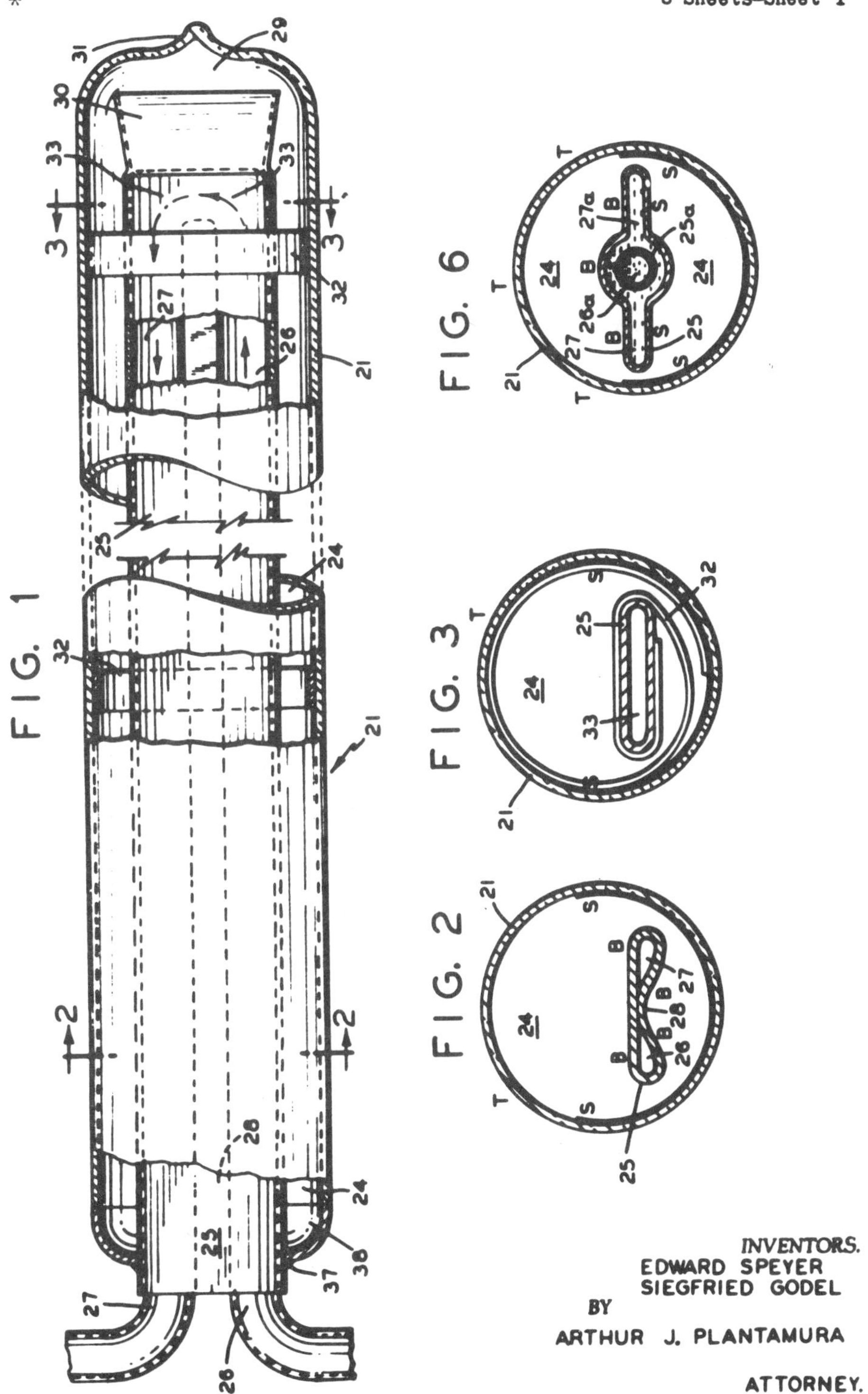

INVENTORS.
EDWARD SPEYER
SIEGFRIED GODEL
BY
ARTHUR J. PLANTAMURA
ATTORNEY.

Jan. 4, 1966 S. GODEL ETAL 3,227,153

SOLAR COLLECTOR

* 3 Sheets–Sheet 2

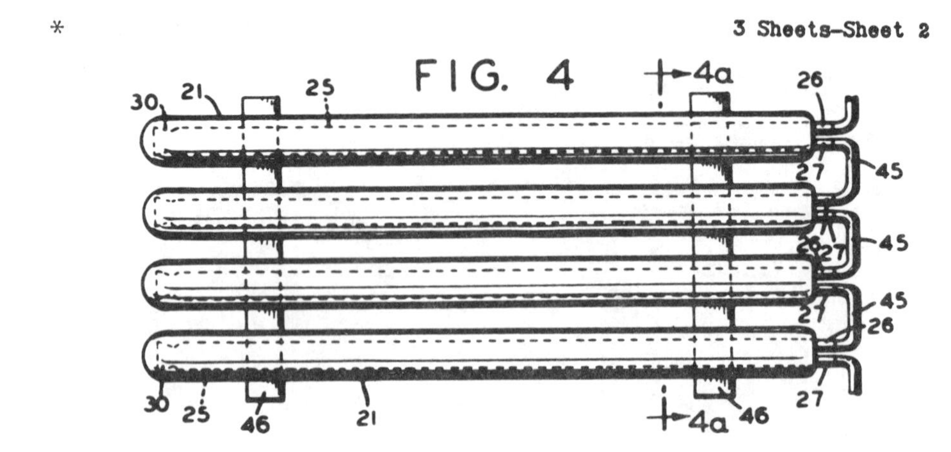

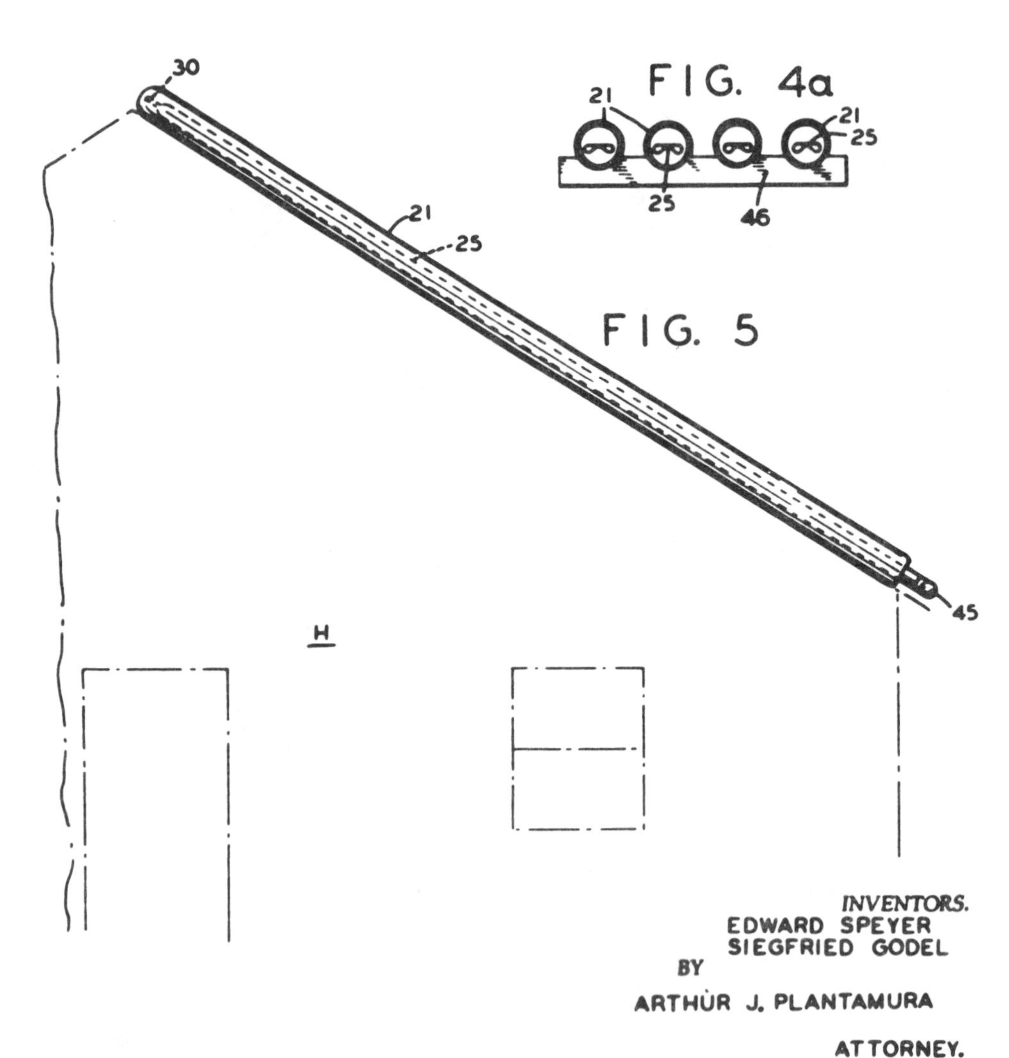

INVENTORS.
EDWARD SPEYER
SIEGFRIED GODEL
BY
ARTHUR J. PLANTAMURA
ATTORNEY.

Jan. 4, 1966 S. GODEL ETAL 3,227,153

SOLAR COLLECTOR

3 Sheets-Sheet 3

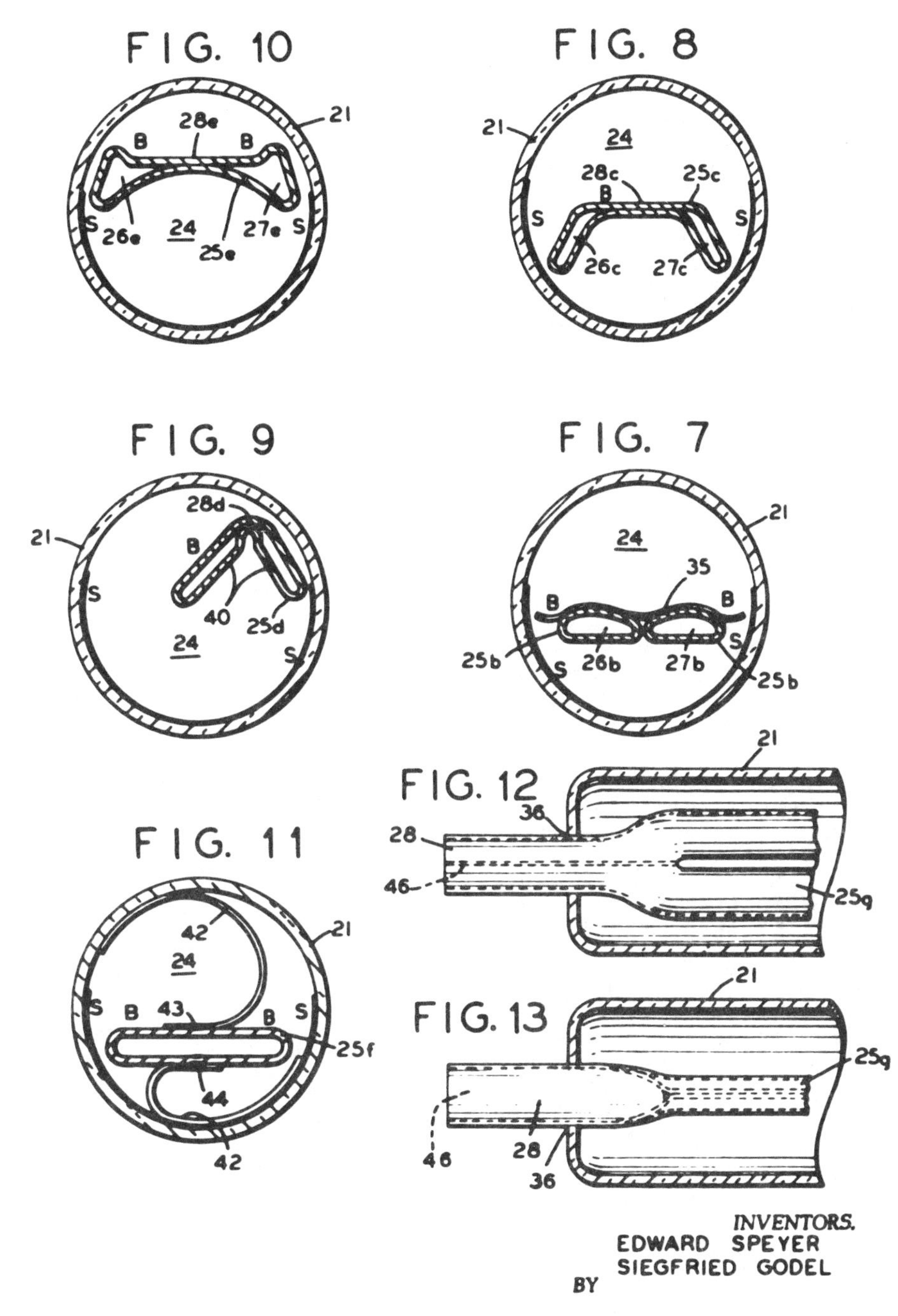

INVENTORS.
EDWARD SPEYER
SIEGFRIED GODEL

BY

ARTHUR J. PLANTAMURA

ATTORNEY.

3,227,153
SOLAR COLLECTOR

Siegfried Godel and Edward Speyer, Norwalk, Conn., assignors to American Machine & Foundry Company, a corporation of New Jersey

*

* This invention relates to solar energy collectors. More particularly, this invention relates to a relatively inexpensive module or unit of excellent efficiency which is useful in absorbing heat from solar energy. The collectors of this invention comprise a unit which includes essentially a transparent evacuated tube or envelope which is sealed at the factory such that when employed in situ the collector does not present a sealing problem because pipes or conduits carrying the liquid to be heated are connected to each other and to a pump by plumbing fittings external to the evacuated tube.

A solar energy collector intercepts a certain area of sunlight, that is, presents a certain area perpendicular to the direction of the sun. The blackened (energy absorbing) surface area of the collector, however, which actually absorbs the sunlight which enters the collector may be somewhat smaller than this.

In flat-plate collectors, the two areas are nearly equal, so that the ratio of the two, called the concentration ratio, generally has a value between 1 and 2. In solar furnaces, at the other extreme, the concentration ratio may have a value of several hundred.

Collectors with concentration ratios higher than 3 or 4 must track the sun to maintain efficiency, that is, change their position during the day. This requires a driving mechanism which makes the construction expensive. Flat-plate collectors, on the other hand, have not in the past gěnerally produced high enough temperatures to be useful for the more desirable applications such as operating air-conditioning equipment, or for generating significant amounts of steam. Our invention overcomes this problem, by providing elements or modules that provide collectively the effect or equivalent of a flat-plate collector of superior performance characteristics.

The main problem heretofore obstructing the widespread use of flat-plate collectors and thus hindering diverse solar energy applications is the cost of the collectors. Collectors in most cases in the past have been designed to be hand-built, rather than mass-produced in modern factories. Our invention takes advantage of the mass production methods used in the glass bottle and tube manufacturing arts thus opening up certain commercial uses for solar energy which heretofore have been too high-priced to be competitive.

In accordance with the invention, collectors are made which incorporate the advantages of evacuated chambers for insulation above and below the absorbing layers of the collector. Such design permits an integrally formed unit in which the evacuated spaces are permanently sealed at the factory. The collector tubes are made preferably of glass and the conduits, contained within the tubes, of relatively thin-walled metal tubing, although conduits comprising glass as described in conjunction with FIG. 6 of the drawing are also contemplated. Of important practical advantage is the fact that the plumbing problem (at installation) is completely separated from that of sealing the evacuated chambers which is effected at the factory.

A perfect collector has no heat loss from the absorbing surface, that is, all the heat absorbed by the blackened surface remains in the surface or is passed into the fluid. The evacuation of the region around the absorbing surface to a pressure of 10^{-4} mm. of mercury, or less, completely eliminates convection heat loss from the absorbing surface, and very nearly eliminates the heat loss by conduction through the air. Evacuation under factory conditions permits vacuum of this order in the collector of the present invention. The only remaining heat losses are:

(1) Conduction through the conduit supports (illustrated in FIGS. 3 and 11); this loss is small because the cross-section of the supporting members is small.

(2) Radiation from the absorbing surface; this radiation loss is reduced by using a selectively black coating on the absorber. This remains, however, the largest cause of heat loss.

(3) Conduction along the conduit walls through the end of the evacuated tube. If the conduit is thin-walled, of steel rather than copper, and much longer than its cross-sectional dimensions, this heat loss will be small.

A valuable feature of our invention is that it may be utilized if desired so as to replace that portion, having greater exposure to the sun, of the roof of a conventional house, thus substantially defraying the cost of installation of the solar collector system. The collectors may be mounted directly on cross boards nailed on the rafters or may comprise modular structural unit comprising a plurality of collectors which are shipped and used preassembled (see FIGS. 4, 4*a* and 5). In such cases, the collectors, in fact, provide a much better insulated roof than one of conventional construction.

It is an object of this invention to provide a novel solar energy collector unit of simplified and practical construction.

It is another object of the invention to provide a novel inexpensive solar energy collector unit or module of excellent efficiency.

It is still another object of the invention to provide a solar collector unit of exceptional low cost relative to units heretofore proposed.

It is a further object of the invention to provide a solar energy collector of simple design and easy factory construction which requires a minimum of assembly at the sites where the collector is to be employed.

Other objects and advantages will become apparent from the following description considered in conjunction with the accompanying drawings in which:

FIG. 1 is a longitudinal view, partially in section, of the collector as seen by the sun.

FIG. 2 is a transverse section taken along the line **2—2** of FIG. 1.

FIG. 3 is a transverse section taken along the line **3—3** of FIG. 1, at a conduit support and positioner.

FIG. 4 shows a panel of collectors of the kind illustrated in FIG. 1, ready for installation.

FIG. 4*a* is a view taken along line 4*a*—4*a* of FIG. 4 illustrating the preassembled package containing a plurality of solar collectors.

FIG. 5 shows the collector panel of FIG. 4 installed on a roof.

FIG. 6 shows a collector of an alternative arrangement to that of FIG. 2.

FIGS. 7–10 show still other alternative arrangements of solar collector units within the contemplation of the invention.

FIG. 11 shows an alternative design for a conduit support and positioner.

FIG. 12 illustrates an alternate connection arrangement for the inlet end of the conduit into the vacuum chamber.

FIG. 13 is a view similar to FIG. 12 rotated 90 degrees.

Solar collectors which are designed to be exposed permanently to the weather must be sealed against dust and moisture. Since the seal must remain tight through a wide range of temperatures, the sealing problem has heretofore constituted a major difficulty. A vacuum tight seal is not very far beyond the dust-and-moisture requirements; however, the usual designs of flat-plate collectors do not provide sufficient strength to withstand atmospheric pressure on only one side, i.e. to withstand evacuation. Our design provides sufficient strength, and thus achieves the very considerable insulation advantages of evacuation, besides maintaining a practically perfect seal against dust and moisture. No one, to our knowledge, has considered the commercial production of an evacuated collector heretofore because of the cost of providing satisfactory strength and seal.

The construction of the collector of the present invention, as most fully detailed hereinafter, is such that it freely admits sun's rays while it substantially minimizes dissipation of heat from the collector other than through the liquid circulant. Water or other fluid is passed through the units under a suitable pressure to effect circulation. After being heated during circulation, the fluid or steam is discharged for application as a heat source or it may be used to drive an engine, distill water, make ice, or stored for subsequent tranformation into power or as a heat store.

Referring more particularly to the figures of the drawing in which like numerals refer to similar components, FIG. 1, the collector of the invention is constructed in the form of a transparent tube **21** which encloses an evacuated space **24** in which is suspended a conduit **25** for the inflow **26** and outflow **27** of the fluid being heated by the sun. The vacuum chamber **24**, surrounds the conduit **25** and is substantially uninterrupted inside the entire tube **21**. The fluid enters and exists at the same end, through suitable connections to the inflow and outflow channels to which the plumbing connections are attached. The closed end **30** of the conduit floats free, i.e. there is a space at **29** between the closed end **30** and the vacuum seal-off point **31** of the tube wall. This floating arrangement for the conduit **25** allows for differential thermal expansion and contraction between the conduit **25** and the tube **21**. The fluid circulated through the conduit **25** flows in a U-shaped path through **26** reversing direction near the floating end at **33** returning via channel **27**. At the entrant end, the conduit may be attached to a metal cap or dome **38** as by welding at **37**. The dome **38** is in turn sealed to the tube **21**. Optionally, as shown in FIGS. 12 and 13, the conduit may be brought out through glass envelope **21** without the use of the meal dome. When this construction is used, the open end of the metal conduit **25*g*** is formed with a round shape at the point **36** where it penerates the glass to facilitate the sealing operation and to provide a better seal. To separate the channels, **26** and **27**, at the open end of the conduit, a suitable baffle or divider **46** may be employed.

Any suitable means such as metal clips **32** of diverse configurations may be utilized to support the conduit in an appropriate location in the tube **21**.

In FIG. 6, the conduit **25*a*** is double-walled, one wall being essentially cylindrical and within the other, which provides fins for the absorption of solar energy. In this embodiment, circulation is in at **26*a***, reversed at the closed free end of the conduit, and out at **27*a***. Where there is only a little clearance between the fin ends and the tube wall **21**, it is more efficient to coat the underside of the conduit **25*a*** with silver S rather than with black B.

In FIG. 7, two separate conduits **25*b*** are provided with a covering sheet or strip **35** welded to the conduit channels and of blackened material which conducts heat to the conduits and the fluid. Preferably, these conduits **25*b*** as well as strip **35** are formed of metal.

In FIG. 8, the inflow channel **26*c*** is not adjacent to the outflow channel **27*c***, the channel being separated by fluid path divider portion **28*c*** but both paths are contained as an integral part of a single element comprising the conduit **25*c***. This conduit as well as each of the various alternates illustrated in connection with FIGS. 2, 9 and 10 as well as additional configurations may be formed from a cylindrical tube closed at one end, e.g. by crimping as illustrated at **30** in FIG. 1, and shaped by suitable means known to those skilled in the art to provide divider **28** to produce the circulating in and out paths for the heat exchange fluid.

In FIG. 9, the design of the conduit **25*d*** is asymmetrical, with a considerable fraction of the sun-light being reflected upward to the lower surface **40** of the conduit **25*d***.

In FIG. 10, the conduit **25*e*** is mounted above the axis of the tube **21**, so that oblique rays of sunlight or skylight cannot as easily leave the tube **21**, i.e. avoid striking either the conduit **25*e*** or the silvering S.

In FIG. 11, a view similar to that of FIG. 3 is shown, except that the conduit support and positioner **42** is made of two parts rather than one as **32** in FIG. 3. One part bonded to the upper surface at **43** of the conduit **25*f*** and the other bonded to the lower surface at **44**. In either design, tha is, that of FIG. 3 or FIG. 11, the positioner element **32** or **42** respectively may be a flexible metal wire or a flexible ribbon such as of spring steel.

In general, the lower half of the collector **21** is silvered S so that heat passing into the collector tube but not impinging on the conduit will be reflected toward the conduit. The fluid conduit is selectively blackened B such as by the method described by Tabor (see Tabor, Selective Radiation. I Wavelength Discrimination Bulletin of the Res. Coun. Israel, vol. 5A, 1956, pp. 119–128). Also further studies on Selective Black Coatings, H. Tabor, J. Harris and H. Weinberger United Nations Conference on New Sources of Energy, Apr. 21, 1961.

Other suitable configurations of the conduit will occur as a consequence of the teaching of the present invention to those who contemplate the geometrical and radiometric requirements for efficient collection, or capturing, of solar energy and of radiation from the sky. Similar considerations and computations will suggest various extents and boundaries for the silvered area S of the tube **21**.

As shown in FIGS. 4 and 5, the units may be suitably employed as on a roof of a dwelling H and water or other fluid may be pumped under pressure such as through header pipes **45**. Optionally, the solar collector units may be arranged so that the passage of water or other fluid follows a parallel route or any suitable variant alternate path such as one using a combination of series and parallel arrangements. Moreover, where the roof or other collector surface is of a length which makes a single collector impractical, two or more collectors may be arranged in tandem. Water or other fluid which is withdrawn after passing through the units may be used to furnish heat or stored in a known manner to be subsequently utilized as a source of heat, such as for the operation of an absorption cycle air conditioning system.

As shown in FIG. 4*a*, the solar collectors may be arranged so that a plurality of the collectors **21** are combined into an integral package affixed to supports **46** by any suitable means. The elements **46** may comprise wood metal solid or cellular plastic etc. In addition to its function as a mounting such supports may also serve as a shipping carton component which offers suitable protection for the collectors during shipment. *

May 23, 1967 D. E. HERVEY **3,321,012**

SOLAR HEAT EXCHANGER

*

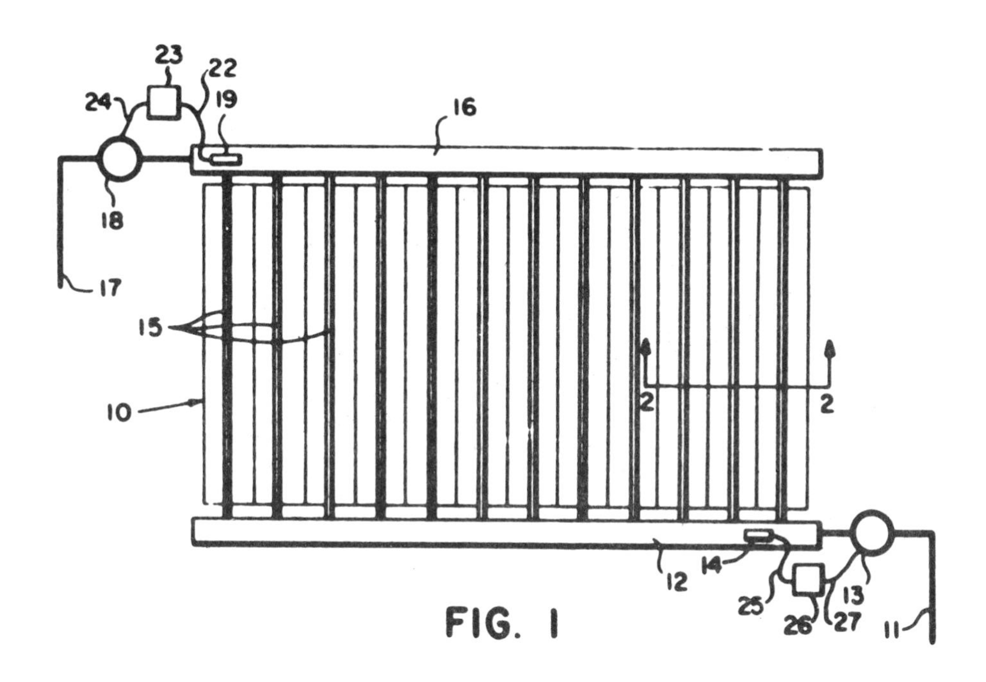

FIG. 1

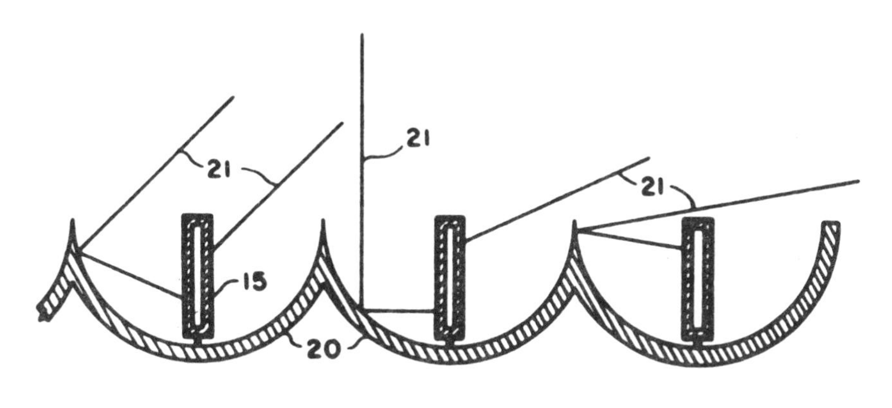

FIG. 2

DAVID E. HERVEY
INVENTOR
BY [signature]
ATTORNEY

3,321,012
SOLAR HEAT EXCHANGER
David E. Hervey, Elm City, N.C., assignor to Industrial Institution International, Ltd., Elm City, N.C.

*

* This relates to heat-exchanging devices and more particularly to devices adapted to selectively, in the alternate, collect heat and dissipate cold or collect cold and dissipate heat.

Heretofore, heat exchangers, particularly of the type adapted to collect cold or heat, have been constructed either with a series of tubes imbedded in a flat reflective surface or have comprised a curved or semi-cylindrical reflector with a round tube mounted at approximately its focal point. Relative to this latter form of the prior art, fins or vanes have been mounted about the tube in an effort to obtain more efficiency from the unit.

Even at best, the prior art heat exchangers have been extremely inefficient even to the point where it is necessary to incorporate thereinto an elaborate system of gears and racks or other means to shift or otherwise change the position of the exchange or collector unit so that its relative position to the source of heat will remain constant.

Applicant, on the other hand, after much research and study has developed and designed a very efficient heat-exchange device for collecting solar radiations as well as cold from natural climatic conditions. This invention consists of a flattened tube so mounted within a semi-cylindrical reflector that each ray of solar radiation will fall upon the tube either directly or by reflection. This collection of each ray of radiation falling upon the device is inherent in its design and, therefore, eliminates the necessity of mechanical or other means of maintaining a pre-defined relationship between the source of radiations and the collector.

It is, therefore, an object of the present invention to provide a heat-exchange means which is extremely efficient in its collection of solar radiations.

Another object of the present invention is to provide a heat-exchange means for collecting solar radiations and cold from natural climatic conditions which does not require a shifting of positions in order to operate at top efficiency.

Another object of the present invention is to provide a solar energy collector having flattened heat-fluid-transfer tubes cooperatively associated with a generally semi-cylindrical reflector means to increase the efficiency of collecting and dissipating energy.

A further object of the present invention is to provide a solar energy collecting means comprising at least one semi-cylindrical reflector having a flattened fluid-heat-transfer tube mounted longitudinally in the radial plane perpendicular to the chord defining the extremities of the arc of said reflector.

Another object of the present invention is to provide a heat-exchange means which is extremely inexpensive to manufacture and install.

Other objects and advantages of the present invention will become apparent and obvious from a study of the following description and the accompanying drawings which are merely illustrative of the present invention.

In the drawings:

FIG. 1 is a plan view of the collector; and

FIG. 2 is a cross-section of lines 2—2 of FIG. 1.

With further reference to the drawings, FIG. 1 discloses a heat-exchange unit **10** having a flow-line **11** entering a manifold **12** by way of fluid circulator **13**. Within said manifold **12** is a sensing probe **14** which is operatively connected to fluid circulator **13** by electrical circuits (not shown).

The manifold **12** is communicatively connected to fluid-bearing tubes **15** in such a manner that a heat-exchange fluid passing through flow-line **11** and into manifold **12** may then pass into said tubes.

When the heat-transfer fluid within said tubes **15** reaches a pre-determined temperature level, as will be discussed in more detail hereinafter, the fluid is forced into a second manifold **16**; and exits through a second flow-line **17** by way of a second flow circulator **18**.

A second sensing probe **19** is located within said manifold **16** in a similar manner to the probe **14** mounted within manifold **12**.

FIG. 2, which is a cross-section of lines **2—2** of FIG. 1, clearly discloses the relationship of the semi-cylindrical reflector **20** of the flattened tubes **15**. This figure also discloses the manner in which the tubes collect either heat from solar radiations or cold from natural climatic conditions as exemplified by radiation lines **21**.

As is readily apparent from the cross-section disclosed in FIG. 2, the flattened fluid-bearing tubes **15** are mounted in a plane defined by the radius which is perpendicular to the chord extending from the extremities of the arc of the curved reflector.

It might also be noted that it has been found advantageous to coat the tubes **15** with a heat receptive color such as dark brown or soot black to aid in the absorption of radiations.

In operation the present invention may be used, for example, in conjunction with a structure heating and cooling system such as that disclosed in my co-pending application hereinbefore referred to. When it is desired to collect solar radiations and to transfer the heat thereby accumulated, the heat-transfer fluid within the manifold tubes **15** will rise to a pre-determined temperature of, for example, 180°. Upon reaching the pre-determined temperature, the sensing probe or aquistat **19** with capillary **22** activates electric switch **23** which in turn will activate the fluid circulator **18** by way of electrical line **24** to cause the heat-transfer fluid to pass into the system through flow-line **17**. Since cool fluid will be entering from the system through line **11** and manifold **12**, sensing probe **19** will automatically shut down circulator **18** upon reaching a pre-determined low temperature.

When it is desired to collect cold from the natural climatic condition, sensing probe or aquistat **14** is set at a pre-determined point, for example, 35°. This probe will activate fluid circulator **13** by way of capillary **25**, electrical switch **26** and electric line **27** upon realization of the pre-determined temperature thereby causing fluid flow from the collector **10** through flow line **11** into the system. Upon the reaching of a pre-determined high temperature, probe **14** will automatically stop the circulation of fluid by shutting off fluid circulator **13**.

It will thus be seen that the collector embodied in the present invention may collect either heat or cold depending on pre-determined temperatures selected to control the operation of the device. It will likewise be obvious that there are substantial improvements in the design of the present heat exchanger over that disclosed by the prior art. *

No. 682,658. Patented Sept. 17, 1901.

J. M. WISHART.

SOLAR HEATER.

(No Model.)

*

*

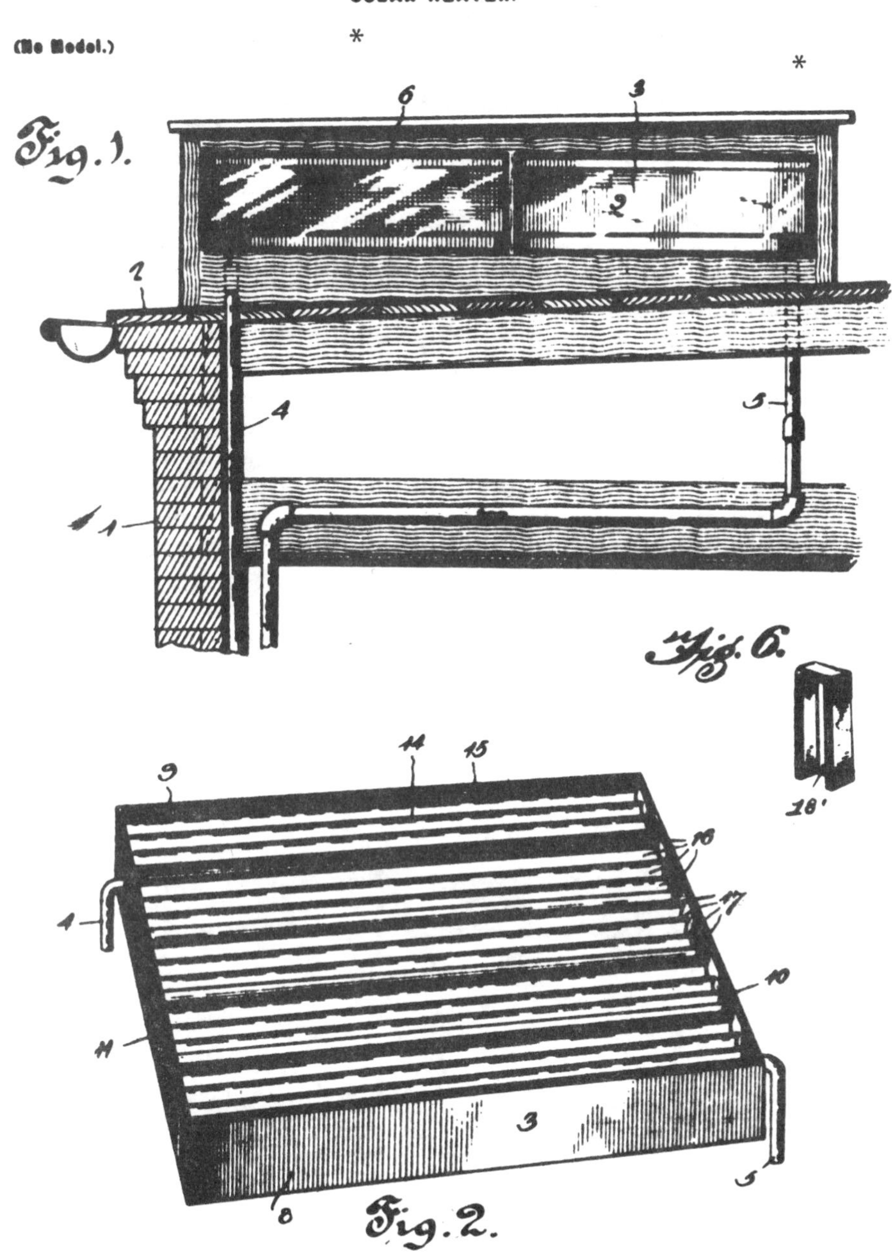

Witnesses,
J. Kauf Culverwell.
Lucius C. Julihn

James Macdonald Wishart, Inventor.
By his Attorneys,
C. A. Snow & Co.

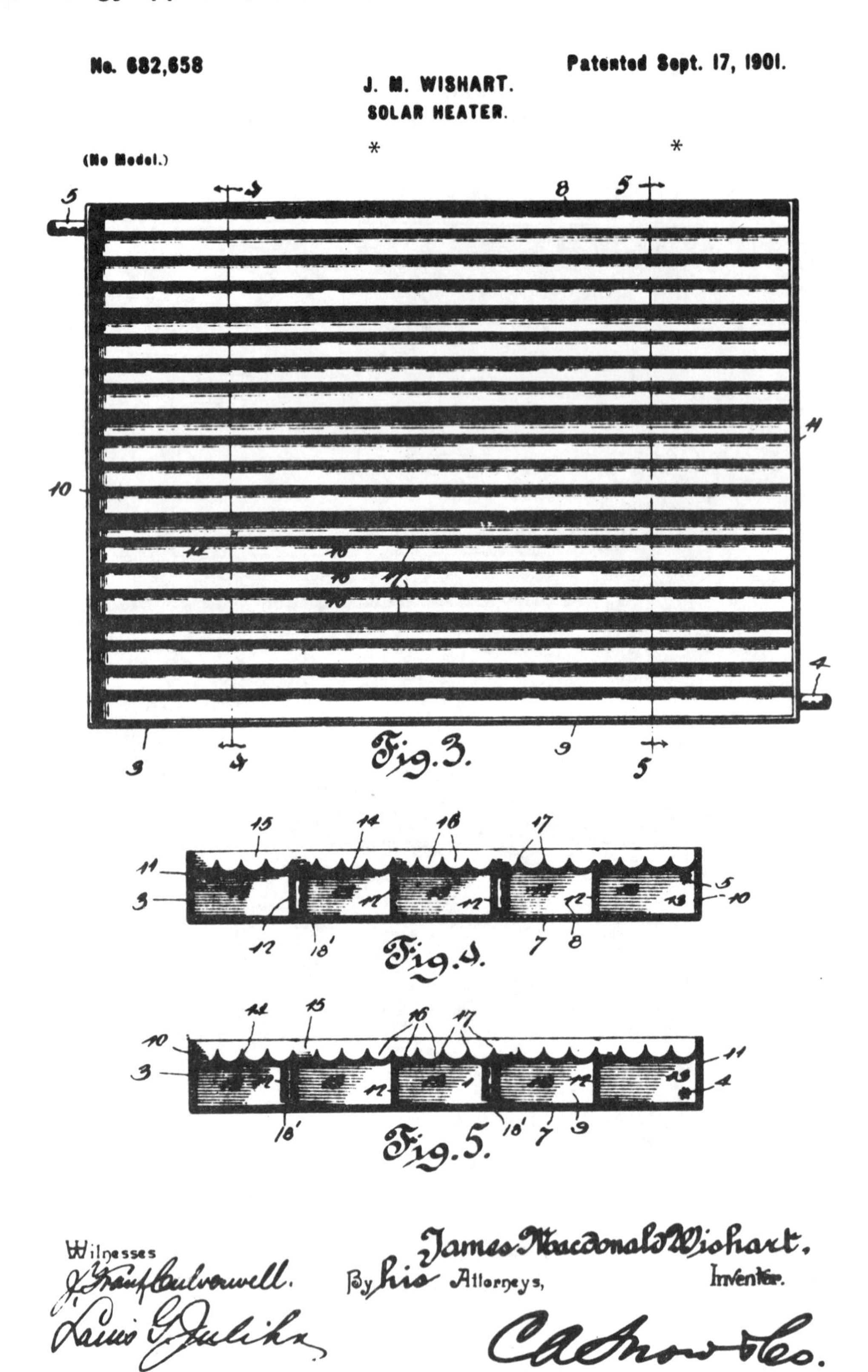
No. 682,658
Patented Sept. 17, 1901.
J. M. WISHART.
SOLAR HEATER.
(No Model.)
Fig. 3.
Fig. 4.
Fig. 5.
Witnesses
By his Attorneys,
Inventor.

UNITED STATES PATENT OFFICE.

JAMES MACDONALD WISHART, OF OAKLAND, CALIFORNIA.

SOLAR HEATER.

SPECIFICATION forming part of Letters Patent No. 682,658, dated September 17, 1901.

To all whom it may concern:

Be it known that I, JAMES MACDONALD WISHART, a citizen of the United States, residing at Oakland, in the county of Alameda and State of California, have invented a new and useful Solar Heater, of which the following is a specification.

This invention relates to solar heaters, and has for its object the production of a heater designed for the utilization of heat generated by the sun's rays to heat water or other liquids.

Specifically, the object of the invention is to provide a heater of this class designed to constitute a part of a circulatory system, the liquid being caused to circulate through a number of chambers, the circulation being maintained by the effect of the solar heat.

Subordinate to these objects are others, which will more fully appear as the necessity for their accomplishment is developed in the succeeding description.

Referring now to the drawings, Figure 1 is a sectional view through a fragment of a house and showing the heater supported upon the roof thereof. Fig. 2 is a perspective view of the heater proper. Fig. 3 is a plan view of the heater. Figs. 4 and 5 are vertical sections taken on lines 4 4 and 5 5, respectively, of Fig. 3 and looking in the directions indicated by the arrows. Fig. 6 is a detail perspective view showing one of the bent plates forming the pipes for communicating the bottom of one compartment with the opening leading to the top of the adjacent compartment.

Referring now to the numerals of reference, each of which is employed to designate a corresponding part in the several views of the accompanying drawings, 1 indicates a fragment of a house, upon the roof 2 of which is located my heater 3, communicating with the direct and return pipes 4 and 5 of a circulatory system and protected by a glass housing 6. Elements capable of these broad designations have been heretofore employed in analogous connections; but I shall now proceed to a description of the specific construction and arrangement constituting the embodiment of my invention.

My heater 3 comprises a substantially rectangular receptacle composed of a bottom 7, front and rear walls 8 and 9, and end walls 10 and 11, respectively. The receptacle thus formed is provided with a series of equidistant longitudinal partitions 12, terminating somewhat below the upper edge of the receptacle and dividing the latter into a number of longitudinal circulating-chambers 13. The top wall or absorption-plate 14 of the heater, formed in a single piece or in a number of sections, as desired, is supported upon the upper edges of the partitions 12 in a manner to leave a space 15 between its surface and the upper edge of the receptacle, and is longitudinally fluted, as indicated at 16, to form an extended series of longitudinal concavities, the contiguous edges of which converge to form ribs 17. By means of this configuration of the absorption-plate I am enabled to get a maximum exposed surface or effective heating area, and as the ribs 17 constitute braces or stiffening devices exceedingly thin sheets of metal are available for employment in this connection.

The direct pipe of the circulating system pierces the end wall 11 at the lower front edge of the chamber 13 at one side of the receptacle. At the rear end of the partition which separates this first chamber from the second and adjacent the upper edge of the partition there is formed a perforation which communicates with a pipe 18, which leads downwardly and opens into the bottom of the second chamber, the pipe 18 being wholly within this second chamber, as shown. This pipe 18 is in the form of a bent plate, as shown, the edges of which are soldered to the partition excepting at the bottom of the plate, so that there is formed what is in effect an open-bottomed pipe. The opposite wall of the second chamber, which is formed by the second partition 12, has a perforation adjacent its upper edge, and at the opposite end of the receptacle from the first perforation described and leading from this second perforation is a second pipe 18', which lies entirely within the third compartment or chamber and opens into the bottom portion of the compartment or chamber. A third perforation is formed in the third partition at the same end of the receptacle with the first perforation and has a pipe lying in and communicating at its lower end with the fourth compartment or chamber. This arrangement is continued throughout the receptacle, so that the bottom of one compartment is connected with the top of the compartment at one side while its top is connected with the bottom of the compartment at the other side, the connections of each chamber or compartment being at opposite ends thereof.

From the foregoing it will appear that the rays of the sun being directed upon the absorption-plate the water within the heater will be heated from the surface, which will induce circulation from end to end and from bottom to top of succeeding heating chambers or compartments and in alternately opposite directions, and the water within the circulatory system connected with the heater will in this manner be kept in continuous motion and will be raised to the desired temperature. *

J. M. KENNEDY & J. O'HARA.
SOLAR WATER HEATER.
*

1,034,465. Patented Aug. 6, 1912.

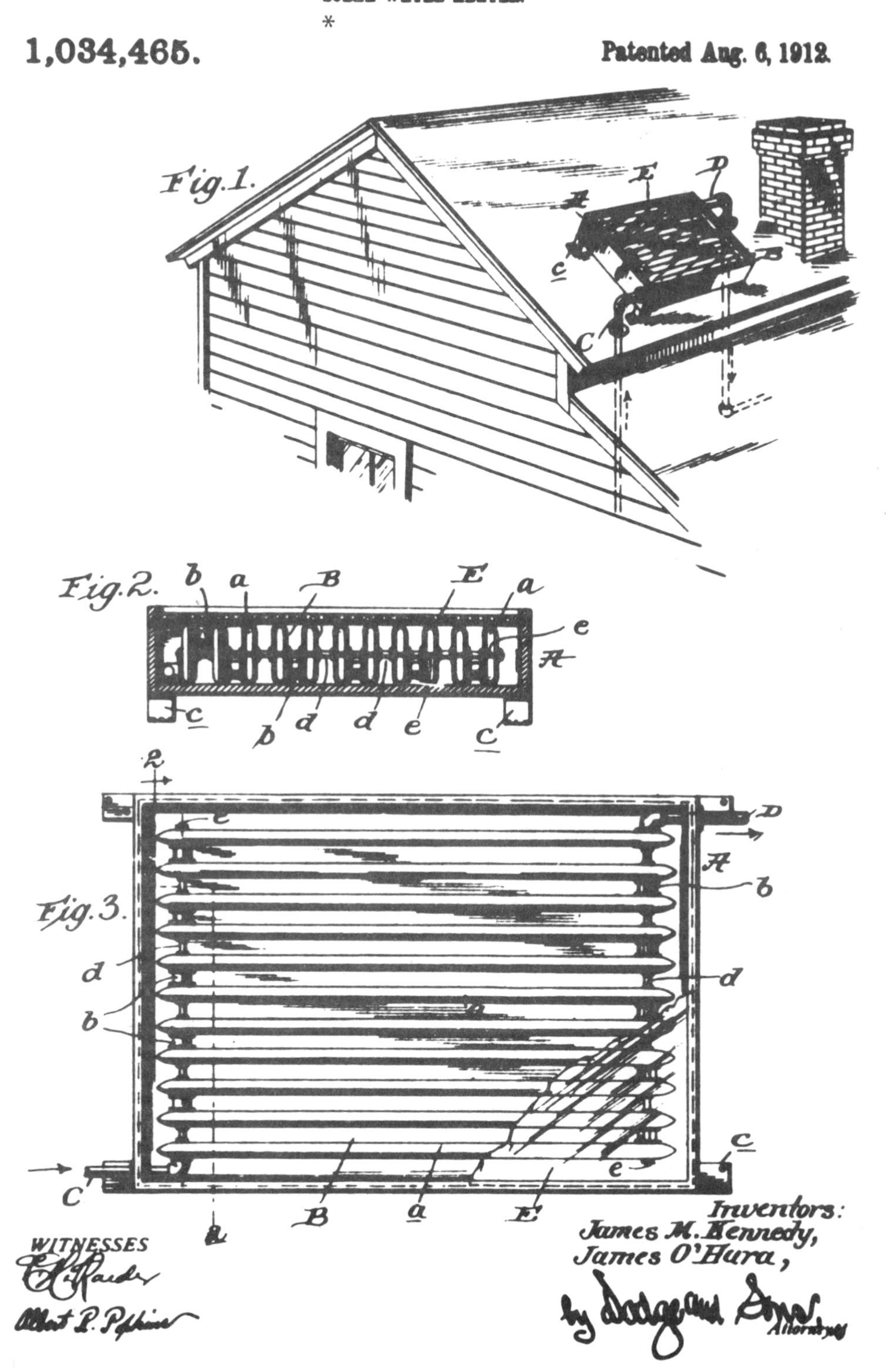

UNITED STATES PATENT OFFICE.

JAMES M. KENNEDY AND JAMES O'HARA, OF BALTIMORE, MARYLAND.

SOLAR WATER-HEATER.

1,034,465. Specification of Letters Patent. Patented Aug. 6, 1912.

*

* This invention pertains to that class of water heaters which utilize the heat of the sun's rays, and it consists in a novel construction of the heater whereby efficiency and cheapness are insured, and ready construction, with whatever capacity may be desired, is rendered practicable in almost any place.

The invention is illustrated in the accompanying drawings, wherein:

Figure 1 is a perspective view of the apparatus mounted in position upon the roof of a building, the water-supply pipe being here represented as rising from a supply main which will afford the necessary head or pressure, though it may, of course, be connected with an elevated tank or other source; Fig. 2 is a transverse vertical section on the line 2—2 of Fig. 3; and Fig. 3 is a plan view with the glass top or cover partially removed, better to show the arrangement of the heater proper.

The utilization of the direct rays of the sun for heating both air and water has frequently been essayed, and various forms of apparatus having this object in view have been devised.

Our purpose is to make use of this source of heat, and to provide a construction which shall insure the rapid heating of, and the maintenance of heat in, a considerable body of water, so that at any time a reasonable supply of highly heated water may be drawn out.

A further object is to render practicable determination of or variation in the capacity of the apparatus.

We also aim to avoid any interference with the free discharge of water from the roof of the building or structure on which the apparatus is placed, or the clogging or failing of the apparatus itself.

With these objects in view we construct the heater in the manner illustrated in the drawings, and which we will now explain.

We first construct a suitable inclosing box or casing A, the dimensions of which will vary according to the desired capacity of the apparatus, which will preferably be such as to contain at one time a volume of water sufficient to supply any demand likely to be made upon it in the situation in which it is used. In other words, its capacity should be approximately that of an ordinary domestic water heater, suitable for a like building. Within the casing A is arranged the heater B, which is composed of a series of sections *a* of hollow or tubular form, similar to or identical with the sheet metal sections of radiators now commonly employed for the heating of buildings. These sections *a* will preferably be made of about an inch to an inch and a half by six to eight inches cross section, and of a length determined by the place and requirements of use, six feet, more or less, being deemed a convenient and suitable length. The cubic contents of these sections *a* being known or readily ascertainable, a heater of any desired capacity may easily be constructed by simply assembling as many sections as are needed, and coupling these sections one to another in such manner as to insure a flow of water through the several sections in series. To insure this proper travel, the water-supply pipe C is connected with one end of the lowermost section *a* of the heater, preferably near the bottom or lower level thereof, as seen in Fig. 2. Connection with the succeeding section is made by a suitable nipple or short pipe *b*, preferably at the top or upper level, as seen in the same figure, and this alternation of ends and elevations it is desirable to maintain throughout the structure with a view to better insuring proper travel of the water through every portion of the heater. The delivery pipe D is connected with the terminal end of the heater, that is to say, with the extremity of the suppermost section *a* thereof, said pipe being led to the cocks or faucets in the building in the same manner as from the ordinary domestic water heater.

As before mentioned, the supply pipe C may come from any source of supply having a suitable head, or the flow of water may be had by siphonic action if the reservoir and outlets be properly placed with reference one to the other. Under any of these arrangements a flow of water from the pipe C through the heater B to the pipe D and its discharge cocks or faucets, will take place.

To prevent entrance of rain, leaves, dust, etc., within the box or casing A, and interference with the heater, there is preferably placed over the same a covering E of glass or other transparent material, through which the heat of the sun's rays may readily pass to reach the heater B.

It is desirable that the sections *a* of the heater be spaced sufficiently apart to permit the sun's rays to pass between and reach the sides of the sections from their upper to their lower edges, or substantially so. The position of the heater will, of course, be chosen with reference to the points of the compass and the path of the sun, so as to secure the maximum effect of its rays upon the tops and side walls of the sections *a*.

The cover E serves not only to exclude rain, dust, leaves, etc., but confines a body of air within the chamber, which in a short time becomes highly heated, and surrounding the sections *a* on all sides, materially increases the efficiency of the heating action, and renders less important the position of the heater, provided only its top surface be reasonably exposed to the direct rays of the sun.

With the sections *a* of substantially the dimensions above suggested, we find it expedient to space said sections about two inches apart. It is to be understood, however, that none of the dimensions here suggested are essential, and that we do not in any manner restrict ourselves thereto, or to any specific dimensions or proportions. These may be varied at will. It is deemed expedient, however, to have the sections *a* comparatively thin from side to side, to the end that the heat of the sun's rays may act upon the body of water from wall to wall of each section, and it is also desirable that the separation of the sections be such as to permit the rays of the sun to reach and cover a side wall of each section from the upper to the lower edge, under the ordinary variations of position of the sun in the particular latitude in which the device is used.

In order to leave clear passage for the rain falling upon the building, the box or casing A is provided with feet *c*, raising its bottom a suitable distance above the roof, and thus affording a clear space beneath it. These feet may be secured in any convenient manner to the roof, or other support upon which the heater is used, it being of course obvious that the heater may be used upon the ground, or in any other convenient position, provided suitable means be employed to insure the flow of water from the supply to the discharge pipe. When the heater is used upon a roof, this elevation is further advantageous in that it permits a free circulation of air, and avoids rotting of the shingles, rusting of tin, or other injury to the roof incident to the retention of moisture beneath it.

The sections *a* of the heater may be suitably spaced apart by thimbles or spools *d*, and tied together by tie-rods or long bolts *e* passing through said sections and through the spools, any usual or suitable type of joint, either ground, threaded, or packed, being provided to guard against leakage. The heater sections may be of any suitable metal, copper having high conductivity and being comparatively free from deterioration through corrosion, but pressed steel will be found very satisfactory, and is at once cheaper and stiffer than copper. The sections may also, if desired, be coated with any suitable pigment, preferably applied "flat," to increase the absorption of heat, and the interior of the box or casing A, which latter will be made of wood or other relatively poor conductor of heat, may be painted with white enamel paint or other light-reflecting substance, to throw back against the heater sections the rays falling upon such surface. No claim, however, is made to such coating of the surfaces, as this principle is well known, and has been heretofore utilized.

As the sections *a* of the heater, and the thimbles or couplings, tie-rods, etc., are regular articles of manufacture and commerce, obtainable in all cities and towns of any considerable size, or upon order, and as they are of standard dimensions, it will be seen that a mechanic of very modest ability may readily construct the device with a few simple tools, and make the necessary connections therewith. For summer use particularly, the device will be found useful and desirable, avoiding entirely the necessity for fire, and the consequent heating of the building or room in which the fire is ordinarily present.

It is intended that the box or casing A shall be placed in a position either horizontal, or inclining at the same angle as an ordinary roof, upon which it may be used. The sections *a* of the heater will therefore occupy a substantially upstanding position, and it is in this sense that the term "upstanding" is elsewhere used herein. *

April 21, 1931. C. G. ABBOT 1,801,710

APPARATUS FOR UTILIZING SOLAR HEAT

*

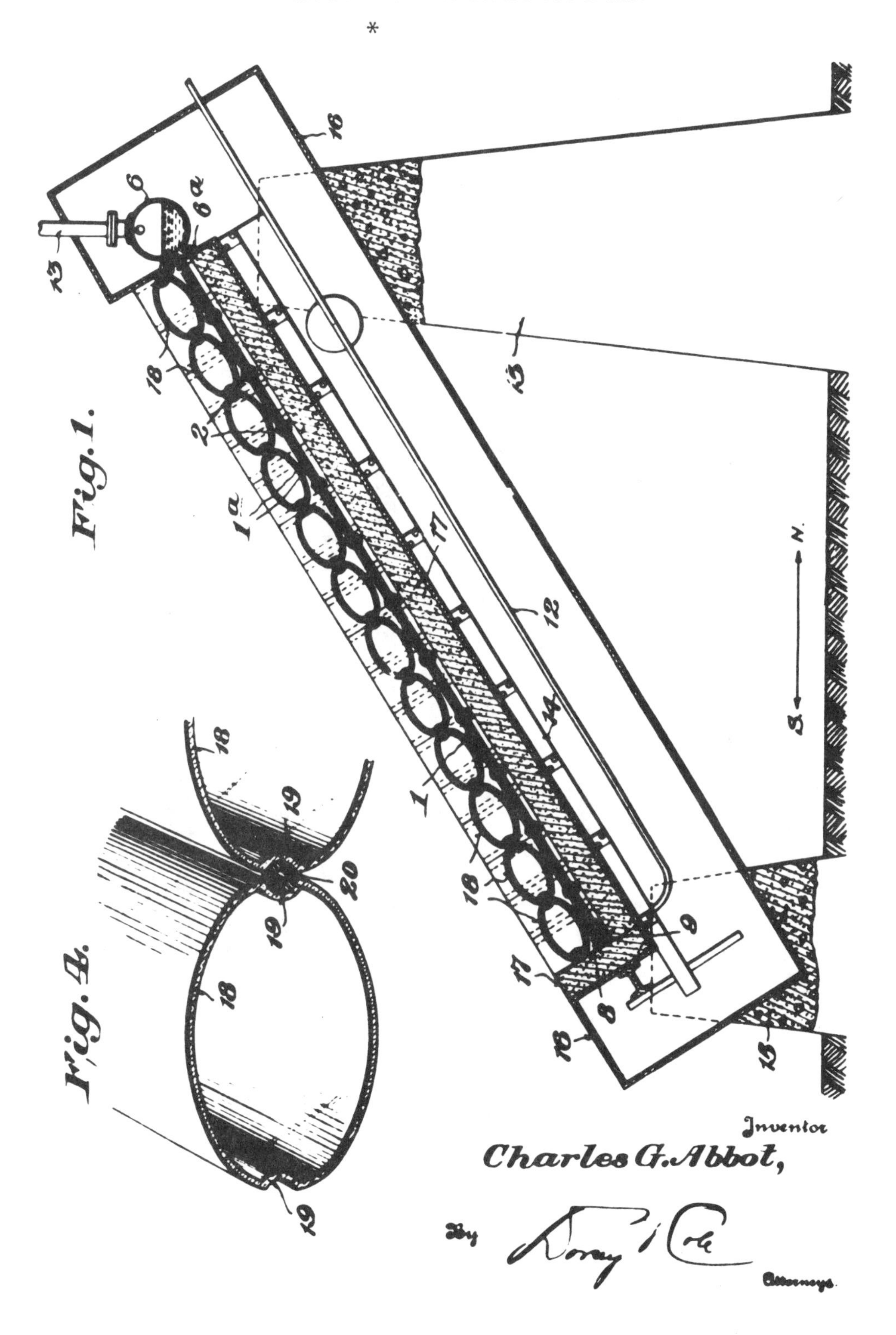

April 21, 1931. C. G. ABBOT 1,801,710

APPARATUS FOR UTILIZING SOLAR HEAT

*

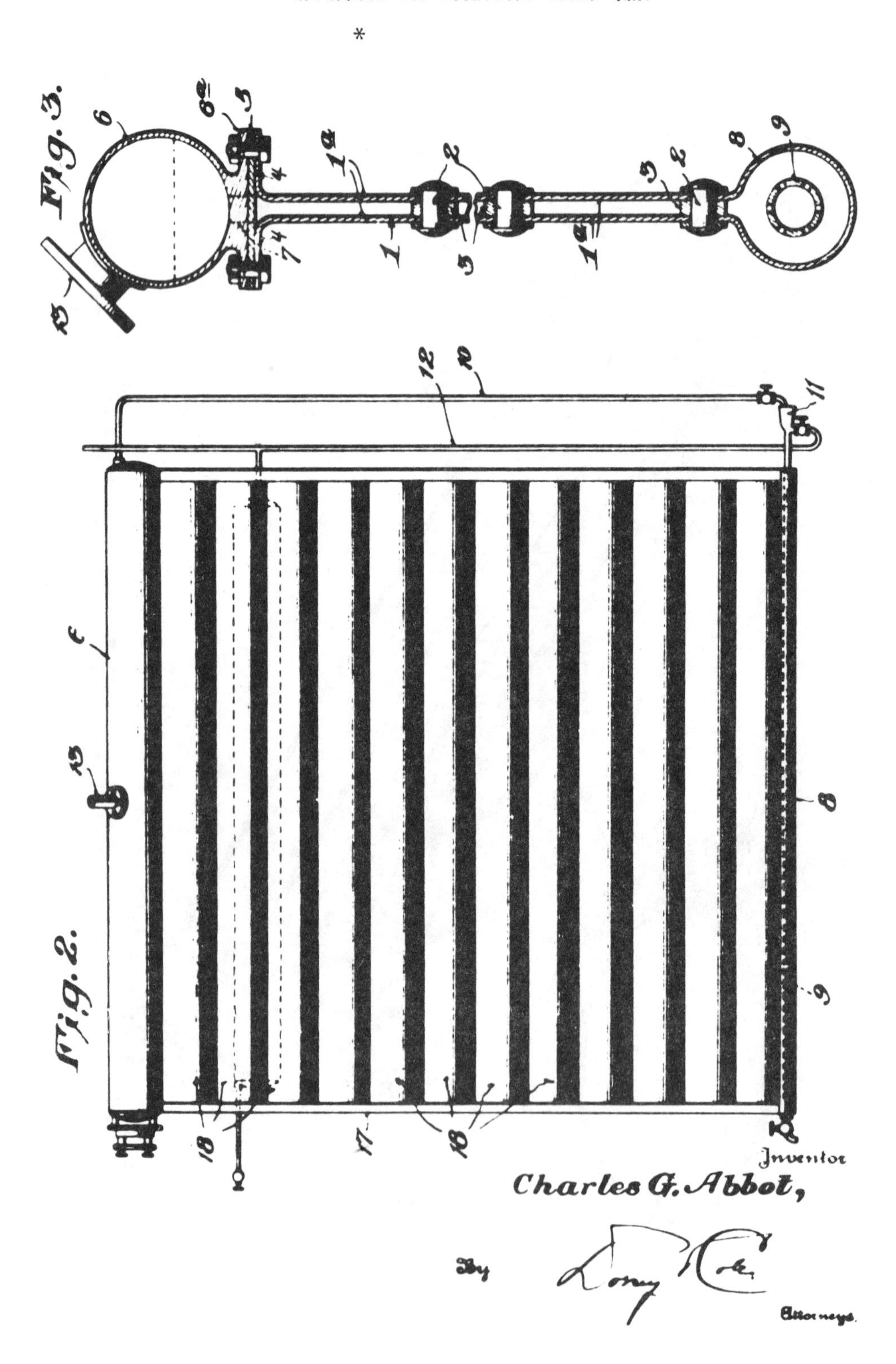

UNITED STATES PATENT OFFICE

CHARLES GREELEY ABBOT, OF WASHINGTON, DISTRICT OF COLUMBIA

APPARATUS FOR UTILIZING SOLAR HEAT

*

This invention relates to apparatus for absorbing the heat of solar radiation and for rendering it useful for various purposes, such as heating liquids for domestic, power, or warming purposes, or for purposes of evaporation.

While many attempts have been made to provide an apparatus of the character named they have been inefficient, due to the failure of the designers thereof to recognize certain conditions which are necessary to the satisfactory utilization of such radiation. The amount of heat per unit area contained in the solar radiation is, under the best conditions, relatively small, and to obtain a substantial rise in temperatures from it, necessitates the use of every refinement possible to reduce radiation and convection losses, while economic reasons demand the simplest and most inexpensive construction.

The apparatus herein described has been designed by me with the above points in view and my invention consists in the construction, arrangement and combination of the parts of which it is composed, as will be hereinafter more fully described and claimed.

Referring to the accompanying drawings in which corresponding parts are designated by corresponding marks of reference,—

Figure 1 is a vertical section through a device embodying my invention.

Figure 2 is a plan view of the device shown in Figure 1.

Figure 3 is a fragmental section through a boiler and connected parts shown in Figure 1.

Figure 4 is a detail through the tubular cover.

As shown in the drawings the device includes a ray-receiver, specifically shown as a boiler which is planar, i. e., is substantially flat, and consists of two parallel sheets 1ᵃ of suitable metal, which sheets at intervals are held together by bolts 2 and spaced apart by washers 3 surrounding the bolts at a distance relatively small in respect to the lateral dimensions of the boiler. The upper edges of the sheets are formed into flanges 4 as shown in Figure 3, to which is fastened a flattened side 6ᵃ of a cylindrical steam chest 6, a plate 5 being interposed between the flanges and the steam chest. The interior of the boiler is in communication with the interior of the steam chest by means of perforations (shown in dotted lines at 7 in Figure 3 in the plate). The lower edges of the sheet 1ᵃ are formed into a cylinder 8, into which passes the perforated intake pipe 9. A steam pipe 10 extends from the top of the steam chest to a suitable injector 11 attached to the water intake pipe 9 and to the water feed pipe 12.

A steam eduction pipe 13 is connected to the top of the steam chest.

The parts as above described are supported upon suitable frame work 14 by pillars 15 in such a manner that the plane of the boiler is approximately parallel to the earth's axis and at right angles to the plane of the meridian at the point where the device is installed, so the rays of the sun may be normal to the upper surface of the boiler at noon on the solstices, and such upper surface of the boiler is blackened to increase the amount of heat absorbed thereby.

The boiler and connected parts as above described are contained in a suitable casing 16 to reduce radiation and convection losses, and to further aid in this the boiler has placed below it and around it heat insulating packing 17.

With the construction as heretofore described, if the boiler is exposed to the sun's rays its contents will be heated, but as radiation and convection losses from the upper surface of the boiler rapidly increase as the temperature of the boiler and its contents are increased, the temperature which it is possible to obtain within the boiler will be limited. To prevent these heat losses from the upper surface of the boiler I provide a cover for the casing 16 and for the boiler contained therein, which casing is diathermous to the rays of the sun, but which is opaque to the rays such as will be thrown back from the darkened surface of the boiler, and which will be non-conductive of heat. For this purpose the cover is made of a series of juxtaposed and preferably closely fitting evacuated vessels of suitable material. I have shown such vessels as glass tubes 18. These tubes are elliptical in cross section with their major axes parallel with the boiler, and each tube has at each end of its major axis a longitudinal channel 19 in its surface. In the channels 19 of adjacent tubes is placed a packing 20 which may be of tubing having a relatively thick wall. The material from which the tubes 18 are made is one highly transparent to rays of the wave lengths contained within the sun's beam, but highly nontransparent to rays emanating from a dark surface and as the temperature of the material of the screen will be raised by this lack of diathermacy to the last named rays, the tubes should be of a material having high thermal endurance and low thermal expansion. The material should have also low conductivity to prevent losses by conduction within the walls of the tube from the lower wall to the upper wall, the vacuum within the tubes reducing convection losses therein.

With a construction as hereinbefore described I have been enabled in locations where the sun has considerable power, to raise the temperature of the contents of the boiler far above 100° C., and to trap enough heat for cooking and heating. The medium within the boiler is preferably water, but I may employ other fluids, such as ammonia, or sulphur dioxide, or for certain purposes, high test oils.

It will be noted that by making the tubes 18 elliptical with the major axes thereof parallel with the boiler, the screen is given a substantially flat upper surface, and that the several tubes present to the sun surfaces which are but slightly curved, and which therefore, when the boiler is oriented, as above described, will be disposed in a manner to result in the minimum of loss by reflection. *

Sept. 30, 1941. A. DE BOGORY **2,257,524**

SOLAR WATER HEATER

*

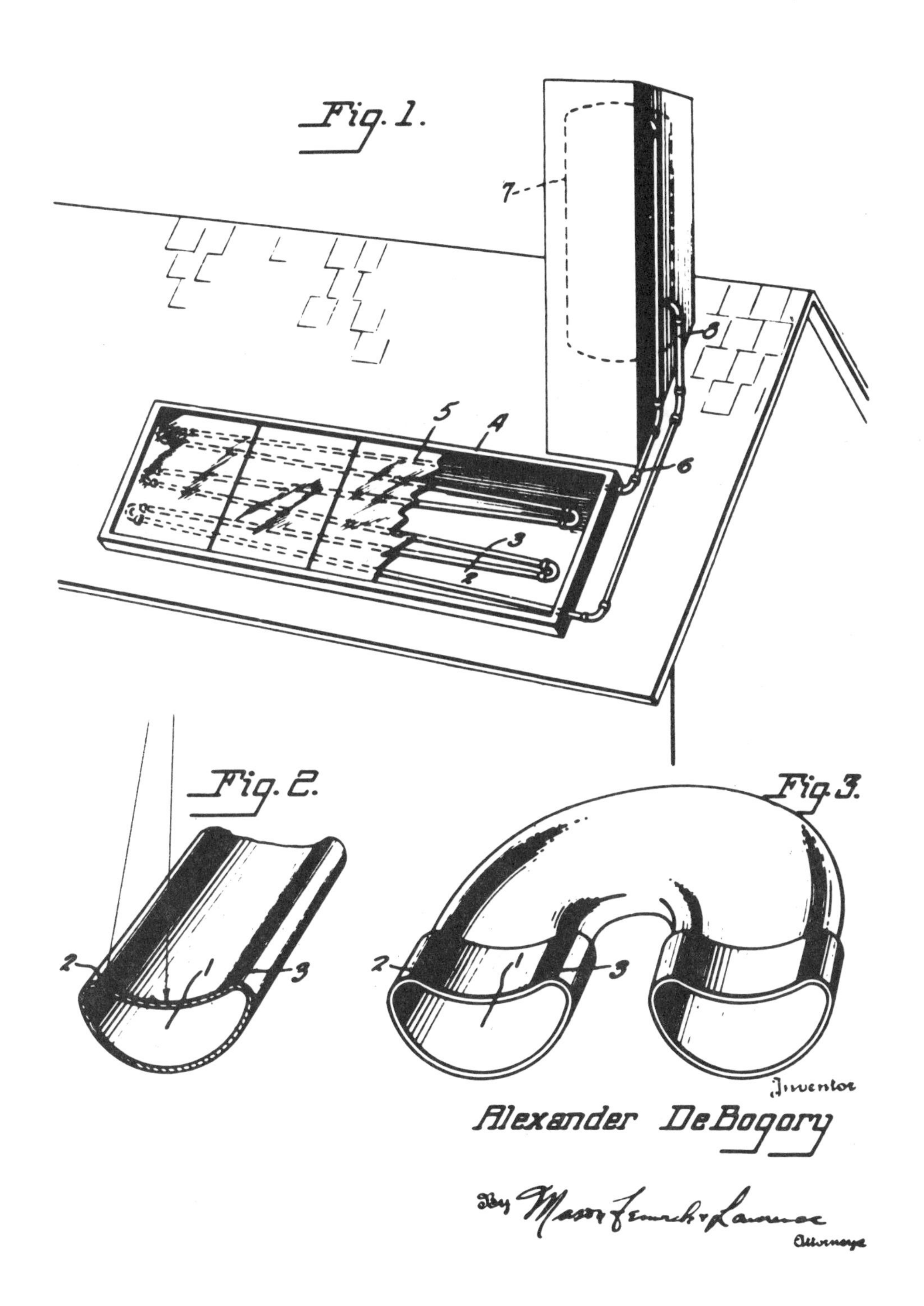

UNITED STATES PATENT OFFICE

2,257,524

SOLAR WATER HEATER

Alexander De Bogery, Miami, Fla.

*

My invention relates to a solar water heater used to heat water for household use or any other purpose where hot running water is used.

The object of my invention is to provide a solar water heater with an improved type of tube or pipe which carries the water and also transmits the heat of the sun to the water which by gravity flows into a reservoir or tank to be stored for use.

The conventional tubes heretofore used in this type process are of a round construction, with heavy non-heat-conducting return bends of the same round shape, which round construction does not allow a maximum absorption of sun heat rays in relation to the surface exposed on account of the convex surface of the round tube being exposed to the heat rays of the sun, thereby diffusing the heat rays. An example of this is the earth with its north and south poles covered with perpetual snow and ice, and in turn the perpetual heat at the equator.

In the drawing,

Figure 1 is a partial perspective view of the apparatus showing a preferred embodiment of this invention.

Figure 2 shows a cross-section view of a tube incorporating features of this inventive concept.

Figure 3 shows a return bend tube having features of this invention.

To overcome the foregoing fault, as will be seen with reference to the drawing, Fig. 1 shows a cut-away section of a solar heater, with the heater coils in place, Fig. 2 shows a cross section of my new design improved tube, this tube as shown has a concave surface exposed to heat rays of the sun and allows a more concentrated amount of heat to be transmitted to the water than can be done with a round tube of the same peripheral circumference. This improved design tube also allows a concentration of heat at the most needed place—that is, Fig. 2, No. 1, the lowest section of the tube, where the water is the coldest, the hot portion of the water being driven by gravity to the uppermost section of the tube as indicated by 2 and 3, Fig. 2. This action causes a faster, more thorough and uniform, heating of the water in the tube thereby creating a faster gravity movement in the tube longitudinally and consequently heating a greater amount of water than can be attained by the conventional type tube.

It is evident that the concave design of the tube allows of a more direct concentration of heat at its central or lowest point, Fig. 2, No. 1. The radiation of sun rays from the upper sides of the concave surface Fig. 2 at 2 and 3, causes the heat from upper sides of the concave surface of the tube to radiate or reflect towards the center of the arc of concave surface, thereby mingling with and superheating the direct vertical rays of the sun which fall on and vertically with the lowest portion and most essential part of the tube to be heated.

It will also be readily seen the cross section of the pipe or tube in my improved solar water heater, Fig. 2, allows a more even distribution of heat to the water by reason of a more uniform depth of water exposed to the heating surface.

In Figure 1 is illustrated an application of the invention in which the improved tubes are arranged in an open boxlike structure 4 having a glass top to prevent air circulation all positioned on a roof and associated with a tank 7, the top of which communicates with the upper reach of the heater by pipe 6 while a pipe 8 completes the circulation of water between the bottom of the tank and the lowest reach of the heater tube. Fig. 3 of the drawing illustrates the return bend, which is of the same design as the concave-convex tube, thereby allowing a continuous maximum absorption of heat throughout the entire length of the tube, and causing no interruption of heat penetration or flow of water through this return bend which is an advantage over the cast return bend of the conventional sun water heater.

This construction also overcomes the danger of the tube bursting in case of freezing, as the concave-convex surface of the tube or pipe can easily adjust itself to this expansion. *

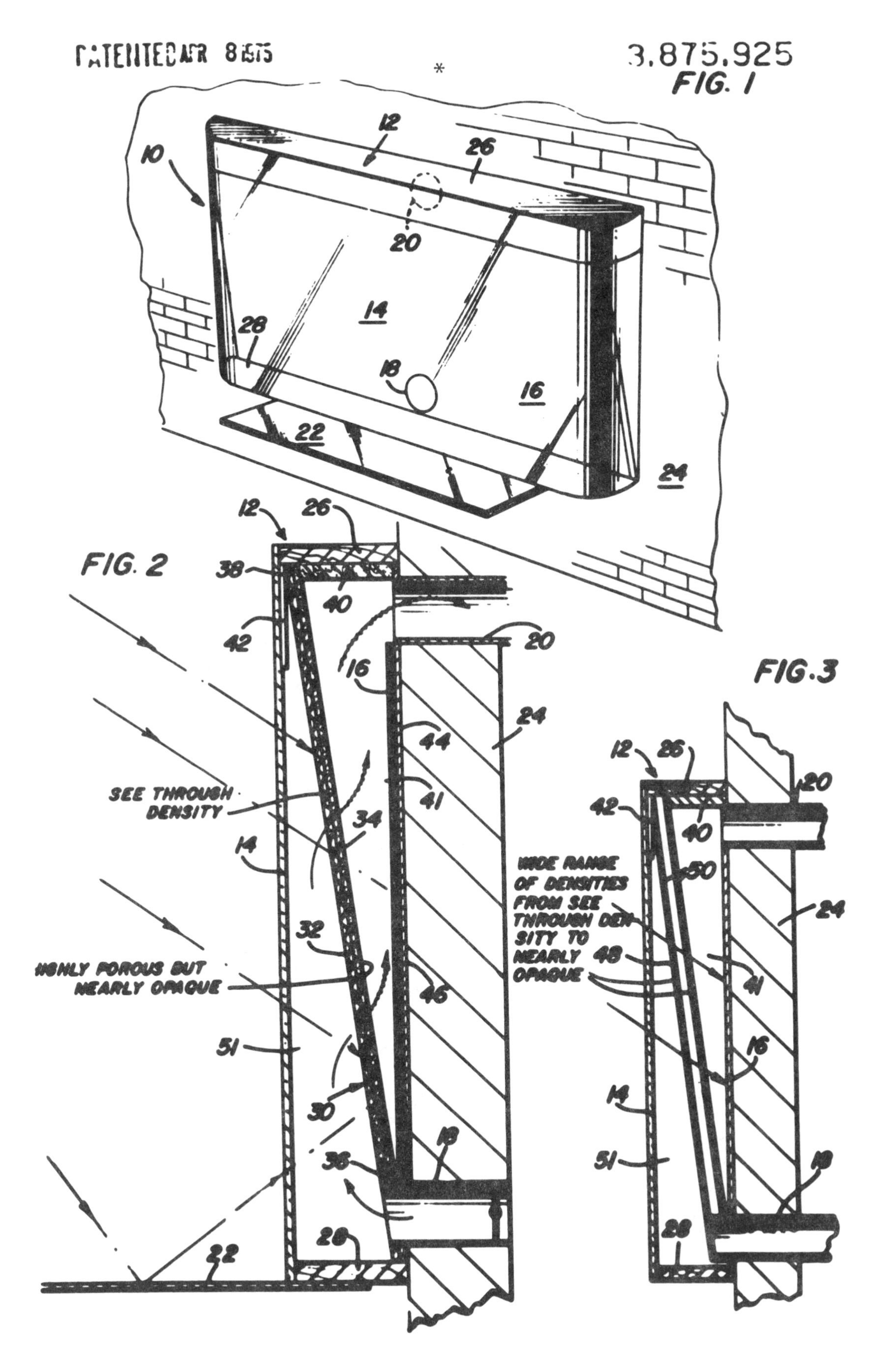
PATENTED APR 8 1975
3,875,925
FIG. 1
FIG. 2
FIG. 3
SEE THROUGH DENSITY
HIGHLY POROUS BUT NEARLY OPAQUE
WIDE RANGE OF DENSITIES FROM SEE THROUGH DENSITY TO NEARLY OPAQUE

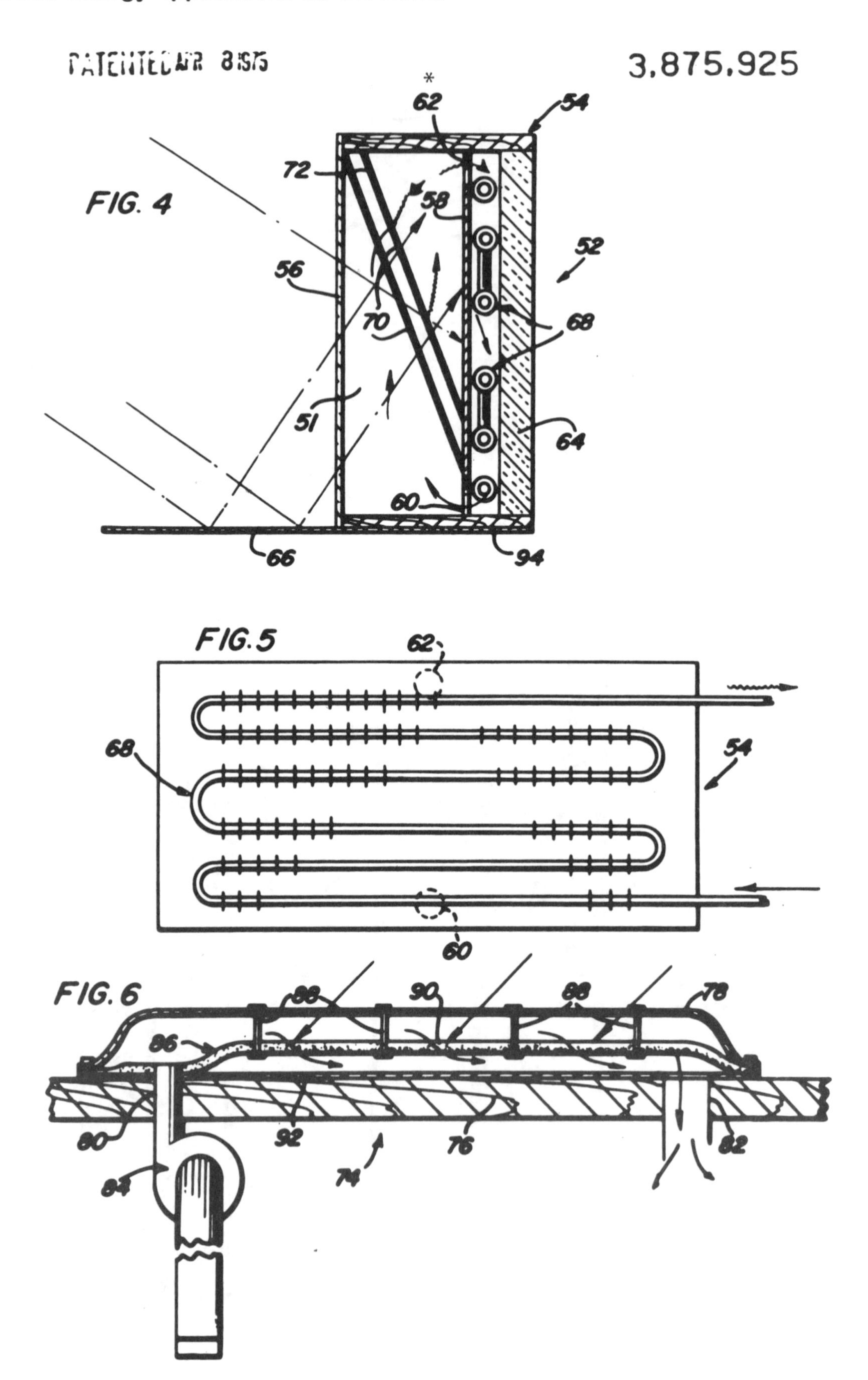
PATENTED APR 8 1975
3,875,925
FIG. 4
62
54
72
58
52
56
68
70
51
64
60
66
94
FIG. 5
62
68
54
60
FIG. 6
88
90
88
78
86
80
92
76
82
84
74

SOLAR HEATER

BACKGROUND OF THE INVENTION

1. Field of the Invention

This invention relates generally to heliotechnology, and particularly to solar heating. 2. Description of the Prior Art

It is known that glass will readily emit shortwave solar radiation, but will block the transmission of longer wavelength radiation. See, for example: Baumeister and Marks, *Standard Handbook for Mechanical Engineers*, 7th Edition, McGraw Hill, New York, 1967, pages 9–212 to 9–218, for a general discussion of heliotechnology, and specifically page 9–214 for a discussion of the "Greenhouse effect" of glass. This property of glass causes solar energy to be passed into an enclosure and not be re-radiated from same.

A disadvantage of a material such as glass in this regard, however, is that although glass does not readily pass long-wave radiation of 5 microns or more, glass does readily conduct heat. Further, convection within the enclosure will transmit the trapped heat back to the glass, thus substantially reducing the efficiency of heat collection.

My prior U.S. Pat. No. 2,998,005, issued Aug. 29, 1961, discloses the use of a fibrous mat to recover heat. Air passes transversely through the mat so as to absorb heat therefrom.

SUMMARY OF THE INVENTION

It is an object of the present invention to provide a material having poor thermal conduction and convection characteristics, but will readily admit solar radiation.

It is another object of the present invention to provide an improved solar heater which substantially eliminates losses by radiation or convection to the face which admits the solar radiation.

It is yet another object of the present invention to provide an improved heliothermal process for heating fluids by means of solar radiation.

These and other objects are achieved according to the present invention by providing: a housing forming a flow path for a fluid to be heated, and including a face arranged for passing solar rays impinging thereon, and a heat check valve arranged in the housing across the flow path for accepting heat received from the face and blocking the passage of heat back toward the face.

A preferred housing for a heliothermal device according to the present invention includes a back wall spaced from the face. An inlet and an outlet are provided in this back wall, and are arranged forming part of the flow path for a fluid to be heated.

The heat valve according to the present invention may be constructed in any one of various forms. A preferred embodiment of the heat valve has a substantially planar mat of a porous, preferably fibrous, material formed from two layers. One of the layers is arranged directed toward the housing face and is constructed from, for example, a fibrous material having a very low density, and the other of the layers is arranged directed toward the back wall and is constructed from, for example, a fibrous material having a density higher than the density of the one layer.

Another preferred embodiment of a heat valve according to the present invention has a pair of spaced screens of predetermined mesh. One of the screens is advantageously arranged directed toward the housing face and the other of the screens toward the back wall.

Although the fluid medium passed about the flow path defined by the housing may simply be air, and the like, directed from the housing outlet to an enclosure to be heated, alternatively this air, and the like, may be passed over the tubes of a heat exchanger in order to warm water, and the like, for more convenient storage and distribution.

These together with other objects and advantages which will become subsequently apparent reside in the details of construction and operation as more fully hereinafter described and claimed, reference being had to the accompanying drawings forming a part hereof, wherein like numerals refer to like parts throughout.

BRIEF DESCRIPTION OF THE DRAWINGS

FIG. 1 is a fragmentary, perspective view showing a solar heater according to the present invention.

FIG. 2 is a fragmentary, vertical, transverse sectional view showing the solar heater of FIG. 1, but drawn to a larger scale.

FIG. 3 is a fragmentary, vertical, transverse sectional view, similar to FIG. 2 but drawn to a smaller scale, showing a second embodiment of a solar heater according to the present invention.

FIG. 4 is a vertical, transverse sectional view, similar to FIGS. 2 and 3, but showing yet another embodiment of a solar heater according to the present invention.

FIG. 5 is a schematic elevational representation showing the solar heater of FIG. 4.

FIG. 6 is a fragmentary, vertical, longitudinal sectional view, showing still another embodiment of a solar heater according to the present invention.

DESCRIPTION OF THE PREFERRED EMBODIMENTS

Referring more specifically to the embodiment illustrated in FIGS. 1 and 2 of the drawings, a solar heater 10 according to the present invention has a housing 12 forming a flow path for a fluid, such as air or other suitable gas, to be heated. Housing 12 includes a face 14 arranged for passing light rays impinging thereon, and especially shortwave solar radiation, and the like. It is to be understood that face 14 may be constructed in a conventional manner from suitable, known materials, such as glass, or a thermoplastic resin. If the latter, one important parameter to use in selection is that the material should be clear and readily transmit solar radiation.

Housing 12 further includes a back wall 16 spaced from and arranged substantially parallel to face 14, and provided with an inlet 18 and an outlet 20 spaced from inlet 18. Both inlet 18 and outlet 20, which may be constructed in a suitable, known manner as from the illustrated conduit, are arranged forming part of the flow path formed by housing 12. As shown, a reflector 22 may be arranged beneath housing 12 and connected thereto for additionally increasing the efficiency of operation of heater 10 by increasing the amount of solar radiation reflected thereinto. Also as shown, housing

12 is mounted in a conventional manner on a wall 24 of a building structure to be heated. This wall 24 must, of course, be provided with openings for receiving the conduits forming inlet 18 and outlet 20. Housing 12 is completed using conventional construction techniques to include a top wall 26 and a bottom wall 28. It is to the latter wall that reflector 22 is attached in a suitable manner.

A heat valve is arranged in the housing 12 across the flow path thereof for accepting light received from face 14 and blocking the passage of heat back toward the face.

The heat valve advantageously, although not necessarily, is in the form of a substantially planar mat 30 which may be considered a filter medium in that it is constructed from a porous material, such as a fibrous synthetic resin, and formed from two layers 32 and 34. Fiber glass such as conventionally used as insulation, air filters, and the like, may be employed for constructing mat 30. Layer 32, being the layer arranged directed toward face 14, is selected to have a very low density, while layer 34, arranged directed toward back wall 16, has a density higher than the density of layer 32. It may be stated in general terms that layer 32 is of minimum density, and layer 34 of medium density. Examples of specific values for the density and radiation ratio of each layer 32, 34 is provided in the form of labels associated with FIG. 3 of the drawings. Further, layers 32 and 34 should generally be colored black, or a dark color, while layer 34 may be of a lighter color, such as gray or white.

The mat 30 employed with heater 10 is arranged extending from a point 36 on the inner end of the conduit forming inlet 18 on a side thereof oriented toward outlet 20 across the flow path to a point 38 on face 14 opposite outlet 20. As can be readily appreciated from FIG. 2 of the drawings, outlet 20 is arranged at a higher level than inlet 18 for creating a natural-circulation of the air or other medium being passed along the flow path defined by housing 12. A piece of insulation 40, which also may be conventional fiber glass insulation, and the like, is arranged along the inner surface of top wall 26 in order to cooperate with mat 30 and form a chamber 41 in which heat is collected. A double facing 42 constructed from a suitable, known material is desirably arranged along the upper edge of face 14 adjacent top wall 26 and extends from the latter to the depth of outlet 20. While back wall 16 may be constructed from an inexpensive material such as plywood which affords minimum insulation, conductance through back wall 16 can be tolerated since heat dissipated therethrough goes into the enclosure to be heated. A thin layer of an insulation 44, which may be aluminum foil, and the like, covers back wall 16, and a preferably black fabric 46, such as a cheesecloth, covers insulation 46. The latter covering absorbs heat, or more specifically solar radiation, passed through mat 30, and completes the heat collecting chamber 41.

The embodiment of a solar heater shown in FIG. 3 of the drawings is similar to heater 10 illustrated in FIGS. 1 and 2, but differs in that the heat valve is formed by a pair of spaced, parallel screens 48 and 50 in place of the multi-layered mat 30. Screen 48, which is preferably of less density than screen 50, is arranged directed toward face 14, and screen 50 is arranged opposite back wall 16. It is to be understood that although insulation 44 and fabric 46 have been omitted from FIG. 3 for reasons of clarifying that figure, such installation of fabric may be provided as desired. Screens 48 and 50 may be construcred in a conventional manner from fiber glass, cloth, or a metal. Examples of conventional materials which may be used for such screening are fiber glass, cloth, certain curtain material, cheesecloth, and door screening. I have discovered that screening that will allow nearly whole penetration by solar rays will effectively block a return of other heat rays. In any event, solar rays changed to heat in the screening, or any long-waves radiated to the screening from back wall 16, are cooled by the flow of cool air from the chamber 51 formed to the face 14 side of the screening into compartment or chamber 41. This flow of cool medium together with the wavelength changes caused by the screening and back wall 16 negate any likelihood of radiation to face 14 from chamber 41.

Referring now to FIGS. 4 and 5 of the drawings, a solar water heater 52 according to the present invention is similar to the heaters shown in FIGS. 1 to 3 of the drawings, but is modified so as to use a heated gaseous medium in the flow path to heat a liquid such as water, and the like. Heater 52 has a housing 54 provided with a face 56 similar to face 14. A back wall 58 is similar to back wall 16, but is spaced inwardly from the rear of top and bottom walls of housing 54 in the manner of a partition. This back wall is provided with an inlet 60 in the form of an opening or aperture in the wall, and an outlet 62 similar to inlet 60 but spaced therefrom. An outer wall 64 advantageously constructed from a material having good thermal insulating properties, completes housing 54. A reflector 66 similar to reflector 22 may be connected to the bottom wall of the housing as shown in FIG. 4.

Back wall 58 and outer wall 64 form a compartment 67 in which is arranged a bank 68 of preferably thin heat exchanger tubes, best seen in FIG. 5. As can be appreciated, bank 68 is arranged within housing 54, but on a side of back wall 58 facing away from face 56 for absorbing heat from a flow path medium, such as air, and heating a fluid, such as water, passing through the tubes of the bank. A pair of screens 70 and 72, similar to screens 48 and 50, form the heat valve for heater 52. It is to be understood, however, that a mat such as that designted 30 in the embodiment of FIGS. 1 and 2 may be substituted for screens 70 and 72 if so desired.

A flat solar heater 74 is shown in FIG. 6 of the drawings. This heater 74 is advantageously arranged on a roof 76, and the like, or other suitable horizontal surface. Heater 74 has a cover 78 which forms both the housing and face of this heater and is advantageously constructed from an optically clear synthetic resin such as those described above in connection with face 14. An inlet 80 and an outlet 82, both in the form of openings in roof 76, place the area under cover 78 in communication with the enclosure to be heated arranged beneath roof 76.

A conventional blower 84, and the like, is arranged in the opening forming inlet 80 to create a draft which moves air, and the like, along the horizontal extent of the flow path formed by roof 76 and cover 78. A black filter media 86, which may be a fibrous mat or a screen as described above, is arranged beneath cover 78 and connected thereto at points 88 as by conventional stitching or the use of a suitable adhesive. The median portion 90 of the heat valve is arranged parallel to the face formed by cover 78 and to roof 76 over which is advantageously arranged a layer of black heat-collecting material 92. Thus, roof 76 forms a surface equivalent to back wall 16, 58. Operation of heater 74 is similar to that of the heaters described above.

Cover 78 is advantageously constructed from a flexible sheet of plastic, and more specifically from three flexible sheets secured to a wall or roof 76 as by the illustrated bats. The inner layers, black porous filter media or cloth, are secured to cover 78 as shown so that pressure from blower 84 expands cover 78 away from back seal layer 92. The chamber when blown up forms a flow path next to the face, or cover 78, then through the filter media 86 to the rear or lower chamber and out outlet 82. Although the heater illustrated in FIG. 6 is specifically intended to be mounted horizontally, it is to be understood that it may also be mounted vertically if so desired.

In operation, all embodiments are similar in that the solar rays, designated by the long, straight arrows, enter through the associated face of the heater and partially or fully penetrate the heat valve. On this penetration, the solar rays change to heat rays of longer wavelength, and hence are absorbed by the air or other flow path medium for heating same. This will expand air or other gas and cause it to rise, thus creating a current drawing in cold air through the inlet 18. From chamber 51, the medium passes through the heat valve, into chamber 41, and out the outlet into the area to be heated. Although the illustrated embodiments are effective enough without the use of a reflector 22, 66, the reflectors arranged at the base can be desirable in extremely cold climates.

Since the heat is formed within the filter media, or heat valve, outward radiation is prevented by that portion of the filter media through which solar rays have penetrated. The back wall or layer, 16, 58, or 92, is covered black to receive rays penetrating completely through the filter media and radiation to the glass face in this case is blocked by the complete layer of filter mediia. When screens are used as the filter media to form a heat valve, the screens should be of minimum density. That is, they should have a high number of openings per unit length. Examples of screen densities suitable for use in such an application are given in the form of labels associated with FIG. 3 of the drawings.

The heaters illustrated in FIGS. 1 through 5 of the drawings need no external power as is. They are silent and efficient, and adaptable to automatic operation. Although no blower is required in any of the embodiments of FIGS. 1 to 5 such a blower can be installed at either the inlet or the outlet of same. Further, a damper valve (not shown) can be draft operated by a thermostatic spring (not shown), a solar eye operated blower (not shown), a flap valve actuated by air pressure (not shown), and the like. A damper valve need only be provided on the lower, or inlet duct or opening. Heavy, cold air will not enter through the top, or outlet duct or opening when the bottom duct or opening is closed.

It is evident that the common operation of the various embodiments described above is based on two elementary concepts. These concepts are: Firstly, as solar rays strike the outer reaches of the filter media and are changed to heat, the heat is immediately dissipated to the on-rushing cooler air on the flow path thus preventing radiation back to the face of the unit. The further into the filter media the solar rays are changed to heat, the warmer the on-rushing air becomes, but the more protection from radiation back to the unit face is effected by the additional portion of filter media between this area and the face. Rays completely penetrating through the filter media strike the black back wall and are afforded the protection of the complete thickness of filter media. Secondly, the complete separation of the heated area from contact with the face of the unit is achieved by the filter media and by the air flow pattern.

In the water heater embodiment illustrated in FIGS. 4 and 5 of the drawings, air circulation is continuous, thus permitting the addition of heat to the air as it is absorbed by the tubes of heat exchanger bank 68. This unit is capable of efficient water or fluid heating or steam generation. As mentioned above, either a fibrous mat or screens may be used as the heat valve. A damper 94 is advantageously provided to control speed of the circulating air. This action will synchronize the heating and cooling cycle to permit full utilization of the heated air before it is returned via the face compartment 51. With a given demand, this can merely be a predetermined restriction. Face 56 of this unit can be double-faced or partially double-faced at the top portion only for use with high operating temperatures. A unit of this kind has been found satisfactory for heating water coming into bank 68 at a temperature of, for example, 60°F. to a temperature of, for example, 170°F.

To again summarize the operation of a heater according to the present invention, solar energy is changed to heat, then to heated air half-way or more through the heat valve where the heated air rises from the face compartment into the back wall compartment. This action creates a circulatory motion drawing in air at the inlet and expelling it at the outlet. The heated air is not exposed to the outer face of the housing. Solar energy is transferred inside the heat valve so heat is not radiated outward. Heat is swept inward by the continuous air action.

As will be readily appreciated from the above description and from the drawings, a heater according to the present invention captures heat energy internally and eliminates radiation to the face and conduction by convection to the face. The efficiency of a heater according to the present invention approaches the maximum possible for this kind of device. Further, a heater according to the present invention permits attainment of temperatures in the range of, for example, 150° to 220°F. in conjunction with the quick conversion and release of solar light rays to heat energy. *

ABSTRACT

A fluid such as air is heated by a heliothermal device which provides a flow path for the fluid, and arranges across the fluid flow path a porous barrier which passes solar rays in one direction, but blocks heat from returning through the barrier in a direction opposite to that of the impinging solar rays. The barrier may be constructed in layers from a fibrous material, or as a fabric, metal, or synthetic resin mesh forming a screen.

* **6 Drawing Figures**

PATENTED SEP 2 1975 PYLE, D. L. 3,902,474

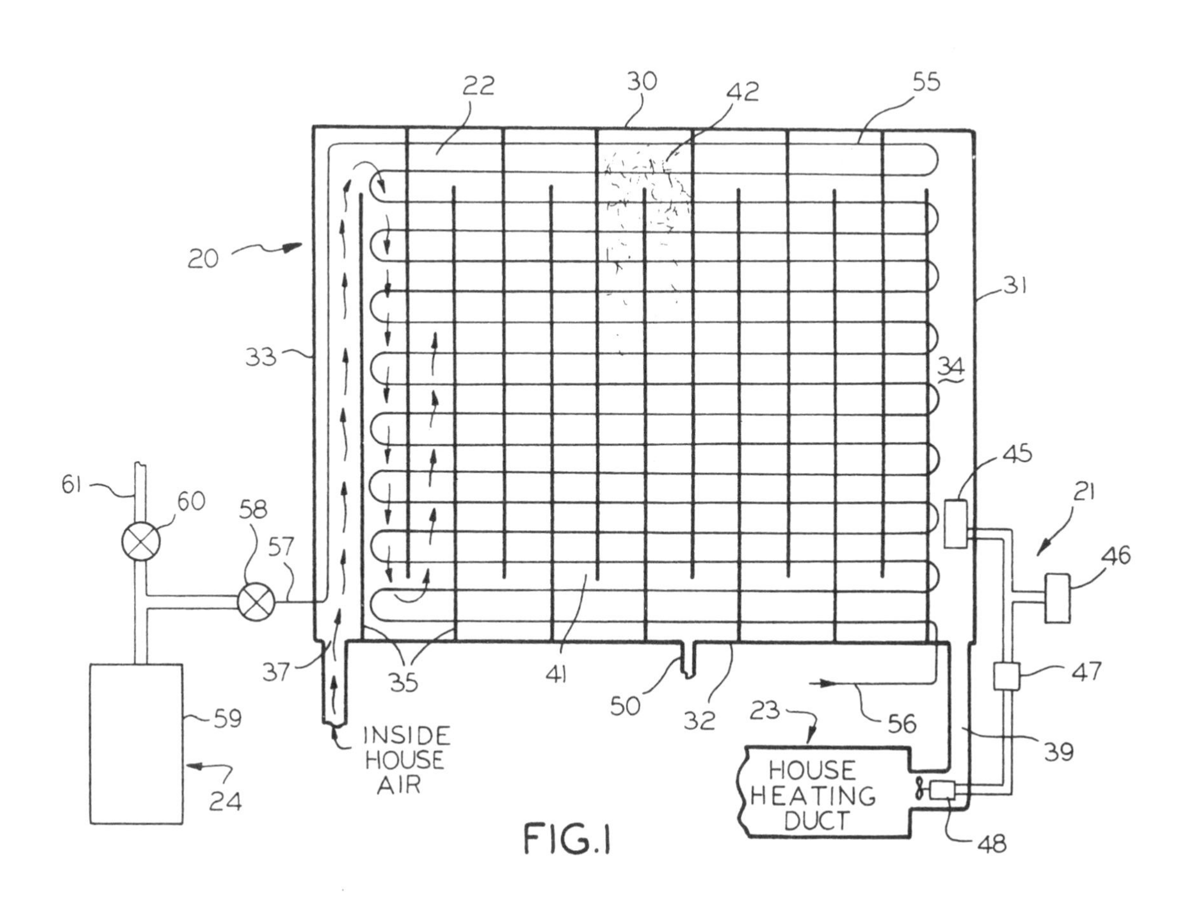

FIG.1

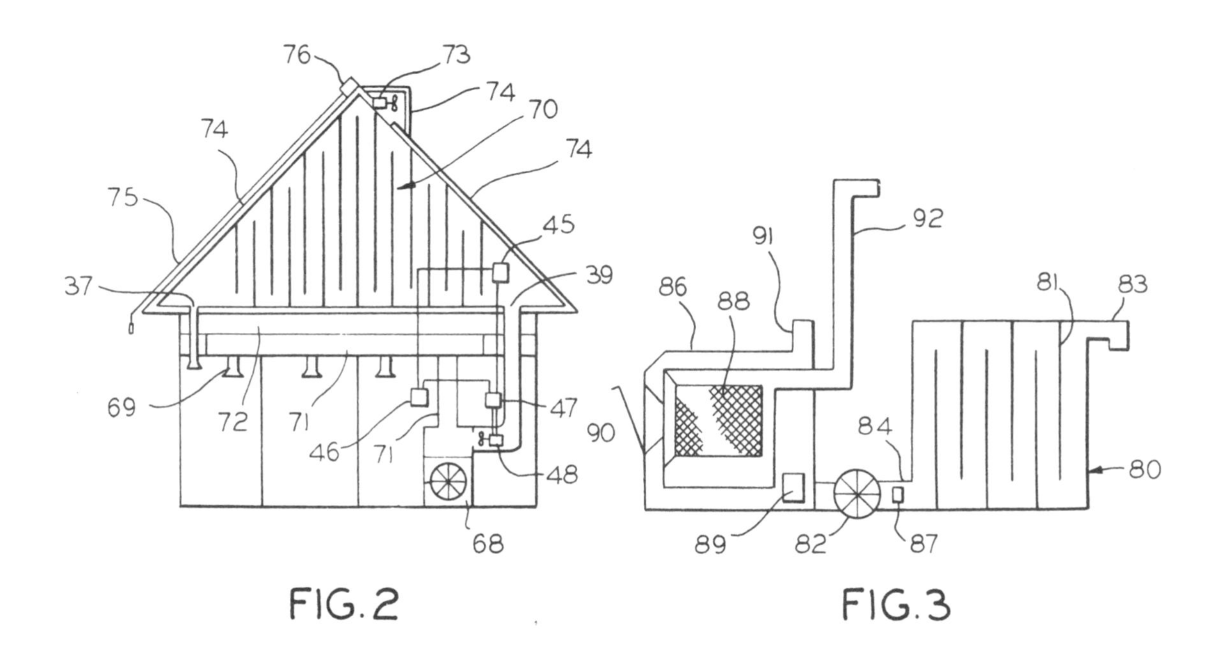

FIG.2

FIG.3

* **ABSTRACT**

A solar heat converter comprises a box of any convenient size with a maze of air passageways within the box. The passageways are partially filled with shredded heat conductive material, preferably having a black color. The heated air is forced through the passageways by means of fans or pumps, and the interior of the box is exposed to sunlight by a covering of thermal glass. In operation, the solar heat converter collects heat which is measured by an internal thermostat. The fans are operated to force heated air through an area to be heated in response to temperatures set on this and another thermostat in the area. *

SOLAR HEAT CONVERTER

This invention relates to solar energy converters and more particularly to means for heating air or fluids, especially although not exclusively for use in homes.

With the growing scarcity of fuel, it becomes ever more apparent that there is a pressing need for low cost, abundant, and inexhaustible energy sources. The sun is the source of the most abundant, and least exhaustible of all energy. Therefore, a better and more efficient solar energy converter is greatly to be desired.

For the home owner, the greatest single criterion is the economic aspect of a solar converter since his funds are not normally as substantial as, say the space program, for example. Therefore, it is not relevant that there may be expensive converters using a high level of technology. For the home owner, durability is also an important consideration. Housing is generally viewed as having a minimum of, say, a 40 year life, and housing parts, such as a roof, as having a 20 year life. Simplicity and ease of maintenance is another important criterion since the home owner is usually his own handy man, who uses conventional tools and skills.

Accordingly, an object of this invention is to provide low-cost solar energy converters meeting these and other criteria. In this connection, an object is to provide solar energy converters which readily mount on conventional homes, but are not unsightly. Here an object is to provide solar converters which may be either built into new homes or mounted on existing homes.

Another object of the invention is to provide an all-purpose solar energy converter module which may be used in large numbers for heating homes or singly (or in small numbers) for supplying heat to small appliances, such as clothes dryers, for example. Here, an object is to provide solar energy converters of various sizes which may be installed, serviced, and operated on any of many scales by the home-owning handy man. In particular, an object is to provide multipurpose solar energy converters for heating air, water, or other fluids.

In keeping with an aspect of the invention, those and other objects are accomplished by providing a box of any convenient size, which may be used as either a large and permanent installation or a small modular unit for assembly into a mosaic of units. Inside the box is a maze of air passageways partially filled with a shredded heat conductive material, such as aluminum, preferably with black surfaces. The box is a completely closed container with one transparent side exposing the maze to the sun. The entire maze is covered on its exposed side with thermal glass. Fans or pumps (which may or may not be thermostatically controlled) are provided for forcing air or liquid through the maze or pipes extending through the box.

The nature of a preferred embodiment of the invention is shown in the attached drawings, wherein:

FIG. 1 shows an exemplary solar energy converting module, incorporating the principles of the invention;

FIG. 2 schematically shows how the solar energy converter of FIG. 1 may be built into a house; and

FIG. 3 schematically shows how the solar energy converting module of FIG. 1 may be adapted for use with home appliances.

The principal elements of a solar energy converting module **20** (FIG. **1**) comprises an electrical control circuit **21,** and a maze **22** connected to a more or less conventional forced air heating or cooling system **23,** and any suitable supplemental appliance **24.**

The solar energy converter **20** may be made of any suitable material and in any convenient size. However, in one embodiment, it is made from materials and in sizes which are compatible with conventional building structures and practices. Thus, the outer perimeter panels **30, 31, 32, 33** of the box may be made from insulation or wooden boards, or plastic panels, about an inch thick, six to ten inches wide and two to four feet long. In one particular case, the box was 40-inches long and 28-inches wide. The back **34** of the box may be made from a sheet of any material having suitable strength which may be joined to the sides **30, 31, 32,** 33 in an airtight manner. The entire outside of the box may be insulated to reduce or preclude a loss of heat to the surrounding air.

Inside the box are any suitable number of baffles or partitions **35** arranged to form a maze or tortuous air passage. Thus, air entering the box at **37** must follow the path indicated, in part, by arrows until it leaves the box at outlet **39.** In the above-cited example of a 40 inch × 28 inch box, there are 13 baffles, each being about **24** inches long, arranged to form fourteen air passageways, one of which is numbered **41.** This arrangement forms a maze having folded air passage which is about 28 feet long, and perhaps 2 inches by 8 inches in cross-section.

All of the baffles inside the box--whether insulated or not--are covered by aluminum foil or other material having a good heat conductive material, which may be painted or otherwise colored black. The air passageway inside box **20** contains at least some shredded black aluminum foil or wire **42** in a sufficient quantity to provide a maximum amount of heat exchange, without seriously impeding the air flow inside the passageway.

A thermostat **45** is positioned inside the box near the outlet thereof and adjusted to close an electrical heating control circuit at a predetermined high temperature and to open the circuit at a predetermined low temperature. A thermostat **46** is positioned in a house, appliance, or other area to be heated by the solar energy converter. This thermostat **46** is connected in series with the thermostat **45** and is arranged to close the heating control circuit at a selected low temperature and to open it at a related high temperature.

The two thermostats **45, 46** cooperate to control a relay or other device **47** in order to demand heat when the house or other area is colder than the temperature selected by thermostat **46**, if there is a sufficiently high level of heat in the solar energy converter **20**. A circuit which is completed by relay **47** operates a fan **48** which draws air from the house through inlet port **37**, the maze inside the box, and the outlet **39** to the fan **48**. A conventional forced air heating system conveys the heated air through the house and back to inlet port **37**.

If the temperature in the solar energy converter **20** is not then hot enough, thermostat **45** is not closed, and relay **47** does not operate. A conventional furnace is then turned on in a normal manner by the thermostat **46**. It is thought that such a supplementary use of a conventional furnace would be required only on extremely overcast and very cold days. However, such usage depends largely upon factors such as the house construction, insulation, storm windows, and the like, which are beyond the scope of the invention.

A water drain **50** is formed in the bottom of the box to drain off condensation.

Any suitable number of the solar energy converters **20** may be formed into a mosaic by connecting their inlets **37** to their outlets **39**--either in series or in parallel--to thereby form a single passageway from the house through one inlet **37** and out a final outlet **39**.

Supplementing the air flow may be a fluid system comprising a pipe **55** which follows a serpentine path through the box. Thus, the fluid may be pumped through piping **55** to a point where it collects and stores heat generated by the solar energy falling on the converter **20**. By way of example, the drawing shows an input connection **56** for leading the pipe to a city water supply, which furnishes suitable fluid pressure. The output end **57** of pipe **55** is coupled through a valve **58** to a hot water tank **59**. As an alternative, valve **60** may also provide means for drawing water directly from the city water supply **61** and into the hot water tank **59**. The hot water in tank **59** may be for any use--such as the normal hot water supply, for example. Of course, any other appliance requiring a heated fluid may be substituted for the hot water tank **59**. In another example, the tank **59** may have a substantial size to provide means for accumulating substantial amounts of heated fluids for heating the house via a conventional hot water distribution system. Further, different fluids may be substituted for water depending upon the user's needs. For example, some of the wellknown refrigerant gases or liquid may be used.

For an existing house, a plurality of the modules of FIG. **1** may be placed in a mosaic assemblage on top of the roof. For new housing, the solar converter may be constructed as taught in FIG. **2**.

In greater detail, the maze **70** is preferably built into the attic area or between roof and ceiling of a house to provide a folded air passage, much as described above in connection with FIG. **1**. The air passage folded into the maze **70** is connected into the normal duct work **71** of a forced air furnace **68** having blower and room vents **69**. The flow of air through the duct is controlled by fan **48** and thermostats **45, 46**. Insulation **72** is interposed between the maze **70** in the attic and the living space in the house.

For summer months, an exhaust fan **73** may draw hot air from the attic maze **70** and vent it through an open insulated door **74**, which is normally closed during the winter months.

Also, at least a part of the roof **74** of the house is covered by thermal glass to expose the maze to the sun during the winter months and thereby heat the air. To cover the thermal glass during summer months a light reflective awning **75** may be unrolled from a box **76** permanently mounted on the roof. Alternatively, a number of louvers may be attached to the roof. A preferred approach is to mechanize the louvers so that they may be opened in the winter and closed in the summer. Another approach is to cover the thermal glass on the roof **74** with louvers preset at an angle which does not block the passage of the angularly slanted winter rays of sunlight, but does block passage of the less slanted summer rays of sunlight. This alternative of using preset louvers has the obvious disadvantage that much less than the full day of solar energy is available for heating the house.

For appliance usage (FIG. **3**), the solar energy converter **80** simply sets at a convenient place outdoors, as in a backyard, where it is struck by the suns rays. Again, essentially the same type of maze **81** is built into the converter with the thermal glass facing the sun exposure. A suitable blower or fan **82** draws fresh outside air through an inlet duct **83**, the maze **81**, and an outlet duct **84** to the appliance **86**, here shown as a clothes dryer, by way of example. Since a dryer, such as this does not depend upon critical heat control, the thermostats may be eliminated. However, it is also within the scope of the invention to provide a controllable fresh air inlet vent **87** between the solar converter **80** and fan **82** to mix fresh air with the heated air when more precisely controlled air temperatures are desirable. Any suitable temperature controlled servo system may open or close vent **87**.

The dryer **86** is here shown as having the usual tumbler **88**, motor **89**, front loading door **90**, control panel **91**, and exhaust vent **92**. However, this is merely representative of appliance usage. Any other suitable appliance may also be used in connection with the solar energy converter. *

U.S. Patent Nov. 11, 1975 3,918,430

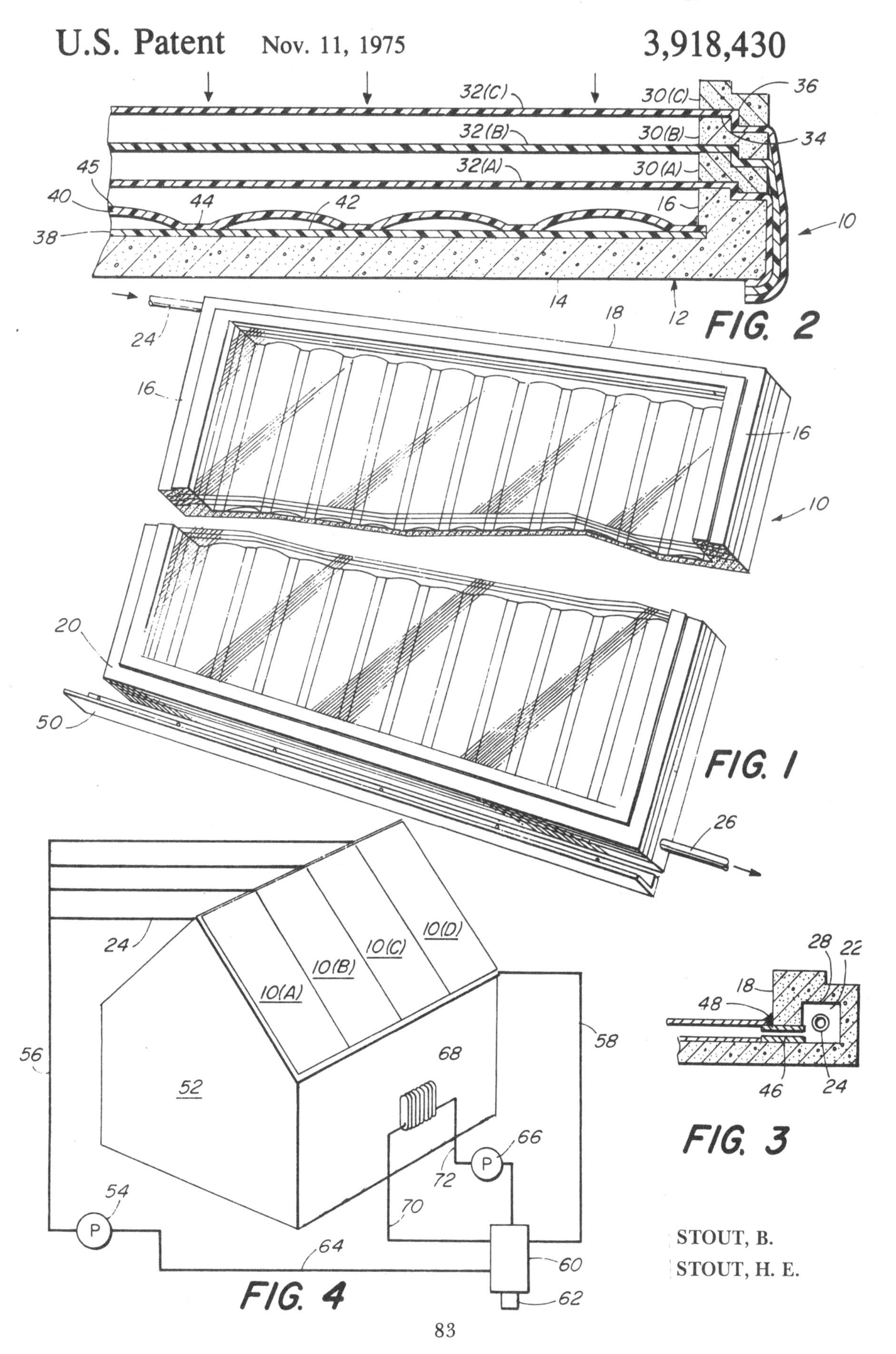

STOUT, B.
STOUT, H. E.

* ABSTRACT

A light weight, low cost, solar heating system is provided for use with homes and other buildings. Solar heating panels are mounted on a roof or other support and connected to the building's heating system. Water or other liquid medium is pumped to the elevated upper end of each unit and is allowed to drain down through each panel by gravity feed back into a storage tank where the heated water is circulated, on demand, through the building. Each heating panel is comprised of a rigid foam plastic frame having a back wall over which is disposed a reflective stratum. A sheet of plastic material having a black surface is bonded to the reflective stratum along spaced parallel lines to define a plurality of parallel channels extending lengthwise of the panel. Manifolds are provided at opposite ends of the panel to feed water into and drain water from the channels. Spaced layers of flexible, transparent plastic film are mounted to the frame across the front of the panel to pass radiant heat from the front to heat water in the channels and trap the heat absorbed by the panel.

* 4 Drawing Figures

SOLAR HEATING SYSTEM AND COMPONENTS THEREOF

BACKGROUND OF THE INVENTION

1. Field of the Invention

This invention relates generally to solar heating systems and more particularly is directed towards a new and improved, solar heating system employing simple, low cost light weight heating panels mountable to the roof of a building or the like.

2. Description of the Prior Art

With the increasing cost of heating fuels as well as the increase experienced in the cost of generating electricity, a greater interest has developed in providing alternate sources of energy, particularly for heating homes and other buildings. Solar heating systems are of particular interest since the sun provides a substantially unlimited source of free energy and various types of solar heating panels have been developed which utilize the sun's rays to heat water or the like with the water, in turn, serving to heat the building which the panels are associated. While solar heat systems of this type have functioned successfully, the high initial capital cost of systems presently available have prevented widespread use of such systems. Also, for the most part, present solar heating systems have required specially designed buildings involving relatively large, expensive and complex components.

Accordingly, it is an object of the present invention to provide a new and improved solar heating system adapted for easy installation on existing buildings. Another object of this invention is to provide a simple, low-cost light weight solar heating system which is compatible with existing structures and heating systems and which may be quickly and easily installed by relatively unskilled workmen.

SUMMARY OF THE INVENTION

This invention features a solar heating system, comprising at least one solar panel fabricated with a light weight frame of a rigid foam plastic material having a back wall and shallow marginal side walls extending about the edges thereof. A reflective stratum is applied over the inner face of the back wall and a layer of waterproof moldable plastic material is bonded to the reflective layer along spaced parallel lines to define a plurality of parallel water channels between the plastic material and the reflective backing. Transparent plastic film is mounted across the frame opening in spaced parallel layers to trap heat generated by radiant energy from the sun passing through the film to heat the water in the channels. The outer face of the plastic material forming the water channels is black to enhance heat absorption. Manifolds are provided in the frame at opposite ends of channels by which water is delivered at one end and drained by gravity from the other end. A pumping system is provided for circulating water and a storage tank is connected to the pumping system to store water heated thereby.

BRIEF DESCRIPTION OF THE DRAWINGS

FIG. **1** is a view in perspective of a solar heating panel made according to the invention,

FIG. **2** is a fragmentary sectional view showing details of the panel construction.

FIG. **3** is a view somewhat similar to FIG. **2** showing further details of the panels, and,

FIG. **4** is a view in perspective, somewhat schematic, of a typical heating system employing panels of the present invention.

DETAILED DESCRIPTION OF THE PREFERRED EMBODIMENT

Referring now to the drawings, the reference character **10** generally indicates a solar heating panel made according to the invention and generally organized about a rectangular frame **12** of a light weight, thermally insulating, inexpensive, material. Preferably the frame **12** is molded from styrofoam or other rigid, foam plastic material which is light in weight, inexpensive yet structually strong and having excellent thermal insulation characteristics. The frame **12** is of a rectangular configuration formed with integral, relatively short surrounding side walls **16.** The dimensions of the frame **12** may be varied over a wide range depending upon particular applications. Typically, the panels are made up of rather long sections on the order of perhaps **10'** to **20'** and in width on the order of perhaps **3'** or so. The dimensions are not critical but rather may be in a wide range. The wall **14** should be relatively thick to provide good thermal insulation for the unit. In this regard, styrofoam is particularly effective as a thermal insulator in addition to its advantageous structual characteristics. The wall **14** may be ½ inch or so in thickness to provide both strength and proper insulating protection for the panel. The side wall **16** is relatively thick being on the order of 1-½ to 2 inches both in height and width to reinforce the assembled panels as well as to provide a clearance of possibly ¾ inch between the inner face of the wall **14** and the top of the wall **16** for reasons that will presently appear. The side walls **16** extend the full length of the panel **10**. End walls **18** and **20** are formed integral with the frame across the full width of the panel and are of the same height as the side walls **16**. The end walls **18** and **20** are hollow to form a manifold chamber **22** for communciation with an inlet conduit **24** for the wall **18** and an outlet conduit **26** for the wall **20**.

The walls **16, 18** and **20**, in the preferred embodiment, are formed with a groove or recessed portion **28** extending about the upper outer edges of the walls to receive in nesting engagement stacked spacers **30**(*a*), (*b*), and (*c*), mounted one on top of the other over the walls **16, 18** and **20** to provide a predetermined spacing between multiple layers of transparent film **32** (*a*), (*b*), and (*c*). The function of the multiple layers of transparent film **32** is to transmit radiant energy from the sun into the solar heating panel **10** while insulating the panel against heat losses through conduction and convection. In the preferred form of the invention, the film layers **32** are spaced apart from one another by a distance of approximately ½ inch and, ideally, are two or three in number. The spacers **30** are of matching size and configuration having a length and width corresponding to that of the panel **10** and formed about its inner lower corner with a recess **34** adapted to nest with the recess **28** of the walls **16, 18** and **20** as well as with a recess **36** formed about the upper outer edges of each of the spacers.

In fabricating the panels, the film layers **32** are stretched over the frame walls **16, 18** and **20** to a relatively taut and smooth surface. In practice, the innermost film layer **32** (*a*) is first placed in position and securely bonded to the frame **14**. One mode of assembly that has been found to be particularly satisfactory is the use of heat shrinking techniques involving thermoplastic films by which the films are shrunk tightly onto the frame. Once the first layer **32** (*a*) is in position, the spacer **30** (*a*) is mounted over the walls **16, 18** and **20** and the second transparent film **32** (*b*) is applied. The same operation is repeated for the next spacer **30** (*b*) and the film layer **32** (*c*). A final optional spacer **30** (*c*) may be applied to form a protective member about the assembled structure. Various types of films may be employed and should be selected according to their light transmission characteristics, durability, weathering characteristics, bonding qualities and the like. Various types of polyethelyne, PVC, and other plastic films are suitable for this purpose. The spacers **30**, preferably of the same material as the frame **14**, are readily moldable from styrofoam or other relatively rigid foam plastic material which is light in weight, structurally strong and displays excellent thermal insulating characteristics.

Within the solar panel there is disposed a reflective stratum **38** applied to the upper face of the frame wall **14** and, for this purpose, aluminized plastic, aluminum foil or other high reflective material, including aluminized paint, may be employed. The reflective stratum **38** covers the entire surface of the frame wall **14** and forms with a ply **40** a plurality of spaced, parallel, water channels **42** disposed lengthwise across the width of the solar panel. The ply **40**, in the preferred form of the invention, is a moldable plastic material such as PVC or the like and is relatively light in weight, waterproof and preferably adapted for thermal-forming techniques. The ply **40** is bonded along seams **44** extending in parallel longitudinal relation to the stratum **38**, as best shown in FIG. **2**. Typically, the bonding seams **44** are about ⅜ inch wide with the channels **42** being about 4 inches in width. As shown in FIG. **2**, the ply **40** between the seams is raised somewhat from the face of the reflective stratum and typically an elevation of perhaps ⅛ inch provides adequate flow of water. The function of the channels is to form water into a relatively thin stream to facilitate heat transfer. In this regard, the ply **40** should be a black body and is either of and entirely black material or has its surface coated as at **45** with a dull black substance which will readily absorb the radiated heat from the sun. The combination of the black body absorption characteristics of the ply **40** along with the reflective characteristics of the stratum **38** causes rapid heating of water flowing through the channels **42**. On a typical sunny day, temperatures on the order of 225° to 250°F are obtainable within a relatively short period of time.

Each of the water channels **42** communicates with the manifold chambers **22** in the upper and lower end walls **18** and **20** as by tubes **46** (FIG. **3**) extending between the chambers **22** and into the ends of the water channel. A fillet **48** of sealing compound may be applied along the joints to prevent leakage.

In practice, each solar panel is mounted in a tilted position with the end wall **18** raised above the end wall **20** in the manner shown so that water fed into the upper manifold through the conduit **24** will flow by gravity down through the water channels **42** into the manifold of the end wall **20** and drain out through the conduit **26**. Typically, the solar panels are mounted on a pitched roof in the manner suggested in FIG. **4** and a number of panels may be installed depending upon the particular requirements of the building. Since each solar panel is relatively light in weight and easily handled, it may be nailed onto an existing roof without the need of reinforcement or extra support. Nails can be readily driven through the side walls of each panel or the unit may be cemented onto the roof. Preferably, an angle iron **50** is secured to the lower end of a pitched roof to provide support for the solar panel against slipping.

A system utilizing the solar panels is illustrated in FIG. **4** and, in the illustrated embodiment, four solar panels **10** (*a*), (*b*), (*c*) and (*d*) are mounted to a pitched roof of a building **52** with the panels extending from the peak of the roof down to the eaves. Feed water is delivered by means of a pump **54** to a conduit **56** through branch lines **24** into the manifold **22** at the upper end of each solar heating panel. The relatively cool water flows by gravity down through the channels **42** in the heating panels becoming heated in the process and drains out through a drain line **58** down into a collecting tank **60**, preferably within the building. The outlet conduits **26** may interconnect with the drain manifolds of adjacent panels with the last connected to the line **58.** The tank **60** should be well insulated and, preferably, is provided with an auxiliary heater **62** which may be electrical, oil fired, gas fired or the like. The auxiliary heater is for use whenever heating requirements are not met by the solar heating system as may occur after a number of cloudy days in succession. The pump **54** is connected by a conduit **64** to the tank **60** and recirculates the water through the system. The heated water in the tank **60** is removed by means of a pump **66** which circulates the heated water through the heating system of the building. The heating system may be preexisting and may include a number of radiators **68** connected by conduits **70** and **72** to the tank **60.** For purposes of illustration, only a single radiator and simple heating system are shown. Obviously, a more complex system may be utilized.

While water has been indicated as the heat transfer medium, obviously a wide variety of liquids and liquefiable materials may be used in the system. For example, alcohol, salt water, liquid hydrocarbons, salt solutions and various other heat transfer media may be employed in the system. *

Feb. 5, 1963 E. W. GOUGH ET AL 3,076,450

PLASTIC SOLAR HEATER

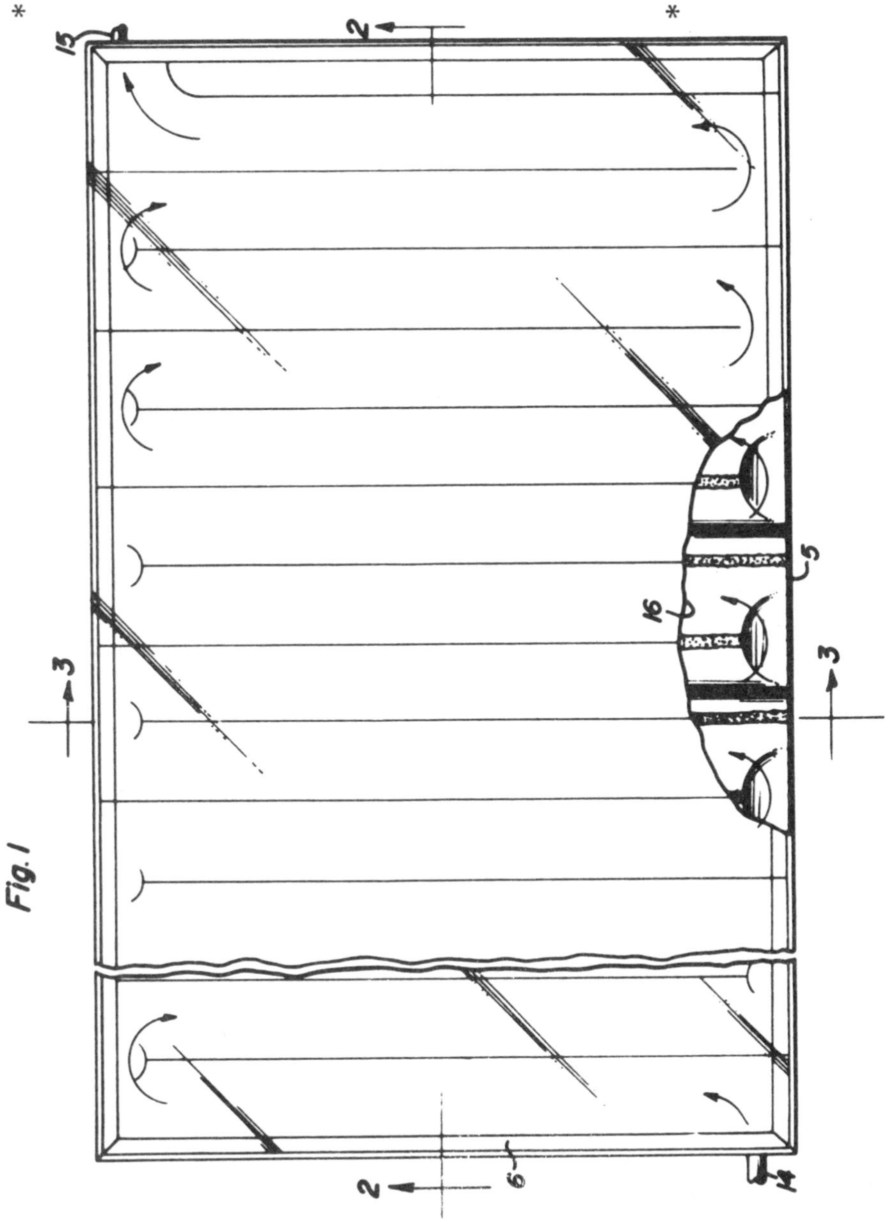

Fig. 1

Edward W. Gough
Paul D. Irwin INVENTORS.

BY

Feb. 5, 1963 E. W. GOUGH ET AL 3,076,450

PLASTIC SOLAR HEATER

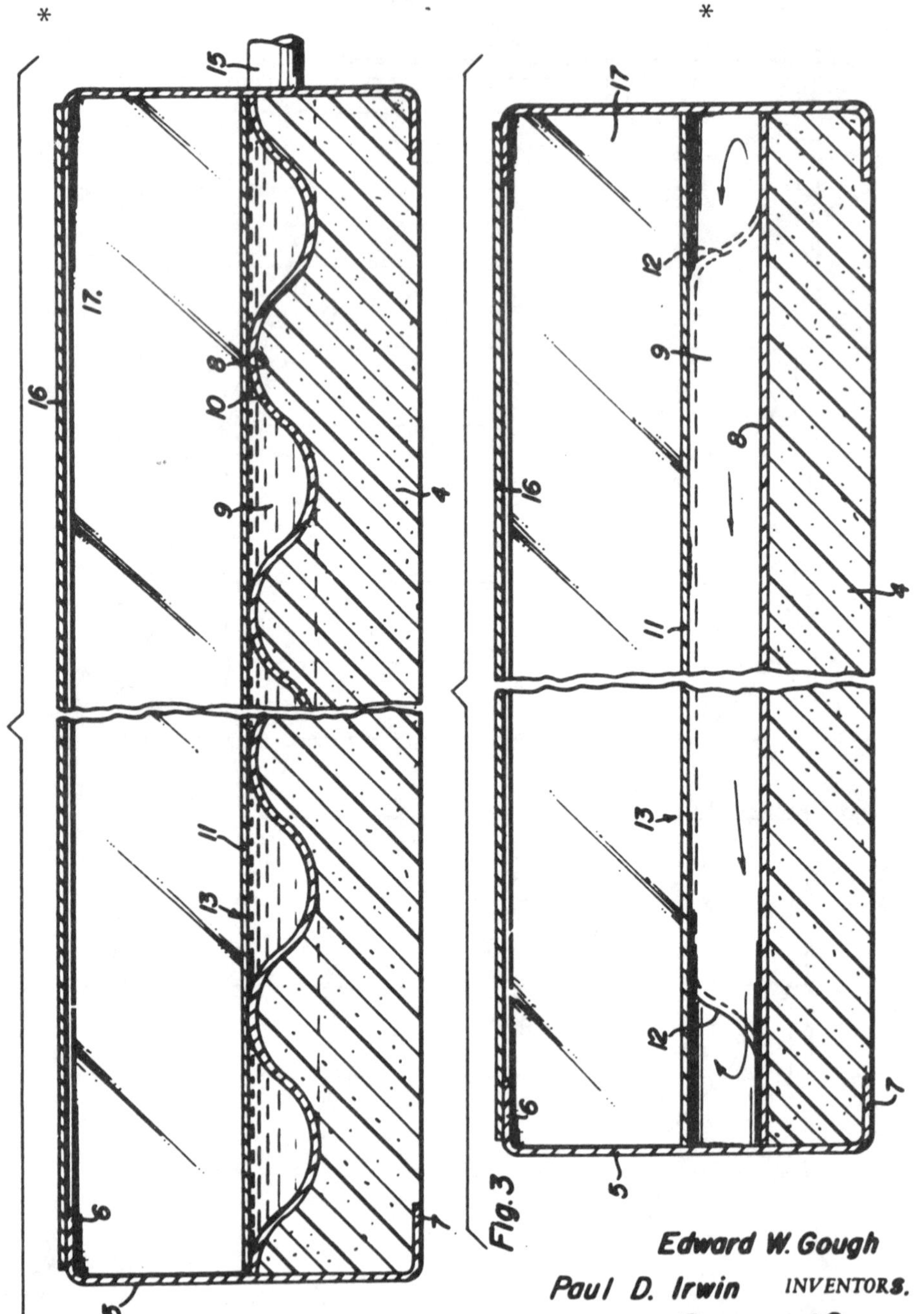

Fig. 2

Fig. 3

Edward W. Gough

Paul D. Irwin INVENTORS.

BY

3,076,450
PLASTIC SOLAR HEATER

Edward W. Gough, 4911 Farber Ave., Covina, Calif., and Paul D. Irwin, 2300 Brigden Road, Pasadena, Calif.

*

This invention relates to new and useful improvements in solar heaters to be used particularly, although by no means necessarily, for heating water for residences, swimming pools, etc.

Present solar heaters are inefficient for a number of reasons. The design is such that the heat must transfer over a considerable distance through metal to a copper tube containing water. Each time the heat transfers from one medium to another there is a loss in efficiency. The metal is usually coated with black paint which in itself is a poor conductor of heat, even though its absorption of solar energy may be excellent, depending on several factors, such as density, gloss, etc.

Because of the fact that the metal itself must transfer the heat, there is a tendency for the water passing through the tubes to release lime deposits as it picks up heat, further lowering efficiency. Also, because the chemicals used in swimming pools are corrosive, the copper tubing soon acquires an insulating deposit of lime and corrosive elements, which deposit is difficult to remove and which still further reduces efficiency.

The volume of water available as a heat absorbing medium is limited by the size and amount of tubing per square foot. Since it is economically unfeasible to lay the tubing side by side over the surface of the heat exchanger, a thin, flat copper sheet to which the tubing is soldered us used. The tubing is kept to a minimum size because of economic and weight considerations.

As a result of the foregoing factors, the present methods employed to heat water through the use of solar energy have not achieved a practical degree of efficiency. Furthermore, because of the choice limitations of material, present solar heaters are unsightly and consequently have limited application. Accordingly, the primary object of the present invention is to provide, in a manne s hereinafter set forth, a greatly improved solar water heater which is made entirely of plastics whereby the aforementioned and other deficiencies in present solar heaters will be substantially eliminated.

Another important object of this invention is to provide an all-plastic solar heater of the aforementioned character which is fabricated in a novel manner to define what may be considered a flat coil or the like through which the water to be heated circulates.

Other objects of the invention are to provide an improved all-plastic solar water heater of the character set forth which will be comparatively simple in construction, strong, durable, compact, of light weight, highly efficient and reliable in use, attractive in appearance and which may be manufactured at low cost.

These together with other objects and advantages which will become subsequently apparent reside in the details of construction and operation as more fully hereinafter described and claimed, reference being had to the accompanying drawings forming a part hereof, wherein like numerals refer to like parts throughout, and in which:

FIGURE 1 is a view in front elevation of a solar water heater constructed in accordance with the present invention, a portion of the device being broken away in section;

FIGURE 2 is a view in vertical longitudinal section on an enlarged scale through the device, taken substantially on the line 2—2 of FIGURE 1; and

FIGURE 3 is a view in transverse section on an enlarged scale through the device, taken substantially on the line 3—3 of FIGURE 1.

Referring now to the drawings in detail, it will be seen that the embodiment of the invention which has been illustrated comprises a polyurethane foam plastic, heat insulative base, slab or bottom **4** of suitable dimensions, said base being substantially rectangular. The base **4** is mounted in the lower or rear portion of a rectangular molded plastic frame **5** comprising, in the embodiment illustrated, inturned marginal flanges **6** and **7**.

The base **4** includes a corrugated or undulated top portion **8** defining a series of parallel water ducts or channels **9**. The corrugated or undulated top **8** of the base **4** is provided with a black plastic liner **10**. Sealed on the crests of the corrugations or the undulations of the liner **10** is a transparent plastic panel **11**. The ducts **9** defined by the construction and arrangement described communicate at alternate ends, as at **12**. Thus, what may be considered a flat coil is provided through which the water to be heated circulates. This coil is designated generally by reference numeral **13**. Inlet and outlet pipe connections **14** and **15**, respectively, communicate with the coil **13** at the ends thereof. Mounted on the top or front of the frame **5** is a panel or cover **16**, also of a suitable transparent plastic. The cover **16** is sealed on the flange **6** of the frame **5** and provides a dead air space **17** above the coil **13**.

It is thought that the operation of the heater will be readily apparent from a consideration of the foregoing. Briefly, the water enters the device at **14** and flows through the continuous duct or channel provided by the passages **9** and **12**. Of course, the water is heated in an obvious manner as it flows through the device and is discharged therefrom at **15**. The cover **16** and the panel **11** are of a transparent plastic having excellent solar heat transmitting characteristics. The black plastic liner **10** absorbs heat and thus materially promotes the efficiency of the device. The efficiency is further increased by the insulating characteristic of the plastic base **4**. The solar heat energy passes through the transparent cover **16** and the panel **11** and impinges on the black plastic liner **10** where it is taken off by the water flowing through the device, resulting in a direct heat transfer. *

July 13, 1965 M. AMAT BARGUES 3,194,228

SOLAR HEATER

* *

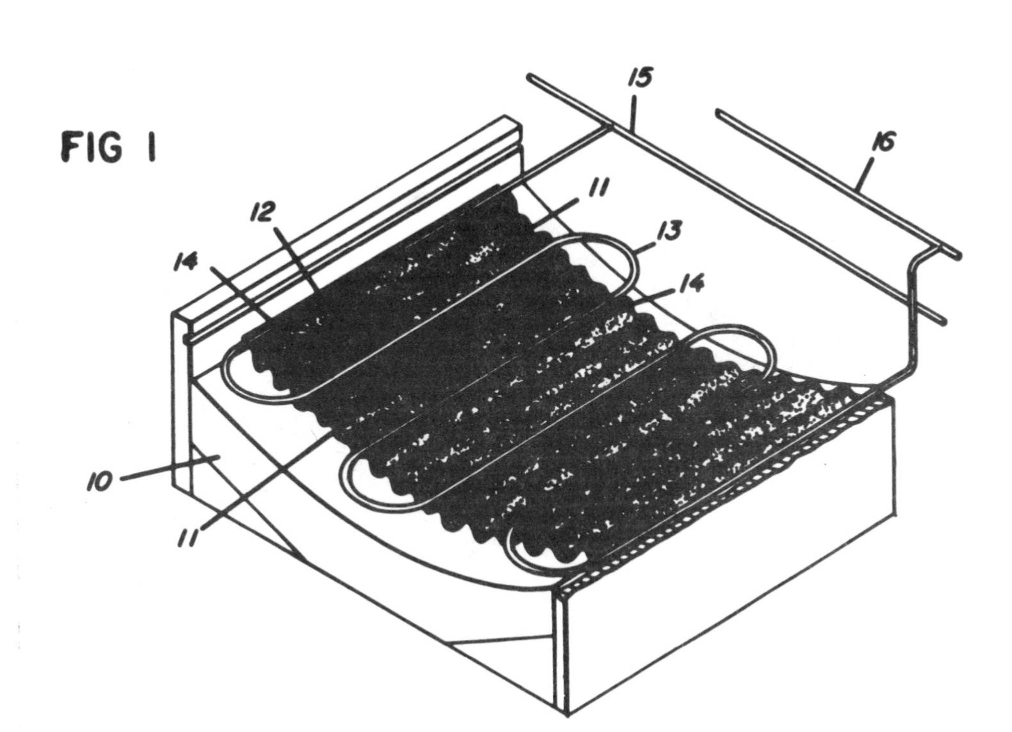

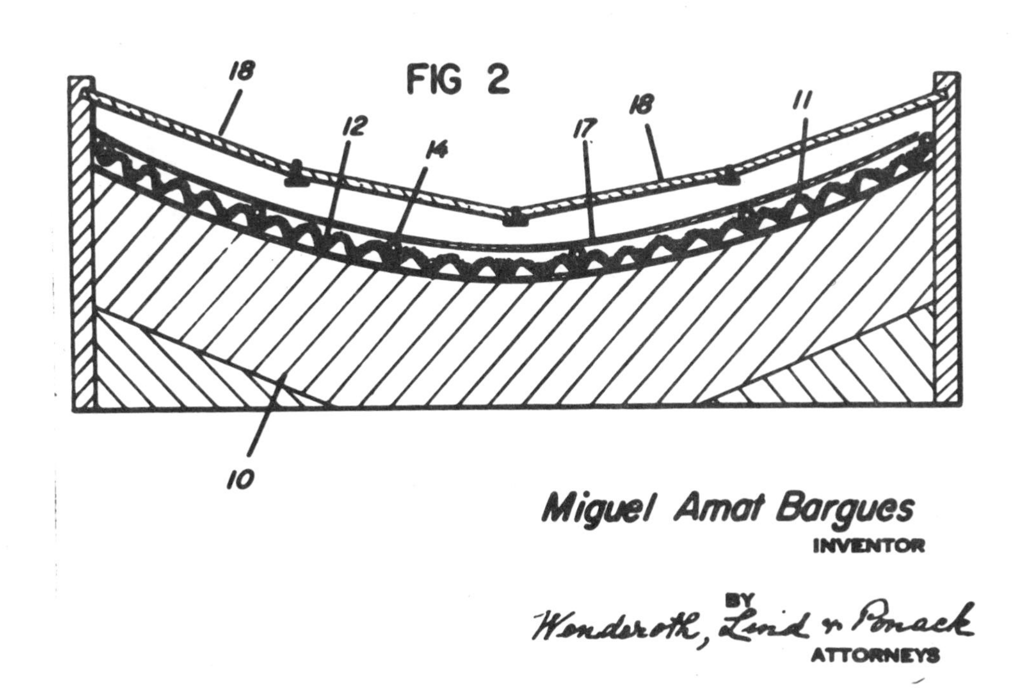

Miguel Amat Bargues
INVENTOR

BY
Wenderoth, Lind & Ponack
ATTORNEYS

July 13, 1965 M. AMAT BARGUES **3,194,228**

SOLAR HEATER

* *

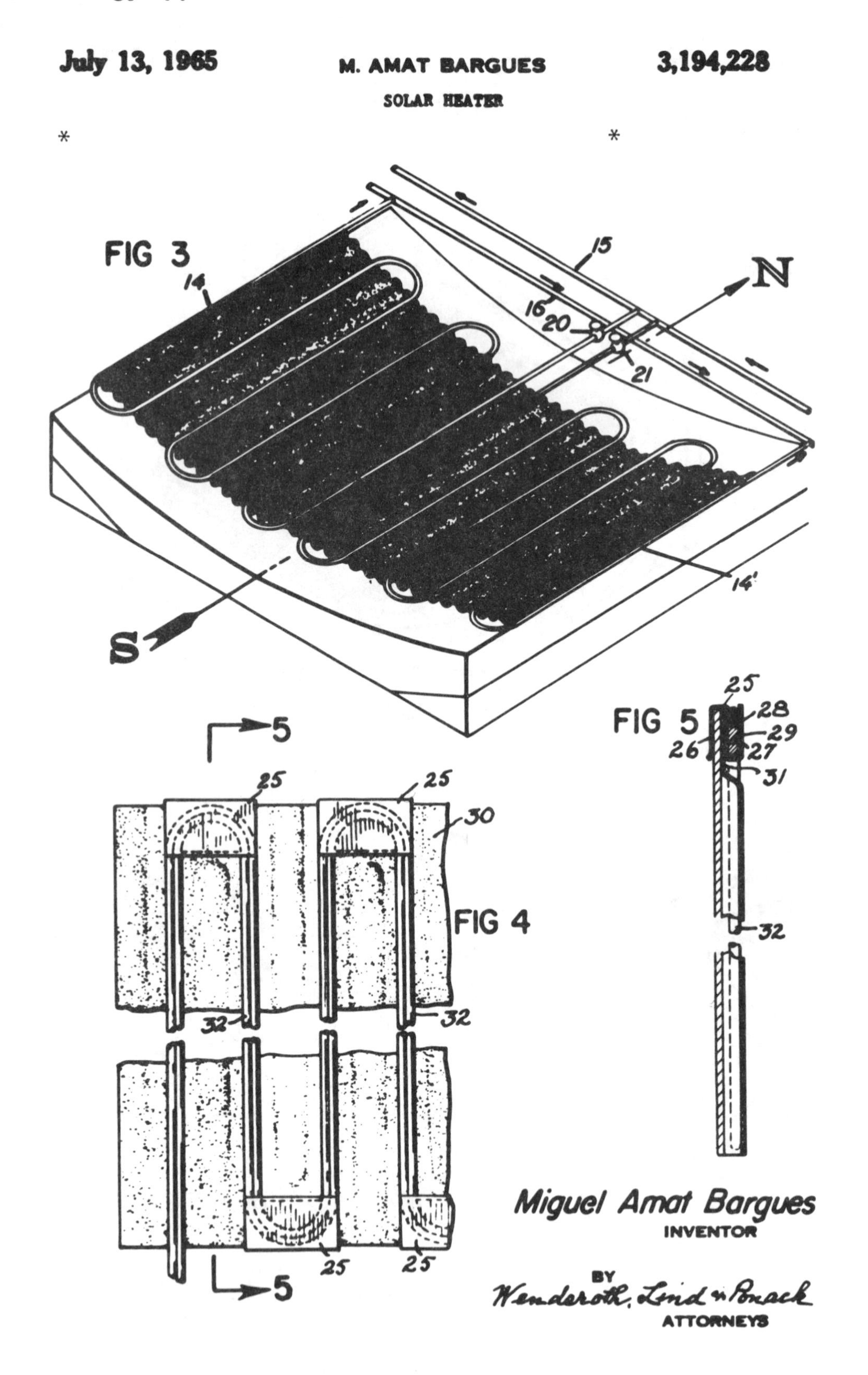

3,194,228
SOLAR HEATER
Miguel Amat Bargues, Paseo de Gracia 77, Barcelona, Spain

*

The present invention relates to a solar heater for the economic production of power by means of warm fluids.

An object of the invention is to provide a solar heater that can compete with the usual means of producing energy.

A further object of the invention is to provide a device wherein it is possible to raise water to a temperature of 160° C., thereby permitting a good performance and yield.

The system according to this invention consists essentially in arranging a special surface highly absorbent of the sun's rays, in combination with the means or a device permitting the circulation, in contact with the said surface, of a fluid, liquid or gas directly or indirectly heated by the said rays, and being completed by a means of protection against loss of heat, thereby setting up the circulation of the fluid at a relatively high temperature which can be easily used in a heat transforming apparatus.

A further object of the invention is to provide an absorbent surface comprising a sheet of corrugated cardboard of the usual type whose surface has been blackened with an application of amorphous carbon in the form of a paint or varnish which is deposited by any desired means on the cardboard and such a corrugated cardboard may be manufactured from a pulp in which a sufficient quantity of powdered carbon has been incorporated.

On the corrugated cardboard so prepared means are provided for procuring the circulation of a fluid, such means being the setting up of a bundle of tubes of a relatively small diameter or of one tube suitably bent in a serpentine shape and having several branches or sections parallel to each other at a suitable distance each of them being placed in contact with the bottom of one of the channels of the corrugated cardboard. In general, the whole installation may be sub-divided to form panels or parts with a surface of 1 m.² and in this case, the most advantageous arrangement for each part is that of tubes of small diameter, 5 mm. for instance, bent in a zigzag, its branches being lodged in definite spaced channels of the corrugated cardboard, leaving a certain number of empty channels, 2 to 10 for example, between one branch and the next.

Finally, the whole group of the absorbent surface and the fluid-circulation tubes is protected against loss of heat. In the first place, the corrugated cardboard is mounted on a supporting sheet of some suitable insulating material so as to avoid loss of heat through the back or under surface of the corrugated cardboard. On the upper surface, i.e. the part exposed to the sun's rays, a protection may be laid, consisting of a sheet of glass covering the whole of the absorbent surface, but separated from it by a few centimeters, and which opposes to the movement of the hot air.

This glass protector may be divided into a series of strips or panels placed side by side and, in order to reduce the weight, may be thin, and, if necessary, these strips may be joined together by any suitable means to ensure that the joints are hermetic and air tight.

This kind of protection is enough in most cases, but it has been found that it is advantageous to complete it by means of a sheet of another protective material laid directly on the absorbent layer, i.e. in contact with the grain of the carbon or with the corrugated cardboard. This said second protective sheet may be made of very thin glass or of any other transparent material, such as cellophane, cellulose acetate or other, and by means of this arrangement, the temperature reached by the absorbent surface is higher and the yield greater.

The above described installation is also completely heat insulating on all its sides and at the back.

Through the above-described tubes a fluid is caused to circulate that may be a gas or a liquid, though a gas and a liquid may be employed jointly. The gas may be put into circulation by means of a very powerful ventilator and at a feeble pressure, going in at one of the faces of the apparatus and leaving at the opposite one, for its conduction to the apparatus in which it will give up its excess heat, then going back to the absorbent apparatus to carry out its fresh cycle.

In the case of gases it is preferable to use steam, especially water steam, for the temperature of the absorbing apparatus is sufficient to boil the water at pressure of the atmosphere and even at a reduced pressure. Moreover, after being condensed, the steam goes back in the form of liquid through small diameter tubes that are easy to insulate thermically.

In the case of liquids, water or a watery uncongealable solution is used, so chosen as to avoid rust in the piping or the formation of deposits. The liquid is caused to circulate through the action of a feeble pressure pump, it being preferable to adopt the above-mentioned arrangement of tubes laid in parallel branches separated from each other for each panel or section, and moreover, the branches should not be too near together, for, on the one hand, the weight and price would be excessive for each part and, on the other hand, a considerable pressure would be needed to cause the liquid to circulate through the tubes.

To assure the best transmission of the heat the corrugated cardboard should be placed on a thin metal conductor sheet, such as, for example, ½ mm. aluminium, which will help to make the heat pass from one channel to the next and contribute to its greater utility. Tubes of plastic material may also be used, the conductability itself of the material they are made of is of small importance but in every case the tube should be black to obtain a greater absorption of the heat rays. At the outlet all the tubes are joined together in a single collector that transmit the hot liquid to the apparatus that is to use it, and after the liquid has given up its excess heat to this utilizing apparatus its carried by another collector to the absorbing apparatus and continues circulating thus in a closed circuit. One has to bear in mind that the liquid ought not to contain any dissolved gases, so as to avoid any giving off of these gases under the influence of the heat, causing the obstruction of the tubes.

In practice, panels or surfaces of determines sizes may be used, suitable coupled together to form a surface of the necessary extent for the energy it is desired to obtain, and the said individual panels may also be advantageously arranged so as to form curved surfaces to assist the absorption of the heat during the hours near to the rising or the setting of the sun. The bundle of tubes may, at option, be divided into two or more sections connected independently to the collector, in combination with a means of cutting off the circulation in one or other of the sections so as to isolate these that eventually receive the solar rays at a tangent.

A still further object is to provide a construction wherein the tubes used are secured by means of special clips at their bending points so as to securely fasten them in place.

With the above and other objects in view which will become apparent from the following detailed description.

some preferred forms of the invention are shown in the drawings, in which:

FIGURE 1 is a perspective view of a unitary panel with certain parts omitted for greater clarity.

FIGURE 2 is a cross-sectional view of the form of the invention illustrated in FIGURE 1 with additional parts added thereto.

FIGURE 3 is a perspective view of a modification wherein the circulating tubes are divided into two sections.

FIGURE 4 is a partial plan view of a further modification illustrating particularly the means for fastening the tubes to the absorbent surface, and

FIGURE 5 is a cross-sectional view taken upon section line 5—5 of FIGURE 4.

The drawings show an elementary form of constructing a sun rays absorbing panel comprising a base **10** of a suitable material and having a curved surface to which a sheet of corrugated cardboard **11** is applied, blackened or covered with a layer **12** of a composition of amorphous carbon or some other sunray-absorbing material and, in the channel formed by the corrugation a serpentine piece **13** is fitted, being composed of a zigzag bent tube with parallel branches **14** that fit into the bottom of certain spaced-out channels and corrugations.

The ends of the said serpentine piece extend as far as the margin of the panel and end in a suitable shape that allows it to be coupled to two collector tubes **15**, **16**, constituting the feeding line connecting several contiguous panels. Each of the panels thus formed is covered, as was stated above, by means of a thin, transparent sheet **17** situated very near to the blackened surface and at a certain distance from it there is a protection **18** of thick glass or of some suitable transparent material either in one single piece or made up of several smaller pieces so arranged that the absorbing elements are completely insulated from the weather.

A most advantageous arrangement is that shown in FIGURE 3 wherein the bundle of tubes is divided into two sections, as **14** and **14'**, each one of which extends on opposed parts of the curved supporting surface, forming two symmetrical sections of tubes that are independently coupled to the collector tubes **15** and **15** through the cocks **20** and **21**, which permit independent functioning of the said sections, coupling either one of the sections, or both at the same time according to the altitude of the sun on the horizon.

The heat absorbent surface has its surface corrugated and is made of cardboard.

In the first place, cardboard is a highly insulating and heat absorbent material, and moreover it is cheap and light. In the second place, the disposition of the corrugated surface forming parallel channels results in that in each channel there is formed an accumulation of clarific rays of the sun, which are received by the portion of the fluid conducting tube, which is situated in the central part of said channel or corrugation.

In this apparatus therefore each one of the portions of the fluid conducting tube receives heat under three forms:

(a) By direct incidence of the rays of the sun.

(b) By contact of the lower part of the tube with its support surface.

(c) By radiation of the walls of each one of the channels or corrugations of the support plate.

All this results in a better utilization of the solar heat, all other conditions being equal, since the very nature of the cardboard avoids heat loss, because, in comparison with a metallic surface, it is to be taken into account that a metallic surface, being a good conductor of heat, has heat loss at the posterior side of the plate, and moverover has also heat loss due to the reflection of the calorific rays which strike the side receiving these rays.

When metallic surfaces are used in a solar heater the loss by reflection is quite important and such loss should be avoided as is done in the present device. Furthermore, the corrugated cardboard support surface is bent in a cylindrical form according to an axis parallel to the axis of the channels of the corrugated cardboard and the panel when placed in its operative position is disposed with the axis of the cylindrical surface thereof parallel to the axis of the earth and in South-North direction as indicated in FIGURE 3.

FIGURES 4 and 5 illustrate a constructional detail for securing the plastic tubes firmly in place upon a corrugated cardboard surface which extends over all the length of the tubes. This is accomplished by providing clips **25** of S-shape as shown particularly in FIGURE 5. The rear leg **26** together with the median portion **27** is designed to clamp the clip upon the edge of the cardboard absorbent surface **30**. The median portion **27** together with the front **28** of the clip forms a channel or groove in which semi-circular guiding pieces **29** are inserted. The guiding pieces **29** are secured to the clip **25** in any desired manner. When the clip **25** is applied to the edge of the cardboard surface it will crush the same somewhat as indicated at **31** in FIGURE 5.

The clips **25** are fastened to the cardboard as shown in FIGURE 4 and extends between every two supporting channels thereof. It is then an easy matter to wind the tubes **32** in the groove of the clips **25** and supported by the semi-circular guiding pieces **29**. By the use of the clips **25** and associated parts the plastic tube or tubes will be properly aligned and at the same time properly fastened to the cardboard sheet.

The cardboard sheets may be suitably corrugated or bent and the channels therein may be designed of the proper size which is deemed suitable for the number of tubes which it may be desired to use. As shown in FIGURES 4 and 5 two tubes are used but this number may be increased as desired.

When using plastic tubes it is preferable to use tubes which have a relatively small diameter since this permits the use of two or more tubes in contact thereby forming a bundle and the correct portions thereof may be placed jointly in the same channel.*

Feb. 27, 1962 S. ANDRASSY 3,022,781

HEATER

*

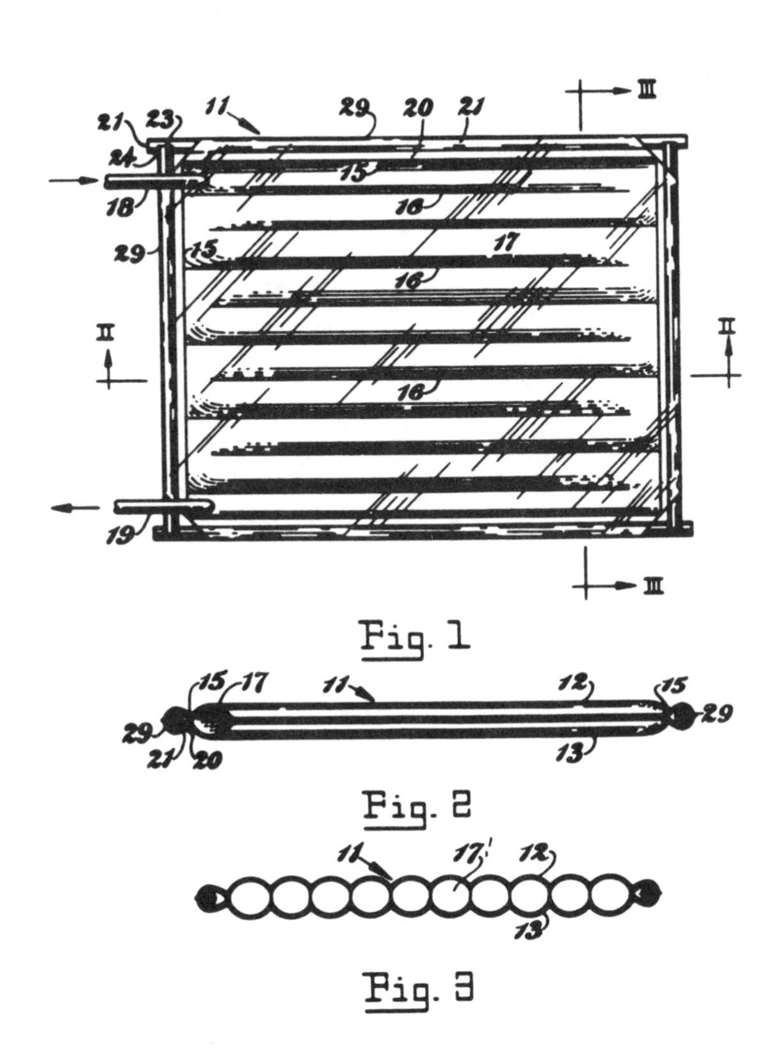

Fig. 1

Fig. 2

Fig. 3

INVENTOR.
STELLA ANDRASSY
BY Philip Mintz
ATTORNEY.

3,022,781

HEATER

Stella Andrassy, Princeton, N.J. (Ridge Road, Kingston Post Office, Monmouth Junction, N.J.)

*

This invention relates to a new and improved solar fluid heater unit. More particularly, this invention relates to a solar water heater unit which is flexible, easily portable, and which will not be damaged in the event of freezing.

Many devices have been developed for utilizing solar energy. One broad class of these devices utilizes solar energy in the form of heat collected at moderate temperatures. This is frequently done by using solar energy to heat water to elevated temperatures in the solar heat collector of such devices. The heated water from such a solar heat collector may be utilized for heating houses, preparing hot water for domestic use, heating swimming pools, etc.

The currently used solar water heaters are usually made of metal, frequently in the form of metallic tubing soldered in a serpentine fashion to the face of a blackened metal plate. Such a structure is unwieldy due to its weight and rigid construction. In addition, fabrication costs are high. In the winter or when there is danger of nocturnal freezing, such a solar water heater must be drained or else antifreeze must be used therein. If antifreeze is used, it is necessary to have an additional heat exchanger for heating water to be used for domestic purposes. This clearly reduces the operating efficiency of such apparatus, and further adds to the costs.

One of the objects of the present invention is to overcome the disadvantages of conventional solar water heaters. Another object of the present invention is to provide a solar fluid heater unit which is light in weight, readily collapsed for transportation and storage, is easily and economically fabricated, and in which the advent of freezing produces no damage.

With the above objects in view, the present invention mainly consists of a solar fluid heater unit having two flexible film members secured to each other adjacent their periphery and further being secured to each other in preselected regions interiorly of the periphery to provide a fluid passageway between the two members. The fluid passageway may be serpentine, or in the form of a pair of headers with a plurality of fluid conduits interconnecting the headers, or of any other configuration.

The novel features which are considered as characteristic of the invention are set forth in particular in the appended claims. The invention itself, however, both as to its construction and its method of operation, together with additional objects and advantages thereof, will be best understood from the following description of a specific embodiment when read with the accompanying drawings, in which:

FIGURE 1 is a plan view of a solar fluid heater unit incorporating the principles of this invention;

FIGURE 2 is a vertical cross section taken along line II—II of FIGURE 1; and

FIGURE 3 is a vertical cross section taken along line III—III of FIGURE 1.

Referring to the drawings, there is shown a solar fluid heater unit 11 constructed according to the principles of this invention.

The solar fluid heater 11 is made of a flexible plastic film which is folded over upon itself so as to form an upper layer 12 and a lower layer 13. Alternatively, layers 12 and 13 may be made from two separate pieces of flexible plastic film, or from a single flattened tube of flexible plastic film.

The plastic film used may be polyethylene, vinylite, polytetrafluoroethylene, polychlorotrifluoroethylene, or any other plastic film which is flexible and which can withstand solar radiations without deterioration.

Layer 12 and layer 13 are secured to each other adjacent their periphery as along line 15, 15 so as to enclose a rectangular region. Layers 12 and 13 are further secured to each other along lines 16, 16, 16 so as to convert the enclosed rectangular region into a serpentine fluid passageway 17. Secured to opposite ends of serpentine fluid passageway 17 are a plastic inlet tube 18 and a plastic outlet tube 19.

For some uses, it may be more desirable to produce a larger volume of warm water rather than a smaller volume of hotter water. For such a use, the enclosed rectangular region may be formed into a tubular passageway providing multiple parallel flow paths. This can be accomplished by securing layer 12 and layer 13 to each other along a series of lines which convert the enclosed rectangular space to the form of two headers along opposite sides of such region connected to each other by a plurality of parallel conduits. The inlet and outlet are respectively connected to opposite ends of the two headers, substantially at diagonally opposed corners of the enclosed rectangular region.

The various joinings of plastic to plastic referred to herein in the construction of the solar water heater unit may be made by heat sealing or by use of suitable adhesives as may be desired.

In order to maximize the collection of solar energy as heat at least one of the plastic film layers 12 and 13 should be highly absorbent of radiant energy. Preferably flexible plastic film layer 13 is made absorbent to radiant energy by painting it black or by incorporating black pigment, such as carbon black, within the plastic composition.

Exteriorly of the line 15, which joins film 12 and film 13 to provide the periphery of the serpentine fluid passageway, there is another joining of plastic film 12 and 13 as at line 29. This provides a hem-like space 20 between lines 15 and lines 29 at the periphery of solar water heater unit 11.

Into each hem-like space 20 is inserted a rod 21. The rods 21 can be made of wood or the like. The four rods 21 are provided at their respective ends with means to temporarily assemble the four rods into a substantially rigid rectangular configuration. Such means may take the form of a slot 23 in one rod into which the butt end 24 of another rod is inserted. In order to facilitate the insertion of rods 21 into hem-like portions 20 and the assembly of such a joint, the corner portions of films 12 and 13 are cut away so as to expose the ends of rods 21.

To use such a solar fluid heater unit for heating water, the plastic film is rolled out upon the ground or other supporting surface and the wooden support members 21 are inserted in the hemlike portions 20 and joined at the corners. This provides desired rigidity. The inlet 18 is connected to a source of flowing water, and outlet 19 is connected to a receptacle for the heated water. The radiant energy in the sunlight impinging upon blackened plastic film layer 13 is converted to heat, raising the temperature of layer 13. The water in the solar water heater unit 11 in contact with layer 13 is thereby also heated. The provision of a serpentine water passageway 17 makes for increased turbulence in the water being heated by increasing its velocity and frequency of changes in direction, thus making for more efficient transfer of heat from blackened layer 13 to the water. Therefore, the sunlight shining upon solar water heater unit 11 will rapidlv heat the water contained therein and flowing therethrough.

To disassemble the solar fluid heater unit for storage or for removal to remote locations, the above sequence of steps is reversed. The plastic part of the solar water heater unit can be rolled around the rigid parts, thereby forming a small package for convenience in shipping or storage.

It is thus seen that there has been provided a solar water heater unit which is readily portable, which is light in weight, which is easily and economically fabricated, and which is not subject to damage upon freezing. Yet, the water heater unit is sufficiently rigid for practical use and provides a substantially long water path for the total cross-sectional area of the unit.

The heater unit can be provided with an insulated bottom layer, made of flexible light-weight thermal insulation and a solar radiation transmitting flexible cover to provide an air space on top, to prevent heat losses.

Sept. 3, 1968 F. L. SUHAY 3,399,664

SOLAR HEATER

*

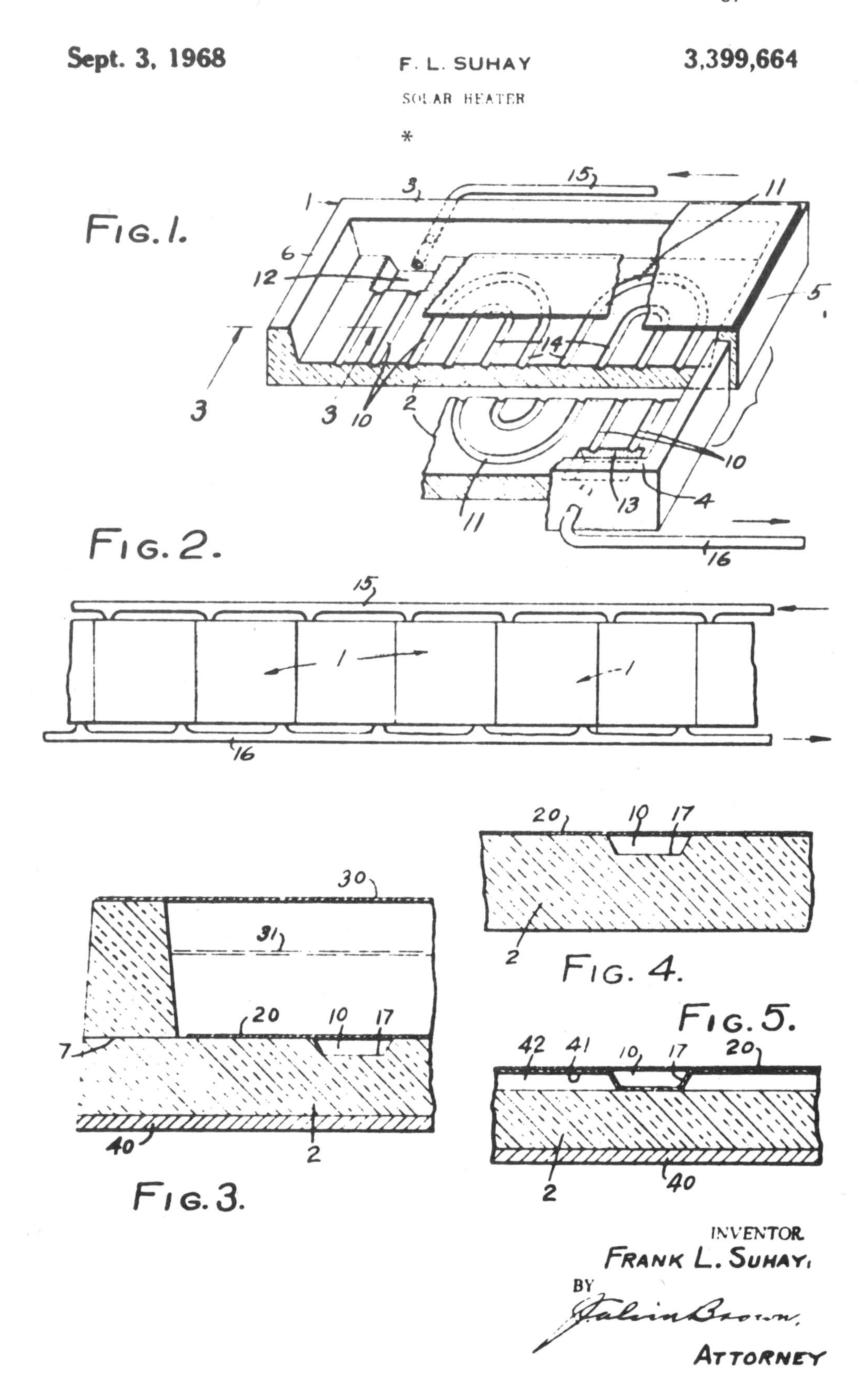

3,399,664
SOLAR HEATER
Frank L. Suhay, Burbank, Calif.

ABSTRACT OF THE DISCLOSURE

The invention comprises a solar heater having a casing the base of which is formed by molding or otherwise with a fluid ductway, the ductway communicating with the surface of the base. Outlet and inlet conduits are provided at the ends of the ductway and overlying the ductway is a high heat conducting metal plate which encloses the ductway.

The present invention relates to solar heaters and has for an object a solar heater which may be fabricated with a minimum of expense and erected on the job or delivered to a site fully assembled.

A further object is the provision of a solar heater of attractive appearance and which does not detract from surrounding objects such as trees, dwellings and the like.

Primarily the solar heater of the invention may be used for the heating of water in a pool, particularly when it is desired that the pool water be maintained at a temperature during both summer and winter months. It is a known fact that the average electrical or gas heater for heating pool water performs at great expense even for a small pool whereas the present solar water heater depends on solar energy and the efficient use thereof for the heating of water.

An object of the invention is the provision of a solar water heater adapted to absorb a maximum of solar heat and the efficient use of said heat in the heating of water or other fluids.

A further object is the provision of a solar water heater of light weight which may be assembled in units as needed, which may be used in such a manner as to provide a patio cover, or a carport cover and which may be installed either by a professional or by the individual without the necessity of providing special structural basing supports and wherein lightweight frames may be utilized.

With the above and other objects in view, the invention consists in the novel and useful provision, formation, construction, association, and relative arrangement of parts, members and features, all as shown in certain embodiments in the accompanying drawing, described generally, and more particularly pointed out in the claims.

In the drawing:

FIGURE 1 is a fragmentary, partially sectional perspective view of one unit of the solar heater of the invention;

FIGURE 2 is a fragmentary plan view of a series of connected solar water heaters;

FIGURE 3 is a fragmentary sectional view on an enlarged scale, taken on the line 3—3 of FIGURE 1;

FIGURE 4 is an enlarged, fragmentary sectional view of a portion of the base of the solar water heater; and,

FIGURE 5 is a modified form of the heater shown in FIGURE 4.

Referring now to the drawing, a solar water heater unit 1 includes a shallow flat casing having a base 2 and encircling side and end walls 3, 4, 5 and 6. The casing may be molded to form so that the end and side walls are integral with the base or the side and end walls may be separate therefrom but secured together as indicated in FIGURE 3 at 7, and in any appropriate manner such as by mechanical bond or by gluing.

The casing 1 as an entirety, is formed from an insulating material which may be a plastic such as polystyrene, expanded polystyrene beads, cork, or other material. The base 2 is so molded or formed as to provide ducts, channels, or ways 10 which ducts may be of serpentine form as shown at 11, and which ducts communicate with depressed well portions 12 and 13 for inlet to said ducts and outlet therefrom. Depending upon the area of the base of the unit, multiple ducts may be arranged in parallel relationship, as shown in FIGURE 1 at 14, the ducts all communicating with the inlet and the outlet wells 12 and 13. The side walls 3 and 4 are bored to allow communication of an inlet conduit 15 with the well 12 and an outlet conduit 16 with the well 13. The section of each duct may vary in geometrical cross section, however, that shown in FIGURES 3 to 5 inclusive is of polygonal form, as shown at 17. Overlying the base 2 and in contact therewith so as to cover all of the ducts, is a thin plate 20 of metallic material having a high thermo conductivity. I prefer to use copper and a thin sheet thereof due to inexpensiveness, as copper has a higher thermo conductivity than most metals other than silver. As shown, the thin plate of copper may or may not be bonded to the base 2 but said sheet constitutes a means totally overlying the base within the marginal limits of the side and end walls. To further enhance the overall efficiency of the solar heater, I provide either a thin transparent plastic sheet or a thin sheet of glass at 30 resting on the top of the side and end walls and above the metallic plate 20. As generally known, glass is athermanous, that is, opaque to heat rays and consequently the interior of the casing is heated or warmed while the objects within the casing, because of low temperature of the waves, are too long to be transmitted by the glass. While I have shown in FIGURE 3 the use of an additional clear plastic unit 31 interposed between the metallic plate 20 and the unit 30, this is for illustrative purposes only. Various refinements of construction may be utilized such as providing the base of the shallow flat casing with reinforcement or stiffening members 40, as shown in FIGURES 3 and 5. Stiffening members would be utilized for various types of insulation for the casing, particularly if the base 2 was subject to shear.

In FIGURE 5 I have shown a modified construction wherein a formed plastic 41 provides a space 42 between plastic 41 and the top of the base 2. It is well-known that air is a poor conductor of heat and the space 42 aids in this regard against dissipation of heat. Also, in FIGURE 5, the metallic member 20 may be chemically or mechanically bonded to the formed plastic.

In FIGURE 2 I have shown a series of the units of the character shown in FIGURE 1, interconnected with inlets and outlets leading to said units. Thus, individual units may be interconnected to provide any size solar heater whether it is for water, gas, or other fluids to the end that the desired size of solar heater may be corrected on the site in accordance with heating requirements.

The operation, uses, and advantages of the invention are as follows.

A considerable savings in heater construction results due to the fact that the casing 2 may be molded to form from insulation material with the ducts or channels molded in the base thereof. The walls leading to the intake and to the outlet from said ducts or channels is also molded into the top surface of the base of the casing. Thus, initial forming of the casing provides the ductways. The thin metallic plate which may be copper overlies and is bonded either chemically or mechanically to the top surface of the base and substantially covers an area equal to the interior area of the base, as shown in FIGURES 3, 4 and 5. It is known that copper is an excellent heat conductor and as a consequence, the metallic plate rapidly conducts radiant heat from the sun to the fluid within the duct ways. The large area of the plate 20 aids in heating fluid in the ducts as the plate overlaps the ducts and rests on the insulation base 2. Thus the plate continuously transfers heat to fluid in the ducts as the large plate area affords a constant source of heat supply from areas adjacent the ducts. By providing the glass 30 overlying the interior of the casing, the heat is concentrated within the space included between the metallic plate and the glass without heat loss and, as stated, affords an efficient solar water heater at less expense than the average solar water heater which uses pipes adapted to be heated by solar radiation as the pipes have less area of direct contact with the solar rays. *

UNITED STATES PATENT OFFICE

CERTIFICATE OF CORRECTION

Patent No. 3,399,664 September 3, 1968

Frank L. Suhay

It is certified that error appears in the above identified patent and that said Letters Patent are hereby corrected as shown below:

In the heading to the printed specification, lines 3 to 5, "Burbank, Calif., assignor to Farbenfabriken Bayer Aktiengesellschaft, Leverkusen, Germany, a corporation of Germany" should read -- 1816 N. Rose St., Burbank, Calif. 91505 --.

Signed and sealed this 23rd day of September 1969.

(SEAL)
Attest:

Edward M. Fletcher, Jr. WILLIAM E. SCHUYLER, JR.
Attesting Officer Commissioner of Patents

E. D. ARTHUR AND W. G. CARTTER.
SOLAR HEATER.

1,338,644. Patented Apr. 27, 1920.

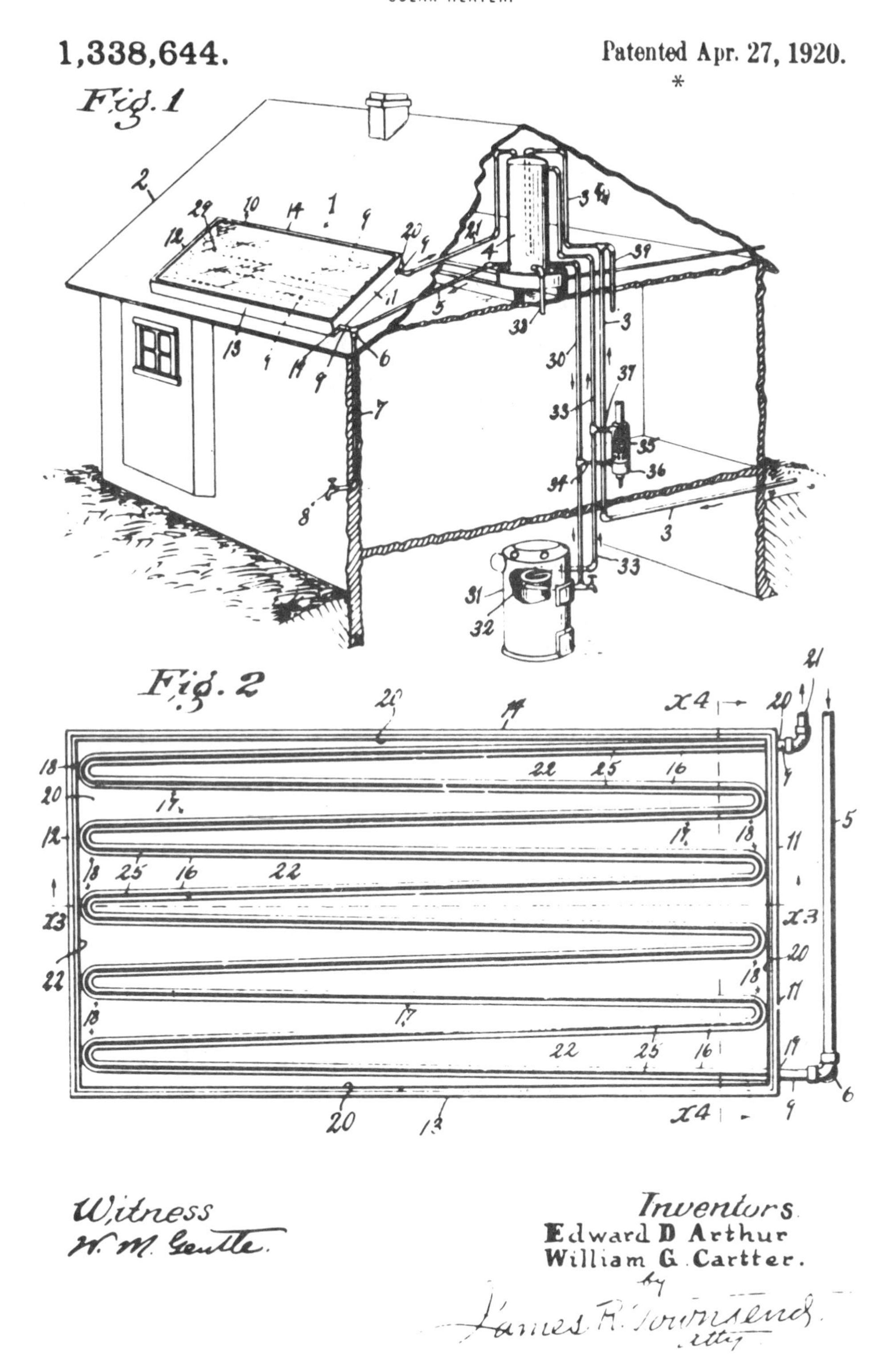

E. D. ARTHUR AND W. G. CARTTER.
SOLAR HEATER.

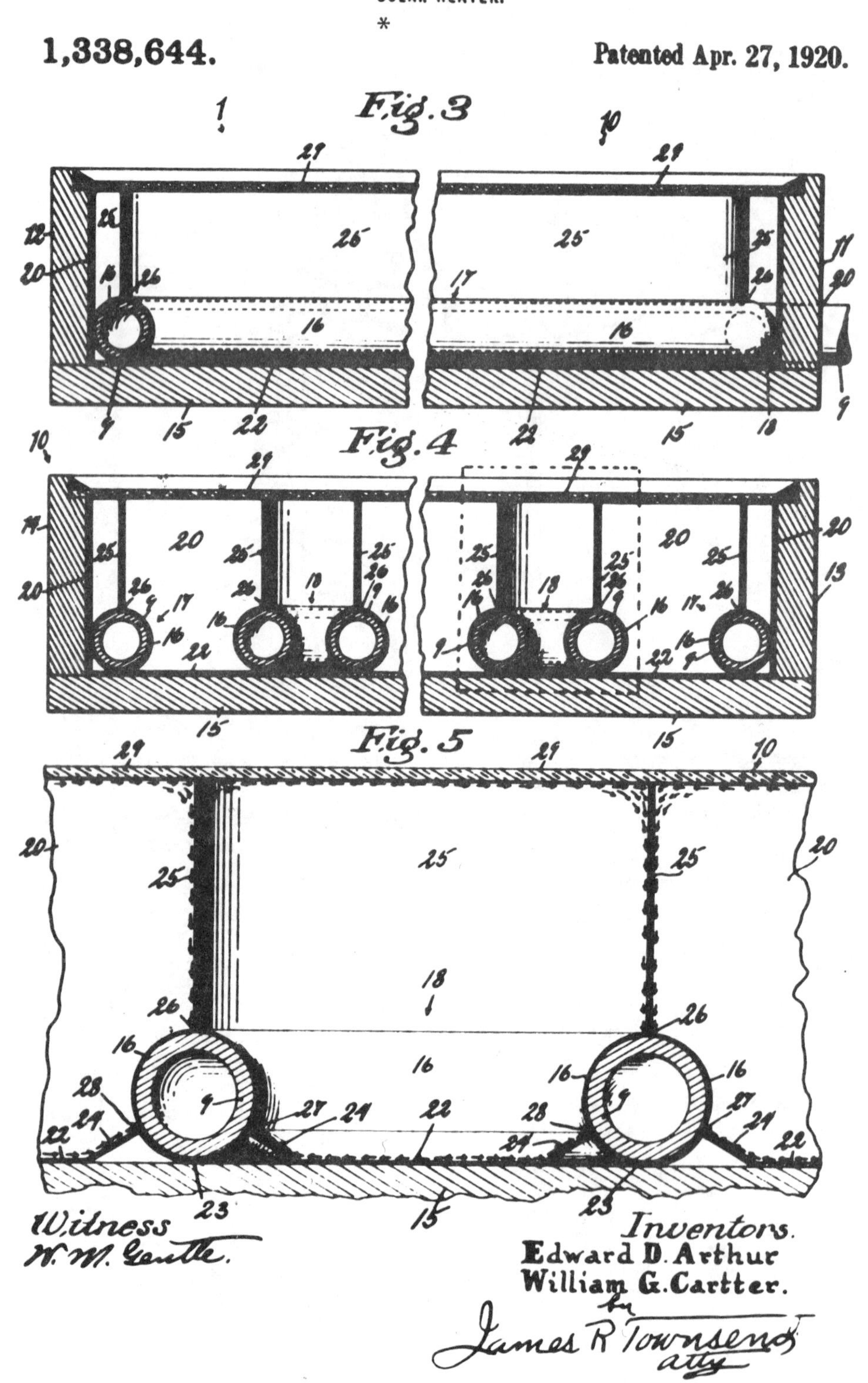

UNITED STATES PATENT OFFICE.

EDWARD D. ARTHUR AND WILLIAM G. CARTTER, OF ARCADIA, CALIFORNIA.

SOLAR HEATER.

1,338,644. Specification of Letters Patent. Patented Apr. 27, 1920.

*

To all whom it may concern:

Be it known that we, EDWARD D. ARTHUR and WILLIAM G. CARTTER, citizens of the United States, residing at Arcadia, in the county of Los Angeles and State of California, have invented new and useful Improvements in Solar Heaters, of which the following is a specification.

This invention relates to solar heaters, and consists in the novel and useful features and improved construction arrangement and combination of parts, the purpose of which will be apparent to those skilled in the art *

The principal object of this invention is to provide a means for more effectively utilizing solar heat to raise the temperature of the water of an ordinary dwelling house water system to a sufficient degree for domestic purposes. Our solar heater is connected directly to the usual water system piping of a dwelling and practically becomes an element in that system.

Another object of the invention is to provide a solar heater with a water pipe that is not only best adapted to absorb the solar heat, but which is also free from internal corrosion such as would leave a mineral taint in the water; that is to say, any pipe may be used that is best adapted to convey the water without injury to its purity.

Another feature of the invention is to provide a pipe construction that will best resist freezing and the effects of frozen pipes; as the solar heater will be in an exposed position where it will be subjected to a low or freezing temperature during the winter season. The pipe is constructed with a heavy wall which in cross section would be of considerable thickness and sufficient to withstand any ordinary internal strain incident to internal pressure.

Another object is to provide a jacketed surface to the water pipe of the solar heater, which, in addition to reinforcing the pipe, adds thereto the feature of increased heat conduction; being preferably of copper, the best heat conducting material.

Another object is to provide a means for utilizing both the conduction and radiation of heat to the pipe through the solar heater.

Another feature of the invention is the connection of the solar heater with a house water system in which a gas or furnace heater is connected, either of which heaters may be used, or both, to raise the water temperature.

Further objects, advantages and features of novelty and invention may appear from the accompanying drawings, the subjoined detail description and the appended claims.

The invention is illustrated by the drawings, in which,

Figure 1 is a perspective view of the solar heater installed in a dwelling the end of which is broken away to show the connection of the solar heater with the water system and the other heaters.

Fig. 2 is a plan view of the solar heater with the glass cover removed for the purpose of showing the pipe and its associated parts.

Fig. 3 is an enlarged section through the solar heater taken on the line x^3—x^3, Fig. 2, the center portion being broken away.

Fig. 4 is an enlarged section through the solar heater taken on the line x^4—x^4 of Fig. 2, the center portion thereof being broken away.

Fig. 5 is a fragmentary view of a part of Fig. 4 enlarged to full size; and a modification shown of the base plate. The part taken from Fig. 4 is indicated by the rectangular dotted line inclosure.

In detail, the solar heater 1 is installed on the roof of a house 2, and secured in place by any well known means, and in such a position that during the day it will be exposed to the sun, and so positioned that the sun's rays will contact with the glass covering of the heater in a line perpendicular to the plane of the glass.

A water pipe 3 leads from some water supply, not shown, into the house and discharges into the tank 4, which may be of any size and located in the upper part of the house so that the water in it may be of a higher elevation than the water in the solar heater.

From the bottom of the tank 4 a pipe 5 leads to one opening in the T joint 6, and from another of such openings in the T 6 a pipe 7 leads downward to the discharge cock 8.

From the remaining opening in the T 6 a pipe 9 leads through the wall of the solar heater 1, near the bottom and right hand corner thereof. The portion of the pipe 9 within the solar heater frame 10 formed of the ends 11 and 12 and the side plates 13 and 14, and bottom plank 15, is incased in a copper jacket 16.

As seen in Fig. 2 the copper jacketed portion of the pipe 9 which is within the solar heater frame 10 is bent to form a plurality of lengths 17 that are integral with the turned ends 18. As seen in Fig. 2, each of the lengths 17 is inclined upward from its intake to its discharge end so there will be a continual rise in the flow of the water as it travels through the heating coil from the inlet point 19 to the discharge point 20. These copper jacketed lengths 17 and turns 18 form the heating coil.

A pipe 21 connects the upper or discharge end of the coiled pipe 9 with the tank 4 so that the water in the tank can pass to the solar heater 1 and return to the tank when the water is heated; and this flow is induced as soon as the temperature of the water in the solar heater rises above that in the tank.

As shown in Figs. 3, 4 and 5 additional means are supplied for raising the temperature of the heating coil 9 and consequently raising the temperature of the water flowing therethrough.

The frame 10 has its interior surface lined with the sheet copper 20, and the copper jacketed coil 9 lies directly upon the bottom portion of the copper 22, and may be soldered thereto in order to form a close contact between the bottom sheet copper 22 and the pipe casing copper 16. As seen in Fig. 5, the contacting surface between the sheet copper 22 and the copper jacket 16 can be enlarged by having the sheet copper bottom 22 stamped into a channel 23, substantially the same length, contour and radial curvature as the exterior surface of the copper jacket 16, forming thereby a bed in which the coil 9 can lay.

Preferably the channel 23 would be of a depth sufficient to produce a contacting surface to engage about one third of the bottom circumference of the jacket 16 when viewed in cross section as seen in Fig. 5. With such contacting surface in the channel 23 the bottom copper place 22 would have the inclined walls 24 connecting it with the top edges of the channel 23.

A copper ribbon 25, whose lower edge is integral with or is soldered to the jacket 16 the entire length of the coil, at a point 26 in a line perpendicular with a longitudinal line through the center of the coil 9, and which is about one third of the circumferential distance from the points 27 and 28, has its upper edge in contact with the glass cover 29 of the case. This glass cover is secured to the frame 10 by any well known means. The ribbon 25 also provides an additional supporting means for said cover 29 whereby a single pane of glass can be used if desired thereby eliminating the cooling effects of shadows on the coil 9.

In this solar heater shadows will be practically eliminated as the apparatus is positioned so that the sun's rays will enter the solar heater in lines parallel to the sides of the ribbon 25.

In the preferred form of construction, as shown in Fig. 5 the inclined walls 24 will eliminate the shadows under the sides of the coil 9. With the cooling shadows effects eliminated from the solar heater, practically all of the heat entering therein will be conveyed to the coil 9 by radiation and conduction.

The travel of heat by conduction is shown in Fig. 5 by the short arrows paralleling the course of travel, both from the heated glass and the copper plated bottom of the solar heater, directly to the coil 9 which the heat enters at about equal distances around the circumference when viewed in cross section. A great deal of emphasis is placed upon the foregoing, for it is well known that the transmission of heat from one body to another is more effectively accomplished by conduction than by radiation. However, it is not to be understood from the foregoing that the radiated heat is not to be utilized, as a provision is made for conducting the heat thus formed to the coil 9. In other words, the heat rays passing through the glass 29 that do not contact directly with the coil 9 are collected in the copper bottom 22 and through it transferred to the coil 9 by conduction.

From the foregoing it will be readily seen that all the heat rays entering the solar heater will be utilized toward heating the coil 9 and consequently heating the water in the tank 4 sufficiently for domestic purposes.

If by reason of cloudy or cold weather the solar heater does not heat the water sufficiently, auxiliary means are provided to assist it. From the bottom of the tank 4 is a pipe 30 that extends down to the basement furnace 31 in which is located the coil 32 to which one end of the pipe 30 is connected; and the other end of the coil 32 is connected to a pipe 33 that leads back to the upper end of the tank 4, by means of which pipe connection to the furnace 31 the water in the tank 4 can be additionally heated.

Connected to pipe 30 is the branch pipe 34 that leads to one end of the coil pipe 35 shown in the gas heater 36; and the other end of the coil pipe 35 is connected by a pipe 37 to the pipe 33, so that by means of the gas heater 36 the temperature of the water in tank 4 can be additionally raised when the solar heater is semi-active and the furnace 81 not in use.

Extending from the bottom of the tank 4 is the hot water pipe 38 which is broken away the hot water system not being shown. Connected to the inlet pipe 3 is a cold water pipe 39 that is broken away, the distributing system not being shown.

In operation the water from some source of supply, not shown, passes through the pipe 3 to the tank 4, and from thence through the pipe 5 to the coil 9 of the solar heater 1, where the heat rays of the sun will by radiation and conduction be conveyed to the coil 9 and from thence into the water. The coil 9 is so positioned that there is less frictional engagement of the water with the interior wall of the pipe as the lighter heated water travels upward. *

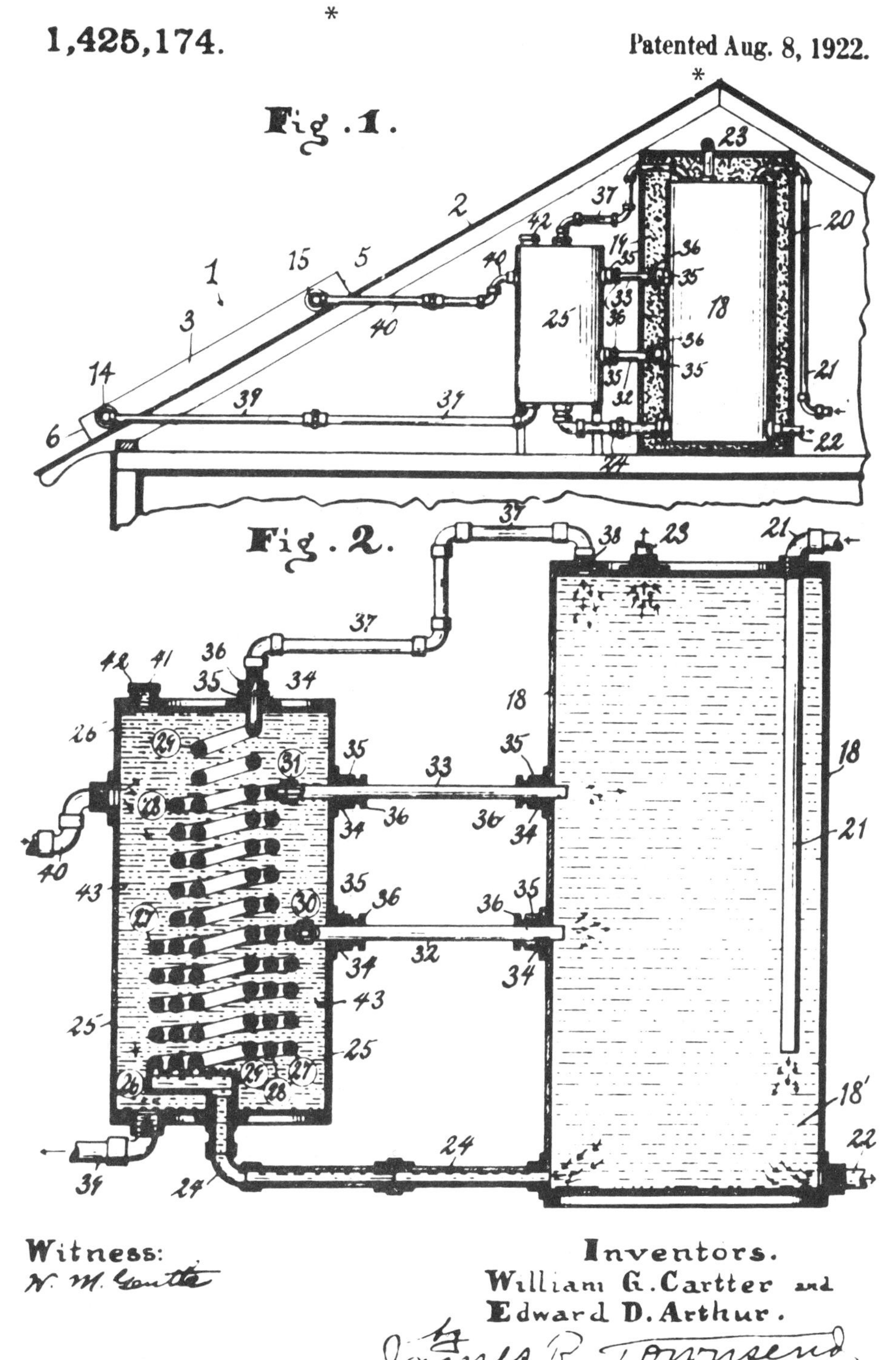
W. G. CARTTER AND E. D. ARTHUR
SOLAR HEAT COLLECTING APPARATUS.
1,425,174.
Patented Aug. 8, 1922.
Fig. 1.
Fig. 2.
Witness:
Inventors.
William G. Cartter and
Edward D. Arthur.

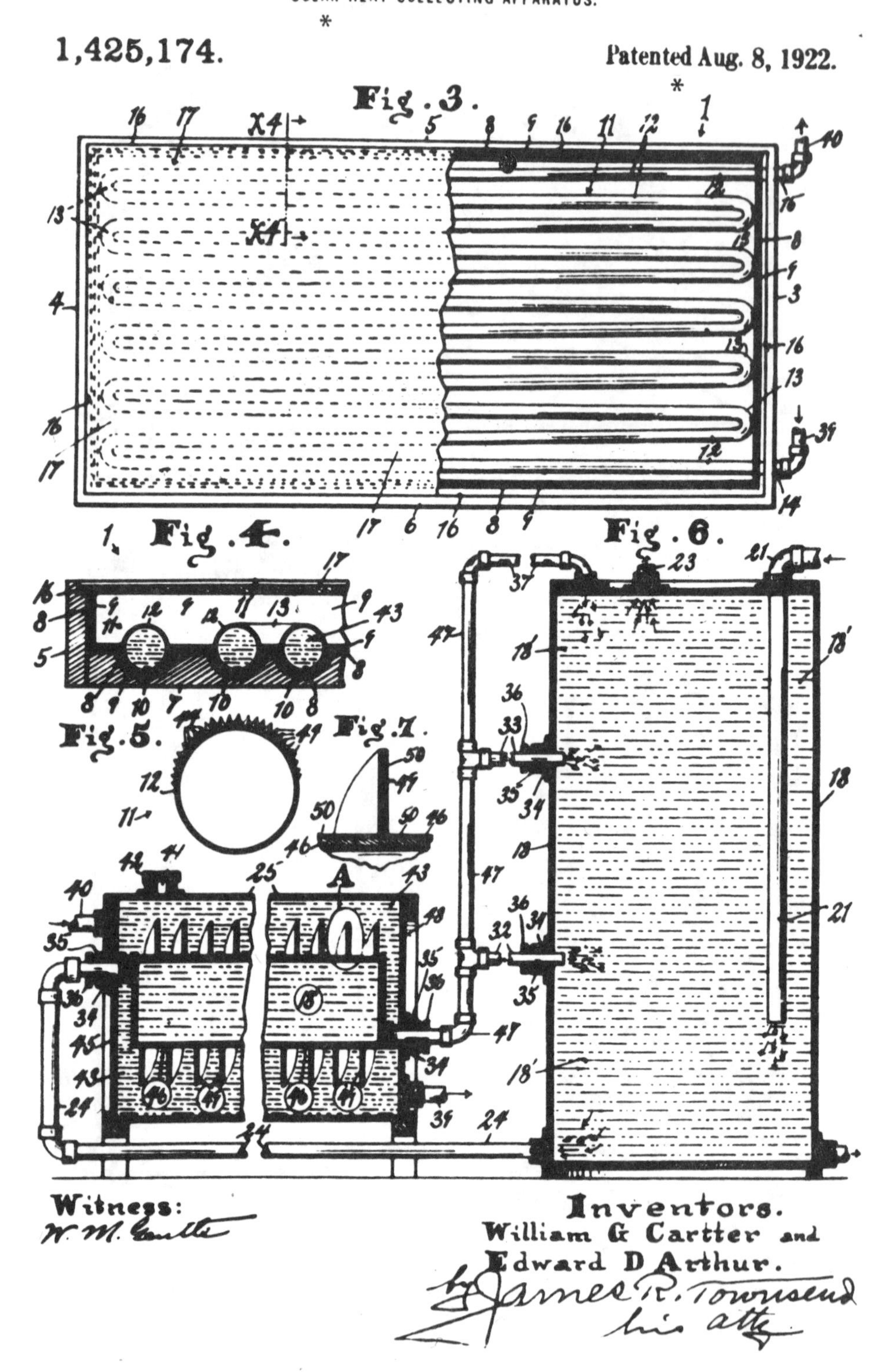
W. G. CARTTER AND E. D. ARTHUR.
SOLAR HEAT COLLECTING APPARATUS.
1,425,174.
Patented Aug. 8, 1922.
Fig. 3.
Fig. 4.
Fig. 5.
Fig. 6.
Fig. 7.
Witness:
Inventors.
William G Cartter and
Edward D Arthur.

UNITED STATES PATENT OFFICE.

WILLIAM G. CARTTER AND EDWARD D. ARTHUR, OF ARCADIA, CALIFORNIA.

SOLAR-HEAT-COLLECTING APPARATUS.

1,425,174. Specification of Letters Patent. **Patented Aug. 8, 1922.**

*

To all whom it may concern:

Be it known that we, WILLIAM G. CARTTER and EDWARD D. ARTHUR, citizens of the United States, residing at Arcadia, in the county of Los Angeles and State of California, have invented a new and useful Solar-Heat-Collecting Apparatus, of which the following is a specification.

This invention relates to an apparatus for collecting and using solar heat, and it may be said to consist of the new and useful features and in the improved construction, combination and arrangement of parts the purposes of which will be apparent to those skilled in the art from a consideration of the preferred form of construction herein shown.

One of the principal objects of this invention is to provide an apparatus that will be proof against injury by low temperatures; for as is well known solar heat collectors necessarily have a part thereof in the open where it is exposed to changing temperatures which latter, when below the freezing point, is liable to injure the apparatus.

Another object of the invention is to provide an apparatus that will be more efficient in collecting the solar heat and for storing and conserving said heat when collected.

Another object of the invention is to provide an apparatus in which a heat storage tank of large size will be interposed between the heat collector and the heat utilizing means: the purpose of which will be hereafter explained.

Another object of the invention is to provide a means for evenly distributing through the water tank the heated water that has passed through the heat storage tank which distribution is accomplished by providing a plurality of discharge pipes for the heated water at different heights in said water tank.

Other objects and advantages of this invention will be apparent from a consideration of the preferred form of construction herein shown described and claimed.

The drawings illustrate the invention.

Figure 1 is a side elevation of the apparatus installed in a house; part of the latter being shown in section and parts broken away.

Fig. 2 is a central vertical section through the tanks associated with the apparatus.

Fig. 3 is a plan elevation of heat collector removed from the house roof; a part of the glass covering broken away; showing the coil pipe associated therewith.

Fig. 4 is a section taken on the line x^4—x^4 of Fig. 3 the parts being enlarged and showing in detail the construction of the heat collector.

Fig. 5 is a section through one pipe of the heating coil showing a modified form of heat collector.

Fig. 6 is a modified form of what is shown in Fig. 2.

Fig. 7 is an enlarged view of a portion of the interior tank enclosed in the ellipse A in Fig. 6.

In detail the heat collector 1 is secured to the roof of a house 2 by any known means; and in a position that will expose the top surface of the heat collector to the sun's rays; and this exposure is preferably such that at the noon hour the rays of the sun will contact with said surface in a line perpendicular thereto.

The frame of the heat collector 1 consists of the ends 3 and 4, and the sides 5 and 6 respectively which are secured to the bottom 7 by any well known means; forming thereby an open top box in which the heat collecting apparatus is secured.

The interior surface of the box is first lined with a non-heat conducting material such as asbestos 8 and over this material 8 is laid a bed of copper 9 which latter is one of the best heat conductors known; and the purposes of these linings will be hereafter explained.

As seen in Fig. 4 the bottom 7 is provided with the channel 10 which in cross section is the contour of a circle, and into which channel is fitted the linings 8 and 9 thus forming a bed for and in which the coil of pipe 11 is partly embedded.

The coil of pipe 11 is formed of the lengths 12 and turned ends 13 which are integral and which form a continuous passageway from the inlet to the outlet ends 14 and 15 respectively; and the lengths 12 are positioned so that from the inlet to the outlet ends of the coil there is an upward inclination, and this upward inclination is for the purpose of reducing the resistance to the flow of the fluid in said coil.

The upper inner edges of the ends 3 and 4 and the sides 5 and 6 are recessed to form the seat 16 for the glass covering 17 which latter can be secured in place by any well known means.

Within the building 2 and preferably in the attic thereof is a water tank 18 which is enclosed in the non-heat conducting material 19 within the casing 20.

Through a pipe 21 the water 18' is supplied to the tank 18 from a source not shown; and through the pipes 22 and 23 cold and hot water respectively are supplied to the water distributing system of the house 2; which distributing system and also the lower part of the house are broken away.

To the bottom of the tank 18 there is connected one end of the pipe 24 the other end of which is threaded through the bottom of the heat storage tank 25 and has the end thereof secured to the distributer head 26 (see Fig. 2).

Within the storage tank 25 there are three coiled pipes 27, 28 and 29 respectively each of which has one end connected to the distributor head 26; and these coils extend upward in the tank 25 to different heights.

The coils 27 and 28 have threaded sockets 30 and 31 respectively into which the respective pipes 32 and 33 are fitted and these pipes extend through the casing of the tank 25 and also through the casing of the tank 18.

To prevent leakage from the tanks 18 and 25 the pipes 32 and 33 are encased at the point of egress through said tanks with the packing rings 34 which latter are seated in the sockets 35 and held in place by the screw plugs 36.

The upper end of the coil pipe 29 passes upward in the tank 25; and has the end thereof extending through the end of said tank; and to prevent leakage the pipe 29 is provided with a packing similar to that encasing the pipes 32 and 33.

The end of the pipe 29 is secured to one end of a pipe line 37 which has its other end screwed into the socket 38 on the top of the tank 18.

From the foregoing it can readily be seen that the water in the tank 18 is free to pass through the pipe 24, distributor head 26 and coils 27, 28 and 29 and discharge back into the tank 18 through the pipes 32, 33 and 37 when the temperature of the water in this circulatory system is unbalanced by heat.

As heretofore indicated the change of temperature is accomplished by the solar heat collector: and the solar heat is transmitted to the water by the following means.

Secured to the bottom of the tank 25 is one end of the pipe 39 which extends outward through the roof of the house 2 and has its other end connected to the inlet end 14 of the coil pipe 11.

To the outlet end 15 of the coil pipe 11 is secured one end of the pipe 40 which latter extends inwardly through the roof of the house 2 and has its other end attached near the upper end of the tank 25.

The tank 25 has on the top end thereof the inlet 41 that is closed by the cap screw 42; and through the inlet 41 the tank 25 is kept filled with a non-freezing fluid 43; which of course fills the coil 11 and its pipe connections to said tank.

When the heat rays of the sun contact with the coil 11 the heat thereof is transmitted to the fluid 43; which transmission of heat induces a circulation of said fluid; the colder fluid passing from the bottom of the tank 25 through the pipe 39 to displace the warmer fluid in the coil 11 which passes upward through the coil as it is heated and back to the tank 25 through the pipe 40; and through this circulation the heat from the sun is transferred from the collector 1 to the storage tank 25.

It will also be apparent that as the heat is transferred from the collector 1 to the storage 25 that the stored heat will be transferred to the coil pipes 27, 28 and 29 and transferred to the water therein which transition of heat causes a circulation of the water in the tank 18 and its pipe connections to the aforementioned coils; consequently the water in the tank 18 will acquire practically the same temperature as the temperature of the non-freezing liquid 43 in the tank 25 and the temperature of the liquid in the latter tank will be the same as that in the collector 1 before the circulations in these systems is stopped by a balancing of temperatures.

In order to more efficiently collect the heat rays in the coil 11 either by radiation or conduction the sides and bottom of the collector 1 are lined with a non-heat conducting material 8 preferably asbestos so that the heat rays will be deflected by said lining; and by conduction through the copper lining 9 transmitted to the coil 11.

Also as seen in Figs. 6 and 7 a modified form for transferring the heat from the storage tank 25 to the water supply is shown. In this modification the tank 25 has its end in a vertical position and its center portion is broken away.

The pipe 24 has one end connected to the tank 18 and the other end thereof passes through the end 45 of the tank 25 and is secured in one end of the cylinder 46 and near the top edge thereof; and to prevent leakage the pipe 24 where it passes through the end 45 is provided with a packing similar to that heretofore described.

To the other end of the cylinder 46 at the bottom edge thereof is secured one end of the pipe 47 which latter extends through the end 48 of the tank 25 and is packed in like manner to pipe 24 to prevent leakage.

The pipe 47 is turned upward and to it are connected one end of the pipes 32, 33 and 37; so that the water in the tank 18 can pass through the pipe 24, cylinder 46, pipe 47 and the branch pipes 32, 33 and 37 back into the tank 18.

The pipe connections from the tank 25 to the heat collector 1 are practically the same as in the other form.

In order to produce a greater heat conduction area the cylinder 46 it provided with a helical ribbon 49 which latter and also the exterior surface of the cylinder can be encased in a copper jacket 50 as seen in Fig. 7.

In operation the heat rays from the sun either by radiation or conduction are transmitted to the coil 11; and from this coil are transferred to the non-freezing liquid therein: thereby unbalancing the temperature thereof as heretofore stated and causing a circulation of said fluid by which means the heat is carried to the storage tank 25.

The heat accumulated in storage tank 25 is transferred to the water in tank 18 by circulation of water through coil pipes 27, 28 and 29.

It is thus seen that the coiled pipes in the storage tank are heated by the heat collector and that as the temperature rises a circulation of water to and from the water tank is produced and the temperature of all the water is raised eventually to the approximate temperature of the non-freezing fluid in said storage tank.

From the foregoing it can readily be seen that after the water in the tank 18 has been raised to a temperature sufficient for domestic use, that a large accumulation of heat is stored in the tank 25; which heat will be transferred to the water entering the tank 18 as the heated water thereof is drawn off: thereby greatly increasing the bulk of heated water without altering the size of the water tank and this feature of the invention is an improvement in the art.*

June 19, 1962 S. ANDRASSY 3,039,453

HEATER

*

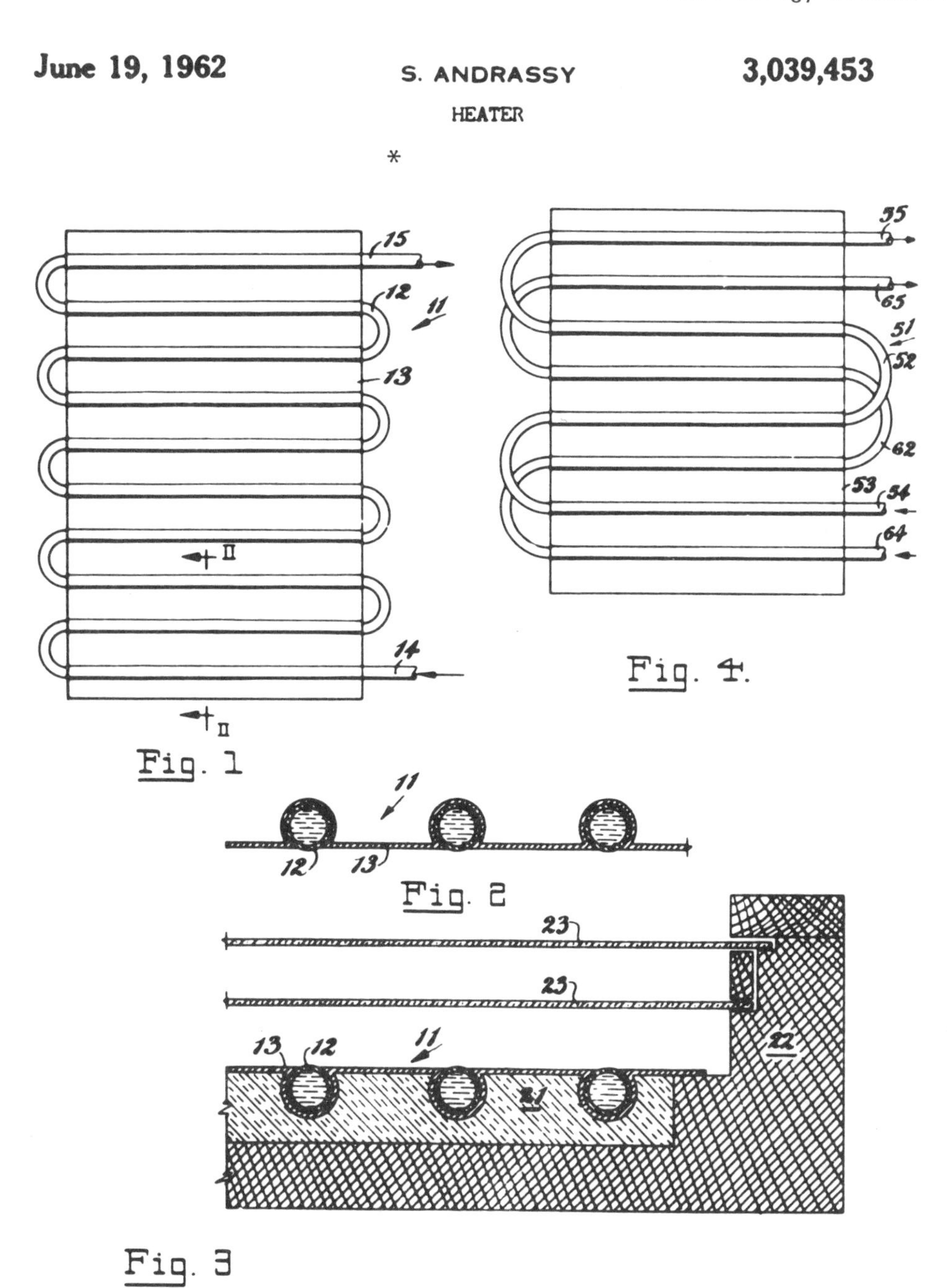

INVENTOR.
STELLA ANDRASSY
BY Philip Mentz
ATTORNEY

3,039,453
HEATER
Stella Andrassy, Princeton, N.J.
(Ridge Road, Kingston, N.J.)

*

This invention relates to a new and improved heat exchanger unit. More particularly, this invention relates to a solar water heater unit which can be economically fabricated, is relatively light in weight, which is corrosion resistant, and which will not be damaged in the event of freezing.

Many devices have been developed for utilizing solar energy. One broad class of these devices utilizes solar energy in the form of heat collected at moderate temperatures. This is frequently done by using solar energy to heat water to an elevated temperature in the solar heat collector of such devices. The heated water from such a solar heat collector may be utilized for heating houses, preparing hot water for domestic uses, heating swimming pools, heating other liquids, etc.

The currently used solar water heaters are usually made of metal, frequently in the form of metallic tubing soldered in a serpentine fashion to the face or back of a blackened metal plate. Such a structure is expensive due to high fabrication costs and heavy weight of metal used. In the winter or when there is danger of nocturnal freezing, such a solar water heater must be drained or else antifreeze must be used therein. If antifreeze is used, it is necessary to have an additional heat exchanger for heating water to be used for domestic purposes. This clearly reduces the operating efficiency of such apparatus, and further adds to the cost.

One of the objects of the present invention is to overcome the disadvantages of conventional heat exchangers.

Another object of the present invention is to provide a solar fluid heater unit which is light in weight, is easily and economically fabricated, is free from corrosion, and in which the advent of freezing produces no damage.

Still another object of the present invention is to provide a heat exchanger unit which is light in weight, easily and economically fabricated, is free from corrosion, and which may readily be modified for different heat exchange applications.

With the above objects in view, the present invention mainly consists of a heat exchanger having a flexible plastic conduit secured to a crimped heat conductive plate.

The novel features which are considered as characteristic of the invention are set forth with particularity in the appended claims. The invention itself, however, both as to its construction and its method of operation together with additional objects and advantages thereof, will be best understood from the following description of specific embodiments when read with the accompanying drawings, in which;

FIGURE 1 is a plan view of a solar fluid heater unit incorporating the principles of this invention;

FIGURE 2 is a vertical cross section taken along line II—II of FIGURE 1;

FIGURE 3 is a vertical cross section showing a solar fluid heater unit incorporating the principles of this invention incorporated within a housing for producing higher temperatures; and

FIGURE 4 is a plan view of another heat exchanger unit incorporating the principles of this invention.

Referring to the drawings, and more particularly to FIGURES 1 and 2, there is shown a solar fluid heater unit 11 constructed according to the principles of this invention.

The solar fluid heater 11 is made of a flexible plastic conduit 12 secured to a crimped metallic plate 13. Conduit 12 is provided with a fluid inlet 14 for fluid to be heated and with a fluid outlet 15 for exhausting the heated fluid.

To construct such a fluid heater 11, metallic plate 13 is first crimped to a configuration such as shown in FIGURE 2. Flexible tube 12 is then snapped into the grooves in crimped metallic plate 13 with a suitable tool.

The configuration of the groove in metallic plate 13 is of substantially circular cross section and is greater than 180° in circumference. This enables the flexible tube 12 to be retained in the grooves without the use of additional fastening means if desired.

Crimped metallic plate 13 may be of aluminum or copper or other highly heat conducting material, and is preferably coated with a radiant energy absorptive coating, such as black paint, on one side.

Flexible plastic conduit may be of such materials as "boilable" polyethylene tubing which is black pigmented to resist sunshine, or polytetrafluoroethylene, or any other plastic which is flexible, and which will resist the action of sunshine and contact with the liquid being heated. It is to be noted that the plastic conduit must be sufficiently flexible as to allow for expansion without breakage when water within the conduit freezes.

To use such a solar fluid heater unit for heating water, heater unit 11 is placed in a position where sunshine may fall upon it. That side of crimped metallic plate 13 which is coated with a radiant energy absorptive coating is placed upward. The incident sunlight, impinging upon the absorptive coating is converted to heat, raising the temperature of metallic plate 13. The heat is conducted through metallic plate 13 and is transferred to the fluid flowing through conduit 12, thereby heating the fluid.

Where the requirements are for a large volume of water to be heated only slightly above the ambient air temperature such as for swimming pool heaters, fluid heater 11 may be used by itself as illustrated in FIGURES 1 and 2. However, where the requirements are for a smaller volume of substantially hotter water; i.e., substantially hotter than ambient air temperature such as for preparing hot water for domestic uses; the solar fluid heater unit may be placed within an incasement as illustrated in FIGURE 3.

As illustrated in FIGURE 3, solar fluid heater unit 11 is provided with an insulated backing 21, which may be foam plastic or glass wool, etc. Solar fluid heater unit 11 with insulated backing 21 may be placed within a wood incasement 22 which incasement also supports one or more glass or transparent plastic films 23 above solar fluid heater unit 11. The inclosure of solar heater unit 11 by insulation below and transparent glass or plastic films 23 above, greatly increase the temperature which may be achieved in solar fluid heater unit 11.

It is thus seen that there has been provided a solar water heater unit which is easily and economically fabricated, which is light in weight, which is not subject to corrosion, and which is not subject to damage upon freezing.

Of course, unit 11 may be used as a heat exchanger by passing a fluid to be either heated or cooled through flexible conduit 12. Such fluid will be either heated or cooled by the action of the surroundings external to unit 11. Alternatively a fluid may be passed through conduit 12 for the purpose of either heating or cooling the area surrounding unit 11. For such applications, the use of flexible plastic tube 12 provides a corrosion-free passageway for the fluid contained therein. Heat conductive plate 13 provides an extended heat transfer surface for increasing the rate of heat transfer between the fluid within tube 12 and the surroundings.

As illustrated in FIGURE 4 two flexible plastic conduits **52** and **62** may be placed in alternate grooves in crimped metallic plate **53**. This provides two substantially parallel fluid passageways, one being in tube **52** from inlet **54** to outlet **55**, the other being in tube **62** from inlet **64** to outlet **65**. Of course the positions of inlet and outlet may be reversed depending upon whether it is desired to have parallel flow or countercurrent flow in tube **52** and tube **62**. If a relatively hot fluid is passed through conduit **52**, it may be used to heat a relatively cool fluid passing through conduit **62**. The heat exchange between conduit **52** and conduit **62** is facilitated by crimped heat conductive metallic plate **53**.

Should it be desired to exchange heat among more than two fluids, more than two conduits are placed in parallel grooves in a crimped heat conductive metallic sheet in a manner analogous to that illustrated in FIGURE 4.

Since the flexible conduits **12**, **52**, and **62** are retained in contact with heat conductive plates **13** and **53** by means of the grooves in these plates, the heat exchanger may readily be modified for other applications. This may easily be accomplished by removing the flexible tubes from the heat conductive plates and replacing them in other configurations. For example, the heat exchanger of FIGURE 1 can readily be converted into the heat exchanger of FIGURE 4. *

June 5, 1928. W. CHRISTIANSEN **1,672,750**

SOLAR HEATER

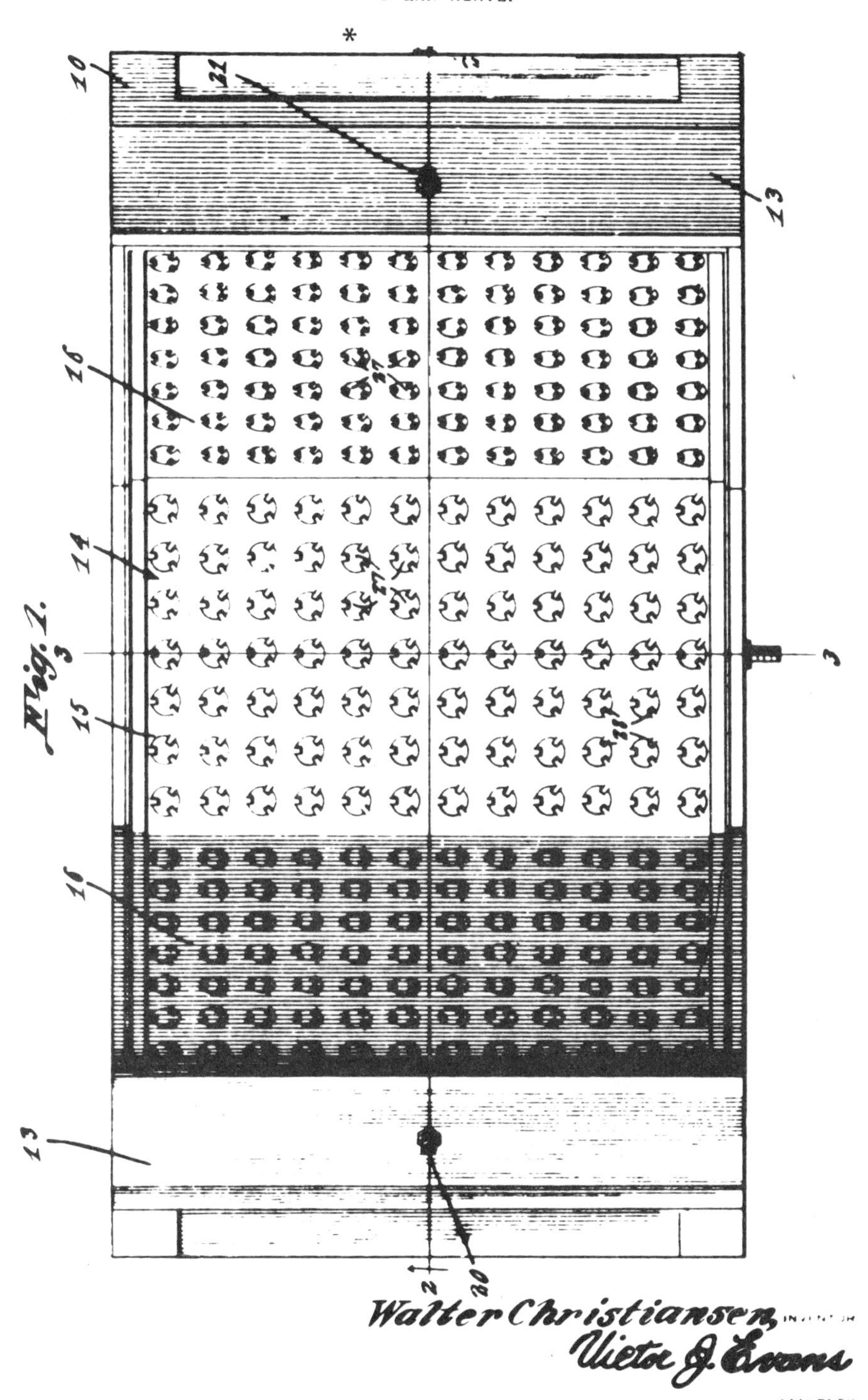

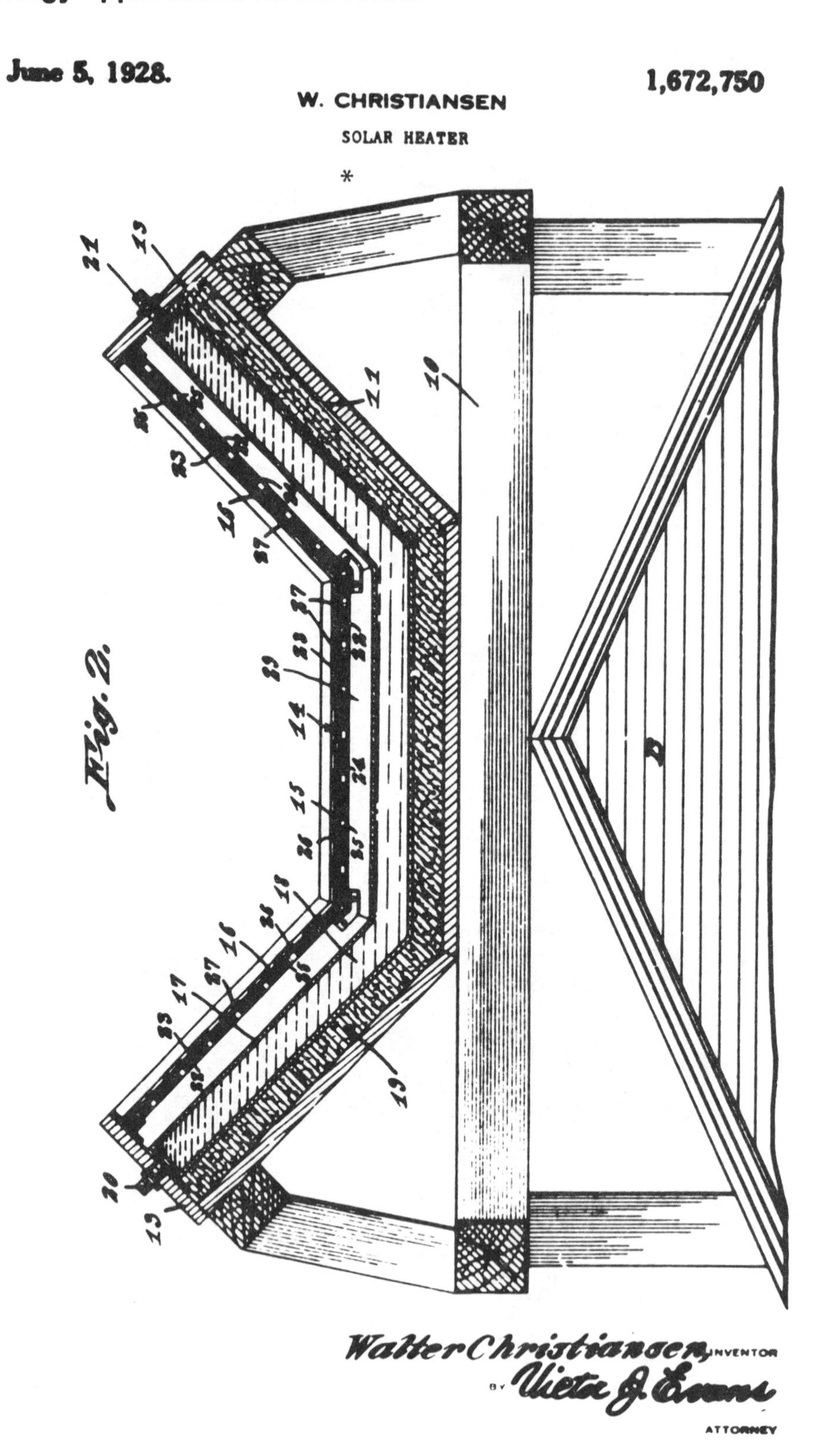
June 5, 1928.
1,672,750
W. CHRISTIANSEN
SOLAR HEATER
Fig. 2.
Walter Christiansen, INVENTOR
BY Victor J. Evans
ATTORNEY

June 5, 1928. **1,672,750**

W. CHRISTIANSEN

SOLAR HEATER

*

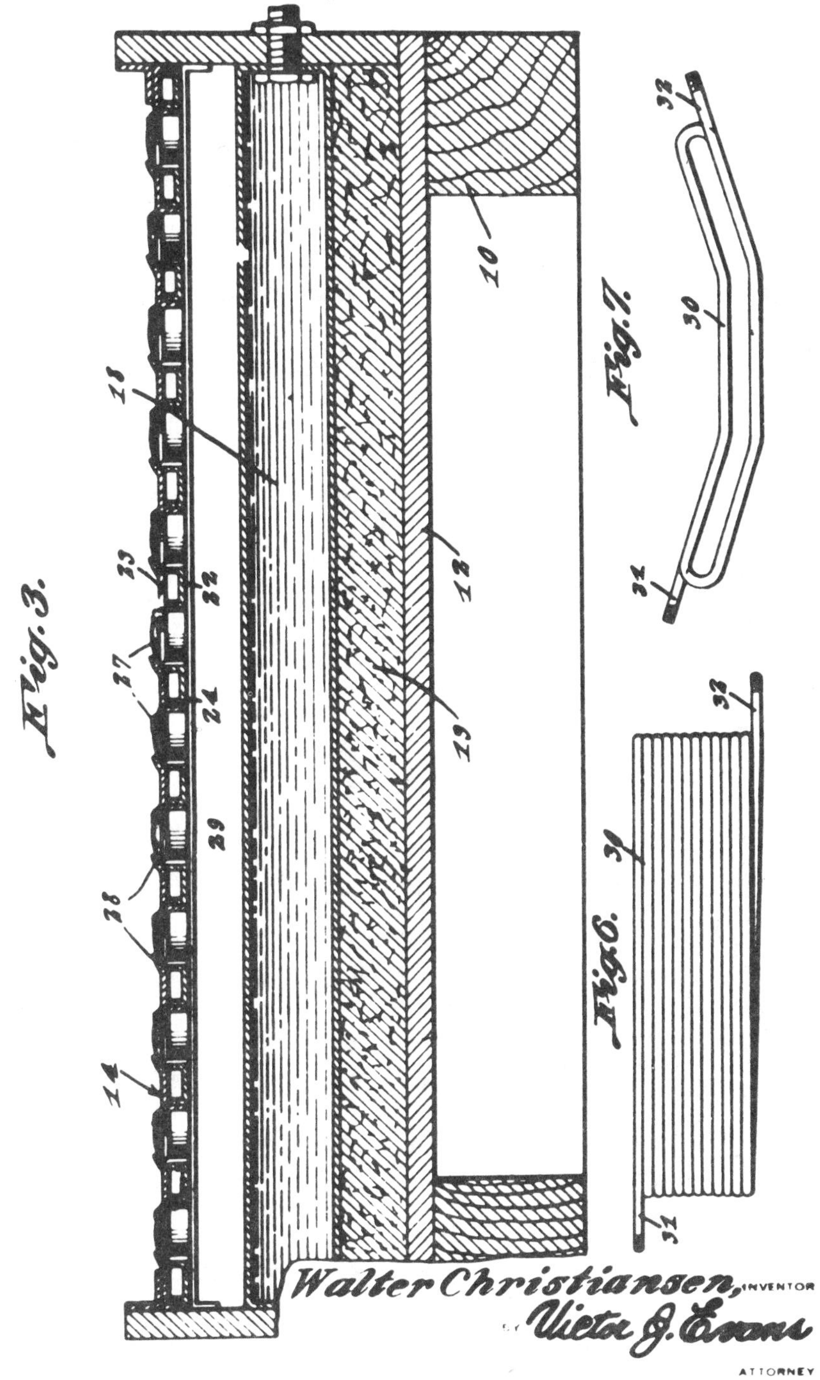

Fig. 3.

Fig. 7.

Fig. 6.

Walter Christiansen, INVENTOR

BY Victor J. Evans

ATTORNEY

June 5, 1928. **1,672,750**

W. CHRISTIANSEN

SOLAR HEATER

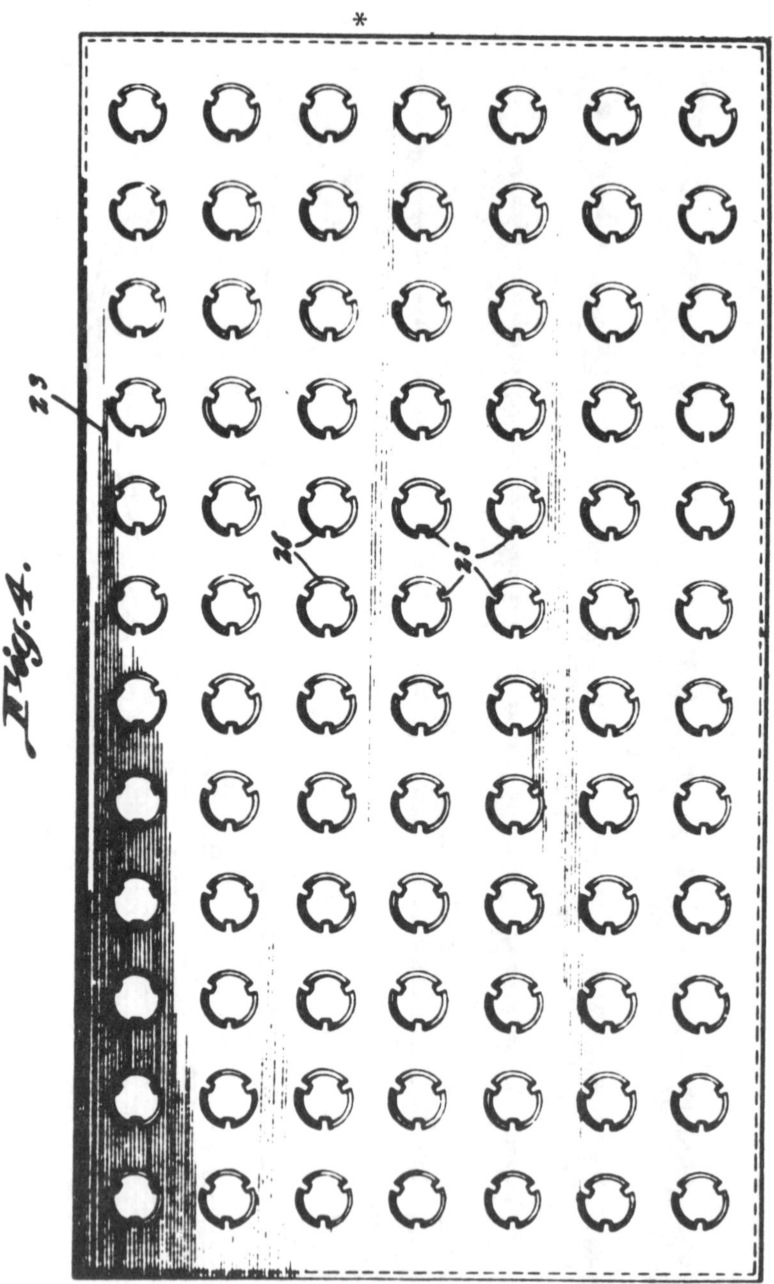

Walter Christiansen, INVENTOR

BY *Victor J. Evans*

ATTORNEY

June 5, 1928. 1,672,750

W. CHRISTIANSEN

SOLAR HEATER

*

Fig. 5.

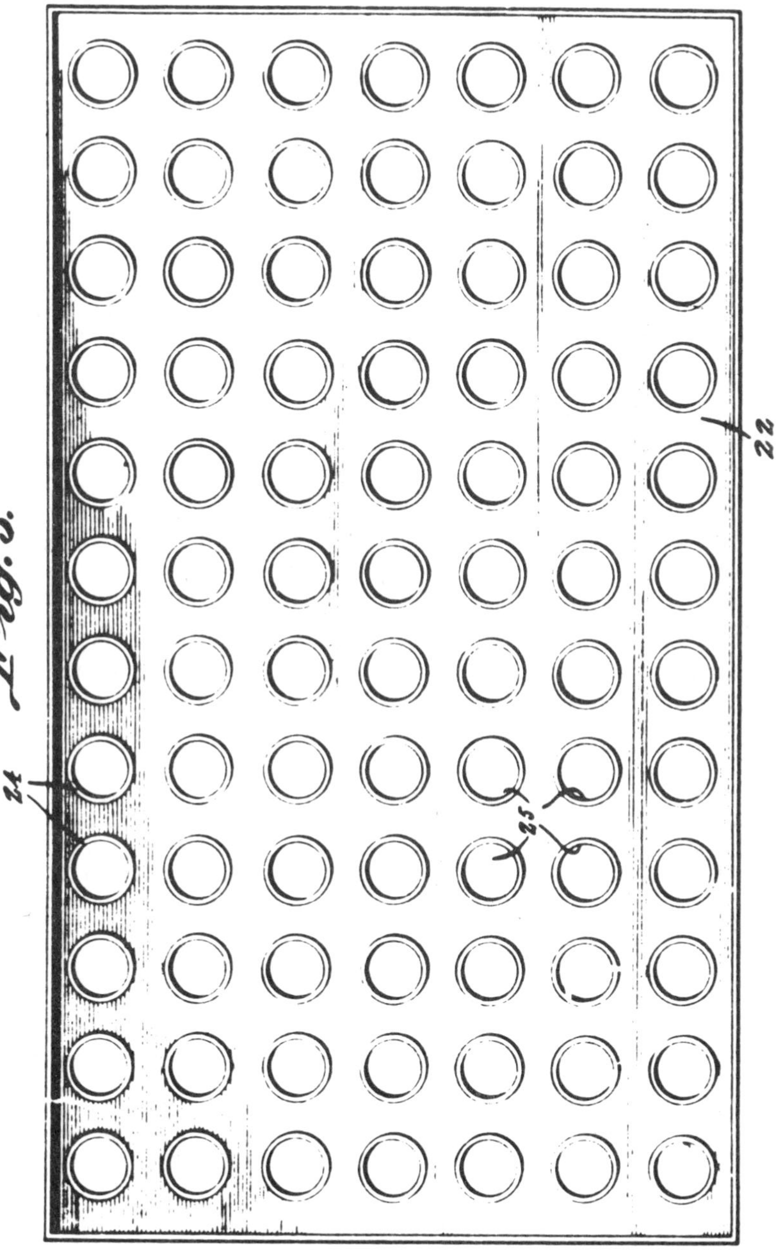

22

24

25

Walter Christiansen, INVENTOR

BY Victor J. Evans

ATTORNEY

UNITED STATES PATENT OFFICE.

WALTER CHRISTIANSEN, OF MIAMI, FLORIDA.

SOLAR HEATER.

*

This invention relates to heaters, an object being to provide means for utilizing the heat of the sun rays for heating water.

Another object of the invention is the provision of a heater of this character which is constructed of sections arranged so that one or more sections will be positioned transversely of the direct rays of the sun as the latter travels across the horizon, together with means for directing the sun's heat upon a receptacle or container for water or other liquid and to provide a circulation through the receptacle.

With the above and other objects in view, the invention further includes the following novel features and details of construction to be hereinafter more fully described, illustrated in the accompanying drawings and pointed out in the appended claims.

In the drawings:—

Figure 1 is a top plan view of a solar heater constructed in accordance with the present invention.

Figure 2 is a sectional view on the line 2—2 of Figure 1.

Figure 3 is an enlarged section on the line 3—3 of Figure 1.

Figure 4 is a top plan view of the outer panel of one of the top wall sections.

Figure 5 is a plan view of the inner panel of one of the top wall sections.

Figure 6 is a detail plan view showing a different form of liquid receptacle or coil.

Figure 7 is a side view of the coil shown in Figure 6.

Referring to the drawings in detail wherein like characters of reference denote corresponding parts, the heater which may be placed in any advantageous position, is shown as supported upon the top of a building, a portion of which is indicated at B. The heater comprises a supporting frame 10 and a housing 11, the latter being of suitable configuration. This housing comprises a bottom wall 12 and side walls 13. The top wall of the housing is indicated at 14 and is shown as comprising a horizontal section 15 which has extending from its opposite edges, oppositely inclined sections 16. The sections 16 are arranged at a suitable angle, the purpose being to provide a maximum amount of surface for exposure to the sun's rays irrespective of the position of the sun, and within a relatively small area

Located beneath and spaced from the top wall 14 is a receptacle 17. This receptacle is preferably of the same configuration as the top wall 14 and is adapted to contain water or other liquid 18. Located within the housing between the bottom of the wall of the receptacle 17 and the bottom wall 12 of the housing is a lining of heat insulating material 19. The receptacle is provided with an inlet 20 and outlets 21 and these inlets and outlets may be connected respectively with a suitable source of water supply and with receptacles or the like to which the heated water may be conducted.

The top wall 14 is of novel construction, each of the sections being formed of an inner panel 22 and an outer panel 23. These panels are provided with openings which are surrounded by flanges 24, the flanges 24 of one of the panels being telescopically received within the flanges 24 of the other panel. Passages 25 are thus provided through the top wall 14. Located at the outer ends of these passages are seats 26 which receive magnifying lenses 27, the latter being held in place by fingers 28 which extend from around the edges of the openings of the outer panels. The wall 14 is spaced from the top wall of the receptacle 17 and this space provides a heat chamber 29 with which the passages 25 communicate. An unobstructed passage for the sun's heat from the lenses 27 is thus provided for the upper wall of the receptacle 17, so that water within the said receptacle may be heated within a relatively short time. By reason of the relative angles of the sections of the top wall 14, a maximum amount of this wall will be presented to the rays of the sun as the latter moves over the horizon while heat within the chamber 29 may circulate through this chamber over the surface of the receptacle even though one of the end panels 16 is not exposed to the direct rays of the sun.

If desired, a coil such as is indicated at 30 in Figures 6 and 7 of the drawings may be substituted for the receptacle 17. This coil includes an inlet 31 and an outlet 32 for connection with sources of supply and distribution. *

PATENTED JUN 28 1971 3,587,559

SHEET 1 OF 3

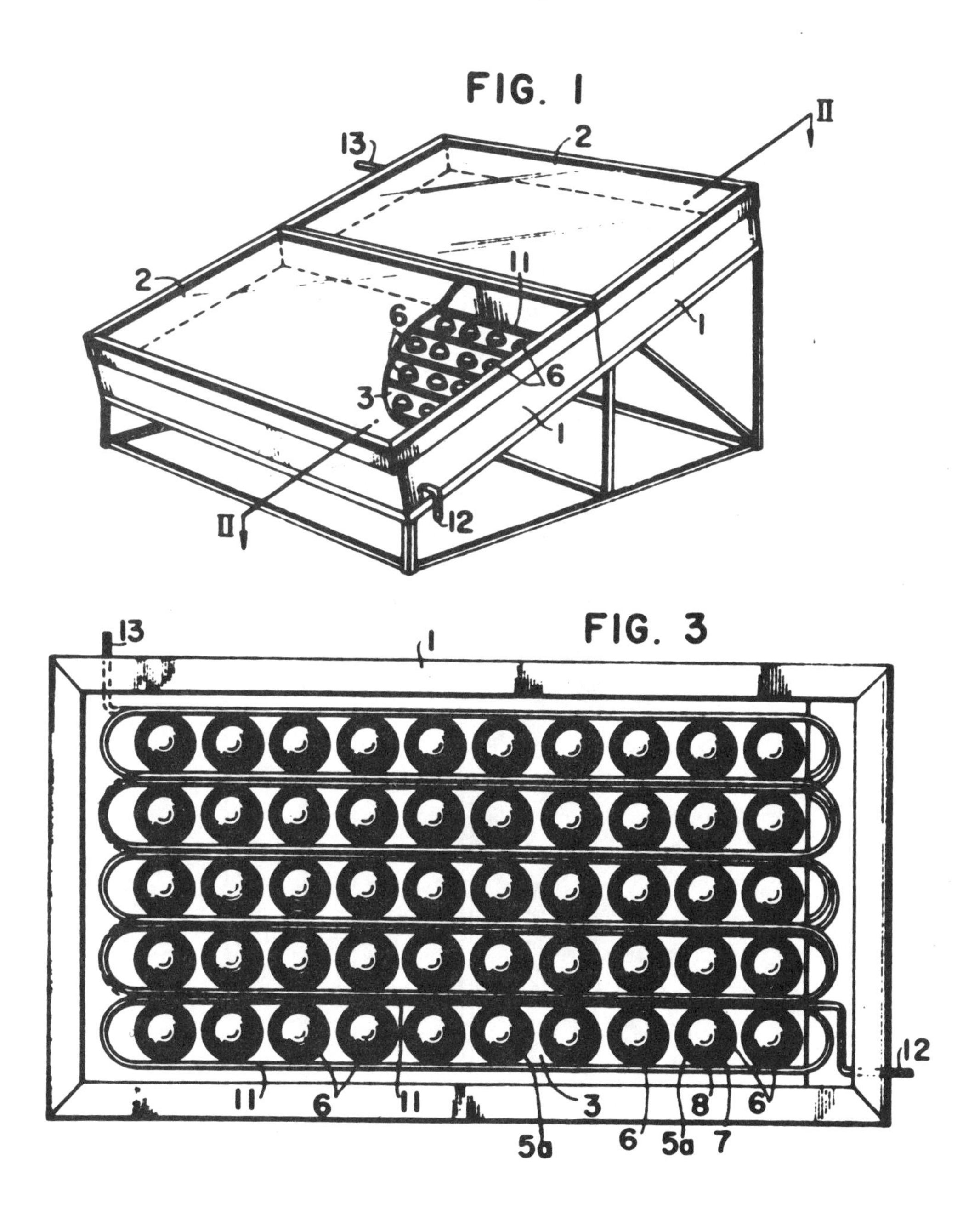

INVENTOR

Kenshichi Nonaka

BY

Cushman, Darby & Cushman
ATTORNEYS

PATENTED JUN 28 1971

3,587,559

SHEET 2 OF 3

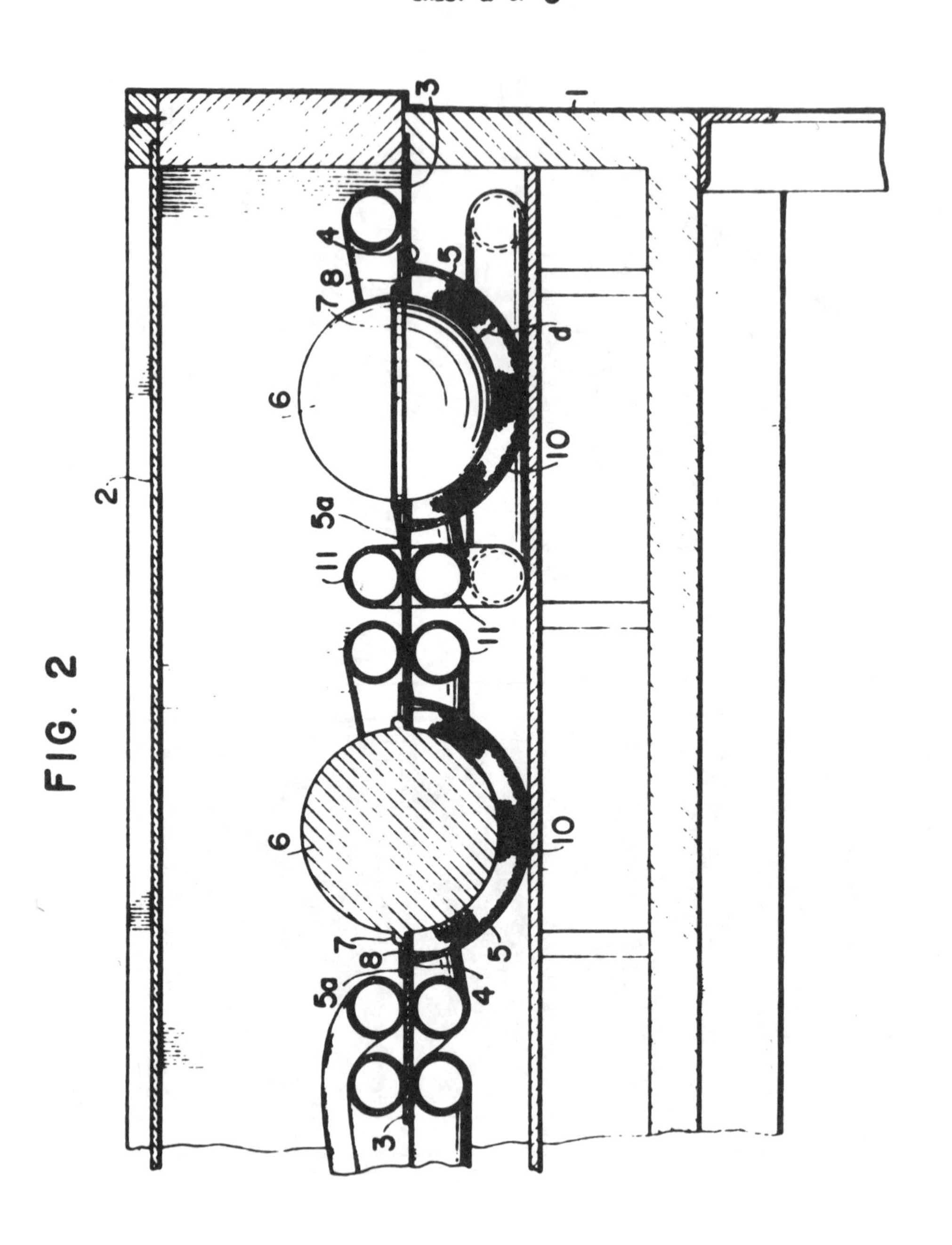

INVENTOR

Kenichi Nonaka

BY

Cushman Darby & Cushman
ATTORNEYS

PATENTED JUN 28 1971

3,587,559

SHEET 3 OF 3

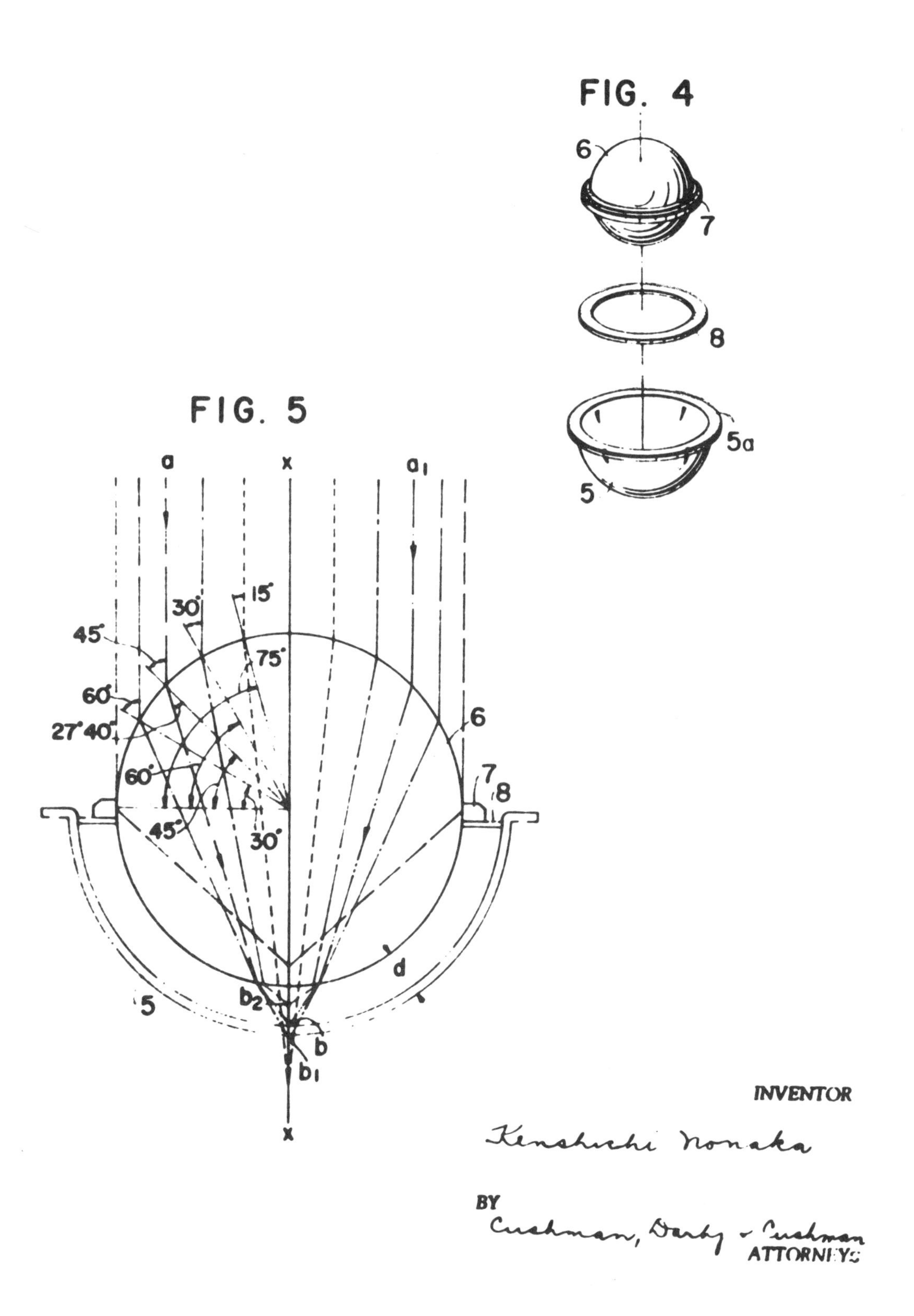

INVENTOR

Kenshichi Nonaka

BY

Cushman, Darby & Cushman
ATTORNEYS

WATER-HEATING APPARATUS UTILIZING SOLAR RAYS

BACKGROUND OF THE INVENTION

the present invention relates to a system for collecting solar heat, more particularly to an apparatus for heating water by solar rays.

An apparatus for heating water by solar rays in which ordinary convex lenses (plano-convex or convexo-concave lenses) are employed have heretofore been known. Such a conventional apparatus does not efficiently heat water as such lenses are not effective all through hours of sunlight but only while rays of the sun are hitting the lenses at certain angles of incidence. Further, it has been noted in such a conventional apparatus that any metal part thereof which is subjected to intense heat of focused rays is apt to be damaged.

SUMMARY OF THE INVENTION

The object of the present invention is to provide an apparatus which is efficient in heating water and free from the above-mentioned shortcomings.

According to the present invention, an apparatus for heating water by solar rays includes a number of spherical lenses which enable it to receive a maximum of radiation from the sun. Such lenses effectively converge solar rays all through hours of sunlight. The rays focused from the lenses subject intense heat to a superheat resisting carbon impregnated cloth which lines the metallic material forming part of a heat collecting member. A large number of such lenses are held by a suitable means within a glass covered box. The heat which is absorbed by the heat collecting members and which is trapped in the closed box warms the water contained in or circulating through a continuous pipe extending in convolutions within the box.

Therefore, the present invention provides an apparatus for heating water by solar rays comprising a plurality of spherical lenses positioned in a box covered by a glass at the side facing the sun, a plurality of heat collecting members each positioned below each of said spherical lenses, each of said heat collecting members being lined with a superheat resisting carbon impregnated cloth at the area subjected to focused rays, and a continuous water pipe extending in a number of convolutions within said box.

BRIEF DESCRIPTION OF THE DRAWINGS

A preferred embodiment of the present invention is hereinafter described by making reference to the attached drawings in which:

FIG. 1 is a general perspective view of an apparatus for heating water by solar rays according to the present invention (two units being combined);

FIG. 2 is a partially enlarged section view of the apparatus cut at the line II–II of FIG. 1;

FIG. 3 is a plan view of a part of the apparatus (a single unit);

FIG. 4 is a perspective view of a spherical lens, a ring for supporting the lens, and a hemispherical member; and

FIG. 5 is a diagram showing a state in which solar rays passing from the lenses converge on the inner face of the hemispherical members.

DESCRIPTION OF THE PREFERRED EMBODIMENT

Referring to FIG. 1, the apparatus comprises a box 1 covered by a glass 2 which functions to trap solar energy The box is placed at an appropriate angle in an elevated position, for example, on the southern slope of a roof. The box 1 in this example consists of two units, but the member of the units may be decreased or increased according to the need.

As seen from FIG. 3 and 4, the box 1 is partitioned by a a partition plate 3 having a plurality of regularly spaced holes 4 in rows. Each of these holes 4 receives a hemispherical member 5 having at its mouth a brim 5a which is welded to said partition plate 3.

A spherical lens 6, as seen from FIG. 4 may be made of glass and formed with a flangelike projection along its largest diameter. This flangelike projection sits on a ring 8 which is placed on said brim 5a of the hemispherical member 5. The diameter of the lens 6 is smaller than that of the mouth of the hemispherical member 5 so that the face of the lower hemisphere of the lens 6 and the inner face of the hemispherical member 5 are spaced at such a distance *d* that the solar rays passing from the lens 6 focus on the surface of a superheat resisting carbon impregnated cloth 10 which lines the inner face of said hemispherical member 5. The focused rays heat said carbon impregnated cloth 10 to high temperatures which in turn heat said hemispherical members 5 and said partition plate 3. A continuous water pipe 11 is arranged in convolutions enclosing each row of said hemispherical members at both sides of the partition plate 3. Water is supplied to said water pipe 11 from a water inlet 12 and is discharged via an outlet 13. As water passes through said water pipe 11, it absorbs the heat from said partition plate 3 within said box 1 and is thereby heated to a high temperature.

Since the spherical lenses 6 are sued in the present invention, parallel rays incident on the entire surface of the upper hemisphere of each lens are refracted therein in the ways as shown in FIG. 5. If, for example, the angle of incidence of rays a, a_1 is 45° and the index of refraction 1.518, the rays are refracted at an angle of 27°40′, and when the refracted rays pass from the lower hemisphere of the lens to the air within said box 5, they are again refracted at an angle of 45° The rays a, a_1 thus refracted converge at a point b on the principal axis X–X. In the same way, the rays incident at an angle of 30° and 60° converge at a point b_1 and b_2, respectively. Therefore, if the space between the opposite faces of the hemispherical member 5 and the lens 6 is predetermined at an appropriate distance d (for example, 8 mm. for a lens having a diameter of 40 mm.) with the point b used as a reference, it is possible to constantly focus the rays on a portion of the carbon impregnated cloth 10 which lines the inner face of said hemispherical member and subject intensive heat thereto. The focal distance d remains the same even when parallel rays incident on the lens 6 come from an oblique angle, as would happen just after sunrise and just before sunset Therefore, as long as the sun is shining, that is from sunrise to sunset, the rays passing through the lenses focus at some portions on the carbon impregnated cloth on the hemispherical member 5. If there is no such heat-resisting cloth at the points where the rays focus, a material forming the hemispherical member would be damaged at such area. If the material used is aluminum whose melting point is 658° C., the focused rays would burn holes in such material. The carbon treated cloth 10 used in the present invention is that which is made by impregnating carbon therein and giving heat treatment thereto. Such a carbon treated cloth has the property of superheat resistance and can therefore withstand temperatures as high as 3000° C. Thus, even when the focused rays passing from the spherical lens result in as high a temperature as 1,400° C., which is possible on summer days, the carbon cloth used therein withstands such heat without being burnt. Thus the heated carbon cloth may be raised to a high temperature which is transmitted to the air inside the hemispherical member 5 and the intensive heat is conducted to said partition plate 3.

Since the water pipe 11, arranged in convolutions at both sides of said partition plate 3, could have a continuous length of some 30 meters, the water contained in or circulating through said pipe is effectively heated. The heating efficiency could be increased according to the need by combining two or more units of this apparatus. In such as case, the water heated in the first unit may be further communicated to the second unit. The heated water discharged from the outlet 12 is led to an appropriate hot-water storage tank which is not shown in the drawings. *

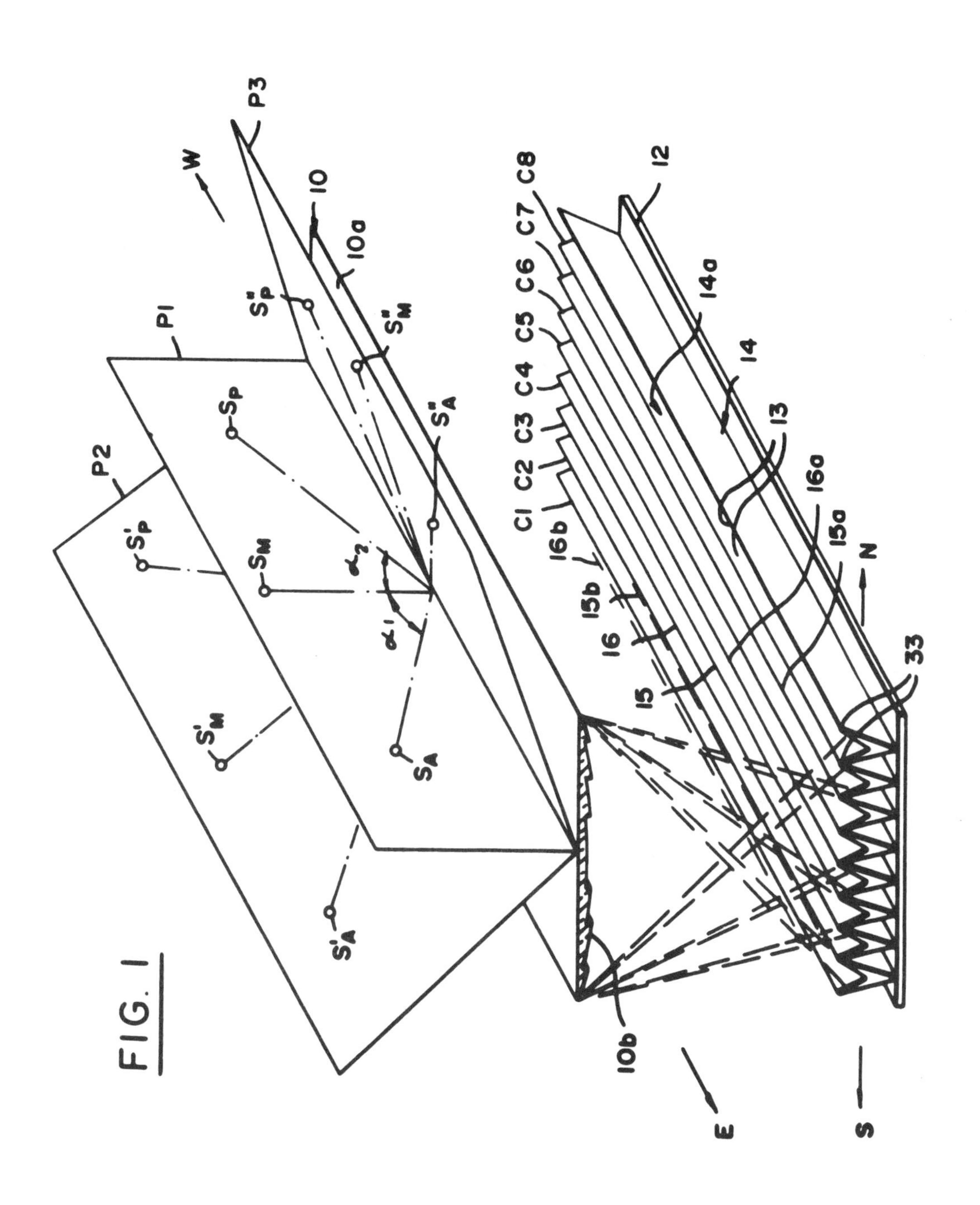

U.S. Patent Oct. 28, 1975 * 3,915,148

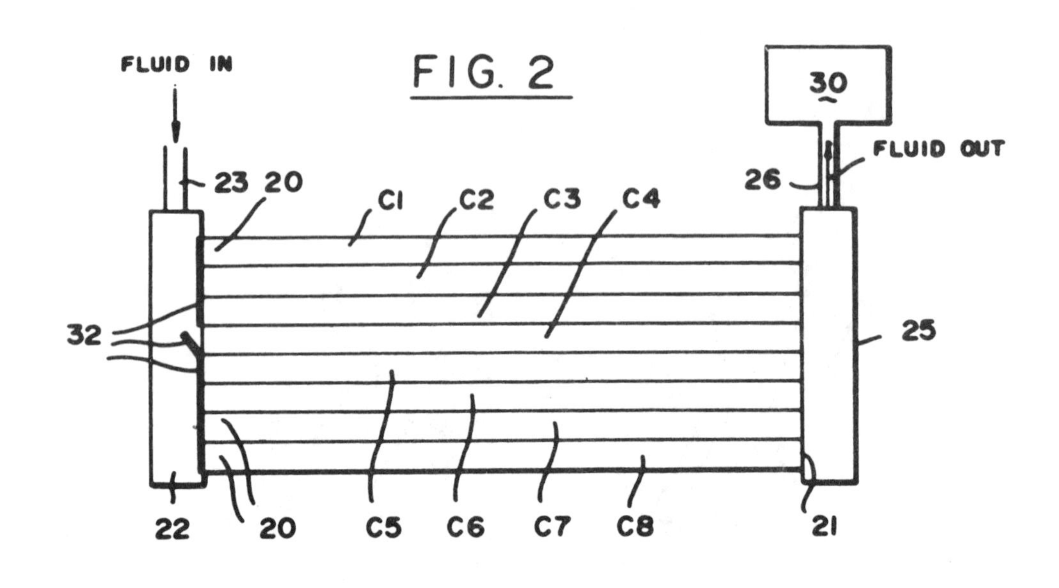

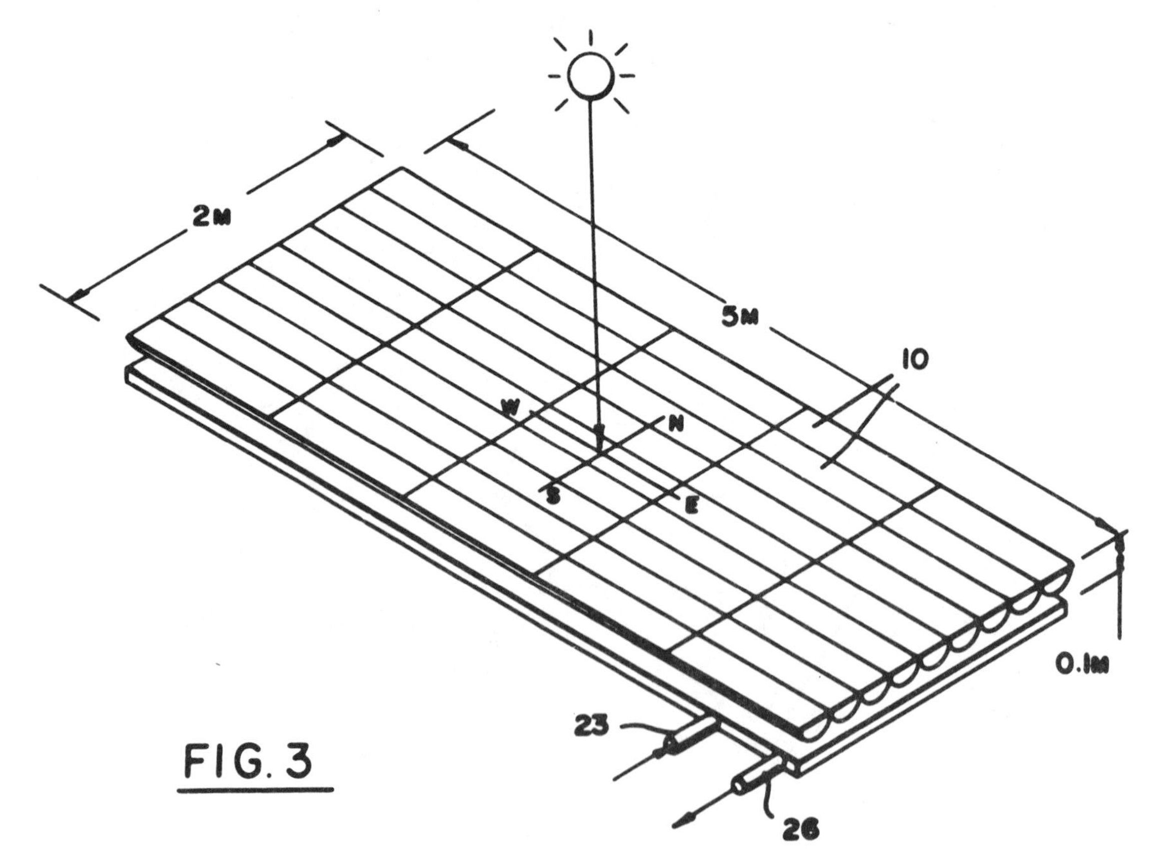

U.S. Patent Oct. 28, 1975 * 3,915,148

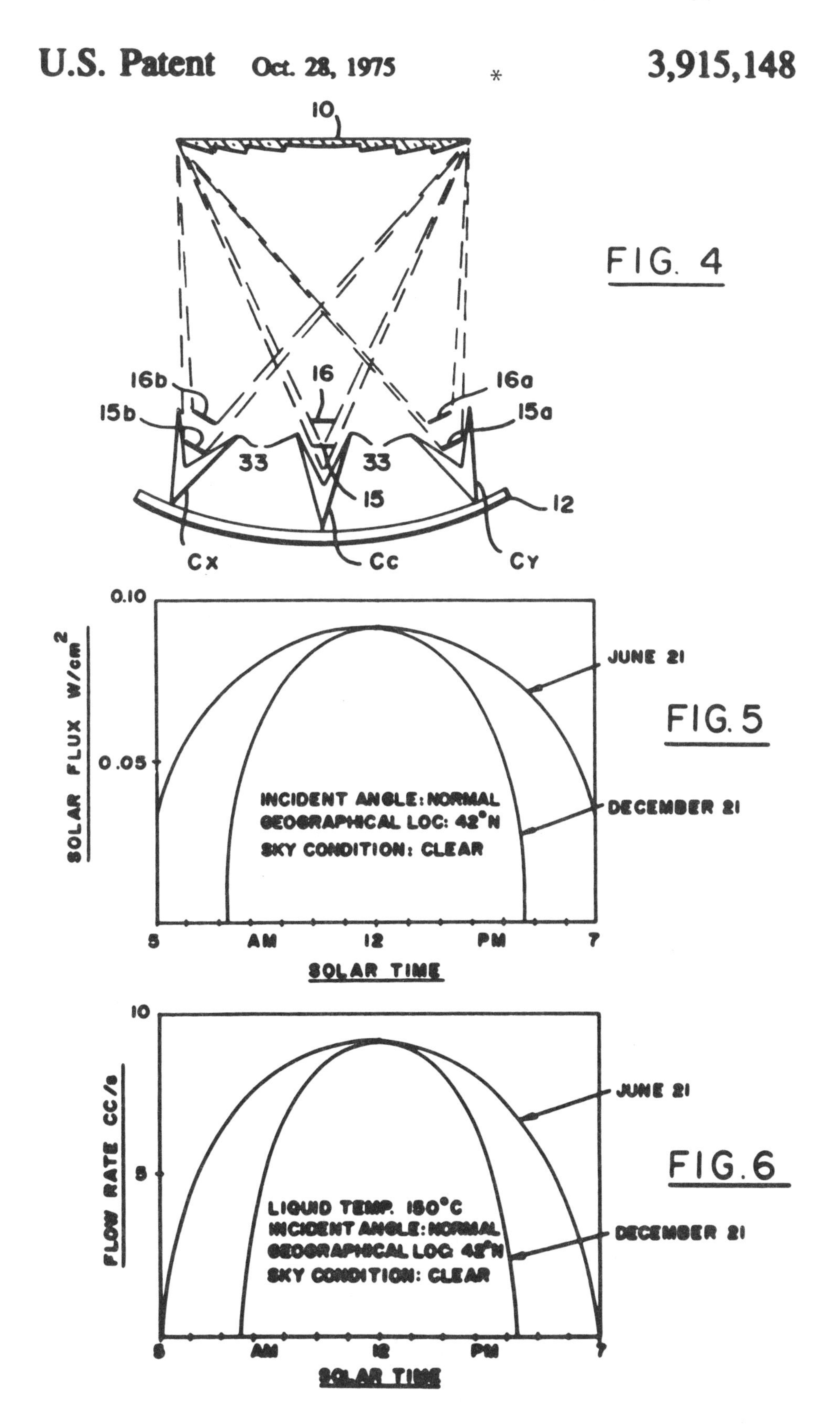

FIG. 4

FIG. 5

FIG. 6

Inventors: **James C. Fletcher**, Administrator of the National Aeronautics and Space Administation, with respect to an invention of **Katsunori Shimada**, Pasadena, Calif.

* **ABSTRACT**

A solar energy concentrator comprises an array of cylindrical Fresnel lenses, all of which are fixedly aligned in the East-West direction. Each lens concentrates the sun rays and forms a line image which extends in the East-West direction. Located below the lenses are individual fluid channels which extend in the East-West direction and are spaced apart in the South-North direction. Each line image focuses onto preferably not more than two of the channels which absorb heat of the concentrated sun rays. Each channel has a thermostatically controlled valve which controls fluid flow through the channel to take place only when the channel's temperature and/or the fluid therein exceed a threshold temperature level. *

THERMOSTATICALLY CONTROLLED NON-TRACKING TYPE SOLAR ENERGY CONCENTRATOR

ORIGIN OF INVENTION

The invention described herein was made in the performance of work under a NASA contract and is subject to the provisions of Section 305 of the National Aeronautics and Space Act of 1958, Public Law 85-568 (72 Stat. 435; 42 USC 2457).

BACKGROUND OF THE INVENTION

1. Field of the Invention:

The present invention relates to solar energy concentrators and, more particularly, to a thermostatically controlled non-tracking solar energy concentrator.

2. Description of the Prior Art:

There are many devices which have been developed to extract thermal energy from solar energy or light. These devices are essentially collectors, which are adapted to absorb the thermal component of the solar energy, to heat a fluid, e.g., water. Without the use of some type of concentrator, the temperature to which the water can be raised is generally quite low, so that efficient use of the collected energy is not attainable. Thus, most of the useful devices employ some type of concentrator, and are generally referred to as solar energy concentrators.

In order to increase energy collection efficiency most prior-art concentrators are of the tracking type. They employ a tracking mechanism in order to track the sun movement which changes with time of day and season of the year. These tracking mechanisms are quite expensive, since they require costly pivoting and rocking assemblies and power for operating them, thereby increasing the initial concentrator cost. Also, since these tracking mechanisms include moving parts additional costs are incurred for maintenance and repair. Thus, a need exists for a new solar energy concentrator which exhibits relatively high efficiency, i.e., efficient thermal energy collection, yet does not include a tracking mechanism.

OBJECTS AND SUMMARY OF THE INVENTION

It is an object of the present invention to provide a new efficient solar energy concentrator.

Another object of the invention is to provide a new non-tracking type solar energy concentrator.

A further object of the invention is to provide a relatively new efficient solar energy concentrator which eliminates the need for a tracking mechanism.

These and other objects of the invention are achieved by providing a solar energy concentrator in which solar energy is concentrated by means of an array of cylindrical Fresnel lenses all of which are fixedly positioned and aligned in the East-West direction. Located below the array of lenses is a stationary array of collector elements through which fluid, e.g., water to be heated, is capable of flowing. The collector elements are also aligned in the East-West direction. Fluid flow through each collector element is controlled by a valve which enables fluid to flow therethrough only when the element's temperature exceeds a selected threshold temperature level.

Each lens concentrates the solar light forming an image which extends in the East-West direction, parallel to the lens length. The width of the image in the South-North direction depends on the lens width in this direction and the concentration ratio provided by the lens. Hereinafter the image will be referred to as a line image. The collectors are arranged so that regardless of the sun angle, which due to sun movement changes with time of day and season of the year, the line image produced by each lens focuses on very few, preferably not more than two of the collector elements.

The novel features of the invention are set forth with particularity in the appended claims. The invention will best be understood from the following description when read in conjunction with the accompanying drawings.

BRIEF DESCRIPTION OF THE DRAWINGS

FIG. **1** is an isometric diagram useful in explaining the basic principles of the invention;

FIGS. **2** and **3** are diagrams related to an array arrangement;

FIG. **4** is a diagram showing variations of the arrangement shown in FIG. **1**; and

FIGS. **5** and **6** are diagrams of curves of solar flux and flow rates, respectively.

DESCRIPTION OF THE PREFERRED EMBODIMENTS

Attention is first directed to FIG. **1** wherein a single cylindrical Fresnel lens **10** is shown, with its flat planar surface **10***a* assumed to face upwardly, so as to face the sun. The lens **10** is fixedly aligned in the East-West (E-W) direction. That is, the lens is located with its long side or length in the E-W direction and its width in the South-North (S-N) direction. Located below the multifaceted side **10*b*** of the lens **10** is a plurality of stationary collector elements, which for explanatory purposes, are limited to eight and are designated by **C1-C8.** The collector elements are supported by a support structure **12,** which is preferably a good thermal insulator. Each of the collector elements is actually a channel through which fluid can flow. Therefore, hereinafter the terms collector element and fluid channel may be used interchangeably.

As shown in FIG. **1,** the collector elements, which together define a heat absorber **14,** are also aligned in the E-W direction. Each is shown V-shaped. That is, its cross-section, in a direction perpendicular to its length is in the shape of a V. The tips of the elements are interconnected so that the V-shaped top surfaces **13** of the elements define a top corrugated surface **14*a*** of the heat absorber. The elements are parallel to one another and are spaced along the S-N direction.

As is appreciated, the sun angle with respect to any horizontal plane, such as surface **10*a*** of lens **10** changes with the seasons of the year. Also, during any given day, as the sun moves from the East to the West, the sun angle changes somewhat by a few degrees. However, for all practical purposes during any given day the sun movement from a few hours preceding and following the noon hour can be thought of as taking place in a common plane. One such plane is designated in FIG. **1** by **P1**, which for explanatory purposes only is shown to be perpendicular to surface **10*a*.** Therein, S_M, S_A, and S_P represent sun positions at the meridian, before noon, and after noon.

Irrespective of the sun position in plane **P1** the lens **10** concentrates the sun rays and forms a line image thereof. In FIG. **1,** numeral **15** designates the line image formed when the sun is at position S_M, i.e., at the meridian. As the sun moves from the meridian a line image is also produced, but at a reduced focal distance from the lens, i.e., closer to the lens and farther away from the fluid channels. Numeral **16** designates the line image for the sun positions S_A and S_P.

The width of the line image in the S-N direction depends on the concentration ratio, provided by the lens **10** and its width in the S-N direction. For explanatory purposes, a concentration ratio of 10:1 is assumed for lens **10.** To simplify the drawings, line images **15** and **16** are shown of minimum width, i.e. as dots in the S-N direction rather than as short lines of widths (1/10)W, where W represents the lens width in the S-N direction.

In FIG. **1, P2** and **P3** designate two other planes in which the sun is assumed to move during different seasons of the year. Three sun positions in plane P2 are designated by S'_M, S'_A and S'_P and three similar positions in P3 are designated by S''_M, S''_A and S''_P. When the sun is in plane P2, line images **15*a*** and **16 *a*** are formed which, as shown in FIG. **1,** focus the concentrated sun rays on elements C7 and C8, which are to the right or North of Element C4. On the other hand, when the sun moves in plane P3, line images **15*b*** and **16*b*** are formed which concentrate the sun rays and focus them on elements C2 and/or C1, which are to the left or South of element C4. Thus, the only effect of the sun angle variations is a shift of the location of the line image in the S-N direction. As a result, the sun rays are focused onto different ones of the collectors which are spaced in the S-N direction.

From the foregoing, it should thus be seen that in accordance with the present invention, the cylindrical Fresnel lens is fixedly placed in the E-W direction. Also placed in the same direction are a plurality of collector elements which are spaced apart in the S-N direction. The elements are shaped and spaced apart from each other and the lens so that the sun rays, concentrated by the lens as a line image, are focused on a minimum number of elements, generally not more than two, irrespective of the sun angle which varies with time of day and seasons of the year. This is achieved with both the lens **10** and the collector elements being in fixed stationary positions. Thus, the concentrator of the present invention is of the non-tracking type. In the present invention, sun movement is accounted for by providing a plurality of fluid channels, spaced in the S-N direction.

As previously pointed out, each collector element is one through which fluid is adapted to flow. In accordance with the present invention, each of the collectors has a thermostatically controlled valve associated therewith. These valves permit fluid to flow only through the channel or channels on which the sun rays are focused and whose temperature exceeds a selected threshold temperature level.

As shown in FIG. **2,** the inlet ends **20** of channels **C1-C8** are shown connected to a common inlet manifold **22** into which fluid to be heated enters from an appropriate source (not shown) through conduit **23.** The outlet ends **21** of the channels are connected to a common outlet manifold **25** from which the heated fluid flows through a conduit **26** to any appropriate utilization device **30.** Associated with each channel is a separate thermostatically controlled valve **32.** Each valve is generally in the closed position. It opens to enable the fluid to flow through its associated channel only when the latter's temperature exceeds the selected threshold temperature level. Thus, the valves control fluid flow to take place only in the channel or channels which are heated by the solar energy to a temperature above the threshold level. In FIG. **2** all the valves **32,** except for the valve **32** associated with channel **C4,** are in the closed position, representing a case in which only the temperature of C4 exceeds the threshold temperature level. In such a case, the fluid entering inlet manifold **22** flows only through the heated channel C4 and the heated fluid exiting the channel C4 passes to the utilization device **30** through manifold **25** and conduit **26.** Thus, even though fluid can flow through all the channels, it is limited only to those whose temperature exceeds the threshold temperature level.

Although the invention was described in conjunction with a single lens **10,** in practice a plurality of such lenses are arranged in an array of a desired surface area, with all the lenses in the E-W direction. One example of such an array is shown in FIG. **3.** It is assumed to be 5m long in the E-W direction and 2m wide in the S-N direction. Assuming each lens to be 1m long and 10cm wide, 100 lenses are required. Also, assuming that each lens has an f number of about 1.0 to 1.5, the image of the sun at the meridian will be located at about 10–15cm from the lens. With a lens width of 10cm and a concentration ratio of 10:1, it will be about 1cm wide in the S-N direction. The lens focal distance, i.e., the image distance from the lens will decrease as the sun moves from the meridian.

With present day technology such lenses can be made from molded plastic to have good efficiency and durability. They can be made quite thin, on the order of 1–2mm thick, even with relatively short focal length. Since a concentration ratio of 10:1 and an *f* number on the order of 1 to 1.5 are assumed, it can be shown from physical optics calculations that it corresponds to an angular precision of 5° in ray direction. Therefore, the usual lens design considerations, including chromatic aberration, off-axis aberration (i.e., solar declination) and precision of fabrication will not present any problems. Thus, the lenses can be made quite inexpensively, with relatively wide fabrication tolerances.

Based on basic physical optics calculations, it can be shown that with a Fresnel lens with a marginal element of apex angle 30°, which corresponds to a marginal element of f/1.5 lens, a concentration ratio of 10:1 is attainable for declination angles of up to 30° from the meridian, which corresponds to 2 hours before and after the sun is at the meridian. This is for the case with flat face **10***a* of the lens pointing upwardly, as shown in FIG. **1.** With the multifaceted side **10***b* pointing toward the sun and the flat side **10***a* toward the channels, the concentration of 10:1 is attained for declination angles of up to 45° from the meridian which corresponds to 3 hours before and after the sun is at the meridian. In FIG. **1,** the declination angles before and after the meridian position in plane **P1** are designated by α_1 and α_2, respectively.

The spacing or distance between the channels and the lenses of course depends on the focal distance of the lenses. In FIG. **1,** the channels are shown below the image lines **15** and **16,** i.e., at a distance greater than the lenses' focal distance. In practice, the channels are located so that the concentrated rays, regardless of declination angle, are intercepted by a minimum number of channels which may be located either ahead or beyond the image plane, i.e., the plane where the image is formed. With an assumed image width of 1cm the tips of each channel should preferably be spaced apart not less and preferably more than 1cm. The tips of the channels are designated in FIG. **1** by numerals **33.** The number of channels which need be associated with each lens depends on the width (in the S-N direction) of each channel and the extent of the shift of the image in the S-N direction as the sun angle changes with the seasons of the year.

In FIg. **1,** all the channels are shown with their tips **33** above the image plane of any of the image lines formed by the lens **10.** Also, all the channels are shown with their tips in a plane parallel to the flat surface **10***a* of the lens and in addition the channels are shown of equal widths, i.e., equal spacing between their tips **33.** Such an arrangement is shown for explanatory purposes only. In order to minimize the number of channels on which the concentrated rays focus or impinge, an arrangement as shown in FIG. **4** may be employed. As shown therein, the channels may be supported on a curved rather than flat support member **12.** Also, the tips **33** may be closer to the lens so that some of the line images, such as **15, 15***a* and **15***b* are formed beyond the channels' tips. In FIG. **4,** the images are shown as short lines in the S-N direction rather than as points, as in FIG. **1.** As appreciated, the widths of these lines are 1/**10** of the lens width for a concentration ratio of 10:1.

Also, the channels may be of variable widths. As shown in FIG. **1,** for the sun in either planes **P2** and **P3** the concentrated rays are assumed to be absorbed by at least two channels, such as **C1** and **C2** for the sun in plane **P3** and channels **C7** and **C8** for the sun in plane **P2.** If desired, the outer channels designated C_x and C_y in Fig. **4** may be wider than the width of the center channel C_c, thereby reducing the number of channels receiving the concentrated rays when the sun is at other than in a plane **P1** perpendicular to the lens surface. With the channel arrangement of FIG. **1,** the maximum number of channels on which the concentrated rays are focused may be limited to three even with channel width of not less than the image width. With the channel arrangement of FIG. **4,** the maximum number may be reduced to two. It should also be pointed out that the lens **10** needs to be placed with its flat surface **10***a* in a horizontal tip. In practice, it may be tipped so that during the particular season when highest efficiency is desired, the sun would be moving in a perpendicular plane and its associated rays absorbed by preferably one channel.

The use of the V-shaped channels is believed to be advantageous for several reasons. In such a channel the area of the channel opening defined by the distance between the tips **33** times the length is considerably less than the total area of the top or upper surface **13,** thereby reducing the reradiation losses area. Also, each channel can be welded to adjacent channels only at its two tips and to the support member **12** at its apex point, thereby reducing the area of contact through which heat from the heated channel is conductable to adjacent elements. If desired, the space between the lens and the channels and/or the spaces between the lower sides of the channels and the support member **12** may be evacuated to reduce the convection of heat from the heated channel. Furthermore, the spaces between the channels and support member **12** may be packed with insulating material. Any and all of these approaches may be used to reduce heat losses and thereby maximize the amount of heat which is received by each channel to heat the fluid passing therethrough.

The surfaces **13** of the channels which are exposable to the concentrated sun rays should preferably be covered with an infrared (IR) selective coating in order to reduce IR reradiation, and thereby increase the thermal energy absorbed by the channels from the concentrated rays for delivery to the fluid flowing through the heated channel. Various IR selective coatings for such a purpose are available commercially. They include silicon carbide and combinations of molybdenum and silicon oxides.

It should be appreciated that the working fluid need not be limited to water. It can include ethylene glycol, pressurized water or other organic compounds. The utilization device **30** to which the heated fluid is supplied may be any system in which heated fluid is utilized. For example, the heated fluid may be directed to heat exchangers to provide domestic or commercial heating or hot water, or for effecting refrigerative cooling or operating heat engines for electricity generation. Since the ultimate use of the heated fluid is not part of this invention it will not be described in any detail.

As previously pointed out, each channel has at least one valve **32** associated therewith, to control fluid to flow through the channel only when its temperature exceeds a desired level. The valve may be one with a bimetallic snap action element with two positions, one stable when hot and the other when cold. Alternately, a valve which proportionately controls fluid rate as a function of temperature may be used to maintain the desired output temperature of the fluid. Also, each valve may be mounted to be influenced directly by the solar energy striking the outside of the channel surface as well as by the actual temperature of the fluid in the heated channel.

It can be shown that at 42°N latitude under clear sky conditions conversion efficiency of the order of about 60% is achievable with a lens with a transmission coefficient β=.9, a channel with an equivalent absorptivity α=.9, and a concentration factor γ=10. The power received by the heat absorber **14** may be defined as P_i and expressed as

$$P_i = \alpha\beta p_{in}A, \qquad (1)$$

where p_{in} is the solar flux in w/cm² and A is the area of the receiver facing the sun. In FIG. **3**, A is assumed to be 10m² = 10⁵cm². The received power p_i is equal to the power removed by the fluid, represented by P_o, plus the losses due to reradiation P_r, structural conduction P_c and convection P_{cv}. That is,

$$P_i = P_o + P_r + P_c + P_{cv} = P_o + P_L, \qquad (2)$$

where P_L is the total power loss. It is reasonable to estimate P_L to equal 1.5 times the reradiation loss P_r from one active channel surface at a temperature of T + 273°K. Thus, one obtains that

$$P_L = 1.5e(5.670\times10^{-12})\ (T+273)^4\gamma A \qquad (3)$$

where e is the infrared emissivity and γA is the area on which the sun's image is formed and from which reradiation takes place.

Substituting expressions 1 and 3 in expression 2, one obtains,

$$\alpha\beta p_{in}A = P_o + 1.5e(5.670\times10^{-12})\ (T+273)^4\gamma A \qquad (4)$$

Thus, the output power per unit of the collector area is

$$P_o/A = \alpha\beta p_{in} - 1.5e\gamma\ (5.670\times10^{-12})\ (T+273)^4 \qquad (5)$$

and the efficiency can be expressed as

$$\eta = \frac{P_o}{p_{in}A} = \alpha\beta - \frac{1.5e\gamma\ (5.670\times10^{-12})\ (T+273)^4}{P_{in}} \qquad (6)$$

Assuming an infrared emissivity e=.9 for a case without special IR coating on the outer surfaces **13** of the channels and a channel temperature of T=150°C with an adjusted flow rate to obtain such a temperature, and further assuming p_{in} = **0.1**w/cm², representing one solar constant

$$\eta = .9 \times .9 - \frac{1.5\times0.9\times0.9(5.670\times10^{-12})(150+273)^4}{1}$$

$$\cong .81 - .24 \cong .57 \text{ or } 57\%$$

It is of interest to derive the relationship between the fluid temperature and flow rate. In addition to water possible choices of the fluid among others are water with a boiling temperature higher than 300°C, i.e., pressurized water, ethylene glycol, or other orgainic compounds. Let the removed power in watts be

$$P_o = 4.18 \times (T-30) \times V \qquad (7)$$

where V is the flow rate in cc/s, and T the final temperature. The number **30** represents an assumed inlet temperature. Substituting expression (7) in expression (4) with T=150°C, one obtains

$$.9 \times .9 \times p_{in} \times 10^5 = 4.18(150-30)V + 1.5e(5.670\times10^{-12})\ (150+273)^4 \times .1 \times 10^5 \qquad (8)$$

Assuming that e=.9 and using FIG. 5 which is a plot of the diurnal variation of solar flux at 42°N latitude which is available from the U.S. Weather Bureau, one can derive the flow rate at 150°C for different times of day and seasons of the year. The derived flow rates are shown in FIG. **6.** In FIG. **6** it is seen that a minimum flow rate of 3cc/s, equaling 2.38gal/h, at 150°C is obtainable for approximately 8 hours per day during the winter (December 21) and for approximately 12.6 hours per day during the summer (June 21), provided the sky is clear. Integrating the flow rates under the curves the total output at 150°C per day can be shown to equal about 47.5 gallons on December 21 and 76 gallons on June 21. The corresponding energy deliveries are 24.6kW-h and 39.3kW-h, respectively. When compared with the integrated power input under the curves of FIG. **5** it is seen that even without the IR coating reasonable output power is obtainable, due to the relatively high concentrator efficiency. With the selective coating even higher efficiencies are achievable. This should be apparent from equation (8) since with the IR coating e=.1 can be assumed rather than e=.9, used in deriving the flow rates shown in FIG. **6.**

Fresnel lenses with a concentration ratio of 10:1 (γ=.1) and a transmission coefficient β=.9 are easily attainable. Also, the channels due to their V-shaped cross section can be produced with an equivalent absorptivity of α=.9. Thus, the novel concentrator of the present invention can be produced to provide relatively high efficiency without the use of any tracking mechanism. Also, IR coatings are presently available with which the channels' IR emissivity e can be made to be quite small, e.g., e=.1.

April 17, 1962 YOSHIMATSU OKUDA 3,029,806

SOLAR HOT WATER HEATER

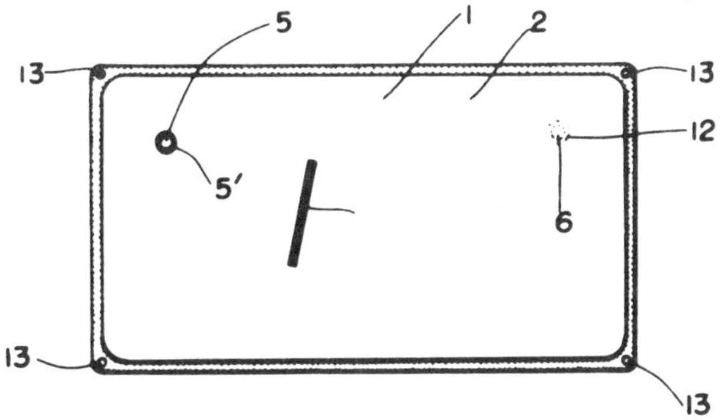

Fig. 1.

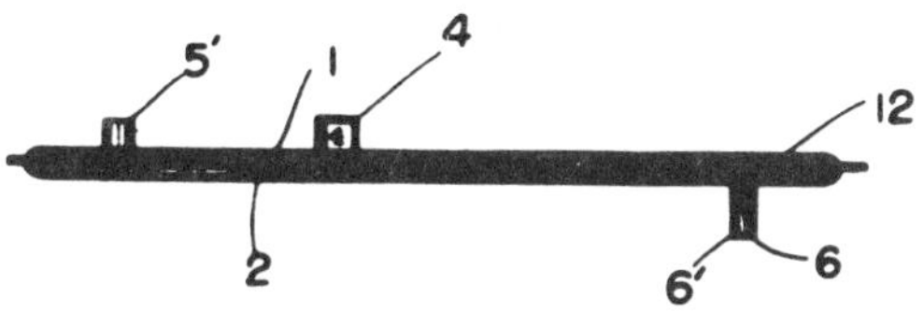

Fig. 2

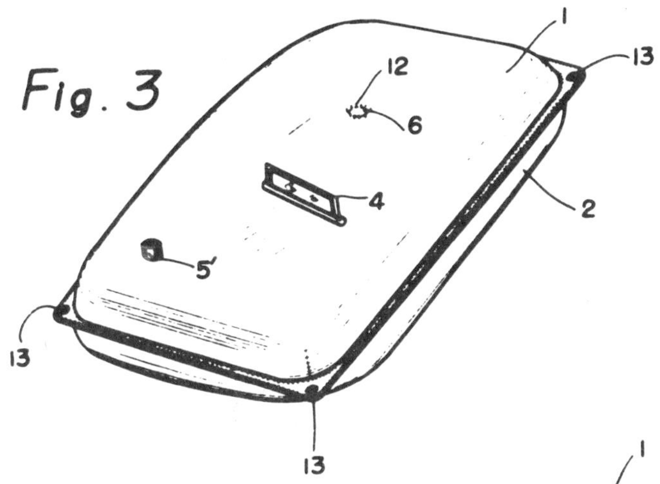

Fig. 3

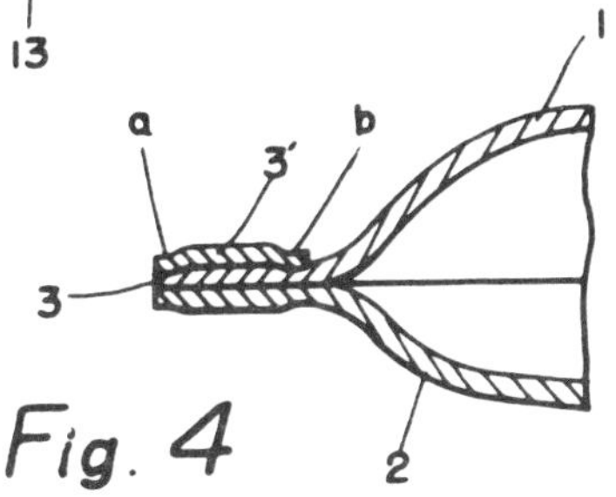

Fig. 4

INVENTOR
YOSHIMATSU OKUDA
BY
ATTORNEY

April 17, 1962 YOSHIMATSU OKUDA 3,029,806

SOLAR HOT WATER HEATER

* *

Fig. 6

10 8 1 11 15 11 14 7 9

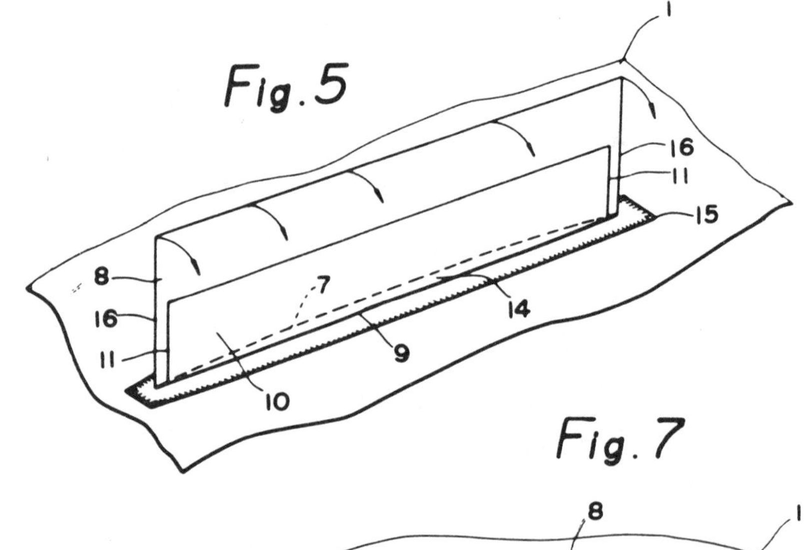

Fig. 7

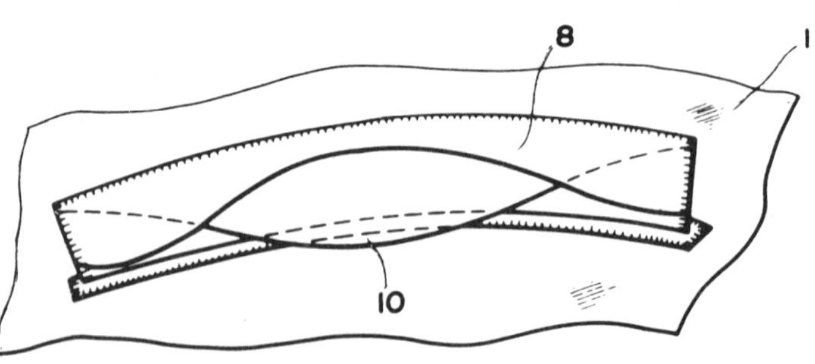

INVENTOR
YOSHIMATSU OKUDA
BY
ATTORNEY

April 17, 1962 YOSHIMATSU OKUDA 3,029,806

SOLAR HOT WATER HEATER

* *

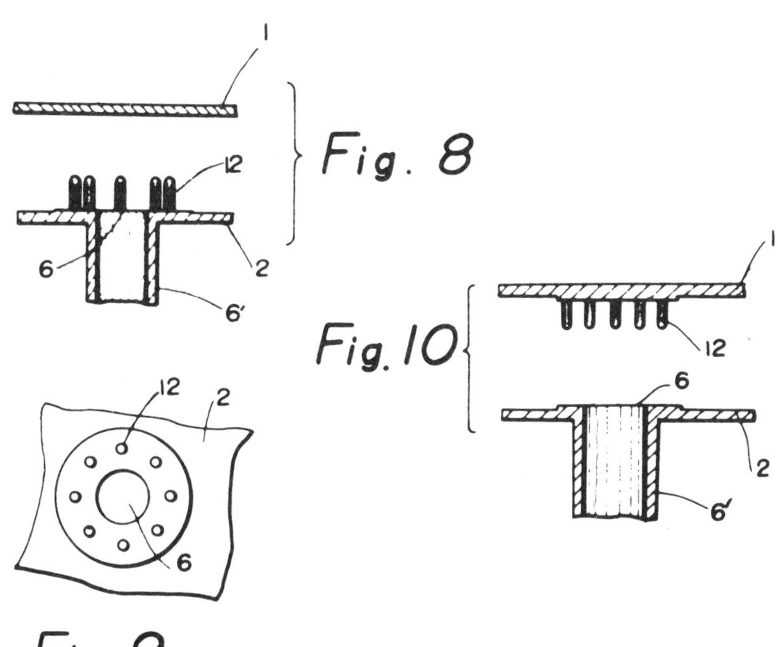

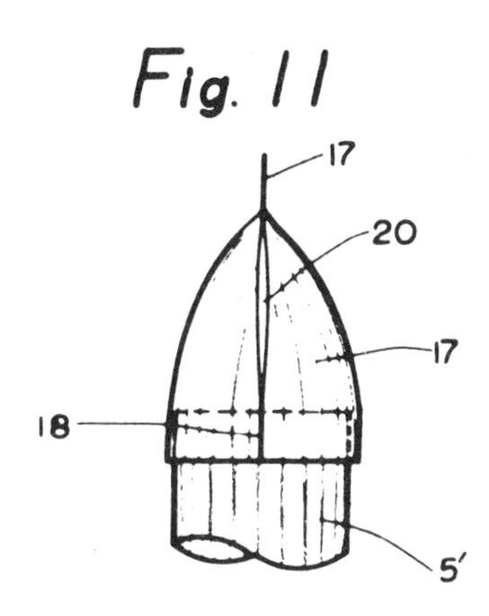

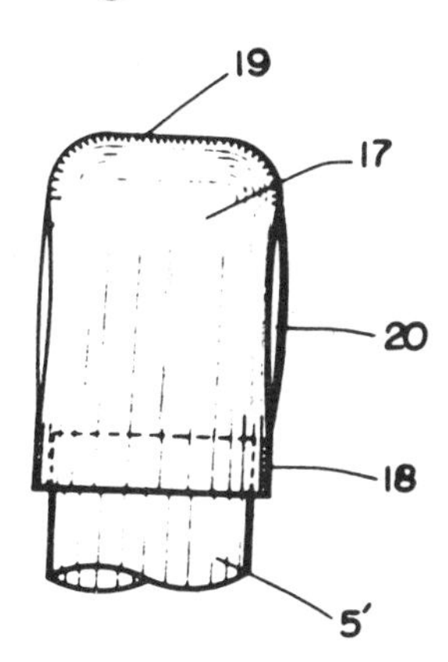

INVENTOR
YOSHIMATSU OKUDA
BY
ATTORNEY

3,029,806
SOLAR HOT WATER HEATER

Yoshimatsu Okuda, 143 3-chome Koshienguchi, Nishinomiya-shi, Hyogo-ken, Japan

*

This invention relates to a solar heat hot water heater. Of the hot water heaters that are installed in the open and by utilizing the solar heat rays hot water is obtained, that is, a so-called solar hot water heater, the invention relates in particular to a novel solar hot water heater in which all of its members are constituted of a soft plastic, such as polyvinyl chloride, in which the special technical problems that arise from the uniqueness of the material used have been solved.

The solar hot water heaters that have been heretofore known are either those in which the interior surfaces of a tank made of wood or metal were painted black for absorbing the rays of the sun, to which glass covers were fitted, or those in which several pipes whose outside surfaces were painted black were connected together. These, however, were either heavy in weight and required for their installation much labor and a large amount of expense or had the defect as would permit the ready admittance of dust into the hot water.

An object of this invention is to provide a solar hot water heater from which such a defect as this of the conventional heaters has been removed, and which is light in weight as to be easily installed.

Another object of the invention is to provide a solar hot water heater made of soft plastic which is not just merely light in weight but has been reinforced such that it possesses sufficient strength to withstand the water pressure that is exerted when in use.

Still another object is the provision of a solar hot water heater made of soft plastic which possesses a structure capable of preventing the admittance of dust by making as small as possible that part in which the water is exposed to the atmosphere, while on the other hand, providing for means as will not prevent on account of the aforesaid structure the cleaning of the interior of the hot water heater.

A further object of the invention is to provide a solar hot water heater made of soft plastic in which a spacing means has been provided to ensure that the discharge of water is not stopped on account of the negative pressure that occurs in the vicinity of the water outlet during discharge of water.

In the accompanying drawings, a preferred embodiment of the invention is illustrated, wherein:

FIG. 1 is a top plan view of one example of a solar hot water heater in accordance with the present invention;

FIG. 2 is a side elevation thereof;

FIG. 3 is a perspective view of the hot water heater when filled with water;

FIG. 4 is an enlarged sectional view showing in detail the sealed part;

FIG. 5 is a perspective view of the construction of the opening for cleaning;

FIG. 6 is a perspective view showing the state wherein the opening for cleaning has been closed;

FIG. 7 is a perspective view showing the above opening in its opened state;

FIG. 8 is an enlarged fragmentary side elevation showing in detail the spacing means;

FIG. 9 is a top plan view of the above spacing means;

FIG. 10 is a side elevation illustrating a modification of said spacing means;

FIG. 11 is a side elevation of the overflow outlet cap; and

FIG. 12 is a front elevation of the above overflow outlet cap.

Now, while referring to the drawings the present invention will be described. As shown in FIGS. 1 to 3, the solar hot water heater in accordance with this invention consists of a soft, transparent plastic top sheet **1** provided with an opening for cleaning **4** and an overflow outlet **5** and a bottom sheet **2** of a soft plastic, which is black in color, provided with a water supply and discharge port **6**, which top and bottom sheets are sealed threefoldly at the perimetric edge **3**. And as shown in FIG. 3 when water is supplied from the supply port **6** when being used, it swells up like a water pillow or a bag-shaped water tank. Since the sealed portion at the perimetric edge **3** is easily ruptured by water pressure, in the present invention, as shown in FIG. 4, the top sheet **1** and the bottom sheet **2** are placed one on top of the other and a strip-like sheet **3'** is further superposed, and the thus three-deckered sheets are sealed together at points *a* and *b* by means of high frequency heat sealing. By thus doing, the thinning of the sheets during heat sealing is prevented, and the tank is reinforced along its entire perimeter. Needless to say, the top sheet **1** and the bottom sheet **2** must not only be such that they can withstand the water pressure but also must be capable of withstanding the heat of the sun as well as hot water. While for this purpose polyvinyl chloride is the most suitable material, those which consist of two or more sheets bonded together are still more suitable. The solar hot water heater of the present invention using such a material and having its perimeter three foldly sealed and reinforced as above can withstand a pressure of 0.7–0.8 atmosphere with the temperature of hot water at 50° C. Hence, there is no possibility of an accident occurring as a result of its bursting under normal conditions of use as a solar hot water heater. The holes **13** provided in the four corners are for passing ropes through for installing and securing the hot water heater.

The opening for cleaning **4** has been provided for the purpose of removing the slime and algoid growths that deposit and adhere to the inside surface of the bag-like water tank during its use over a long period of time. Thus it is possible to keep the tank clean at all times. The details of it are shown in FIGS. 5 to 7. As shown in FIG. 5, a slit **14** at least large enough to permit the entry of a hand is first made at a suitable location in substantially the middle part of the top sheet **1**. And after having provided, if necessary, a reinforcing washer **15**, a tongue piece **8** is attached to an edge **7** of the slit **14** and a tongue piece **10** to the other edge **9** thereof. The length of the tongue piece **8** is about 1.2 to 1.8 times that of the tongue piece **10**. That portion of the tongue piece **8** in excess is folded over in the arrow direction, and both side edges **11** of the tongue **10** and both side edges **16** of the tongue **8** as well as the folded edge of the tongue piece **8** are heat sealed. Thus, as shown in FIG. 6, by the tongue piece **8** which extends from one edge **7** of the slit **14** assuming the form wherein it envelopes the tongue piece **10** extending from the other edge **9** in the bag-like portion formed by heat sealing of the folded over portion at its both side edges, the opening for cleaning **4** is constituted. Since the construction of the opening for cleaning of the hot water heater is as hereinabove described, it is readily opened by passing of the tongue piece **10** under the bag cover **8**, and cleaning of the inside surface can be performed by inserting the hand from this opening.

In the top sheet **1** there is also provided an overflow outlet **5** at a suitable location. The overflow outlet **5** is for allowing the excess water to flow out from here when the bag-like water tank of the solar hot water heater of the present invention becomes full of water. As shown in FIGS. 1 to 3, a cylindrical tube **5'** is attached here. By suitably regulating the length of this overflow tube **5'** the amount of water that is to be put into the water tank may be regulated. There is however the possibility that dust might enter from this opening into the water tank as to contaminate or pollute the hot water. Hence, preferably a cap **17** such as is shown in FIGS. 11 and 12 should be provided. This cap **17** is made by superposing two sheets of soft plastic of the same material as that of the sheet **1** and heat sealing that part **18** which fits over the overflow tube **5'** and also the summit part **19**. By doing thus, that part which has not been heat sealed forms a slit **20** from which the excess water overflows.

In lieu of providing an overflow outlet such as above, it is possible to have the aforesaid opening for cleaning **4** perform also the function of an overflow outlet. Precisely, while the opening for cleaning is in its normal state maintained in a closed state as in FIG. 6, when the water tank becomes filled with water, on account of the pressure exerted it opens up naturally as in FIG. 7. Thus, it is seen that by opening up in this manner it can be utilized as an overflow outlet.

In the bottom sheet **2** there is provided a water supply and discharge port **6**, which functions both as the supply inlet for supplying water to the water tank as well as the discharge outlet for the discharge of water therefrom. To this port, a water supply and discharge pipe **6'** is connected. Instead of having one pipe performing both the functions of supplying as well as discharging water, it is possible to provide two. For example, a water supply inlet may be provided in the top sheet **1** separately from the discharge port, as described above.

Inasmuch as the hot water heater of the present invention is constituted of soft sheets, there is the tendency of the top sheet **1** being sucked towards the water discharge port **6** due to the negative pressure occurring in the vicinity of the water discharge port during discharge of water. Thus the discharge of water, in some cases, becomes impossible on account of the top and bottom sheets coming in close contact with each other. In order to remove such a trouble as this, in accordance with the present invention, a spacing means **12** may also be provided. In FIGS. 8 and 9 can be seen as this spacing means the provision of a number of verrucose projections **12** around the water discharge port **6** of the bottom sheet **2**. On the other hand, in FIG. 10 verrucose projections **2** facing downwards are provided annularly in the top sheet in a location opposite the water discharge port **6**. In either of these cases, even if a negative pressure does occur in the vicinity of the water discharge port **6** and the top sheet **1** is sucked towards the port, the coming into close adherence of the top and bottom sheets would be prevented, and thus it is apparent that the water discharge port will not be closed. The spacing means is not to be limited to such verrucose projections as this, and any and all equivalents capable of producing the same results can all be used.

While I have shown and described a preferred embodiment of my invention, it will be understood that it is not to be limited to all of the details shown, but is capable of modification and variation within the spirit of the invention and within the scope of the claims. *

PATENTED OCT 15 1974

3,841,302

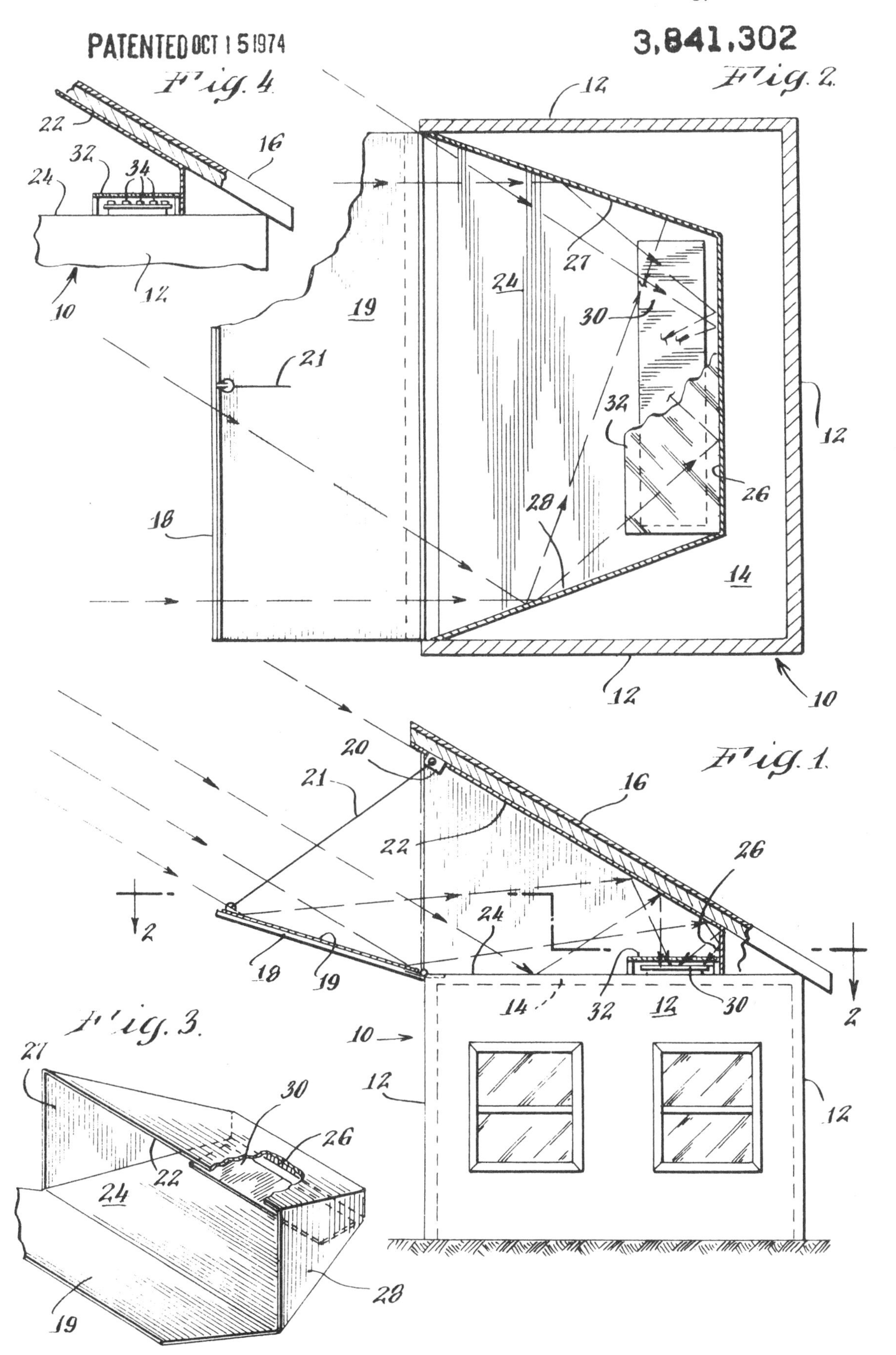

Solar Energy Applications for the Home

Inventor: **Gerald Falbel,** Stamford, Conn.

Assignee: **Wormser Scientific Corporation,** Stamford, Conn.

* **ABSTRACT**

A solar energy system is provided in which a solar collector is positioned inside what would be the attic under a conventional roof of a building. The inside surfaces of the roof rafters and top surfaces of the ceiling joists are utilized to mount reflective surfaces thereon to reflect and focus incoming rays from the sun onto a small collector mounted on the ceiling joists of the structure. These reflective surfaces mounted in the attic form a pyramidal reflector which focuses the sun's rays onto the collector. A movable hinged reflective panel which forms the base of the pyramidal reflector when closed is opened and closed by a geared electric motor. This movable reflective panel is opened when the sun is out, and may be closed when it is cloudy, or at nighttime. It may also be positioned at an optimum angle, depending upon the elevation angle of the sun. The solar collector may be utilized to heat a medium for providing a heating and hot water system for the structure, as well as providing cooling and/or air conditioning, and/or may include solar cells for generating electricity from the collected sun's rays. *

SOLAR ENERGY SYSTEM FOR A BUILDING

BACKGROUND OF THE INVENTION

This invention relates to a solar energy system for a building, and more particularly to such a system associated with a building or structure to be heated and/or cooled, and/or provided with electrical power by solar energy.

The use of solar energy for heating a structure has been utilized in many forms, including applicant's U.S. Pat. No. 3,179,105 entitled "Off-Axis Focused Solar Heater" which discusses some of the problems involved in the solar heating of a structure. Until the present energy crisis, solar heating, or the generation of electricity from the sun's rays for supplementing the energy supply of a building has not been economically competitive, due to the ready availability of cheap energy sources. Spiraling energy costs and shortages now make solar energy utilization in residential and commercial structures more economically competitive. Even if economically competitive under present changing conditions, many of the prior art systems for converting the sun's energy into heat required large collectors or reflectors which were continually exposed to the elements and could thereby degrade with time or become useless when snow covered. Many such systems also required special expensive structural changes in buildings to accommodate the solar collectors and/or reflective systems for gathering the sun's energy and applying it to a collector on which it could be converted into heat or electrical energy. Many of these structural features to accommodate the collecting and focusing of the sun's rays on a collector were prohibitively expensive and/or unsightly.

Accordingly, it is an object of this invention to provide a new and improved solar energy system for a building which utilizes a standard roof construction in a building, therefore not requiring any special structure or structural changes in a building's external appearance or aesthetics, to collect the solar energy.

A further object of this invention to provide a new and improved solar energy system for a building in which the reflector for collecting and focusing the sun's rays for producing the desired solar heat may be selectively completely enclosed to protect it from the elements, or to close off additional solar heat input when and if the collector plate becomes overheated.

A further object of this invention is to provide a new and improved solar energy system for a building which is simple to construct and a more efficient collector of the solar energy, and lower in weight, size, and cost than existing collector systems utilized in buildings.

A further object of this invention is to provide a new and improved method of cooling the building through the medium of heat radiation from the solar collector, using the pyramidal reflective surfaces to direct the long wavelength infrared emission rays from the collector to the day or night sky in the summer, when the sun is high in the sky and out of the solid angle defined by the pyramid. In order to accomplish this, the hinged reflective panel would be opened on command and at the same time, the glass cover above the blackened collector removed to provide for radiative long wavelength heat emission from the solar collector. In this manner the collector is cooled through radiative exchange with the cold sky and the fluid used for heat circulation is now cooled by the sky and may be used to cool the house, or stored in a separate insulated tank using appropriate controls.

SUMMARY OF THE INVENTION

In carrying out this invention in one illustrative embodiment thereof, the inside roof surfaces and ceilings of a building, normally comprising the attic space of a building, are provided with reflective surfaces to provide a pyramidal specular reflector which directs and focuses the sun's rays on a solar collector for converting those rays into heat, and/or electricity if the collector plate includes solar cells. A movable hinged panel having an inside reflective surface is a part of the pyramidal reflector which is opened and closed by an electric motor to expose the pyramidal reflector to the sun's rays and which positions the panel at any angle to maximize the sun's rays at any season of the year and any latitude of the earth's surface. The interior mounting of the solar collector and the pyramidal reflective surfaces for directing the sun's rays onto the collector, as well as the hinged movable panel, protects the system from the elements.

BRIEF DESCRIPTION OF THE DRAWINGS

FIG. 1 is a side elevation view, partly in section, of a building incorporating the solar energy system embodied in this invention.

FIG. 2 is a sectional view taken along lines 2—2 of FIG. 1.

FIG. 3 is an isometric view, partly broken, of the pyramidal reflector which is formed under the roof surfaces of FIGS. 1 and 2.

FIG. 4 is a partial view of FIG. 1 illustrating the use of solar cells for the generation of electricity for the structure, in addition to providing heating.

DESCRIPTION OF THE PREFERRED EMBODIMENTS

Referring now to FIGS. 1 and 2, one form of conventional building structure is shown and generally referred to with the reference numeral **10**, having side walls **12**, a ceiling **14**, and a slanting roof **16**. Although the type of building structure **10** contemplated herein is directed basically for residential use, the same type of structure may be utilized for commercial type buildings, garages, or other structures. The structure **10** is provided with a hinged movable panel **18** which is positioned between the roof **16** and the ceiling or base member **14** of the structure **10**. The present invention utilizes the space between the roof and the ceiling, which is what is normally considered attic space. The attic space is enclosed by reflective surfaces **22, 24, 26, 27**, and **28**, made of suitable non-corroding reflective material, such as protected polished aluminum foil, aluminized plastic, or any other suitable mirror surface or reflective materials, forming within the attic space a truncated pyramidal reflector **25**, which is best seen in FIG. 3. A "black" solar collector **30** (i.e. absorbing and emitting at all wavelengths) may be positioned on the ceiling joists **14**, near the surface **26** (which may be vertical or some other optimum angle) of the truncated pyramidal reflector **25**. The solar collector **30** is covered by a fixed or removable glass window **32**, appropriately coated or uncoated, which functions to pass solar radiation to the collector **30** while providing some insulation for any conductive loss of heat from the solar plate **30** back into the attic, and the coating (if used) reflects the long-wavelength emitted energy from the collector back onto the collector.

For example: In an optimized system, single or multiple glass surfaces **32** would have anti-reflection coatings on the outside surface to maximize transmission of solar radiation and infrared reflecting surfaces on the inside surface to enhance infrared reflection. The glass surface (**32**) may be removed upon command if the system is used for cooling using the cold summer day or night sky. Alternatively, plastic which transmits long wavelength radiation may be substituted for the glass, in which case it would not have to be removed to achieve the radiative cooling function.

The use of the coated glass covers **32** achieves the so-called "greenhouse effect" which increases the maximum temperature of the black collector **30** reached in the winter. As a further optimization for heating use only, the collector may be coated with a selective spectral absorber surface which has an absorptivity of 0.9μ wavelength or higher in the visible region of the spectrum where there is a maximum of solar radiation and has a low emissivity, approaching 0.1, in the longer wavelength infrared ($3\mu - 15\mu$) where the energy radiated by the heated collector having a temperature between 150°F and 300°F is at a maximum.

If the system is used for both heating and cooling using radiative exchange with the cold sky, as discussed above, a black coating absorbing and emitting uniformly in the visible and infrared regions of the spectrum would be used.

The truncated reflective pyramid **25** which is formed in the attic space may be opened and closed by the movable hinged panel **18** having an inside reflective surface **19** thereon. The panel may be controlled by a motor **20** driving a cable **21** or other suitable means which is attached to one end of the panel **18**, which in turn is hinged to the structure **10** at **17**. The movable panel **18** functions to open the pyramidal reflector **25** to the sun's rays for directing solar energy onto the collector **30**. By controlling the angle of the movable reflective panel **18** by the motor **20**, the panel can be set at any angle to maximize the sun's rays which reach the collector **30** at any season and any latitude. For example, in the winter, the sun's rays come in at a lower angle, and the panel would be open a larger angle, whereas the summer rays (used to heat domestic hot water) are higher, with the panel **18** open less. Similarly, at latitudes nearer the equator the angle of the sun's rays are steeper and hence the panel should be opened to a smaller angle.

The function of the pyramidal reflector **25** is to focus the sun's rays on the collector **30**. For radiative cooling in summer days the glass cover on the collector is removed, and the movable panel is set to the largest angle to prevent the sun's rays from reaching the collector. In this mode the collector sees cold sky over 2π steradians, thus achieving high radiative cooling efficiency. It will also be apparent that the inside mounting of the reflective surfaces and collector eliminates the need for weatherproofing of the type previously used for large solar collectors having glass coverings on which solar energy is absorbed directly without reflection.

The present construction allows for the use of a "black" flat plate collector **30** having a surface area which is reduced in area, weight and cost by a factor of 2 to 10 times, and the temperature differential above ambient obtained at the solar collector **30** under a given set of conditions is roughly proportional to the energy density and hence proportional to the focusing factor of the pyramidal reflector. This increases the temperature differential of the working fluid used to transfer energy from the flat plate collector to the storage tank by a factor of 2 to 10 which increases the energy content of the transfer fluid by this factor and thus reduces the amount of energy storage required by this factor which results in an additional important saving in size, weight, and cost of the energy storage tank required.

Other advantages apply to the system through this increase in temperature of the working fluid. Using water in an unpressurized system the temperature should probably be kept to just below the boiling point of 212°F (100°C). However, through a small amount of pressurization this temperature may be increased to a range between 250°F and 300°F. Alternatively, higher boiling point fluids may be used. The increased temperature of the working fluid makes it suitable for use in powering absorption refrigeration systems for summer airconditioning as an alternative to the aforementioned radiative cooling technique.

The solar collector **30** will normally contain a medium such as water which is heated by the sun's rays which are absorbed by the collector. This medium can then be pumped to a heat sink for storing the heat provided by the sun's rays until it is ultimately utilized for heating the structure **10.** The system for storing and circulating the heat for heating the structure **10** is conventional, and does not form a part of this invention, and accordingly is not discussed herein.

As is shown in FIG. **4,** the collector **30** may include solar cells **34** for converting the sun's rays into electrical energy, which may be utilized for supplementing the electrical requirements of the structure **10.** The collector **30** may be a combination of a heating and/or electrical generating system, provided it includes some solar cells for generating the desired electrical current. The aforesaid focusing gains applicable to the generation of heat also apply to the generation of electricity by the solar cells.

The present system functions to collect and focus by reflection or multiple reflection of solar energy on a suitable collector of greatly reduced size and weight. The reflective surfaces forming the portion of the pyramidal reflector are mounted in and on structure which exists in a standard configuration, namely utilizing the structural components of the attic of a building, thereby simplifying the construction of the solar system. Since a hinged movable reflective panel is utilized, the collector system, whose optical axis should be oriented near the noon orientation of the winter sun, may be selectively exposed to the sun's rays at an angle for optimizing those rays, and may be closed when it is cloudy, at night, or in inclement weather, or when the collector overheats, thus protecting the reflective surfaces in the system from the elements and the collector from damage or fire. The motor control for raising and lowering the movable panel **18** may be manually or automatically controlled. In the automatic control, a small insulated solar collector plate on which a thermal sensor is mounted is positioned to be always exposed to the sun, and is designed with a suitable time delay for controlling the motor **20,** this time delay preventing continuous raising and lowering of the movable panel **18** during partly cloudy conditions. Control circuits can be provided for programming the movement in accordance with the seasons, thus the position of the sun, to properly position the panel **18** at an optimum angle. In a more optimized system an arrangement of solar cells can be used to cause the hinged panel to continually track the elevation angle of the sun.

The solar collector **30** may be positioned horizontally as shown, across the ceiling **14,** or in a vertical position on the surface **26** covering the top of the truncated pyramidal reflector **25,** or an inclined position between these two extremes. The horizontal position is preferred, since the heat escaping from the living space below the ceiling **14** can serve to help prevent the liquid transfer medium such as water in the collector **30** from freezing during nights or cloudy days when the solar energy is not collected. Furthermore, less structural modification in the attic is required, since the ceiling joists under the roof can be utilized to support the horizontally extending reduced size solar collector **30.**

The use of the pyramidal reflector in the attic maximizes the application of solar energy to the collector by reflection from its surfaces to the collector, with little loss. This allows for the use of smaller collectors by a factor of 2 to 10 than would be possible using unfocused collector plates for gathering the sun's energy. As was pointed out, the present system may be utilized as the main or auxiliary installation for providing heat, cooling, and electrical power for a structure such as **10.** The structure **10** is the preferred form, since it accommodates the principles of the present invention without numerous structural changes. The structure **10** may be the principal structure, or may form a part of another structure or be an addition thereto. It will be apparent, however, that the use of a movable (or stationary) panel enclosing or being part of a pyramidal type reflector having a solar reflector mounted therein may be used in other forms of structure than that shown in FIG. **1.** It will be apparent that the structure **10** is preferably positioned so that the panel **18** opens toward the direction for the optimum receipt of the sun's winter rays.

Chapter 2

Solar Energy Collectors - Air

E. MOREAU.
Apparatus for the Produotion of Hot Air.

No. 201,439. Patented March 19, 1878.

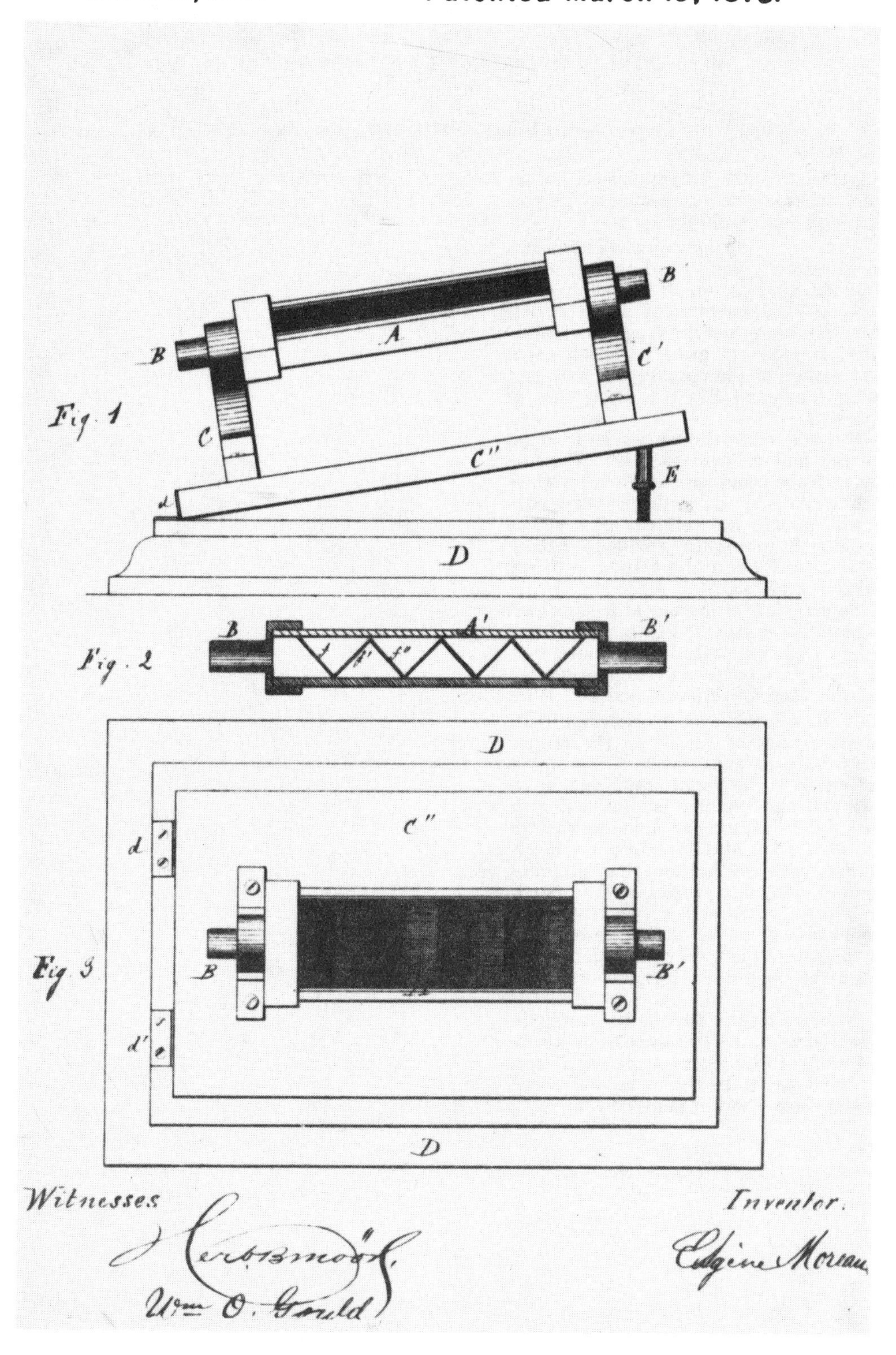

UNITED STATES PATENT OFFICE.

EUGÈNE MOREAU, OF SAN FRANCISCO, CALIFORNIA.

IMPROVEMENT IN APPARATUS FOR THE PRODUCTION OF HOT AIR.

Specification forming part of Letters Patent No. 201,489, dated March 19, 1878; *

*

My invention relates to that class of hot-air apparatus where the air is heated by its passage through hot diaphragms, *

and consists in an improvement whereby the said diaphragms are heated by the direct action of the solar rays.

For the better description of my invention I will refer to the annexed drawings, in which—

Figure 1 is a side elevation. Fig. 2 is a longitudinal section of the diaphragms and box containing them, and Fig. 3 is a top view of the apparatus.

A is the box or flue, open at both ends, through the hollow bearings B B′. The flue A is made of wood, and provided with a glass cover, A′. Any good diathermanous substance will answer as well as glass. The bearings B B′ fit into holes provided for them in the stands C C′, and the stands C C′ are fastened to the plate C″.

D is the bed-plate of the machine, to which the platform C is attached by means of the hinges *d d′*. The bed-plate D is provided with a screw, E, for the purpose of regulating the angle of the plate C″ with the bed D. With the aid of the screw E and the bearings B B′ the flue can always be turned in the proper direction toward the sun.

By referring to the longitudinal section in Fig. 2 we see that the flue is provided with partitions *f f′ f″*, running at right angles with the sides of the flue, and at an angle of forty-five degrees with the bottom, thus dividing the flue into triangular spaces. These partitions are made of blackened copper-wire gauze, and are placed there for the purpose of absorbing the heat of the solar rays, which strike them when the apparatus is turned toward the sun.

It is obvious that the air will be heated in its passage through the flue by coming in contact with the hot wire-gauze of the partitions, and will have only to be led, by an additional pipe, to the place where it is needed. *

Aug. 29, 1961 J. G. JOHNSTON **2,998,005**

SOLAR HEATER

* *

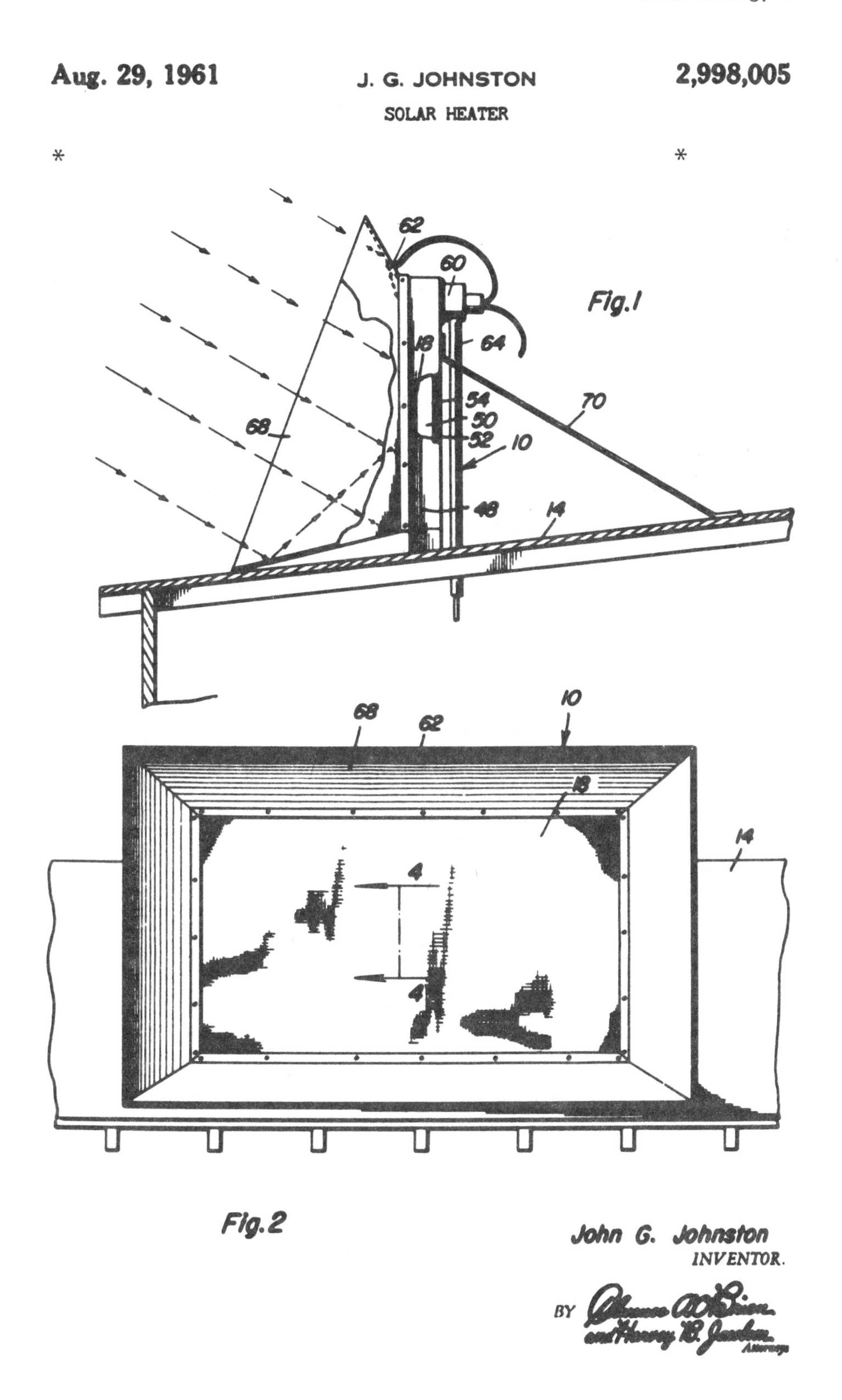

John G. Johnston
INVENTOR.

BY

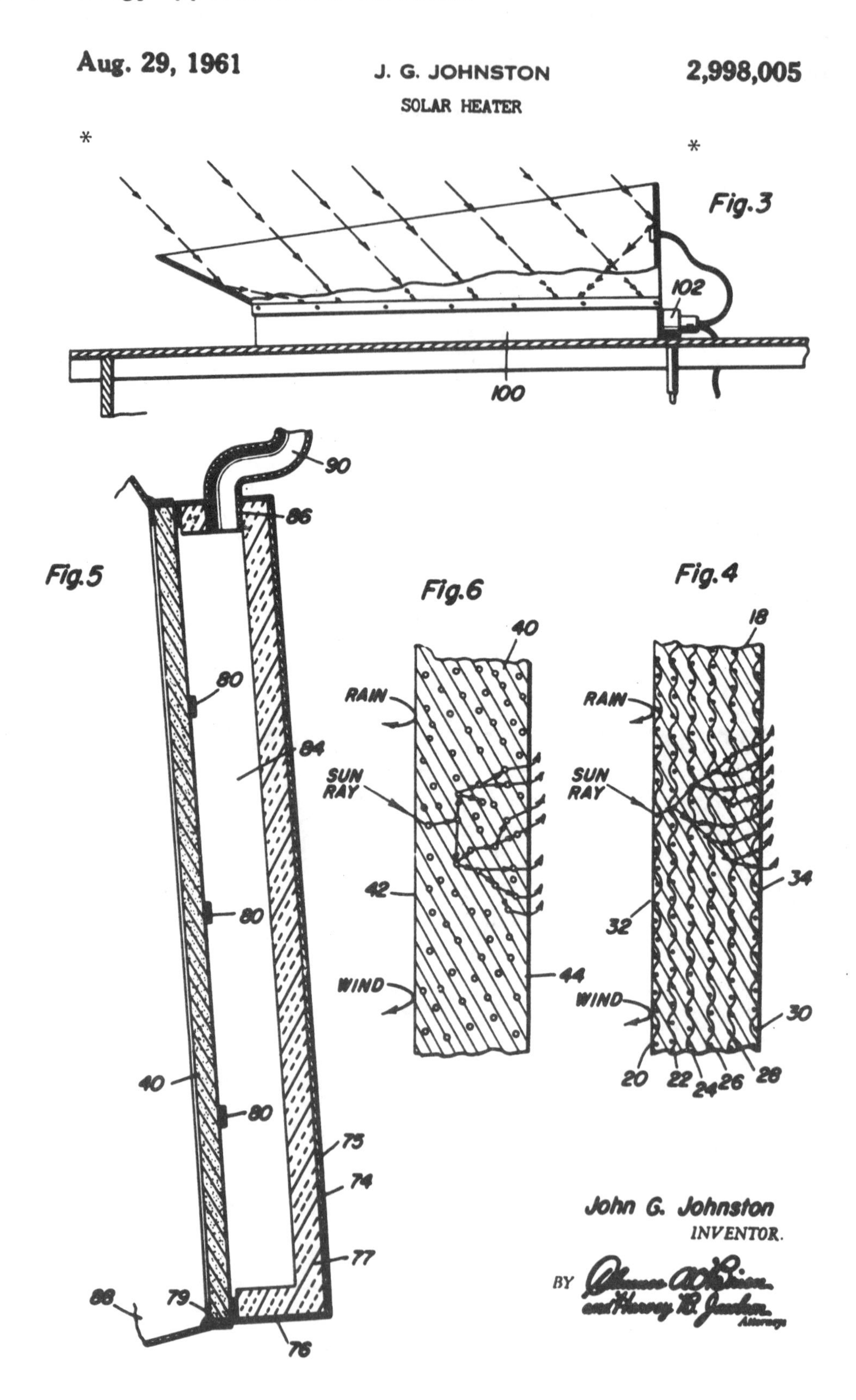
Aug. 29, 1961
J. G. JOHNSTON
2,998,005
SOLAR HEATER
Fig.3
102
100
90
86
Fig.5
Fig.6
Fig.4
40
18
80
RAIN
RAIN
84
SUN RAY
SUN RAY
42
34
32
80
44
WIND
WIND
30
20
22
24
26
28
40
80
75
74
John G. Johnston
INVENTOR.
77
BY
88
79
76

2,998,005
SOLAR HEATER
John G. Johnston, Rte. 3, Box 84A, Palmdale, Calif. *

This invention relates to heating plants and more particularly to solar heaters.

The value of the sun's energy is known to be tremendous. The efficient capture of this energy is certainly well worthwhile.

The principal purpose of this invention is to provide means for efficiently utilizing some of this energy by extracting it in the form of heat. This heat may be used for any purpose such as; heating buildings, heating water or other liquids, chemicals or solids for any purpose, to use the heat in refrigeration or cooling equipment, use the heat for dehumidifying, etc. In the use of this invention for heating occupied buildings it will be noted that the air is heated in the direct presence of sunlight (not through glass or some other transparency), and the air is reduced in germ and bacteria count due to the ultraviolet in direct sunlight. Health advantages are understandable in view of this and moreover, this invention is so constructed that the air in a building is constantly replaced by heated, outside and germ reduced air.

This invention briefly consists in a shallow open-faced case which is insulated throughout and covered with a sunlight-to-heat exchanger face which is preferably in the form of a porous fiber network. This network is of considerable importance in the invention because it has a special action in connection with the extracting of heat from the sun's energy.

It is preferred that the network be formed of glass fibrous material, such as, "Fiberglas," glass wool and others. The sun's rays penetrate into the network striking an inner fiber thereby releasing some energy, and reflecting the rest of the energy to some other fiber farther into the network where additional radiant energy is released in the form of heat, then continuing to additional deeper fibers until the balance of the energy is released and changed to heat. The heated air rises inside the case and forms a draft that promotes continual flow of heated air. The heat released within the network is well protected from being dissipated to the cold outside air and wind currents due to the nature of the fibrous network itself. It is a wind and rain barrier.

Sun's rays will penetrate the fibrous network or mat at any angle without reflecting back into the outer air as in the case of a glass covered heater. This is one main advantage of the fibrous mat. The second main advantage is the conversion of sunlight to heat within the mat where the heat is insulated from radiation to the outside.

To promote efficient extraction of heat, it is preferred that the fibers be painted black or some other very dark color. Moreover, the internal construction of the mat can be varied. It can be one piece or it can be laminated, the latter being slightly superior. The laminations can have a slight space between them with the outermost layer or layers light colored or reflective (refractive in the mat). The innermost layers are black and therefore, absorptive of radiant energy and heat. In the laminar construction, rays strike the outermost meshes and reflect and refract farther toward the inner fibers of the mat before changing to heat. In this way some energy will be saved by preventing backward heat radiation to air currents at the outer fibers of the mat. One of the greater advantages in this type of construction is that it is more durable and resists the inclement weathers, such as rain or snow.

This invention can be applied to any buildings and at various angles. The means of mounting the mat and its box can be varied from the simplest to very complex arrangements with mirrors, reflective surfaces, tilt adjusting mechanisms, blowers that are thermostatically controlled and with the inclusion of many other available attachments. Moreover, the embodiments of this invention can be applied to a top of a building, side or can be at a position remote from the building with the heated air piped into the building. There are many other alternatives, modifications and changes which will occur in following the description of the illustrated forms of the invention.

FIGURE 1 is a side view of one embodiment of the invention;

FIGURE 2 is a front view of the embodiment in FIGURE 1;

FIGURE 3 is a side view, parts being shown in section, of another embodiment of the invention;

FIGURE 4 is an enlarged sectional view taken on the line 4—4 of FIGURE 2 and showing the laminar mat used in the invention;

FIGURE 5 is an enlarged sectional view showing a very simplified version of the invention; and

FIGURE 6 is a fragmentary enlarged sectional view showing an energy absorbing and converting mat.

In the accompanying drawings FIGURES 1 and 2 show a typical installation with solar heater 10 mounted on the top of a sloped roof 14 of a building. This heater has a fibrous network or mat 18 in it. The mat is made of screens of expanded fibrous material whose distance between parallel fibers or particles is great in comparison to the diameter or thickness of the solid elements themselves. Although fibrous materials are referred to herein, inasmuch as fibrous materials that serve the purpose of the invention very well are readily commercially available, it is to be understood that the expression "fiber" does not exclude particles of other shapes and configurations.

Mat 18 is laminar having screens or layers 20, 22, 24, 26, 28 and 30 that may be very slightly spaced from each other and that are made in mesh formation. All of the mat fibers are colored black. The laminated mesh construction using a material such as glass cloth mesh is more durable than the fibrous glass mat to be considered below, although not necessarily more efficient as a heat panel. In utilization, the energy rays from the sun pass the front surface 32 and strike the solid elements of the various layers and accordingly surrender a portion of their energy as heat. It will be realized that the rays which do not strike the outermost layers continue inwardly so as to strike the inner layers to surrender their energy.

As a modification, the outer layers 20 and 22, for example, may be made reflective by dyeing or painting white or silver colored. The sun's rays striking the silvered strands will be reflected toward fibers of the inner layers of the mat 18 (FIGURE 4) before being converted to heat by striking the dark strands. This enables the layers 20 and 22 to act as insulation against cold outside eddying air.

Mat 40 shows a modification. The mat has a front face 42 and a rear surface or face 44. The solid elements of the mats are dyed black throughout. The action of the rain and wind and radiant energy of the sun rays is the same as that of FIGURE 4 as shown by the arrows in FIGURE 6.

Reference is now made again to the solar heater 10. It consists of a box 48 that has four side walls and a back wall. The side walls and back wall are covered with insulation (see FIGURE 1) and the mat 18 is held parallel to the back wall of the box or case. Heater air chamber 50 is between the rear surface of mat 18 and the front surface of the insulation 52 on the back wall 54 of case 48.

A blower 60 is attached to the back wall of the case and has its inlet in registry with chamber 50. The blower can be wired with a thermostat located in the building or it can be merely a manual on-off arrangement. When a thermostat is used in the building, the sensing element 62 thereof is located adjacent to the mat 18 to sense the presence of sunlight which will, through the unshown circuitry, require the blower motor to be energized. The discharge port of the blower has a conduit 64 connected with it and this exhausts in the building.

Hood 68 is attached to case 48 and is around the edges of the mat 18. The purpose of the hood is to receive the sun's energy and reflect it onto the fibers of mat 18. In addition, the hood functions as a protector for the mat 18.

Any means may be resorted to for mounting the solar unit 10 and it may be mounted in any place. The illustration shows an ordinary mounting bracket 70 which is attached to the case and to the building roof 14. Although non-adjustable, the bracket 70 could be substituted by conventional adjustable brackets.

Reference is now made to FIGURE 5. In this embodiment of the invention the details for mounting mat 40 are shown. These details are applied to all embodiments of the invention. The mat 40 is mounted in case 74, the latter having a back wall 75 and side walls 76. An insulating liner 77 is in the case 74. Mat 40 has a frame 79 around its perimeter and this frame is secured to the open front of case 74. Transverse battens 80 across opposing side walls of case 74 and hold the frame 79 and its mat 40 supported parallel to the back wall 75 of the case and spaced from the insulation 77 therein. This forms chamber 84 within which air is heated and conducted to an outlet 86. Hood 88 is attached to the frame 79 and/or the case 74 and serves as a protector as well as a heat reflector as shown in FIGURE 1.

Outlet 86 has a pipe, conduit or the like 90 registered with it through which heated air is adapted to be moved. The heated air of chamber 84 can be drawn through the conduit 90 or can be moved through the conduit by convection. In the case of a convection motion, it is preferred that the case be tilted slightly as shown in FIGURE 5 because this will promote more efficient upward draft to pass through the conduit 90.

In this invention, air is introduced into the heated air chamber by producing a flow of air transversely through the porous fiber mat or network, which results in heating the air by heat exchange with the heat absorbtive fibers of the porous network.

FIGURE 3 shows that the solar heater 100 can be mounted flat. Air can be drawn through and heated by the unit in any position from vertical to horizontal. Here again, this embodiment as well as all others, can be mounted for adjustment by the use of adjustable mounting brackets. Secondly, complex and elaborate parabolic or flat mirrors can be used to attain more of the sun's rays energy or the simpler versions can be used. The mat may have its fibers less dense in the front part thereof and more dense in its rear part to achieve a graduated recovery of heat from the energy rays as they penetrate the mat. All such embodiments fall within the scope of the invention as claimed and all other embodiments as fall within the scope of the following claims may be adopted. *

(No Model.)

E. S. MORSE.

WARMING AND VENTILATING APARTMENTS BY THE SUN'S RAYS.

No. 246,626. Patented Sept. 6, 1881.

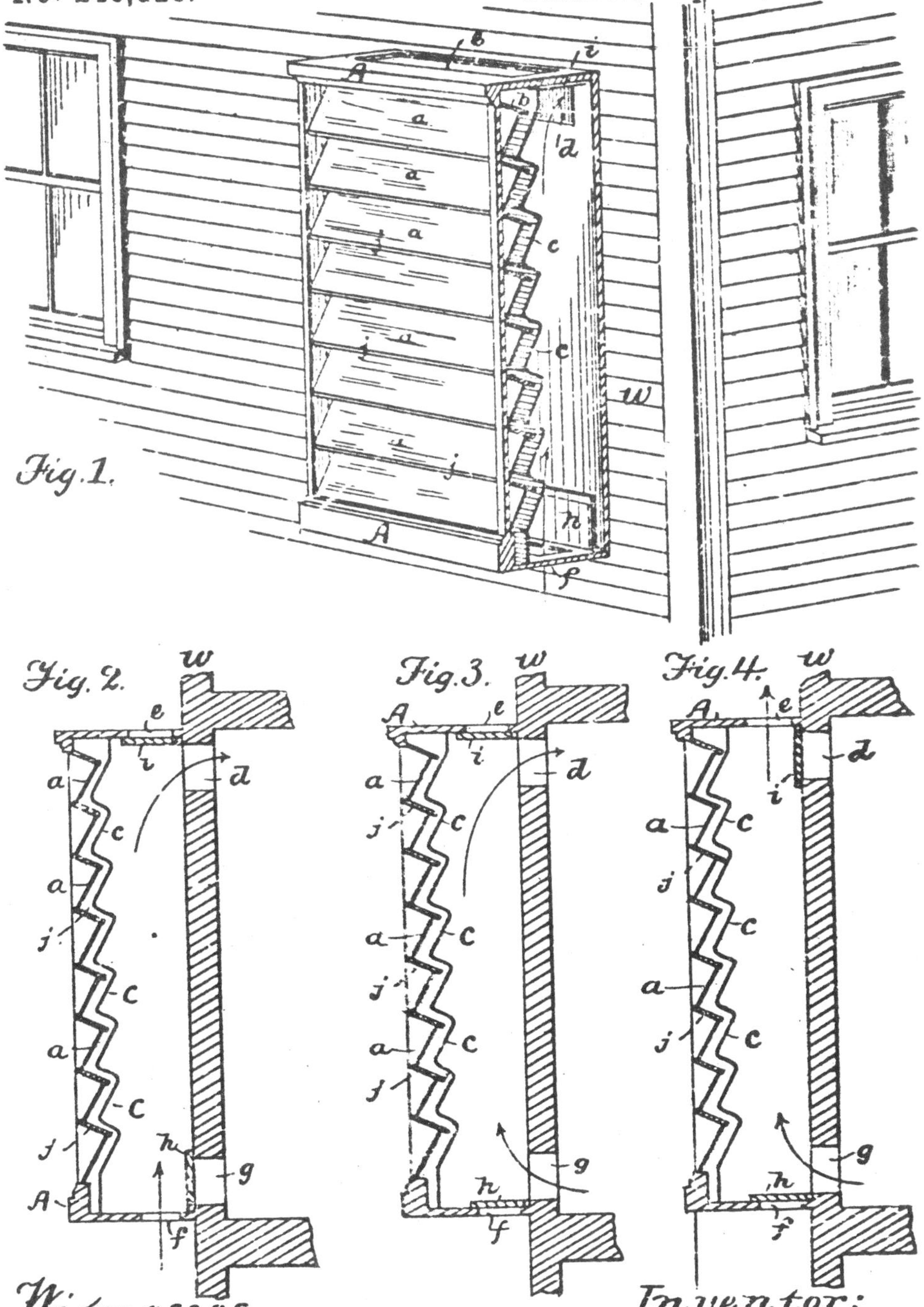

Fig. 1.

Fig. 2.

Fig. 3.

Fig. 4.

Witnesses.
Wm H. H. Emmons
J. Brown Lord

Inventor;
Edw. S. Morse.
by J. H. Adams
Atty.

246,626. Warming and Ventilating Apartments by the Sun's Rays. Edward S. Morse, Salem,

*

My invention relates to a means for utilizing the rays of the sun for the purpose of heating and ventilating rooms and apartments of buildings.

The invention consists in the employment of a casing attached to the outer wall of a building, and provided with a blackened surface of metal, earthenware, or other suitable material, having either a flat or corrugated surface protected by glass in front of the same, and so arranged as to allow the rays of the sun to fall as directly as practicable upon the said blackened surface. Behind the blackened surface is an inclosed air space or flue communicating by apertures at the upper and lower ends with corresponding openings of an apartment or room of a building, and also by separate openings with the outer atmosphere. The action of the sun's rays upon the blackened surface heats the air in the space or flue at the rear, which heated air, as it ascends, may be directed into the room or building, so as to warm the same, or it may serve to draw the air from the room, and thus occasion ventilation.

Referring to the accompanying drawings, Figure 1 is a perspective view of my invention as applied to a building. Figs. 2, 3, and 4 are sectional views of my device, indicating the different directions of the air for heating and ventilating an apartment or building.

A A represent a casing, shown as attached to the outside of a house or building, *w*, at any suitable part of the same which may be exposed to the sun's rays. The sides of the casing are to be closed. In Fig. 1 one side is left open to show its internal arrangement.

c c represent a plate extending from the top to the bottom of the casing and presenting series of inclined surfaces, as shown, and designed to be arranged so that the rays of the sun will fall upon them to the greatest advantage. The said plate is to have a blackened surface in front, and to be composed of metal, earthenware, or other suitable material. In front of this blackened surface is arranged a series of glass plates or strips, *a a*, parallel with the inclined portions *c c*, and set in sashes or strips of wood *j j*.

At the top and bottom of the casing A, respectively, are openings *e* and *f*, and in the wall or side of the building, at the upper and lower ends of the casing, respectively, are apertures *d* and *g*. Between the opening *e* and aperture *d* above and the opening *f* and aperture *g* below are hinged the lids or covers *i* and *h*, so arranged as to close either aperture or opening above or below while the other is open.

The casing A is designed to be placed on the side of the building most exposed to sun's rays, and when properly arranged a very considerable amount of heat will be imparted to the air within the casing, as has been proved by actual experiment.

When a room or apartment is to be heated the lid *h* at the bottom of the casing is opened, thus closing the aperture *g*, and the lid *i* at the top closes the opening *e*, leaving the aperture *d* open, as shown in Fig. 1. The air passing into *f* becomes warmed in its passage through the casing and enters the apartment at aperture *d*.

In Fig. 3 the openings *e* and *f* are shown as closed; the air entering the casing from the apartment and passing through the casing reenters the apartment, and so continuing the circulation and adding to the supply of heated air in the apartment.

When ventilation only is required the bottom opening, *f*, is closed by lid *h*, leaving aperture *g* open. Aperture *d* is then closed by lid *i*, leaving *e* open, as shown in Fig. 4. As the air becomes heated it passes up and out of opening *e*, drawing air all the time from the apartment through aperture *g*.

My invention may be applied to a house already built. In adapting it to a house while building the casing may be so arranged as to admit of its being turned to adapt the blackened surface to the changing position of the sun.

Instead of the corrugated plate showing a series of inclined surfaces, and a corresponding glass covering, the blackened plate may be of an entire plane surface with a plane plate of glass. *

March 9, 1954 C. W. HARRIS **2,671,441**
VARIABLE HEAT INSULATING APPARATUS AND SOLAR HEATING SYSTEM COMPRISING SAME
*

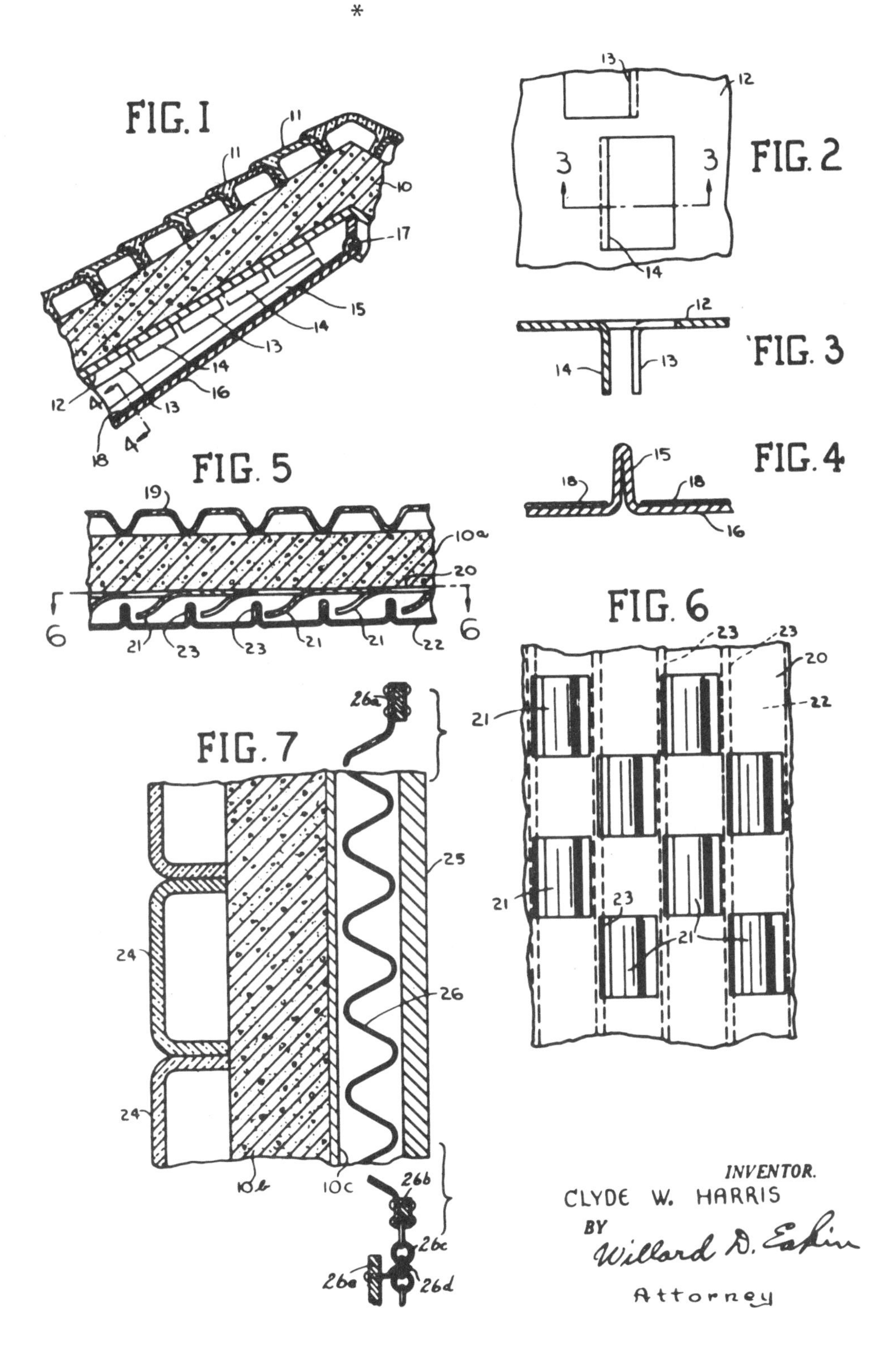

UNITED STATES PATENT OFFICE

2,671,441

VARIABLE HEAT INSULATING APPARATUS AND SOLAR HEATING SYSTEM COMPRISING SAME

Clyde W. Harris, Akron, Ohio

*

This invention relates to variable heat-insulating apparatus and to a solar heating system inclusive of such apparatus.

Its chief object is to provide a solar heating system having provision for storing solar heat and variable heat-insulating means for controlling the rate at which the heat passes to the space wherein a controlled temperature is desired, so that stored solar heat can be economically used and its use thus distributed over a long period of time.

Further objects are to provide improved variable heat-insulating means, having the advantages of efficiency and economy of construction.

Of the accompanying drawings:

Fig. 1 is a fragmentary vertical section of a roof structure embodying my invention in one of its preferred forms.

Fig. 2 is a fragmentary face view of one of the elements shown in Fig. 1.

Fig. 3 is a section on line 3—3 of Fig. 2.

Fig. 4 is a fragmentary section on line 4—4 of Fig. 1.

Fig. 5 is a fragmentary section of a modification.

Fig. 6 is a fragmentary face view of one of the elements shown in Fig. 5, on line 6—6 of Fig. 5, with an underlying member shown in dotted lines.

Fig. 7 is a fragmentary vertical section of another modification.

Referring first to the embodiment shown in Figs. 1 to 4, the structure there shown comprises a self-supporting roof member 10, permissibly of concrete as shown, having high capacity for storage of heat, and a field of cup-shaped glass members 11, 11 suitably mounted upon it, for * causing rays of sun to heat the underlying structure and providing air pockets for insulation against outward passage of the heat.

Suitably secured to the under face of the concrete member 10 and in extensive contact with it is a metal plate 12 having a multiplicity of rows of stamped out and downwardly bent tabs such as the tabs 13, 13 and 14, 14 in such staggered relation as shown in Figs. 2 and 3 that each double row of staggered tabs is adapted to receive, in sliding contact with the tabs, one of a multiplicity of ribs such as the rib 15 formed by bending or crimping of a sheet of metal 16.

The metal sheet 16 is hinged at one margin, as at 17, Fig. 1, and means (not shown) is provided for holding it at different positions about its hinge axis.

When held in the position in which it is shown in Fig. 1, the sheet 16 defines, with the plate 12 and the concrete, an insulating air space for retarding flow of heat from the concrete roof into the interior of the building. To provide additional insulating effect, the plate 16 can be provided upon extensive areas of its upper face with heat-reflecting means such as aluminum foil 18, 18.

When it is desired to increase such flow of heat the sheet 16 is swung on its hinge to a higher position such that each of its numerous ribs 15 enters with a sliding fit between the tabs 13, 14 of a respective double row of the tabs. Metal to metal contact of a multiplicity of the ribs 15 and tabs 13, 14 thus being established, heat rapidly passes by conduction from the body 10 to the lower face of the metal sheet 16 and thus heats the interior of the building. The rate of flow of heat can be varied by varying the angular position of the metal sheet 16 to vary the number or area of contacts between ribs 15 and tabs 13, 14.

In the embodiment shown in Figs. 5 and 6 a ribbed or bisculted sheet of transparent plastic 19 provides for solar heating and outer-face insulation of a wall or roof member 10a which has in extensive contact with its lower face a metal sheet 20 having a multiplicity of spring-like tabs 21, 21 stamped out and bent obliquely downward from the main body of the sheet.

Mounted below the sheet 20, upon means (not shown) for holding it at different distances from the body of the sheet 20, is a metal sheet 22 formed with crimped ribs 23, 23 for stiffness.

When it is at a low position such that it is out of contact with the tabs 21 the sheet 22 defines, with the sheet 20, an air space having high heat-insulating effect, but when it is raised into contact with some or all of the tabs 21 the metal to metal contacts provide more rapid transfer of heat, and the rapidity of the transfer can be varied by varying the number, extent or pressure of contacts between the sheet 22 and the spring-like tabs.

In the embodiment shown in Fig. 7 a building wall 10b, here shown as a concrete wall, is provided on its outer face with a field of cup-shaped glass members 24 providing solar heating and outer-face insulation of the wall. Spaced inwardly from the wall 10b is a metal sheet or wall 25 having good heat conductivity but defining, with the wall 10b, a heat-insulating air space.

In the said space is suspended, from a fixed supporting bar 26a, a springy, corrugated metal sheet 26. For vertically stretching and relaxing the corrugated sheet 26 its lower margin has secured to it a stiffening bar 26b and a chain 26c, the chain being adapted to have its links selectively engaged with a hold-down hook 26d projecting from a fixed standard 26e, to hold the lower margin of the corrugated sheet at different heights. The corrugations are of such dimensions in relation to the thickness of the space that when the sheet is relaxed the flutes on one side of the sheet will strongly contact the wall 10b while those on the other face of the sheet strongly contact the metal sheet 25, for rapid transfer of heat, but when the sheet is stretched and the angles of the corrugations thus changed the sheet will have less contact, or no contact, with the member 10b or the member 25, and the air space between those two members will provide effective insulation. Such insulation is especially effective when the corrugations are horizontally disposed, as in Fig. 7, so that they serve as baffles against gravity convection currents. Preferably the concrete wall 10b is provided with a sheet metal facing 10c for effective transmission of heat to the member 20.

While supplementary insulation is not shown in Fig. 5 or Fig. 7, the use of supplemental insulation, as in Figs. 1 and 4, is not excluded.

In all of the embodiments shown, insulation is in effect by-passed by a set of heat-conducting members of high conductivity, and the well known greater comfort of radiant heating, as compared with convection heating, is provided. *

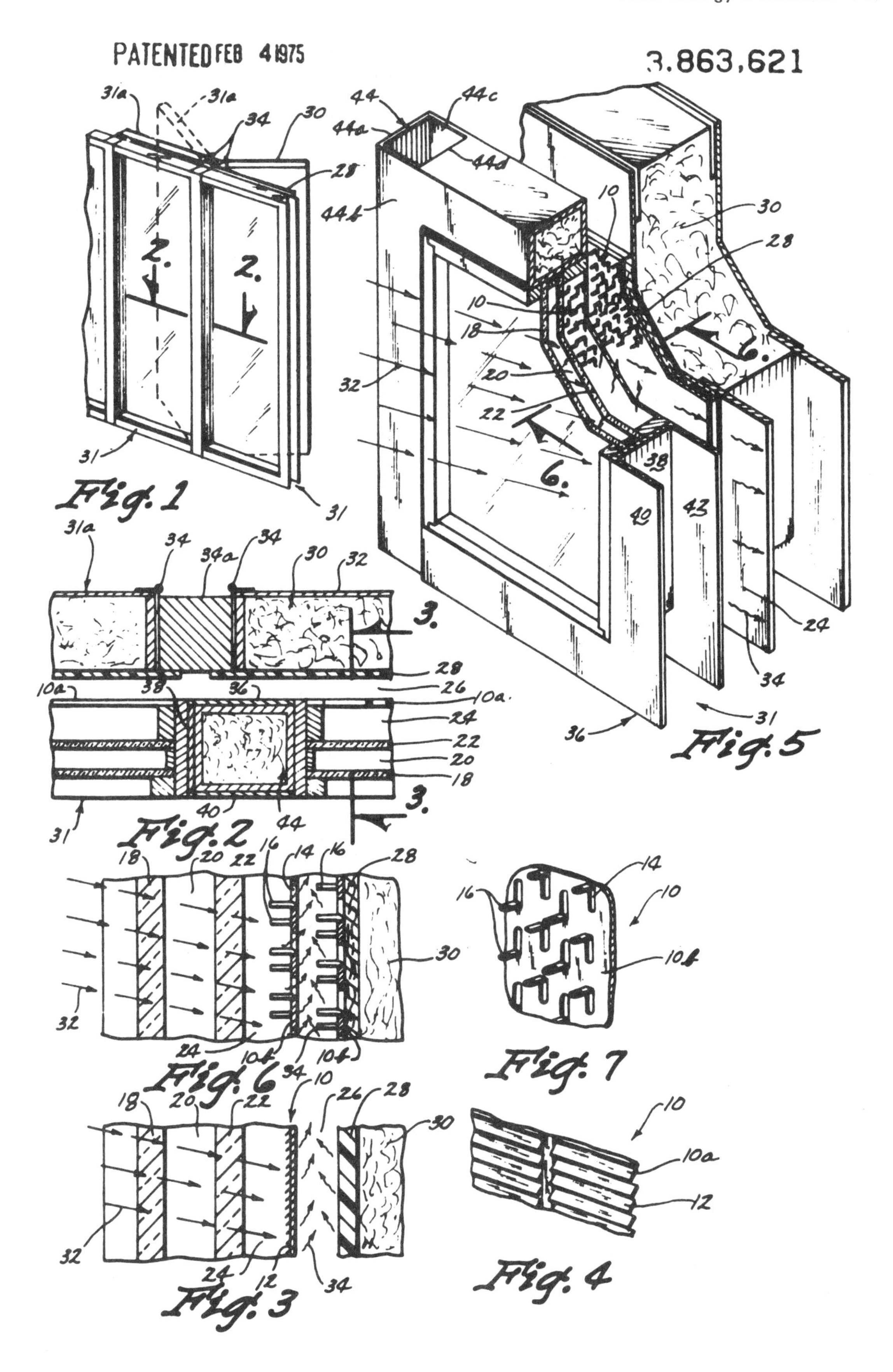
PATENTED FEB 4 1975
3.863,621
Fig. 1
Fig. 2
Fig. 3
Fig. 4
Fig. 5
Fig. 6
Fig. 7

SOLAR WALL SYSTEM

BACKGROUND OF THE INVENTION

Solar heat collecting wall systems represent one possible method of relieving a part of our current energy crisis. Approximately one-third of all energy consumed in this country during the year 1971 was for space heating and air conditioning. This is a tremendous drain on our country's fuel reserves. Efficient and consumer acceptable solar wall systems which would utilization of solar energy as an alternative to fossil fuels for heating and lighting would be a great aid in relieving this current crisis.

Solar wall systems have been developed heretofore. However, no solar wall system yet developed has generally been accepted by the public as a convenient heat source for homes and other building structures. Part of the problem with prior art solar wall systems is that most, if not all of them, have been opaque. Thus while the wall system will allow for capturing solar energy and converting it into heat energy, it is at the sacrifice of allowing light to enter to the interior of the building structure. Prior art solar wall systems have been opaque because it was thought that in order to efficiently collect solar energy an opaque wall system was deemed essential. In other words, a solar wall system which would allow light into the interior of a building structure would not be as efficient since it would allow escape of heat energy. Of course, since building structures having large opaque areas in the walls thereof, are not favored by the public this factor has considerably decreased the acceptability of solar heat as a means of heating homes and other buildings. Accordingly, there is a real need in the art for the development of a solar wall system which will efficiently collect solar energy, convert that energy into heat energy and at the same time, allow for transmission of light into the interior of the building structure.

An additional deficiency of prior art solar wall systems relates to their general inability to efficiently collect solar energy and convert that energy into heat without a substantial loss of the heat. It has now been discovered that solar wall systems, utilizing special collector plates for the solar energy, will allow for increased efficiency in gathering solar energy and converting that energy into heat energy. In other words, the amount of heat energy which is allowed to dissipate without being utilized is decreased.

Another deficiency with many prior art solar wall systems relates to their generally complicated structure and the long times necessary for jobsite construction. The solar wall system of this invention can, if desired, be built in modules or units which can quickly and efficiently be constructed at the construction jobsite.

Accordingly, one object of this invention is to develop a solar wall system which will efficiently collect heat energy and still allow for passage of light into the interior of a building structure.

Yet another object of this invention is to provide a solar wall system having a special type of solar energy collection plate which more efficiently will convert solar energy into heat energy.

Still another object of this invention is to provide a solar wall system in modular units which can be quickly constructed at the construction jobsite with a minimum of required skill and with great efficiency.

The method of accomplishing these and other objects will become apparent from the following description of the invention.

SUMMARY OF THE INVENTION

This invention relates to solar wall systems employing a unique and specially designed apertured collector plate. The utlization of the collector described hereinafter allows for increased efficiency in conversion of solar energy into heat energy. In one embodiment the invention relates to a transparent, or see-through, wall system which allows light to pass into the interior of a building structure and which allows those within the building to see out.

In another embodiment the invention relates to an extremely efficient opaque solar wall system. In yet another embodiment of the invention relates to a solar wall system, comprised of modular units, which can be put together at a construction jobsite efficiently and with a minimum of required skill.

DESCRIPTION OF THE DRAWINGS

FIG. 1 is a perspective view of a transparent solar wall system employing exterior and interior modular units.

FIG. 2 is a sectional view along line 2—2 of FIG. 1.

FIG. 3 is a sectional view of FIG. 2 along line 3—3 showing a cross section of a transparent wall construction where a louvered collector plate is employed.

FIG. 4 is a fragmentary view of a louvered collector plate.

FIG. 5 is an expanded perspective view of exterior and interior modules for a solar wall system employing gang-nail collector plates.

FIG. 6 is a sectional view of FIG. 5 along lines 6—6 showing in cross section wall construction where gang-nail collectors are employed.

FIG. 7 is a fragmentary review of a gang-nail collector plate.

DETAILED DESCRIPTION OF THE INVENTION.

A collector plate, as utilized herein, refers to a metal sheet which is utilized to collect the solar energy. Typically collector plates are painted a dark highly absorbtive color such as flat black color. Solar rays hit the plate and are converted thereon into heat energy as the plate is warmed by the solar energy. Such collector plates can be made of any suitable material of high solar absorbtivity and are typically made from copper, aluminim, steel and galvanized iron. Many types of collector plates have been employed in the prior art. For example, the prior art has utilized flat sheet-like collector plates, corrugated collector plates, collector plates faced with copper water pipes and metallic fibrous materials. For examples of typical prior art collector plates see the following U.S. patents: Harris, U.S. Pat. No. 2,671,441; Anderegg, U.S. Pat. No. 2,601,905; Gay, U.S. Pat. No. 2,559,870; Johnston, U.S. Pat. No. 2,998,005; Thomason, U.S. Pat. No. 3,295,591; and Hay, U.S. Pat. No. 3,563,305. The efficiency of any solar wall system depends directly upon the efficiency of the collector plate in gathering solar energy and converting it into heat energy.

It has now been discovered that increased solar energy conversion into heat energy can be otained when specially designed collector plates are utilized. These plates can generally be described as apertured collector plates. An apertured collector plate, as that term is used herein, does not mean a collector plate which merely has holes punched therein. A collector plate having holes punched therein will naturally have a materials loss when compared to a solid plate of like material, weight and dimensions. Thus, the surface area of the overall collector plate will be decreased. In accord with this invention it has been discovered that apertured collector plates which have substantially no materials loss when compared to a solid plate of like material, weight and dimension, provide increased surface area, and in addition, will transmit light therethrough. The increased surface area results in a greater increased efficiency for collection of solar energy and conversion of that energy into heat energy. Thus, while the collector plate does have apertures therein, the material displaced in forming the apertures is not completely removed from the collector plate. Examples of such collector plates, formed without a materials loss, are shown in FIGS. 4 and 7. FIG. 4 shows a louvered collector plate wherein the metal is punched or otherwise pressed in a dye to provide louvers therein. Thus there are apertures present but the material displaced in forming the apertures is not removed from the collector plate. Obviously then, the overall surface area for collection of solar energy is increased. The collector plate is referred to herein as **10** and the louvered collector plate is referred to as **10*a*** with the gang-nail collector plate, to be described in detail hereinafter, referred to as **10*b***.

The louvered collector plate, **10*a*** formed by having generally downwardly and outwardly displaced louvers **12** formed in a metal sheet. These louvers will provide increased surface areas for gathering solar energy and converting it into heat energy and, as explained in more detail hereinafter, will allow light to be transmitted therethrough. As a result, one looking through a solar wall system employing louvered collector plates can see out to the exterior of this structure.

Collector plate **10*b*** is a gang-nail collector plate. Gang-nail collector plate, **10*b***, has apertures **14** and upstanding tabs **16**. Of course, other collector plates having apertured surfaces wherein the apertured collector plate has no materials loss when compared with a plate of like size, weight and dimensions can easily be made. Thus, the louvered collector plate **10*a***, and the gang-nail collector **10*b***, are shown herein as representative only. The key feature being that these plates have no materials loss when compared with like plates of similar size, weight and dimension but on the other hand, do have an increased surface area. A description of the action of these plates in collecting solar rays will be provided hereinafter.

FIGS. **1**, **2**, **3** and **4** represent a solar wall system having a louvered collector plate and are designed to provide a transparent, or more accurately perhaps a see-through solar wall system wherein light is transmitted to the interior of the structure and one standing there within can see out to the exterior thereof. FIGS. **5**, **6**, and **7** represent an opaque solar wall system having enhanced efficiency for collection of solar energy, conversion of that energy into heat energy and distribution thereof within the building structure. For purposes of general description of the invention and for clarity, the invention will first be described in connection with the cross sectional views of FIGS. **3** and **6**. FIG. **3** is a sectional view of a solar wall construction employing a louvered collector plate. FIG. **6** is a similar cross sectional view of a solar wall construction employing gang-nail collector plates.

While the collector plates shown in the drawings generally relate to a preferred modular unit solar wall system, it should be appreciated that the solar wall system can equally as well, if desired, be built as an entire wall section. Where this is done the views of FIGS. **3** and **6** generally will represent, a sectional view of the various layers, in laminar relationship, comprising the wall structure. Conventional wall frame means can be utilized to hold the various solar wall system layers into their hereinafter described relationship and thus this conventional frame structure will not be described here in detail.

In both FIGS. **3** and **6**, the left hand side thereof, represents the exteriorly exposed portion of the wall, with the right hand side thereof representing the interiorly disposed portion of the wall. Speaking now with specific reference to FIG. **3**, there is shown a transparent or see-through solar wall system. This system comprises an exteriorly exposed transparent member **18**, a void space **20**, and spaced apart from but behind the exteriorly exposed transparent member **18** is an interiorly disposed transparent member **22**. Of course, there can be more than two transparent members and if desired, the number can be from two up to four. However, for purposes of cost efficiency two transparent members are preferred. The transparent members can be conventional plate glass, or made of transparent plexiglass material. Thermopane glass can also be employed. Behind the most interiorly disposed transparent member **22**, is an additional air space **24** and spaced apart from transparent member **22** and behind said member is a louvered collector plate **10*a***. Immediately behind louvered collector plate **10*a*** is an air space chamber **26** for collection and movement of warm air. The rear wall of space chamber **26** can be defined by any conventional panel material **28** which in FIG. **3** is transparent. Behind panel **28** and in abutting relationship therewith is an insulation layer **30**. Insulation layer **30** can comprise any well known insulating material. For example, it can be foam plastic insulation such as urethane foam; it can be a fiber insulation such as fiberglass butt; or it can be a loose fill insulation such as fiberglass pellets and the like. Insulation layer **30** is the most interiorly disposed portion of the solar wall system. Of course, behind insulation layer **30** can be any wall panel construction suitable for exposure within the internal wall of the building. This could conceivably be wood paneling, any conventional dry wall construction, or the like. As will be explained hereinafter, with regard to the embodiment shown specifically in FIG. **3**, the insulation layer is movably connected to the remainder of the solar wall system so that the insulation layer can be moved away therefrom to allow light to pass through the solar wall and to allow those within the building structure to see outside. In this specific embodiment, therefore, panel 28 is preferably another see-through panel of glass or plexiglass material.

During in use operation the solar wall system described in FIG. 3 operates as follows. Sun rays represented by arrows 32 pass through transparent members 18 and 20 and hit the louvers 12 of louvered collector plate 10*a*. The collector plate is warmed by the sun rays 32 and the collector plate 10*a*, which is typically painted flat black, converts the sun rays 32 into heat energy. Because of the increased surface area of collector plate 10*a* over a simple metal sheet collector plate or over a corrugated collector plate, the absorption and coversion of solar energy into heat energy is increased. The heat energy warms the air in air space chamber 26 and the warm air 34 can be swept away for heating the building structure. Heat loss of the collected heat energy is significantly decreased by the presence of panel 28 and insulation layer 30. Heat loss by conduction to the exterior of the wall construction system is prevented by design of collector plate 10*a*, and the spaced apart relationship of the transparent members 18 and 22. The means for sweeping away warm air and circulating it through the building structure are conventional but will briefly be described hereinafter.

The wall construction shown in FIG. 6 is similar to that shown in FIG. 3 but is specifically designed for highly efficient opaque solar wall system. Those portions of the structure of like construction to those previously described will not be described here in detail. Like numerals have been utilized to represent like structure. In FIG. 6 there is shown a first gang-nail collector plate 10*b* and spaced apart therefrom but behind first gang-nail collector plate 10*b* is a second gang-nail collector plate also represented by numeral 10*b*. There chamber 26, then, is defined by the back of first gang-nail collector plate 10*b* and the front of second gang-nail collector plate 10*b*. Behind second gang-nail collector plate 10*b* is a panel 28 which can be wood or other opaque conventional materials since this wall system is an opaque one. Spaced directly behind panel 28 and in abutting relationship thereto is insulation layer 30. In the construction of FIG. 6, those rays which pass through the apertures of the first gang-nail collector plate 10*b* will strike the second collector plate 10*b* which is preferably in offset relationship with regard to the first collector plate 10*b*. As a result an enhanced efficiency of solar energy collection is achieved. Moreover, the combined increased exposed surface areas of gang-nail collector plates 10*b* make them extremely efficient in solar energy collection.

FIGS. 1 and 2 show with particularity the solar wall system construction wherein the wall is comprised of modular units with an exterior modular unit generally designated at 31 and a movably mounted interior modular unit generally designated at 31*a*. This system is designed for utilization wherein the solar wall system is to be a see-through solar wall. the interior modular unit comprises the insulation layer 30 and any appropriate covering thereover. Positioned in front of the interior modular unit 31a is a stationary transparent member. The movably mounted interior modular unit when in closed position is in abutting relationship with the interiorly disposed transparent member 28. Thus when the interiorly disposed modular unit is moved away from abutting relationship with interiorly disposed transparent member 28 light can pass through transparent members 18 and 22, through louvered collector plate 10*a*, and through transparent member 28 and into the internal structure of the building. It is desirable to keep the movably mounted interior modular unit in a closed position during early morning hours so that collector plate 10*a* can satisfactorily reach a warm temperature. Thereafter once sufficient heat exchange is occuring, interior insulation layer 30 and the modular unit which incorporates it can be moved away from the exterior modular unit by the movable connection to provide a see-through condition. For exemplary purposes, this can be seen in FIG. 2, interior modular unit 31*a* is shown as being hingedly connected by hinge 34 to a post member 34*a* so that it can be swung rearwardly.

Exterior modular unit 31 comprises the exposed exteriorly disposed transparent member 18, any interiorly disposed transparent members 22, and the collector plate 10*b*. The frame of exterior modular unit 31 is uniquely designed to provide for easy jobsite construction of solar walls. The frame can be aluminum, or any other suitable metal or wood. The modular unit is preferably rectangular in shape and has two adjacent sides forming open frame members of U-shaped cross section. This is best seen in FIG. 5 wherein the open frame members generally designated in FIG. 5 as 36 are comprised of an outwardly extending sidewall 40 a back standing sidewall 38 and an additional outward extending sidewall 42. The other sides of the modular unit 31 comprise closed frame member 44 formed by walls 44*b*, 44*a*, 44*c* and a wall 44*d*, not depicted in FIG. 5. The dimensions of closed frame member 44 are such that it will matingly receive the open frame member 36. Thus as can be seen in FIG. 2, open frame member 36 will matingly receive closed frame member 44 to provide a solid fit. In this fashion modular units can be built one matingly receiving the other until a solar wall system of desired size is achieved. Preferably, the open space in closed frame member 44 is filled with insulation. This will allow for an even increased efficiency in thermal retention. As can be seen from FIG. 5, the interior modular unit 31*a* can also be comprised of like configuration having open frame members and closed frame members which will matingly receive one another. In such a manner a solar wall system can be built by unskilled labor and does not require a detailed familiarity with the intricate construction of the entire wall system. In addition each modular is in and of itself surrounded by an insulation layer which makes heat loss significantly less.

As heretofore mentioned, the method of storing and circulating warmed air 34 which is warmed in air chamber 26 is conventional. For example, a fan system and warm air storage unit can be located remotely in building structure with the fan system being in communication with warm air 34 in air chamber 26. The warmed air is swept into a storage system wherein it is forced throughout the interior of the building by conventional warm air conveying and conduction means. Cold air from the home can be recirculated back into the fan system wherein it is warmed by incoming hot air and then recirculated throughout the home. This cyclical process can continue in a generally continuous fashion. Heat storage, can be accomplished in conventional means by utilization of conventional heat sinks such as water which is warmed, sodium sulphate salt which is warmed, and the like.

As can be seen, the various combinations of structure of this invention provide an extremely efficient solar heat collection means and wall system therefor. The system also provides a solar wall system which will allow light to pass therethrough and yet extremely efficiently collect solar energy. Additionally, the solar wall system provides for convenient modules which can be easily made, transported and constructed on the job-site. Thus the invention accomplishes all of the heretofore stated objectives. *

ABSTRACT

A solar wall system wherein the wall has a collector plate for gathering solar energy and converting it into heat energy. The collector plate is an apertured collector plate having substantially no materials loss when compared to a solid plate of like material, weight and dimensions, but has increased surface area. One embodiment of the invention relates to a transparent solar wall system capable of transmitting light to the internal parts of a building structure. The transparent wall system utilizes the louvered collector plate. Another embodiment of the invention relates to a very efficient opaque solar wall system which employs gang-nail collector plates.

M. L. LITTLE.

SOLAR HEATING PLANT.

*

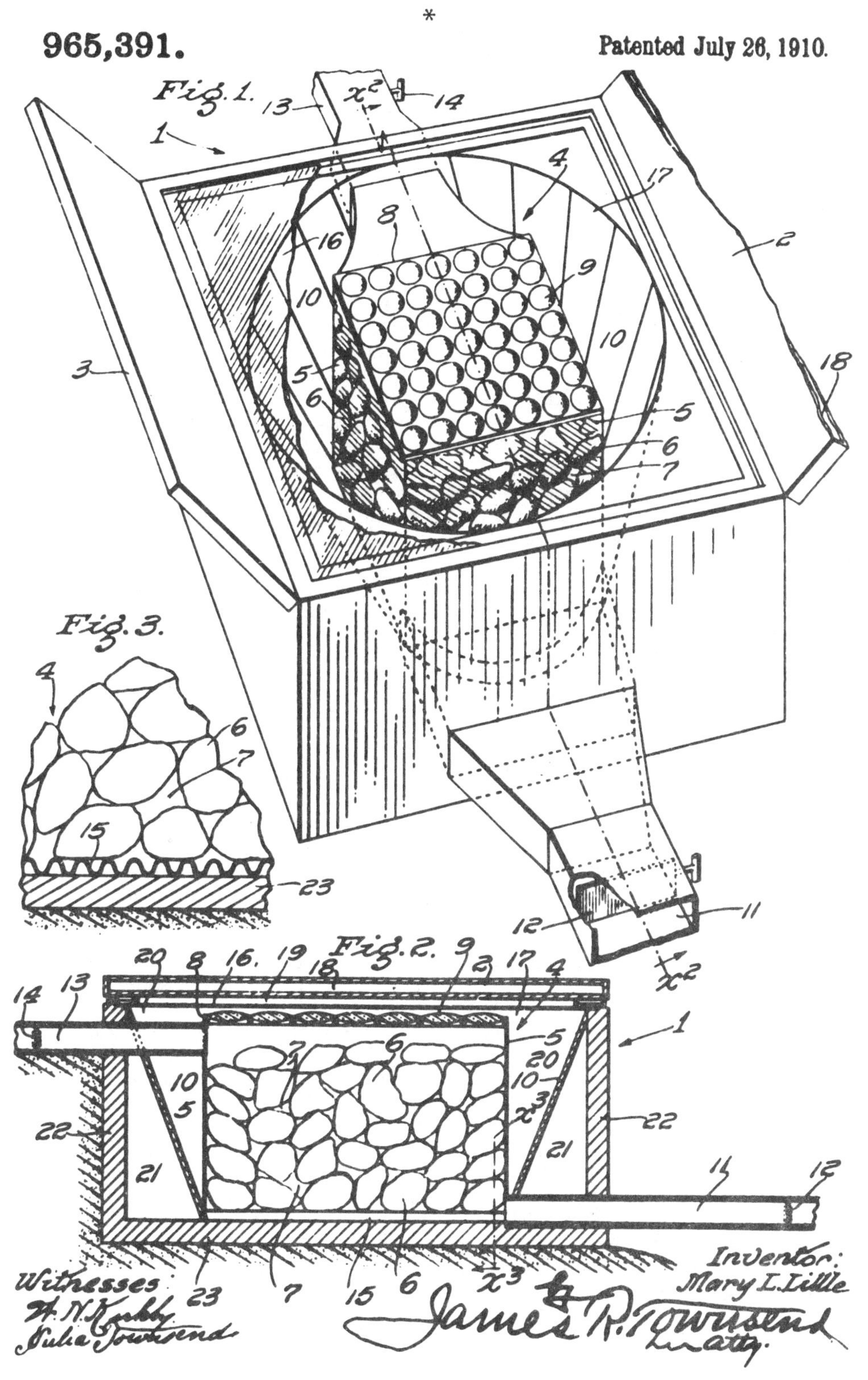

UNITED STATES PATENT OFFICE.

MARY L. LITTLE, OF LOS ANGELES, CALIFORNIA

SOLAR-HEATING PLANT

965, 391. Specification of Letters Patent **Patented July 26, 1910.**

*

The object of this invention is to provide means for warming apartments by the heat of the sun at night and during cloudy weather, such warming to be as convenient and effective by artificial means heretofore in use, and also being thoroughly sanitary.

The accompanying drawings illustrate the invention.

Figure 1 is a perspective view of apparatus constructed in accordance with this invention and set aslant. Fig. 2 is a longitudinal sectional elevation of an analogous apparatus set level. Line x^2, Fig. 1 designates the plane of section. In this view the floor of the receptacle is level. Fig. 3 is a fragmental sectional view on line x^3, Fig. 2.

1 represents an insulating receptacle in the form of a box, the walls of which may be of concrete or other material and of any suitable construction for retaining the heat. A cover formed of two hinged doors 2 and 3 extends over the same. 4 represents a case having translucent walls 5 through which the sun's rays may penetrate to heat loosely arranged heat-absorbing bodies 6 between which are communicating air-spaces 7. In the form shown, the case 4 is a rectangular prism, and all of the walls thereof above the base are transparent, and the top 8 is also open to the sun's rays and may be provided with lenses 9 as shown, in order to concentrate said rays upon the heat-absorbing bodies 6 inside the case.

I do not limit the construction to the use of lenses for the top, but such lenses are deemed advisable in some instances.

In case the lenses 9 are used, care is taken that the bodies 6 be so arranged as to receive the concentrated rays of the sun when the apparatus is subjected to the sun's rays.

Around the case 4 is provided a series of reflectors 10 arranged to direct to the case the sun's rays that fall upon the reflectors. The purpose is to heat the heat-absorbing bodies as fully as possible during the time that the sun's rays fall upon the apparatus. The reflectors should be constructed and arranged in such manner as to receive the sun's rays from a wide area and to direct such rays to said bodies 6.

The apparatus may be arranged with a southern inclination in northern latitudes for the purpose of most advantageously receiving the rays and directing them upon the heat-absorbing bodies.

In cloudy weather at night and whenever it is deemed advisable to close the apparatus, the doors 2 and 3 will be shut down thus closing the insulating receptacle and retaining the heat within the device.

11 designates a valved air inlet and 12 a valve therefor. Said inlet opens into the bottom of the case to supply cold air thereto. 13 represents a valved air outlet leading from the top of the case to the apartments, not shown, that are to be heated. 14 designates a valve for the hot air outlet.

The heat-absorbing bodies 6 may be stones of such form that when the stones are placed together, open air-spaces or interstices will occur between them as indicated at 7. The stones may be boulders and should be thoroughly washed and dried before they are placed in the case.

15 designates a corrugated iron support for said stones, the purpose being to allow air to flow underneath the stones from the cold-air inlet 11 when the valves 12 and 14 are open.

A transparent glass top or inner cover 16 may be provided over the orifice of the cavity 17 around the case 4 so as to prevent the heat from being carried away by air-currents.

The cover may be provided with a dead air space 18, and a dead air space 19 may be provided between the cover and the glass top or inner cover 16. Another dead air space 20 may be provided between the case 4 and the glass top 16 and reflectors 10. Another dead air space 21 may be provided between the reflectors and the walls 22 and floor 23 of the insulating receptacle 1.

In practical use, when the sun is shining, the doors 2 and 3 may be opened so that the sun will heat the contents of the case. When the heat of the sun is no longer effective upon the apparatus the doors will be closed, thus to insulate the interior of the apparatus and retain the heat until it is desired to be used in the building, not shown, with which the hot-air outlet 13 is connected.

When it is desired to heat such building the valves 12 and 14 will be opened, thus to allow the air to pass into the case 4 and thence up through the outlet 13 to the building.

By constructing large plants of this character and arranging to concentrate a large amount of sun's rays upon the heat-absorbing bodies, the same may be brought to a high heat and such heat may be largely retained until the time of use, and great economy of fuel result. *

Chapter 3

Solar Collectors with Heat Storage/ Exchange Units

April 22, 1952 C. L. STOCKSTILL 2,594,232

SOLAR HEATER AND HEAT EXCHANGER

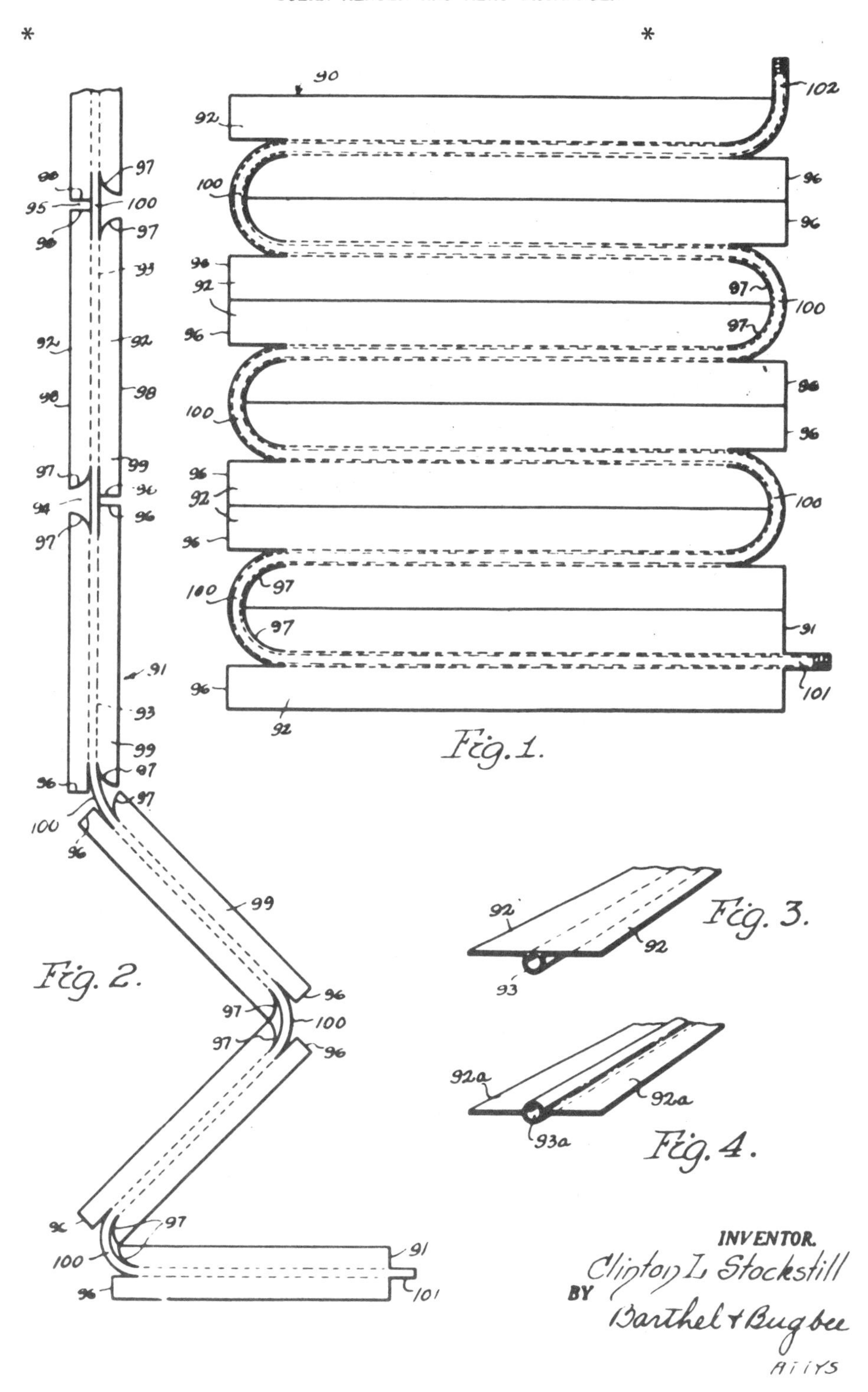

April 22, 1952 C. L. STOCKSTILL 2,594,232

SOLAR HEATER AND HEAT EXCHANGER

* *

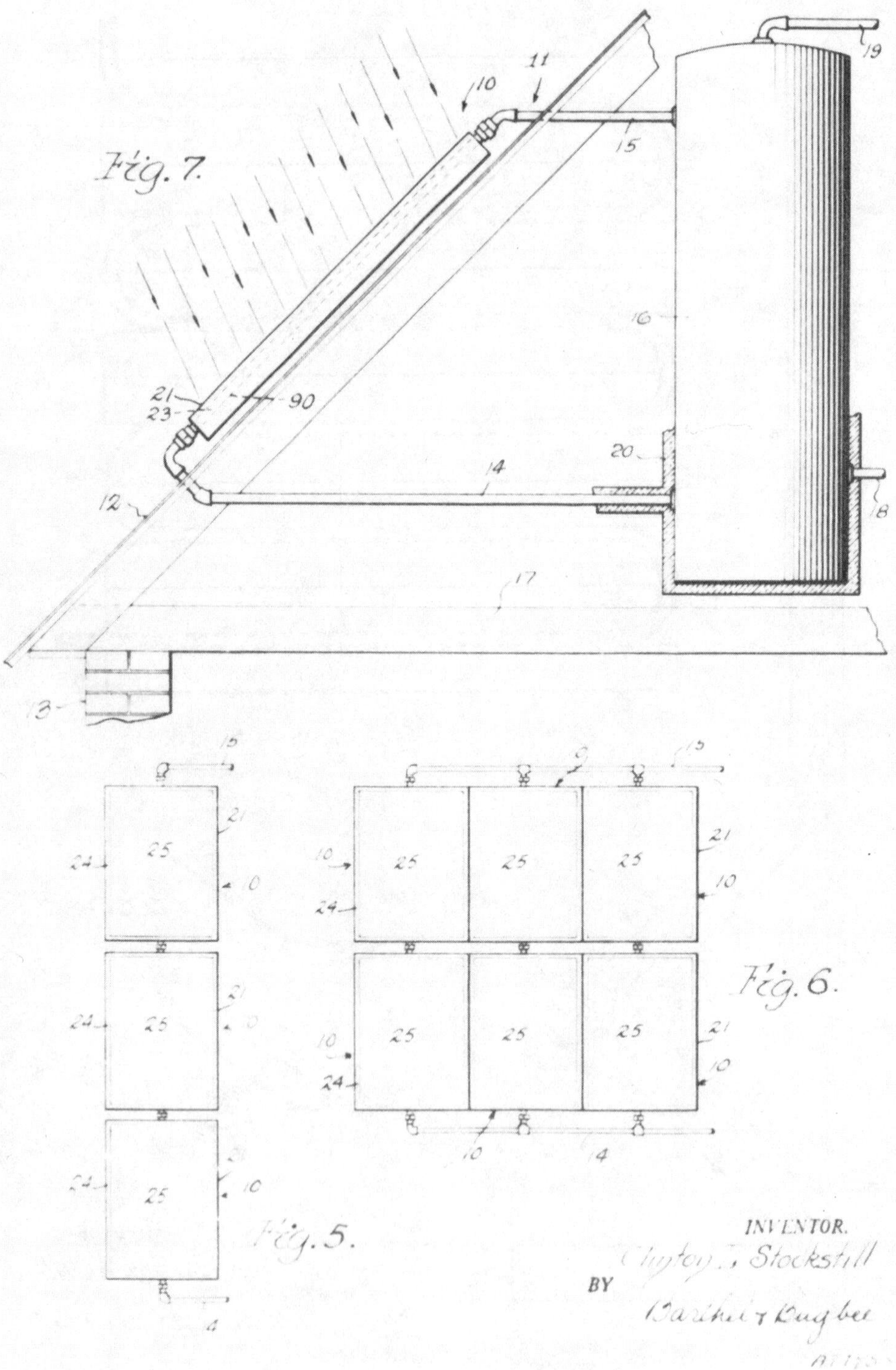

Fig. 7.

Fig. 6.

Fig. 5.

INVENTOR.
Clayton J. Stockstill
BY
Barthel & Bugbee
ATTYS

UNITED STATES PATENT OFFICE

2,594,232

SOLAR HEATER AND HEAT EXCHANGER

Clinton L. Stockstill, Detroit, Mich.

Application September 16, 1947, Serial No. 774,220

*

This invention relates to solar heaters, or devices for utilizing the heat of the sun to heat water or other liquids.

One object of this invention is to provide a solar heater which is simply and inexpensively constructed and which employs heat-absorbing elements which are capable of production by stamping or extrusion processes.

Another object is to provide a solar heater formed from extruded metal parts, wherein the heat exchanger includes tubular heat absorbing elements having integral fins thereon and connected at their opposite ends to headers which receive the cool water or other liquid at one end and carry away the heated water from the other end, the headers being also optionally provided with integral fins, these fins increasing the heat-absorbing ability of the heater.

Another object is to provide a solar heater as set forth in the preceding objects, wherein the heat exchanger is formed from an elongated tubular member with fins along its opposite sides, these fins being transversely cut away at intervals so as to enable the tubular member to be bent in a zigzag manner into a sinuous form with the fins arranged edge to edge.

Another object is to provide a solar heater as set forth in the preceding objects, wherein the integral construction of the tubular members and their flanges or fins eliminates the costly and inefficient manufacture of these elements in separate parts, as well as the interference with the conduction of heat through the layers of solder or other dissimilar metals previously used in uniting the various parts.

Figure 1 is a front elevation of a heat exchanger unit, wherein the unit is formed from an elongated finned tubular member bent into a sinuous form;

Figure 2 is a front elevation of the elongated finned tubular member from which the heat exchanger unit of Figure 1 is constructed, with the bending operation partially performed;

Figure 3 is a perspective view of a portion of the tubular member shown in Figure 1;

Figure 4 is a perspective view similar to Figure 3 but showing a modification thereof;

Figure 5 is a diagrammatic front elevation of three solar heaters of the present invention, connected in series;

Figure 6 is a diagrammatic front elevation of six solar heaters of the present invention, connected in a series-parallel arrangement; and

Figure 7 is a diagrammatic side elevation, partly in section, of a solar heater system installed in the upper portion of a building and employing one of the solar heaters of the present invention.

Referring to the drawings in detail, Figures 1 and 7 show a solar heater generally designated 10, according to a preferred form of the invention, as contained in a solar heating system 11 (Figure 7). The solar heater 10 is preferably mounted upon the roof 12 of a building 13 where it will be exposed to the maximum amount of direct sunlight and connected at its lower and upper ends by pipes 14 and 15 to the lower and upper portions of a tank 16 mounted in any suitable location, such as upon the attic floor 17 of the building 13. Connected to the lower portion of the tank 16 is a water inlet pipe 18 and to its upper end is connected a water outlet pipe 19 for conveying the heated water to the location where it is used. The tank 16 is preferably surrounded by an insulation layer 20, which may also be extended around the pipes 14 and 15 to conserve heat.

The solar heating system 11 may contain but a single solar heater 10 or it may include a battery of such heaters 10 as shown in Figures 5 and 6. In Figure 5 the heaters 10 are connected in series between the cool water pipe 14 and the heated water pipe 15. In Figure 6, however, the heaters 10 are connected in a series-parallel arrangement whereby pairs of individual heaters 10 are connected in series and these pairs are in turn connected in parallel between the pipes 14 and 15.

The solar heater 10 consists generally of a box-like glass-covered casing or housing 21 containing a heat exchanger 90. The heat exchanger 90, removed from the housing 21, is shown assembled in Figure 1 and with its parts separated in Figure 2. The casing or housing 21 is a box-like structure having sides 23 (Figure 7) of wood or other suitable material, assembled in a rectangular arrangement. Secured to the front edges of the sides 23 for example by metal bars forming a frame 24 which holds a glass pane or panel 25 positioned to cover the opening between the sides 23, the latter being recessed or grooved to receive the pane 25.

The heat exchanger 90 shown in Figures 1 to 3 inclusive is formed by preparing an elongated finned tubular member 91, preferably by extrusion, with aluminum as the preferred material. The fins 92 on opposite sides of the tubular portion 93 are discontinuous, gaps 94 and 95 being cut alternately on either side thereof from one end to the other (Figure 2). The gaps 95 are in the form of rectangular notches having spaced straight edges 96 whereas the gaps 94 are provided with arcuate edges 97 diverging toward the tubular portion 93 from a minimum width of gap at the outer edges 98. Thus the elongated tubular member 91 is provided with spaced heat exchanger tube portions 99 at intervals along its length. The gaps 94 and 95 are preferably formed by punching or stamping but may be formed in any other convenient way. The fins

92 are either formed tangentially (Figure 3) to the tubular portions 93 or diametrically to the tubular portion 93a as at 92a in Figure 4.

When the elongated finned tubular member 91 has been prepared and slotted in the manner shown in Figure 2, it is bent at points adjacent the gaps 94 and 95 and alternately in opposite directions. Figure 2 shows the commencement of the bending operations and Figure 1 the finished heat exchanges. The arcuate edges 97 are formed with radii of curvature substantially equal to the widths of the fins 92 so that when the spaced heat exchanger tube portions 99 are bent edge to edge upon one another (Figure 1) the connecting tubular portions 100 will curve into arcs coinciding with the arcuate edges 97. The latter as a result of the bending operations, unite to form semicircles as shown at the opposite sides of Figure 1.

In this manner the heat exchanger 90 is formed in a single piece with its fins 92 integral with the tubular portions 93 and their connection portions 100. Tubular extensions 101 and 102 at the opposite ends of the elongated member provide inlet and outlet connections for the liquid. The heat exchanger 90 when thus assembled, may be used either by itself or in a suitable housing, such as the housing 21 of Figures 5 to 7 inclusive.

The solar heaters 10, employing the heat exchanger 90, may be mounted in units which are conveniently shipped and carried up to their positions on the roof. Typical arrangements of such units are shown in Figures 5 and 6 as previously described. A typical circuit is shown in Figure 7 also previously described.

The operation of the invention will be understood from Figure 7. Water is supplied to the tank 16 such as through the pipe 18. As the tank 16 is filled, the water likewise flows through the pipe 14 into the solar heater unit 10. As the sun's rays, indicated by the arrows in Figure 7, beat down upon the solar heaters 10, the heat of the sun is transferred to the heat exchanger tubes, assisted by their fins, and this heat passes into the water in the tubes. The fins on the lower and upper headers also assist in collecting the heat, and an insulation layer (not shown) behind the heat exchanger 90 in the casing 21 (Figure 7) prevents loss of the heat into the roof 12. As the water becomes heated, it becomes lighter and hence flows through the pipe 15 into the upper portion of the tank 16. This sets up a circulation by convection currents, and this re-circulation causes the water to become hotter and hotter upon each passage through the solar heater 10. The heated water is drawn off through the pipe 19 for service to the household or other installation where the solar heater is used. In actual installations the operation of the circuit shown in Figure 7 is somewhat improved if the pipe 15 is inclined slightly upward from the solar heater 10 toward the tank 16, so as to facilitate the flow of the heated water from the solar heater 10 to the tank 16.*

July 2, 1968 C. D. SNELLING 3,390,672

SOLAR HEATING DEVICE

* *

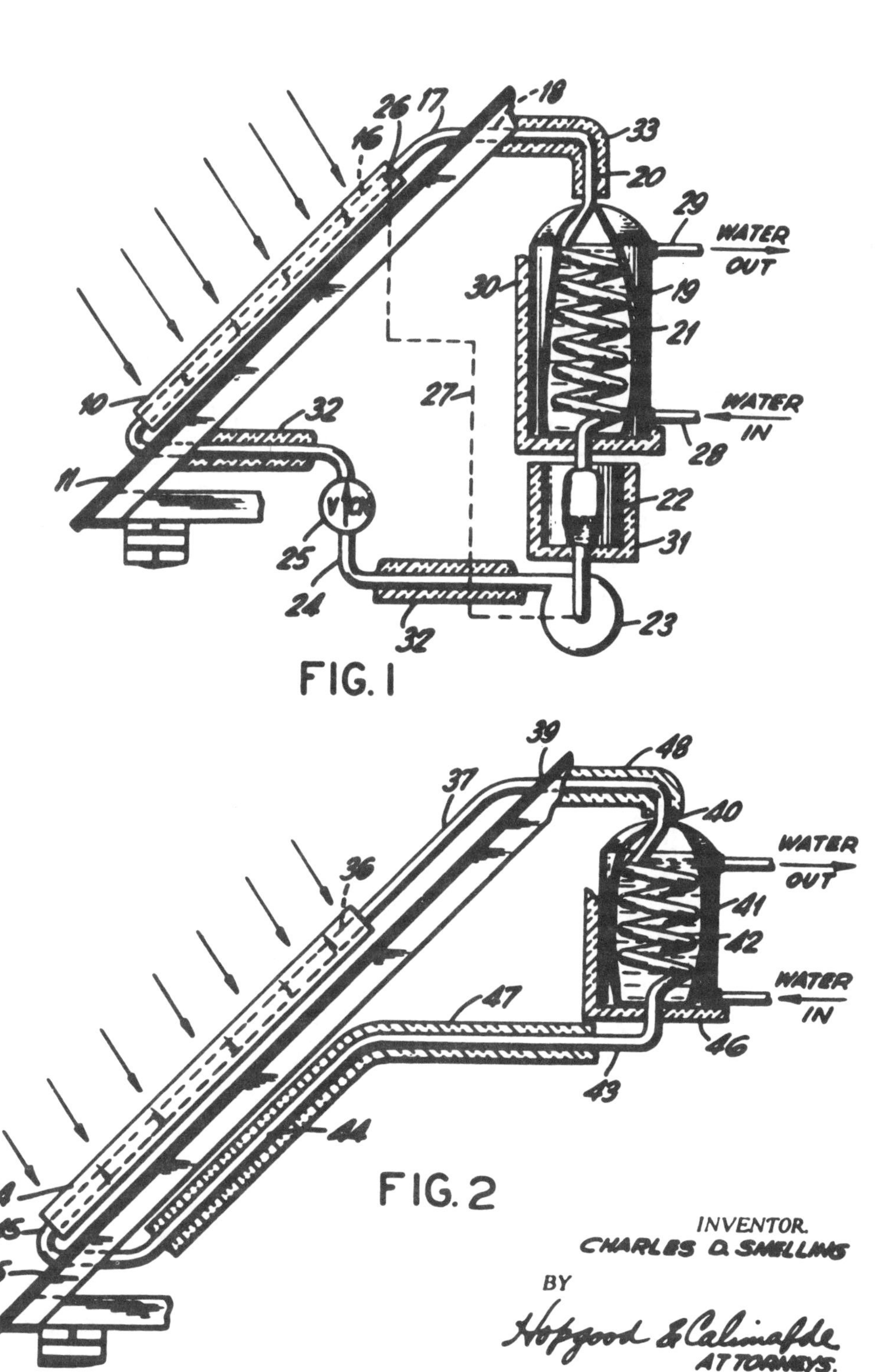

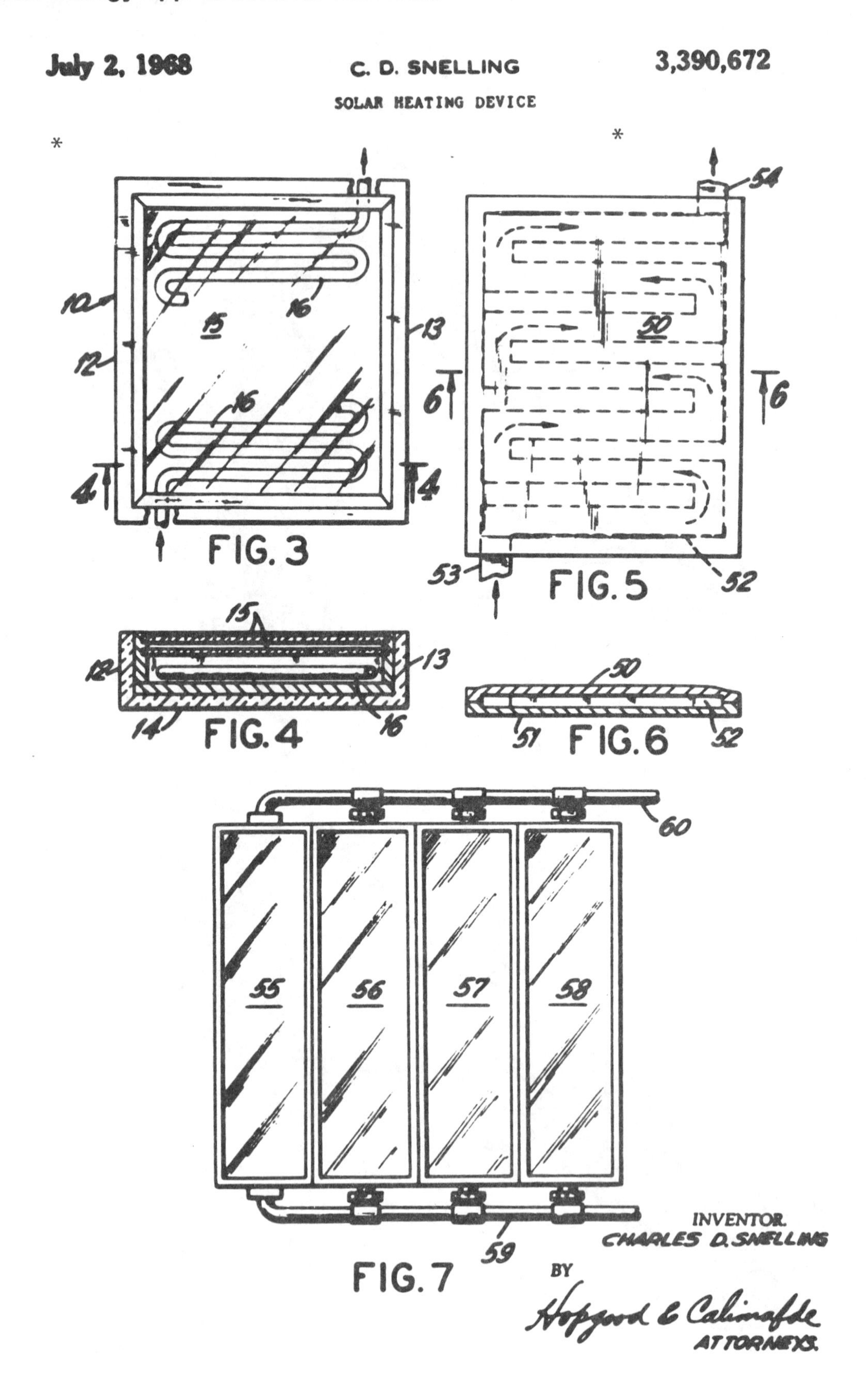
July 2, 1968
C. D. SNELLING
3,390,672
SOLAR HEATING DEVICE
FIG. 3
FIG. 5
FIG. 4
FIG. 6
FIG. 7
INVENTOR.
CHARLES D. SNELLING
BY
Hopgood & Calimafde
ATTORNEYS.

3,390,672

SOLAR HEATING DEVICE

Charles D. Snelling, Allentown, Pa., assignor, by mesne assignments, to Melpar, Inc., a corporation of Delaware

*

ABSTRACT OF THE DISCLOSURE

A solar heating system in which a heat-collecting chamber has an evaporation zone communicating with the fluid-conducting condenser of a heat exchanger via an evacuated, hermetically sealed heat-transfer fluid circulating system forming a closed path with the chamber and the exchanger. The circulating system contains a vaporizable heat-transfer fluid in a quantity in the condensed form just sufficient, when the spacing between chamber and exchanger along the closed path is considered, to flood the evaporation zone of the chamber.

This invention relates to solar heaters and, in particular, to a solar heating and heat exchange system and a method of utilizing solar energy.

The principal object of the invention is to provide a method of and a system for solar heating of homes and other habitable structures which is more practical than systems and methods heretofore used.

Broadly speaking, solar heaters comprise a solar heat collector which absorbs heat energy from the sun and delivers it via a heat transfer fluid into a house or to a heat storage unit. The heat collector generally comprises a black plate to absorb solar radiation, one or more air-spaced glass panes for transmitting solar radiation to the collector and for trapping the heat within it, and a circulating heat-transfer medium, e.g., water, for transferring heat from the collector to rooms in a house or to a heat storage device.

The heat collector may be in the form of a flat tank placed on top of a roof or may comprise a zig-zag arrangement of pipes in a well-insulated box covered by one or two air-spaced panes of glass. Water circulated in the pipes on the roof is heated by the sun and is accumulated in an insulated storage tank, or the pipes with the heated water may pass through a heat exchanger and the heat of the water transferred to a heat exchange fluid, such as water in a boiler or to a stream of air used to heat the home.

The foregoing systems have their limitations insofar as heat capacity is concerned in that the heat energy transferred is generally in the form of sensible heat. Assuming the heat-transfer fluid is circulating water, and the water is heated to a temperature of say 50° F. above its original temperature, this amounts to an increase in heat content due to heat absorption of 50 B.t.u.'s per pound of water. By circulating the heated water through heat-exchanger tubes, some or all of the heat is extracted. The rate at which heat is extracted will depend on the rate at which the circulating water absorbs heat, the rate of circulating water, the efficiency of the heat collector, the efficiency of the heat exchanger, etc.

Attempts to improve the foregoing types of hot water heaters have generally been in the direction of re-designing the collector to improve its heat absorbing characteristics. Another modification has been to utilize the heat pump principle in conjunction with the solar collector in which ammonia gas is employed as the heat-transfer fluid. This modification, which is described in U.S. Patent No. 1,765,136, comprises passing ammonia gas through the collector where it absorbs heat, and then adiabatically compressing the gas before it enters a heat exchange apparatus, in this case a steam boiler.

My system differs from the foregoing in that I utilize an evacuated hermetically sealed circulating system containing a heat-exchange fluid adapted to boil over a range of temperatures so long as there is a temperature difference between the temperature at the collector and the temperature at the heat exchange unit. Thus, instead of relying on only sensible heat to effect heat transfer, I am able to provide a system in which the latent heat of vaporization is utilized at any temperature to assure high heat capacity within the system so long as the temperature at the heat collector is higher than that at the heat exchanger.

The objects of my invention will be more clearly apparent from the following disclosure and the drawing, wherein:

FIGS. 1 and 2 are illustrative of two apparatus embodiments for carrying out my invention;

FIGS. 3 and 4 depict in plan and cross section one form of heat collector which may be used in carrying out my novel inventive concept;

FIGS. 5 and 6 also show in plan and cross section another form of a heat collector; and

FIG. 7 is illustrative of a bank of heat collectors.

My invention comprises the combination of a solar heater and a heat-exchange system consisting of a heat-collecting chamber having an evaporation zone associated therewith, a heat exchanger associated with fluid-conducting condensing means, and an evacuated heat-transfer circulating system connecting the heat-collecting chamber to the fluid-conducting condenser means in a closed path which communicates with the heat-collecting chamber. A predetermined amount of vaporizable heat-transfer fluid is hermetically sealed in the evacuated circulating system, the heat-collecting chamber being spatially disposed relative to the heat exchanger such that the contained predetermined amount of heat-transfer fluid is preferably just sufficient in the condensed form to flood the evaporation zone of the heat-collecting chamber, means being provided to insure flooding of the evaporation zone with the predetermined amount of heat-transfer fluid. Such means may comprise a pump or a gravity leg may be provided extending from the condenser, the gravity leg being disposed relative to the evaporator so as to insure flooding of the evaporator with heat-transfer fluid.

Referring to FIG. 1, I show one embodiment of a solar heating system comprising a solar collector **10** associated with roof **11**, the solar collector being of the type, for example, as that shown in FIGS. 3 and 4 comprising a flat box having side walls **12**, **13** (FIG. 4) and an insulated bottom **14**. The side and end walls support a pair of air-spaced panes of glass **15**, the box or collector having contained therein a bank of tubing **16** arranged in a tortuous path, and specifically in zig-zag fashion as shown in FIG. 3, the tubing making up the evaporation zone of the collector.

Tubing **16** is part of and coextensive with a circulatory system comprising tubing **17** emerging from the collector, passing through the roof at **18** and entering a hot water **19** at **20** in communication with coiled tubing or heat exchanger **21**. The heat exchanger may be coupled to a sump **22** below the hot water tank, although a sump is not necessary. The sump is connected to a pump **23** which removes the heat-transfer fluid from the sump to the collector via tubing **24** which has a one way check valve **25** across it to prevent back flow of condensed fluid. The pump is driven by a motor which may be controlled by a conventional switch actuating means at **26** of the collector through line **27** coupled to the motor. The switch actuating means may comprise a float which actuates a micro-switch at **26**, or other conventional actuating device. Where the amount of heat transfer fluid employed is just sufficient to flood the evaporator, a cut-off switch would not be necessary since the sump would be empty and there would not be any additional fluid to pump. In this connection, the pump which is generally small and operated by a one-sixteenth to one-eighth horse power motor may run continuously and need not stop.

As stated above, the circulating system is evacuated and a heat-transfer fluid added to it in a predetermined amount just sufficient to maintain a reservoir in the sump and to keep the evaporation zone of the solar collector flooded. Examples of heat-transfer fluids are those sold under the trademarks Freon 11, Freon 113, Freon 114 as well as such fluids as ethyl alcohol, ethyl ether and similar heat-transfer fluids. By hermetically sealing the fluid in the circulating system under sub-atmospheric pressure, for example under vacuum, it will develop its own equilibrium pressure at each temperature. Thus, assuming ethyl alcohol is sealed under vacuum in the system, the pressure developed in the system at, for example 60° F. as the alcohol evaporates will be about 32 mm. (about 0.6 p.s.i. absolute). If the temperature at the collector is higher than the temperature in the condensing zone, then the alcohol in the evaporating zone of the collector will boil and remove heat from the collector as latent heat of vaporization. No matter what the temperature is at the collector, so long as it is higher than the temperature in the storage tank, there will always be some boiling of fluid until the temperature of the storage tank reaches that of the collector and the system reaches equilibrium.

I prefer hermetically sealed systems having fluids with fairly low vapor pressures at temperatures upwards of about 175° F. Freon 11 is very practical in that it exhibits a vapor pressure of about 39 lbs./in.^{2} absolute at 130° F. Freon 113 exhibits a lower vapor pressure of about 18.5 lbs./in.^{2} at the same temperature, while Freon 114 exhibits a vapor pressure of about 73.8 lb./in.^{2}. Hermetically sealed ethyl alcohol, on the other hand, can be boiled in an evacuated system at temperatures of up to about 172° F. before it reaches a pressure of one atmosphere absolute or 14.6 lbs./in.^{2}. in the system. Some temperatures and vapor pressures (lbs./in.^{2} absolute) of fluids which may be employed are given as follows:

VAPOR PRESSURE (LBS./IN.^{2})

Temp., ° F.	Ethyl Alcohol	Ethyl Ether	Carbon Tetrachloride	Freon 11	Freon 113
60	0.6	7.1	1.38	10.1	4.3
68	0.85	8.5	1.75	10.3	5.1
77	1.14	10.3	2.22		
86	1.5	12.4	2.74		
95	2.0	14.6	3.4	20.1	9.4
104	2.6	17.7	4.15		
122	4.75	24.5	6.2	30.4	16.0
131	5.4		7.3	39.1	18.5
140	6.8	33.2	8.65		
149	8.65		10.2	50.5	24.5
158	10.42	43.9	12.0		
172	14.6		14.0	70.0	30.2
176	15.6	57.6	16.1		
194	23.0	73.8	21.4	98.0	50.0

As will be noted from the above, a fairly wide range of evaporation temperatures is possible over a fairly low range of pressures, provided the circulating system is evacuated before the heat-transfer fluid is added to the system. Thus, no matter how small the temperature difference between the collector and the condensers, so long as the collector is higher in temperature, there will always be some heat transfer since there will always be some heat transfer fluid going from liquid to vapor and back to liquid again. The sensible heat is transferred as well as the latent heat of vaporization. Such heat transfer fluids may be adapted to boil from about +50 to +250° F. at vapor pressure of about 1 to 200 lbs./in.^{2} absolute. In the conventional devices using the convection flow of water as the heat-transfer liquid, the heat transfer at low temperature differences is quite sluggish and not as positive acting as the system of the invention.

Referring again to FIG. 1, after the requisite amount of heat transfer fluid, let us say ethyl alcohol, has been charged into the evacuated circulating system, pump **23** is started to insure flooding of collector **10** with alcohol. When the temperature at evaporator **10** exceeds that of condenser **21**, the alcohol will boil and pass into the condenser to heat the water therein. Cold water is fed into tank **19** via pipe **28** at the bottom and heated water drawn off via pump at pipe **29** at the top. Assuming that the water in the tank starts off at a temperature of about 70° F. and the temperature of the collector is such as to be substantially above the water temperature, let us say about 130° F., the alcohol in the evaporating zone will boil: the vapor will pass through pipe **17** into condensing coil **21** where it will condense and give up its sensible and its latent heat to the surrounding water, and the condensed heat-transfer fluid will then flow by gravity to sump **22** from which it will be drawn by pump **23**.

The circulation of the heat-transfer fluid will continue through the pump until evaporation ceases. This will occur when the temperature of the water tank reaches and is the same as that of the collector. Since no fluid is being evaporated, the pump will shut off via a signal from switch actuating means at point **26** of the evaporator. However, as stated hereinabove, a switch may not be necessary where the amount of fluid is just sufficient to flood the evaporator. It will be appreciated that in the evening, the collector may cool down below the temperature prevailing in the sump. Where this occurs and the temperature is higher in the sump, the fluid in the sump will tend to boil and its vapor flow upwards through condenser coil **21**, remove heat therefrom and then condense in the cooler piping on the roof and dump the heat outside the house. To prevent the cycle from reversing itself in the evening, a check valve **25** is provided as shown in line **24**. Since no circulation can take place against the valve, the cycle reversal is prevented. However, so long as the amount of fluid is just sufficient to flood the evaporator, the reverse flow of heat is prevented, since the sump would be empty. In prior art solar heaters, extra care must be taken to prevent the reverse flow of heat.

In order to prevent loss of heat in the house, it is preferred that water tank **19** be insulated. An insulation **30** is shown fragmentarily of suitable material, such as asbestos and the like. Sump **22** is likewise preferably covered with an outer sheath of insulation **31**. Similarly, the pipes should be insulated as shown fragmentarily at **32**, **33**, etc.

In FIG. 2, I show another modification of my invention in which a pump is not required to insure flooding of the evaporation zone with the vaporizable heat-transfer fluid. In this instance, the means to insure flooding is a gravity leg or trap lying below the water tank. In FIG. 2, a collector **34** is shown associated with roof **35**. The evaporator zone may comprise a zig-zag arrangement of tubing **36** which is part of and coextensive with a hermetically sealed heat-transfer circulating system comprising a tubing **37** emerging from the collector and passing through the house at **39** and entering a hot water tank **41** and **40** in communication with coiled tubing or heat exchanger condenser **42**. The exit end of the condenser communicates with tubing **43** which terminates into a gravity leg or trap **44** below the water tank, which leg communicates with the collector at **45** on the roof. Preferably the pipe lines in the house and the water tank should be insulated as shown fragmentarily by insulation **46**, **47** and **48**. The vapor passes one way to the heat exchanger via pipe **37** while the gravity leg serves as a trap or stop in the other direction. As is apparent, the embodiment shown in FIG.

2 is self-operable so long as the amount of fluid hermetically sealed in the circulation system is just sufficient to fill up leg or trap **44** and evaporation zone **36** in the solar collector. As stated above, so long as the temperature at the collector is higher than the temperature in the circulating system within the house, the fluid will boil, evaporate and transfer its latent heat to the heat exchanger. The structure shown in FIG. 2 by its very nature prevents flow of heat to outside the house.

Embodiments of other types of solar collectors are shown in FIGS. 5 to 7. Preferably the material of construction of the evaporation zone should be a good heat conductor so as to insure rapid transfer of the absorbed sun's rays to the heat-transfer fluid. In FIG. 5, I show what is known in the trade as a flat tube sheet made of two superimposed sheets of aluminum **50** and **51** bonded together at their contact faces except for a tortuous pathway **52** shown in dotted lines in FIG. 5 and by the cross section in FIG. 6. The heat transfer fluid enters the evaporator at **53** and exits at **54** as a vapor to the circulating system in the house or other enclosure. The evaporator would preferably be encased in an insulated box with two air-spaced glass panes as shown in FIGS. 3 and 4 and would have an anodized black finish so as to insure a high efficiency of heat absorption.

The solar collector may comprise a parallel arrangement of collector segments **55** to **58** as shown in FIG. 7 with a manifold inlet of fluid at **59** and a manifold outlet for the vapor at **60**. *

Aug. 15, 1950 G. E. PRESSER ET AL 2,519,281

WATER HEATER AND STORAGE UNIT

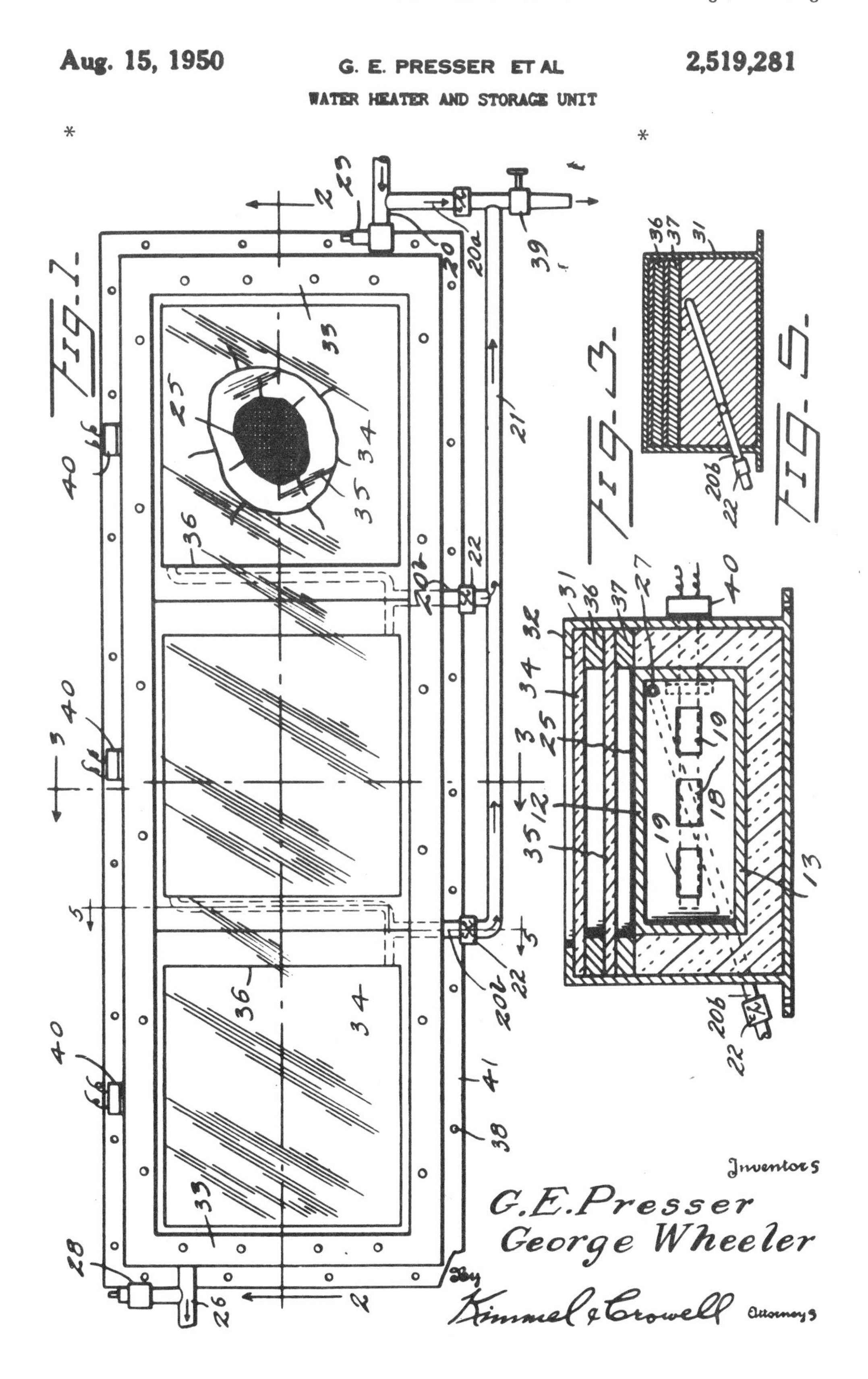

Aug. 15, 1950 **G. E. PRESSER ET AL** **2,519,281**

WATER HEATER AND STORAGE UNIT

*   *

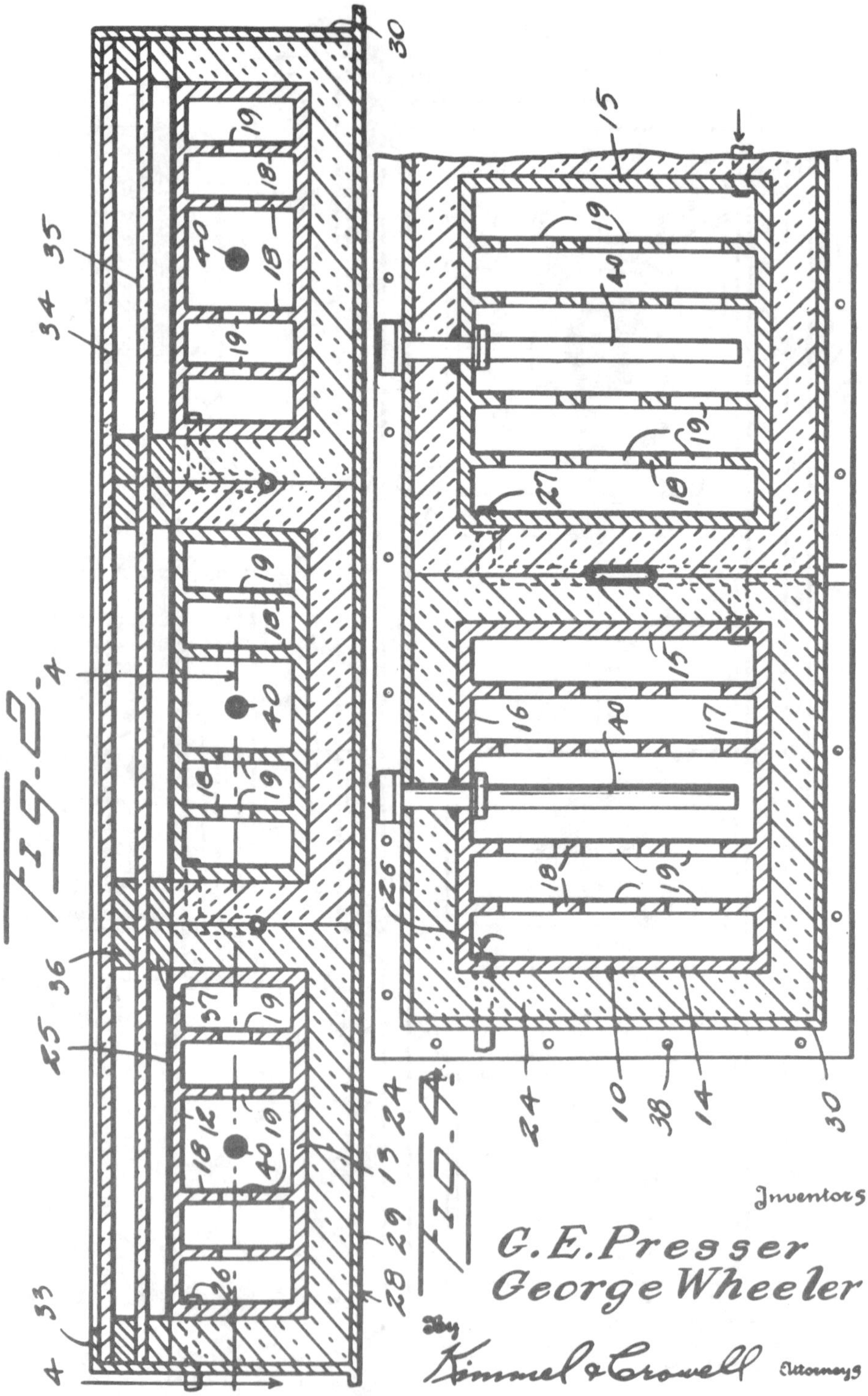

Inventors

G. E. Presser
George Wheeler

By Kimmel & Crowell Attorneys

UNITED STATES PATENT OFFICE

2,519,281

WATER HEATER AND STORAGE UNIT

Glenn E. Presser and George Wheeler, Miami, Fla.

*

This invention relates to solar heaters.

An object of this invention is to provide a solar water heater and storage reservoir which includes single units or a series of coupled units which are imbedded in heat insulation with one side thereof exposed to the sun rays through glass.

Another object of this invention is to provide a solar water heater and storage reservoir constructed in one unit, including a booster heating means so that the water may be heated to the desired degree above the temperature of the water obtained from the sun rays.

Another object of this invention is to provide a solar heater which may be used with a pressure water system and when they are installed in more than single units include check valves for establishing the flow of water from each solar heater and storage reservoir unit to a drain valve.

A further object of this invention is to provide a heater of this kind wherein the heating and storage units may be cast out of metal, or formed of welded parts. *

In the drawings,

Figure 1 is a plan view, partly broken away, of a solar heater constructed according to an embodiment of this invention,

Figure 2 is a sectional view taken on line 2—2 of Figure 1,

Figure 3 is a sectional view taken on the line 3—3 of Figure 1,

Figure 4 is a fragmentary sectional view taken on the line 4—4 of Figure 2,

Figure 5 is a sectional view taken substantially along the line 5—5 of Figure 1.

Referring to the drawings, the numeral 10 designates generally one unit of a series of connected solar heaters which are constructed according to an embodiment of this invention. These heaters have been shown in the drawings mounted in a single casing, but it will be understood that any desired number of these heaters may be mounted as a single water heating and storage means.

The heating unit 10 comprises upper and lower walls 12 and 13 respectively, which are connected together at their opposite ends by end walls 14 and 15. Upstanding side walls 16 and 17 are secured to the opposite lengthwise edges of the walls 12 and 13 and the side and end walls constitute a means for providing a closed housing through which water is adapted to pass.

The heating unit 10 is adapted to be braced to withstand inside pressure by means of a plurality of bracing plates 18 which are fixed between and secured to upper and lower walls 12 and 13 respectively, and are secured to and between the side walls 16 and 17. The bracing members 18 are formed with elongated holes 19 therethrough, whereby the water may freely pass through these bracing members from the inlet to the outlet of the heater and storage unit.

An intake pipe 20 is secured to the end wall 15 and the pipe 20b is connected to a common drain pipe 21 extending lengthwise of the multiple assembly. A check valve 22 is interposed in the pipe 20b so as to provide for movement of the water in only one direction, that is, toward the drain cock. The endmost heating member 10 has connected thereto an intake pipe 20a which is also connected to the drain pipe 21 by pipe 20b and a pressure relief valve 23 is interposed in the intake pipe 20.

The heating element and storage unit 10 is adapted to be imbedded in a heat insulating medium 24 which engages the bottom, the opposite sides and the opposite ends of the unit, leaving the top wall thereof free for exposure to the sun rays through glass. The top wall 12, on the upper surface thereof, is coated black, as indicated at 25, so that the sun rays will be absorbed by the top wall 12.

The heating and storage unit 10 in single unit installations also has connected thereto an outlet pipe 26 which extends through the insulating means 24 and the outlet pipe 26 is connected to a hot water pipe distributing system. A pressure relief valve 28 is interposed in pipe 26 so as to provide for safety from over heating.

The heating and storage member 10, when installed in more than single units, has a cold water supply pipe 20 connected to lower end of wall 15, through which cold water enters the first unit 10. In top end of wall 14, an outlet pipe is provided. Through this pipe 27 hot water passes to the next unit inlet in the lower end of wall 15, which is repeated with each succeeding unit in the installation. From the last unit 10 hot water leaves heater and storage units through pipe 26. The water moves from the heater and storage units as same is used at the hot water faucets or hot water appliances.

The heat insulation 24 has disposed thereabout an outer casing or jacket 28 which includes a bottom wall 29, end walls 30 and opposite side walls 31. An inwardly extending flange 32 extends from the side walls 31 and a similar inwardly extending flange 33 extends from the end walls 30. A pair of transparent panels 34 and 35 are disposed above the top wall 12, being supported in spaced relation with respect to each other by spacer members 36, and supported in spaced relation to the top wall 12 by spacer members 37. The top flanges 32 and 33 engage over the uppermost transparent panels 34 so as to hold these panels in proper position.

The flanges 32 and 33 may, if desired, be made removable, in a conventional manner, so that the panels 34 and 35 may be replaced when broken or when first mounted in the unit. Base flanges 41 carried by the jacket are formed with openings 38 so that securing bolts may be passed through the flanges in order to attach the device on a suitable support. A drain valve 39 is connected to the pipe 21 for draining water from this pipe, and the valve 39 may be connected to a suitable drain means.

In order to provide a means whereby the temperature of the water heated in one or all heating and storage units may be boosted, we have provided an elongated electrical heating unit 40 which projects through the side wall 16 and is adapted to be connected to a suitable source of electric current supply. The electrical booster heating element may also be used for heating the water in each heating and storage unit at a time when the sun rays do not strike the device. At other times, the booster heater 40 may be used for raising the temperature of the water above the point to which the water is heated by the sun rays.

In the use and operation of this heater, the pipe 21 is connected to a source of water supply and the pipe 27 is connected to the hot water connections in the house. The unit is placed in a position where it will receive the sun rays, these rays passing through the transparent panels and striking the black surface 25 of the heating element. The water as it becomes heated circulates through the openings 19 of the bracing members 18 and remains stored in the unit until drawn through the outlet connections 26. In the event it is desired to raise the temperature of the water above that obtained from the sun rays, the electric booster members 40 are energized. These booster members 40 are of conventional construction. *

Jan. 20, 1953 C. W. HARRIS 2,625,930

SOLAR-HEATING STRUCTURE

* *

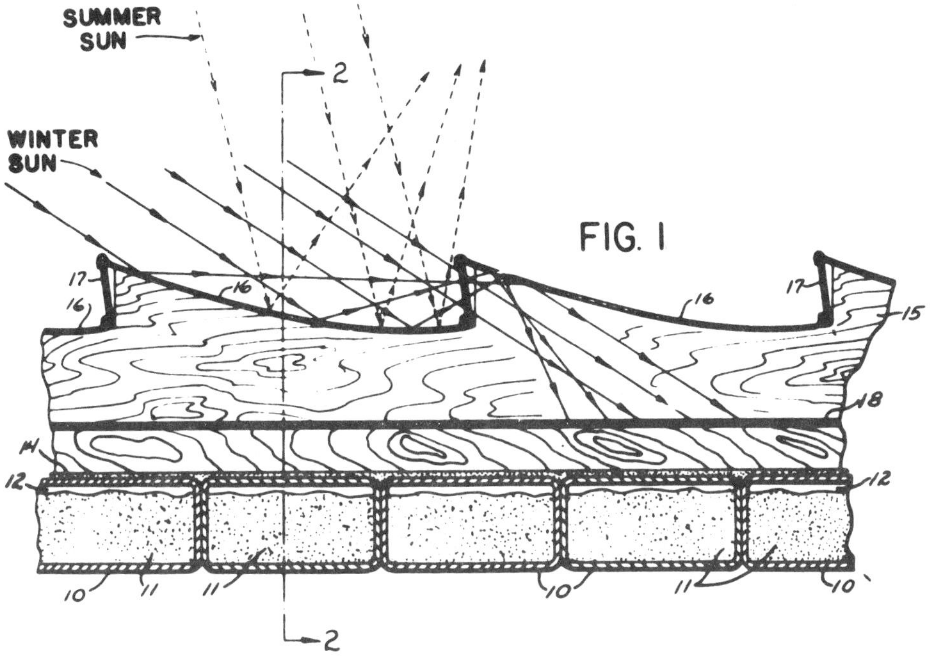

SUMMER SUN

WINTER SUN

FIG. 1

FIG. 2

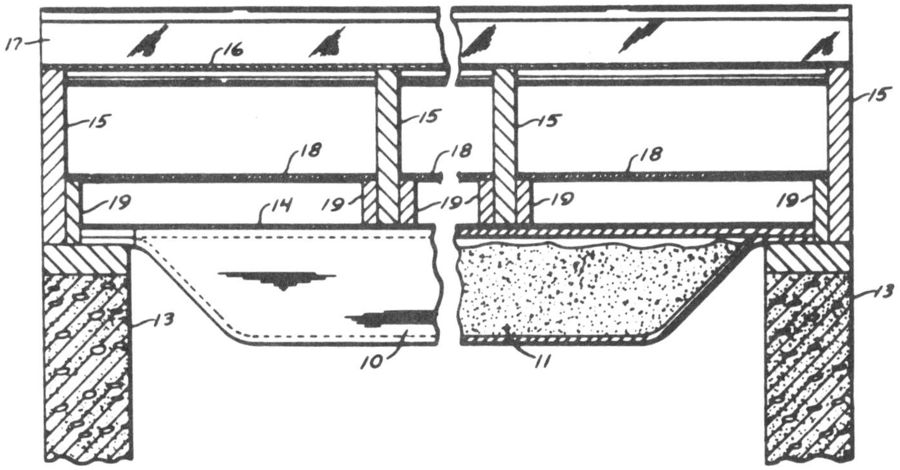

INVENTOR.
CLYDE W. HARRIS
BY Willard D. Eakin
ATTORNEY

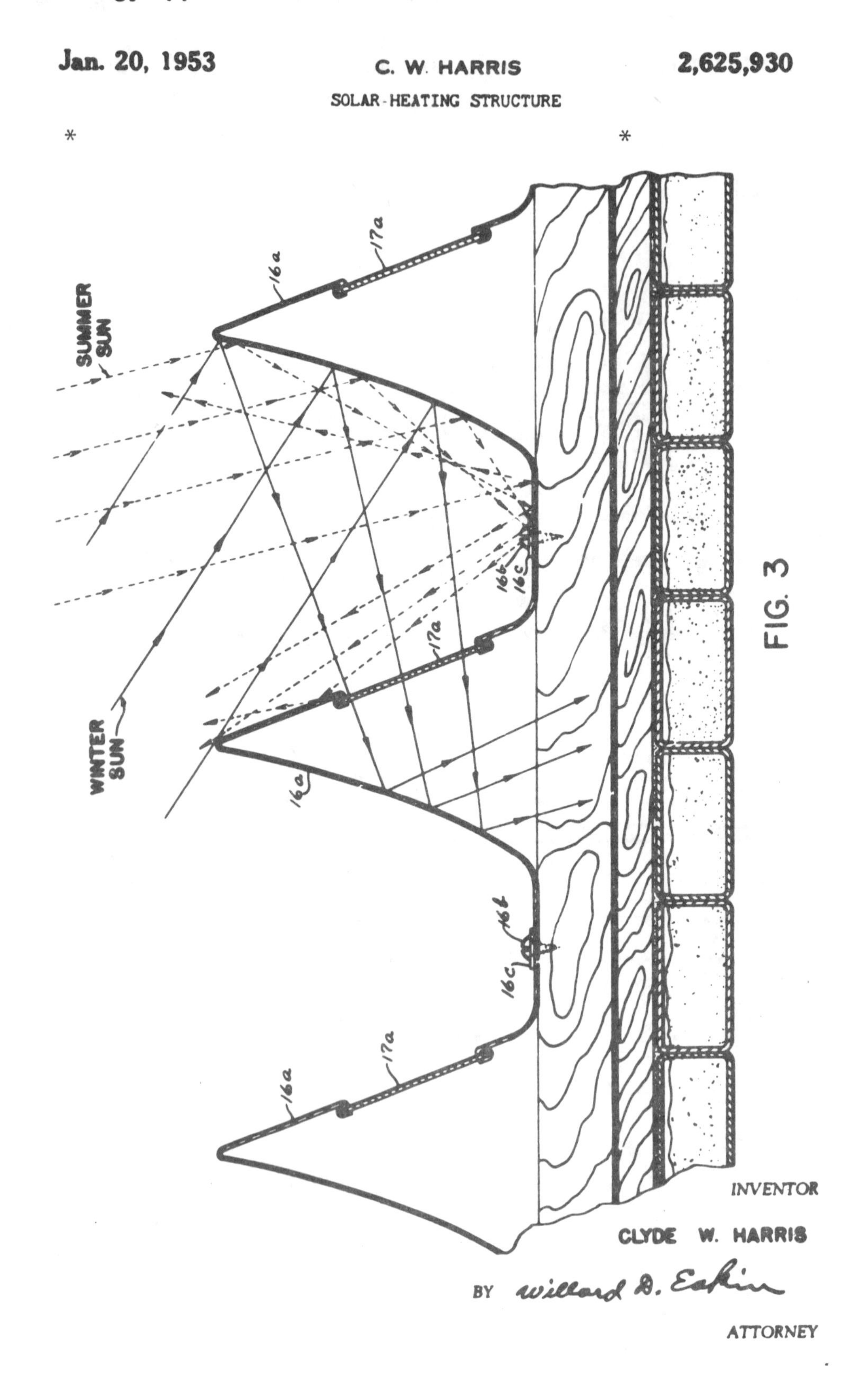
Jan. 20, 1953
C. W. HARRIS
2,625,930
SOLAR-HEATING STRUCTURE
SUMMER SUN
WINTER SUN
16a
17a
16b
16c
FIG. 3
INVENTOR
CLYDE W. HARRIS
BY Willard D. Eakin
ATTORNEY

UNITED STATES PATENT OFFICE

2,625,930

SOLAR-HEATING STRUCTURE

Clyde W. Harris, Socorro, N. Mex.

*

This invention relates to building structures adapted for solar heating of the interior of the building. *

The chief objects of the present invention are to provide a simple, inexpensive, durable and highly effective structure for the above stated purpose.

More specific objects are to provide a compact and efficient structure, localized in a single space-enclosing element of the building, such as a wall or the ceiling-and-roof structure, for performing the three functions of (1) collecting solar energy, (2) storing the energy for use at night or on cloudy days and (3) transmitting the stored heat to the interior of the room when it is needed.

A further specific object is to provide economically and effectively for conservation of heat by providing heat-storage means effectively insulated against escape of heat therefrom except to the interior of the room.

Of the accompanying drawings:

Fig. 1 is a north-and-south section of a ceiling-and-roof structure embodying my invention in one of its preferred forms.

Fig. 2 is a section on line 2—2 of Fig. 1, with the middle part of the structure broken away.

Fig. 3 is a north-and-south section of a modification.

The embodiment shown in Figs. 1 and 2 comprises a set of laterally abutted hollow metal ceiling beams 10, 10 each containing a substance 11 having a temperature of reversible transition a little higher than the desired room temperature, a good example of which is tertiary butyl alcohol (trimethyl carbinol), which melts at 77.7 degrees F. and stores 21 B. t. u. per lb. of the material in melting and releases a corresponding amount of heat in freezing.

The beams are filled not quite full of the material, so that an air space 12 above the material in each beam is left to provide for expansion and contraction of the material.

The beams are closed at their ends, as shown clearly in Fig. 2, and the ends of each beam are mounted upon respective wall structures 13, 13.

Upon the set of beams is a layer of opaque and preferably black material 14 which can be merely a coat of paint, for converting the rays of the sun into heat, and preferably the layer is thin, for good transmission of the heat, through the metal of the beam, to the heat-storing material 11.

Mounted upon the hollow ceiling beams, crosswise thereof, are a set of roof joists 15, 15 of which the upper edges are suitably shaped, saw-tooth fashion, to seat with extensive contact a set of approximately horizontal sheet-metal reflectors 16, 16 having both upper and lower reflecting faces.

Each reflector has a margin approximately under the adjacent margin of the next and the said margins, of each pair, are crimped to hold in place a glass or other transparent sheet 17, approximately in a vertical position.

Thus the reflectors and the glass provide an outer wall-element of serrated or stepped form exposed to solar radiation and adapted to transmit the said radiation to the surface of the layer of opaque material 14.

Each reflector, with a concave upper face, has such curvature and is set in such relation to the transparent sheet 17 rising from its margin as to reflect rays of the winter sun, with concentration of the reflected rays, through the transparent sheet and onto the convex lower face of the adjacent reflector, which, with divergence of the reflected rays, reflects the rays onto the conversion or energy-absorbing opaque surface material 14, from which the heat is transmitted by conduction, and to some extent by radiation, to the metal of the beams 10 and thence to the heat-storing material 11.

The reflectors serve as gutters for shedding of rain water and can be given a lengthwise slope for improving their performance of that function.

To lessen escape of heat back into the outer atmosphere, two superimposed sets of insulating air-pockets are provided by dividing each space between joists 15 into an upper pocket and a lower pocket by sheets of glass or other transparent material 18, 18 supported upon ledges provided by spacer strips 19, 19 set against and secured to the side faces of the joists 15.

With proportions as here shown, which are of course subject to variation, and under climatic conditions existing at Socorro, N. Mex., for example, and with suitable control of ventilation, the room temperature will remain within a comfortable range throughout a much greater range of outdoor temperature, the heat-storing material absorbing a large amount of heat in melting and, in refreezing, transmitting a large amount of heat to the interior of the room.

My present invention is well adapted for the use in conjunction therewith of any known or suitable variable-insulation means. *

The modification shown in Fig. 3 corresponds to that shown in Figs. 1 and 2 except that the reflectors, 16a, 16a are of somewhat different shape, are more nearly vertical, and, with greater angles of incidence and reflection, reflect the rays in a southerly direction, instead of a northerly direction, for their passage through the transparent sheets, 17a, 17a, and onto the inner face of the adjacent reflector.

In this embodiment of Fig. 3 it is unnecessary to give the roof joists a saw-tooth edge contour, as the sheet metal members 16a, 16a have such shape that they are self-supporting and strongly resist distortion when secured to straight upper edges of the joists, as shown, by screws 16b, 16b having rubber sealing washers 16c, 16c under their heads. *

An advantage of the structure as described is

that throughout a large part of the summer months, when the sun is higher in the sky, its rays hit the reflectors at such angles that they are reflected back into the sky, instead of through the glass windows, as indicated by the broken lines, so that shades blinds or the like are unnecessary.

3,894,528

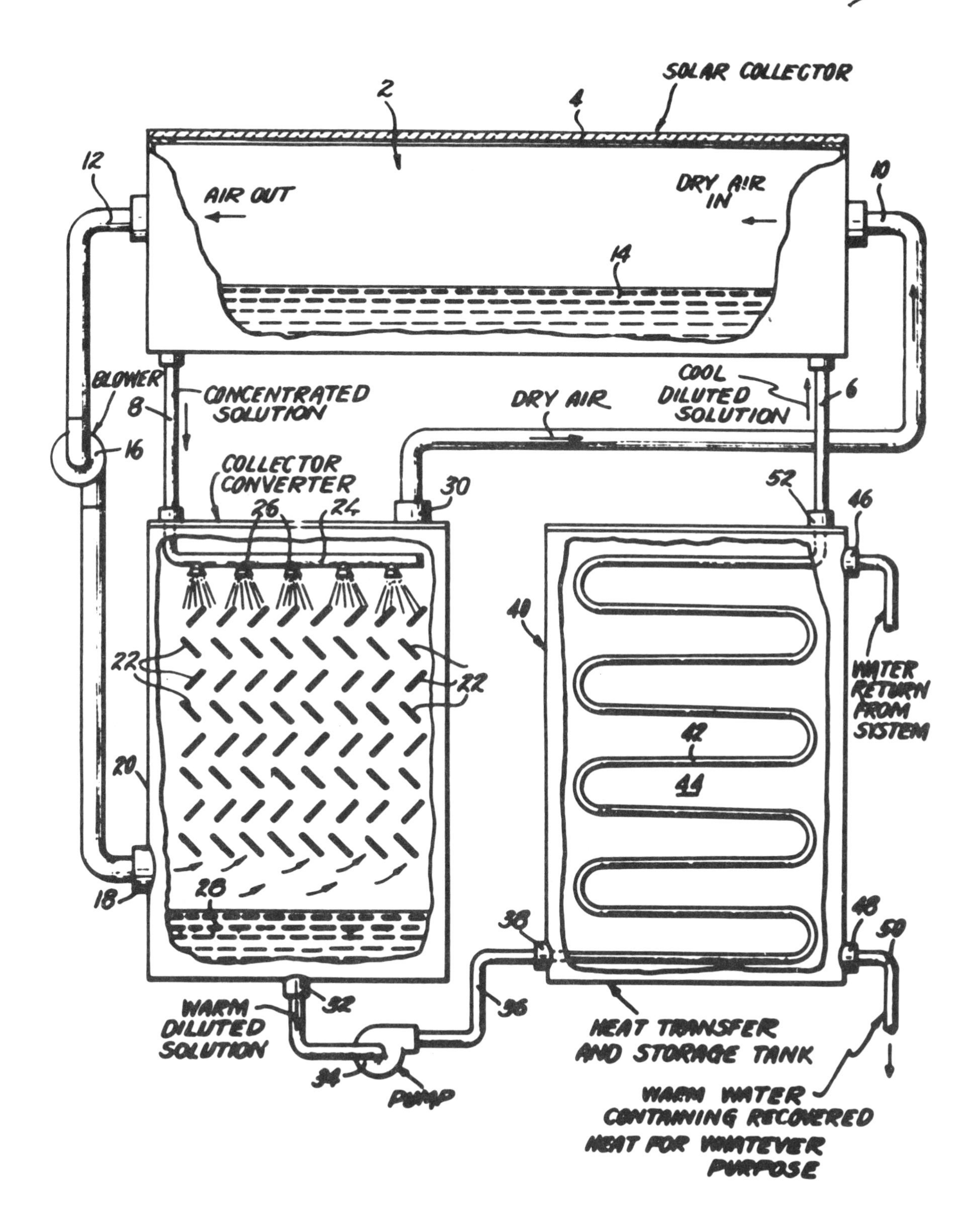
SOLAR COLLECTOR
2
4
12
10
AIR OUT
DRY AIR IN
14
BLOWER
8
CONCENTRATED SOLUTION
DRY AIR
COOL DILUTED SOLUTION
6
16
COLLECTOR CONVERTER
26
24
30
52
46
40
22
22
WATER RETURN FROM SYSTEM
42
44
20
18
28
38
48
50
WARM DILUTED SOLUTION
32
36
HEAT TRANSFER AND STORAGE TANK
34
PUMP
WARM WATER CONTAINING RECOVERED HEAT FOR WHATEVER PURPOSE

Inventor: **Richard R. Stubblefield,** Arnold, Md.

Assignee: **Broyles & Broyles, Inc.,** Fort Worth, Tex.

* **ABSTRACT**

A dilute solution of lithium chloride having a vapor pressure greater than that of relatively dry air is exposed to sunlight to vaporize water from the solution into a body of air, this concentrates the solution and lowers its vapor pressure while increasing the vapor pressure of the air-water vapor mixture. The moist air and concentrated solution are separately conveyed to a chamber where they are mixed and the water vapor is absorbed by the concentrated solution, giving up its latent heat of vaporization, and the solution is thus diluted and heated. Heat is then removed from the solution as converted solar energy and the air and cooled dilute solution are recycled in a continuous process.

*** 1 Drawing Figure**

SOLAR ENERGY COLLECTION METHOD AND APPARATUS

BACKGROUND OF THE INVENTION

This invention is in the field of solar energy and relates particularly to methods and apparatus for converting and collecting solar energy in a usable form.

Many proposals have been made heretofore for collecting solar energy, but they have generally comprised exposing a liquid to sunlight to directly increase the temperature of the liquid sufficiently to be able to extract heat therefrom. It has also been proposed to operate absorption type refrigerating apparatus by employing solar energy as a heat source for separating the refrigerant from a carrier fluid. However, all such previous proposals were relatively expensive and inefficient in requiring the solar energy to directly increase the temperature of a liquid.

SUMMARY OF THE INVENTION

The present invention collects solar energy, not by causing the same to directly increase the temperature of a fluid but by employing trapped solar energy as a source of heat of vaporization without in itself substantially increasing the sensible temperature of a carrier liquid.

It is a principal object of this invention to provide a method and apparatus for capturing a portion of the sun's energy and convert it into a state suitable for beneficial use.

Another object of the present invention is to provide a highly efficient and inexpensive method and apparatus for collecting solar heat.

It is a further object of this invention to provide a method of collecting solar energy by directly converting the same to heat of vaporization of a vaporizable solvent in a carrier solution and thereafter recombining the vaporized solvent and solution to provide an increase in temperature of the solution and thus facilitate heat extraction.

BRIEF DESCRIPTION OF THE DRAWINGS

The single FIGURE of the drawings is a schematic representation of suitable apparatus for practicing the present invention.

DESCRIPTION OF A PREFERRED EMBODIMENT

The following description is directed specifically to the use of water as a vaporizable solvent, air as a carrier gas and a solution of lithium chloride as a carrier solution but it is to be understood that other materials may be employed. The salts of other metals or the like may constitute the materials in the carrier solution and liquid other than water may be employed as the solvent while gases other than air could serve as a carrier gas.

In FIG. **1,** numeral **2** designates a solar collector generally in the form of a container, preferably of shallow dimension but covering a substantial horizontal area and provided with a transparent cover **4** through which sunlight may penetrate. Preferably, the bottom and side walls of the container **2** are opaque and may be provided with either heat absorbing or heat reflective inner surfaces. A conduit **6** is arranged to direct a dilute aqueous solution of lithium chloride into the bottom of container **2** adjacent one end thereof and an outlet conduit **8** is arranged to drain solution from the other end of the container **2.** An inlet duct **10** is arranged to direct air into the container **2** above the bottom thereof and at the end corresponding to the inlet conduti **6.** Likewise, an outlet duct **12** is arranged to receive and remove air and water vapor from the container **2** at the same end thereof as the outlet conduit **8.** In operation, the level of the lithium chloride solution in container **2** will be substantially below the transparent cover **4,** so that only a relatively small volume of the container is occupied by the solution **14,** as shown in FIG. **1,** for example. As stated, the lithium chloride solution introduced into container **2** is dilute, that is, it is sufficiently diluted so that its vapor pressure is greater than the vapor pressure of the relatively dry air introduced through the inlet air duct **10.**

As sunlight traverses the transparent cover **4,** the heat thereof is trapped within container **2** and causes vaporization of water from the solution **14,** thus rendering the solution more concentrated and lowering its vapor pressure as it flows from inlet **6** toward outlet **8** and the heat thus absorbed is essentially only the necessary heat of vaporization and the materials do not exhibit an appreciable rise in temperature but the vapor pressure of the air increases as it entrains the water vapor.

A suitable blower or pump **16** in the outlet duct **12** withdraws air and water vapor from the container **2** and directs the same to an inlet **18** of a second or collector-converter container **20,** adjacent but spaced upwardly from the bottom thereof. As shown, the second container **20** is provided with a multiplicity of baffle plates **22** therein and the outlet conduit **8** from container **2** directs concentrated solution from container **2** to a header **24** in the upper part of container **20.** The header **24** is provided with a multiplicity of downwardly directed nozzles **26** through which the concentrated solution from container **2** is sprayed to cascade downwardly over the baffle plates **22** and the air and water vapor introduced through inlet **18** rises upwardly in countercurrent scrubbing relation to the solution moving downwardly over the baffle plates. The air introduced at **18** contains a considerable amount of water vapor and its vapor pressure is thus quite high relative to that of the concentrated lithium chloride solution introduced into container **20.** As is known, under these conditions, the concentrated solution will reabsorb water vapor in the form of water and the same is condensed therein, thus releasing the latent heat of vaporization, to effect a rise in the sensible temperature of the solution and this also effects a dilution of the lithium chloride solution. A heated dilute solution then gathers in the bottom of the container **20,** as shown at **28.** The dried air leaves the container **20** at outlet **30** and is recirculated to inlet **10** of the first container **2** for recycling. The heated dilute solution at **28** leaves the container **20** through its bottom outlet **32** and pump **34** causes flow thereof along conduit **36** to the inlet **38** of a heat exchanger designated generally at **40.** The heat exchanger **40** may be any suitable type, for example, it may contain internal coils **42,** preferably of the externally finned type, surrounded by a body of water at **44** in the heat exchanger tank, which water is in heat exchange relation to the coils **42.** Water is circulated through the space **44** from an inlet **46** to an outlet **48.** As is obvious, the water circulating through the space **44** will absorb heat from the heated solution in coils **42** and will thus extract the converted solar energy and may be directed through conduit **50** to any suitable place for storage or use. For example, the water could be circulated through the heating system of a residence but obviously could be used for any other heating purpose.

The cooled diluted solution leaves the heat exchanger **40** through outlet **52** which leads directly to the inlet conduit **6** previously described and, thus, the lithium chloride solution is continuously circulated as is the solvent water, and the body of air serving as a carrier gar for the water vapors.

The foregoing description suggests that the sun's heat entering collector container **2** is all used to provide the latent heat of vaporization for the solvent without appreciably raising the temperature of the solution at **14.** However, some heating of the solution will take place, to a lesser degree if the inner surfaces of the side walls and bottom of the container **2** are heat reflective or transparent and to a greater degree if they are heat absorbing. In any event, such heat is recoverable in heat exchanger **40.**

J. S. HITTELL & G. W. DEITZLER.

APPARATUS FOR COLLECTING, STORING AND UTILIZING HEAT.

No. 188,517. Patented March 20, 1877.

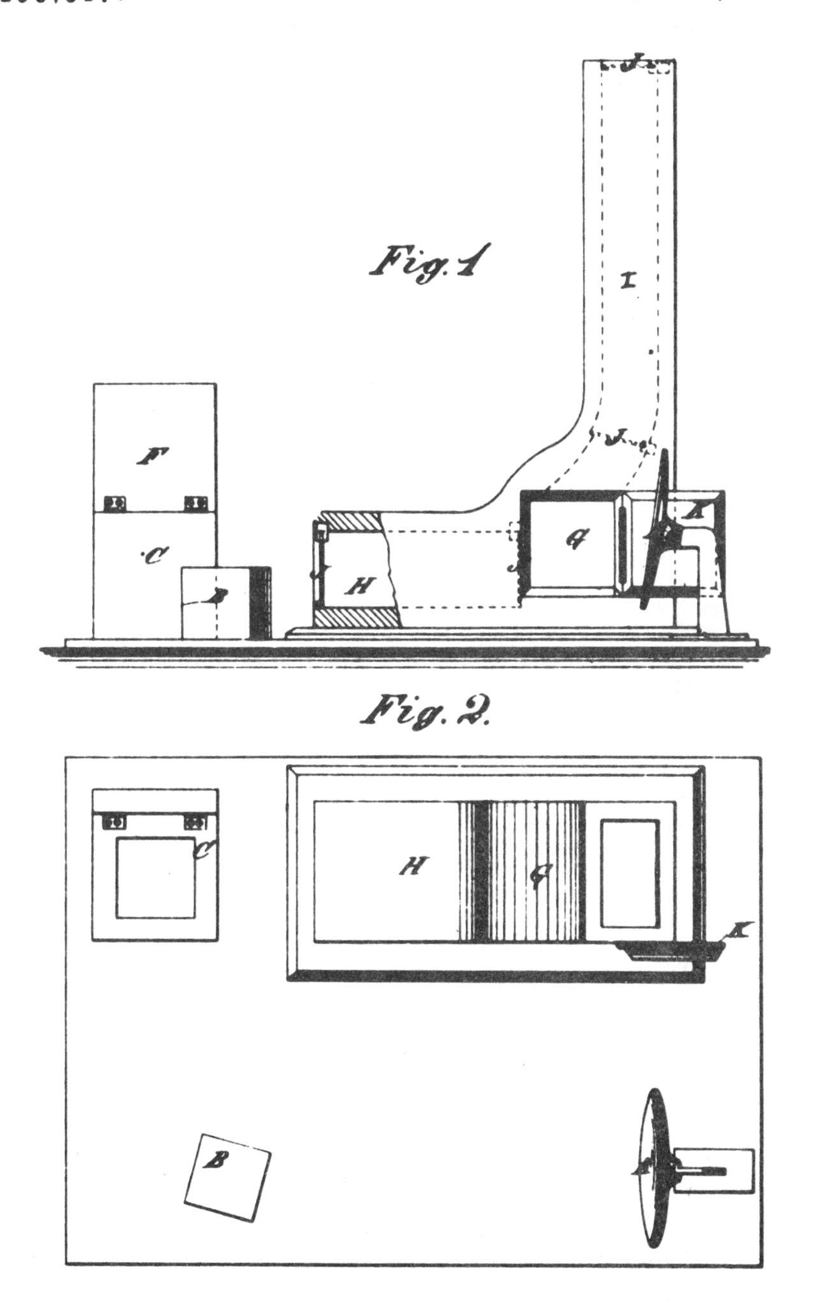

WITNESSES:

INVENTORS
Jno. S. Hittell
Geo. W. Deitzler
BY
Munn & Co
ATTORNEYS.

UNITED STATES PATENT OFFICE.

JOHN S. HITTELL AND GEORGE W. DEITZLER, OF SAN FRANCISCO, CAL.

IMPROVEMENT IN APPARATUS FOR COLLECTING, STORING, AND UTILIZING HEAT.

Specification forming part of Letters Patent No. 188,517, dated March 20, 1877; *

To all whom it may concern:

Be it known that we, JOHN S. HITTELL and GEORGE W. DEITZLER, of the city and county of San Francisco, California, have invented a new and Important Apparatus for Collecting, Storing, and Utilizing Heat, of which the following is a specification:

This apparatus is devised to collect solar or other heat, store it up in a heat-reservoir—a mass of iron or other suitable material—confine it in the reservoir until needed, keep it in such form that it can be transported from place to place, and utilize it for industrial or other purposes.

The solar-heat-collecting device may be a mirror or mirrors, concave or plain, or a lens or lenses, so arranged as to intensify in a complete or partial focus the light and heat, and all the forces conveyed in the solar rays.

The contrivance for keeping the heat stored up in the reservoir until needed consists of a heat-box with non-conducting walls for receiving and inclosing the reservoir.

The apparatus for utilizing the heat consists of a heat-reservoir chamber with non-conducting walls to inclose the hot reservoir, and doors or valves to let the cold air pass in, and to let the heated air pass out through a pipe or flue to the place where it is to be used.

For special purposes a devaporizing-chamber and a drying-chamber may be connected with the heat-reservoir chamber, all as hereinafter described.

Figure 1 is partly a side elevation and partly a section of our improved apparatus. Fig. 2 is a plan view.

Similar letters of reference indicate corresponding parts.

A is a concave mirror for concentrating the solar rays upon the heat-reservoir B, which is a mass of iron or other suitable material. C is the heat-box for confining the heat until needed, and also for serving as package for transporting the heat-reservoir when hot. The heat-box may have different forms, some movable and others fixed—the latter for keeping the heat without transporting it—and these last may be either under or above ground. The movable heat-box may also be used in keeping the reservoir when the heat is being utilized for some purposes.

G is the heat-reservoir chamber, in which the heat is communicated from the hot reservoir to the air. Under certain circumstances the heat-reservoir may be heated in the heat-reservoir chamber. H is a devaporizing-chamber, for extracting the moisture from the air by means of a deliquescent substance or other material or treatment. A vertical stack or flue, I, communicates with the heat-reservoir chamber, for conveying the heated air away for use.

The device for concentrating the solar rays may be either stationary or movable, and, if movable, may be moved by hand or automatically to follow the sun.

The various chambers mentioned will have valves J at the ends to regulate the passage of the air, and there will be a door or doors, K, at the side or bottom.

The air passing to the heat reservoir chamber may be required to pass through the devaporizing-chamber, so as to deprive it of its moisture, and thus increase its capacity to absorb other moisture. *

Feb. 20, 1968 H. E. THOMASON 3,369,541

HEAT STORAGE

*

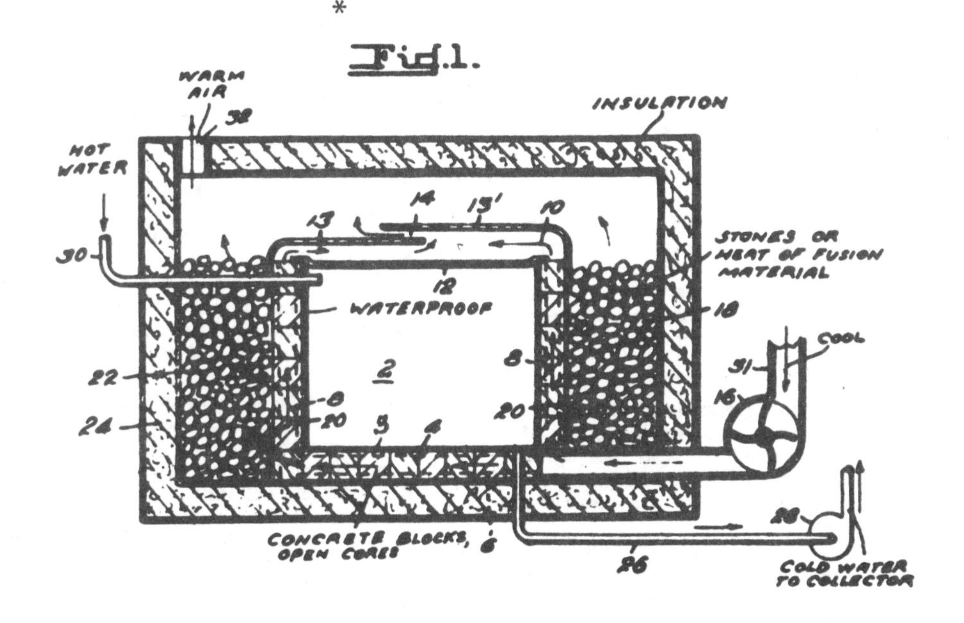

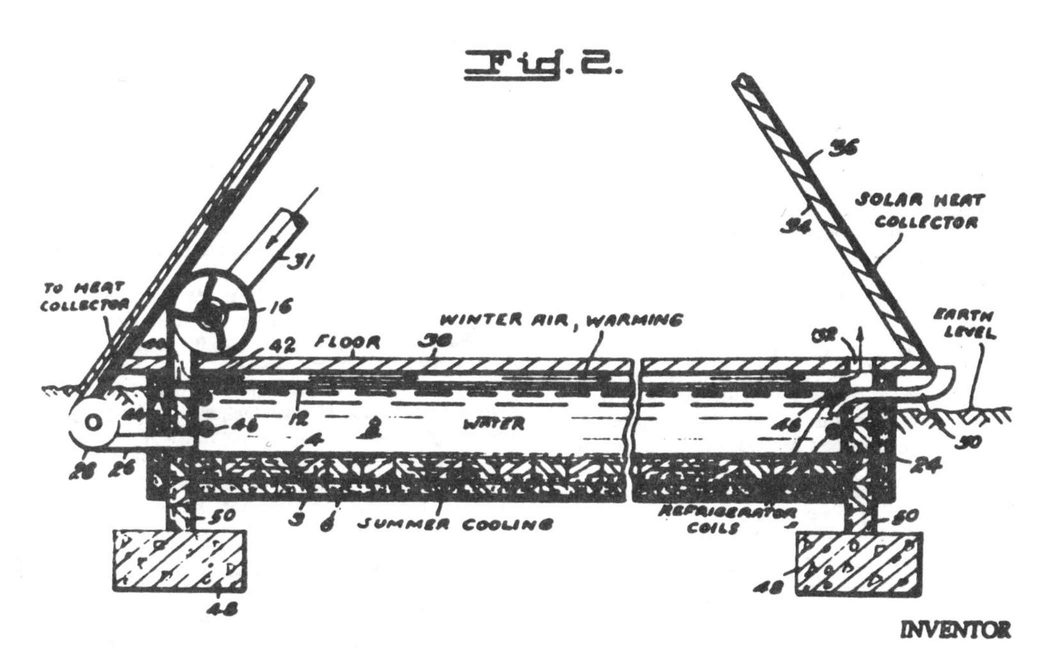

INVENTOR

Harry E. Thomason

3,369,541
HEAT STORAGE

Harry E. Thomason, District Heights, Md.
(6802 Walker Mill Road SE., Washington, D.C. 20027)
*

ABSTRACT OF THE DISCLOSURE

Heat is stored in water in a tank in a heat storage bin. The water may be heated by solar energy, or cooled for use in air conditioning a building. The bin in FIG. 1 contains stones and building blocks forming the tank. Air to be heated is circulated under and around the warm tank and stones.

In FIG. 2 the heat storage bin is of a "pancake" design and is located beneath the floor of an A-frame building. Air to be heated may be circulated above the closed warmed water tank (during winter), or air to be cooled may be circulated below the water tank when the water therein is chilled (during summer).

The present invention relates to apparatus for storage of heat and finds particular utility in storage of solar-produced heat. Such stored heat can then be used, for example, to heat homes or other buildings when the sun is or is not shining. Such heating is commonly referred to as space heating.

The present apparatus is simple and low-cost in construction. The materials are permanent and non-corrosive in nature. In the "pancake" design the invention is usable in a building with no basement. Excavation costs are minimized. Large quantities of heat can be stored. If desired the water or other liquid can be chilled during hot weather to air-condition the building.

In the drawing:

FIG. 1 is a diagrammatic cross sectional view through one form of the invention;

FIG. 2 is a view through a "pancake" modification of storage apparatus.

The storage apparatus may be used to store heat or "coolness," that is, to store heat at a temperature level higher or lower than the level where it is to be used. For example, if a house is to be heated to 70° F., the heat will be stored at a higher temperature level whereas, if the house is to be cooled to 75° F., the heat will be discharged to and stored at a lower temperature level.

In FIG. 1 a water tank 2 comprises masonry such as concrete building blocks, bricks or such at 3. The masonry is waterproofed at surface 4. Air passages 6 provide for circulation of air through the masonry material of the tank itself. Air currents are illustrated at 8 passing in heat exchange relationship with the masonry 3. The masonry, in turn, transfers heat to, or from, the liquid in the tank.

As the air passes out through the top of the masonry tank walls it is preferably diverted across the top of the tank as illustrated at 10.

The top of the tank may be closed by a liquid and vapor resistant member 12 which floats or is otherwise suspended or supported over the liquid. Members 13, 13' serve to deflect the air in tortuous paths across top member 12 to effect a better heat exchange relationship. The air passes out between members 13, 13' at 14. When blower 16 is turned off, and air is no longer introduced under pressure, member 13' settles down onto member 13 thereby closing passage 14 and reducing convection currents. Members 12, 13 and 13' are preferably flexible plastic film, with 13, 13' serving as a flap valve at 14.

Stones, containers of heat-of-fusion material, or other heat storage and heat exchanger material 18, may be used around tank 2 if desired. If material 18 is used a portion of the air supplied by blower 16 may pass out of the masonry tank walls as at 20 and into material 18. Air currents 20 exchange heat with material 18 through which they flow.

The apparatus is preferably inclosed in an airtight storage bin 22 with insulation 24 substantially surrounding the bin.

Liquid to be heated may be withdrawn from tank 2 through pipe 26 and circulated to a solar heat collector or other source of heat by pump 28. Hot liquid is returned to tank 2 by pipe 30.

Air is drawn from an area to be heated through duct 31 by blower 16. The air is warmed as it passes through the warm bin and passes out through duct 32 back to the area to be heated.

If desired the liquid in tank 2 may be cooled, at night on hot summer days for example, to cool the air passing through the bin. The cooled liquid cools the masonry walls of the tank, and adjacent material 18 if such is used, thereby storing "coolness." This storage of heat at a low level is useful for summertime air conditioning.

In FIG. 2 "pancake" heat or "cold" storage apparatus is illustrated for warming or cooling a chalet style or A-frame house 34 with a solar heat collector 36 and floor 38, preferably well insulated to reduce heat losses up from the heat bin. The masonry tank walls 3 have air passages 6 therethrough for passage of air to be cooled when damper 40 is swung up to block passage 42 and passage 44 is open. This directs the air adjacent to the relatively cold bottom of the heat bin for maximum cooling. The cool air, drawn from the interior through duct 31 by blower 16, is returned at 32 to cool the interior of the house.

During the heating season damper 40 is swung to close passage 44 and to open passage 42 as the air flows through the storage bin. Air then flows from blower 16 along the warm top 12 of tank 2 and the warmed air is returned through passage 32 to warm the interior of the building.

It will be noted that only one valve is used to switch the air flow from winter heating to summer cooling.

Refrigeration coils 46, or rooftop cooling as taught in Thomason Patent No. 3,254,703, or other means, may be used to cool the water in tank 2.

The house is customarily supported on footings 48 and foundation walls 50.

The "pancake" form of heat storage apparatus could be used in other environments. As exemplary, it could be used between the ceiling of one level of living quarters and the floor of a higher level.

The heat or "cold" storage tank and bin described is simple and low-cost to construct, even in large sizes, therefore, large capacity can be obtained at low cost. Also, large heat exchange surfaces are provided between the liquid and solid material and between the solid material and air. This permits use of heat stored at a temperature level near the temperature to be maintained in the space to be heated or cooled. This, in turn, increases efficiency of solar heat collection for heating or heat dissipation for cooling. The materials used for construction are permanent and non-corrosive in nature thereby yielding a long life for the apparatus.

For the "pancake" design excavation costs are substantially eliminated and storage bin costs are reduced to a minimum. Further, the entire floor is kept warm in winter and cool in summer to aid in comfort-conditioning the house.

In the "pancake" type the tank is relatively shallow but is long and wide, thereby providing a large area of surface 12. The masonry, stone and sand material could be eliminated. The air to be heated is flowed in the thin space across the large top of the tank 12 and below floor 38. In all forms of the invention the top 12 is preferably made of a heat conducting and vapor barrier material which minimizes evaporation of the liquid while transferring heat to the air flowing thereover. Due to the large area of the tank top, and by confining air flow to rather thin proportions, good heat exchange can be obtained between the liquid and air. This is all the more true where the apparatus is used for storage, and recovery, of heat because the warmer liquid rises to the top of the tank to keep top 12 warm. Also, no insulation is perfect and therefore warmth from the entire top of the tank rises and helps warm the entire floor thereabove. *

Chapter 4

House Heating Systems

May 10, 1949. B. O. CHRISTENSON **2,469,496**

CONDITION CONTROL SYSTEM

*

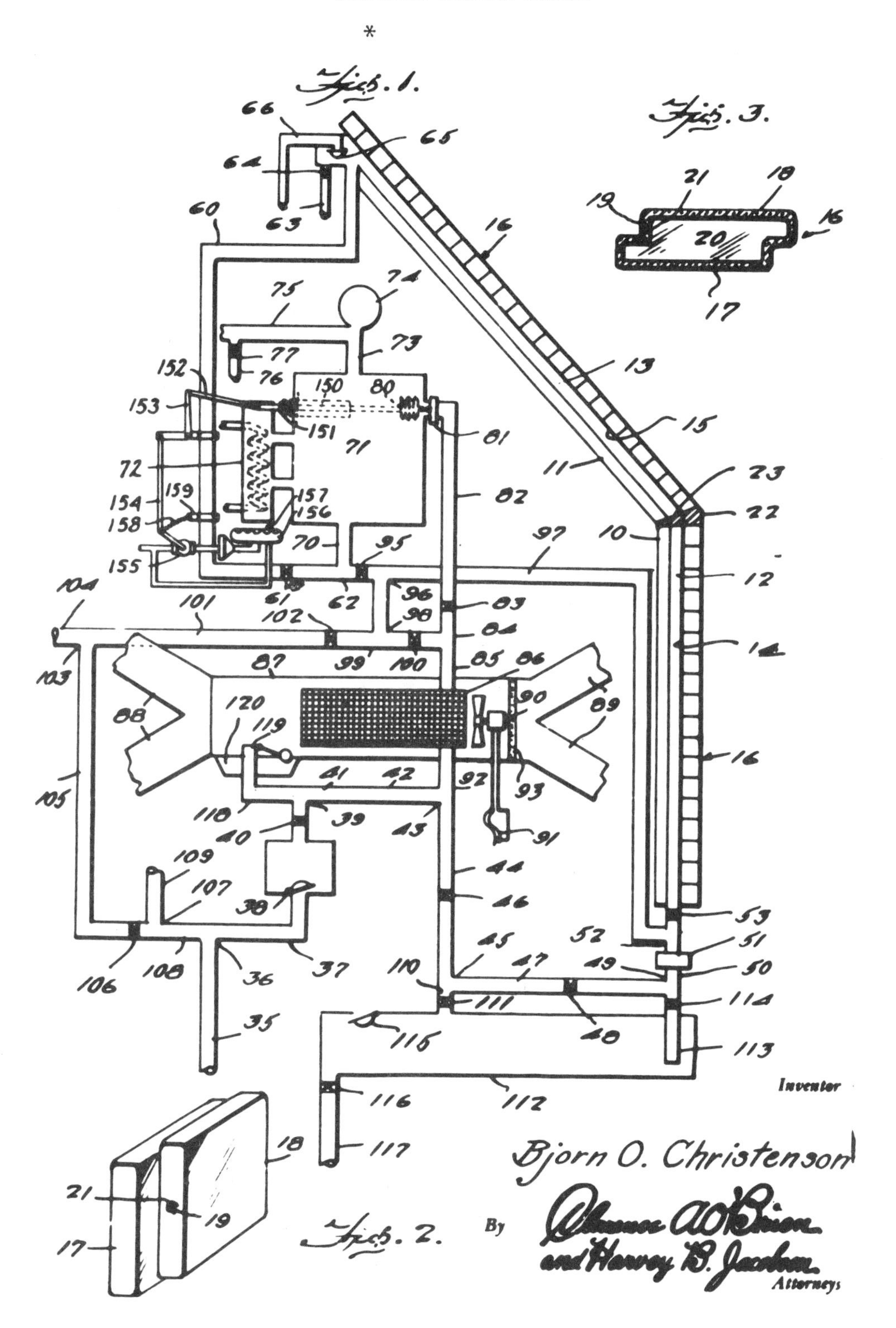

UNITED STATES PATENT OFFICE

2,469,496

CONDITION CONTROL SYSTEM

Bjorn O. Christensen, De Pere, Wis.

*

This invention relates to a condition control system and more particularly to such a system adapted to control the temperatures of air and water for domestic or industrial use or the like.

A primary object of this invention is the provision of such a system whereby the condition control is accomplished by solar radiation.

An additional object is the provision of means whereby such solar radition may be utilized without concentrating the same by the use of mirrors, reflectors, lenses, or similar intensifying devices.

A still further object is the provision of means in such a system for applying such solar radiation to the heating of a building, and the air therein or the like.

A still further object is the provision of means in such a system for utilizing solar radiation to heat the water for domestic or industrial use.

An additional object is the provision of such a system wherein means are provided to readily convert the apparatus to cooling the air in the dwelling or other structure when conditions warrant.

A more specific object is the provision of means of improved structural design for effecting the utilization of solar radiation to achieve the above mentioned objects.

Other objects will in part be obvious and in part be pointed out as the description of the invention proceeds, and shown in the accompanying drawings, wherein there is disclosed a preferred embodiment of this invention.

In the drawings:

Figure 1 is a schematic representation of one form of condition control system embodying this inventive concept.

Figure 2 is an enlarged perspective view of one of the elements adapted to be utilized in conjunction with such a system, and

Figure 3 is a plan sectional view of the element of Figure 2.

Like reference numerals refer to like parts throughout the several views of the drawings.

As conducive to a clearer understanding of this invention, it may here be pointed out that it is well known that vacuum serves effectively as a heat insulating medium. It is further well known that material having heat conductive characteristics when of a dark color, such as black, serves normally as a conductor for heat therethrough rather than as a repellent for such heat.

It is an object of this invention therefore to apply these known principles, to a new and improved condition control system, in order to utilize effectively the heat occasioned by solar radiation to condition the air or water within a building structure or the like.

Having reference now to the drawings there is, schematically indicated in Figure 1, an embodiment of the system of the instant invention such as might be applicable to a small building, as for example a four-room dwelling.

In Figure 1, 10 indicates, schematically, a side sectional view of a portion of a wall of a house and 11 designates a portion of the roof wall thereof. Suitably affixed to the exterior of walls 10 and 11 are tanks 12 and 13, respectively. Tanks 12 and 13 may be applied to any desired section of the side walls and the roof of a building and cover any desired area, and may be either large unitary structures, in which case suitable spacers (not shown) are provided between the inner and outer walls of the tanks or may be comprised of a large number of relatively small interconnected units.

Tanks 12 and 13 are preferably constructed of metal or similar conductive material and have their outer walls, 14 and 15, respectively, colored both on their inner and outer surfaces a dark color, preferably black.

Positioned outside the exterior surface of tanks 12 and 13 are a relatively large number of transparent hollow blocks 16 of glass, plastic, or other suitable material.

Blocks 16 are comprised as shown in Figures 2 and 3 of two sections 17 and 18, offset from each other in such manner as to preclude the formation of a direct mortar joint passing completely through the surface formed by the blocks. Each block is provided with a recessed aperture 19 through which the block is adapted to be evacuated, the space 20, in the interior thereof, thus forming a vacuum chamber. After each block has been evacuated aperture 19 is sealed as by a sealing tip 21, tip 21 being positioned within the recess 19, in order to preclude the accidental breakage of the same in setting the blocks, and the consequent loss of the vacuum therein.

From the foregoing it will now be seen that water contained within tanks 12 and 13, and introduced therein in a manner to be described hereinafter, is adapted to be warmed or heated, by the passage of the sun's rays through blocks 16 and the subsequent impingement thereof on blackened surfaces 14 and 15. It may here be pointed out that the blocks 16 are adapted to be set in a suitable mortar of an expansible and contractible character to permit relative extension of the sizes of the blocks occasioned by variations in temperature, and that there is a similar expansible and contractible joint 22 positioned between the blocks in adjacent relation on walls 10 and 11 exterior of tanks 12 and 13, the joint 22 extending also between the tanks 12 and 13 and being provided with a communicating pipe 23 therebetween.

Having particular reference now to the system, water is admitted to the same through an inlet pipe 35 connected to any suitable source of supply such as a city water system. Pipe 35 leads to a T 36, one leg 37 of which extends to a suitable one-way valve 38 from which a pipe 39 having a valve 40 therein extends to a T 41. One leg 42 of T 41 extends to a further T 43 from one leg of which latter a pipe 44 extends to a T 45, pipe 44 having a valve 46 therein. One leg of T 45 extends through a pipe 47 having a valve 48 therein to a further T 49 one leg 50 of which has a suitable pump or circulator 51 positioned therein. Pipe 50 leads to a T 52 one leg of which extends through a valve 53 into the lower portion of tank 12. It will thus be seen that when the valves 40, 46, 48 and 53 are in open position, certain other valves to be described hereinafter being closed, water will be fed directly from the source of supply into the heating tanks, being either pumped thereinto by pump 51, or allowed to circulate, after a certain quantity of water in the tank becomes heated, by normal convection current.

From the upper extremity of tank 13 an outlet pipe 60 leads through a valve 61 to a T 62. Adjacent the extremity of tank 13 is also positioned an overflow pipe 63 having a pressure actuated safety valve 64 positioned therein, and above which is positioned a one-way valve 65 communicating with an air pipe 66. Valve 65 is so arranged as to permit the ingress and exit of air into the system as water is drained therefrom, but so designed as to be floated shut when the level in the top portion of pan 13 approaches the mouth of pipe 66.

One leg of T 62, 70, extends into a storage tank 71 provided with an associated water heater 72 of any desired conventional construction, and also having an outlet 73 provided with an air chamber 74 from which an outlet pipe 75 lead to the hot water fixture (not shown) of the building. An overflow pipe 76 provided with a pressure actuated safety valve 77 extends from pipe 75.

Positioned within the tank 71 is a thermostat 80 which when in expanded position engages the adjacent end of the rod 150 which extends through the packing box 151, and whose opposite end is connected by the link 152 to one end of the bell crank lever 153 pivotally supported on the outlet pipe 60. A link 154 is connected between the other arm of the bell crank lever 153 and the gas cut-off valve 155 to turn off the gas burner 156 when said thermostat 80 is in expanded position. The burner 156 is provided with a pilot 157 and a spring 158 is connected between the cut-off valve 155 and an arm 159 on the pipe 60 to again open the valve to cause the burner to again operate when the temperature of the water in the tank 71 drops to a predetermined point. Thermostat 80 is also adapted to actuate a thermostatic valve 81 positioned in a pipe 82, comprising the circulating outlet from the storage tank, when the temperature in tank 71 falls below the level at which the heater is energized.

Pipe 82 extends through a valve 83 to a T 84, one leg of which 85 extends into a radiator 86 of any desired type but preferably of the honeycomb variety.

Radiator 86 is positioned in association with an air duct 87 from which suitable conduits 88 are adapted to conduct heated air to registers or the like. Inlets 89 are also provided to permit circulation of air through the ducts. A blower 90 or the like is positioned within the ducts 87, and controlled by a conventional room thermostat 91 positioned at any desired location, the arrangement being such that when it is desired to heat the house as the temperature falls below a predetermined minimum the fan is energized to draw air through a filter 93 and blow the filtered air over the radiator, heated by water entering the same through pipe 85. After the water has circulated through the radiator it passes therefrom through a pipe 92 which comprises the other leg of T 43.

The other leg of T 62 connects through a valve 95 with a T 96, one end of which extends into a by-pass 97 which communicates with the remaining leg of T 52, between pump 51 and valve 53. The other leg of T 96 communicates with a T 98 one leg of which 99 leads through a valve 100 to the remaining leg of T 84, and the other leg of which 101 leads through a valve 102 to a T 103. One leg of T 103 comprises a connection 104 to the cold water outlet (not shown) of the plumbing system of the household.

The other leg of T 103 extends through a pipe 105 to a valve 106 and a T 107, one leg 108 of which connects through T 36 with the inlet 35 of the system, 109 of which connects with the drinking fixture (not shown) of the dwelling or other structure.

Referring back now to T 45 it will be seen that the remaining leg 110 leads through a valve 111 to a floor tank 112 preferably positioned beneath the floor of the dwelling. A pipe 113 leads through a valve 114 to the remaining leg of T 49. Tank 112 is provided with a one-way valve 115 to permit the ingress and exit of air therefrom, but constructed in a manner similar to valve 65 being adapted to float to closed position when the tank 112 is filled with water. A valve 116 is positioned in an outlet pipe 117, adapted to empty into the city sewage system or any other desired system for the disposal of waste water.

From the foregoing the operation of the system should now be understandable. When it is desired to fill the system the valves 40, 46, 48, and 53 are opened, valves 106, 111 and 114 and 83 being closed, and the pump 51 started, which operation fills the tanks 12 and 13. The pumping is continued, water overflowing tank 13 flowing through pipe 60 to the storage tank 71, valve 61 being open and valve 95 being closed, until such time as the tank is full. The pump may then be shut off until the combined action of solar radiation and the heating element associated with heater 72 function to raise the temperature of the water in the tank to the desired point. When such point is reached thermostatic valve 81 automatically opens, valve 83 is opened and water from the tank flows in to the radiator 86 and therethrough, thence returning through pipe 92 and pipe 47 to pipe 41 to be recirculated, by renewed operation of the pump. It may here be pointed out that one leg of T 41, 118, leads through a float valve 119 to a conventional tank humidifier 120 positioned in the path of air blown over radiator 86 by fan 90. It may also be pointed out that the air dome 74 serves, when the system is full, to preclude the admittance of additional water from supply pipe 35 until such time as water circulating in the system is drawn off from the hot water fixture through pipe 75. As such water is drawn off the pressure in dome 74 is reduced permitting additional water for replacement purposes to be drawn from the cold water supply line 35.

Obviously, when the temperature within the rooms to be heated falls below a predetermined point, the thermostat 91 energizes fan 90 to blow air over the heat exchanger or radiator 86, and humidifier 120 to supply warm humid air as desired through the heating system of the house.

Under certain conditions, as in cold climate at night, it is desirable to drain the water out of the wall and roof pans 13 and 14. For this purpose floor tank 112 is provided, the tank being of a sufficient capacity to permit all the water from the tanks to be drained thereinto. To accomplish this operation the valve 46 is closed and the valves 111 and 114 opened. After the water has all drained from the wall and roof tank valve 46 is reopened, valve 53 is closed, valve 61 is closed and valve 95 is opened.

It will now be seen that during the winter operation of the device the water during the day circulates in the manner above described from the pump 51 through the pans 12 and 13, pipe 60, the storage tank 71, pipe 82 and radiator 86 and thence through pipes 44 and 47 back to the pump 51.

It will also be seen, however, that when the water is drained from the tanks 12 and 13, the circulation is from pump 51, which may or may not be operating in accordance with the temperature of the water and the normal convection current therein through the pipe 97 and the valve 95 through the storage tank 71 and thence back through pipe 82 and the radiator 86 through pipe 44 and connection 110 to floor tank 112 thence back through pipe 113, valve 114 and pipe 50 to pump 51.

Under this latter condition of operation it will be apparent that the heated water in floor tank 112 serves as an additional warming means for the house during the chill of the night, keeping the floor relatively warm, and that any possibility of loss of heat from water in the tanks 13 and 14 is precluded.

It will also be seen that drinking water is provided at all times direct from the normally cool water source through the pipe 35, T 36, leg 108, T 107 and pipe 109. During winter operation valve 106 is normally adapted to be opened, so that water may pass from inlet 35 through pipe 106 direct to the cold water outlet 104.

When it is desired to change the system over for summer cooling operation, the entire system is first drained. This is accomplished by closing valves 40, 106 and 102, and opening all the remaining valves including outlet valve 116. Thus all the water within the system is permitted to drain off while an uninterrupted supply of cold water is permitted to pass from the inlet to the cold water and drinking water outlets. After the drainage has been accomplished valve 116 is closed, as are valves 46, 83, and 95, valves 61 and 100 are opened, and thermostatic valve 81 closed and the thermostat disconnected therefrom. Likewise thermostat 91 is readjusted in such manner that the fan 90 is energized when the temperature rises above a predetermined point and deenergized when the temperature falls below such point. Cold water now enters the system through pipe 35 and passes upwardly through pipe 92 through radiator 86 and thence through pipe 85 and valves 100 and 102 outwardly to cold water outlet 104. When the fan 90 is energized the air blowing over the radiator 86 will give up a certain amount of its heat to the water in the radiator, the water being correspondingly warmed. Thus, cool air will be passed outwardly through the ducts 88 to the room to be cooled and the water being slightly but not materially warmed will be at an adequate temperature for household uses other than drinking. It may here be pointed out that drinking water will still pass from inlet 35 through pipe 109 directly to the drinking water fixture and that such water will retain the relatively cool temperature of the source of supply. A certain amount of the water passing through pipe 99 will be diverted through T's 98 and 93 and pipe 97 to wall and roof tanks 12 and 13 and thence, partially heated, through pipe 60 to storage tank 71. The system under the conditions above mentioned will normally be full except when water is being drained from outlet 104, at which time additional water will enter through inlet 35, and the pressure of such water in the system will tend to retain the water in tanks 71, keeping the same normally full. The thermostat 80 remains connected to the heater 72 and operates in the same manner as when the system is used for winter operation. Accordingly, the water in the tank 71 will be retained at a sufficient heat for the application to normal hot water usages. As normal convection precludes the fall of hot water through cold water the temperature of the water in the lower part of the system will be substantially unaffected by the temperature of the water in storage tank 71 or wall and roof tanks 12 and 13.

From the foregoing it will now be seen that there is herein provided an air and water conditioning system, accomplishing all the objects of this invention and many others including advantages of great practical utility and commercial importance.

It will also be seen that the system may be adapted to various sizes and construction of buildings as desired. Likewise, the various valves disclosed in varying positions throughout the specification may be manually operated directly, or may be suitably operated in a desired manner from a remotely controlled point, or may be automatically operated by any desired suitable means known to those skilled in the art. *

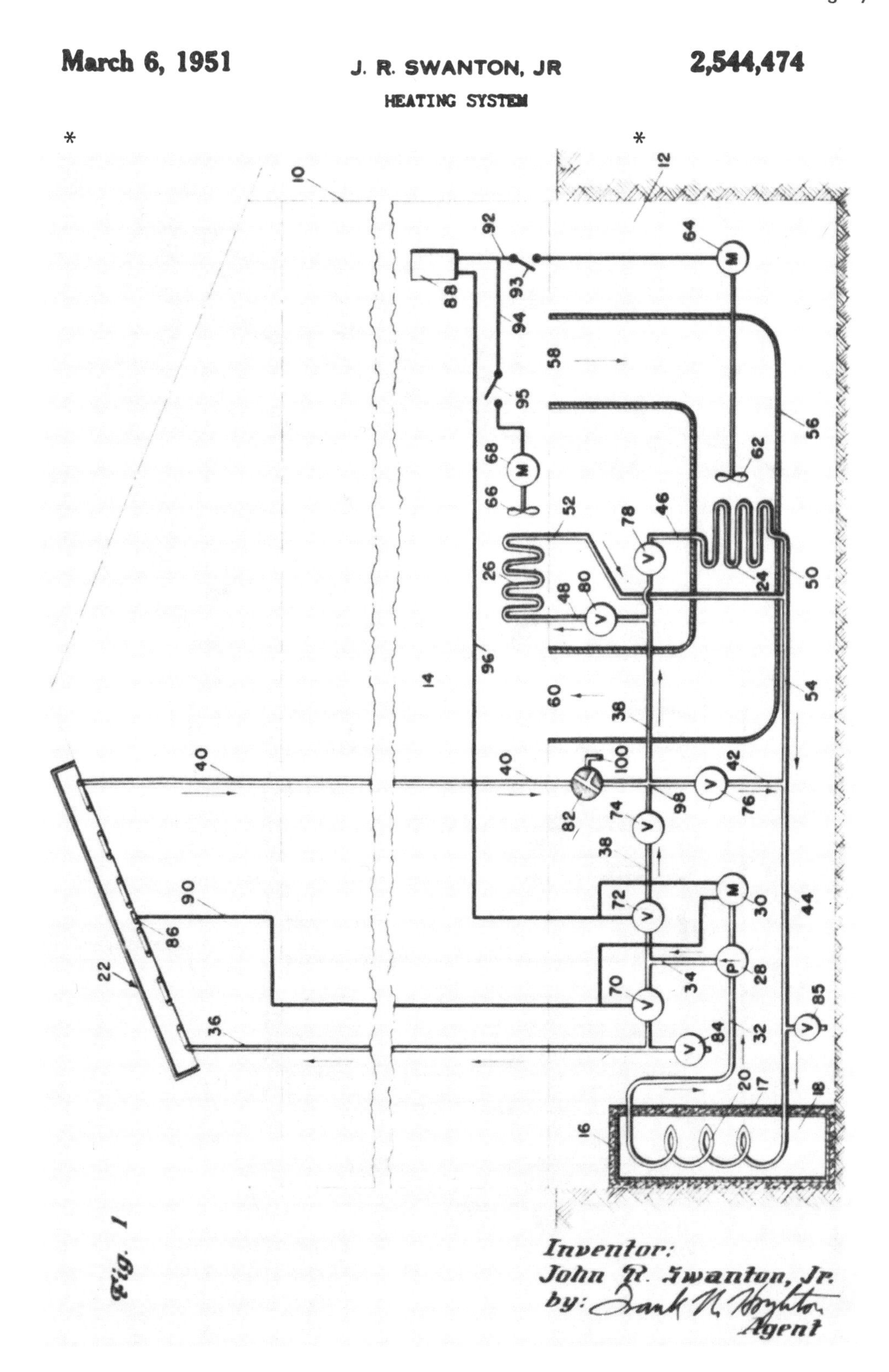
March 6, 1951
J. R. SWANTON, JR
2,544,474
HEATING SYSTEM
Fig. 1
Inventor:
John R. Swanton, Jr.
by:
Agent

March 6, 1951 J. R. SWANTON, JR **2,544,474**

HEATING SYSTEM

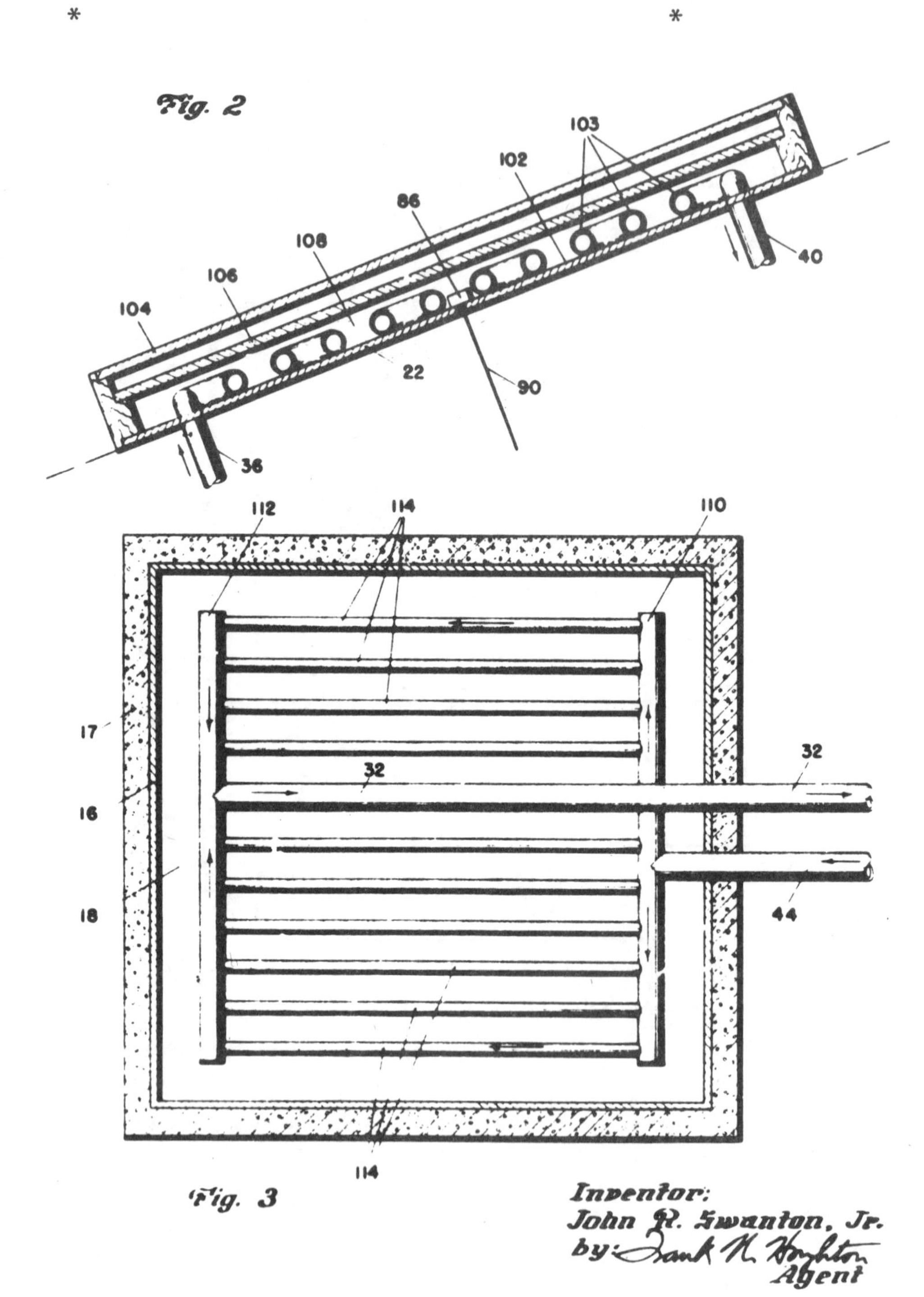

March 6, 1951 J. R. SWANTON, JR 2,544,474

HEATING SYSTEM

* *

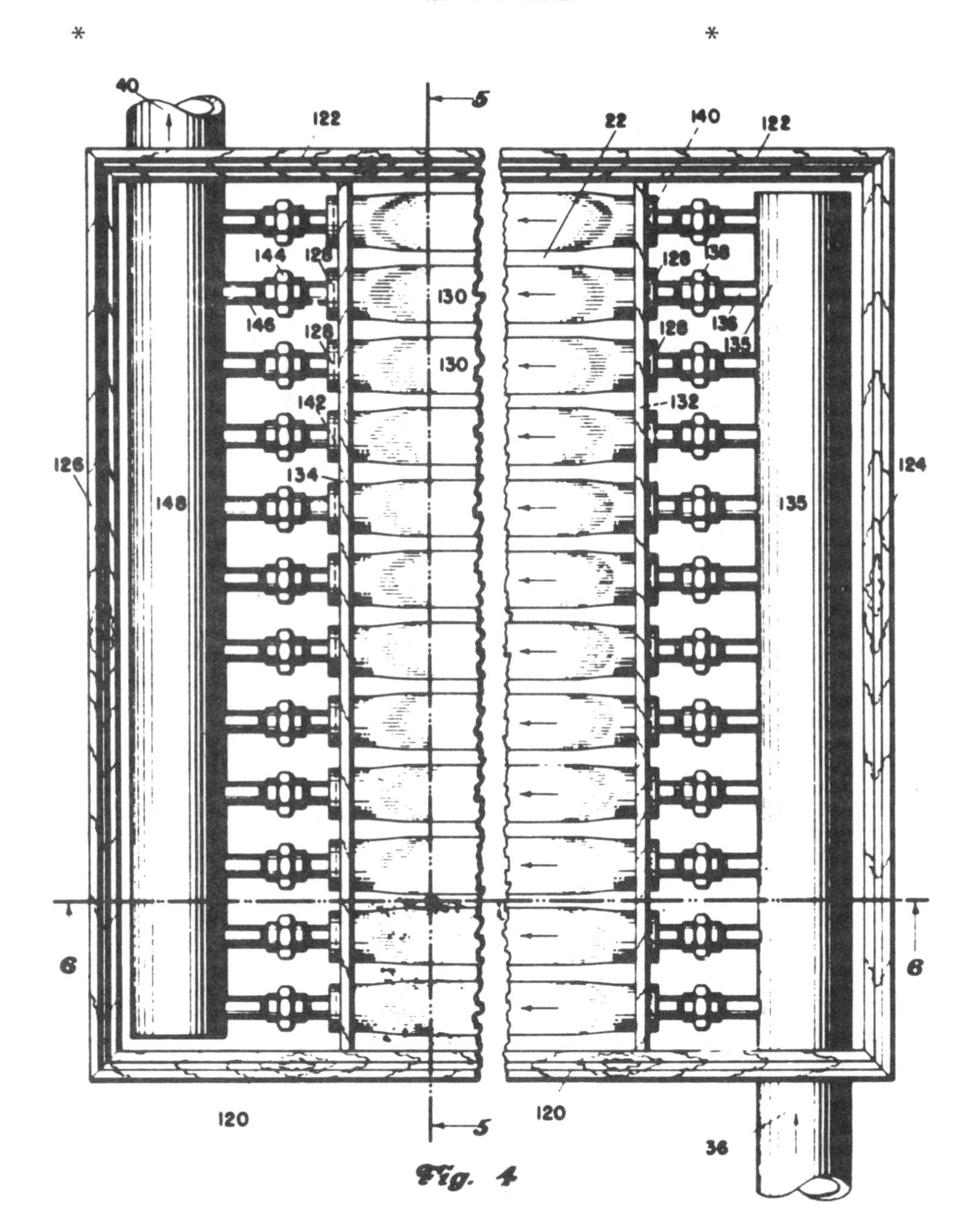

Fig. 4

Inventor:
John R. Swanton, Jr.
by: Frank N. Houghton
Agent

March 6, 1951 J. R. SWANTON, JR **2,544,474**

HEATING SYSTEM

* *

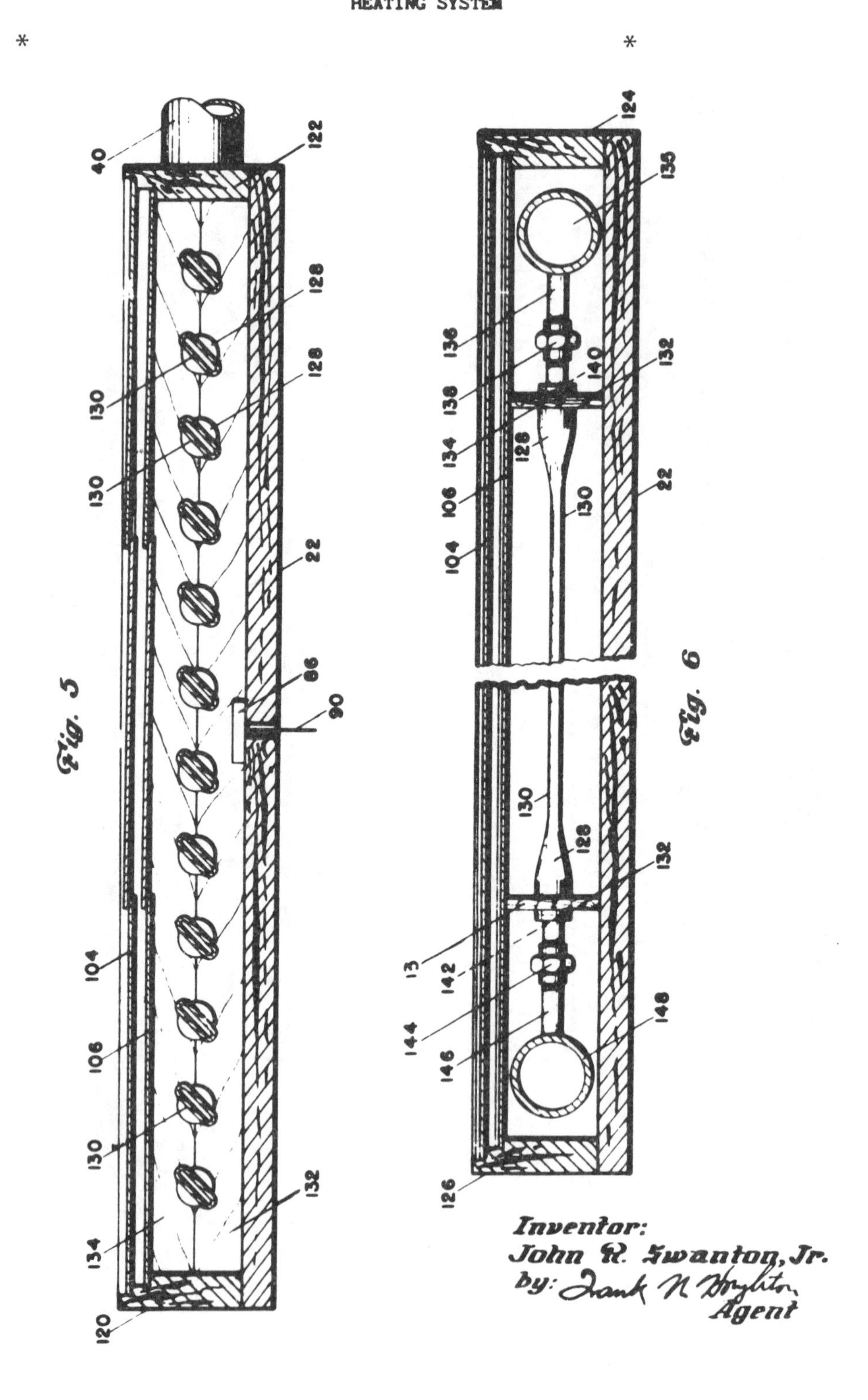

UNITED STATES PATENT OFFICE

2,544,474

HEATING SYSTEM

John R. Swanton, Jr., Newton, Mass., assignor to Arthur D. Little, Inc., Cambridge, Mass., a corporation of Massachusetts

*

This invention relates to the heating of dwellings and other buildings, and is directed in particular to heating such buildings by means of the latent and sensible heat which is available in a stored medium and which has been imparted thereto by exposure to solar energy.

This invention makes it possible to do away with the necessity for using coal, oil, gas, or other fuels—or electrical heat—in the heating of dwellings and other buildings. The system of this invention, once it is installed, operates continuously the year round, substantially without either upkeep cost or attention except for oiling a motor or turning a valve occasionally. Consequently the costs of fuels or electricity for heating, and of repairs and maintenance of more or less expensive heating plants, is eliminated. So are nuisances such as dusty fuels, smoke, disposal of ashes, etc.

The purposes of this invention are accomplished by providing a medium which has a melting point (which may also be referred to as its fusion point or as its freezing point) sufficiently above normal room temperature, and which is stable under the conditions of operation herein described, is substantially inert toward the equipment with which it is used, has a relatively high latent heat of fusion, and is relatively inexpensive. This medium is the heat storage medium of the present invention. Very few substances answer these requirements. The substance which most fully answers the foregoing requirements, I have found to be hydrated disodium orthophosphate, $Na_2HPO_4.12H_2O$, and this I prefer for the purposes of the present invention. Another medium which may be used for these purposes is hydrated calcium chloride, $CaCl_2.6H_2O$. While the latter is less expensive than the hydrated disodium orthophosphate, it has a lower latent heat value and a lower fusion temperature. Hydrated sodium sulfate, $Na_2SO_4.10H_2O$, which is another medium having most of the requirements for these purposes (although having somewhat less favorable latent heat characteristics than those of hydrated disodium orthophosphate), is not, however, considered to be a desirable medium, because of its tendency to precipitate on repeated melting and freezing.

To be suitable for the purposes of this invention, the heat storage medium should have a transition point (liquid to solid and vice versa) of at least about 85° F. for ordinary house heating, or more generally, it should have a transition point of at least 10° F. and preferably at least 15° F. above the temperature of the dwelling or other space to be heated. Lower transition points result in such small temperature differentials between heat storage medium and space to be heated that heat is not effectively transferred, or that excessively large radiation surfaces and amounts of heat storage medium are required. Also, the latent heat of fusion of the heat storage medium should be substantial, at least about 60 gram calories per cubic centimeter. A lower latent heat value means that excessively large amounts of the heat storage medium will usually be required to store sufficient heat for the purposes of this invention. Furthermore, as a practical matter, the heat storage medium must have good enough heat-carrying characteristics and be sufficiently low in cost that the carrying charges on the medium and the installation will not be excessive, in comparison with costs of heating by conventional means.

The heat storage media mentioned above, and others having transition points and latent heat values within the range set forth above, have properties indicated in the following table, wherein column A indicates the temperature, in degrees F., at which the medium changes from the liquid to the solid state and vice versa (i. e. the transition point), column B indicates the latent heat in gram calories per gram, column C indicates the specific gravity, and column D, obtained by multiplying the figures in column B by those in column C, indicates the latent heat in gram calories per cubic centimeter.

Material	A	B	C	D
Gallium	86	19.0	5.88	113.8
$Na_2HPO_4.12H_2O$	94	66.8	1.52	101.5
$Na_2SO_4.10H_2O$	90	57.1	1.46	83.4
$Ni(NO_3)_2.6H_2O$	132	36.7	2.05	74.7
$CaCl_2.6H_2O$	86	40.7	1.68	68.4
OsO_4	104	13.5	4.91	66.3
$Zn(NO_3)_2.6H_2O$	98	31.1	2.06	64.2
$Ca(NO_3)_2.4H_2O$	108	33.9	1.82	61.7

As a practical matter, however, most of the foregoing materials are ruled out of consideration for use on any substantial scale. Hydrated sodium sulfate, as already indicated, is apt to form a precipitate which does not redissolve readily, when it goes through the transition point. Also, as already pointed out, the transition point of hydrated calcium chloride is relatively low for the most effective heat transfer to the space to be heated, unless the temperature to which said space is to be heated is relatively low (e. g. 65° F.). The same is true of gallium. From the point of view of cost, gallium and osmium tetroxide are of course out of the question for practical utilization, at least at present. Also, the three nitrates in the foregoing list are relatively too expensive for most uses. It follows, therefore, that hydrated disodium phosphate is the most suitable heat storage medium for the purposes of the present invention, although others can be used should circumstances warrant. Of these others, the hydrated calcium chloride appears to be the only one at present of commercial interest at prevailing prices.

The purposes of the present invention are accomplished by providing a body of the heat storage medium in suitable containing means, heating this medium by solar energy during sunny days, thereby storing heat in said medium, and then transferring this stored heat into the dwelling or other building to heat the same. The transfer of heat from the sun to the heat storage medium, and the transfer of heat from said medium to the building, are conveniently carried out by the use of water as the heat transfer medium, although other liquids or solutions may be used if desired. Ordinarily water will be chosen for this purpose, for reasons of cost and convenience. However, it may be desirable in some instances to use, for example, a water-alcohol or other anti-freeze mixture in the event that the heat transfer system were to be subjected to below-freezing temperatures, e. g. in a public building to which heat is to be supplied only at intervals.

A heat transfer surface is provided for receiving the solar energy. This surface should be so positioned as to be as nearly as possible at right angles to the rays from the sun at its average noonday position, at a selected time of year. This time will be selected on the basis of the amount of heat given by the sun at that time. For latitudes up to say about 40° north or south, winter would be the selected time, as sufficient heat is radiated by the sun in other seasons of the year that the heat transfer surface need not be then at right angles to the sun at noon to receive adequate heat. On the other hand, at high latitudes where not enough heat is received from the winter sun at noon by the surface when at right angles to the rays of the sun, the surface should be placed at right angles to the rays from the sun at some other time of year, e. g. spring or autumn. Heat will therefore be gathered from the sun at such seasons, and at times nearer to that when the sun is highest, but will not be gathered at times when the sun is lower, thus requiring adequate provisions for storage of heat throughout the period when the sun is too low for heat-gathering in accordance with this invention.

If the building to be heated in accordance with this invention has a roof which faces due south, and is of normal slope, the heat transfer surface may be mounted directly on the roof, or in the roof and more or less flush with it. If the roof does not face due south, or substantially so, or if its slope is too flat or too sharp, or for other reasons, the heat transfer surface may be positioned at a suitable angle to the roof, or in any other location as long as it is at a satisfactory angle to the sun's rays, as stated above.

Alternatively, as a modified arrangement, the heat transfer surface may have a "Venetian blind" configuration, wherein said surface comprises slat-shaped hollow members which can be turned or rotated so that their flat sides are at right angles, or at other selected angles, to the sun's rays at desired times. The heat transfer medium is caused to flow through such hollow members.

During sunny summer days, and also at other times of year when the weather is clear and the sun is hot enough, the heat transfer medium is circulated in heat exchange relation with the heat transfer surface, thereby becoming heated, and then in out-of-contact heat exchange relation with the body of heat storage medium, thereby transferring heat to the latter. The heat transfer medium continues this cycle as long as adequate heat is supplied by the sun.

The heat storage medium, which is a solid at temperatures below about 85° to 90° F., thereby becomes heated above its melting point, thus absorbing both latent and sensible heat. When cold weather arrives, so that it becomes necessary to heat the building in which the apparatus is installed, the heat transfer medium is caused to move in a closed circuit between the heat storage medium and heat transfer means (such as radiators) in the building to be heated.

Suitable valve, thermostat, and pump means are provided, as may be desired, to cause the heat transfer medium to flow through the desired circuits. The valves may be operated manually, or may be caused to operate by thermostats set to act at desired temperatures. The pump or pumps necessary to cause the heat transfer medium to flow where desired may also be turned on and off automatically by the thermostats. Blowers may be installed if desired to cause air in the building to circulate over the radiators, and these blowers may also be turned on and off automatically by the thermostats, if desired.

This invention will now be described in more detail by reference to the accompanying drawings, which are to be considered as illustrative of a preferred form of the invention, but not as limiting it in any way other than as expressed in the accompanying claims. In the drawings,

Fig. 1 shows, more or less diagrammatically, a sectional side view of a dwelling or other building containing the apparatus of this invention;

Fig. 2 shows a sectional side view of a simple form of the heat transfer surface mounted upon a roof or other suitable exposure to the sun's rays;

Fig. 3 shows a sectional side view of a suitable reservoir for the heat storage medium, with provisions therein for circulation of the heat transfer medium and

Figs. 4, 5 and 6 shows a "Venetian blind" type of heat transfer surface, wherein

Fig. 4 is a top view thereof, with the glass covering removed;

Fig. 5 is an end elevation thereof, in section along the line 5—5 of Fig. 4; and

Fig. 6 is a side elevation thereof, in section along the line 6—6 of Fig. 4.

Fig. 1 is on a smaller scale than the other figures. Fig. 5 is on a slightly larger scale than Figs. 4 and 6.

Referring now to Fig. 1, numeral 10 represents a dwelling or other building, having a basement 12 and living or other commonly habited quarters 14. In basement 12 is located reservoir 16 having an insulated covering 17 and filled with heat storage material 18 and containing pipes or coils 20 carrying the heat transfer medium. On the roof or in any other suitable location is placed the heat transfer surface 22 for gathering solar energy. Within building 10 are located one or more radiators or other heat transfer means (hereinafter called radiators) 24, 26. A pump 28 driven by motor 30 is provided to cause the heat transfer medium to move in the circuit desired at any particular time.

Conduit 32 leads from coils 20 to the intake of pump 28, and the outlet of pump 28 connects with conduit 34, which is provided with branches 36 and 38. Branch 36 leads to the heat transfer surface 22, through which the heat transfer medium passes, while conduit 40 is provided to convey the said medium back to coils 20 via conduit 42 and main return conduit 44. Branch conduit 38 leads to radiators 24 and 26 via branches 46 and 48 respectively. Return branch conduits 50 and 52 lead back from radiators 24 and 26 respectively to conduit 54 and thence connect with main return conduit 44.

Radiator 24 is located in air duct 56 which is conveniently located in basement 12 and is provided with inlet 58 and outlet 60. Within duct 56 is fan 62 driven by motor 64, so as to cause circulation of air from quarters 14 through duct 56 over radiator 24 and back, in heated condition, to quarters 14. Similarly, radiator 26 may be associated if desired with a fan 66 driven by motor 68 to improve heat transfer from radiator 26.

A number of different valve arrangements may be used for directing the flow of heat transfer medium through the various conduits. These valves, as well as the motors 30, 64 and 68, may be manually controlled or may be controlled by thermostats. One suitable system of valves and thermostats is shown in Fig. 1, wherein valves 70, 72, 74, 76, 78, 80, 82, 84 and 85 are provided, and thermostats 86 and 88.

Thermostat 86 is positioned in contact with heat transfer surface 22, and is set to operate at a suitable temperature as hereinafter set forth. Thermostat 88 is positioned in quarters 14 and is likewise set to operate at a predetermined temperature. Thermostat 86 is operatively connected through electrical lead 90 with motor 30 and valve 70 to actuate them. Thermostat 88 is operatively connected through electrical leads 92, controlled by switch 93, and 94, controlled by switch 95, to motors 64 and 68 respectively, and through electrical lead 96 with motor 30 and valve 72.

Valve 70 controls flow of heat transfer medium through heat transfer surface 22, while valve 72 controls the flow of said medium through all the radiators. Valves 78 and 80 control the flow of said medium to each of radiators 24 and 26 respectively. Since conduits 38, 40 and 42 have a common intersection at the X connection 98, valves 74 and 76 are also provided for better controlling the flow of heat transfer medium. If for any reason it might be desired to drain the heat transfer medium from the circuit leading to and from surface 22, or from the entire circuit, suitable drain valves such as 82, 84 and 85 may be provided. Valve 82 is a three way valve which, when turned so as to close conduit 40, causes any liquid above valve 82 to drain out through pipe 100, while pipe 100 is closed when valve 82 is set to maintain the circuit through conduit 40 open. Valves 84 and 85 are simple drain valves.

Fig. 2 shows in more detail one form of the heat transfer surface 22 and its connections, including conduits 36 and 40, thermostat 86, and lead 90 already described. This surface 22 consists of a metal plate 102 to which are thermally bonded the tubes 103 which form a closed circuit leading from conduit 36 to conduit 40. Metal plate 102 and tubes 103 are preferably provided with black, heat absorbent surfaces. Over this structure are placed the double glass panes 104, 106, which assist in maintaining high temperature within space 108 between them and plate 102. Thermostat 86 is positioned in or upon plate 102 so as to be actuated by the temperature thereof.

Fig. 3 shows in more detail a form of the storage reservoir 16. Main return conduit 44 leads to header 110, while header 112 is connected with conduit 32. Between the headers 110 and 112 is a series of connecting tubes 114. The heat transfer medium enters through main return conduit 44, passing thence into header 110 whence it is distributed via tubes 114 to header 112, wherein it is collected and passed to conduit 32 and thence out of the heat storage reservoir 16. Heat exchange takes place between the heat storage material 18 and the heat transfer material flowing in headers 110 and 112 and tubes 114. Other arrangements may of course be used, such as the coils shown in Fig. 1.

Figs. 4, 5 and 6 show the "Venetian blind" form of heat transfer surface. This arrangement comprises the surface 22 which may be placed on or adjacent the roof as already described, and which carries thermostat 86 to which lead 90 is connected, and above which are placed the double sheets of glass 104, 106, all as already described with respect to Figs. 1 and 2. These sheets of glass are supported above surface 22 by side walls 120, 122, 124 and 126. Between the glass and the surface 22 are positioned the pipes or tubes 128, which are round at each end and which are flattened throughout most of their length, as shown at 130. These pipes are rotatably supported at each end by lower supports 132, and upper supports 134, which have round holes to accommodate pipes 128. Conduit 36 for heat transfer medium is connected via header 135, nipples 136 and flare unions 138 to pipes 128, which latter are plugged at each end against escape of liquid by plugs 140 except for a hole centrally of each plug to permit passage of liquid from header 135 into the pipe. Similarly at the other end of each pipe 128 are plugs 142, flare unions 144 and nipples 146, so that the pipes may discharge into header 148 which leads to conduit 40 previously described.

The operation of the system described herein is as follows: During hot weather, when the temperature within the house or building 10 rises above normal comfort temperature of 72° F. or so, and the temperature at the heat transfer surface 22 is sufficiently high (say at least 95° F., or in any event at an operable temperature—about 5° F. or more—above the fusion temperature of the heat storage medium 18), the thermostat 86 opens valve 70 and causes motor 30 to operate pump 28. At the same time valve 72 is closed by thermostat 88, valve 76 is open, and valves 78 and 80 closed. Valves 82, 84 and 85 are, of course, closed against drainage of heat transfer medium from the system. Motors 64 and 68 are not operating, regardless of whether or not switches 93 and 95 are closed, since thermostat 88 is set so as to actuate these motors only at temperatures below normal comfort temperature in the building 10. Consequently, the heat transfer medium is impelled through conduit 36 to heat transfer surface 22, passing through pipes 103 and absorbing heat; thence said heated medium passes downward through conduits 40, 42 and 44, and to coil 20 (Fig 1), or to header 110, connecting tubes 114, and header 112 (Fig. 3), where it gives up heat to the heat storage medium 18. Then the heat transfer medium flows back through conduit 32 to to pump 28, whence it resumes the circuit.

When the sky is overcast or the weather is so cold that the temperature at surface 22 is too low to permit heat to be transferred therefrom to medium 18 above the fusion temperature of the later, thermostat 86 causes valve 70 to close. Consequently, flow of heat transfer medium to surface 22 is cut off. If the roof temperature is so low or such other conditions exist, that there is danger that the heat transfer medium in conduits 36 and 40 or at surface 22 will freeze, drain valves 82 and 84 may opened and said medium drained out. If the temperature in space 14 falls below normal comfort temperature, thermostat 88 acts to open valve 72, and to cause motor 30 to actuate pump 28. Thermostat 88 also starts motor 64, if switch 93 is closed, or motor 68, if switch 95 is closed, or both, if both switches are closed. Valve 74, and valve 78 and/or valve 80 are opened, and valve 76 closed. Consequently, heat storage medium 18 gives up heat to the heat transfer medium in coil 20 (Fig. 1) or in tubes 114 and headers 110 and 112 (Fig. 3), which latter medium then flows out through conduit 32 and is impelled by pump 28 through conduit 38 to either radiator 24 or radiator 26, or both of them, where heat is given up, and is distributed by means of fans 62 and/or 66. The heat transfer medium then returns via conduit 54 and main return conduit 44 to pick up more heat by heat exchange with medium 18. As heat is thus supplied to space 14, and the temperature therein rises above that at which the thermostat 88 is set, the latter acts to shut off motors 64 and 68, as well as motor 30, and to close valve 72. Thus, heat transfer medium ceases to flow through radiators 24 and 26, until the temperature in space 14 falls below the temperature at which thermostat 88 is set, at which time the cycle described above is repeated.

It should be noted, as already indicated, that either radiator 24, or radiator 26, with their associated conduits, motors, and fans, may be used, or both may be used. The circuits, connections, and operations obtaining when either radiator is used alone, or both are used together, will be obvious from the foregoing disclosure.

The arrangement shown in Figs. 4, 5 and 6 collects heat as already described with respect to the device of Fig. 2, except that the pipes 128 may be rotated so that thin flat surfaces 130 are at right angles (or any other desired angle) to the rays of the sun at the desired time of day and year. The pipes 128 may be turned on their axes by hand in the arrangement shown, by adjusting the flare unions, but a mechanical rotation may be provided for if desired, with the use of stuffing boxes at the points where the tubes rotate, in the conventional manner. The pipes 128 rotate between supports 132, 134, and the flare unions 138, 144 permit adjustment. The axes of these pipes 128 are preferably horizontal, for reasons which will be obvious from the present disclosure, although they may be placed at an angle to the horizontal, if desired. By this arrangement, the pipes 128 can be turned to receive the maximum amount of heat from the sun at any or all desired times of year. In Fig. 6, the flat surfaces 130 of pipes 128 are shown parallel to surface 22, while in Figs. 4 and 5 they are shown at an angle to said surface, as illustrations of different possible positions.

At some times of the year when the sun is hot enough to provide a sufficiently high temperature at surface 22, and yet the ambient temperature is such that space 14 is below the normal comfort temperature at which thermostat 88 is set, a combined operation may advantageously be used. In such operation (see Figs. 1, 2 and 3), valves 70, 78 and 80 are opened, and valves 72, 74 and 76 are closed. Valves 82, 84 and 85 are, of course, closed against drainage of heat transfer medium from the system. Accordingly, the heat transfer medium is impelled by pump 28 driven by motor 30 actuated by thermostat 86, to pass through conduit 36, tubes 103, and conduit 40 to X connection 98, and thence via conduit 38 to radiator 24 or radiator 26, or both, returning then via conduit 54 and main return conduit 44 to the heat exchange surface within reservoir 16, whence it is recirculated. Thus the heat transfer medium, heated in tubes 103, gives up part of its heat to space 14 and part of its heat to heat storage medium 18. During such periods of combined operation, the heat storage medium will frequently be at its fusion point and partly in liquid and partly in solid form. Hence, it will still have a high heat content while being capable of taking up still more heat. *

May 15, 1951 L. W. CORNWALL 2,553,302

SOLAR HEATING ASSEMBLY

* *

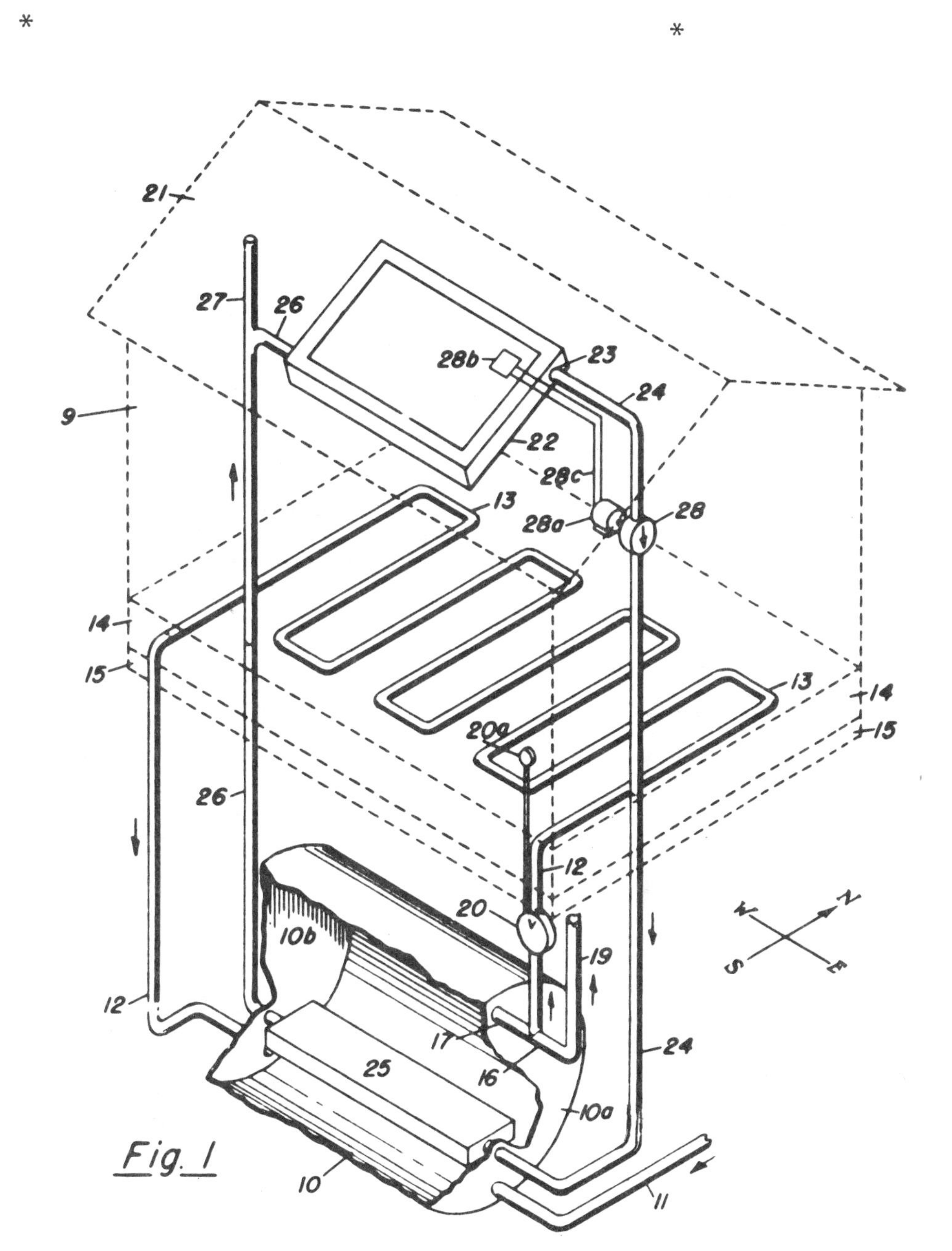

Fig. 1

INVENTOR.
LEO W. CORNWALL
BY Everett H. Curtis
ATTORNEY

May 15, 1951 L. W. CORNWALL 2,553,302

SOLAR HEATING ASSEMBLY

* *

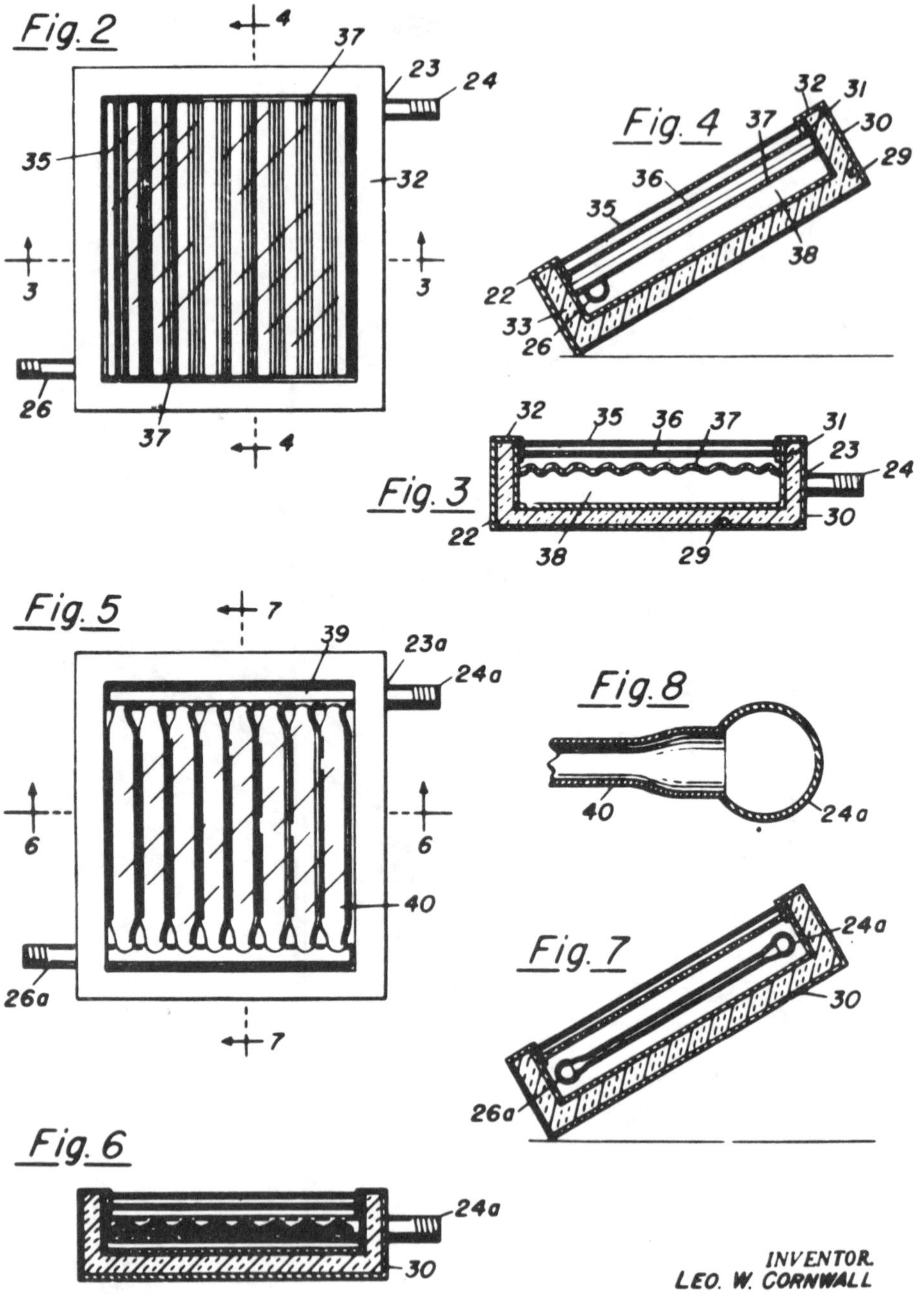

Fig. 2

Fig. 4

Fig. 3

Fig. 5

Fig. 8

Fig. 7

Fig. 6

INVENTOR.
LEO. W. CORNWALL
BY [signature]
ATTORNEY

May 15, 1951 L. W. CORNWALL **2,553,302**

SOLAR HEATING ASSEMBLY

* *

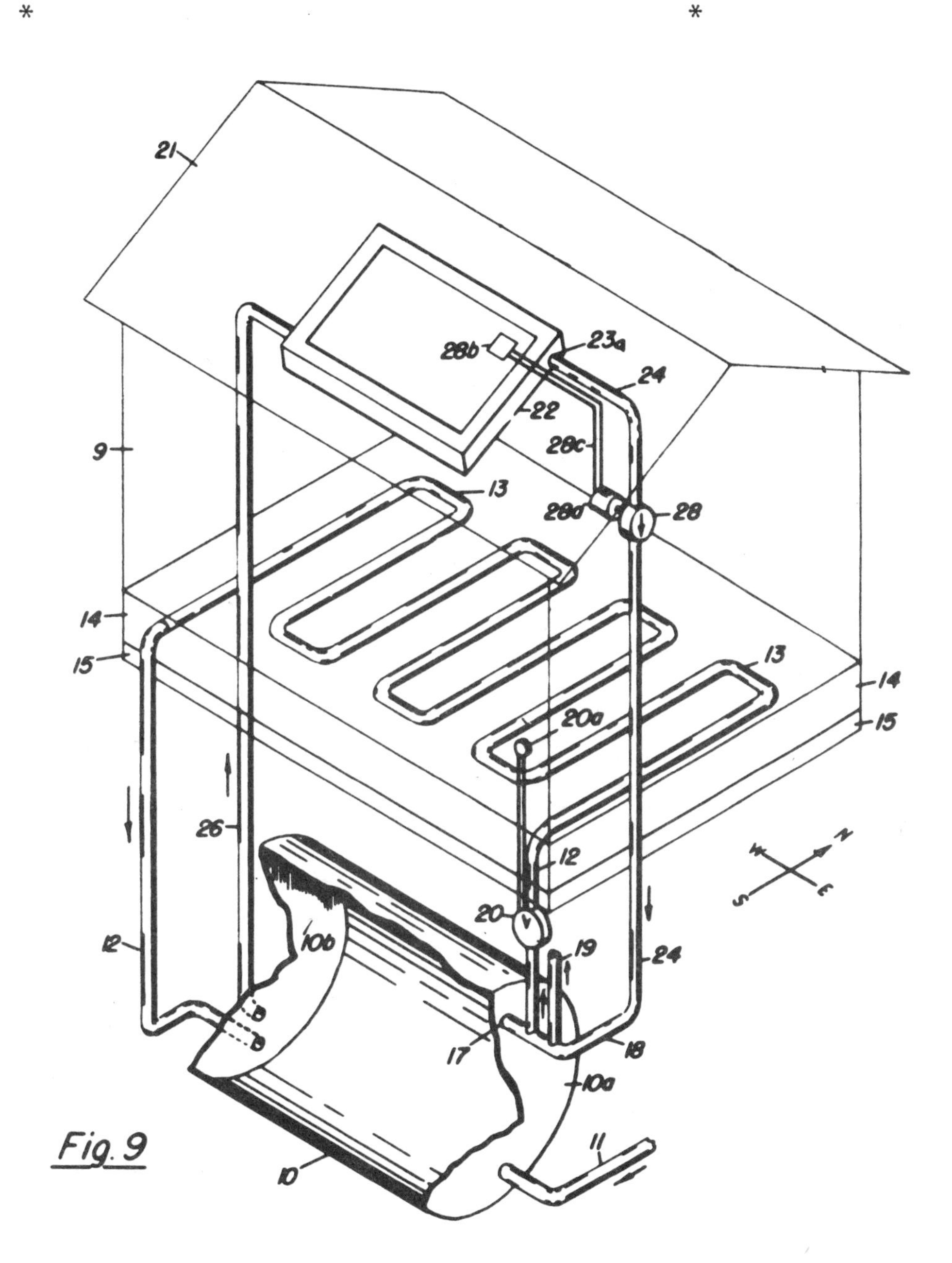

Fig. 9

INVENTOR.
LEO W. CORNWALL
BY Everett McCurtin
ATTORNEY

UNITED STATES PATENT OFFICE

2,553,302

SOLAR HEATING ASSEMBLY

Leo W. Cornwall, San Diego, Calif.

*

My invention relates to solar heating assemblies, and its objects are to utilize in a manner heretofore unknown in the art, the rays of the sun for heating and maintaining the temperatures of the water of hot water circulating and storage systems so as to render such water available for domestic purposes; to provide automatic thermostatic means for controlling as desired the said temperatures and to guard against overheating of the water circulating through said systems; to furnish either gravity or pressure means for maintaining said circulation and for guarding against undue pressure against the walls of the tanks or pipes of said system; to insulate, shield and protect against injury from outside sources the various parts of said system; to provide as an important part of said system a special form of hot water heater in which the direct rays of the sun are constantly utilized and employed for heating the liquid contents thereof; to provide a portable form of heater which can be used in said system or readily used apart therefrom for camping or out of door purposes; to render said system available for buildings used for household purposes and to be built in and to form a permanent part of the structure thereof; to render the parts of said apparatus readily accessible for inspection, adjustment, removal, replacement and repair; and in general to provide an apparatus which is economical of construction, efficient in action and of prolonged life and durability. These and other objects will appear from the drawing and as hereinafter more fully set forth and described. *

Figure 1 is a diagrammatic representation of the closed circuit assembly embodying my improved heating apparatus, illustrating the application thereof to a dwelling house, an outline view of which is shown; also shown in dotted lines is an adaption of said apparatus to a pressure system;

Fig. 2 is a plan view of the solar heat absorption unit shown in Fig. 1;

Fig. 3 is a section on line 3—3 of Fig. 2, looking in the direction of the arrows;

Fig. 4 is a section on line 4—4 of Fig. 2, looking in the direction of the arrows;

Fig. 5 is a plan view of a solar heat absorption unit of the pressure type, the tubes thereof being shown flattened in form;

Fig. 6 is a section on line 6—6 of Fig. 5, looking in the direction of the arrows;

Fig. 7 is a section on line 7—7 of Fig. 5, looking in the direction of the arrows;

Fig. 8 is an enlarged section of the end of one of the tubes shown in Fig. 5, showing its connection with intake or outlet conduit, and

Fig. 9 is a view of a modification of the assembly shown in Fig. 1, illustrating the adaptation of the same to the pressure type of my invention.

Referring to the drawings, in Fig. 1, I have shown an outline view of a conventional building 9, showing an assembly of water tanks and conduits embodying my invention; including a closed unreplenished water circulatory system directly connected with the solar heat absorption unit and an open circulatory system connected with and supplied by the main water line. As shown, a well insulated hot water tank 10 is installed in the basement or under the bottom floor of the building; the lower part of one end 10a of said tank being connected to the supply pipe 11 leading from said main water supply, and the upper part of said end 10a being connected with the egress pipe 16, from which extends upwardly the conduit 12 leading to and merging into the heating coils 13 and the take-off pipe 19 leading to bathrooms, toilets, laundry, kitchen or other outlets from which hot water may be dispensed as required. These heating coils are preferably embedded in a layer 14 of ordinary concrete, resting upon a layer of light weight aggregate concrete 15; the two layers forming the floor of the building. From the said coils 13, the conduit 12 leads downwardly and is connected with the lower part of the end 10b of the tank 10, discharging into the same. Preferably the flow of hot water coming from the coils 13 is automatically controlled or arrested by the thermostatic valve 20, which valve is one made responsive only to the temperature control 20a of the room just above said heating coils

Located upon the slanting roof 21 of the building 9, or preferably made a part thereof and flush therewith, is the closed box 22 of the solar heating unit 23, preferably in the Northern hemisphere inclined so as to face south toward the orbit of the sun. Leading out of the upper part of the hollow of said box 22 is an outlet pipe, the threaded end of which is detachably secured to the conduit 24, which, extending downwardly, enters the lower part of the tank 10, through its end 10a where it leads into and is connected with one end of the elongated closed box of the heat dispensing unit 25, and connected with and leading out of the other end of said elongated box and through the adjacent end 10b of said tank 10, is the conduit 26, which passing upwardly is connected with the threaded end of the inlet pipe leading into the lower part of the hollow of the box 22 of the heater unit 23. By reason of the connections of conduits 24 and 26 with the respective threaded ends of the inlet and outlet pipes of the box 22, the said solar heating unit 23 is obviously readily detachable therefrom, and is thereby made portable for camping or out of door purposes. If desired, at some portion of this closed circulatory system may be installed and connected a conventional air chamber 27 to guard against excessive pressure from the water therein, resulting from its expansion upon the heating thereof. Also a conventional pump 28, suitably connected to the conduit 24 and actuated by a motor 28a, is provided for the purpose of maintaining the circulation of water to and from the unit 23, and for bringing such water to, and keeping it at, the desired temperatures; a conventional thermostat 28b connected by the electric wiring 28c with both said unit and pump serving to guard against circulation of the water above excessive temperatures.

In Figs. 2, 3 and 4, I have illustrated a form of my solar heat absorption unit 23, comprising the square or rectangular double walled box 22, the space 29 between the walls 30 and 31 of which is closed by the frame 32 and is filled with rock wool 33 or other suitable heat insulation material. Hermetically closing the mouth of the said box are two panes 35 and 36 of glass or other suitable transparent material, in parallel relation, and preferably spaced one quarter of an inch apart. Just below the pane 36 and closely spaced therefrom is the corrugated metal partition 37, extending from wall to wall in the interior of said box, and hermetically sealed therefrom; the said corrugations being preferably positioned due north and south and contoured so as to receive on some part thereof the direct rays of the sun. Below the said partition is formed the hollow 38 of the box forming a shallow reservoir within which the flowing water of the system is exposed and subjected to the heat of the sun, and into and out of which reservoir such water is pumped by the pump 28 in effecting the circulation thereof to raise the same to the desired temperatures.

In the operation of the closed circuit assembly shown in Figs. 1 to 4, inclusive, the solar heating unit 23, conduit 24, heat dispensing unit 25, and conduit 26, are first completely filled with clean water, to which may be added an anti-freezing mixture if necessary in climates where freezing temperatures are to be encountered. This step when accomplished forms a self contained circulating system without necessity of replenishment or cleansing except at rare and extended intervals. At the same time or previous thereto, the tank 10, conduit 12, coils 13, and egress pipe 16 and outlets therefrom, have been filled and continuously supplied with water coming through the pipe 11 connected with the water main. Thereafter, the face of the solar heating unit 23 is exposed to the rays of the sun, and the temperature of the water of said unit rises, and when it reaches from 140 to 150 degrees Fahrenheit as indicated by the thermostat 28b, the motor 28a is automatically started and the pump 28 caused to operate, pumping the heated water from the reservoir 38 of said unit 23 down through the conduit 24 into the hollow of the box of unit 25 inside the tank 10, the contents of which tank are thereby caused to be heated. Thence, the water of unit 25 passes upwardly through the conduit 26 back to the heating unit 23, and thereafter continues to be pumped and to circulate through the system. If the said temperature of the water in the heating unit 23 drops below the range above specified, or rises above 212 degrees Fahrenheit, the thermostat 28b is adjusted automatically to stop the motor 28a and to shut off the pump 28.

As the result of the rise in temperature of the mass of water concentrated by the heat dispensing unit 25, and passing in and out of the same, the temperature of the larger volume of water contained in the tank 10 and contacting the wall of said unit will rise correspondingly; and following the law of heat transfusion in liquids and solids will of its own accord tend to pass out of said tank upwardly through conduit 12 from the egress pipe 16 into and through the coil 13, where it will serve to heat the room above, such heat being diffused upwardly through concrete layer 14. Here the temperature of the room is controlled by the thermostatic valve 20, which acts automatically to arrest the circulation of the water upwardly through the lower portion of the conduit 12 when the desired temperature is reached; while allowing the heated water to be drawn off for domestic purposes from the top of said tank through take-off conduit 19.

In Figs. 5 to 9, inclusive, I have illustrated a form of heat absorption unit 23a, adapted to be used for the pressure type of my invention, and being substantially identical with the unit 23, except that for the corrugated metal partition 37, I have substituted a tubular assembly 39, comprising the extended intake tube or conduit 26a, the extended outlet tube or conduit 24a, and the series of tubes 40 communicating therewith and extending in parallel formation therebetween; the said tubes being flattened with connected adjacent walls so as to eliminate waste absorption areas and so as to take full advantage of the direct impact of the rays of the sun. Also further to adapt the said unit 23a to the pressure type of my invention, I eliminate the heat dispensing box 25, and as indicated in dotted lines 18 in Fig. 1, I move the connection of the discharge end of the conduit 24 to the upper part of the tank 10, while leaving open the egress connection of said tank with the conduit 26. Through such changed arrangement of conduits, the hot water coming from the heating unit 23a is pumped first into the top of the tank 10, from whence the water of the tank passes outwardly through the conduit 26 back to the heating unit 23a, and through the egress pipe 16 to the coils 13 or to the takeoff conduit 19; the water from the coil 13 being returned to the tank through the end of the conduit 12 discharging into said tank through its end 10b. *

Nov. 26, 1968 H. E. THOMASON **3,412,728**

SOLAR HEATING EQUIPMENT

*

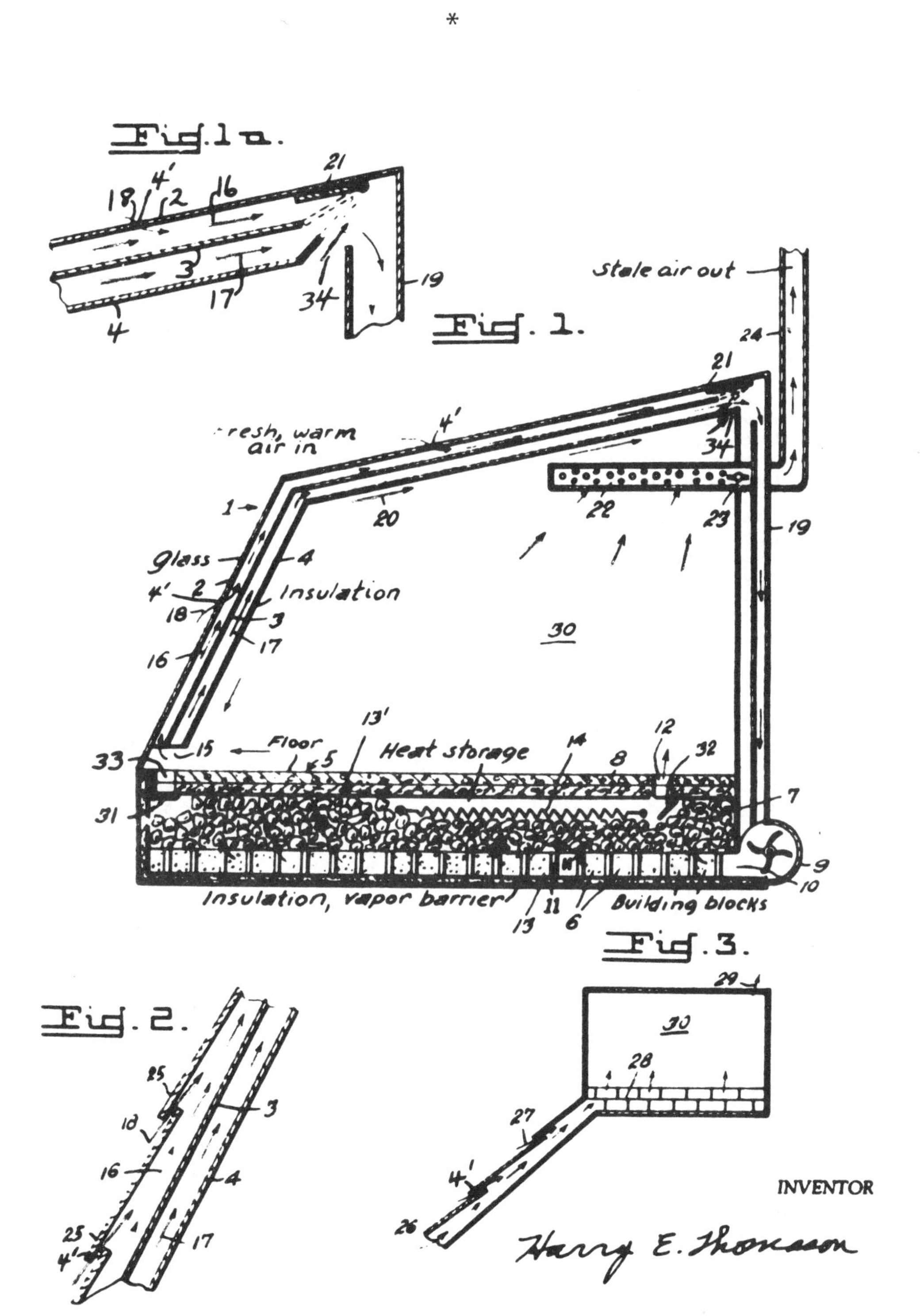

3,412,728
SOLAR HEATING EQUIPMENT
Harry E. Thomason, District Heights, Md.
(6802 Walker Mill Road SE., Washington, D.C. 20027)

*

ABSTRACT OF THE DISCLOSURE

Solar heat collector 1 on a building warms air and the warmed air is circulated by blower 9 to warm heat storage material 7 and the building space 30. Stale air goes out at 22 and fresh, prewarmed air, enters the system at 4'.

This invention relates to equipment to collect and utilize solar heat, in a building, for example.

The building to be warmed, and in which the air is to be conditioned, may be a home or animal shelter, a lumber or crop drying kiln, a greenhouse, or other. In a home, for example, water vapor continuously passes into the air from cooking, bathing, floor mopping, the bodies of occupants and so on. Carbon dioxide is released into the air by the breathing occupants. In a lumber or crop drying kiln water vapor is continuously entering the air from the material being dried. The humidity in greenhouses is sometimes excessive and damaging to the plants being grown. In each case the air tends to become stale, polluted, excessively humid and so on and should be changed.

The present invention provides for automatic introduction of fresh warm air into the system and expulsion of stale spent air which is no longer desirable. Also, solar heat collection and heat storage equipment are simplified, thereby lowering construction and operating costs. Efficiency of heat collection, storage and retrieval from storage are also increased.

In the drawing:

FIG. 1 is a diagrammatic cross-section through the apparatus;

FIG. 1A is an enlarged detail of a damper control of FIG. 1;

FIG. 2 is an enlarged detail of a section of a solar heat collector of preferred construction;

FIG. 3 is a diagrammatic representation of a modification of the apparatus.

Detailed description:

Referring to the drawings in greater detail solar heat collector 1 has an outer transparent covering 2 and a heat collecting sheet 3, preferably treated on its outer surface to absorb sunrays and convert them to infrared heat. This sheet may be corrugated metal, for example. An inner member 4 may be ordinary insulation material, such as glass fiber or foam, or may be reflective insulation such as reflective foil, reflective corrugated aluminum, or other. The transparent covering 2 is preferably provided with passage means 4' to admit warm air from outside to the inside of the collector as illustrated at 18. The passage means may be provided as holes, slits, cracks, overlapping glass panes without airtight seals, jet-venturi devices or other.

Heat storage apparatus 5, otherwise known as a heat bin, preferably comprises a layer of heat storage masonry such as building blocks 6 with passageways therethrough and with non-liquid heat storage material 7 and a floor 8 thereabove. Floor 8 may comprise a heat storage material such as concentrate, for example. If desired, a layer of insulation 13' (e.g. foam insulation) may be provided between material 7 and floor 8 to reduce heat transfer therebetween. Blower 9 preferably draws warm air from the top of the structure through duct 19 and introduces it to blocks 6 through distributor manifold 10, such air passing out into material 7 through cracks 11 between the blocks. The air may pass out of the storage material through one or more holes or registers 12. Insulation 13 is preferably provided for the walls and floor of the heat storage bin.

If desired an auxiliary heat source 14 may be provided and dampers 31, 32 may be provided to close or open passageways 33, 12 respectively.

Air passing through passageway 12 into area 30 may leave through passageway 15 back to heat collector 1, or may leave by passageway 34 for recirculation by blower 9, or may leave the building by passageway 22, 24, or may leave area 30 by two or more of these passageways depending on adjustment of the various dampers 21, 23, 31, 32, as will be explained more fully hereinafter.

Convection currents of warm air are illustrated at 16, 17, 18, 20.

Operation:

The air just above or outside of the transparent solar heat collector cover 2 is generally warmer than ambient air which is not close to the cover due to several factors as follows: (1) the transparency itself is warmed because it intercepts approximately 10–30% of the sunrays passing through the transparency; (2) the warmed air inside of the collector warms the transparency and the air just outside; (3) infrared heat is radiated from the hot solar heat collector sheet 3 to the transparency thereby heating the transparency and the air just outside; (4) if the transparency seal is not perfect, warm air leas out of the collector, thereby warming the air just outside.

In the present invention leakage of warm air out of the collector is prevented or reduced and use is made of the heat above the collector glazing 2 as follows. The air inside of the collector is warmed by heat generated at the solar heat collector sheet 3. Such warmed air rises in natural convection currents 16. The upward movement of the air is enhanced by a partial vacuum in ductwork 19 produced by blower 9. Fresh warm air from outside of the heat collector transparency may enter the stream of ascending air through openings 4'. If openings 4' are designed as in FIG. 2 for example, ascending air currents 16 whisk past the openings and tend to create a venturi effect, thereby aiding the introduction of fresh warm air at 18 into the stream of ascending air.

As illustrated in FIG. 3, if the point of storage 28 or use 30 of the warmed air is at an elevation higher than the solar heat collector, it is possible to use the system without a power blower. Ascending air currents 26 transfer the heat from inside of the collector to storage 28 and out of the building at 29 and also induce fresh warm air entry through openings 4' as illustrated at 27.

As a practical approach, if a power blower is to be used to produce a slight vacuum inside of the solar collector, the transparency seals may be constructed for slight air leakage therethrough into the collector. However, even here, introduction of warm air from outside will be enhanced if the openings are constructed to utilize a jet-venturi effect, or in other ways whereby the ascending convection currents 16 draw the fresh warm air in from the outside. A "shingling" of panes of glass, with a slit 4' therebetween as at 25 in FIG. 2, is one practical way of achieving the desired result.

Movement of the warm air outside of the collector glazing tends to be upwardly and, at times, this upward movement is accelerated by a breeze or wind blowing onto the glazing and being deflected upward along the sloping surface. These factors enhance flow of the warm air in through openings 4'.

Although only one transparent collector cover is illustrated it is to be understood that two or more transparencies could be provided. The warm air between transparencies would preferably be allowed to ascend, as convection currents, and then pass on to storage or a point of use.

Warm air from the outside would be permitted to enter through slits or other openings in the outer transparency in a manner similar to that described for one transparency.

For some purposes constant circulation of air through the system and interior 30 of the building is desirable, e.g. lumber or crop drying. In other instances it is desirable to bypass the interior 30 and circulate air from the top of solar collector 1 to heat storage apparatus 5 and directly back to the solar collector. As exemplary of such operation the interior 30 may be warm enough but additional heat is to be stored for later use. In such instance damper 31 may be opened, or partially opened, and damper 32 may be closed, or partially closed, to reduce or temporarily eliminate circulation through interior 30. Thus the air is returned from the storage apparatus directly to the solar heat collector through opening 33.

Some of the solar energy entering through transparency 2 and warming collector sheet 3 warms the air therebetween which rises at 16. Some of the heat warms air between sheets 3 and 4 and this warmed air rises at 17. Some of the heat warms sheet 4 and, at least to a limited extent, the heat gets through sheet 4, even if it is insulating in nature. This, in turn, warms air inside the building. This heated air rises as illustrated at 20.

Warm sheet 4 also radiates some infrared heat to the interior of the building. The amount of heat so radiated may be minimized, if desired, by a high degree of heat insulating reflectivity of sheet 4, or by glass fiber, foam or other insulation, or by both reflective and fiber or foam insulation. Or, the amount of heat radiated may be increased by reducing the insulating value of the material or by completely eliminating sheet 4 and all insulating materials.

Damper 21 may be moved to any desired position to allow air to flow only from space 30, through opening 34, to duct 19, or from space 30 plus the space between sheets 3 and 4, or from these spaces plus the space between transparency 2 and sheet 3.

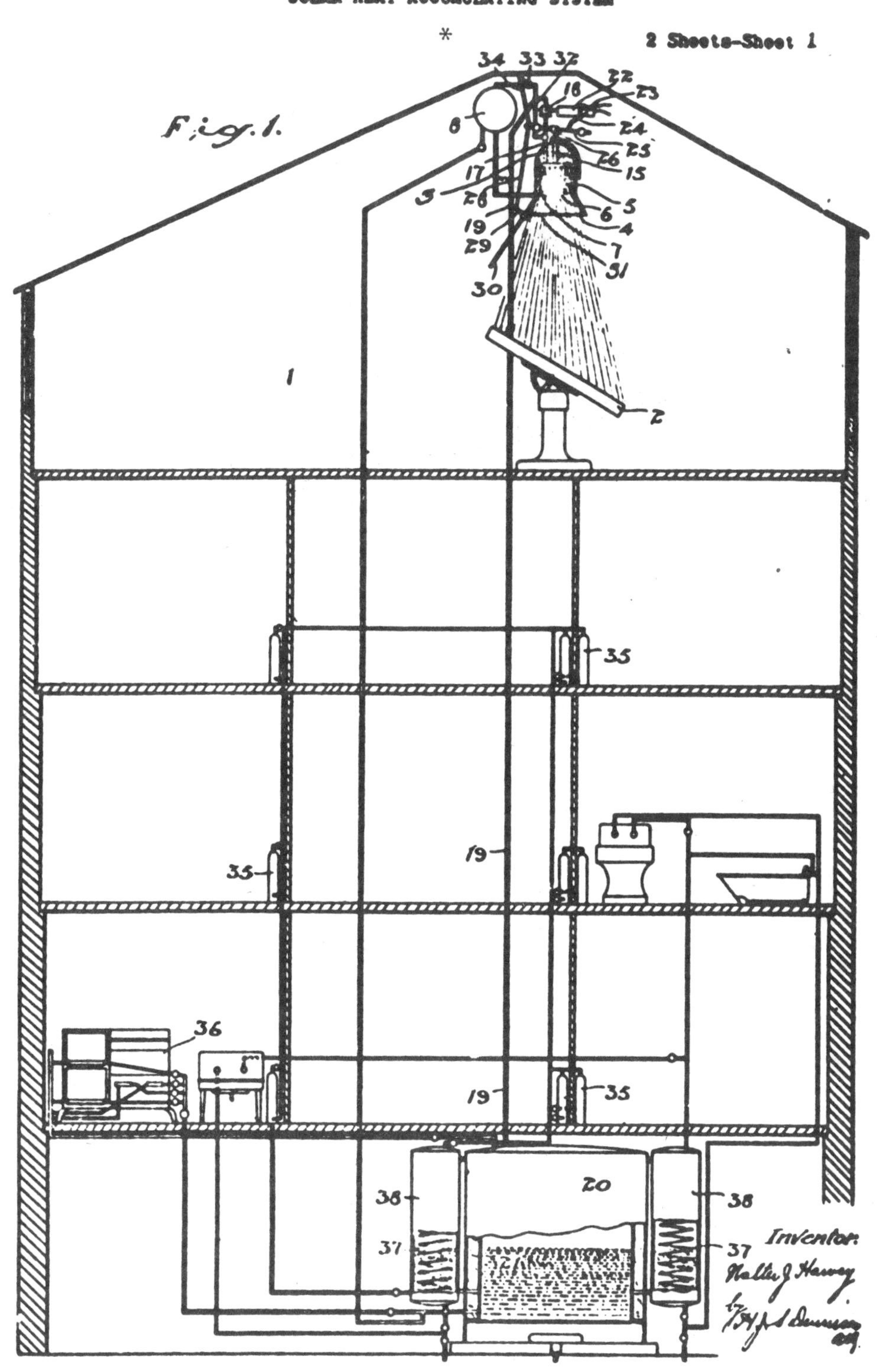
Dec. 18, 1928.
1,696,003
W. J. HARVEY
SOLAR HEAT ACCUMULATING SYSTEM
2 Sheets-Sheet 1
Fig. 1.
Inventor:

Dec. 18, 1928.

1,696,003

W. J. HARVEY

2 Sheets-Sheet 2

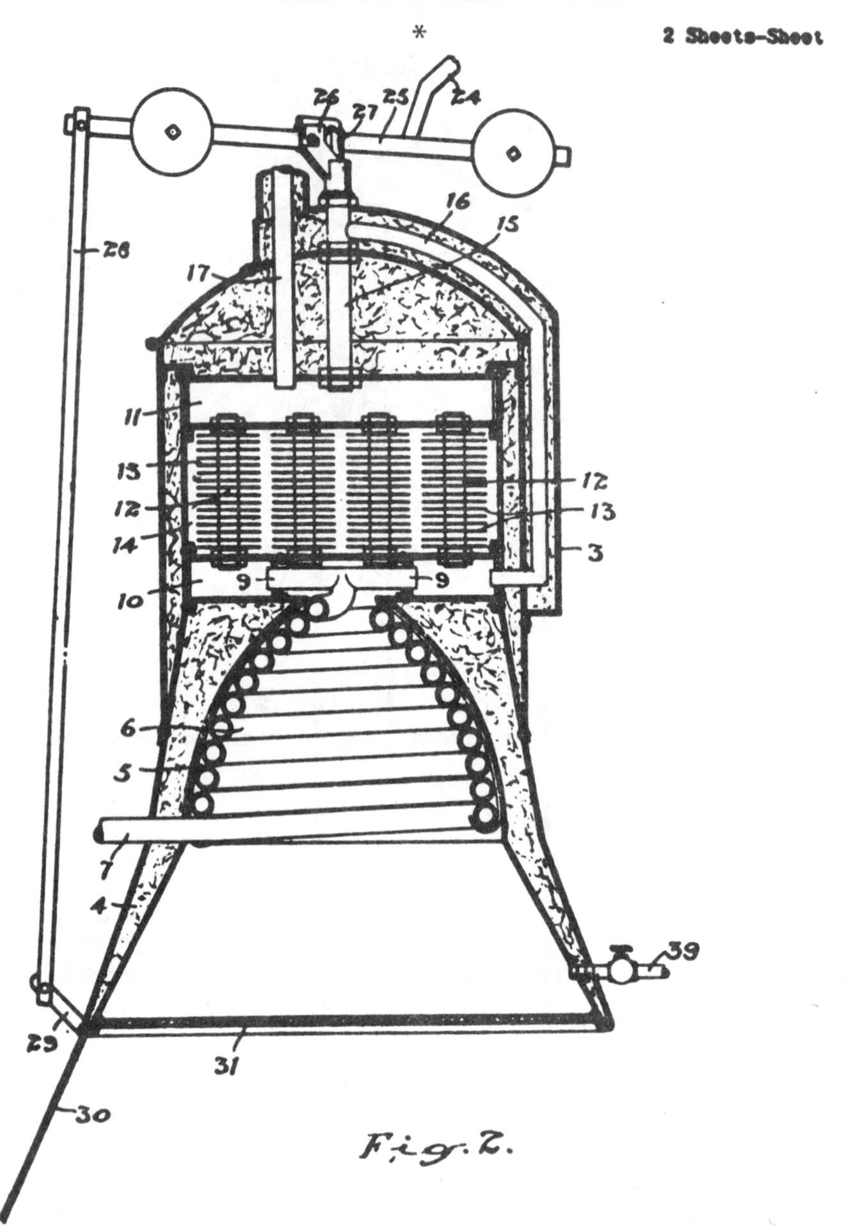

Inventor.
Walter J. Harvey
G. H. J. S. Dennison
atty.

UNITED STATES PATENT OFFICE.

WALTER J. HARVEY, OF TORONTO, ONTARIO, CANADA.

SOLAR-HEAT-ACCUMULATING SYSTEM.

*

The principal objects of this invention are, to accumulate and store the heat of the sun's rays for commercial heating purposes, and to devise a simple and economical form of automatic device for accomplishing the desired object.

The principal features of the invention consist in the novel arrangement of means for concentrating the sun's rays with a means for transferring the heat energy of the rays to a circulating storage fluid.

In the accompanying drawings, Figure 1 is a vertical sectional diagram of a heating installation for a house.

Figure 2 is an enlarged vertical sectional view through the concentrating heater.

The active heat of the sun's rays is of course a well known fact and many devices have been conceived for concentrating the rays so that the heat may be utilized for instance, by the direct application of the rays to heating a boiler.

The present invention contemplates the utilization of the heat of the rays to heat a medium which will retain a high temperature for a considerable period of time and which will dispense the accumulated heat as may be desired for various purposes.

In the method of utilizing the sun's heat illustrated herein, the diagram shown in Figure 1 illustrates a house equipment. On the upper floor of the house is arranged a room 1 which is open to receive the rays of the sun through glazed walls and roof and within this room is arranged a suitable form of reflecting device 2 which is so constructed as to reflect the sun's rays to a fixed point throughout the day. The construction of this reflecting device is not herein shown as different forms may be devised and such construction does not form part of the present invention.

Arranged above the reflecting device 2 is the heat receiving and transmitting device 3, which is here shown in the form of a hood having its walls formed of heat insulating or refractory material. This hood is formed with a circular converging apron 4 leading to a chamber 5 of concave form. Opening downwardly and within the chamber 5 is arranged a tubular spiral coil 6 having its inlet end 7 at the bottom connected with a tank 8 arranged above the device 3.

The upper end of the coil 6 is preferably branched with laterally arranged leads 9 connected with an annular chamber 10 and this chamber is connected with a chamber 11 arranged thereabove by a plurality of tubes 12.

The tubes 12 are shown provided with a plurality of heat absorbing discs 13 within the chamber 14 enclosing the tubes and the heat reflected into the transmitting device after heating the coil 6 is further absorbed by the discs 13 and the tubes 12.

A tube 15 leads upwardly from the top of the chamber 11 and contains a thermostat. A circulating tube 16 leads from the top of the tube 15 back to the chamber 10 so that there will be a constant circulation of the fluid medium for transmitting the heat through the tube 15 carrying the thermostat.

An outflow tube 17 leads from the upper chamber 11 and is connected to a circulating pump 18 which forces the heated fluid medium through a conduit 19 to a storage receiver 20 which is here shown arranged in the basement of the building and which is enclosed within an insulating casing 21.

The pump 18 is of any suitable design operated by any suitable form of motor indicated in Figure 1 by the numeral 22. This motor can be controlled by any desirable form of switch mechanism and the switch 23, the details of which are not shown, is connected with an arm 24 extending from the pivoted bar 25 carried on the bracket 26 mounted on the top of the transmitting device and which is actuated by the thermostat rod 27.

The bar 25 has connected to its outer end a rod 28, the lower end of the rod being connected to the arm 29 of the shutter 30, which is pivotally supported at the lower rim of the apron 4.

The apron 4 is preferably provided with a shield 31 of quartz through which the reflected rays from the reflector 2 are directed and the shutter is adapted to close over the quartz plate in the event of the heat becoming too intense.

When the thermostat rod expands it tilts the bar 25 on its pivot and through the rod 28 its swings the shutter.

A branch pipe 32 is connected to the outflow pipe 17 and leads to the top tank 8 and is provided with a valve 33. The valve 33 is connected by a link 34 with the bar 25 and is so adjusted that when the thermostat expands to a predetermined point it will open the valve 33 and allow the flow of the fluid medium to the tank 8 and thus provide a local relief.

Oil of a high flash point is the preferred fluid medium for receiving and storing the heat and as the sun's rays are reflected from the surface of the reflector 2 into the concave chamber 5 they are absorbed by the coil 6 and the oil contained therein flows upwardly into the chamber 10 through the tubes 12 into the chamber 14 and from thence through the outflow tube 17 from which it is pumped to the storage receiver 20.

A temperature in the neighborhood of 700° F. may be attained by the oil but in the event of the heat being so intense as to raise the temperature of the oil in the heater coil above a predetermined point the shutter 30 is operated by the thermostat to deflect the rays from the reflector and also to open the local relief through the branch pipe 32.

In the diagram illustrated in Figure 1, various pipes are connected to the receiver 20 and oil may be taken therefrom at high temperature to the various heating appliances throughout the house, such as the radiators 35 or the stove 36.

The return circulation carries the oil back to the receiver at a low point.

Water heaters 37 are shown in the form of coils passing through tanks 38 through which the hot oil is circulated and the water from these coils is carried to the various heating appliances throughout the building.

It may be found desirable to exhaust the air from the chamber 5 and a pipe 39 is provided for this purpose.

In the use of this device the storage medium will retain a high temperature for a considerable period but in the event of protracted dull weather when the sun's rays are obscured a supplementary heating means is provided beneath the storage receiver 20 which means may be in the form of an oil burner, a gas burner or an electric heater.

The equipment shown is of course merely diagrammatic and the construction of the apparatus is also largely diagrammatic as it may be altered in details to a considerable extent without departing from the spirit of the invention.

What I claim as my invention is:—

1. In a solar heat accumulating system, a diurnal reflector adapted to direct the sun's rays to a fixed point, a receiver adapted to contain a fluid heat absorbing medium, a circulating conduit connected with said receiver, a helically shaped tubular coil introduced in said conduit and arranged at said fixed point, a chamber connected with the upper end of said coil, tubes leading upwardly from said chamber, an annular chamber connected with the upper ends of said tubes, a pipe leading from the upper chamber and forming part of the circulating conduit, a pump arranged in said upper pipe, and means for operating said pump to effect the circulation of said heat absorbing fluid.

2. In a solar heat accumulating system, an insulated receiver adapted to contain a fluid heat absorbing medium, a circulating conduit connected with said receiver, a heat exchange device connected with said circulating conduit, a diurnal reflector adapted to concentrate the sun's rays on said heat exchange device, a shutter adapted to be interposed between the reflector and said heat exchange device for controlling the reflected rays, a thermostat arranged in said heat exchange device, means operatively connecting said thermostat with said shutter for operating the latter, and means for circulating the fluid medium through said conduit and receiver.

WALTER J. HARVEY.

April 20, 1965 G. FALBEL 3,179,105

OFF-AXIS FOCUSED SOLAR HEATER

*

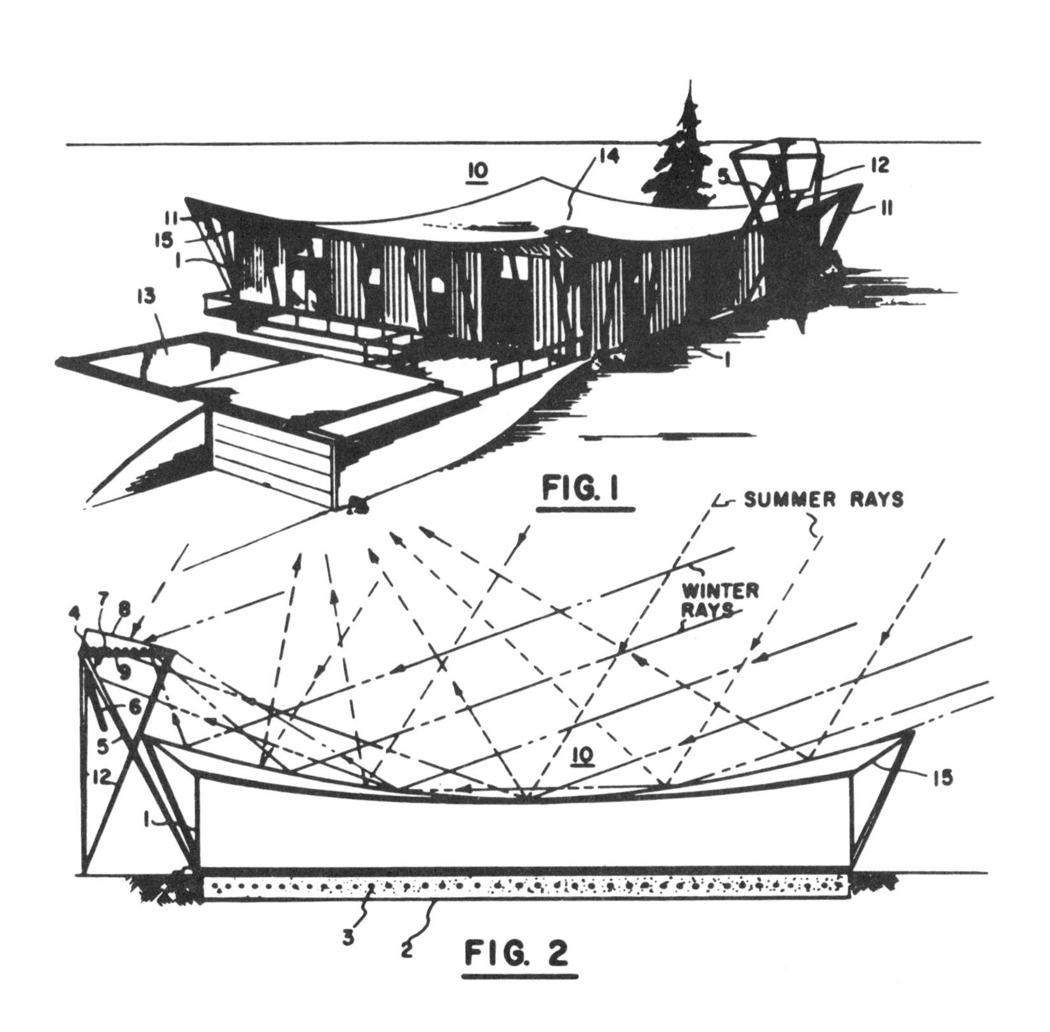

INVENTOR
GERALD FALBEL

BY Robert Ames Norton

ATTORNEY

3,179,105
OFF-AXIS FOCUSED SOLAR HEATER
Gerald Falbel, 59 Glen Ave., Stamford, Conn.

*

This invention relates to an off axis solar heating system and more particularly to such a system associated with a house to be heated by solar energy.

In the past solar energy has been used extensively for heating but in general this has been done in two ways. In the case of a solar heated house the roof or walls or both are provided with a heating medium which may be water or some other liquid. The sun's rays striking the surfaces heat up the medium which can be pumped to a heat sink, for example a chamber with a large mass of material such as rocks so that the heat can be stored. This is of course of importance because, except in unusual climates for example southwest United States, there are periods during which the sun does not shine for a day or two at a time and so it is necessary to accumulate heat in a heat sink. The heat is then used when needed for heating the house by pumping the same or a different medium in heat exchanging relation with the heat sink and with the interior portions of the house. Solar heated houses, although they have been practical in locations such as the southwest United States where the duration of cloud cover rarely exceeds a day, have not proven to be satisfactory in climates for example, the northeastern United States, where it is not unusual for the sun to be obscured by clouds for a number of days in succession and even occasionally for a week. It is true that in such cases a relatively small auxiliary system may be used and the solar heating utilized for a major portion of the heat during the heating season. But there is still insufficient heating area for climates that do not have many hours of intense sunshine and so solar heating of buildings has been seriously limited in its practical utilization.

Other types of solar heating have been proposed and in smaller units have been practically used. These involve focusing mirrors. When an accurate focusing mirror is used and is aimed directly at the sun it is possible to achieve extraordinarily high temperatures and this has been utilized for the melting or otherwise heat processing of highly refractory materials. A somewhat similar use has been for heating at lower temperatures by means of cylindrical mirrors or troughs which have been employed for stream generation and similar power purposes.

The on axis focusing of solar heat requires some means for turning the mirror so it is pointed at the sun throughout the period of time when the sun is shining. In the case of heating of buildings this requires quite elaborate mechanical drives which add to expense and present maintenance problems. A second disadvantage of the on axis or focused solar heating is the relatively higher temperatures which are reached. Even if the area of the heat absorbing surfaces are comparatively large, temperatures are produced which are too hot for many media although they can be used for relatively high temperature steam for power generation. The temperature factor is perhaps less serious than the great complication required in the drive for large mirrors which must be continuously pointed at the sun.

The on axis focused solar heating has constantly striven for accurate focusing. This is one reason why the mirror has to be continuously driven to point at the sun. For maximum efficiency of course accurate focusing has many advantages but the disadvantages of the cumbersome drive and high temperature at the focus have rendered this method of heating buildings economically undesirable and there has been no extended success in solar heated homes or other buildings utilizing on axis heating.

The present invention depends for its operation on a deliberate departure from the conditions which were considered necessary for focused solar heating. It is based on the use of an off axis focusing mirror which need not be perfect in its surface contour and reflects, focusing with a low degree of resolution, onto a fairly large surface of the heat collector such as a tank for water or other heat absorbing means. It is deliberately intended to utilize the resulting aberrations which destroy the resolution at the focus because now the heat is not focused sharply in a small area but is distributed over a larger area because of the large circles of confusion introduced by the aberrations inherent in off axis operation. These aberrations and the lack of sharp imaging are deliberately used in order to produce a better system for solar heating, particularly of homes.

By means of the present invention an off axis mirror can be erected over the top of the house, for example, it may be a thin aluminum, or coated steel sheet supported by pylons. The aluminum sheet may constitute part or all of the roof which can effect building economies. The resulting catenary curves of the edges produce rough approximation of a paraboloid. No attempt is made for great precision. The reservoir of liquid medium acting as an exchanger, for example in the form of a shallow tank or flat black plate with attached pipes, is mounted on a tower which is higher than the building and of course higher than the off axis mirror. This tower is located opposite the sun, for example in the case of the northern hemisphere to the north of the building. When the building faces north, a tower structure may be utilized to form part of an entrance structure for the building.

For a period of several hours around local apparent noon, the sun's radiations striking the off axis focusing mirror are imaged, if one may call the extremely rough resolution produced an image, onto the heat absorbing reservoir. If the mirror is a paraboloid there will be produced a comparatively large circle of very poorly focused radiation. This circle will not produce temperatures that are too high for the transfer medium and therefore one of the extremely serious drawbacks of on axis solar heaters for home heating is avoided. At the same time with a reasonable size of heat exchanger the roughly focused radiation will remain on the heat exchanger for a considerable period of time either side of local apparent noon. It should be remembered that accurate focusing with low aberration produces high temperatures but adds nothing to the heat because the same amount of heat from the sun is distributed over the larger circle when the highly aberrant off axis system of the present invention is employed. Thus there is nothing lost in efficiency and there is achieved the great gain of completely stationary mirrors with no driving means and with no danger of excessive temperature on the absorbing vessel. At the same time the light supported mirror presents no maintenance problems which are encountered with moving drives. In the preferred embodiment where the mirror forms part or all of the roof structure proper there is involved but little or, in some case no additional investment.

The mirror extends normally beyond the walls of the house and makes gutters unnecessary. It is of course necessary to provide a drain pipe in the center so that water which collects will be allowed to flow off. This however presents no serious construction problem and in the case of many architectural styles for modern houses can be combined with a small central court.

While the present invention is not limited to the use of a particular type of heat sink, two types of heat sinks which can be directly applied will be discussed here. In the first of these a covered swimming pool is used with water as the heat storing medium. On an economical basis, a covered swimming pool, is an ideal sink for the following reasons:

(1) A swimming pool has a large water capacity and can thus provide a desirable long term heat sink.

(2) Swimming pools are usually made of concrete which is a good insulator.

(3) Since the water is kept in the pool all year round, the cost of emptying and refilling the pool in the spring and fall is saved.

(4) The use of an insulated removable cover on the pool is highly desirable from a safety standpoint where there are small children in the household.

(5) Since the swimming pool provides family recreation, its cost does not constitute a cost chargeable entirely to the present invention.

In addition, since the swimming pool may be opened, which is not the case with a normally used buried water tank, aluminum barrels of paraffin may be inserted into the pool in the winter to greatly increase its heat storage capacity as a heat sink. The function of this paraffin as a medium to increase the sink's heat capacity is discussed as a part of the description of the second type of heat sink which follows.

The water is heated by circulating liquid from the heat exchanger through suitable pipes.

The second type of heat sink which can be used with this invention, consists of a thick concrete slab below the house. This concrete slab of course contains embedded pipes which circulate the heating medium from the heat exchanger and it is possible to utilize a very simple change of phase heat storing means which is not practical with ordinary solar heating. High molecular hydrocarbons such as paraffin wax melt at temperatures from 40 to 60 or 80° C. and have a very high latent heat of fusion, not too greatly less than that of water. Concrete is easily made with incorporation of large amounts of paraffin wax dispersed therein. The wax does not react with any constituents of the concrete or with pipes and it is stable and does not deteriorate over many years of use. Paraffin or similar compounds which store heat by change of phase could not be used in the ordinary solar heated house because the rays striking a surface frequently did not produce sufficiently high temperature to melt the paraffin. While the present invention does not produce the enormous temperatures of an axis focused solar heating, the temperature is considerably higher than is produced by the unfocused sun's rays on an ordinary flat surface and is amply high to impart to the circulating liquid absorbing medium in the heat exchanger a temperature sufficient to melt paraffin. The aluminum barrels full of paraffin referred to above perform the same function of increasing the heat storage capacity of the swimming pool.

Solar heating is only needed in the winter. In the summer it is not only not needed but is undesirable. Therefore considerable problems are presented in the ordinary solar heated house because the relatively large amounts of heat transfer medium are heated up by hot sun on long summer days and remain hot during the night, thus presenting either uncomfortable temperatures or extra load on an air conditioning system if such is employed. The present invention solves this problem and at the same time makes an improved house for summer. During the summer months the sun's altitude is so high near local apparent noon that the focused image misses the heat absorbing reservoir on the tower altogether. In other words, the heating is automatically shut off. At the same time the aluminum mirror reflects the sun's rays and keeps the house much cooler than an ordinary house. Thus the same element performs two entirely different functions at different times in the year which is an important added advantage of the present invention when used for the solar heating of homes.

The invention will be described in greater detail in conjunction with the drawings in which:

FIG. 1 is an isometric view of a house utilizing the invention,

FIG. 2 is a simplified section through the center of the same house.

The wall of the house is shown at **1** the same reference numeral being used for the west wall of FIG. 1 and the north wall of FIG. 2. In fact in the two figures the same functional elements all bear the same reference numerals. The house is provided with a thick concrete slab heat sink **2** with embedded heating pipes **3**. The concrete also contains dispersed therein a relatively large amount of paraffin which of course cannot be shown on the drawing.

Over the ceiling of the house, and preferably spaced therefrom, is an aluminum mirror shown generally at **10**. This is a moderately thin sheet of aluminum which is supported by four pylons **11**. Each edge of the mirror hangs as a catenary and is normally reenforced with wire or light cable (not shown). The four catenaries cause the mirror as a whole, to assume the approximate form of a paraboloid.

On the north side of the house is a tower formed of four columns **12** and two pipes **5**. At the top there is supported a blackened plate **7** of considerable area to which is attached a grid of pipes **4** which connect to the pipes **5**. Transparent or translucent upper and lower surfaces **8** and **9** respectively are situated on either side of the plate **7**. These surfaces transmit short wave radiation but do not transmit long wave infrared and produce a "greenhouse" effect on the plate **7** with its pipes **4**. A hinged double faced mirror **6** is mounted adjacent an edge of the plate **7**. When swung down it serves to reflect some additional radiation from the mirror and when swung up cuts off radiation to the plate **7**. This latter function sometimes of importance on hot days in the late fall and early spring.

The liquid medium which is circulated through the pipes **4** may have any suitable composition which will resist freezing at the temperatures encountered. It can be a hydrocarbon or water with suitable antifreeze additives. The liquid, is circulated by conventional circulating pumps (not shown), through pipes in heat exchanging relation with the water in a swimming pool **13** which is shown in FIG. 1 and/or through heating pipes **3** in a concrete heat slab **2** as is shown in FIG. 2.

The location and height of the heat exchanger **7** is chosen with respect to the curvature of the mirror **10** so that during the winter months near local apparent noon the sun's rays will be focused at points on the lower surface **9** of the heat exchanger. The circle moves across the surface from west to east as the sun passes from the easterly meridional angle in the morning to a westernly meridional angle in the afternoon. As the sun's declination changes throughout the heating season the circle of the roughly focused image moves across the plate **7** from north to south. This is taken into consideration in constructing the mirror and the heat exchanger which should have the proper distance and the mirror the proper curvature for the latitude of the building which is to be heated. The drawings do not show dimensions accurately to scale but approximate the general dimensions and curvature useful in the latitude of northern New England.

FIG. 2, on which it has been stated before similar elements bear the same reference numerals, is a section in diagrammatic form and shows rays for winter and summer. It also illustrates the concrete slab heat sink modification.

Rain accumulating in the mirror **10** flows off at the center of the building through an opening **14** above a small courtyard. The sides of the mirror act as overhangs making it unnecessary to provide gutters thus performing automatically an additional useful function. It is, however, necessary to keep driven rain from striking the ceiling of the house. This is effected by the tilted soffit **15**. In a fairly large house, such as shown, it is desirable not only to provide cables along the edges of the mirror but to provide two transverse diagonal supports from pylon to pylon. As the nature of these supports involves conventional building design and they are not a necessary functional part of the present invention they are not shown on the drawings.

The invention has been illustrated in conjunction with a solar heated home. This is the most important single field of utility for the invention but it should be realized that the off axis solar heating can be applied quite generally and does not need to be used for heating of a dwelling or for that matter for the heating of a building at all. While therefore in a more specific aspect the present invention is directed to solar heating of homes in a broader aspect it is not so limited and this use is merely a typical illustration.

While the relative positions of the mirror and heat exchanger must be maintained for the particular latitude in which the invention is to be used, it is not necessary that the mirror be exactly centrically located over the roof of a house. Nor is it necessary that the house be approximately square. There is an advantage where terrain and other constructional considerations permit in having the mirror more or less centered over the roof of the house because it then provides overhangs and heat insulation in the summer. But of course as far as the operation of the present invention is concerned the location of the mirror with respect to the building may be varied. *

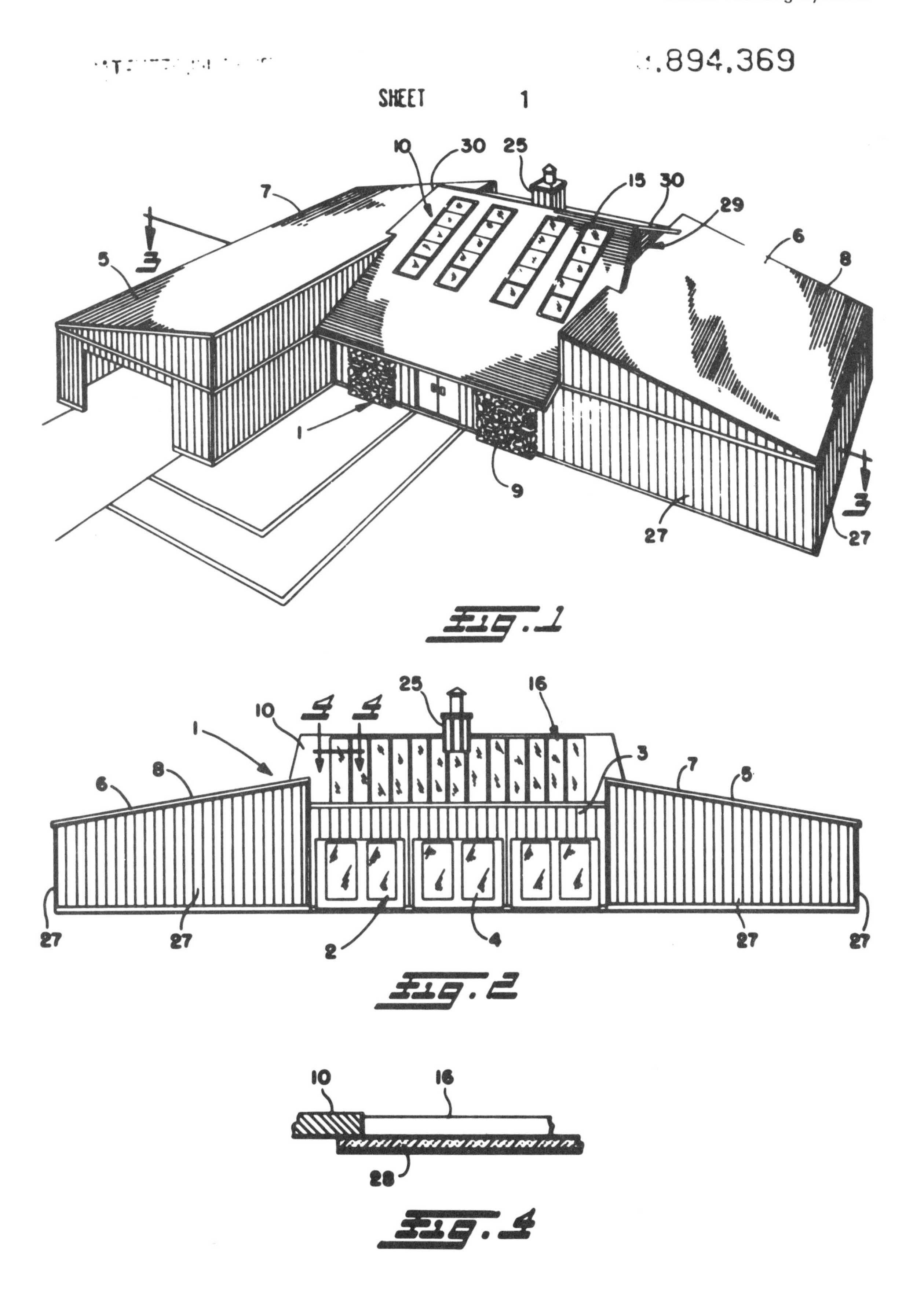
.894,369
SHEET 1
Fig. 1
Fig. 2
Fig. 4

PATENTED JUL 15 1975 3,894,369

SHEET 2

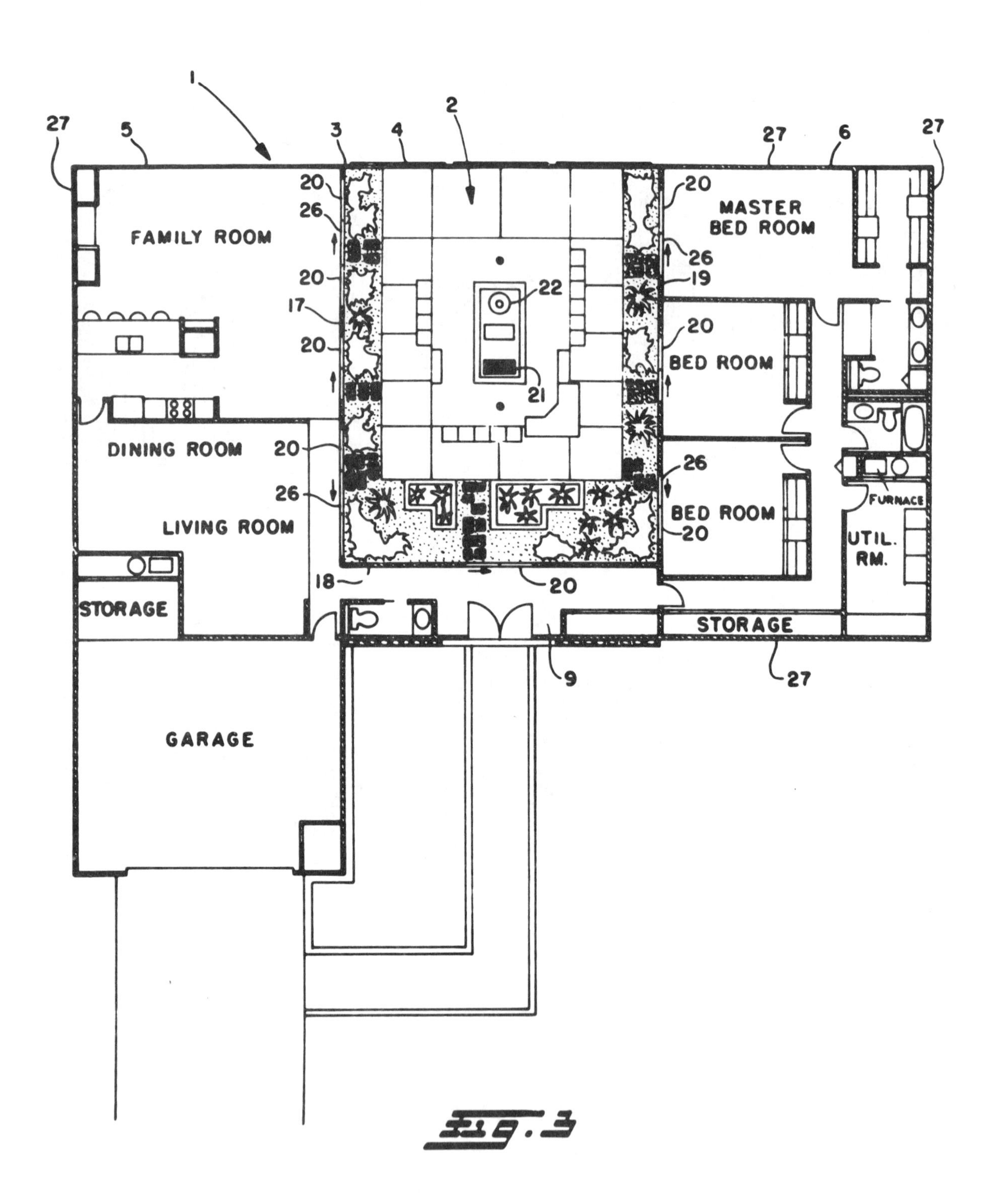

Fig. 3

Inventors: **Robert F. Schmitt,** 399 Crossbrook Dr.; **Edward A. Schmitt,** 690 Wyleswood Dr., both of Berea, Ohio 44017

* **ABSTRACT**

A building structure in which most or all of the exterior glass area is exposed to an outdoor area which is enclosed during cold weather and has a transparent roof permitting passage of solar energy therethrough for heating the enclosed area and thereby minimizing the loss of heat through the exterior glass area without sacrifice to natural lighting or outdoor viewing. A fire in the enclosed area is readily visible from virtually every room in the structure and may be used to provide supplemental heat to the enclosed area at night or during poor solar days in cold weather. Sliding glass doors and the like may also provide easy access to the enclosed area from virtually every room in the structure, and because of the solar heating effects on the enclosed area, it may be used for various outdoor patio activities substantially the year around.

* **4 Drawing Figures**

BUILDING STRUCTURES

BACKGROUND OF THE INVENTION

This invention relates generally as indicated to building structures, and in particular, to building structures of a unique design including solar heated patio areas which may be effectively used both to substantially reduce the amount of heat loss from the interior of the structures during cold weather, and to provide an outdoor atmosphere having both functional and amenity values the year around which may be made readily accessible and visible from virtually every room.

Much work has of course already been done to make use of solar energy to assist in heating houses and other building structures. However, heretofore such efforts have primarily been directed toward transferring or storing solar heat for use in heating the structures or water with little or no effort having been made to obtain other desirable benefits from the solar energy, for example, to permit greater use of window and patio areas to create an atmosphere of outdoor living year-round without incurring the large amounts of heat loss which would normally occur through the windows during cold weather.

While it is possible with existing materials and knowledge to reduce energy consumption for heating and cooling new homes and other structures in the order of **50%** as compared to typical heat loss characteristics of homes built in the past, nevertheless a major source of heat loss from any such structures has been through the exterior glass area even when insulating glass is used. For instance, at a **75**°F. temperature difference between the interior and exterior, **1** square foot of ¼ inch air space insulating glass loses approximately **48** BTU per hour not counting the infiltration loss characteristics of the window, which is in the order of **10** times more than the heat loss than through a well insulated opaque wall. Such high heat loss through the exterior glass area is of more concern now particularly in view of the permanent fossil fuel shortage and corresponding higher costs of procuring the dwindling supply of such fuel.

SUMMARY OF THE INVENTION

With the foregoing in mind, it is a principal object of this invention to provide a building structure which utilizes solar energy to substantially conserve on the fuel required to heat the structure and also obtains other functional and amenity benefits therefrom.

Another object is to provide such a building structure which substantially reduces the heat loss through the exterior glass area and in many instances provides a heat gain through the exterior glass area even when there is a substantial temperature difference between the interior and exterior of the structure.

Still another object is to provide such a building structure which permits substantial use of exterior glass area without incurring the large amounts of heat loss which would normally occur therethrough.

Yet another object is to provide such a building structure in which substantial portions of the interior space are exposed to a solar heated patio area to substantially reduce the amount of heat loss from the interior space and also provide an open, outdoor environment the year around in cold climates.

Still another object is to provide such a building structure in which the solar heating effects on the structure provides protection against freezing of the mechanical heating and cooling systems for the structure and maintains tolerable room temperatures even during fuel and energy interruptions in cold weather.

These and other objects of the present invention may be achieved by providing a building structure in which most or all of the exterior glass area is exposed to an outdoor area that is enclosed under a transparent roof with insulated wall enclosure during cold weather to create a "greenhouse" effect which substantially reduces or completely eliminates the loss of heat through the exterior glass area depending on the temperature differential between the enclosed outdoor area and the interior space exposed to the outdoor area. If the temperature of the enclosed solar heated area is only slightly less than the interior temperature, there will be very little heat loss through the exterior glass area, whereas if the temperature of the enclosed solar heated area is higher than the interior temperature an interior heat temperature gain will result by the heat passing directly through the exterior glass area or by opening the glass area to permit transmission of the heat by convection.

By eliminating most or all of the exterior glass area along the exterior walls of the structure not exposed to the enclosed solar heated area, the major source of heat loss through the building structure is eliminated with little or no sacrifice to natural lighting and outdoor viewing. In fact, the enclosed outdoor area provides an excellent patio setting which may be used for outdoor patio activities and to grow flowers and other plants the year around in colder climates because of the solar heating effects on the area.

Supplemental heating for the entire structure may also be obtained from the patio area on cold nights or during poor solar days by providing a fire in a fireplace and/or potbellied stove in the patio area. In addition to the heating effects, a patio fire may be used for outdoor cooking, and there are also the psychological benefits obtained from the patio fire which is visible from virtually every room in the house. A patio fire also eliminates the heat loss from a fire in a conventional interior fireplace and its unbalancing effect on the house heating system, and a patio fire is also much safer since it is not near any combustible materials.

During warm weather, the solar heating effects on the patio area may be minimized by opening large glass doors or windows in the insulated wall of the patio area and large louvers in the gable ends of the glass covered roof area and vented openings at the bottom of the front roof slope glass area which create a chimney effect inside the patio area for continuously removing excess heat in the summer. Insulating panels may also be installed over the patio glass areas to assist in keeping the patio area cool in warm weather and also minimize heat loss through the patio glass area during cold weather when the sun is not shining.

To the accomplishment of the foregoing and related ends, the invention, then, comprises the features hereinafter fully described and particularly pointed out in the claims, the following description and the annexed drawings setting forth in detail a certain illustrative embodiment of the invention, this being indicative, however, of but one of the various ways in which the principles of the invention may be employed.

BRIEF DESCRIPTION OF THE DRAWINGS

In the annexed drawings:

FIG. 1 is a schematic perspective view of one form of building structure constructed in accordance with the present invention;

FIG. 2 is a rear elevation view of the building structure of FIG. 1;

FIG. 3 is an enlarged horizontal section through the building structure of FIG. 1 taken on the plane of the line 3—3 thereof; and

FIG. 4 is a partial section through one of the glass panels in the patio roof showing an insulating panel in place, taken on the plane of the line 4—4 of FIG. 2.

DESCRIPTION OF THE PREFERRED EMBODIMENT

Referring now in detail to the drawings, one type of building structure, a single floor house, is shown incorporating the various novel aspects of the present invention. However, it will be apparent that the same design principles are applicable to a wide variety of different house plans, and also to other building structures which may include more than one story.

The particular building structure **1** illustrated by way of example is generally in the shape of a U, providing a central outdoor patio or court area **2** enclosed along three of its sides by the walls of the house and along the fourth side by an insulated wall **3** having large glass portions **4** which may be opened or removed for a purpose to be subsequently described. The two wings or sides **5** and **6** of the house **1** may have separate roof portions **7** and **8**, respectively, whereas the connecting portion **9** of the house between the two sides and the patio area **2** may be covered by a single gable roof **10** as clearly shown in FIG. **1**.

Substantial portions **15** and **16** of the gable roof **10** over the outdoor patio area **2** are glass or other transparent material to provide for the solar heating of the patio area enclosed under the roof, thereby minimizing the loss of heat through the walls **17, 18** and **19** of the house exposed to the patio area. Moreover, since a major source of heat loss from any building structure is through the exterior glass area, a substantial savings in the heat loss may be obtained by locating most or all of the exterior glass area **20** along the walls **17, 18** and **19** of the structure which define the patio area **2** where the interior and exterior temperature differential is minimized due to the heating effects of the solar energy on the patio area. This may be done with little or no sacrifice to natural lighting or outdoor viewing, and in fact in many instances such natural lighting and outdoor viewing may be enhanced by providing a greater concentration of glass area **20** along the exterior walls **17, 18** and **19** exposed to the patio area than would normally be provided without sacrificing any heat loss. Since heat loss is a direct function of temperature difference, the solar heating effects on the outdoor patio area **2** will greatly reduce the amount of heat loss through the exterior glass area **20**. Indeed, a heat gain to the interior will occur if the temperature within the enclosed patio area rises above the interior temperature, which is a distinct possibility on a good solar day even during quite cold weather.

During the night or on extremely cold days, supplemental heating for the interior of the structure may still be obtained from the patio area **2** by providing a fireplace **21** and/or potbellied stove **22** in the patio area. There are also other benefits which may be obtained from a patio fire. For instance, a patio fire may be used for outdoor cooking virtually any time of the year, and there are also the psychological benefits obtained from a patio fire which is visible from almost every room in the house. Having a fire in the patio rather than in a fireplace in the house also eliminates the disadvantages of an indoor fire, including its unbalancing effect on the heating system of the house and the heat loss caused thereby. A patio fire is also safer than an indoor fire because of the latter's closer proximity to combustible materials. A chimney or vent pipe **25** extending through the patio roof **10** is needed to vent a patio fire.

Many benefits other than a reduction in heat loss from the house interior may also be derived from a solar heated patio. Not only does the patio give the house a more open, outdoor atmosphere, it is also readily accessible from virtually every room in the house by providing sliding glass doors **26** or the like for each room facing the patio. Moreover, the patio may be used for various outdoor patio activities substantially the year around, and flowers and other plants may also be grown and maintained in the solar heated patio the year around.

While it is preferable not to have any glass areas in the exterior walls **27** of the structure not exposed to the patio area **2** as shown, it will be apparent that such additional glass areas may be provided if desired with some sacrifice in heat loss. Moreover, while the particular location of the solar heated patio in the house design shown in this application has substantial advantages in providing solar heat and amenity characteristics, it will be apparent that the same principles may be applied to a wide variety of house plans, and may also be readily adapted to buildings of two or more stories if desired.

For each building configuration and location, calculations and tests will be required to determined the amount of transparent area **15, 16** in the roof **10** necessary to produce the desired solar heat gain in the patio area **2** during cold weather. Moreover, insulating panels **28** or the like may be used to cover the glass area as schematically shown in FIG. **4** when the sun is not shining during cold weather and also during warm weather to keep the patio area cool. Also during warm weather the glass doors or windows **4** in the insulated wall **3** of the patio area **2** and the large louvers **29** in the gable ends **30** of the glass covered area may be opened to create in conjunction with the vented openings at the bottom of the front roof slope glass area a chimney action inside the patio to continuously remove excess heat during the summer. Moreover, since the glass area **20** along the exterior walls **17, 18** and **19** exposed to the patio area are normally not exposed to direct sunlight, the average conditions contributing to heat gain to the interior of the structure are reduced both in respect to direct radiation and air temperature, thereby aiding cooling in the same but reversed manner as the heating.

The effects of the solar heat in assisting in maintaining the desired room temperature in the structure will be most noticeable in the fall and spring and should be sufficient to supply substantially all of the heat necessary to maintain the entire interior of the house at the desired room temperature when the outdoor temperature is in the **40°** to **60°**F. range. The solar heat absorbed during the day by the concrete, stone, and other objects in the patio area **2** will also assist in maintaining the interior temperature at the desired level during the nighttime which may be supplemented by moderate use of the fireplace or potbellied stove in the patio area at night and during very cold weather. Using dark colors in the patio area will also increase the amount of heat absorption in the patio area during the day for use in maintaining the interior room temperature at night. Of course, when the interior temperature drops below a predetermined level, the interior house heating system will come on to provide whatever supplemental heat is needed to maintain the interior temperature at the desired level.

While an important function of the solar heated patio area is to provide assistance in heating the interior of the structure or minimize the heat loss therefrom during cold weather, it may also be used as a sheltered and screened patio area for outdoor patio activities substantially the year around. The patio area is free from rain and insects in warm weather while still providing an outdoor feeling, and is directly viewable and readily accessible from virtually every room. Moreover, a patio fire not only has the functional value of providing heating assistance and permitting outdoor cooking, but it also provides the psychological benefits of a fireplace in a house without the aforementioned disadvantages of conventional indoor fireplaces. *

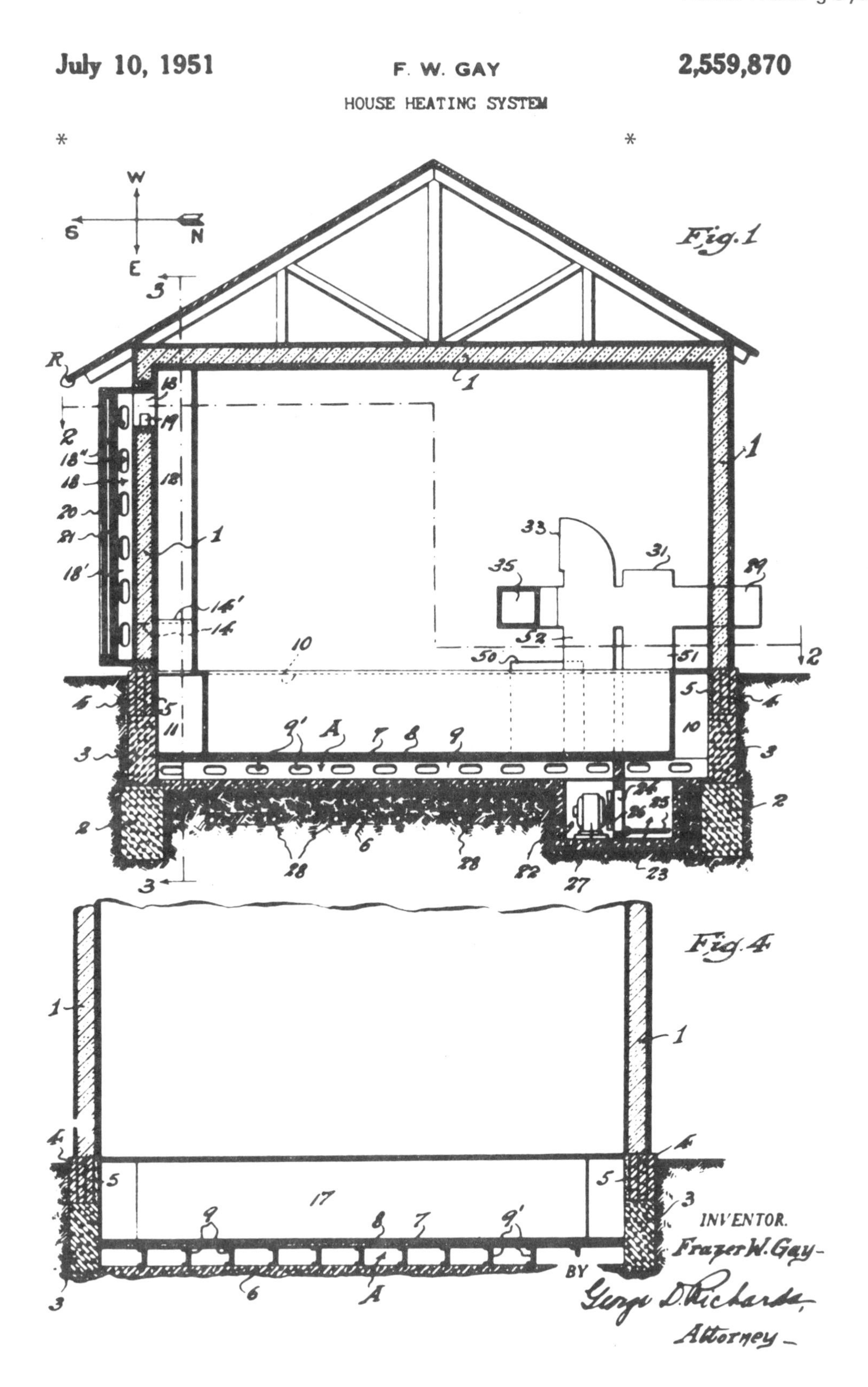
July 10, 1951
F. W. GAY
2,559,870
HOUSE HEATING SYSTEM
Fig. 1
Fig. 4
INVENTOR.
Frazer W. Gay
BY
George D. Richards
Attorney

July 10, 1951 F. W. GAY **2,559,870**

HOUSE HEATING SYSTEM

* *

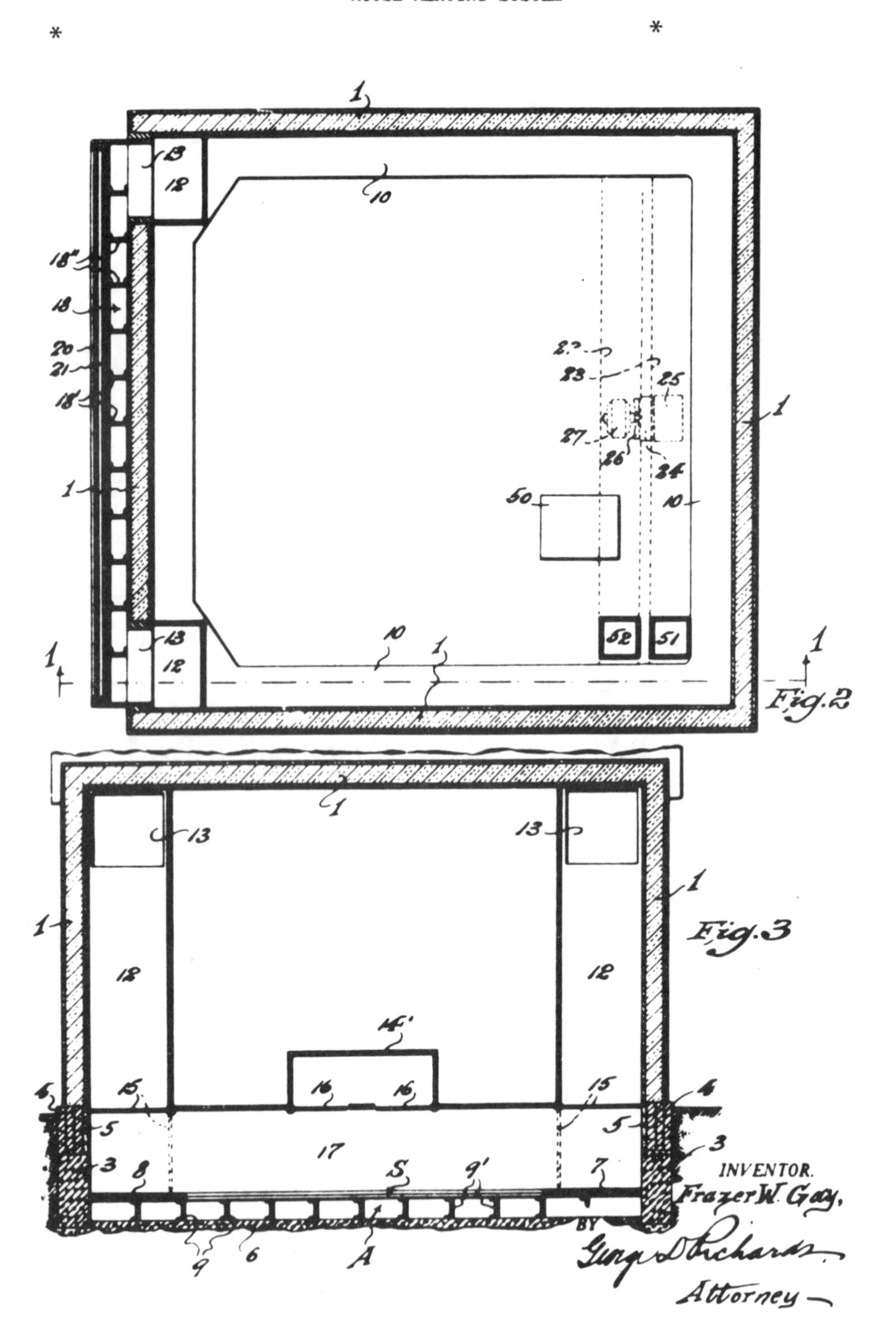

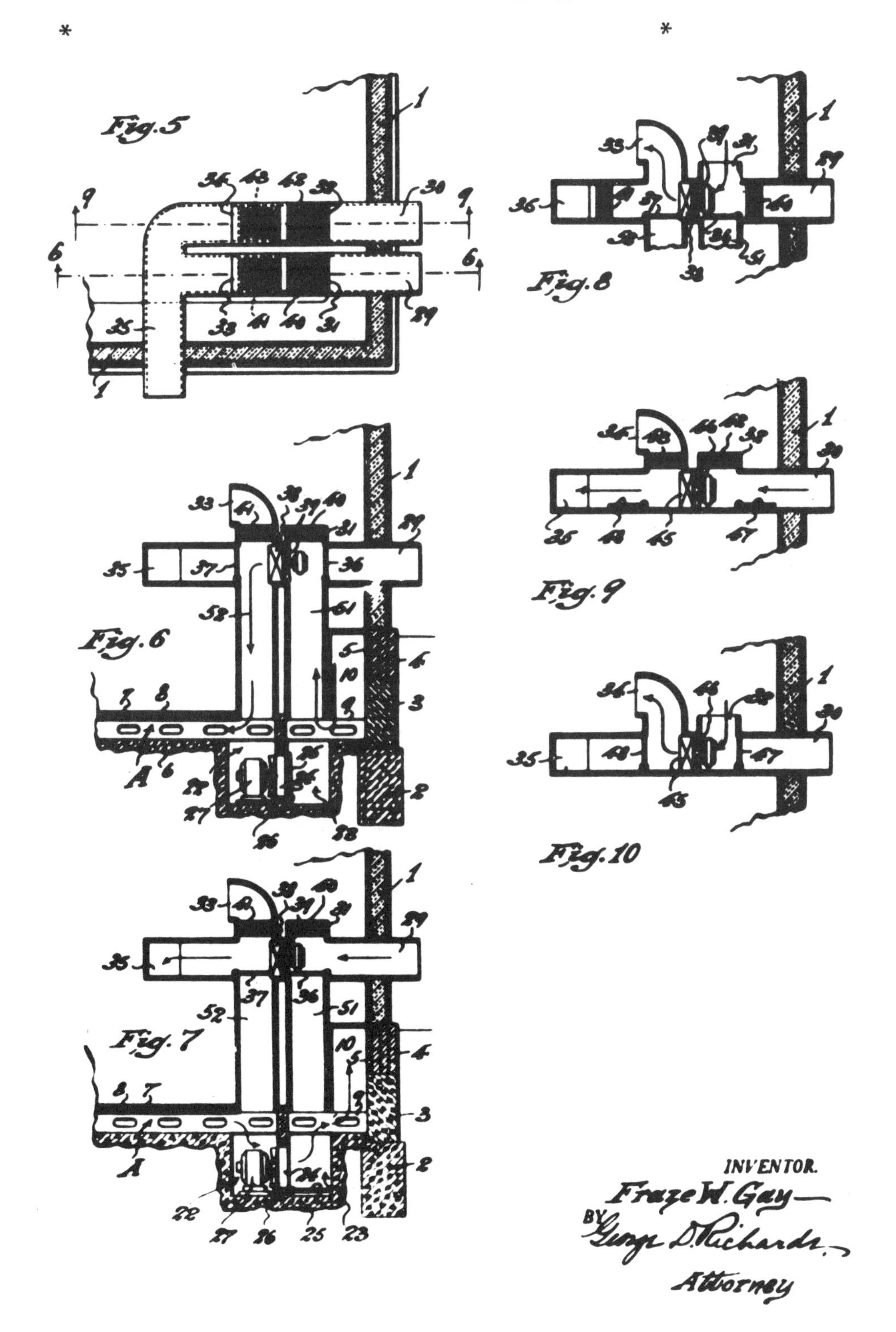
July 10, 1951
F. W. GAY
2,559,870
HOUSE HEATING SYSTEM
Fig. 5
Fig. 6
Fig. 7
Fig. 8
Fig. 9
Fig. 10
INVENTOR.
Fraze W. Gay
BY George D. Richards
Attorney

July 10, 1951 F. W. GAY **2,559,870**

HOUSE HEATING SYSTEM

*   *

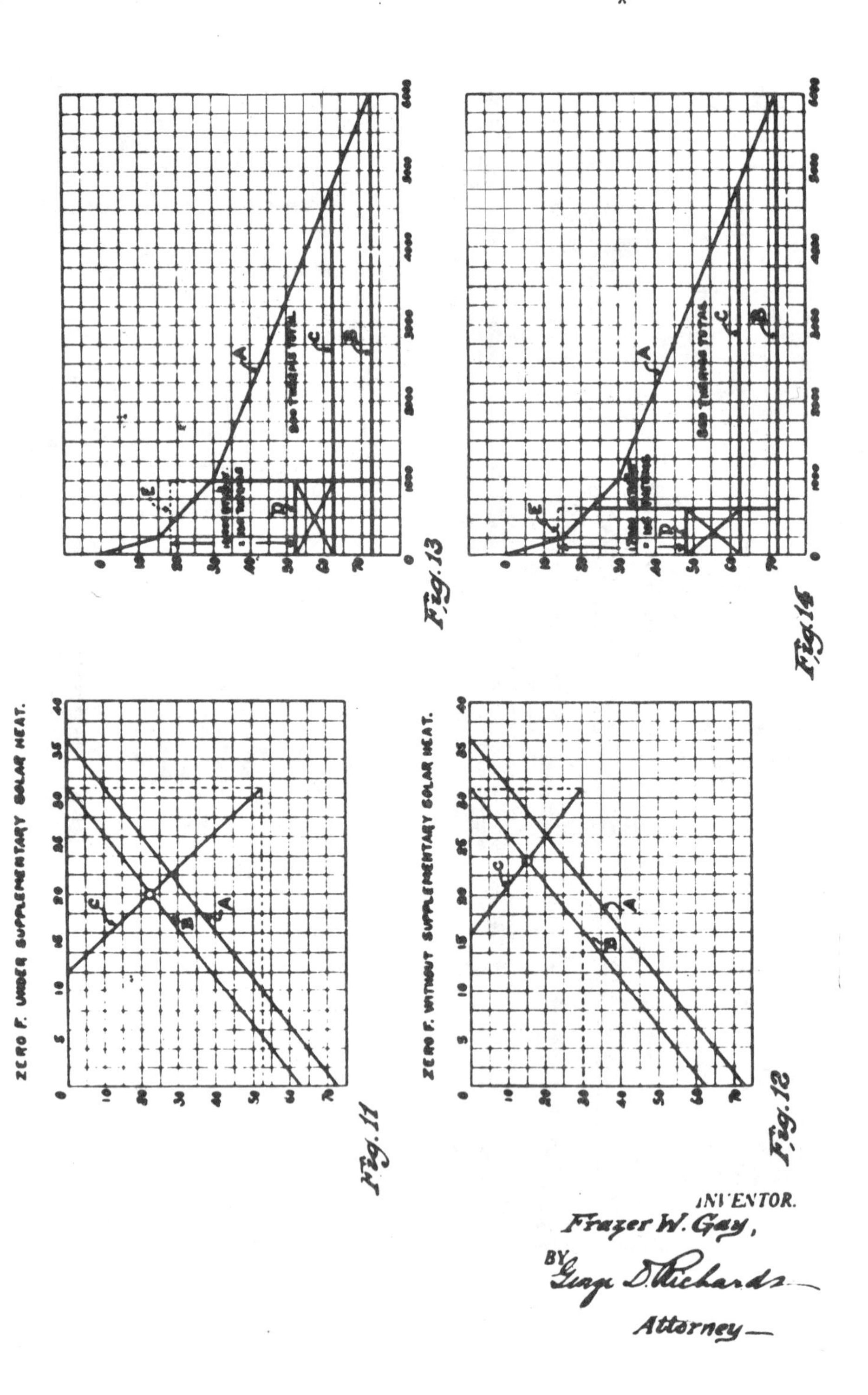

UNITED STATES PATENT OFFICE

2,559,870

HOUSE HEATING SYSTEM

Frazer W. Gay, Metuchen, N. J.

*

This invention relates to a novel house structure and heating system therefor whereby the house is heated by a reversed refrigeration cycle or heat pump; the system including novel means for extracting heat from the ambient air and storing such heat in the earth under the house; and further including means to supplement the stored heat by heat derived from solar radiation, together with means to make the stored heat available to the evaporator of the heat pump during extremely cold weather.

The purpose of the invention is to provide an envelope of recirculating air contiguous to the earth under and around the basement of a house, the outside walls of this envelope comprising a concrete structure bedded against the earth and the inside walls of said envelope being of heat insulating character and serving to separate the air in the envelope from the air within the house; means being provided for circulating the air in said envelope, the envelope including a solar heat trap, and damper means to direct the circulated air through the latter during periods of solar radiation, whereby heat is captured by the circulated air from the solar heat trap and conducted to the earth for storage therein; means being also provided for passing air from the envelope through an evaporator in a heat pump refrigerant circuit, whereby, in extremely cold weather the heat pump receives its major supply of heat from the earth stored heat.

It is a further object of this invention to extract a portion of the latent heat in a hot condensed refrigerant liquid by passing such liquid through pipes buried in the earth under the house before delivering the condensed refrigerant through expansion valves to the evaporator of a heat pump, whereby heat thus extracted from condensed refrigerant liquid is also stored in the ground; means being provided for making this stored heat available as a source of heat for a heat pump in very cold weather.

These and other objects of the invention will become more apparent as the description proceeds with the aid of the accompanying drawings, in which:

Fig. 1 is a transverse vertical section through the house structure, taken on line 1—1 in Fig. 2; Fig. 2 is a horizontal section, taken on line 2—2 Fig. 1; Fig. 3 is a cross sectional view, taken on line 3—3 in Fig. 1; Fig. 4 is a cross-sectional view similar to that of Fig. 3, but omitting the solar heat trap; and Fig. 5 is a plan view, with house walls in section, showing the exchanger compartments for a heat pump.

Figs. 6, 7 and 8 are vertical sectional views, taken on line 6—6 in Fig. 5, and respectively showing various settings of dampers for supplying air to the evaporators of an exchanger compartment for a heat pump; and Figs. 9 and 10 are vertical sectional views, taken on line 9—9 in Fig. 5, respectively showing different settings of dampers for controlling air circulation through a condenser of the heat pump.

Figs. 11 to 14 are graphs illustrating performance results of the heating system according to this invention.

Similar characters of reference are employed in Figs. 1 to 10 inclusive to indicate corresponding parts.

Referring to the drawings, the reference character 1 indicates the shell of the house structure which is packed with insulating material, such e. g. as mineral wool, between the studs in the vertical walls and between the beams of the ceiling, thus to provide, in well known manner, a house structure with all of its outside walls fully insulated.

The house shell 1 is supported on a foundation comprising masonry walls 3 carried by footings 2. Included in the upper portion of the foundation walls 3 are external brick sections 4 faced on inner sides with heat insulating sections 5, such as coatings of vermiculite cement. Contiguous to the inner faces of the north, east and west sides of the foundation walls 3 is a continuous air duct structure 10. Contiguous to the inner face of the south side of the foundation wall is a center chamber 17 which terminates at its respective ends in end chambers 11. In the corners of the house shell 1, at the south side thereof, are vertical duct structures 12 which respectively connect the respective end chambers 11 with respective openings or ports 13 through which recirculating air may be delivered to and through a solar heat trap 18 which is externally mounted on the south wall of the house structure. The lower portion of the solar heat trap 18 communicates with a collection chamber 14' through an opening or port 14.

The basement of the house structure is provided, contiguous to the underlying earth, with a concrete sub-floor 6. Supported upon this subfloor 6 are a plurality of spaced apart metallic channel or I-beams 9, the webs of which are pierced by a multiplicity of openings or holes 9'. Supported upon the channel or I-beams 9 is a main floor 7, which is made of suitable insulating material, such as vermiculite concrete; the upper or exposed surface of said main floor being faced with suitable overlaid flooring 8 to provide a desirable wearing surface. The floor construction thus formed provides an air space A between the sub-floor 6 and main floor 7; the compartments of this air space A, which are defined by the channel or I-beams 9, intercommunicate through the openings or holes 9' of the latter.

The solar heat trap comprises an air space 18 formed between the south wall of the house structure and an external wall formed by double glassed windows 20 and 21. Said windows 20 and 21 are supported by metallic channel or I-beams 18' which are provided with openings or holes 18'' in their webs so that the compartments of the air space 18, which are defined by said channel or I-beams, intercommunicate so as to provide in effect a single air space from side to side of the solar heat trap. The roof of the house structure is extended as at R so as to overhang the south side of the house, and thus shade the south wall thereof and the included solar heat trap.

Two parallel air ducts 22 and 23 are countersunk in the earth beneath the basement of the house structure so as to extend between its east and west sides. These air ducts 22 and 23 are connected for communication by an opening or port 24. An air impelling fan 26, preferably driven by an electric motor 27, when in operation, moves air from air space A through duct 22 into duct 23, whence the air may pass from the latter into that part of the air duct 10 which extends along the north wall of the house, and thence through the air duct 10 along the east and west walls of the house into the chambers 11. When dampers 15 between the chambers 11 and vertical ducts 12 are disposed in the positions thereof shown by broken lines in Fig. 3, air from air duct 10 passes upwardly through the vertical ducts 12, and thence through openings or ports 13 into the solar air trap 18. Air heated by solar radiation within the solar air trap 18 is discharged therefrom through the opening or port 14 into the collection chamber 14' which communicates with chamber 17; such communication being controlled by dampers 16. When these dampers 16 are open, the air heated by solar radiation may flow from the chamber 17 through slots S in the basement floor 7 into the air space A, and thence back into duct 22 in its recirculating course. The opening or port 24 may be opened and closed, according to operating conditions involved, by a damper 25. The dampers 15, 16 and 25 are adapted to be electrically actuated, and the motor 27 is adapted to be started and stopped by electrical control means. An electric eye 19, operated by solar irradiation, is provided to actuate the damper and motor controls, so as to set the dampers and run the motor 27 during periods of sunshine, whereby to recirculate air through the solar air trap 18, but so as to close the dampers and stop the motor 27 at all other times.

A conventional heat pump 50 is connected to its evaporator unit 38 and to its condenser unit 45 in manner to provide a reverse refrigeration cycle.

The evaporator unit 38 is mounted across a cold air duct 29 leading into the interior of the house from the outside ambient air. This cold air duct 29 terminates at its inner end in a discharge branch 35 which extends through the house wall back to the outer ambient air. A riser 51 extends from the air duct 23 to communicate with the cold air duct 29 adjacent to the air intake side of the evaporator 38. A similar riser 52 leads from the cold air duct 29 adjacent to the air discharge side of the evaporator 38 for communication with the air duct 22. A damper 36 is manipulable to open the intake portion of the cold air duct 29 while closing the riser 51 and vice versa. Similarly, a damper 37 is manipulable to close the discharge branch 35 of the cold air duct 29 while opening communication between said cold air duct and the riser 52 and vice versa. An air impeller fan 39 is mounted within the cold air duct 29 adjacent the air intake side of the evaporator 38, the same being operative to move the air through the latter. Adjacent to the air intake side of the evaporator 38, the cold air duct 29 is provided with an intake passage or port 31 leading thereinto from the house interior, and is further provided, adjacent to the air discharge side of the evaporator 38, with an air discharge passage or port 33 which communicates with the house interior. Said passages or ports 31 and 33 may respectively be closed, when desired, by respective removable insulating blocks or partitions 40 and 41 adapted to be disposed across the same.

The condenser unit 45 is mounted across a second air intake duct 30 leading into the interior of the house from the outside ambient air, the inner end of said duct 30 being connected with and for discharge through the discharge branch 35 to the exterior atmosphere. An air impeller fan 46 is mounted within said air intake duct 30 adjacent to the air intake side of the condenser 45, said fan being operative to move air through the latter. Adjacent to the air intake side of the condenser 45, the air intake duct 30 is provided with an intake passage or port 32 which leads thereinto from the house interior, and is further provided, adjacent to the air discharge side of the condenser 45, with an air discharge passage or port 34 which communicates with the house interior. A damper 47 is manipulable to close the intake end of the air intake duct 30, when it is desired to pass air from the house interior, received through the intake passage or port 32, through the condenser 45, and another damper 48 is manipulable to close the discharge end of the air intake duct 30, whereby to discharge the air, thus passed through the condenser 45, back to the house interior through the air discharge passage or port 34. Said passages or ports 32 and 34 may be respectively closed, when desired, by respective removable insulating blocks or partitions 42 and 43 adapted to be disposed across the same.

A line of piping 28 is buried in the earth a short distance beneath the sub-floor 6, said piping being looped back and forth in the earth, and so connected between the condenser 45 and heat pump 50 that the hot condensed refrigerant leaving the condenser first flows through the piping in the warmest earth which is near the south wall of the house and last through coolest earth which is near the north wall of the house. In a well designed system, about 15 per cent of the heat leaving the heat pump can be recovered from the hot infrigerant condensate and stored in the earth around the piping 28, whereby to make a large part of this stored heat available to the heat pump in very cold weather. Furthermore the extraction of this heat renders the heat pump more efficient for summer cooling operation, since the heat extracted by the earth would otherwise be dumped back into the cold space of the heat pump. Such extraction of heat, however, has little effect upon heat pump operation under winter conditions. Attention may here be called to the fact that, where solar energy is not available, the piping 28 may supply most of the heat, a small amount being extracted from the earth. This latter condition is that the heat pump can and will pump all the heat required to heat the house interior directly from outdoors down to a temperature of 28.5° F. In the illustrative case it is assumed that outdoor air is passed across the evaporator 36 as a source of heat down to a temperature of 30° F., and that below this temperature earth stored heat and that of the envelope air is utilized as a source of heat delivered across the evaporator.

The average temperature drop across the inner wall of the air circulating envelope during the 1000 coldest hours of the year will be 72° F. less the average envelope air temperature of 51° F., i. e. 21° F., so that 21,000 B. t. u. per hour, on the average, will be required to pass through the inner wall 6 of the envelope. Of this 5000 B. t. u. will come from living losses and 16,000 B. t. u. from the heat pump. With a coefficient of performance of 4, 4000 B. t. u. will be converted from pump actuating electric current. This 4000 B. t. u. and the 5000 B. t. u., or 9000 B. t. u. per hour total, will pass through the outside wall 5 of the air envelope, thus producing a thermal drop of 9 F. However, the average drop across the outside wall 5 of the air envelope is 32° F. so that on the average 23,000 B. t. u. per hour will be required from earth stored heat or a total per year of 230 therms. About 800 therms per year will be required to heat the house interior, so that 230/800 or about 29 per cent of the total heat will be taken from earth stored heat, the balance less living losses being supplied by the heat pump pumping heat from outdoor air. *

July 10, 1951 F. W. GAY **2,559,871**

HOUSE STRUCTURE AND HEATING SYSTEM THEREFOR

* *

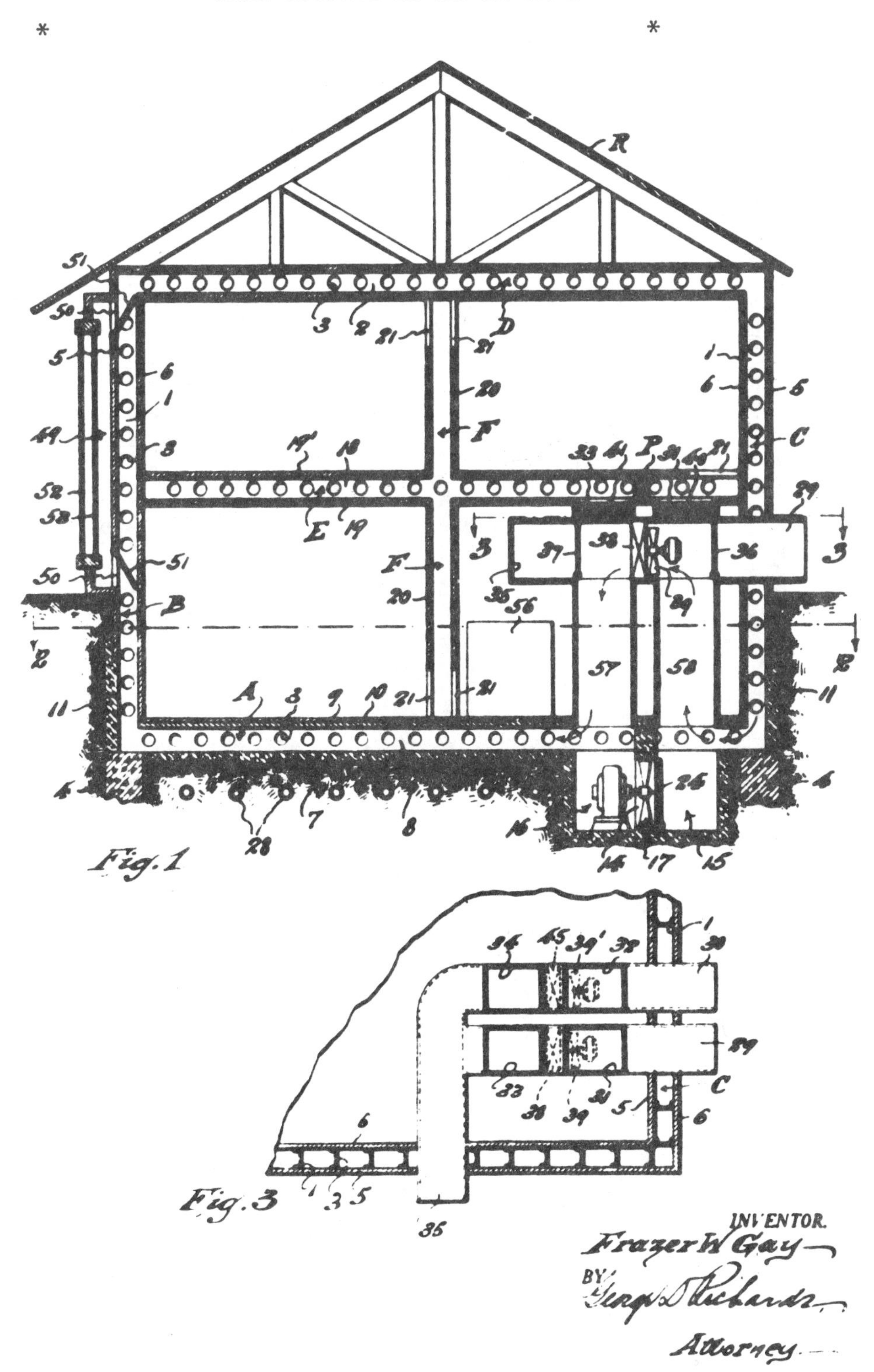

July 10, 1951 F. W. GAY 2,559,871

HOUSE STRUCTURE AND HEATING SYSTEM THEREFOR

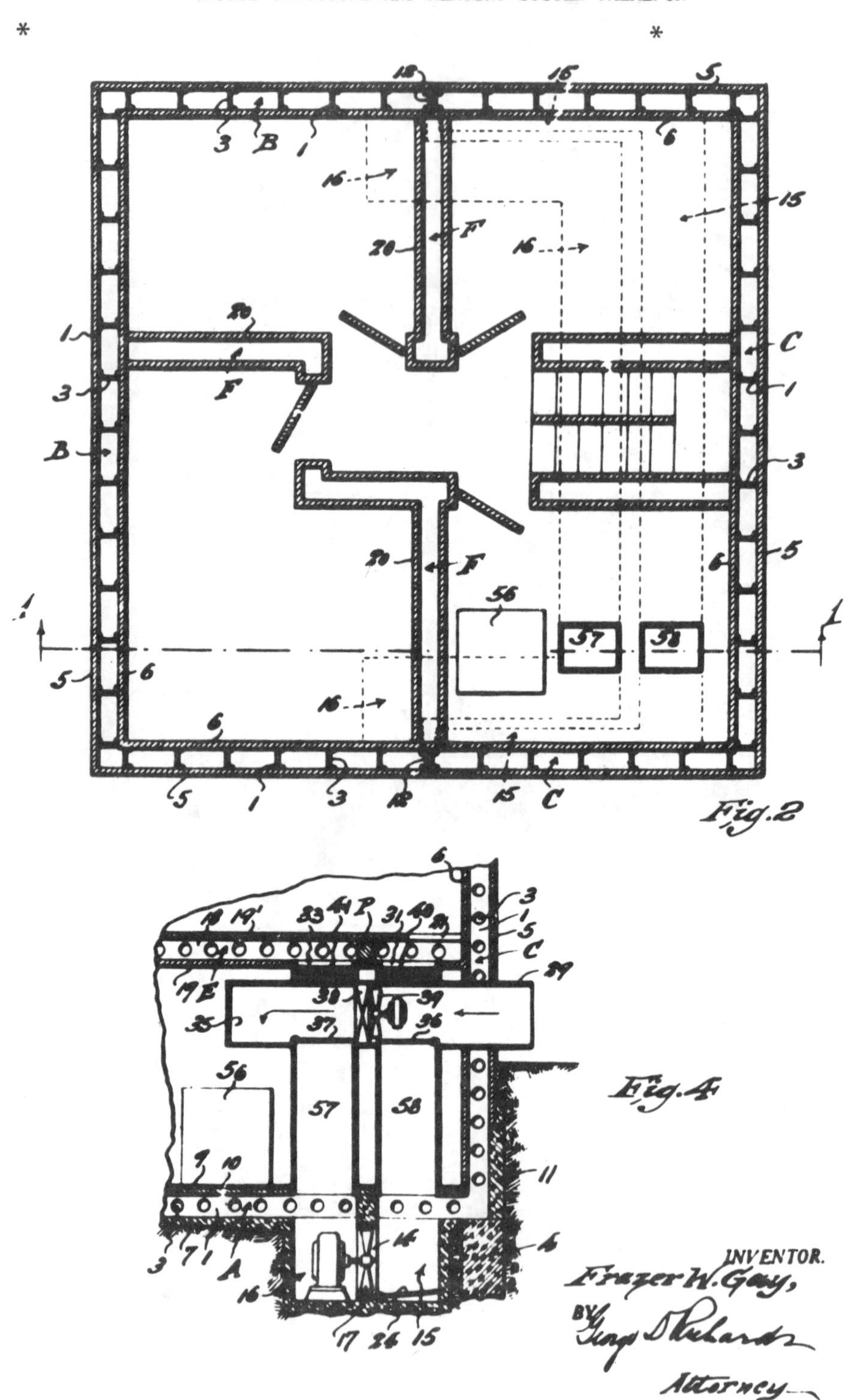

July 10, 1951 F. W. GAY **2,559,871**

HOUSE STRUCTUFE AND HEATING SYSTEM THEREFOR

* *

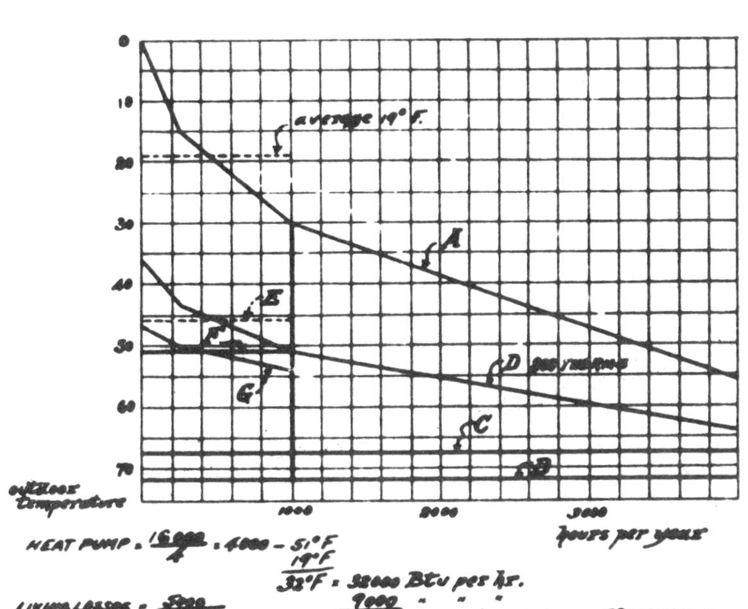

Fig. 5

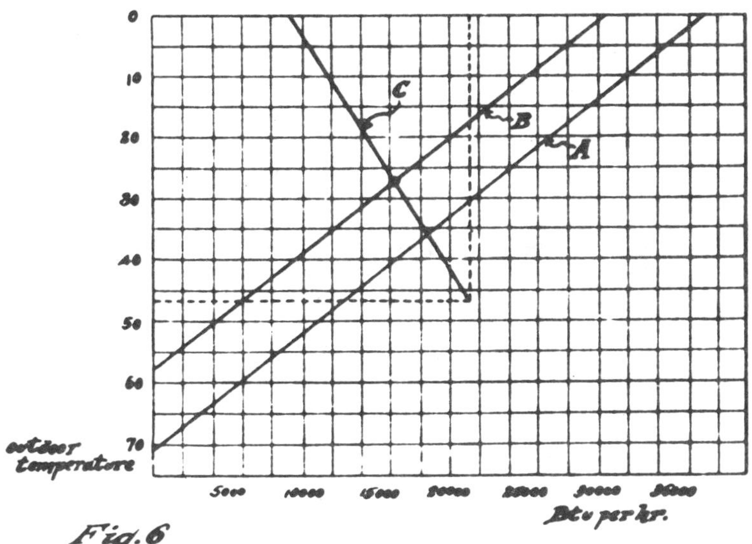

Fig. 6

INVENTOR.
Frazer W. Gay
BY George Richards
Attorney

UNITED STATES PATENT OFFICE

2,559,871

HOUSE STRUCTURE AND HEATING SYSTEM THEREFOR

Fraser W. Gay, Metuchen, N. J.

*

This invention relates to a novel house structure and heating system therefor, and, more particularly, to a house structure and heating system therefor which includes a heat pump of the reversed refrigeration cycle type such as shown in my patent 2,559 870 wherein * means is provided for extracting heat from the ambient air and storing said heat in the earth beneath the house, together with means for supplementing the stored heat by heat derived from solar radiation, and means to make the stored heat available to the heat pump evaporator during extreme cold weather.

It is an object of the instant invention to provide a house structure the surrounding walls of which are constructed to provide an envelope of recirculating air enclosing the house interior and including a passage extending contiguous to the earth beneath the house and around the below ground level part of the latter; the inside walls of this envelope being made of heat insulating material, and the outside walls of this envelope, which extend above frost line, being also made of heat insulating material but which include heat conductive walls bedded against the surrounding earth below frost line. A solar heat trap is provided in the south wall of the house, including damper means for including or excluding communication thereof with the air envelope, means being provided for circulating air through the envelope; all whereby the circulated air may be caused to traverse the solar heat trap during periods of solar radiation, so that heat derived from solar radiation may be taken up by the circulated air and transferred therefrom to the earth beneath the house, as said air traverses that portion of the envelope which extends contiguous to said underlying earth. Means is provided whereby heat stored in the earth may be conducted by the circulating air through the evaporator of the heat pump, so that the heat pump, in extreme cold weather, may receive the major supply of operating heat from the earth stored heat.

It is a further object of the invention to provide internal walls of the house structure with air flow passages in communication with the house interior, through which air heated by passage across the condenser of the heat pump may, in cold weather, be circulated through the house interior.

It is a further object of this invention to provide air duct means operative to deliver outdoor air across the evaporator of the heat pump and thence back out of doors; said ducts including adjustable damper means which can be disposed to exclude the passage of out door air during extremely cold weather while directing passage of air across the evaporator for transfer transfer thereto of heat from earth stored heat; the air envelope being so constructed and arranged that the air passes through the evaporator so as to give up heat thereto, the cool air being reheated as it again, in its recirculation, passes contiguous to the heat storing earth beneath the house.

Other objects of the instant invention, not at this time more particularly enumerated, will be understood from the following detailed description of the same.

An illustrative embodiment of the invention is schematically shown in the accompanying drawings, in which:

Fig. 1 is a transverse vertical section through a house structure according to this invention, taken on line 1—1 in Fig. 2; and Fig. 2 is a horizontal section, taken on line 2—2 in Fig. 1.

Fig. 3 is a fragmentary horizontal sectional view, taken on line 3—3 in Fig. 1.

Fig. 4 is a fragmentary vertical sectional view, similar to that of Fig. 1, but showing another adjustment of the air circulating dampers controlling air movement across the evaporator of the heat pump means.

Figs. 5 and 6 are graphs illustrating performance results of the heating system according to this invention.

Similar characters of reference are employed in Figs. 1 to 4 inclusive to indicate corresponding parts.

Referring to the drawings, the reference character 1 indicates the studs of the exterior walls of the house building, and 2 the beams of the upper floor ceiling which support the building roof structure R. Said studs and beams are made of suitable metal in channel form, the webs of which are provided with openings 3 spaced along the length thereof. The studs 1 extend a substantial distance below the ground level of the building site, and are supported by footings 4 which are countersunk in the earth. The studs and beams 1—2 are faced at their outer sides by outer walls 5, and at their inner sides by inner walls 6; said walls being of heat insulating character, such e. g. as vermiculite plaster or similar material supported by metal lath (not shown) which is affixed to the studs and beams 1—2. The outer and inner walls 5 and 6 are spaced apart by the studs and beams 1—2, so as to provide intermediate passages which form an air circulation envelope by which the house interior is surrounded. The side walls of the house extend downwardly into the ground well below frost line, and, within the thus extended side walls, the earth is excavated to corresponding depth. The outer walls 5 penetrate the earth substantially to frost line depth, and terminate in heat conductive sections 11 of concrete which are contiguous to the surrounding earth below frost line. A concrete base-floor 7 of suitable thickness is laid upon the earth within the building interior, and extending over this base floor 7 are metallic sleepers 8 of channel or I-beam form, similar to the studs and beams 1 and 2, and also provided with openings 3 spaced therealong. Supported upon the beams 8 is a main floor 9, which is made of suitable insulating material, such as vermiculite concrete; the upper or exposed surface of the main floor 9 is overlaid with flooring 10 of material adapted to provide a desirable wearing surface. The intervening space between the base floor 7 and main floor 8 provides an air flow space A in communication with the air flow passages with which the side and top walls of the building are provided. The spaces between the studs 1, beams 2 and sleepers 8 intercommunicate through the openings 3 with which said studs, beams and sleepers are provided.

That part of the air circulating envelope which extends through the side wall structure is subdivided by imperforate studs or partitioning members 12, which respectively extend centrally of the building through the front and back sections of wall structure, thus providing an air flow section B in one half of the building for movement of air through the envelope in one direction, and an air flow section C in the other half of the building for movement of air through the envelope in opposite direction. These air flow sections B and C communicate with an air flow section D formed in the top wall, and through which air is conducted from one said section to the other.

Countersunk in the base floor 7 of the building, to extend between the front and back of the building, are ducts 15 and 16 which communicate with the earth contiguous air flow space A. The duct 15 communicates at its ends with the air flow section C, while the duct 16 communicates at its ends with the air flow section B. The air ducts 15 and 16 are connected for communication by an opening or port 14. A reversible motor driven air impelling fan 17 cooperates with the opening or port 14 to move the air from duct 15 to duct 16 or vice versa. The opening or port 14 can be opened and closed by a manipulable damper 24.

A solar heat trap 49 is provided in the south wall of the house, and is formed by spaced glass windows 52 and 53. The solar heat trap 49 communicates at its upper and lower ends with the air flow section B through ports 50. The ports 50 are adapted to be opened and closed as conditions may require, by manipulable dampers 51. During periods of sunshine these dampers 51 are opened, and the air impeller fan 17 is driven in direction to move air from duct 16 to duct 15, thence through air flow section C and air flow section D for descent through air flow section B, whence a considerable volume of the air flow is by-passed through the solar heat trap 49 to take up heat therefrom. The thus heated air is delivered to and passes through the earth contiguous air flow space A so as to transfer its solar derived heat to the underlying earth for storage therein, subject to use in extreme cold weather. When solar radiation is not available, dampers 51 and damper 24 are closed and fan 17 is stopped, thus removing the solar heat trap from the air flow circuit.

A conventional heat pump 56 is connected to its evaporator unit 38 and to its condenser 45 in manner to provide a reverse refrigeration cycle.

The evaporator unit 38 is mounted across a cold air duct 29 leading into the interior of the house from the outside ambient air. This cold air duct 29 terminates at its inner end in a discharge branch 35 which extends through the house wall back to the outside ambient air. A riser 58 extends from the air duct 15 to communicate with the cold air duct 29 adjacent the air intake side of the evaporator 38. A similar riser 57 leads from the cold air duct 29 adjacent to the air discharge side of the evaporator 38 for communication with the air duct 16. A damper 36 is manipulable to open the intake portion of the cold air duct 29 while closing the riser 58 and vice versa. Similarly, a damper 37 is manipulable to close the discharge branch 35 of the cold air duct 29 while opening communication between said cold air duct and the riser 57 and vice versa. An air impeller fan 39 is mounted within the cold air duct 29 adjacent the air intake side of the evaporator 38, the same being operative to move air through the latter.

The interior of the house is suitably subdivided to provide upper and lower room spaces by an intermediate floor structure comprising perforate beams 18 which support a lower storey ceiling 19 and an upper storey flooring 19', thus providing an intermediate air flow passage E. The upper and lower storeys are partitioned to provide suitable room spaces by hollow partition walls 20 the interiors of which provide air flow passages F which communicate with the air flow passage E. Air from the passages E and F is communicated to and from the rooms by way of openings or ports 21 with which the walls of the partitions 20 are provided.

Adjacent to the air intake side of the evaporator 38, the cold air duct 29 is provided with an air intake passage or port 31 which communicates with the air flow passage E on one side of a partition P which subdivides the same, and is further provided, adjacent to the air discharge side of the evaporator 38, with an air discharge passage or port 33 which likewise communicates with the air flow passage E on the opposite side of said partition P. Said passages or ports 31 and 33 are normally closed, in winter weather, by removable insulating blocks or partitions 40 and 41.

The condenser unit 45 is mounted across a second air intake duct 30 leading into the interior of the house from the outside ambient air, the inner end of said duct being connected with and for discharge through the discharge branch 35 to the outer atmosphere. Motor driven fan means 39' similar to the fan means 39 in duct 29, is mounted within the air intake duct 30 adjacent the air intake side of the condenser 45, whereby to move air across the latter, and dampers (not shown), similar to the dampers 36—37 in duct 29, are provided for opening and closing the duct 30 to and against admission of outdoor air. Adjacent to the air intake side of condenser 45, the cold air duct 30 is provided with an air intake passage or port 32 which communicates with the air flow passage E on one side of its partition P, and adjacent to the air discharge side of condenser 45, the cold air duct 30 is provided with an air discharge passage or port 34 which communicates with the air flow passage E on the opposite side of the dividing partition P. Said passages or ports 32 and 34 are normally closed by removable insulating blocks or partitions (not shown) similar to the blocks or partitions 40 and 41 which close corresponding passages or ports 31 and 33 of the cold air duct 29.

In the winter time, the dampers in cold air intake duct 30 are disposed to shut off admission of outdoor air, and the passages or ports 32 and 34 are opened so that air from the house interior may be circulated through passages E and F across the condenser 45, whereby cool air enters the passage or port 32, is driven across the condenser 45 so as to be warmed and then returned through passage or port 34, and by way of passages E and F to the house interior.

In extreme cold weather, the dampers 36 and 37 in the cold air intake duct 29 are positioned as shown in Fig. 1, whereby to shut off admission of cold outside air, and so as to receive air from riser 58 which is supplied from the air circulating envelope by way of air flow passage C and duct 15. The air thus moved is driven across the evaporator 38 and is cooled, thereafter passing down the riser 57 and thence through duct 16 to traverse the earth contiguous air flow space A where it takes up heat from the earth stored supply of heat so as to be warmed thereby, thence flowing by way of the air flow passages B and D back to air flow passage C for recirculation.

In moderately cold winter weather, the dampers 36 and 37 are set, as shown in Fig. 4, to close the risers 58 and 57, and to open the air intake duct 29 to flow of outdoor air across the evaporator 38, thus utilizing the heat of outdoor ambient air for evaporator operation, and conserving the earth stored heat.

A line of piping 28 is buried in the earth a short distance beneath the base floor 7, said piping being looped back and forth in the earth, and so connected between the condenser 45 and heat pump 55 that the hot condensed refrigerant leaving the condenser first flows through the piping 28 before returned to evaporator 38. In a well designed system, about 15 per cent of the heat leaving the heat pump can be recovered from the hot refrigerant condensate and stored in the earth around the piping 28, whereby to make a large part of this stored heat available to the heat pump in very cold weather, and augments the supply of stored heat which is derived from solar energy through the agency of the solar heat trap. The operation and performance effects of the novel house heating system of this invention is indicated by the graphs of Figs. 5 and 6. In the graph of Fig. 5, curve A shows the assumed temperature degree F. against accumulated hours per year; that is for the coldest 250 hours (not consecutive) of the year when outdoor temperature varied from zero degree F. to 15° F. and for the next 750 hours (not consecutive) when the outdoor temperature varies from 15° F. to 30° F.

In the graph of Fig. 6, curve A is plotted to indicate the amount of heat consumed (B. t. u. per hour as abscissa) at any outdoor temperature (degrees F. as ordinate).

Curve A in the graph of Fig. 5 indicates that a heating rate of 500 B. t. u. per hour is required to raise the internal temperature of the house 1° F., or 1000 B. t. u. per hour, which passing through the inside wall 6 will cause a drop of 1° F. across that wall, and 1000 B. t. u. per hour passing through the outside wall 5 will cause a drop of 1° F. across the latter wall. It is assumed that living losses will be 5000 B. t. u. per hour, and that these losses will pass through both walls. Curve B, therefore, shows the net B. t. u. per hour that must be released within the house in order to maintain an interior temperature of 72° F. To heat the house, the heat pump should have a heat pumping capacity, at zero degree F. outdoor temperature, in B. t. u. per hour of one-quarter the 35,000 B. t. u. per hour required, i. e. about 9000 B. t. u. per hour. Curve C indicates how the capacity of this heat pump will increase with a rise in air temperature. For example, at the coldest assumed temperature of the air in the envelope surrounding the house interior, the heat pump will be able to pump from its evaporator, when the envelope air is at a temperature of 46.5° F., approximately 21,700 B. t. u. per hour into the house interior. This 21,700 B. t. u. per hour plus the 5000 B. t. u. per hour living loss, or 26,700 B. t. u. per hour, will pass through the inner wall 6 of the envelope, thus producing a thermal drop of 26.7° F. This drop added to the 46.5° F., the envelope air temperature, will produce a maximum house interior temperature of 73.2° F. If the coefficient of performance is taken as 3.8 then the electric pumping energy (taken as heat) will amount to 21,700/3.8 or 5700 B. t. u. per hour. Of the 21,700 B. t. u. per hour delivered into the house interior, 5700 will pass out through the outer wall 5 of the envelope to the house exterior and 16,000 B. t. u. will return to the evaporator. In other words, the heat pump will recirculate 16,000 B. t. u. per hour, since 5700 B. t. u. per hour of electric energy will pump 16,000 B. t. u. per hour through the envelope inner wall 6 to be picked up by the evaporator and added to said 5700 B. t. u. per hour which is electrically produced, thus making up a total of 21,700 B. t. u. per hour pump output.

In the graph of Fig. 5 the curve D indicates the temperature of the air in the envelope between the walls 5 and 6 when the air is not in circulation and the solar heat trap is not contributing heat; i. e. the air in the envelope under such conditions would have a temperature about half-way between the indoor and the outdoor temperatures.

The graph of Fig. 5 further shows that for the 1000 coldest hours of the year the average outdoor temperature is 19° F., and curve E shows that the average temperature of the air in the envelope (without solar heat trap contribution or circulation) is about 45.5 degrees F.

In the operation of the system, enough heat derived from solar radiation and salvaged from hot refrigerant condensate is gained to raise the average of the air in the envelope to 51° F., this being indicated by curve F of the graph of Fig. 5; and, furthermore, with the air in the envelope circulating in juxtaposition to the underlying earth, the variation of temperature (indicated by curve G of this graph) from the mean (curve F) will be only one-half that shown between curves D and E, and a minimum temperature will approximate 46.5° F.

In the graph of Fig. 6, the curve C indicates

illustrated in Fig. 4 wherein the solar heat trap 18 and its damper controls are omitted, and the air duct 10 is arranged to pass around the south side of the building as well as the north, east and west sides thereof. Under these modified conditions the piping 28 is depended upon to furnish most of the stored heat that is required in operation of the system.

In Fig. 6 is shown the conditioning of the heat pump for operation in extreme cold weather, and so as to draw upon heat stored in the earth. To thus condition the heat pump, the dampers 36 and 37 are set to close the cold air intake duct 29 and open communication between the risers 51 and 52 through the evaporator 38. When the heat pump is thus conditioned, air passes from the air duct 10 into the duct or chamber 23, thence upwardly through the riser 51 to pass through the evaporator 38, and thence downwardly through the riser 52 and duct chamber 22 so as to be directed through the air space A to chamber 17, and thence back to air duct 10. The air thus circulated picks up heat from the supply thereof which has been stored in the earth contiguous to the air space A. When the heat pump is thus conditioned for extreme cold weather operation, the insulating blocks or partitions 42 and 43 are removed to open the passages or ports 32 and 34, and the dampers 47 and 48 are disposed to close the intake and discharge portions of the cold air duct 30, all whereby air from the house interior may be delivered through the passage or port 32 so as to be driven through the condenser 45 to take up heat therefrom, and then returned to the house interior through the passage or port 34 (see Fig. 10).

In Fig. 7 is shown the conditioning of the heat pump for operation in moderate winter or less than extreme cold weather. To thus condition the heat pump, the dampers 36 and 37 are set to close the risers 51 and 52 against recirculation of air therethrough, and so as to open the air intake duct 29 for passage of outer air through the evaporator 38 and back to the atmosphere through the discharge branch 35; thus utilizing heat of the ambient air for evaporator operation, and conserving the earth stored heat. Under these circumstances, the setting of the dampers 47 and 48 in the air intake duct 30, which serves the condenser 45, remains the same as shown in Fig. 10, and as above described.

In Fig. 8 is shown the conditioning of the heat pump for operation in summer or hot weather. To condition the heat pump for service under such conditions, the blocks or partitions 40 and 41 are removed from and so as to open the passages or ports 31 and 33, and these or similar blocks or partitions are positioned across the intake section and discharge section of the air intake duct 29, respectively outwardly of or beyond the respective passages or ports 31 and 33. At the same time the dampers 36 and 37 are disposed to shut off the risers 51 and 52. When such changes are effected, and the heat pump is put in operation, air from the house interior enters the duct 29 and passes through the evaporator 38, so as to give up heat thereto, the cool air leaving the evaporator being thereupon returned to the house interior through the port or passage 33. During such summer or hot weather operation of the heat pump, as shown in Fig. 9, the ports or passages 32 and 34, communicating between the house interior and the air intake duct 30, are respectively closed by the blocks or partitions 42 and 43, whereby air from out of doors enters through the intake duct 30, to pass through the condenser 45, so as to take up heat therefrom, the hot air leaving the condenser being thereupon discharged to the out door atmosphere through the discharge branch 35 with which the intake duct 30 communicates.

Referring now to the graph of Fig. 11, curve A is plotted between outdoor temperature as ordinate and B. t. u. per hour heat requirement as abscissa. Curve A shows that at a zero degree F. outdoor temperature, 36,000 B. t. u. per hour is assumed to be required to heat the house. It is further assumed that losses will amount to 5,000 B. t. u. per hour flowing continuously. Curve B indicates the house heating requirement demand on the heat pump. Assuming that the heat pump possesses a heat pumping capacity from zero degree F. of 12,000 B. t. u. per hour; the capacity of the heat pump to supply heat will increase with rise in temperature of the air entering the evaporator 38 approximately in accordance with curve C. Curve C shows that the heat pump will be able to pump all the heat required to heat the house directly from outdoor air down to an outdoor temperature of 22° F.; i. e. at an outdoor temperature of 22° F., the house will require 20,000 B. t. u. per hour from the heat pump (curve B) and this will be the output of the heat pump at 22° F. (curve C).

Since the house will require 31,000 B. t. u. per hour at an outdoor temperature of zero degree F., and since curve C shows that at 31,000 B. t. u. heat pump capacity the temperature of the air delivered to the evaporator 38 must be 51.5° F.; then under the conditions shown in Fig. 6, the air temperature may be boosted to the required degree by circulation through the air space A so as to take up heat from heat stored in the underlying earth. Such supplementary or boosting heat may be easily stored in the underlying earth by utilizing the solar heat trap and by heat salvaged from hot refrigerant liquid circulating through the piping 28.

If the solar heat trap is omitted and only the heat transfer piping 28 is used to furnish heat for earth storage, then the temperature of the air circulated through the flow air space A will be much lower than the required 51.5° F. above mentioned. By reference to the graph of Fig. 12 it will be seen, if a minimum temperature of 30° F. is found, then the heat pump must be of greater capacity, as indicated by curve C of the Fig. 12 graph. This larger heat pump should have a capacity of 16,000 B. t. u. per hour at zero degree F., about 23,500 B. t. u. per hour at 15° F., and about 31,000 B. t. u. per hour at 30° F. Such heat pump will be able to heat the house, using outdoor air as a source of heat, down to about 15° F.

Referring to the graph of Fig. 13, curve A is plotted between outdoor temperature as ordinate and hours per year is abscissa. The first 250 hours at the left indicates that the coldest 250 hours vary between zero degree F. and 15° F.; it being understood that these coldest hours are not consecutive, but are arbitrarily grouped together as shown. Curve B indicates the constant indoor temperature at 72° F. The vertical distance between curves A and B at any temperature indicates the drop in temperature across the insulated house shell or walls at 72° F., and if the house shell or walls pass 500 B. t. u. per hour per degree F. difference in temperature, then the vertical distance in degrees F. multiplied by 500 will give the B. t. u. per hour that is required to maintain the house interior at 72° F. for that temperature. If, for example, the living losses are taken to be 5000 B. t. u. per hour, the distance between curves B and C will represent these living losses. At any temperature, the vertical distance in degrees F. between curves C and A multiplied by 500 indicates the reouired heat pump output at that temperature. Assuming the system makes use of stored heat derived from the solar heat trap and from heat salvaged from hot condensate, if the heat pump operates to pump heat from outdoors at all temperatures above 30° F. and pumps stored heat from the earth at all temperatures below 30° F., e. g. during the 1000 coldest hours of the year, and the average temperature for these hours is e. g. about 19° F., as indicated by curve E, the distance between curves C and E is 43° F., therefore, the heat pump must pump 43 times 500 or 21,500 B. t. u. per hour as an average. If the co-efficient of performance is taken to be about 4, then the heat pump losses will be, on estimate, about 5500 B. t. u. per hour, and the balance, viz. 16,000 B. t. u. per hour, will have to be taken from earth stored heat, or about a total of 160 therms from combined solar energy storage and heat salvaged from hot condensed refrigerant.

Assuming, however, that a solar heat trap is not used or not available, and that only stored heat derived from hot condensed refrigerant plus some heat extracted from the earth itself is available to supply the heat pump, then the temperature of the air recirculating in contact with the earth in space A will be much lower, say about 30° F. (see Fig. 12). Under these circumstances the heat pump must be of much larger capacity so as to pump the required 31,000 B. t. u. from the 30° F. air circulating in the space contiguous to the earth. Assuming this larger heat pump to have a capacity of 16,000 B. t. u. per hour at zero degree F., it will have sufficient capacity at 15° F. to supply the 23,500 B. t. u. per hour which is required to be pumped using outdoor air as a heat source. However, from the standpoint of efficiency, it is desirable to draw all heat from earth storage for temperatures lower than 22.5° F.

Referring to the graph of Fig. 14, it is assumed that the average outdoor temperature for 625 coldest hours of the year is 14° F., and that the total (average) heat demand from the heat pump is 62–14 or 48° F., i. e. about 24,000 B. t. u. per hour. Under these circumstances, if the coefficient of performance is taken as about 3.5, then the heat pump losses will approximate 7,000 B. t. u. per hour, and the balance required to be taken from earth stored heat will be about 17,000 B. t. u. per hour, or about 106 therms. The major part of this heat will be taken from the stored supply although an appreciable part will be taken from residual heat of the earth. This is possible for the reason that average earth temperature at a depth of ten feet, where the earth surface is exposed to the elements in winter weather, is about 45° F. Under small houses, however, the average temperature of the underlying earth is about 50° F., and under very large heated buildings such earth temperature, at ten foot depth, may be as high as 60° F. It will, therefore, be understood that a recirculating air stream in the space A contiguous to the earth under the building, if at a low temperature of 30° F. will also draw heat from the residual heat of the underlying earth. *

Feb. 5, 1952 F. W. GAY 2,584,573

METHOD AND MEANS FOR HOUSE HEATING

* *

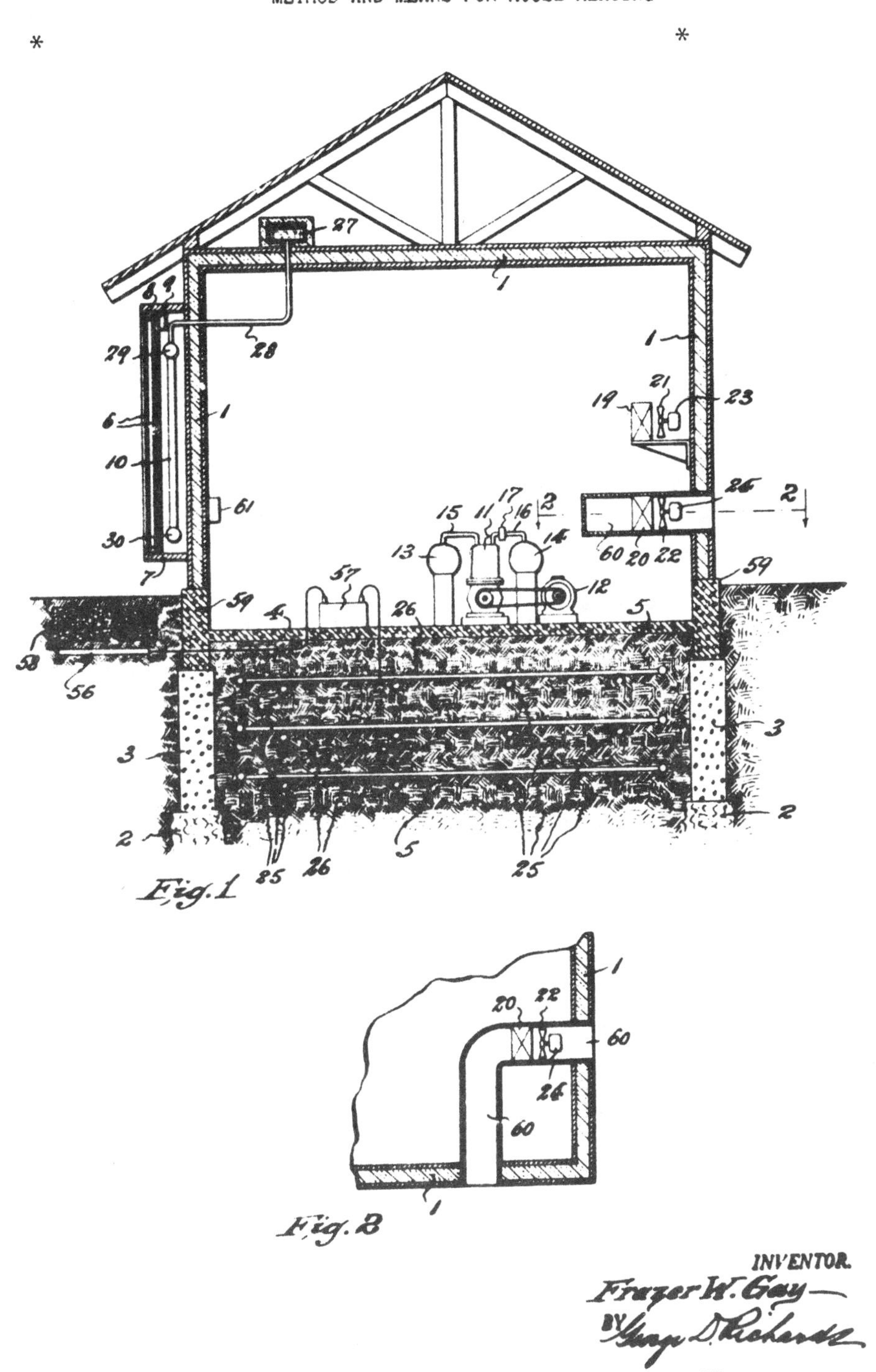

Fig. 1

Fig. 2

Feb. 5, 1952 F. W. GAY 2,584,573

METHOD AND MEANS FOR HOUSE HEATING

* *

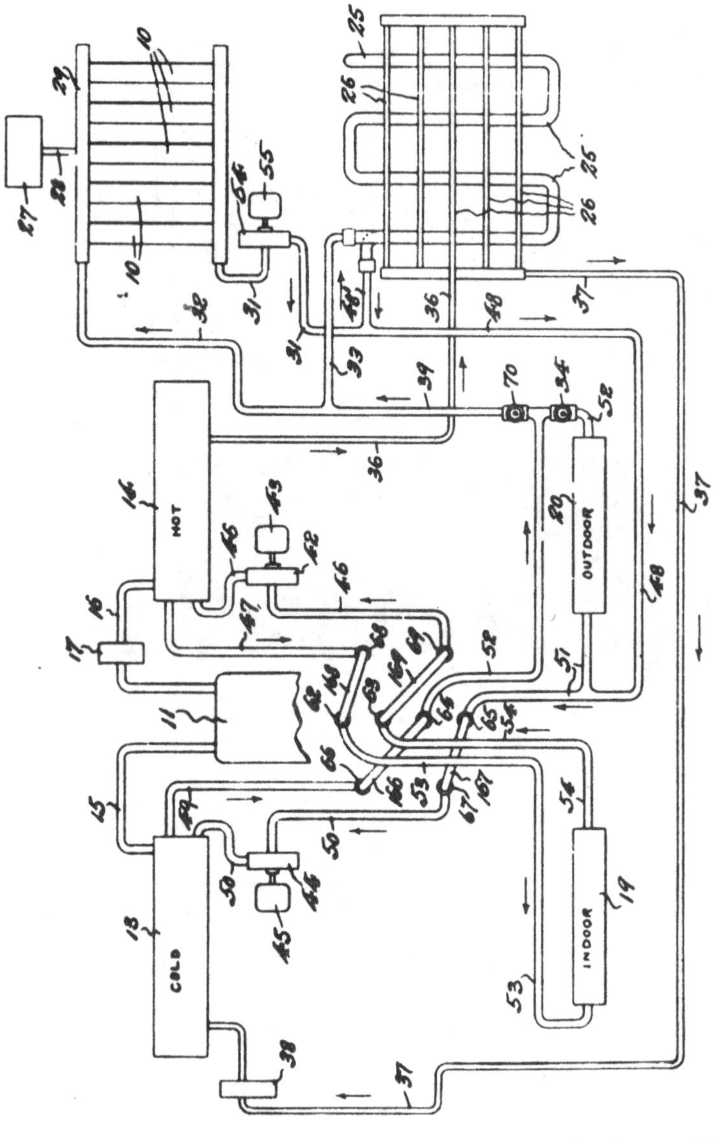

INVENTOR.
Frazer W. Gay
BY George D. Richards
Attorney

Patented Feb. 5, 1952 2,584,573

UNITED STATES PATENT OFFICE

2,584,573

METHOD AND MEANS FOR HOUSE HEATING

Fraser W. Gay, Metuchen, N. J.

*

This invention relates to a novel method and means for house heating by means of a heat pump.

House heating by means of a heat pump operative to pump heat from outdoor air into the house is known to the art, and can be effectively carried on except in very cold weather. House heating by heat pump operation can be improved by the provision of means for storing a reserve of heat in the ground under the house, which reserve heat can be drawn upon for heat pump operation in very cold weather, but even then efficiency of operation is diminished by reason of the fact that the relatively small area of ground beneath the house, which is usable for heat storage, cannot long supply a sufficient amount of heat to maintain heat pump operation during a prolonged spell of very cold winter weather.

Having the above in view, it is an object of this invention to increase the efficiency of house heating by heat pump, with respect to operation during a prolonged spell of very cold winter weather, by providing improved means for storing heat in the earth or ground beneath the house, and by providing means for continuously pumping heat to the storage means by operation of the heat pump in moderate winter weather, and by using the stored heat as a source of heat supply to the pump in very cold winter weather, and to this end to transfer heat to ground storage from hot condensed refrigerant liquid, as such liquid flows from the condenser of the heat pump back to the evaporator thereof.

This invention has for a further object to additionally provide means for supplying solar heat to the ground storage means, whereby to increase the amount of stored heat available for heat pump operation in very cold winter weather.

Other objects of this invention, not at this time more particularly enumerated, will be understood from the following detailed description of the same.

The invention is illustrated by the accompanying drawings, in which:

Fig. 1 is a transverse vertical sectional view showing a house equipped with a heat pump operated heating system according to this invention; Fig. 2 is a fragmentary horizontal section, taken on line 2—2 in Fig. 1; and Fig. 3 is a schematic view showing the components of the heating system and the operative interconnected relation thereof.

Similar characters of reference are employed in the above described views, to indicate corresponding parts.

Referring to the drawings, the reference character 1 indicates the insulated walls and ceiling of a house structure. When building the house, the excavation therefor is made deeper than would ordinarily be customary, and the foundation walls 59 are then supported upon a plurality of piers 3, the latter being, in turn, supported upon suitable footings 2. Beneath the basement floor 4 is a fill of clay or other heat conductive earth 5.

Buried in the fill 5, at suitably spaced apart levels are runs of piping suitably interconnected to provide a labyrinth of pipes 25, through which is circulated a heat transfer liquid, such e. g. as a water-alcohol mixture. The interconnected pipes 25 thus comprise a plurality of layers thereof connected in series, intermediate and surrounding which are masses of clay or other heat conductive earth, by which the fill 5 is comprised. The fill 5 and labyrinth of pipes 25 buried therein provide a heat storage reservoir or stored heat exchanger. To promote maximum thermal conductivity of the clay or earth of which the fill 5 is comprised, a source of D. C. voltage, such e. g. as storage battery 57, is provided. The positive pole of battery 57 is connected to a metallic plate 56 which is buried in the earth exteriorly of the house, and preferably beneath a dry well 58 which receives house roof drainage water. The negative pole of battery 57 is connected to the labyrinth of pipes 25. In operation, this arrangement draws moisture into and through the fill 5 around the pipes 25 by electrical osmosis, thus keeping said fill 5 damp and its thermal conductivity at a maximum.

Suitably located within the house interior is a heat pump comprising a compressor 11, which is driven by an electric motor 12, an evaporator 13 and a condenser 14. The compressor 11 receives a refrigerant gas, such e. g. as freon, from the evaporator 13 through pipe 15, and delivers the same to the condenser 14 through pipe 16, in the line of which is included an oil filter 17. The liquid refrigerant fluid, such as Freon, is returned from the condenser 14 to the evaporator 13 through piping, including an expansion valve 38; the association of this piping with the heat storage means, in accordance with the principles of this invention, being hereinafter more particularly set forth.

An outdoor heat exchanger 20 is mounted in a duct 60, one end of which enters through a house wall from the exterior of the house, and the opposite end returns through a house wall to the house exterior (see Fig. 2), thus permitting outdoor air to pass across said heat exchanger 20. The outdoor air is driven across the heat exchanger 20 by a fan 22 operated by an electric motor 24.

An indoor heat exchanger 19 is suitably located within the house. Through this indoor heat exchanger 19, indoor air is drawn by a fan 21 operated by an electric motor 23, so that this heat exchanger functions to control the temperature of the house interior.

Heat is delivered to the evaporator 13 and discharged from the condenser 14 by recirculated heat transfer liquid, such e. g. as a water-alcohol mixture. The means for circulating the heat transfer liquid between the heat exchangers 19 and 20, ground storage serving pipes 25 and evaporator 13 and condenser 14, as well as movement of hot condensed refrigerant liquid from the condenser 14 to the evaporator 13 through the ground heat storage means or exchanger, will be best understood by reference to Fig. 3 of the accompanying drawings.

Over the respective layers of heat transfer liquid conducting pipes 25 of the ground heat storage means is laid a system of multiple interconnected layers of tubing 26 which is connected between the condenser 14 and evaporator 13 for return of liquid refrigerant from the former to the latter. Preferably the tubing 26 is of smaller diameter than that of the heat transfer fluid conducting pipes 25, and also of a total length relatively greater than the length of the latter. The relation of the layers of tubing 26 to corresponding layers of heat transfer fluid conducting pipes 25 is such, that the runs of tubing 26 cross the runs of pipe 25 at right angles, and so that the tubing 26 is in contact with said pipes 25 at points of intersection therewith.

In operation of the system, cold heat transfer liquid passes from the evaporator 13 by way of pipe 49 to an exchange connection 66 and interconnecting conduit 166 to exchange connection 64, and thence through the pipe 52 and its normally open valve 34 to the outdoor heat exchanger 20 through which the cold transfer fluid passes. After passing the outdoor heat exchanger, the transfer fluid is discharged through pipe 51, to flow thence through exchange connection 65 to exchange connection 67 by way of interconnecting conduit 167, and thence through pipe 50 and circulating pump 44, driven by electric motor 45, back to the evaporator 13. When thus circulated through the outdoor heat exchanger 20, heat is absorbed by cold transfer fluid from the outdoor air, and the heat thus taken up is transferred by the fluid to the evaporator 13 and given up therein for evaporation of refrigerant fluid in the heat pump operation.

Also in the operation of the system, hot transfer fluid passes from the condenser 14 by way of pipe 47 to exchange connection 68 and thence to exchange connection 62 by way of interconnecting conduit 168, thence through pipe 53 to the indoor heat exchanger 19. The transfer liquid is discharged from the indoor heat exchanger through pipe 54 to exchange connection 63 and thence to exchange connection 69 by way of interconnecting conduit 169. From exchange connection 69, the transfer fluid flows through pipe 46 and circulating pump 42, driven by electric motor 43, back to the condenser 14. When thus circulated through the indoor heat exchanger 19, heat is given up by the transfer fluid and discharged to the house interior for house heating effect.

Communicating with the cold transfer delivery pipe 52, which leads to the outdoor heat exchanger 20, at a point beyond the intake side of the valve 34, is a pipe 39 which includes a normally closed valve 70. Leading from the pipe 39, for connection with the intake end of the labyrinth of pipes 25 of the ground heat storage means or exchanger is an admission pipe 35. From the outlet end of the labyrinth of pipes 25 of the ground heat storage means or exchanger extends a pipe 48' to return pipe 48, which connects with the pipe 51 by which the transfer fluid is returned to the evaporator under the circulating effect of the pump 44 and connected piping hereinabove already described.

Hot refrigerant liquid is discharged from the condenser 14 of the heat pump through pipe 36, and is delivered by the latter to the intake of the runs of tubing 26 which form part of the ground heat storage means or exchanger, whereby said hot refrigerant liquid is caused to flow through the tubing 26, being returned therefrom to the evaporator 13 of the heat pump by pipe 37 and expansion valve 38. The hot refrigerant liquid thus circulated through the tubing 26 gives up part of its heat to the surrounding fill 5 of the ground storage area, whereby to be stored therein.

In moderate winter weather, valve 34 being open and valve 70 being closed, cold transfer fluid is circulated through the outdoor heat exchanger 20, whereby to take up heat from outdoor air for transfer to the heat pump evaporator 13. In extremely cold winter weather, if the outdoor heat exchanger 20 cannot supply from outdoor air enough heat for heat pump operation, or if the outdoor heat exchanger should become frosted up, then valve 34 is closed and valve 70 is opened, whereby to circulate the heat transfer fluid in such manner as to by-pass the outdoor heat exchanger 20, but to flow through the pipes 25 of the ground heat storage means or exchanger. In the latter case heat is taken up by the heat transfer fluid from heat stored in the ground heat storage means or exchanger, and transferred to the evaporator 13 for evaporation of refrigerant fluid in heat pump operation.

It will be apparent that the arrangement of the pipes 25 and tubing 26 of the ground heat storage means or exchanger is subject to considerable variation. In a preferred arrangement thereof, however, it is desirable to cause the hot refrigerant liquid to enter the tubing 26 at a central portion thereof, so that, when partially cooled, it leaves from outlying portions thereof. On the other hand, it is desirable to have the heat transfer fluid enter the pipes 25 at outlying portions thereof and leave the same at the central portion thereof; the flow of refrigerant liquid thus being in counterflow relation to flow of heat transfer fluid. In such arrangement, the cold transfer fluid enters the coolest area of the ground storage means and is discharged from the hottest area of the latter. Since the hot refrigerant liquid conducting tubes 26 cross or intersect the transfer fluid conducting pipes 25 in contact therewith, it will be obvious that there will be a multiplicity of spaced apart points of intersecting contact of the tubing 26 with the pipes 25. The respective layers of intersecting tubing 26 function to transmit heat to the respective layers of pipes 25. Since the tubing 26 directly transmits but a relatively small percentage of the heat carried away by the pipes 25, the liquid in the tubing tends to cool where the tubing directly touches the pipes 25 at a contacting intersection thereof, then the liquid in the tubing warms up as it passes through the tubing to the next point of intersecting contact with the pipes 25, and this effect is repeated throughout the area of the associated tubing 26 and pipes 25. Due to this arrangement and mode of operation, the network of tubing 26 and pipes 25 functions to deliver heat from the ground storage to the heat transfer fluid to which the heat is delivered to the evaporator 13 of the heat pump, when stored heat is depended upon for heat pump operation. When heat pump operating heat is derived from the outdoor heat exchanger 20, then the network of tubing 26, through which hot refrigerant liquid flows, functions to deliver heat to and for storage in the ground storage fill 5.

In the operation of the heating system, the pump driving motor 12, the fan motors 23 and 24, and the pump motors 43 and 45 are all simultaneously started and stopped by control of a house thermostat 61 in accordance with temperature drop and rise within the house.

The operational advantage of the house heating system according to this invention may be illustrated as follows:

A pound of Freon 12 at 30° F. outdoor temperature contains about 81 B. t. u. total heat above base (−40° F.) as a gas. The heat pump will raise the pressure and temperature of this gas to allow condensation at the indoor radiator temperature of, say 130° F. and the total heat will then be about 90 B. t. u., or the heat pump will have added about 9 B. t. u. per pound. This pound of Freon 12 will condense into a liquid containing about 38 at 130° F. 90 less 38 or about 52 B. t. u. will be given up by condensation to heat the house. In the conventional heat pump this pound of Freon would be valved directly into the evaporator and its heat would pass into the cold gas by evaporation. If, however, this pound of hot Freon 12 liquid is run through tubing 26 underground and has its temperature reduced to, say, 60° F. (at which temperature the total heat will be about 21 B. t. u.), then 38 less 21 or about 17 B. t. u. will be given up to and stored in the earth; i. e., 17/52 or the equivalent of about 32 per cent of the total heat pumped into the house will be stored in the earth instead of being dumped back into the evaporator. It is obvious that, in the system of the instant invention, the evaporator must be increased in size about 30% in order to supply the approximate 17 B. t. u. taken out of each pound of Freon 12 during the passage of the hot Freon 12 condensed liquid through the tubing 26 buried in the earth. It is thus obvious that a large part of the heat pumped up to high temperature for indoor use will be salvaged instead of being dumped back into the evaporator for recirculation.

It is also an object of this invention to provide means to supplement the amount of heat derived from heat pump operation, by heat derived from solar energy and added to heat stored in ground heat storage means. To this end, a solar heat trap is built into the south side of the house served by the heating system. This heat trap, in an illustrative form thereof, is provided by an enclosure, the back of which is formed by the house wall, and which is formed by a bottom wall 7, a top wall 8 and side walls extending therebetween. The outer wall or front face of the enclosure is provided by spaced apart glass panels 6. Within enclosure is arranged a plurality of heat transfer fluid conductive pipes 10 which extend between headers 29 and 30. A heat insulated tank 27 is located in the house attic, and communicates with the pipe 10 through interconnecting service pipe 28, thus serving to maintain the system of pipes 10 full of heat transfer fluid at all times. The system of pipes 10, as exposed to solar rays, is operative to absorb solar heat into the transfer fluid circulated therein.

Heat transfer fluid is circulated between solar heat trap pipes 10 and pipes 25 of the ground heat storage means during sunshiny weather, whereby to deliver heat derived from solar energy to ground storage. To this end, heat transfer fluid is delivered from the pipes 10 to the pipes 25 by pump 54, operated by electric motor 55, through conduit 31 to pipe 48', returning to pipes 10 by way of pipe 33 and pipe 32 to said pipes 10. The operation of electric motor 55 may be controlled by a thermostat 9, whereby to put said supplementary heat supplying means in operation during hours of sunshine. It will be apparent that through the described agency and by the circulation of heat transfer fluid therethrough, heat derived from solar energy can be delivered to the ground heat storage means to supplement the supply of heat stored in the latter subject to use in furnishing heat for heat pump operation in extremely cold winter weather. *

Jan. 7, 1930. C. F. JOHNSON 1,742,861

BUILDING

*

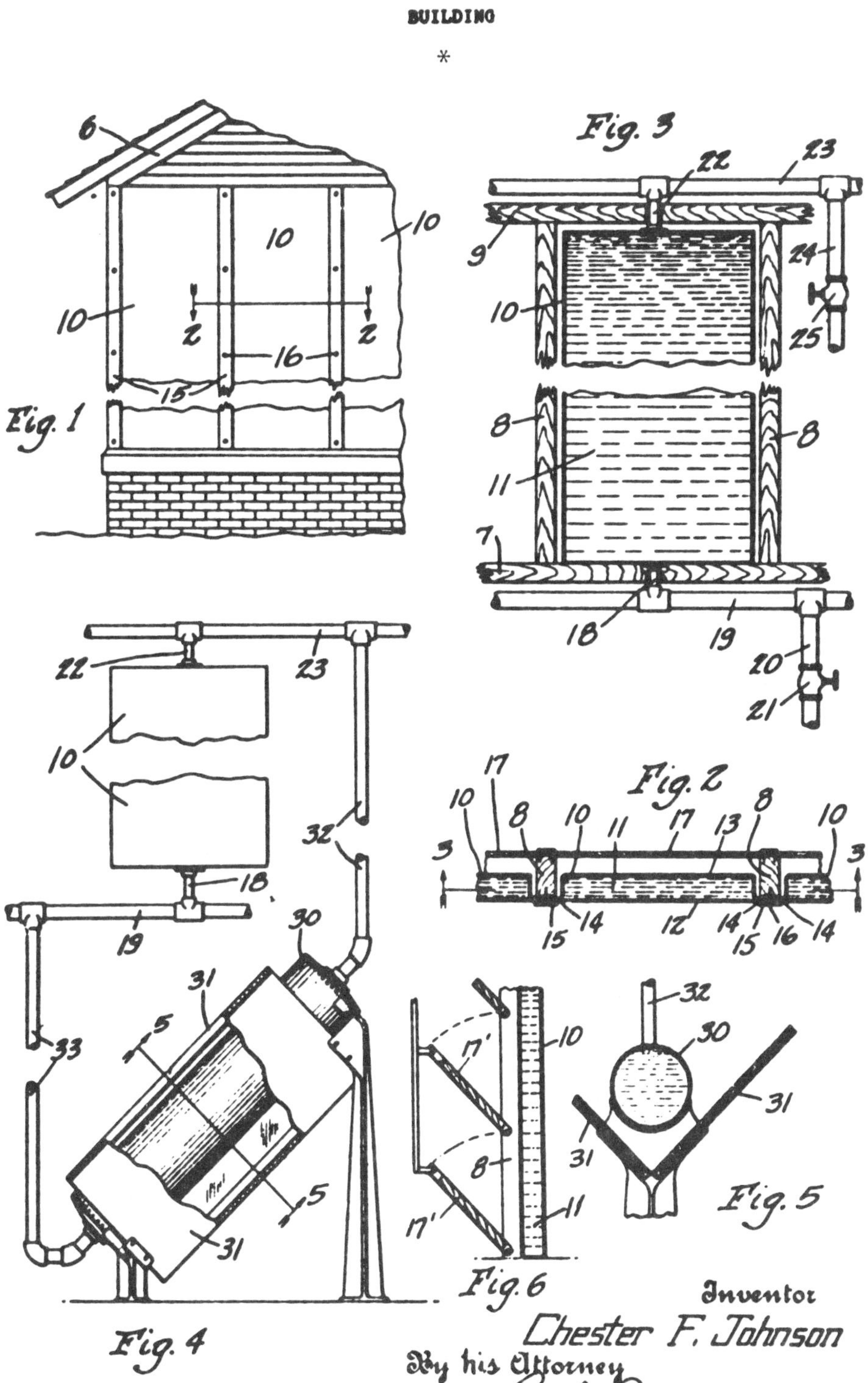

UNITED STATES PATENT OFFICE

CHESTER F. JOHNSON, OF DETROIT, MICHIGAN

BUILDING

*

The invention relates generally to buildings, such, for example, as dwelling houses, in the interior of which it is desirable to maintain a relatively constant temperature and is especially concerned with the provision of means of particular utility where the climatic conditions are favorable whereby the temperature within the building may be maintained approximately uniform without necessitating the use of fuel.

In some localities, such, for example, as the warmer sections of the south-western United States, where the air is dry and rain is infrequent, the diurnal range of temperature is comparatively great, the temperature during the day in situations exposed to the direct rays of the sun being very high and the night temperature falling to a point such that the comfort of the occupants of a dwelling requires the use of heavy clothing or the provision of special domestic heating means.

In accordance with my invention, it is proposed to store up the heat energy obtainable from solar radiation when the sun is shining and to utilize the same for warming the interior of the building at other times. It is further proposed to provide heat-storage means of such character that the building in connection with which it is utilized may be protected from excessive heating during the hours of direct sunshine and may be prevented from rapid cooling when the external atmospheric temperature has fallen.

To this end the invention comprises the provision of wall portions or elements containing a suitable heat-storage medium which elements or portions are, or may be, exposed to the heating effect of the sun's rays. The heat-storage capacity may be increased and the heating effect enhanced by providing additional heating agencies, which may also be designed to utilize solar energy, associated with the wall elements of the building in such manner that the temperature of the heat-storing medium within the wall elements may be raised to a higher point than would be possible by the mere exposure of the elements themselves. Means may also be provided to restrict excessive loss of heat energy to the exterior atmosphere during the time when the temperature on the outside is less than that of the heat-storage medium which means may be movable or adjustable in order to permit exposure of the wall elements to the sun when desired.

In the accompanying drawings illustrating one mode of carrying out the invention,

Fig. 1 is an elevation of a portion of a building having wall portions adapted to provide storage spaces for liquid, parts being broken away;

Fig. 2 is a horizontal section on line 2—2 of Fig. 1;

Fig. 3 is a vertical section on line 3—3 of Fig. 2, parts being broken away;

Fig. 4 is a view with parts broken away showing in side elevation an auxiliary heating means and also showing diagrammatically the connections between said means and the wall structure;

Fig. 5 is a section on line 5—5 of Fig. 4; and

Fig. 6 is a fragmentary view showing movable means for covering or protecting the surface of the liquid-storing elements.

Referring to the drawings, 6 indicates a building, such as a dwelling house, which may be of any usual or desired configuration. The building may have the usual frame elements as sills 7, studding 8, and plates 9. The wall portions of the building, however, consist, at least in part, of elements 10, preferably of sheet metal, which are formed as containers for a material having high heat-storage capacity, such as water, indicated at 11.

The containers as shown comprise walls 12 and 13 which may be connected at their edges to form flanges 14 adapted to rest against either the inner or outer faces of the studding. They may be supported at their lower ends upon the sills 7 and be of such dimensions as to substantially fill the spaces between the studding. As a convenient means for retaining the containers in place I have shown the flanges 14 secured by battens 15 which cover and conceal the edges of the flanges and are fixed to the studding by suitable fasteners 16. The walls 12 and 13, while illustrated as flat or plane, may be shaped as desired and may be suitably finished or decorated to present a neat and pleasing appearance. If desired, however, additional wall elements may be mounted upon either the inside or the outside, or both, of the wall, which elements would then constitute the visible or exposed portions of the wall. In Fig. 2, such additional elements 17 are shown as forming the inner wall surface, the containers 10 forming the outer wall surface. In Fig. 6, the reverse arrangement is shown, the additional wall elements 17′ being mounted outside of the containers 10. With this arrangement, it may be desirable to support the additional elements pivotally, for example at the lower edges, as shown, so that they may swing, somewhat in the manner of shutters, thereby permitting, when in open position, the direct impingement of the sun's rays upon the containers. These pivoted members may be of heat-insulating or radiation-preventing material, as wood, cork or the like, adapted, when closed, to prevent radiation of heat from the containers, thus conserving the heat energy acquired during the period of exposure.

Each container 10 is connected at its lower end by a pipe 18 to a pipe 19 whereby the liquid utilized, as water, may be supplied to the containers to fill them to any desired extent. Any available source of supply may be utilized, such as a connection to a city water system, such connection being shown at 20, the flow of water to the containers being controllable by a valve 21.

Each container is also connected at the upper end by a pipe 22 to a header 23 which is provided with an outlet by means of pipe 24 having a valve 25. Since the containers are entirely closed or liquid-tight, except for the connections to the upper and lower headers, the entire system may be completely filled by admission of water through the valve 21. Pipe 24 may be utilized, if desired, as a source of water supply for domestic use. Since the containers are exposed to the heat of the sun the water therein will normally be warmer than that drawn directly from the city supply system.

Additional means may be provided for employing solar radiation to heat the contents of the containers. Such means is illustrated in Figs. 4 and 5 as including a receptacle 30 suitably supported in a position to receive the sun's rays as efficiently as possible, for example by inclining it in such manner as to expose the maximum heating area. Auxiliary devices, such as reflectors 31, are arranged in such position as to intercept and direct upon the walls of the receptacle 30 the rays from a considerable area adjacent to the receptacle. Pipes 32, 33, join the upper and lower portions respectively of the receptacle 30 to the water system of the building, as by connection to the headers 23 and 19, thus providing for flow of heated liquid from the upper portion of the heater to the wall containers and of cold liquid from the containers to the heater. Any desired form of solar or other heater may be employed in this connection, the form shown being merely illustrative. It will be obvious that roof sections of the building may also be provided with wall elements of similar character either interconnected to constitute an independent circulating system or connected to the circulating system of the vertical wall portions.

In the operation of the structure it will be understood that the liquid-containing elements of the system will be exposed to the heating effect of the external atmosphere and the rays of the sun. The heat energy will be expended largely in raising the temperature of the heat-storage medium which is preferably of such character that it has a high heat capacity. For this reason, as well as by reason of its cheapness and availability, the use of water is preferred. The interconnection of the parts of the system also permits circulation of the liquid contained therein whereby the temperature of various sections of the wall portions is equalized even though they are not all exposed directly to solar radiation.

The wall elements containing the heat-storage medium act to prevent the transmission of the heat to the interior of the building, thereby serving to a certain extent as insulating means to maintain lower temperature of the interior during the day than would otherwise be produced. When the exterior temperature falls, however, as during the night, the heat stored in the system during the day becomes effective to warm the interior of the building while serving at the same time as an insulating means to prevent rapid loss of heat from the interior. As a result, fairly uniform temperature conditions may be maintained within the building notwithstanding the occurrence of relatively great variations in external conditions. *

July 10, 1951 F. W. GAY **2,559,869**

HOUSE STRUCTURE AND HEATING SYSTEM THEREFOR

* *

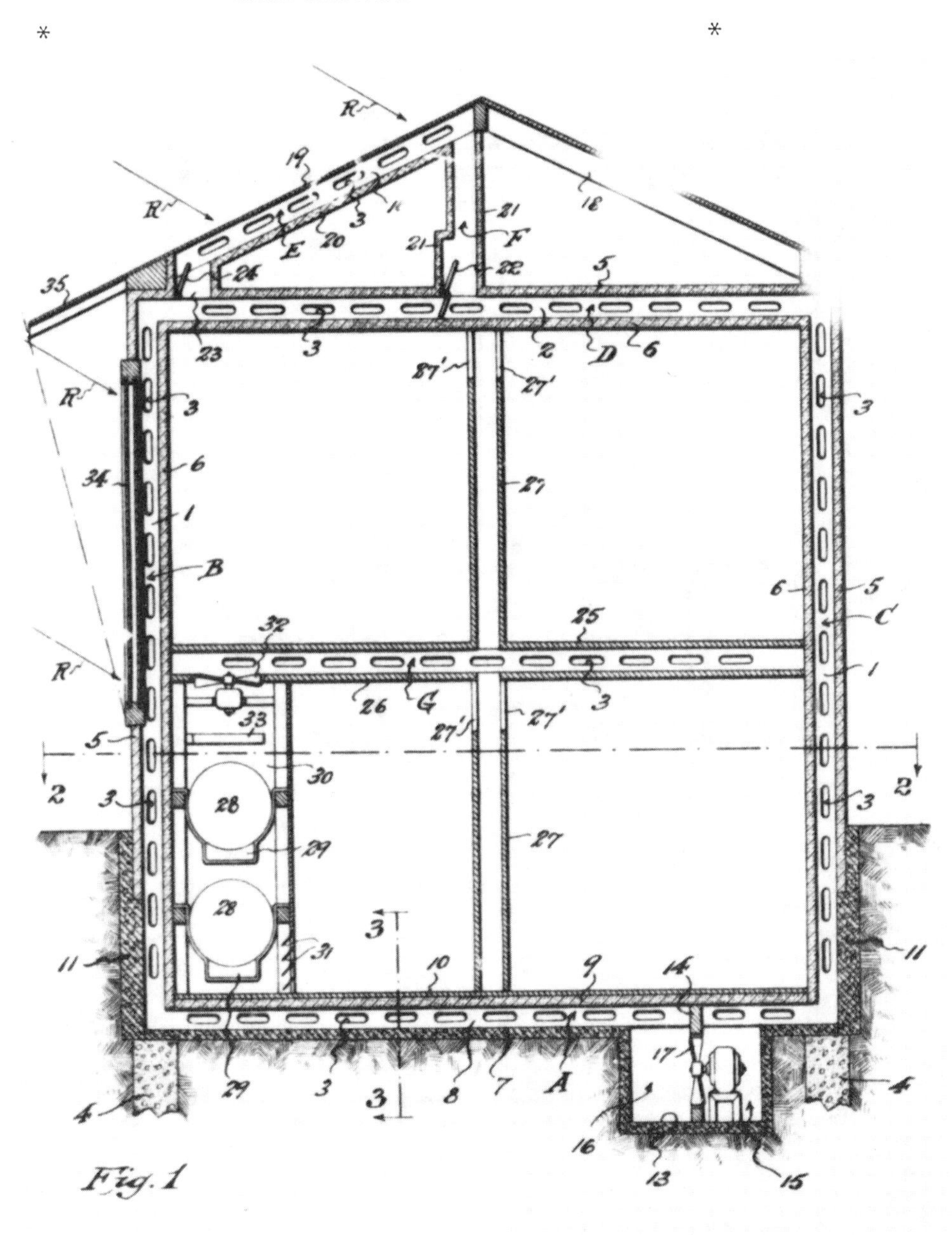

INVENTOR.
Frazer W. Gay
BY George D. Richards
Attorney

July 10, 1951 F. W. GAY 2,559,869

HOUSE STRUCTURE AND HEATING SYSTEM THEREFOR

* *

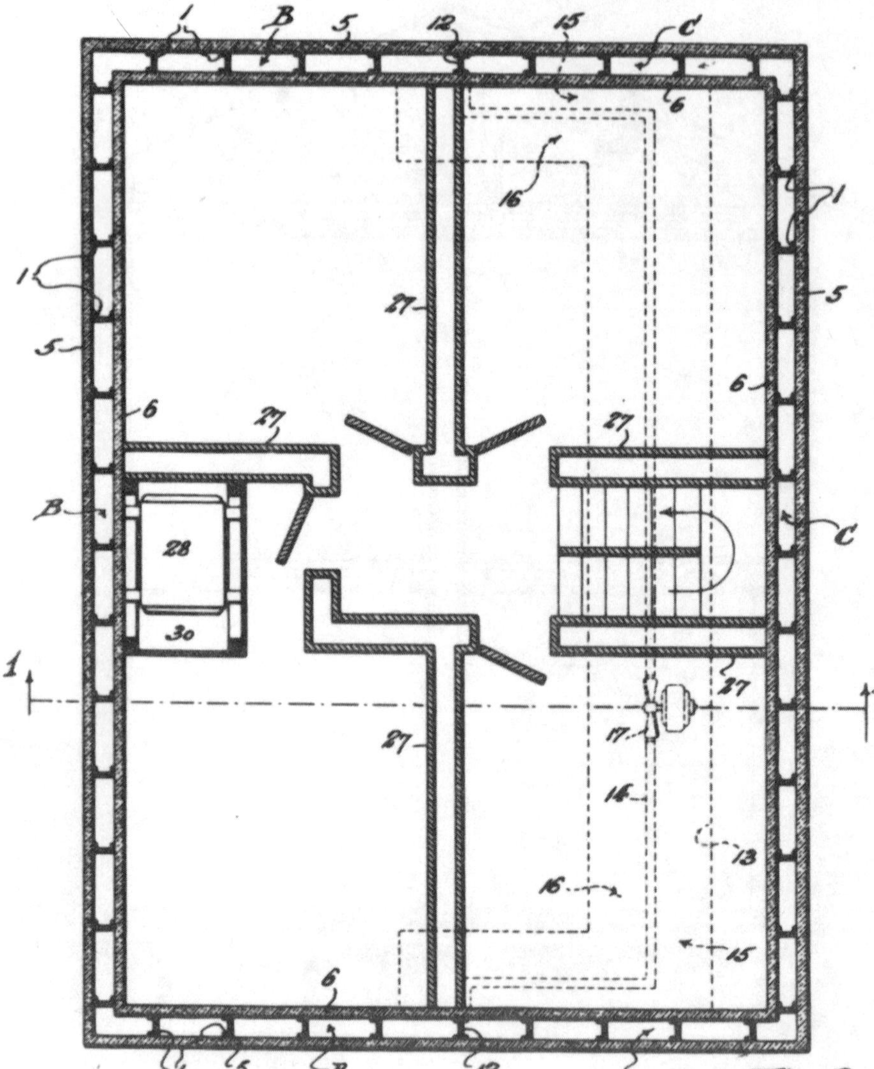

Fig. 2

Fig. 3

INVENTOR.
Frazer W. Gay
BY George D. Richards
Attorney

UNITED STATES PATENT OFFICE

2,559,869

HOUSE STRUCTURE AND HEATING SYSTEM THEREFOR

Frazer W. Gay, Metuchen, N. J.

*

This invention relates to a novel house structure and heating system therefor, including means to conserve generated heat which is employed for interior heating by ground storage; the * instant system including means to supplement the generated heat by heat derived from solar radiation.

The invention has reference, more particularly, to a novel house structure provided with means to greatly increase the availability of solar radiation for interior heating thereof, so as to reduce the total amount of heat energy demand upon any type of heat generator employed as a main source of heat, and especially upon electrically supplied heat produced by the method known to the art as the "Hall" heating method.

In the "Hall" method, electric heaters are provided to heat water stored in tanks. These electric heaters are connected to electric utility company lines, and are assumed to take power therefrom over an approximate period of eight hours comprehended by light load night hours, and, during such period, is assumed to utilize about three times the normal house heat demand; this is not the case, however, since the demand for house heat is much greater than normal during said eight hour night period, and consequently the "Hall" method is found to require an electric power consumption about double that of an ordinary direct electric heating system which only generates and delivers heat when and as required. In theory, under the "Hall" method, the heat storage tanks should be able to store about one-half of the total heat produced per day with a 60° F temperature change, but, in practice, said tanks are sized to provide about twenty-five per cent greater storage capacity, so that some excess of stored heat is available to carry through a particularly cold day.

Having the above in view, it is an object of this invention to provide a house structure so constructed that its habitable interior is surrounded by spaced inner and outer insulating walls which define an enveloping space through which air may be circulated, said envelope space including portions contiguous to the earth so that heat may be transmitted to and stored in the adjacent earth for return to the circulating air in extremely cold weather; said house structure including an interior heat generating and supplying means, and said house structure further including novel means whereby solar energy may also be transferred to the air circulating in said envelope, and thus transferred to the earth for storage therein as an available auxiliary heat supply supplementary to the generated heat, so that the capacity of the interior heat generator employed, or of an electric heating means and associated storage tanks when utilized, may be substantially reduced, e. g. as much as forty per cent, and the total expenditure of electric energy required for adequate interior heating is, in fact, reduced even more in the fall and especially in the spring of the year, since a substantial part of the required heat, at such times, is supplied by solar energy.

Other objects of this invention, not at this time more particularly enumerated, will be understood from the following detailed description of the same.

An illustrative embodiment of the novel house structure according to this invention is shown in the accompanying drawings, in which:

Fig. 1 is a transverse vertical sectional view of the house structure, taken on line 1—1 in Fig. 2; Fig. 2 is a horizontal sectional view of the same, taken on line 2—2 in Fig. 1; and Fig. 3 is a fragmentary cross sectional view, taken on line 3—3 in Fig. 1, but drawn on a somewhat enlarged scale.

Similar characters of reference are employed in the hereinabove described views, to indicate corresponding parts.

Referring to the drawings, the reference character 1 indicates the wall studs of the building structure, and 2 the beams which support the upper floor ceiling and roof. Said studs and beams are preferably of channel form produced from steel, aluminum or other suitable metallic material. The webs of said studs and beams are punched to provide spaced openings 3 extending along their neutral axes throughout the lengths thereof. The studs 1 are supported on footings 4 which are countersunk in the earth below ground level. Supported by the studs and beams 1 and 2 is an outer wall 5 which completely surrounds the sides and top of the building above ground level. Said outer wall 5 is formed from a material having desirable heat insulating characteristics, such e. g. as vermiculite plaster or similar material. Said vermiculite plaster is applied to metal or other lath (not shown) which is affixed to the outer flanges of the studs 1 and beams 2; such application may be made by hand or gunned into place. An inner wall 6 of like material and construction is mounted on the inner flanges of the studs 1 and beams 2. The walls 5 and 6, as spaced by the studs and beams, define an intermediate air passage envelope which surrounds the building interior.

The side wall structure is extended downwardly below ground level or grade so that the outer side walls 5 extend below frost line; usually for a distance of at least two feet. Within the side wall structure as thus extended the earth is excavated to suitable depth. Contiguous to the subterranean extension of the side walls 5 is arranged a body 11 of concrete or cement of high thermal conductive characteristics, which extends downward to the floor of the excavated interior. Said body 11 is made of suitable thickness, and serves in lieu of a foundation. The concrete or cement body 11 contributes to transfer of heat from the earth to the air circulating within the wall structure envelope.

A concrete base floor 7 of suitable thickness is laid directly upon the earth within the building interior. Laid on this floor 7, to extend between studs 1 at opposite sides of the building structure, are sleepers 8. These sleepers 8 may be of either channel or I-beam form, and are preferably made of steel. Supported by said sleepers 8 is an interior flooring 9, which preferably compises a two inch layer of vermiculite concrete, over which is laid a surfacing floor 10, which may be of standard concrete, asphalt, tile or other material adapted to furnish suitable wearing surface. The intervening space between the base floor 7 and interior flooring 9 extends between said opposite sides of the building structure so as to provide a bottom air flow course A in communication with the air circulating envelope formed in the side and top wall structures. The webs of said sleepers 8 are punched to provide spaced openings 3 extending along the same, similarly as is done with respect to the studs 1 and beams 2, whereby communication is established between the parallel air flow channels intermediate said studs, beams and sleepers.

That part of the air circulating envelope provided by the side wall structure is subdivided by imperforate studs 12 preferably located within the front and back sections of said side wall structure, whereby to form, in one half of the side wall structure, a rising air flow course B, and, in the opposite half thereof a descending air flow course C; communication between the rising and descending courses being established through the upper horizontal part of the air circulating envelope which is defined by the beams 2, and which provides a transfor air flow course D.

Countersunk in the base floor 7 below one-half of the building to extend between the front and back of the latter as shown, is a duct 13. This duct is subdivided along its length by a partition 14, whereby to provide an air receiving chamber 15, with which the descending air flow course C communicates through one end of the bottom air flow course A, and an air discharging chamber 16, which communicates with the rising air flow course B through the opposite end of said bottom air flow course A. Mounted in the partition 14 is a reversible motor driven air impeller fan 17, which moves the air from the receiving chamber 15 to the discharging chamber 16, or vice versa at will.

In an illustrative embodiment of house structure according to the instant invention, the same is provided with a gabled roof structure supported by rafters 18. The rafters at the south side of the roof structure are provided with a roofing 19 of sheet metal, preferably aluminum; the external surface of which is painted a dark color so as to reduce heat reflection and increase heat transmission therethrough. Affixed to the underside of the rafters 18 of said southern side of the roof structure is an internal wall 20 of insulating material, such e. g. as vermiculite. The space between the roofing 19 and wall 20 provides a roof air flow course E. Insulating walls 21 rising between the top exterior wall 5 and the roofing define an intercommunicating air flow passage F between the transfer air flow course D and the roof air flow course E. Air delivery communication between the transfer air flow course D and the roof air flow course E by way of said air flow course F may be opened and closed by a manipulable damper 22, which when opened to flow of air to the course E, will close off flow of air toward the southern side of the building through that part of the transfer air flow course D beyond said damper. Air discharge communication between the roof air flow course E back to the transfer air flow course D, and thence to the air flow course B, is provided by a discharge port 23, adapted to be opened and closed by a manipulatable control damper 24.

Suitably located within the lower storey of the building is a suitable heat generating means. Hot air is delivered from the heat generating means into passage space G between the floor 25 of the upper storey and the ceiling 26 of the lower storey of the building, being distributed thence through hollow partitions 27 which define the rooms of each storey, for discharge, through registers or other outlets 27', into said rooms.

A preferred heat generating means, as shown, comprises water storage tanks 28 which are heated by suitable electrical heaters 29. Said tanks 28 are suitably mounted within an enclosure or hot box 30. Air is admitted into the bottom of said enclosure or hot box 30, through gravity closed louvres 31 provided in an external wall of the latter. The upper end of the enclosure or hot box 30 communicates with the hot air delivery passage G, and circulation of air through the house interior and enclosure or hot box 30 is preferably effected by means of a motor driven impeller fan 32 mounted within the upper discharge end of said enclosure or hot box 30. If desired, an electrical radiator 33 may be used as an auxiliary to the storage tanks 28, although since radiation area in the form of the tanks 28 costs but little more than that provided by electrical radiators, it follows that, with the tanks, the water storage function thereof costs but little if credit is taken for the radiating surface which the tanks provide.

As an adjunct to the solar energy utilizing means of the house heating system, the outer wall 5 at the southern side of the building is provided with transparent window structure 34 of substantial area, and preferably double glazed, thus permitting a considerable amount of solar rays R—R to pass through the window and impinge upon the inner wall 6, being thus converted to sensible heat within the circulating envelope. The solar rays therefore not only impinge upon the sheet metal roofing 19 to warm the air in the roof air flow course E, but also are permitted to additionally warm the air circulated through the air flow course B.

The roofing at the southern side of the building is provided with an overhanging extension 35 so that solar rays R—R are cut off from the window structure 34 during the noon period in the summer season when the sun is high overhead. The extent of said overhanging extension 35 is so limited, however, as not to cut off solar rays R—R from said window structure 34 in the winter season when the sun is low in south even during the noon period.

In cold weather, the fan 17 drives air from the discharging chamber 16 through the bottom air flow course A, thence upwardly through the rising air flow course B, across the transfer air flow course D, and downwardly through the descending air flow course C to the receiving chamber 15. If it is extremely cold out doors, the air moving through the bottom air flow course A in contact with the earth supported base floor 7 picks up heat from the contiguous earth mass, since underground temperature is considerably higher than ambient temperature under cold weather conditions. Illustrative of this, extensive tests show that underground temperatures in the neighborhood of metropolitan New York city e. g. average about 50 F., and this temperature changes but little throughout the year for depths in excess of ten feet. The heat transferred to the air from the earth is dissipated as the air is circulated through the envelope by which the building is surrounded.

From the above it will be obvious that the novel building structure provides a thin envelope of recirculating air which surrounds the building interior, a portion of which envelope is contiguous to the earth so as to promote the transfer of heat to and from the air from and to the earth upon relatively slight temperature differential. In warm winter weather (above 30 F.), the heat passes from the recirculating air into the earth, thus increasing the normal flow of heat from the interior of the building across the inner heat insulating wall 6 so that this increment of heat is largely stored in the underlying ground. In cold winter weather (approximating zero), the stored heat passes from the ground into the recirculating air, and thus greatly reduces the drain on the heating generator, so as to economize operation of the latter.

The heating operations in the novel building structure are substantially as follows: to maintain an interior temperature approximating 72° F.

Assuming the normal average outdoor temperature to approximate 30 F. (as e. g. in the metropolitan New York city area), and that the outer wall 5 of the air envelope possesses a heat conductivity approximating 1000 B. t. u. per hour per degree F., and that the inner wall 6 of said air envelope also possesses a heat conductivity approximating 1000 B. t. u. per hour per degree F.; the air within the envelope would normally possess a mid temperature of

$$\frac{30 \text{ plus } 72}{2}$$

or 51 F., and the drop across the inner wall 6, from heat supplied by furnace 18, would be 21° F., i. e. the furnace 18 would be required to produce an output of approximately 21 × 1000 or 21,000 B. t. u. per hour. However, if the normal earth temperature is 50 F., some heat would be stored in the ground, and the furnace 18 would have a somewhat higher output. For outdoor temperatures higher than 30 F. (e. g. a maximum of 60° F.), the envelope air would normally tend to possess an average temperature of approximately

$$\frac{60 \text{ plus } 72}{2}$$

or 66 F., and the furnace would only supply 6 × 1000 or 6000 B. t. u. per hour. However, the earth can be expected to store heat, transferred thereto from the envelope air, and thus to maintain an envelope air temperature of approximately 55 F., so that the furnace need only supply 17 × 1000 or 17,000 B. t. u. per hour. Under these circumstances, the drop across the outer wall 5 will approximate 5 F. negative, so that 5 × 1000 or 5000 B. t. u. will be transferred to the earth from outdoors, thus a total heat storage in the ground of 17,000 plus 5000 or 22,000 B. t. u. per hour will be accumulated. The conducting underground wall 11 absorbs over 4000 B. t. u. per degree F.

At zero outdoor temperature, without considering earth storage heat, the envelope air would possess a temperature of 0 plus 72/2 or 36° F., and the furnace 18 would be required to supply 36 × 1000 or 36,000 B. t. u. If, however, T is assumed to be the temperature of the envelope air, then (72−T) × 1000 equals output of the furnace, and T × 1000 equals heat passing through outside wall 5 and T × 1000 − (72−T) × 1000 is the amount of heat desired from ground storage. If the ground is assumed to yield 4000 B. t. u. per degree F. of variation above 50° F., then (50−T) × 4000 equals available storage heat, and

$$T \times 1000 - (72 - T) \times 1000 = (50 - T) \times 4000$$

and T equals approximately $45\frac{1}{3}$ F., so that ground stored heat will supply about $4\frac{2}{3} \times 4000$ or 18,700 B. t. u. per hour, of the 45,300 B. t. u. required, leaving but approximately 26,600 B. t. u. necessary to be supplied by the furnace 18, instead of 36,000 B. t. u. normally needed, thus normally effecting a saving in furnace capacity required of 9,400/36,000 or about 26 per cent.

In the use of the solar heat supplied features of the invention, during cold winter weather (below 30° F.), the dampers 22 and 24 are closed to exclude circulation of air through the roof air flow course E, but in warm sunny winter weather (above 30° F), these dampers 22 and 24 are opened to shunt the envelope circulated air through the roof air flow course E, and under the latter conditions the air impeller fan 17 is reversed, to reverse direction of circulation of air through the air envelope, so that the air flows upward through the air flow course C, thence by way of the transfer air flow course D through the roof air flow course E and from the latter down the air flow course B to the bottom air flow course A. The air as thus circulated picks up heat derived from solar energy transmitted through roofing 19, and additionally from solar energy transmitted through the window structure 34. The thus additionally warmed air flows into the bottom air flow course A in heat transfer contact with the earth, to which it gives up heat for storage subject to future demand. The solar energy derived heat, by reason of the reversed circulation of air through the recirculating envelope is mainly transferred to the earth underlying the southern part of the house, so that the earth which underlies the southern part of the house is warmer than that which underlies the northern part of the house.

Since the solar energy converted into sensible heat within the air circulating envelope can gain no direct access through to the house interior by reason of the shielding inner wall 6, which preferably is coincident to the entire area of the south side wall of the building, it is preferable that all windows opening into the house interior are reduced to a minimum, and these located in other than the south wall of the building. From this it follows, that, if desired, substantially the entire outer wall at the south side of the building may be made of solar energy transmitting character so that a maximum amount of sensible heat gain derived from solar energy may be rendered available for storage and later use.

The supplementary heat derived from solar energy according to this invention and transferred to the earth underlying the building may be assumed to raise the normal underlying earth temperature approximately 5° F. As above stated, it is assumed that the outer and inner insulating house walls 5 and 6 possess a thermal conductivity of 1000 B. t. u. per hour per degree F., and that the heat conductive wall 7 between the bottom air flow course A and the earth has a conductivity of approximately 5600 B. t. u. per hour per degree F. At zero outdoor temperature, without heat storage or solar energy aid, the house air temperature within the air recirculating envelope would approximate 36° F., and the house heating generator would be required to supply 36,000 B. t. u. per hour. With the solar energy heat supply considered, the air temperature within the air recirculating envelope may be considered as T, and $T \times 1000$ B. t. u. per hour would pass through the outer envelope wall 5, and $(72-T) \times 1000$ B. t. u. would pass through the inner envelope wall 6. Under these circumstances, the stored heat from the underlying earth would supply $(55-T) \times 5600$ B. t. u. which equals $T \times 1000 + (72-T) \times 1000$ so that T is of the order of 50° F. Consequently about 50,000 B. t. u. passing through the outer envelope wall 5 and 22,000 B. t. u. passing through the inner wall 6, with 28,000 B. t. u. per hour derived from earth stored heat as a maximum stored heat drain. The saving effected with respect to required generated heat capacity, under my novel system including solar energy aid, will approximate 36,000 B. t. u. (normal) less 22,000 B. t. u. or about 39 per cent. *

Oct. 15, 1963 J. F. GARRISON 3,107,052

RADIATION COLLECTORS

*

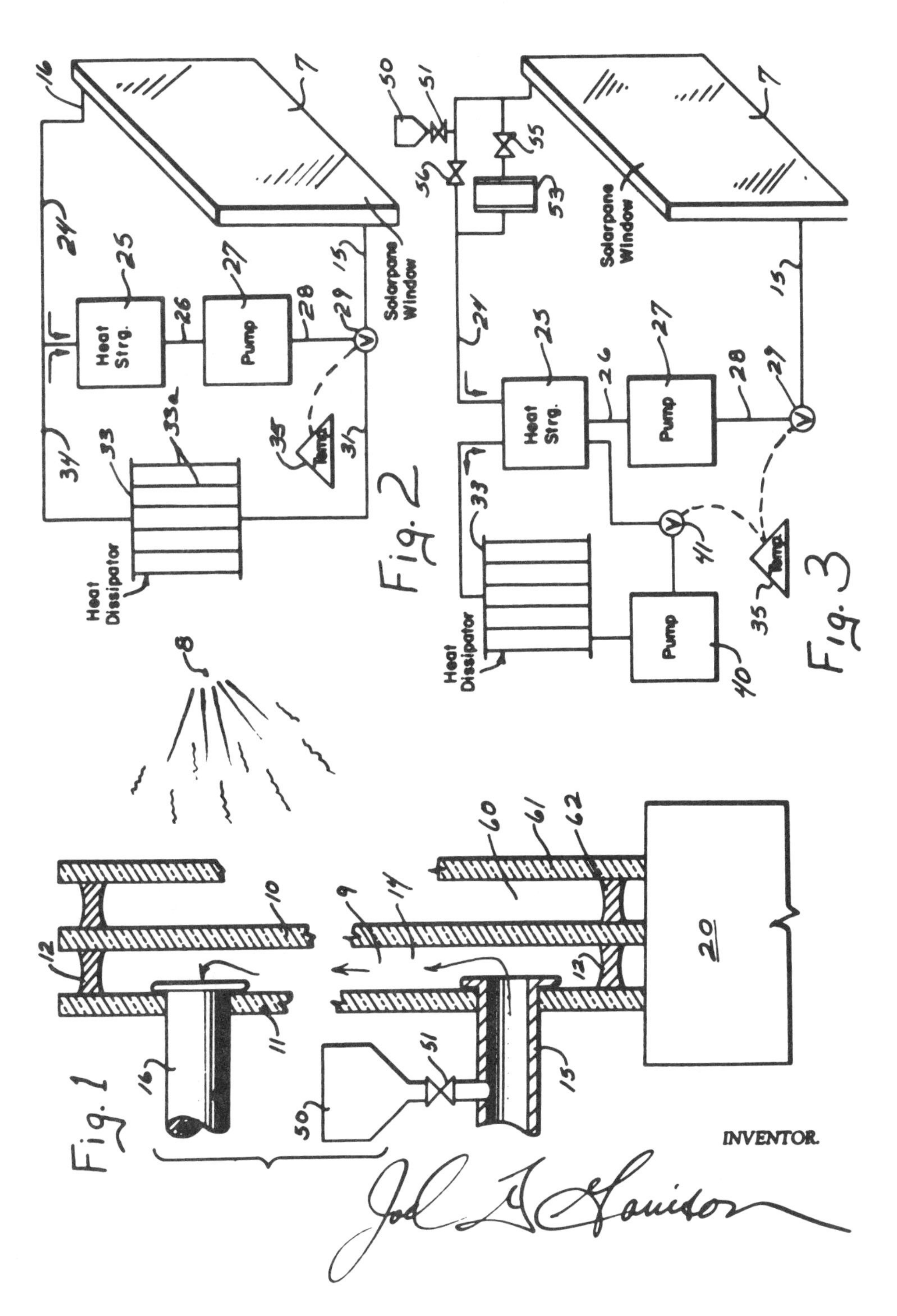

3,107,052
RADIATION COLLECTORS
Joel F. Garrison, San Jose, Calif.
(1174 Denver Drive, Campbell, Calif.)

*

This invention relates to thermal radiation collecting apparatus and particularly concerns solar or other heat collectors which are substantially transparent.

An object of the invention is to provide improved radiation collector-dissipators.

An additional object is to provide a transparent radiation collector-dissipator which has a novel construction.

An additional object is to provide an improved wall closure for a building.

An additional object is to disclose the construction of a transparent solar heat collector-dissipator wall for buildings.

An additional object is to provide an improved system for solar heating a building.

An additional object is to provide an improved system for determining the kinds and intensities of radiation which are permitted to pass a substantially transparent panel such as a window.

Another object is to provide an improved method of heating a building.

Other objects will become apparent as the description proceeds.

In order that my invention may be practiced by others it will be described in terms of express embodiments, given by way of example only, and with reference to the accompanying drawings in which:

FIGURE 1 is a cross-sectional view of a radiation collector-dissipator showing the fluid connections thereto.

FIGURE 2 is a schematic drawing of a system for solar heating a building.

FIGURE 3 is a schematic drawing of another system for solar heating a building.

Solar heated buildings presently available have had limited acceptance by the buying and building public. One reason for this is that the prior art radiation collectors are conspicuously placed at or above or below the main floor level of the building in plain view. This has necessitated unconventional and even unsightly appearing buildings which receive limited public acceptance.

The heat collectors for a building, according to any invention, comprise the windows which are located in the walls of the building. The window or collector area of the building may therefore, be varied within wide limits as determined by architectural and climatic considerations, without departing from the building appearances which are accepted.

I propose windows having dual panes which are separated to allow a fluid to pass between them. The fluid would normally be transparent but could contain substances which would enhance the heat absorbing or dissipating property, or the light and radiation filtering properties of the fluid. The fluid absorbs solar heat while in the window and moves by convection currents or by pumping in a circulation system. The system would normally include a heat storage or a heat exchanger device which forms a part of the system for heating the building. The movement of the substantially transparent fluid between the dual-panes is not detectable and buildings could be constructed to include this form of radiation collectors without having to depart from accepted architectural forms.

Ornamental effects are achieved by introducing substances such as dyes, flakes of metal, colored solid particles and gas bubbles, into the fluid which circulates through the dual pane windows.

My invention can be incorporated in the construction of cubicles for observing sources of intense thermal radiation, such as open hearth furnaces. The cubicle is built to have a duel pane window in which substantially transparent heat absorbing fluid is circulated. Various substances could be added to the fluid to enhance the inherent heat and radiation filtering and absorbing properties. This structure would permit the observer to observe the source in relative comfort because large quantities of heat would continually be being removed by the circulated fluid from the area of the transparent window.

Referring now to FIGURE 1, the radiation collector **7** is seen to comprise an outside pane **10** of substantially transparent or light transmitting material and an inside pane **11** of substantially transparent or light transmitting material. One quarter inch thick glass or plastic is satisfactory. The two panes are separated a short distance. A sealing member **12** is sealed between the edge surfaces of the sheets thus forming an enclosed space **14**.

An inlet tube **15** is connected to the inner pane **11** near the lower edge of the enclosed space **14**; and an outlet tube **16** is connected to the pane near the upper edge of the enclosed space. The inlet and outlet tube connections are sealed to prevent leakage.

The entire radiation collector is supported in an upright position by a support such as a window casement or other part of the building **20**. The collector is most efficient where located in a wall which is exposed directly to the source of radiation **8**. For solar heat radiation in this hemisphere, the radiation collector is most efficient when given a southern exposure.

A substantially transparent or light-transmitting heat absorbing fluid **9** is introduced into the enclosed space **14** by one or more inlet tubes such as inlet tube **15**. The fluid is pumped into the enclosed space and moves upwardly filling the space **14** between the dual-panes and is removed by outlet tubes such as the outlet tube **16**. In this fashion relatively cool fluid is circulated into the space **14** to replace the hot fluid. The newly introduced, relatively cool fluid is heated by heat radiated from the source of radiation **8**.

The heated fluid from the radiation collector is then directed into a heat storage unit or heat exchanger unit which absorbs heat from the fluid so that the fluid is relatively cool when it again enters the collector.

The collector outlet pipe **16** (FIG. 2) is connected by a pipe **24** to a heat storage unit **25** which is in turn connected by a pipe **26** to a pump **27**. The pump is connected by a pipe **28** and a valve **29** to the inlet pipe **15**.

The heat storage unit **25** comprises several containers of Glauber's salt, or similar heat storing material. The heated fluid is brought into contact with the lower temperature containers and thus gives off heat to the material in the containers.

The pump outlet line **28** is connected to the valve **29** which controls the relative volume of fluid moving to the collector **7** and through pipe **31** to a heater unit **33**. The heater unit **33** could comprise, for example, a series of small diameter pipes *33a* in the building floor or walls, which radiate or otherwise dissipate the heat from the fluid passing through them into the room. The heater unit **33** is connected to the heat storage unit inlet by a line **34**.

The most satisfactory results are achieved if the flow valve **29** is controlled by a control device **35** which responds to temperature changes within the building. Such temperature responsive valve controls are well known and available commercially. The temperature responsive control 35 for flow valve 29 responds to high temperatures by causing the valve to direct the major volume of fluid from the pump to the collector 7 and away from the heat dissipator unit 33 in the building. The heat is thereby stored in the storage unit 25. The temperature responsive control 35 for flow valve 29 would respond to low temperatures by causing the valve to direct the major volume of fluid from the pump to the heat dissipating unit 33. Heat is thereby removed from the storage unit 25.

The system just described is simple and the same fluid is used throughout. In operation, however, the volumes of fluid flowing in the collector 7 and in the heat dissipating unit 33 vary inversely with each other.

In order to independently control the volumes of fluid flowing in the collector 7 and in the heat dissipating unit 33, a second system shown in FIGURE 3, is provided. This second system has the heat dissipator 33 for the building and include a pump 40 and a valve 41. The dissipating system is independent of the absorbing system except that the fluid in the dissipating system circulates through the heat exchanger 25 to absorb heat energy from the heat storing medium.

The temperature responsive control 35 is connected to control both the flow valve 41 and the flow valve 29 and the volumes of fluid flowing in each system is thereby regulated.

It has been mentioned that a great number of techniques are available to enhance specific properties of the fluid chosen to circulate in the collector-dissipator. The additives could include:

(1) Substances for enhancing the heat absorbing property;

(2) Substances for enhancing the radiation filtering property;

(3) Substances to color the fluid;

(4) Substances such as colored solid particles, metal powders and flakes, and gas bubbles for particular effects.

In order to introduce and remove such substances an injection chamber 50, FIGURES 1 and 3, is connected by means of a valve 51 into the system. By opening the valve 51 pressurized gas in the head of the chamber forces substances placed therein into the line.

A filter or settling tank 53, FIGURE 3, is provided to remove injected substances from the system. By opening valve 55 and closing valve 56 the fluid flowing in pipe 16 will all pass the filter or settling tank 53. Other means of injecting and removing substances from the system will occur to persons skilled in the art.

Radiated heat raises the heat content of the fluid 9 flowing in the enclosed space 14, FIGURE 1. The fluid loses this heat while between the panes mainly by the process of conduction to the air on either side of the window.

If heat is lost by conduction to the air inside the building, this is not objectionable, but if heat is lost to the outside air, this is objectionable because this decreases efficiency. This objection is overcome by providing a second enclosed space 60, FIGURE 1.

The second enclosed space 60 is achieved by sealing a light transmitting pane 61 to the pane 10 by using a sealing member 62. The enclosed space 60 is evacuated so that no air remains to conduct the heat from the fluid in space 14 to the outside. With this arrangement, most of the heat energy lost by the hot fluid in the collector-dissipator will be lost, not to the outside, but to the room.

It is well known that during cold months, as much heat will be lost through a single window as is lost through an entire wall of an ordinary residence. These standard windows are very cold and cause the room to be cold in the area just inside the window. With the present invention, the windows will be transparent and warm and there will be no appreciable temperature variation at any point in the residence.

It will be observed that the expanse of windows disclosed herein can conduct refrigerated fluids. This alternative would provide a building which could be easily maintained at a cool inside temperature relative to a hot outside temperature because solar heat energy would merely warm the cold fluid and then be dissipated at the refrigerator. This then would prevent such solar energy from warming the inside of the building even though large window areas are exposed to the sun. *

March 29, 1966 E. A. MORGAN **3,243,117**

BUILDING STRUCTURES

* *

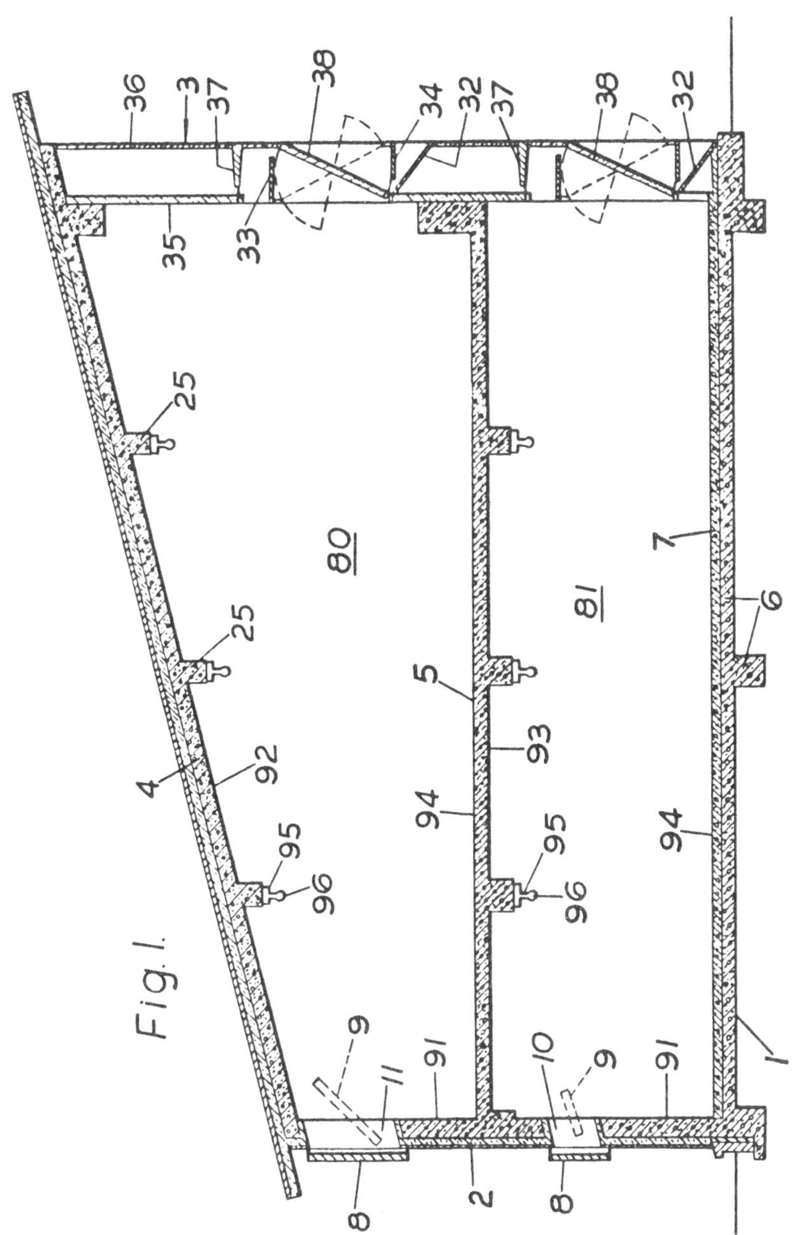

INVENTOR:
EMSLIE A. MORGAN
BY
Brown, Schuyler & Beveridge
ATTORNEYS

March 29, 1966 | E. A. MORGAN | 3,243,117

BUILDING STRUCTURES

* | *

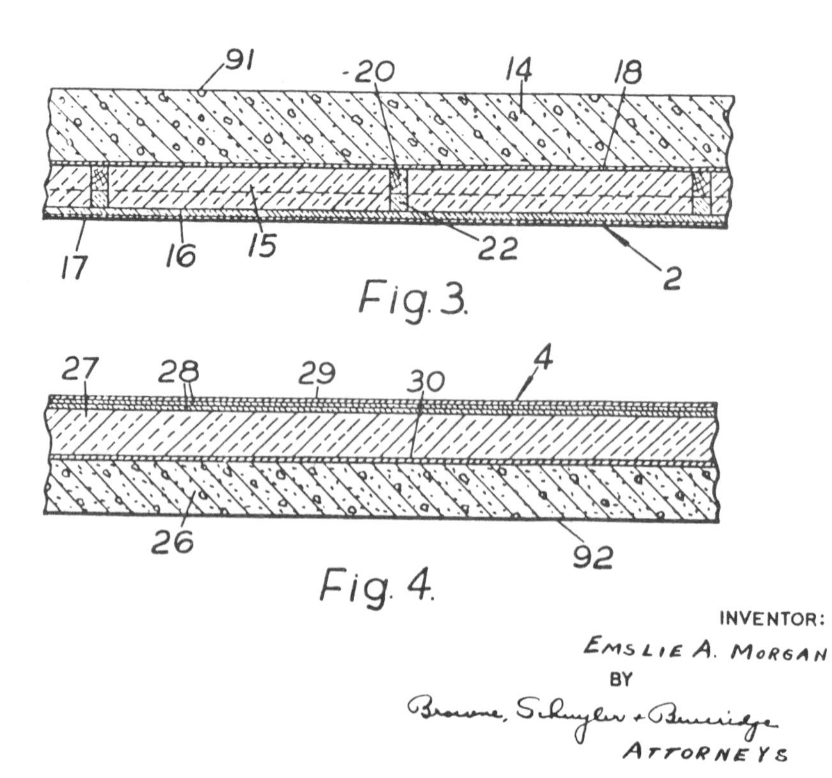

March 29, 1966 E. A. MORGAN 3,243,117

BUILDING STRUCTURES

* *

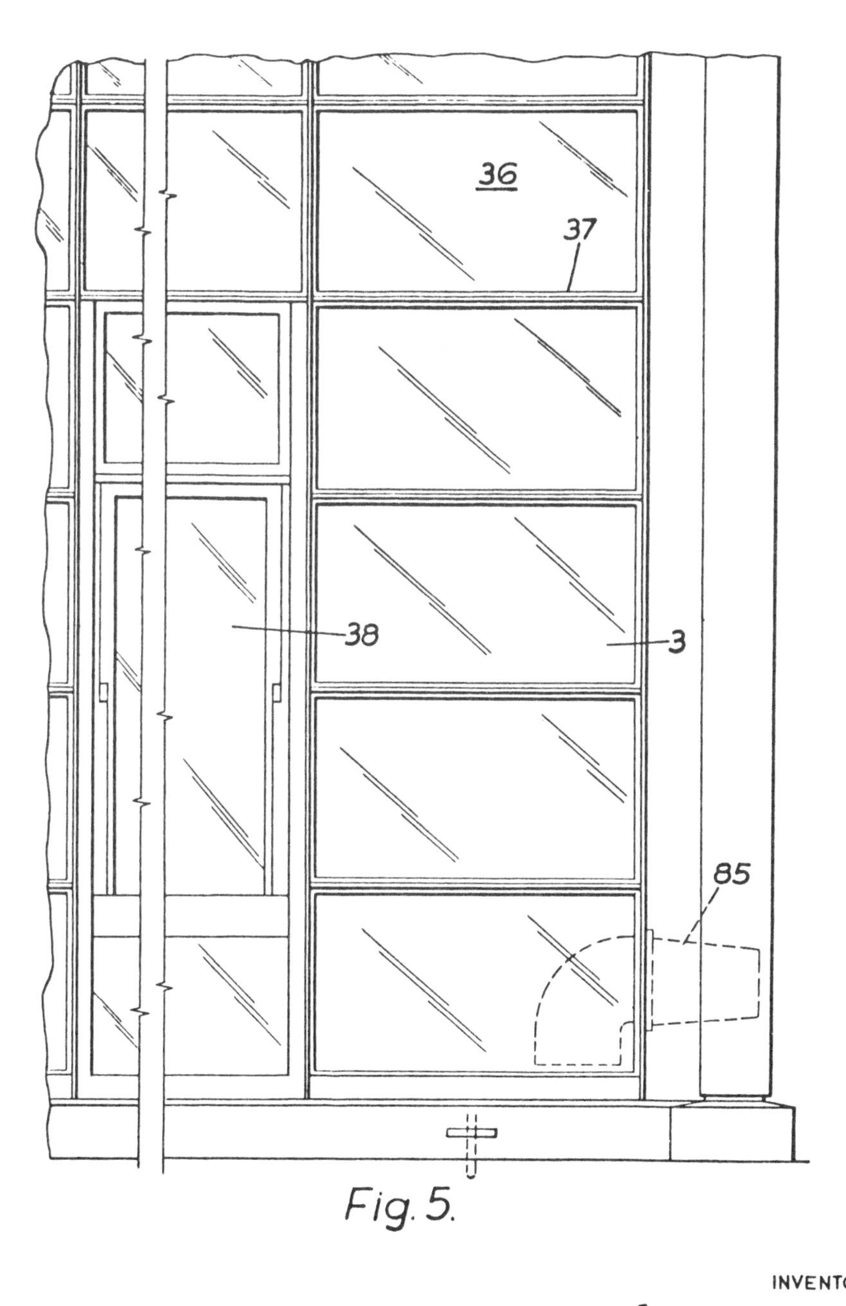

Fig. 5.

INVENTOR:
EMSLIE A. MORGAN
BY
Brown, Schuyler & Beveridge
ATTORNEYS

March 29, 1966 E. A. MORGAN 3,243,117

BUILDING STRUCTURES

* *

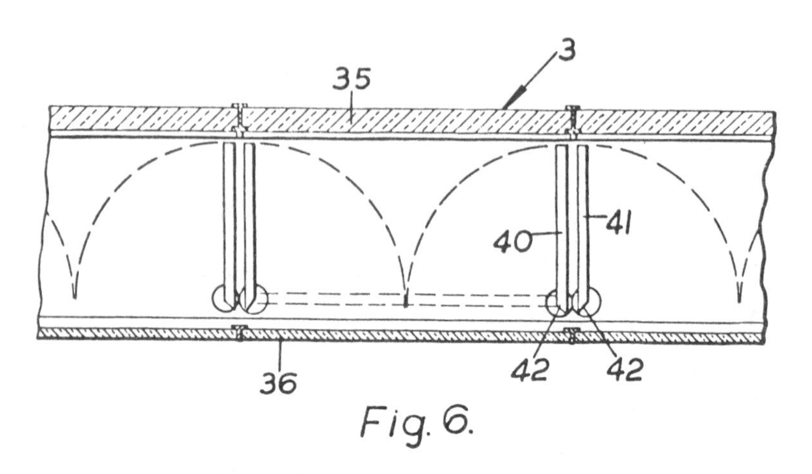

Fig. 6.

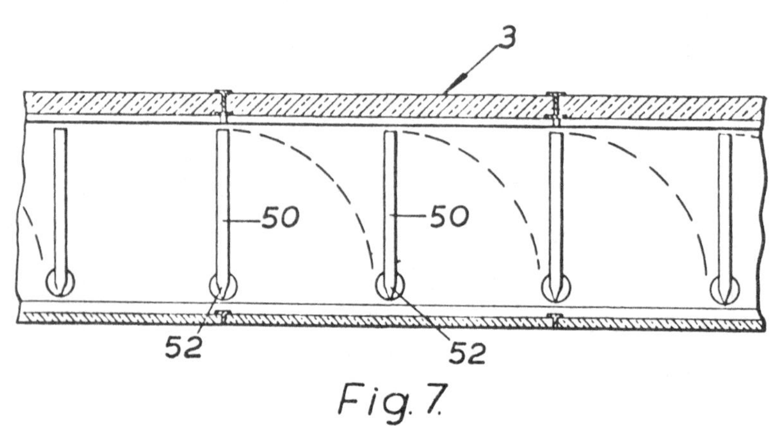

Fig. 7.

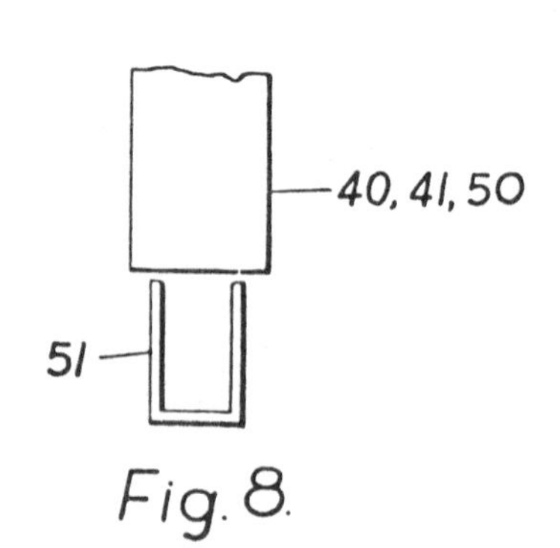

Fig. 8.

INVENTOR:
EMSLIE A. MORGAN
BY
Browne, Schuyler & Beveridge
ATTORNEYS

March 29, 1966 E. A. MORGAN **3,243,117**

BUILDING STRUCTURES

* *

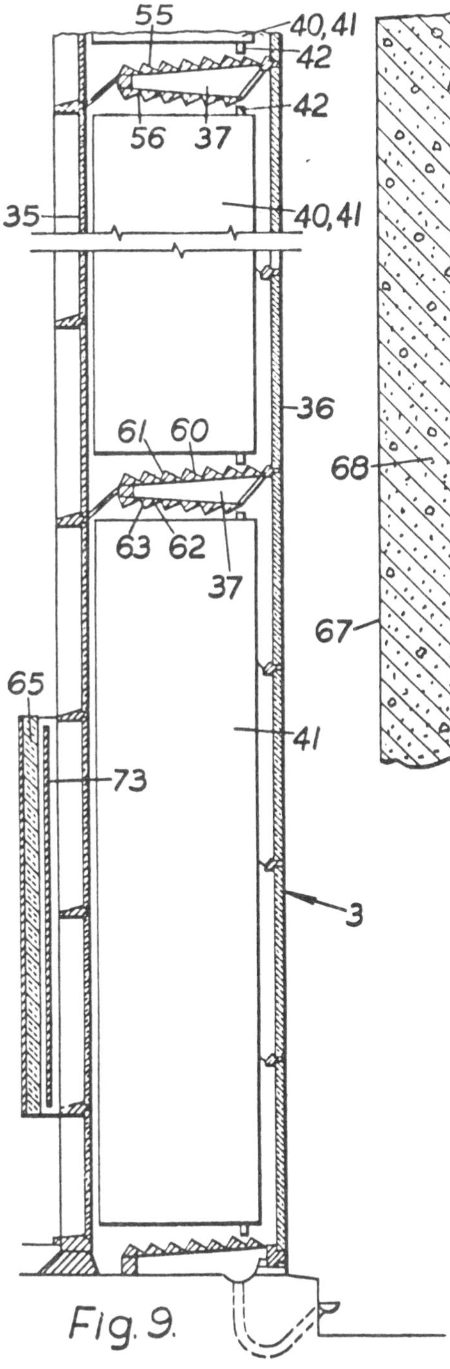

Fig. 9.

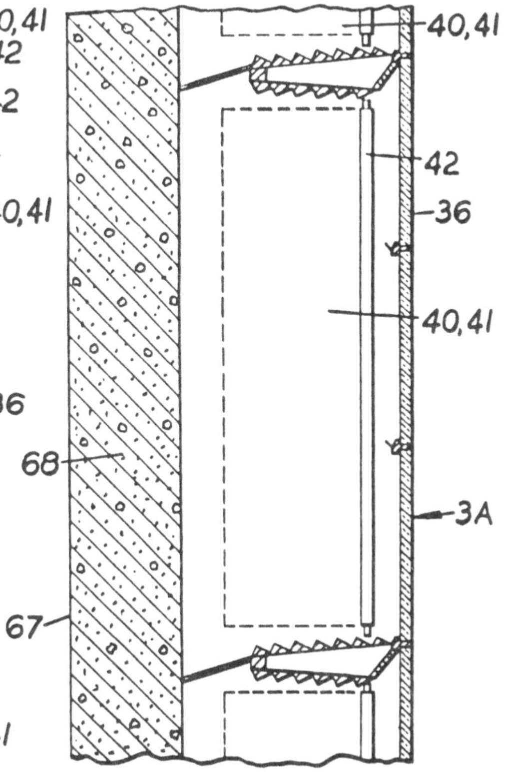

Fig. 10.

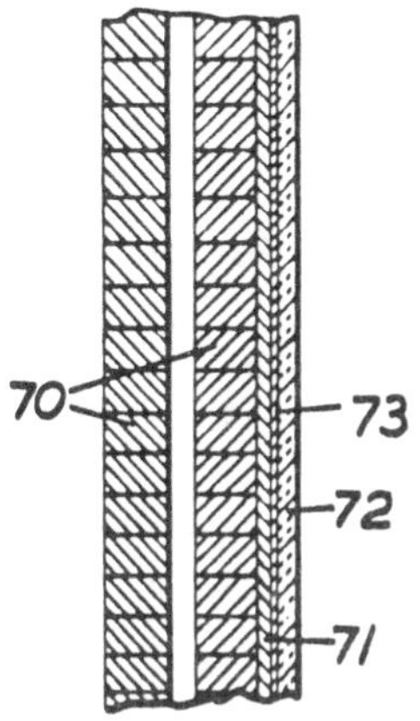

Fig. 11.

INVENTOR:
ENSLIE A. MORGAN
BY
Browne, Schuyler & Beveridge
ATTORNEYS

3,243,117
BUILDING STRUCTURES
Emslie Alexander Morgan, Wallasey, Wirral, England; Westminster Bank Limited, administrator of estate of said Emslie Alexander Morgan, deceased *

*The present invention relates to building constructions and more particularly the heating of useful accommodation within the building. The useful accommodation is that accommodation which is intended to be used for the purpose for which the building is designed and built. For example, in a school the useful accommodation comprises the class rooms but may also include an assembly hall, corridors and the like.

It is common practice to employ central heating to heat the useful accommodation of buildings. Central heating is expensive to install because it requires radiators for radiating heat, piping for circulating the heating fluid and a heater for heating the fluid.

There have been a number of proposals for heating useful accommodation in buildings partly or wholly by the use of solar radiation with the object of reducing or eliminating fuel costs. Whilst such solar heating systems have been successfully used they have hitherto not become a commercial proposition because of the greater expenditure incurred in constructing a building which is capable of being satisfactorily heated by solar radiation.

In some prior art solar heating systems the radiation from the sun is used for heating the useful accommodation whilst the sun is shining and some other heating means is provided for heating the useful accommodation when there is insufficient or no solar radiation. Such a building has to be specially constructed to enable it to be solar heated but also requires a normal heating installation which may be as expensive as a comparable one installed in a conventionally heated building.

In prior art buildings adapted to be heated entirely by solar radiation, a special room, usually a loft is provided for the collection of solar radiation and means is provided in this special room for converting the solar radiation into heat and passing it into a fluid by means of which the heat is transferred to some point of storage from where it can be distributed to the useful accommodation as required. In one particular solar heating system of this kind the solar radiation passes through a large collecting window in the loft and falls upon a collector. The heat is removed from the collector by means of air which is circulated to heat storage "bins" closer to the useful accommodation. The heat is transferred from the heat storage bins to the useful accommodation when required by the further circulation of air.

Thus it will be seen that none of the prior art solar heating systems has obviated the necessity for a heating installation as such, be it only a circulating system for distributing the solar heat to the useful accommodation.

Solar heating systems require the buildings in which they are incorporated to be insulated against heat loss. Thus the expense of the prior art solar heating system has been not only the expense of the installation of the heating system itself but also the expense of additional heat insulation material applied to the walls and roof of the building.

It has never been thought a practical proposition to deliberately apply heat insulating material on a generous scale to buildings adapted to be heated by a conventional heating system because the interest and repayment of capital required to provide and fit such heat insulation is likely to be greater than the cost of fuel saved.

It is an object of the present invention to construct a building, adapted to be heated solely by radiation emanating from at least one incandescent source, such as the sun, without requiring any heating installation as such within the building.

It is another object of the present invention to provide a building, adapted to be heated solely by radiation emanating from at least one incandescent source, that is adapted to store the radiation as heat directly adjacent the useful accommodation so that the heat is always present at the useful accommodation where it is required.

It is a still further object of the invention to provide a building whose useful accommodation is adapted to be heated by the maintenance therein of a flux of warming radiation extending substantially throughout the useful accommodation.

It is yet another object of the invention to provide a building which the walls of the useful accommodation are maintained at a temperature higher than the air temperature in the useful accommodation by impinging on the walls radiation emanating from at least one incandescent source, such as the sun, such radiation being partly reflected by the walls and partly absorbed by the walls so as to pass into storage in the walls until required.

The invention is further described, by way of example only and not for the purposes of limitation, with reference to the accompanying drawings in which:

FIG. 1 is a side sectional elevation of a building, more particularly a school;

FIGS. 2 and 3 are a sectional side elevation and sectional plan view of a typical wall structure;

FIG. 4 is a section through the roof;

FIG. 5 is a fragmentary elevation illustrating the solar wall from the exterior of the building;

FIG. 6 is a fragmentary view illustrating one arrangement of shutters in the solar wall;

FIG. 7 illustrates an alternative arrangement of shutters within the solar wall;

FIG. 8 is a fragmentary view to illustrate the framing of the shutters;

FIG. 9 is a fragmentary sectional elevation through a part of the solar wall designed to transmit solar radiation to the useful accommodation within the building;

FIG. 10 is a fragmentary sectional elevation of another part of the solar wall designed to absorb solar radiation directly into the heat storage material of the building; and

FIG. 11 is a sectional view illustrating one mode of applying insulation to the inside of an existing cavity wall.

More specifically the invention provides a building wherein the wall surfaces bounding the useful accommodation are heat transfer surfaces which are exposed to receive, from time to time, radiation emanating from at least one incandescent source. The incandescent source is usually the sun in which case the building is provided with a solar wall through which the solar radiation passes directly into the useful accommodation to impinge the heat transfer surfaces. The main fabric of the building or at least a major part thereof acts also as heat storage material and is provided with heavy external insulation. The term "fabric" as used herein includes the walls, the floor and roof and ceiling of the building and includes all strength members, such as beams, facings such as tiles, and permanent fixtures. Thus the heat transfer surfaces are surfaces of the fabric of the building and the heat absorbed by the heat transfer surfaces is conducted directly to the fabric acting as heat storage material and is stored therein until required. Thus the useful accommodation may be maintained at a habitable temperature without the use of any heating installation as such since the heat required is conducted as radiation to the useful accommodation where it is stored until it is wanted. No fluid circulating system is required at all, unless ventilating means is required to prevent the useful accommodation becoming too warm in summer. Even then forced ventilation is usually unnecessary.

Artificial illumination means, such as electric lights, may be used in addition to or instead of the sun as incandescent sources for providing the radiation which is to impinge the heat transfer surfaces in the useful accommodation.

The roof and external walls, in so far as they are not designed for the transmission of solar radiation, are heavily insulated down to a U value of from 0.03 to 0.15 (and preferably of from 0.03 to 0.10).

The "U value" referred to herein is the rate of heat loss in British thermal units per hour per square foot of surface of insulation per degree Fahrenheit of temperature difference across the insulation.

The U value of the heat insulating layer is so chosen in relation to the heat storing capacity of the fabric that the average rate of impingement of radiation from the incandescent source balances the rate of heat loss through the building under the coldest weather conditions the building is likely to encounter. The average rate of radiation from the electric lighting installation and body heat may be taken into account.

U values appropriate to the present invention may be achieved by the application of a layer of expanded polystyrene or equivalent heat insulating material of from 2" to 5" thick to the external walls and roof. If the external walls are largely relied upon for heat storage then the insulating layer should be applied to the external surface thereof and provided with a vapour barrier internally and a moisture barrier externally.

If the external walls are not heavily relied upon for heat storage the insulating layer is preferably applied to the internal surfaces thereof with a vapour barrier on the inside of the insulating layer and preferably also on the outside of the insulating layer between the layer and the walls.

The heat storage material, usually forming at least a major part of the fabric of the building should have a heat storing capacity not less than 5 British thermal units and preferably not less than 25 British thermal units per square foot of floor area of the useful accommodation per degree Fahrenheit rise or fall in temperature of the heat storage material.

The heat storage material incorporated in the building and its internal heat transfer surfaces should be such as to provide a thermal path of low resistance from the surfaces to the heat storage material therebehind. The surface itself should be capable of absorbing radiation either solar or from electric lamps of the order of from about 0.3 up to 5.0 microns wavelength. Whether or not it will be desirable for the surface of a room or other space to have an absorptivity nearing 100% will depend upon the design of the particular room. Thus it may be desirable for the surface to have a certain degree of reflectivity so as to build up a radiative flux in the room and to distribute the radiation more evenly over the surfaces of the room. The degree of absorption and reflectivity can to a considerable extent be controlled by the formulation of the paint applied to the surfaces.

The heat transfer surfaces should moreover be capable of absorbing long wavelength radiation from other surfaces in the room and in particular body heat from the occupants. Any surfaces which do not bound heat storage material should be reflective rather than absorbent to short wavelength radiation but should be capable of absorbing long wavelength radiation. The overall effect should be such as to provide heat storage material capable of absorbing a large quantity of heat with a minimum rise in surface temperature. A good example of a traditionally constructed ceiling for embodiment in a building constructed in accordance with the present invention is a ceiling formed from a dense concrete slab with a suitable paint applied to the underside.

To avoid undue heat loss through casual air infiltration it is very desirable in building structures according to the present invention that the external shell of the building should be sealed against undue casual ingress of air and in particular that means should be provided for sealing around the external doors and ventilators.

An important feature of the mode of heating of the present invention is that the internal bounding surfaces of a room tend to be maintained at a temperature slightly higher than that of the air of the room and the air is not used to any significant extent for the distribution of heat. Most conventional forms of heating tend to keep the air temperature above the temperature of a major portion of the bounding surface. This feature of the invention yields certain advantages as follows:

(a) Of two rooms of the same equivalent temperature one having a mean wall surface temperature somewhat higher and the other having a mean wall surface temperature somewhat lower than the air temperature, that with the means wall surface temperature higher than the air temperature will, other factors being equal, be considered the more comfortable by the majority of people.

(b) Maintaining the bounding surfaces at temperatures above the air temperature will greatly reduce the rate of soiling of the decorative surfaces.

(c) Advantages of a medical character.

The solar wall preferably incorporates a light diffusive glass so as to scatter a proportion of the solar radiation and so obtain a more uniform distribution of the radiation falling on the heat transfer surfaces.

To minimise heat loss through the solar wall, such a wall preferably comprises inner and outer walls of light transmitting material, such as glass.

Corrugated reflective surfaces extending approximately horizontally inwardly from the outer skin of the solar wall towards the inner skin may be provided at vertically spaced intervals in the solar wall with the object of reflecting back heat radiation from the inner skin to the outer skin thus improving the U value of the solar wall. These corrugations can be designed to reduce the collection of solar heat from the high summer sun.

The fabric of the building illustrated in FIG. 1 comprises a base **1**, external walling **2**, an upper floor **5** and a roof **4**. The building is suitably framed either by steel or concrete and incorporates a solar wall **3**. The base comprises a concrete mass **6** having a surface layer of concrete **7** with a damp proof layer therebetween.

The walling **2** is formed with ventilating openings **10**, **11** therein. The openings **10**, **11** are each closable by a horizontally pivoted insulated shutter **9** and can be shielded by louvres **8**.

The walling **2** is constructed as illustrated in FIGS. 2 and 3 and comprises 9" thickness of concrete **14**, 5" thickness of foamed polystyrene **15**, ¾" thick insulation board **16**, an outer vapour barrier **17** of bituminous felt and a vapour barrier **18** of bituminous felt between the concrete **14** and the foamed polystyrene **15**. The foamed polystyrene is in the form of slabs supported between wooden rails **19** and wooden posts **20**, the spaces between the rails and posts **19** and **20** and the concrete **14** being filled by strips of foamed polystyrene **21, 22**. The inner surfaces **91** of the concrete **14** are painted with a paint having a suitable coefficient of reflectivity to provide heat transfer surfaces.

The roof **4** incorporates re-inforced concrete beams **25**. The roof section between the beams is illustrated in FIG. 4 and comprises an inner layer **26** of concrete, an outer insulating layer **27** of foamed polystyrene 5" thick, two layers **28** of ½" insulation board with joints staggered and an outer vapour barrier **29** of bituminous roofing felt. A vapour barrier **30** is provided between the concrete **26** and the insulation **27**. The inner surface **92** of the roof concrete **26** is painted to provide a heat transfer surface.

The floor **5** is constructed of re-inforced concrete and divides the building into an upper storey **80** and a lower storey **81**. The ceiling concrete beneath the floor **5** is painted to provide a heat transfer surface. The base **1** and the floor **5** are provided with suitable floor coverings **94**, for example, thermoplastic tiles of a suitable light colour, such as yellow, to provide further heat transfer surfaces. The heat transfer surfaces **91, 92, 93, 94** are so disposed as to receive, at least indirectly and for the most part directly, solar radiation passing through the solar wall and through the useful accommodation **80, 81**.

The solar wall **3** diagrammatically illustrated in FIG. 1 comprises an inner glazed skin **35** and an outer glazed skin **36** which is spaced from the inner skin by about two feet. The framing on the inner skin **35** is 3" x 1½" I-section steel and that of the outer skin **36** is 1½" x 1½" T-section steel. Walkways **37** supported between the inner and outer skins facilitate the cleaning of the glazing in the cavity between the skins. The external appearance of the solar wall is illustrated in FIG. 5.

The inner skin **35** comprises a diffusive or reflective glass capable of scattering the solar radiation so as to distribute such radiation more uniformly over the heat transfer surfaces **91, 92, 93, 94**. The inner skin **35** should not be too diffusive, however, or the solar wall would appear as a complete wall of light and would be unpleasant to the eyes.

Double glazed windows **38** are pivoted at their mid-height between upper and lower horizontal louvre panels **33, 34**. A glass sheet **32** slopes downwardly and outwardly from the inner edge of the lower louvre panel **34**. When a window **38** is upwardly inclined to the right as illustrated in FIG. 1 the window is closed but when inclined upwardly to the left as indicated in broken lines in FIG. 1 the window remains burglar and weather proof but permits ventilation to occur through the louvres **33** and **34**.

Shutters of insulating material are pivoted about vertical axes between the inner and outer skins **35** and **36** of the solar wall. One form of shutter arrangement is shown in FIG. 6 wherein pairs of insulated shutter panels **40, 41** are pivoted about adjacent axes **42** near to the outer skin **36** of the solar wall so that they can occupy positions perpendicular to the skins of the solar wall where they permit the transmission of solar radiation through the solar wall but can be moved to positions parallel with the skins of the solar wall where they serve to insulate the solar wall against the transmission of heat outwardly therethrough, as shown by dotted lines.

FIG. 7 illustrates an alternative arrangement in which shutters **50** are arranged singly at spaced intervals from one another instead of in pairs as in FIG. 6 and which open by angular displacement about axes **52** in the same direction instead of by angular displacement in opposite directions as in FIG. 6.

The shutters of the solar wall when in their closed positions are framed by channel framing **51** as diagrammatically illustrated in FIG. 8, the flanges of the channels being spaced by only a small distance of the order of a sixteenth to an eighth of an inch from the edges of the shutters to obstruct thermal air currents passing around the edges of shutters.

FIG. 9 is a sectional elevation illustrating part of the solar wall **3** in more detail. Corrugated reflective surfaces **55** and **56** are provided above and below the walkways **37** and extend approximately horizontally inwardly from the outer skin of the solar wall towards the inner skin with the object of reflecting back outward heat radiation from the inner skin to improve the U value of the solar wall and also to reflect outwardly a portion of the solar radiation from the high level summer sun. The facets **60, 61** of the upper reflective surfaces **55** may lie at angles of 153° and 243° respectively to the horizontal whilst those, **62** and **63**, of the lower reflective surfaces **56** may lie at angles of 26° and 116° respectively to the horizontal.

A heat insulating screen **65** is provided immediately behind a lower part of the solar wall to protect occupants immediately therebehind from undue exposure to the sun, the solor radiation being absorbed by a metal baffle plate **73** and distributed therefrom as convected heat to the air in the building.

FIG. 10 illustrates an alternative form of solar wall **3A** in which the inner skin **68** thereof is of heat absorbing material rather than heat transmitting material. Heat absorbed by the inner skin **68** from the sun is conducted to the inner surface **67** thereof and then transmitted into the building by convection and radiation therefrom. An important feature of the inner skin **68** is that heat is stored therein with only a relatively small rise in temperature of the material of the inner skin itself. When the sun is obscured loss of heat from the inner skin **68** can be minimised by closing the shutters **40, 41**.

Ventilators **85** (see FIG. 5) containing air filters are preferably provided for ventilating the interior cavity of the solar wall **3** so that the air drawn into this cavity by temperature and barometric variations is cleansed of dust and other impurities which would deposit on and soil the interior surfaces of the solar wall.

The present invention may be applied to existing building structures such for example as dwelling houses by the application of a layer of insulation to the inner surface of the external walls as illustrated in FIG. 11 where cavity walls **70** of brickwork with a layer of plaster **71** on its inner face is provided with a layer **72** of expanded polystyrene.

A vapour barrier **73**, for example of aluminum faced paper, is provided on the concealed face of the polystyrene layer between the plaster **71** and the polystyrene layer **72**. The thickness of the polystyrene layer may be of the order of 2 or 3 inches.

Electric light fittings **95** supporting electric light bulbs **96** are mounted beneath the roof **4** and beneath the floor **5** for illuminating the upper and lower storeys **80** and **81** at night and when there is insufficient sunlight. The fittings **95** are so disposed that the lamps **96** are supported thereby shine on substantially the whole of the heat transfer surfaces **91, 92, 93** and **94.**

The heat transfer surfaces **91, 92, 93** and **94** form substantially the whole of the surfaces bounding the useful accommodation **80, 81.** These heat transfer surfaces are so disposed as to receive solar radiation through the solar wall **3** and through the useful accommodation **80, 81.** Some of the solar radiation is diffused by the inner skin **35** of the solar wall, which preferably has a southerly aspect in the northern hemisphere, to distribute the heat radiation more uniformly over the heat transfer surfaces. A minor proportion of the radiation impinging on the heat transfer surfaces is reflected therefrom and falls mainly on other parts of the heat transfer surfaces. This enables a still more even distribution of the radiation over the heat transfer surfaces to be obtained. Only a minor proportion of the reflected radiation, which itself is a minor proportion of the received radiation, passes outwardly again through the solar wall **3** to be lost.

The major proportion of the radiation falling on the heat transfer surfaces is converted into heat and passes into storage in the concrete **5, 6, 7, 14, 25, 26.** The fabric of the building is thereby maintained at a temperature which in practice is slightly higher than the temperature of the air in the useful accommodation **80, 81.** The stored heat which is reradiated into the useful accommodation is comparatively long wavelength radiation and forms, together with the incident and reflected short wavelength radiation from the sun, a flux of warming radiation throughout the useful accommodation.

The U value of the layers of insulation **15, 16, 27, 28** is chosen in relation to the heat storing capacity of the concrete **5, 6, 7, 25, 26** that, during a normal winter, sufficient heat is stored in the concrete, forming the fabric of the building, to maintain the useful accommodation **80, 81** at a habitable temperature day and night and from day to day. In schools and in most office buildings and the like the habitable temperature is 65° F. to 70° F. In a room, such as a school gymnasium, where the occupants exert themselves physically, the habitable temperature is lower usually 50° F. to 55° F. In very cold weather in winter the daylight hours are short and the lights **96** will usually be lit for at least a substantial proportion of the time the useful accommodation is occupied. The radiation emanating from the lights falls on the heat transfer surfaces **91, 92, 93, 94** and should be taken into consideration when determining the U value of the insulation in relation to the heat storage capacity of the fabric. Also when a large number of persons are likely to occupy the useful accommodation for any length of time, as in school class rooms, the body heat introduced into the useful accommodation should also be taken into account. Furthermore the heat lost at night time may be reduced by closing the shutters **40, 41** in the solar walls to prevent the escape of radiation from the useful accommodation.

In the summer, the useful accommodation would be overheated if certain precautions were not taken. Thus in summer the ventilators **9** and the windows **38** are left open, especially at night, to take away the heat stored in the heat storing fabric during the previous daytime. The windows **38** may be locked in an open position in which the louvres **33, 34** allow free ventilation but prevent burglars from entering the building. In fact in hot summer weather the thermal capacity of the fabric may be relied upon to keep the building cool. Thus the heating system of the present invention may also be used as a cooling system.

The present invention envisages the possibility, in buildings wherein windows are not required, of heating the useful accommodation therein entirely by means of the lighting installation. It should be pointed out that a lighting installation is necessary in almost any building and as the radiation emanating from the lights may be used to heat the accommodation according to the present invention, the useful accommodation can be maintained at a habitable temperature without resorting to a heating installation as such.

In a building constructed according to the present invention, the extra cost of applying the heavy insulation is offset by not having to install a heating system, such as a central heating system, involving expensive pipework and/or duct work, pumps, heating means, etc. Fuel costs are low or non-existent. A low fuel cost may arise in cases wherein it is necessary to have the electric lights illuminated rather longer than is necessary to provide the desired illumination. In other words if any heat additional to or instead of solar radiation is required in a building constructed according to the present invention this can be readily obtained from the electric light fittings which must be installed in any event and it is not necessary to provide any supplemental heating means.

It is characteristic of a building constructed according to the present invention that the heat transfer surfaces **91, 92, 93, 94** are maintained at a temperature a few degrees higher than the air temperature within the useful accommodation. It has been found that this temperature difference is a good indication of the state of ventilation of the useful accommodation. Thus if it is perceived that the air temperature has risen above the wall temperature (for example, due to the presence of extensive body heat) this is an indication that the ventilation is insufficient.

Not all the useful accommodation of a building constructed according to the present invention need be heated by radiation emanating from an incandescent source. For example, in a school constructed according to the present invention it was found that, in view of the remoteness of the kitchens from the solar wall and the ready availability of other sources of heating in the kitchens it was more convenient to use electric or steam heaters for maintaining the kitchens at a habitable temperature. *

May 10, 1966 D. M. SHEROCK 3,250,269

SOLAR HEAT DEVICE

*

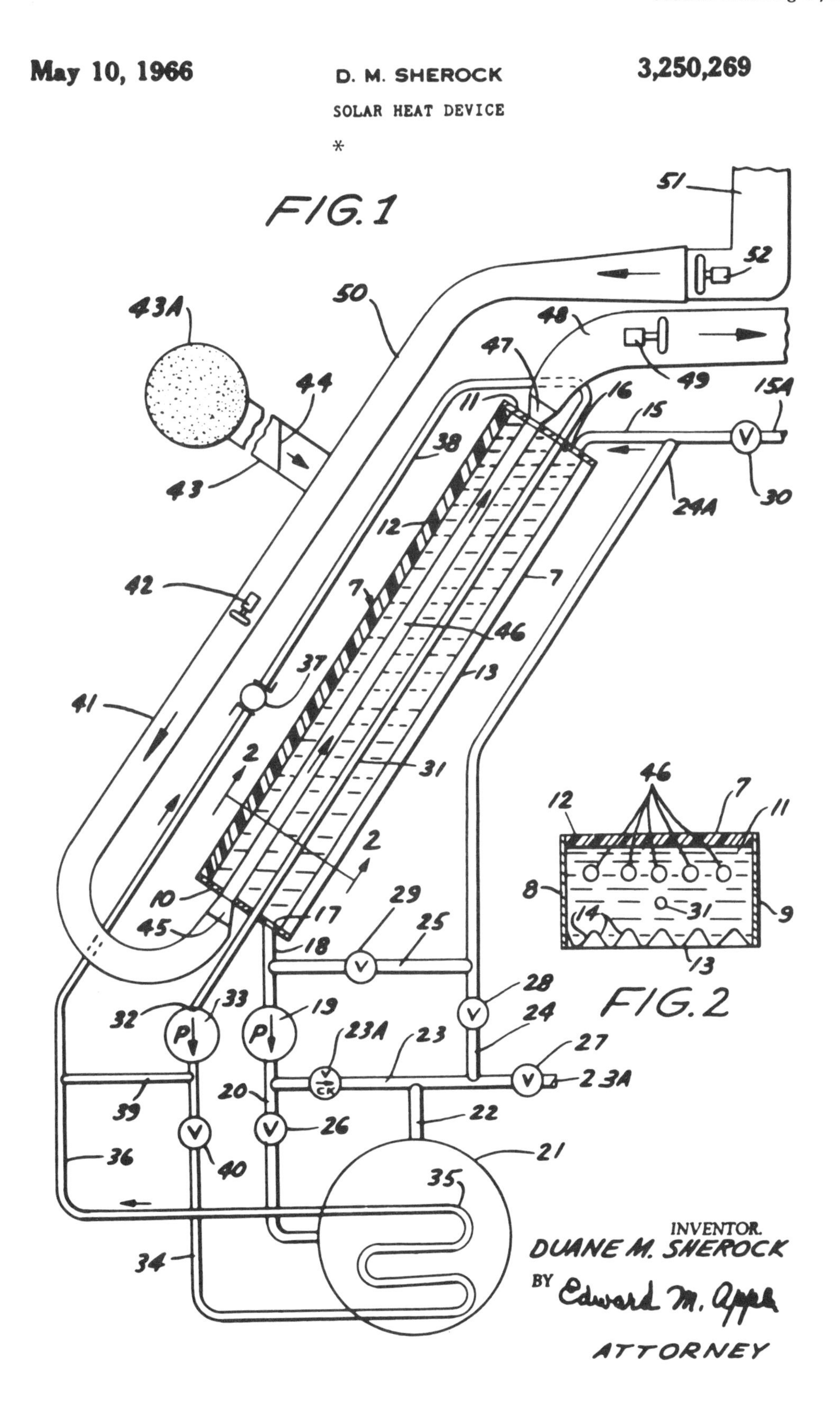

3,250,269
SOLAR HEAT DEVICE

Duane M. Sherock, 32190 Five Mile Road,
Livonia, Mich.

*

This invention relates to solar heat devices and has particular reference to a solar heat system suitable for heating the interior of a building.

Another object of the invention is to provide a device of the character indicated which is constructed and arranged to utilize solar radiation for heating the interior of a building, with means for storing the heat when not called for and means for providing delayed heat exchange.

Another object of the invention is to provide a solar heat exchange system which employs both air and a liquid in the heat exchange cycles.

Another object of the invention is to provide a solar heat exchange system which employs both air and a liquid in the heat exchange cycles with storage means for delayed action in the heat exchange during certain phases thereof.

Another object of the invention is to generally improve solar heating devices, and to provide a device of that character which is simple in construction, economical to manufacture and efficient in operation.

The foregoing and other objects and advantages of the invention will become more apparent as the description proceeds, reference being made from time to time to the accompanying drawing, forming part of the within disclosure, in which drawing:

FIG. 1 is a schematic view, with parts in section, of a device embodying the invention.

FIG. 2 is a section taken substantially on the line 2—2 of FIG. 1.

Referring now more particularly to the drawings, it will be understood that in the embodiment herein disclosed, the reference character 7 indicates in general a substantially rectangular housing, which is provided with side walls 8 and 9 (FIG. 2), end walls 10 and 11 (FIG. 1), and a top wall 12, which is preferably made of glass, or a suitable plastic material, and a bottom wall 13 which has an undulating cross section, as shown in FIG. 2, and is made of a highly reflective material to provide a plurality of reflective surfaces 14, which are arranged to reflect the sun's rays in a number of directions on the interior of the receptacle 7. The bottom surface of the wall 13 is preferably painted black.

The members 8, 9, 10, 11, 12 and 13, are secured together by any suitable means to provide an airtight receptacle 7.

The receptacle 7 is positioned in a suitable opening in the roof of the building (not shown) intended to be heated, so that the rays of the sun, as long as it is shining, may strike and pass through the wall 12, and be reflected back into the receptacle 7 by the wall 13, whereby to heat the interior of the receptacle 7 and a suitable liquid, preferably having a low boiling point, with which the receptacle 7 is filled.

The liquid is supplied to the interior of the receptacle 7 through the liquid intake pipe 15, which extends through a sealed opening 16 formed in the end wall 11.

The liquid is withdrawn from the receptacle 7 through a sealed opening 17, formed in the end wall 10, which opening communicates with the pipe 18, which comprises part of one of the liquid circuits hereinafter described.

A pump 19 circulates the liquid through the receptacle 7, the pipes 18 and 20, the latter being connected to a liquid storage container 21. The liquid flows from the liquid storage container 21 through the pipe 22, and into the pipes 23 and 24, the latter connecting to the pipe 15 as at 24A. The pipes 18 and 24 are connected by a pipe 25.

The pipe 23 is provided with a check valve 23A so that the liquid may flow in only one direction in the pipe 23.

The pipes 15, 20, 23, 24 and 25 are provided with solenoid valves, respectively indicated by the reference characters 26, 27, 28, 29 and 30, in order to control the flow of liquid therein as hereinafter described. The ends 15A and 23A of the pipes 15 and 23 are connected to suitable radiators (not shown) which are located in the area to be heated.

The elements 15–30 are all located in the primary liquid circuit which is employed in the device.

I also provide a secondary liquid circuit which I will now describe.

The secondary liquid circuit consists of a pipe 31 which extends through the interior of the housing 7, and is surrounded by the liquid in the housing 7 and in the primary liquid circuit. The pipe 31 passes through the ends 10 and 11 of the receptacle 7 and is sealed so that none of the liquid in the receptacle 7 may leak around the pipe 31.

The pipe 31 connects as at 32 to a pump 33, which pump 33 is connected to a line 34, which in turn connects to a coil 35 positioned in the liquid storage container 21.

The coil 35 is connected at its opposite end with a pipe 36, which is connected at one side to a generator 37. The opposite side of the generator 37 is connected to a pipe 38, which in turn is connected to the pipe 31 to complete the secondary liquid circuit.

By-pass line 39 connects between the pipes 34 and 36 and is controlled by means of a solenoid valve 40.

In addition to the two liquid circuits which I have described, the device is also provided with an air circuit which consists of the main conduit 41 in which is positioned a fan 42, and which communicates with a stack 43, open to atmosphere, which stack 43 is provided with a damper 44. The stack 43 is intended to supply the conduit 41 with fresh air as occasion demands. The air entering the stack 43 is pre-heated as it passes through a perforated dome 43A, which is made of a heat collecting material and is positioned to receive the direct rays of the sun.

The lower end of the conduit 41 connects to a header 45, which is secured to the end 10 of the receptacle 7. The header 45 is sealed so that there is no leakage around the same.

The header 45 communicates with a plurality of tubes 46, which extend through the interior of the housing 7 (FIG. 2). The tubes 46 are surrounded by the liquid in the receptacle 7 and receive the sun's rays, passing through the wall 12 and reflected from the wall 13.

The opposite ends of the tubes 46 are connected to a similar header 47, which is secured to the end wall 11 of the receptacle 7, and is sealed therefrom as previously described.

The header 47 is connected to an air conduit 48, which in turn connects with suitable hot air registers (not shown) provided in the area to be heated. The hot air conduit 48 is provided with a fan, or blower, 49 to help move the air.

The conduit 41 beyond the stack 43 connects to a conduit 50, which in turn connects to a cold air duct 51, which picks up the cold air from the area being heated. The cold air duct 51 may or may not be provided with a fan 52 to help move the air.

The device functions as follows. The primary and secondary liquid circuits are first charged with a suitable liquid after the receptacle is positioned and hooked up as previously described. Rays from the sun pass through the wall 12 and are reflected back by the wall 13, causing the temperature of the liquid in the liquid circuits to rise. At the same time, air passing through the conduit 41 and pipes 46 is likewise heated. The fluid in the primary circuit picks up the heat and carries it to the radiators positioned in the area to be heated. When sufficient heat is provided in the area to be heated, the solenoid valves 27 and 30 are closed so that the heated liquid remains in the closed circuit through the liquid storage container 21 where the heat may be stored until called for.

With the proper control of the solenoid valves 26, 28 and 29 the liquid may be circulated through the short circuits provided by the pipes 23 and 25 until the liquid is exceedingly warm, at which time it may then be diverted into the liquid storage container 21.

It will be understood that the liquid storage container 21 is properly insulated to retain the heat therein.

When the sun goes down and the temperature falls in the area to be heated, the solenoid valves will then open to permit the circuit to be completed through the container 21, so that the heat stored therein may be utilized in the area to be heated.

The secondary liquid circuit through the pipes 31, 34, 36 is used to heat the coil 35 which in turn helps to heat the liquid in the liquid storage receptacle 21. The coil 35 may be by-passed through the pipe 39 by closing the valve 40 so that the full flow of the liquid through the secondary circuit and its heat exchange potential may be employed to operate the generator 37.

From the foregoing it will be seen that I have disclosed a solar heat exchange device which employs several liquid circuits as well as an air circuit. *

Jan. 24, 1967 H. R. HAY **3,299,589**

APPARATUS FOR MODULATING THE TEMPERATURE WITHIN ENCLOSURES

* *

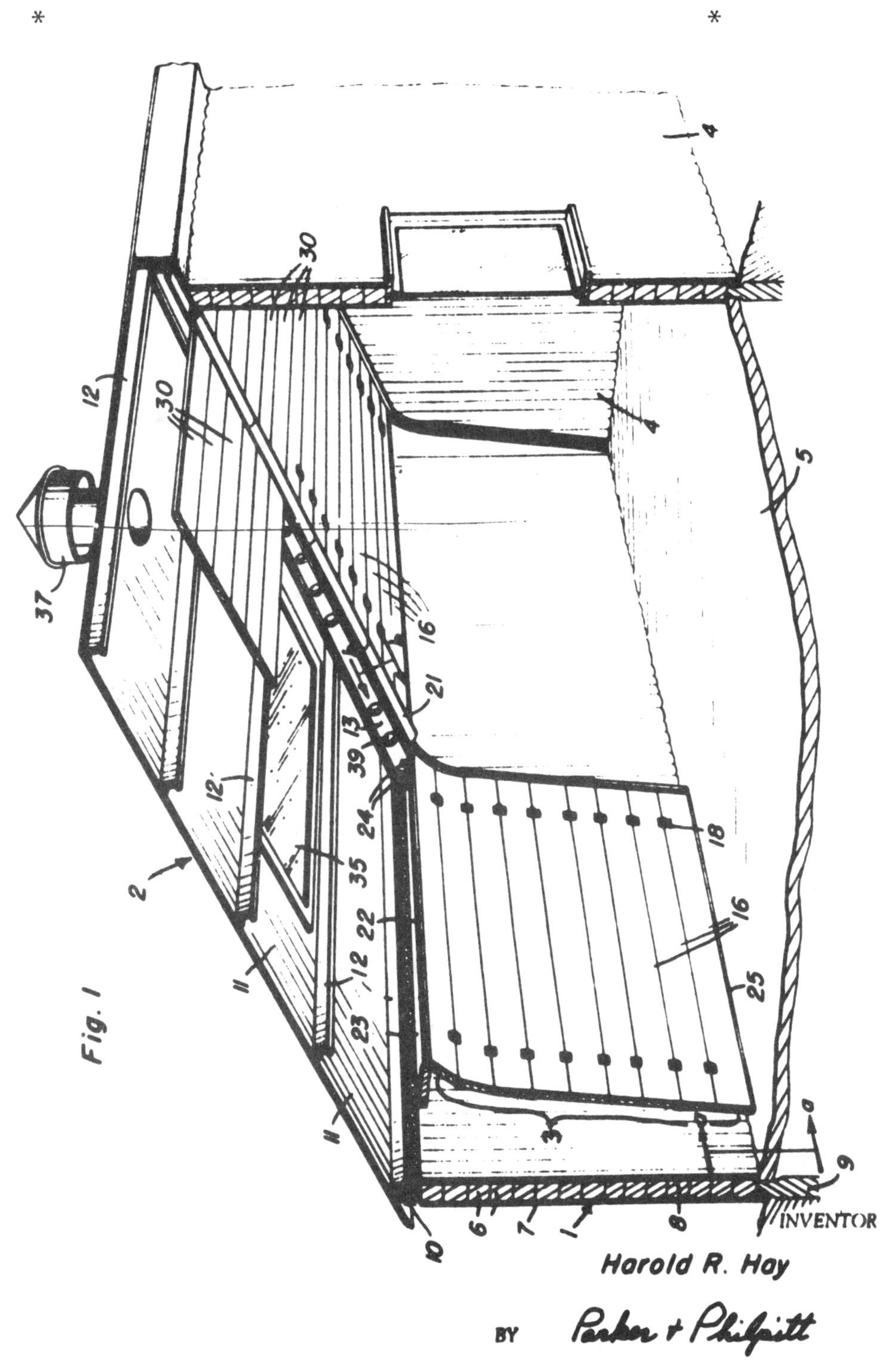

BY Parker + Philpitt

ATTORNEY

Jan. 24, 1967 H. R. HAY **3,299,589**

APPARATUS FOR MODULATING THE TEMPERATURE WITHIN ENCLOSURES

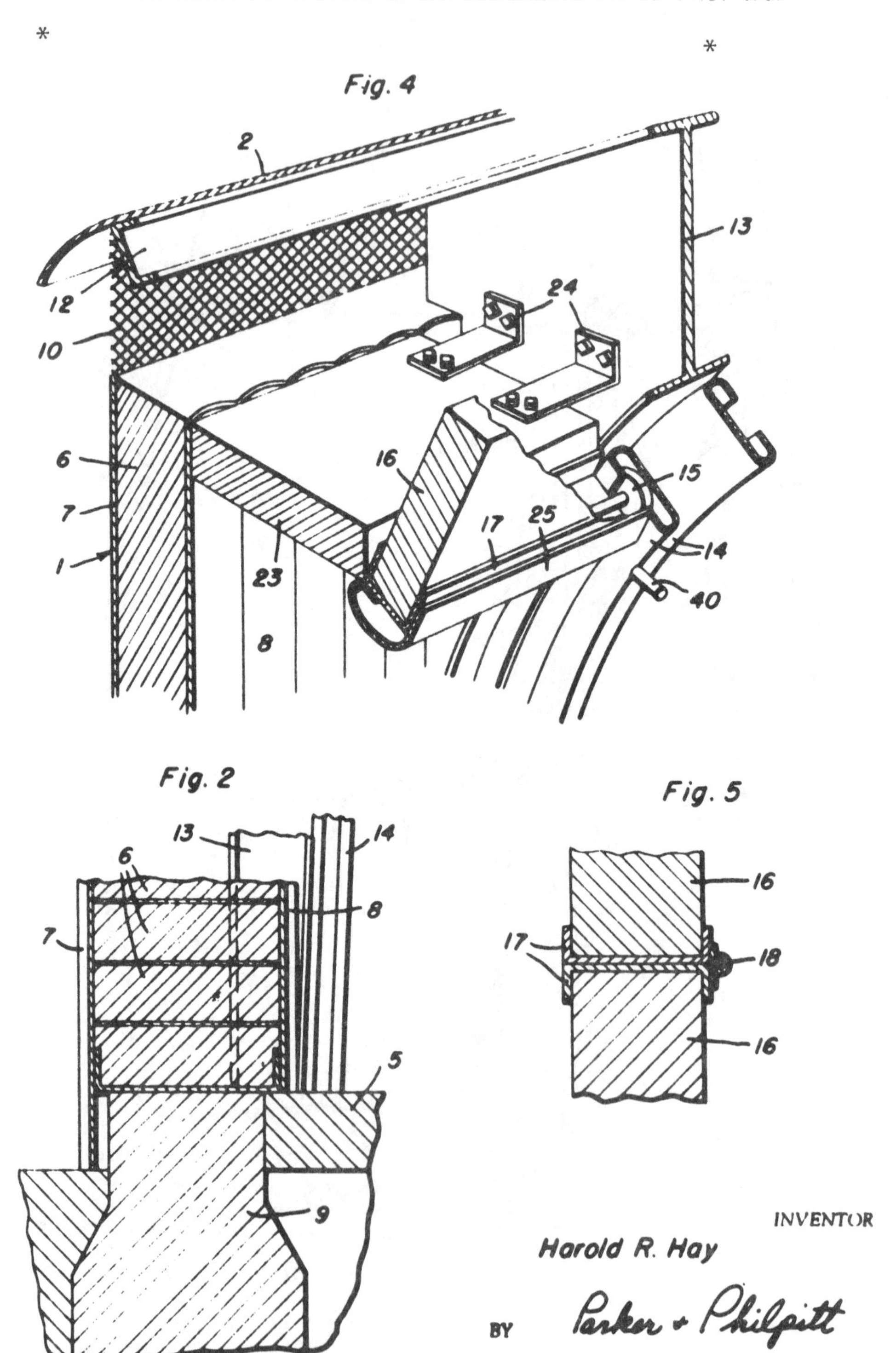

ATTORNEY

Jan. 24, 1967 H. R. HAY **3,299,589**

APPARATUS FOR MODULATING THE TEMPERATURE [illegible]

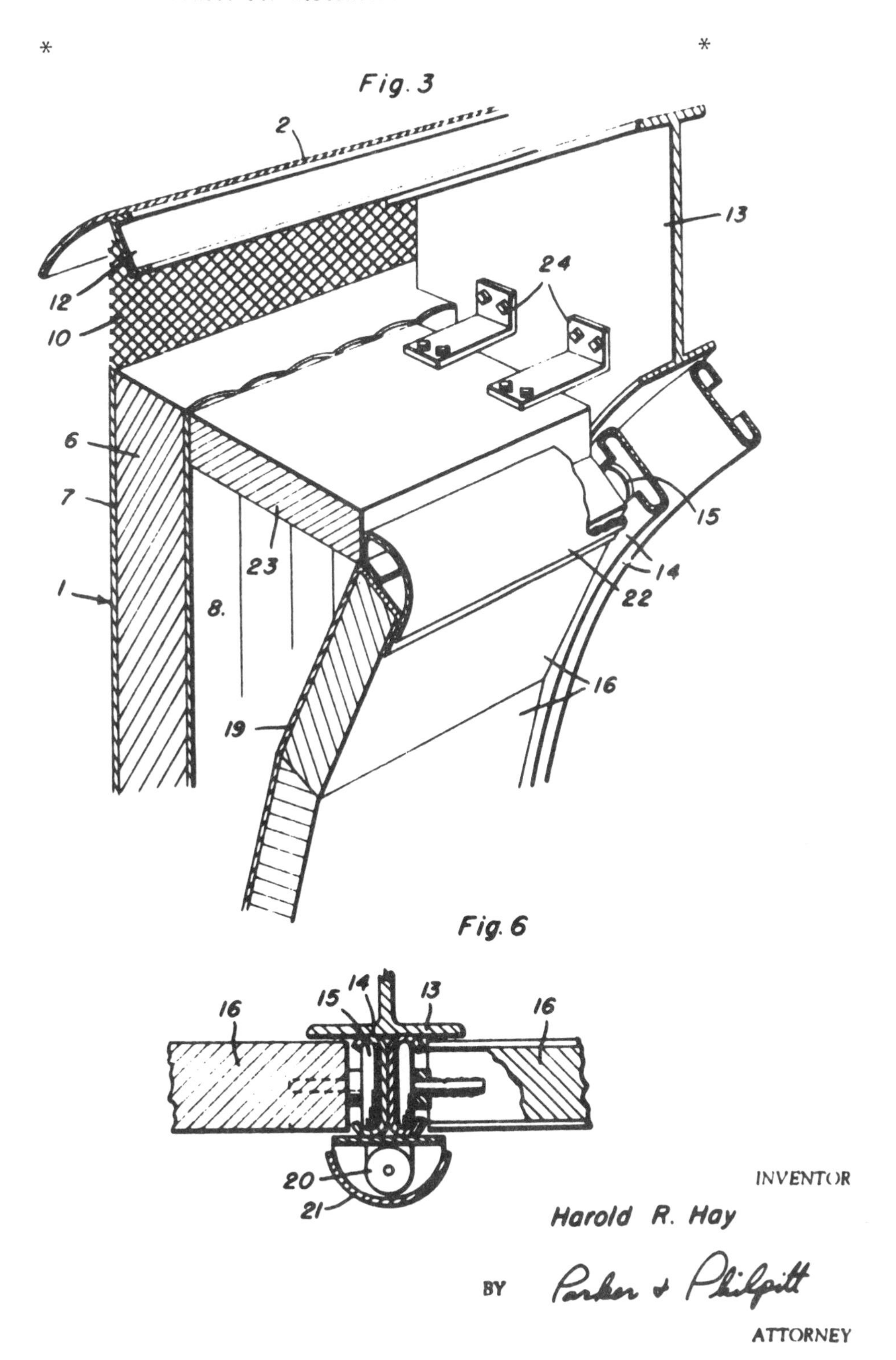

Jan. 24, 1967 H. R. HAY **3,299,589**

APPARATUS FOR MODULATING THE TEMPERATURE WITHIN ENCLOSURES

* *

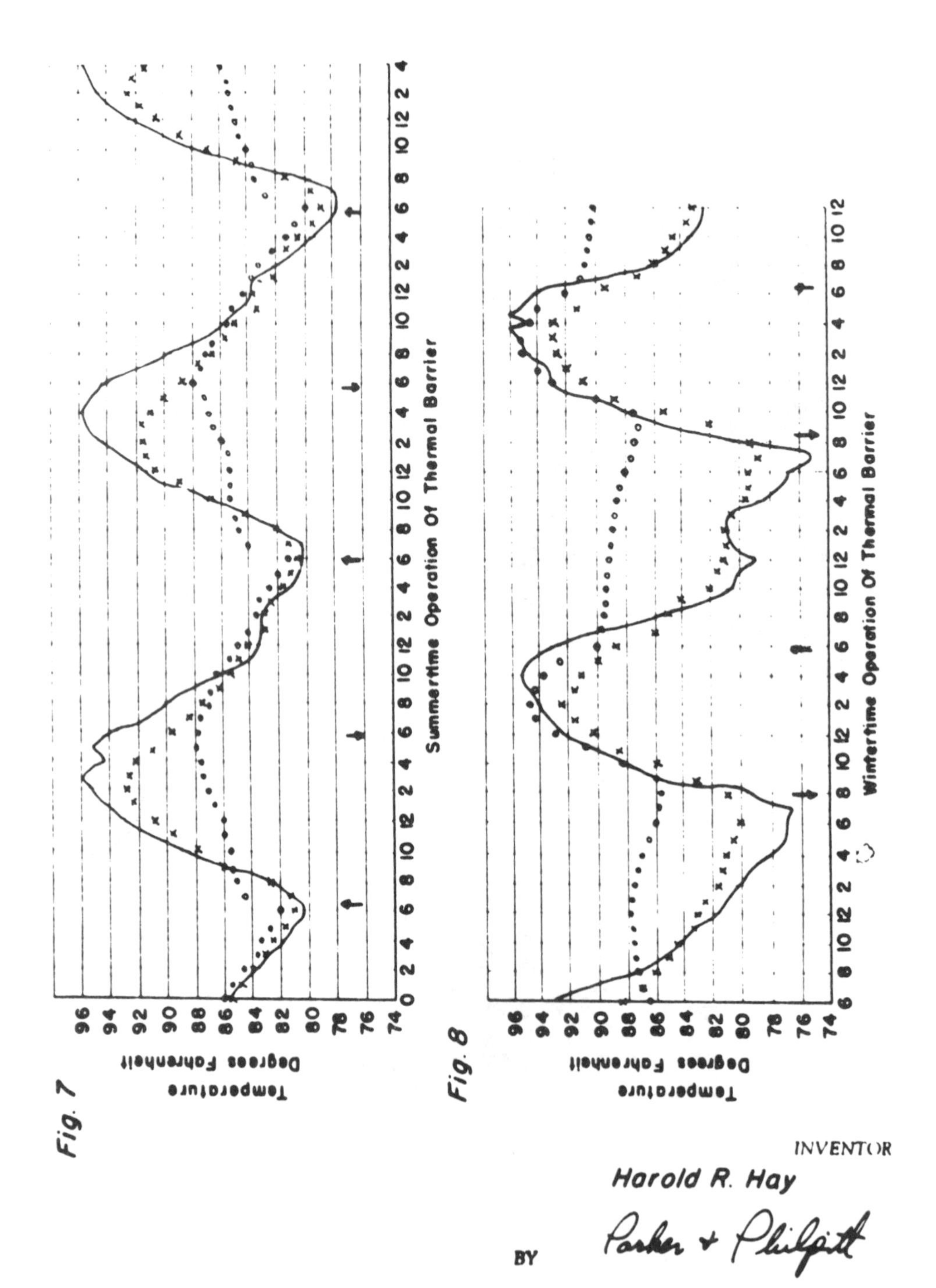

INVENTOR
Harold R. Hay

BY *Parker + Philpitt*

ATTORNEY

Jan. 24, 1967 H. R. HAY **3,299,589**

APPARATUS FOR MODULATING THE TEMPERATURE WITHIN ENCLOSURES

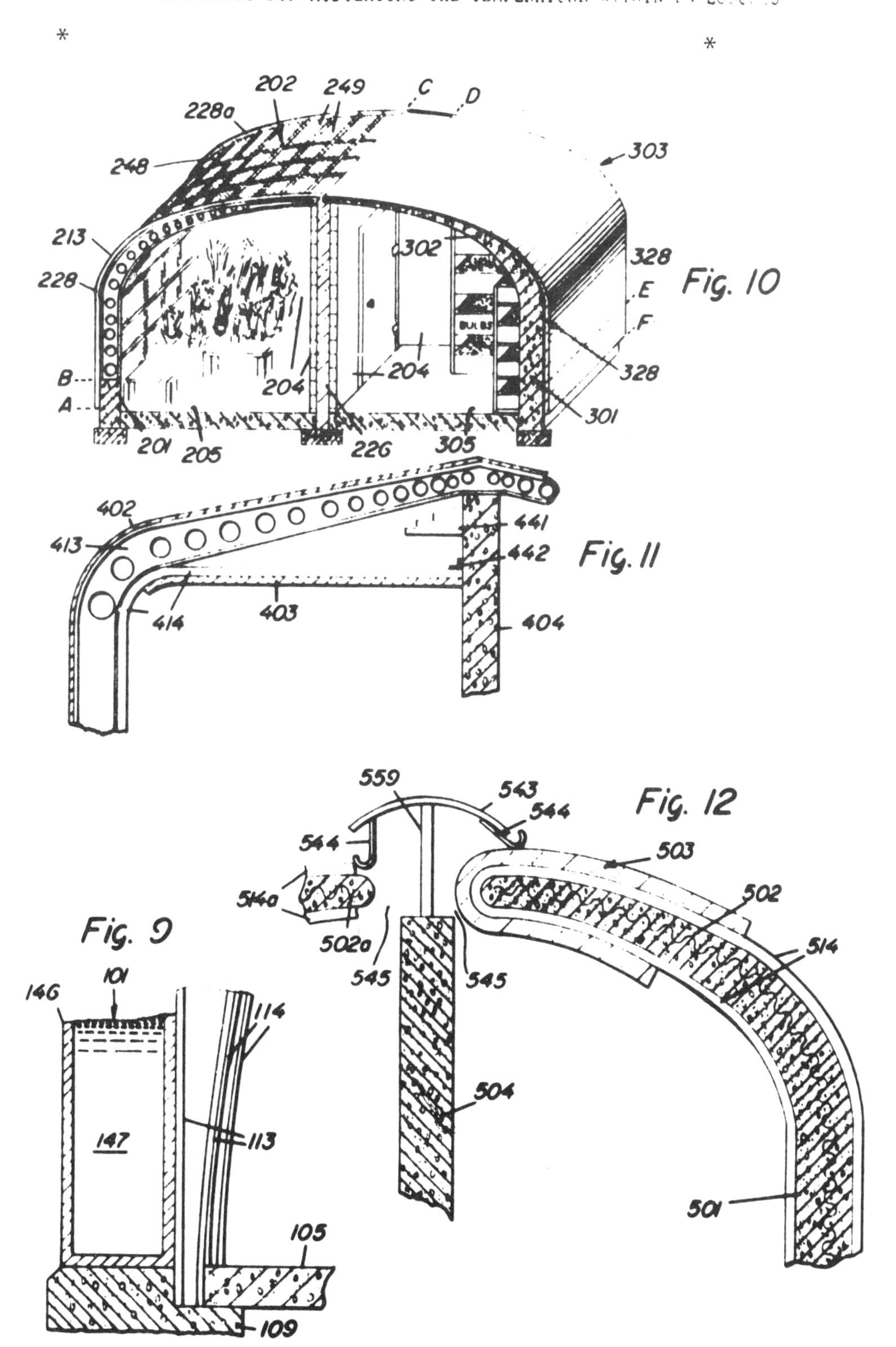

Jan. 24, 1967 H. R. HAY 3,299,589

APPARATUS FOR MODULATING THE TEMPERATURE WITHIN ENCLOSURES

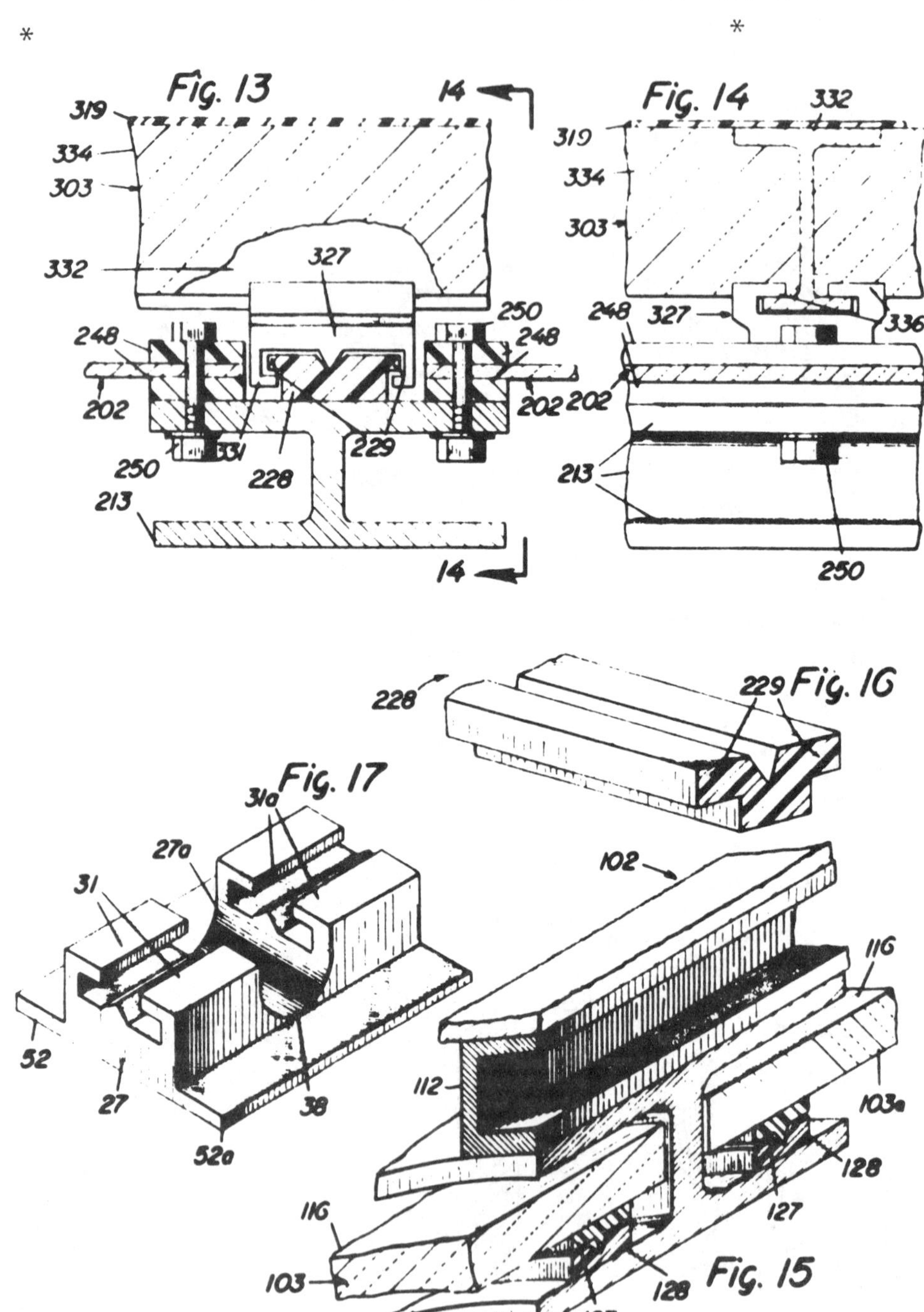

3,299,589
APPARATUS FOR MODULATING THE TEMPERATURE WITHIN ENCLOSURES
Harold R. Hay, 795 Roble, Menlo Park, Calif. 94025

*

This invention is subject to a reservation by the United States Government of a non-exclusive, irrevocable, and royalty-free license with power to grant licenses for all governmental purposes.

This invention generally relates to an apparatus for modulating the temperature within enclosures. More particularly this invention relates to a thermal valve means incorporated into an enclosure so that by simple manual or automatic manipulation of the thermal valve means the temperature within the enclosure as a whole or the temperature of various individual components or contents of the enclosure may be regulated to suit the objectives for which the enclosure is intended.

In one particular embodiment, this invention relates to a novel thermal valve means incorporated into a house and operated in such a manner as to maintain the internal temperature of the house as closely as possible to the most comfortable of the daily external temperatures, said novel thermal valve means consisting primarily of standard building components, the relative location of which within the enclosure may be varied at will and in consonance with external changes in the daily temperature.

In another embodiment, the thermal valve means forms part of a farm structure for the protection of animals. In yet another embodiment the thermal valve means modulates temperatures in a greenhouse and may simultaneously modulate temperatures in an adjacent building or room intended for the storage of vegetables. A similar thermal valve means may be incorporated into a solar still, as disclosed in a co-pending application, wherein it materially influences the rate of distillation of a distilland. Moreover, the thermal valve means may influence the evaporation of water from wet materials such as grain and lumber when they are confined within an enclosure designed as a solar drier of which the thermal valve means is a part. Said thermal valve means may further be adapted to solar water heaters so as to maintain desirable temperatures therein. It is irrelevant in what form of enclosure, or for what purpose, the temperature modulation is achieved by means of my invention.

Before proceeding with descriptions of these embodiments of the invention, attention is directed to certain fundamental propositions which will facilitate an understanding of the detailed description hereinafter made.

It has been historic and current practice to build houses and other building structures from components such as walls, ceilings, roofs and floors which remain permanently fixed in their positional relationship to one another. Thermal comfort within such structures has heretofore been maintained either by a combination of structural design with mechanical and electrical devices such as fans, heaters and air conditioners or through structural design alone. In hot and dry areas, thermal comfort in structures is obtained using walls 18 to 36 inches thick to maintain within the structure a temperature which approaches the average of the external daily variation. Massive walls of this type are costly and the average temperature obtained in this manner is not always as comfortable as the more comfortable of the two extremes. It often would be a distinct advantage to maintain internal structure temperatures nearer the external night temperature during the summer months and nearer the external day temperature during the winter months. Hitherto, structural materials used alone have not attained these objectives.

Today, in most areas of the world, one may compensate for the deficiencies of historic design of structures by adding fireplaces, electric heaters and air conditioners for temperature adjustment in the rooms and fans to increase air movement which lowers body temperature by increasing evaporation. However, these means of obtaining comfort are costly in initial investment, in continuing fuel or power requirements and in maintenance. They cannot be afforded, in some countries, by many families in the lower income levels nor can they be used economically where fuel and electric power are not readily available as in deserts, on mountain tops or in remote areas.

In modern times, many low density materials have been developed and applied by various means to building structures or other objects requiring insulation, thus obviating the use of massive construction. It has been characteristic of the application of this low density insulation that it is fixed in a definite and permanent relation to one or another of the components of the structure such as the side walls or the roof. I have found that there is not only a disadvantage in having said insulation affixed to said components during a part of the day, but that differing components can be either benefited or detrimentally affected by insulation at the same time during the day and that a movable thermal barrier of said insulation can be positioned alternately in differing locations so as to be useful in relation to components requiring insulation while avoiding effect upon components which at that particular time should be free from insulation in order to produce the optimum thermal characteristics within the building structure. I have found that when this movable thermal barrier is combined with building components of ancient or modern types to be described, and when these components of the building structure are oriented properly with respect to the seasonal path of the sun and when the movable thermal barrier is positioned in concordance with the daily path of the sun, a unique effect may be had upon the temperatures within the building structure.

In my invention it is usually characteristic that the movement of the thermal barrier means causes it to be importantly useful in its various possible positionings during portions of the day which are unlike by virtue of solar radiation or temperature. The effective thermal barrier may even act in different capacities during such unlike portions of the day or it may act in relation to different components of the structure and it generally serves a beneficial function in a thermal process in each of its possible positionings.

This invention is herein broadly related to devices for collecting solar energy, for its storage and for control over its dissipation in a manner to add to comfort or to the utility of mankind. While this invention is disclosed with particular reference to maintaining within a building structure temperatures comfortable to life or favorable for the preservation of foods and other products deleteriously affected by excessively high or low temperatures and while it is also disclosed with particular reference to the production of potable water from saline or brackish water, and it can be applied to the drying of grain or lumber, because of the particular utility in these fields as will hereinafter appear, it is expressly understood that the invention is not restricted thereto.

The primary object of this invention is to provide an improved device for controlling the collection and loss of solar energy characterized by low-cost production, operation and maintenance.

Another object of this invention is to provide an improved device for building structures for collecting and storing solar heat during winter months as a continuing source of heat during cold nights while also operating to minimize the effects of the collection and storage of heat during summer months.

Another object of this invention is to provide an improved device for controlling either the collection of solar heat or the prevention of heat loss from storage characterized by the capacity to maintain the temperature of the interior of the structure or of components of the structure or of materials or objects within the structure at the most optimum portion of the diurnal cycle of approximately one half of the day while modulating the temperature during the remainder of the day so as to prevent deleterious effects of adverse thermal conditions.

Another object of the invention is to provide improved natural lighting and improved acoustical conditions within the structure in which this invention is employed while simultaneously controlling the collection and loss of solar heat.

It is another object of this invention to provide comparatively simple and inexpensive means for modulating the temperature within an enclosure.

It is an added object of this invention to provide a measure of heat control within an enclosure by moving well-known building components into different positional relationships with respect to each other dependent upon the changes in the external temperature.

Another object of this invention is to provide a movable thermal valve means within a building structure which can be alternately moved into positional relationship with either the roof or the side wall of the building structure so as to thereby at least partially affect the rate at which heat either enters or leaves the building structure.

An additional object of this invention is to affect thermally sensitive objects and processes such as evaporation, distillation, heat storage or transfer, and all such processes as are influenced by thermal change within an enclosure. Other objects and advantages of the present invention will become more apparent after reading the following descriptions taken in conjunction with the drawings.

The invention is capable of receiving a variety of mechanical expressions illustrated on the accompanying drawings. * For clarity, the description relating to a building structure as illustrated in FIGURES 1 to 17 inclusive will be separated from the description relating to the control of temperatures or processes within specialized enclosures.

A. THERMAL MODULATION IN A BUILDING STRUCTURE

The following description of the invention relates to a building structure in which:

FIGURE 1 is a front cut-away perspective view of a building structure containing the novel apparatus according to this invention;

FIGURE 2 is an enlarged diagrammatic sectional view of the footing and lower side of the wall, taken along line *a—a* of FIGURE 1;

FIGURE 3 is an enlarged perspective view of the wall seal and insulation panel means of FIGURE 1;

FIGURE 4 is another enlarged perspective view of the wall seal and insulation panel, when the panel is in its uppermost position;

FIGURE 5 is an enlarged diagrammatic view of the hinge portion of the mounting for the insulation panel shown in FIGURE 1;

FIGURE 6 is an enlarged diagrammatic sectional view of the trackways and associated structure taken along line *b—b* of FIGURE 1;

FIGURES 7 and 8 are temperature variation charts;

FIGURE 9 is a diagrammatic sectional view of an embodiment in which the high heat capacity wall 101 is composed of a liquifiable material 147 confined within metal 146;

FIGURE 10 is a perspective sectional representation of another embodiment of the invention in which the enclosure is divided into compartments and in which the movable thermal barrier is moved externally from an effective area substantially covering the first compartment to an effective area substantially covering the second compartment;

FIGURE 11 is a fragmentary diagrammatic sectional view of a further embodiment of the invention in which the movable insulation **403** is positioned by means of a trackway located near the high thermal capacity wall or substantially parallel to the floor at a considerable distance from the roof portion **402**;

FIGURE 12 is a fragmentary diagrammatic sectional view of still another embodiment of the invention in which the movable thermal barrier 503 can be positioned alternately on the exterior or the interior portion of the enclosure;

FIGURE 13 is a sectional and partially cut-away view showing one means, a knife-edge runner, for moving the movable thermal barrier, mounted externally on the enclosure;

FIGURE 14 is a sectional view of FIGURE 13 taken along line **14—14** of FIGURE 13;

FIGURE 15 is a diagramamtic sectional representation of a means for moving a plurality of the movable thermal barriers on the inside of a structure by means of knife-edge runners;

FIGURE 16 is a fragmentary sectional and perspective view of a grooved trackway suitable for use with a knife-edge runner as a means for moving the movable thermal barrier;

FIGURE 17 is a perspective view of a dual knife-edge runner of flexible material suitable, in combination with the grooved trackway of FIGURE 16, for moving the movable thermal barrier when connected thereto and also serving as a hinge for separate panels constituting said thermal barrier.

In its simplest form, as embodied in a building structure, this invention usually utilizes three separate and distinct building elements or components having quite different heat transfer characteristics. When these three different building elements are properly incorporated into the design of a building they form a thermal valve means which may be manipulated manually or automatically in relation to the time of day so as to maintain the temperature within the building as close as is possible to the more comfortable of the daily extremes of temperature. These three building elements or components are as follows:

(1) *The high thermal capacity wall*

In accordance with one embodiment of this invention, shown as the building structure in FIGURE 1, the building structure should have at least one substantially vertical wall 1 composed primarily of high thermal capacity material. Said wall should also have moderate thermal transfer characteristics and should preferably be oriented to obtain a southern exposure in the northern hemisphere and a northern exposure in the southern hemisphere. The high thermal capacity wall 1 may consist of brick, stone, adobe, rock, concrete, or other similar materials, or mixtures thereof. The interior and exterior faces of said wall may be finished with a comparatively thin layer of plaster, stucco, concrete, paint, etc., if desired to improve appearance or weather resistance. The interior and/or exterior faces may be sheathed with metal, plastic, thin plywood, hardboard or such other materials as do not substantially alter the thermal characteristics of said wall. In certain circumstances, one might use, instead of the above-described materials, a wall consisting of two opposed metal panels which confine between them either a fluid of high thermal capacity as shown in FIGURE 9 (such as water or solar heat collecting chemicals of the type of sodium sulfate decahydrate, sodium thiosulfate pentahydrate, etc.), or a loose particulate mass of high thermal capacity material (refractory dust, granules or powders).

It is preferred in the type of structure shown in FIG-

URE 1, that the high thermal capacity wall 1 should be of such thickness that it will provide about a twelve-hour heat lag in attaining maximum or minimum temperature by heat transfer from one face to another. Brick, stone, concrete or earth walls of approximately thirteen inches in thickness have been found generally to be most suitable, although a thickness range of as wide as between three and twenty inches may be satisfactory under varied conditions and in diverse localities.

Normally, the type of high thermal capacity wall described above would produce less comfort than a more costly thicker wall and this discomfort could ordinarily only be lessened by means of fireplaces, heaters, fans or air conditioners.

(II) *The roof*

In accordance with this invention as applied to the building structure shown in FIGURE 1, the building structure should have a roof 2 constructed of a material having little resistance to heat transfer and little thermal capacity. Thin sheets of either metal or glass are preferred, but in some instances roofing consisting of asbestos-cement, plastic or similar material so manufactured to have little resistance to heat transfer may be used. The roof 2 preferably should be low with relation to the floor so as to minimize the cubic volume of the room and should be sloping so as to expose the maximum amount of its surface to the southern exposure in the northern hemisphere or the maximum surface to northern exposure in the southern hemisphere. This type of roof has heretofore been considered undesirable for building structures because under normal circumstances it would produce uncomfortably warm internal temperatures during summer daytime hours and uncomfortably cool temperatures during winter nighttime hours.

(III) *Movable thermal barrier*

In accordance with the embodiment of FIGURE 1, a building structure should have what can aptly be generally referred to as a thermal valve 3 and which can be referred to more specifically as a movable thermal barrier 3. Said barrier is preferably composed of low density sheets, panels or blocks of fairly rigid or semi-rigid insulation having low heat capacity and low thermal transfer characteristics. The insulation material may be of the rigid type, such as the vegetable fiber product known by the trade name "Celotex," or it may be cork, balsa wood, foamed glass, foamed polystyrene. The insulation also may be of the semi-rigid type such as batts of wood fiber, mineral wool, glass wool, or the foamed products of rubber, polyurethane, or other plastic or resin materials.

Movable thermal barrier 3 likewise may be formed from non-rigid materials such as mineral wool, glass fiber or wood fiber loose-fill insulations held in flexible cloth, paper or other containers, or from aluminum foil, plastic sheets or other reflective insulation alone or in combination with other insulators. The insulating material may be of the non-rigid type confined within or bonded to a suitable material or in some foreign countries it may consist of woven grass, pithy materials or even plant seeds having cotton-like hairs. The combination of rigid and non-rigid insulating materials, some or all of which may be transparent or translucent, is likewise contemplated.

The above-described material in the movable thermal barrier 3 contrasts with the high thermal capacity wall 1 in that the thermal barrier has a much lower thermal capacity and lower heat transfer characteristics and it contrasts with the roof 2 in that the thermal barrier has a much lower rate of heat transfer. It is these distinguishing properties of the movable thermal barrier which allow it to function effectively as a thermal valve in the building structure embodiment of FIGURE 1.

For the structure shown in FIGURE 1, the movable thermal barrier 3 should be mounted inside the building structure in such a manner that it can be alternately positioned closely adjacent either the inside of high-density wall 1, which has a partially controlled thermal flow or in near proximity to roof 2, which has an essentially uncontrolled thermal flow. When the barrier 3 is so mounted it can act as a thermal valve, in the sense that it is able to control the flow of heat into and out of the building structure. The various ways in which the movable thermal barrier may be mounted so as to achieve these ends will be discussed more fully hereinafter.

(IV) *Other elements of the structure*

In accordance with this invention, as shown in FIGURE 1, the other three walls of the building structure may be constructed of the same material as the high thermal capacity wall 1 or of any other suitable material. High thermal capacity walls are preferred, but where considerations of economy, appearance, design, etc. make the use of such walls impractical or unfeasible, other types of walls having a lower density and a lower thermal capacity may be used as long as it is realized that the temperature cannot be controlled within the same desired limits as if high thermal capacity walls were employed.

The building structure may have a floor of any well-known type. The greater the insulation between the earth and the interior of the building structure, the smaller will be thermal flow to and from the earth and the heat storage in the earth. Poured concrete is preferred, although wooden flooring can also be used.

The above description of the various elements of my invention will be clearer after reading the following description taken in conjunction with the drawings:

FIGURE 1 is a cut-away perspective view of a building structure in accordance with this invention. This structure comprises a substantially vertical high thermal capacity wall 1 constructed of a plurality of stacked bricks or of concrete blocks 6. A roof 2 has its lower edge supported by the upper portion of wall 1 while the opposite end of roof 2 slopes upwardly and away from the top of said wall. A movable thermal barrier 3 is disposed within the building structure. Two other walls 4 are shown, which together with a fourth wall (not shown) and a floor 5 complete the building structure except for doors (not shown) and windows (partially shown).

As shown, the high density wall 1 has outer and inner faces covered and protected by sheath material 7 and 8 which preferably consists of plaster or stucco, of tile, or of rather thin elongated sheets of metallic or plastic material joined to the high density wall by bolts, wires, screws, nails, cement, etc. The plurality of stacked blocks 6 is supported on any suitable type of foundation or footing 9 (see FIGURE 2).

Near the top of the high thermal capacity wall 1 suitable transverse support means in the form of purlins 12 bearing on I-beam frame 13 can be provided for the lower edge of roof 2. In the drawings, ventilation eave 10 has been shown which permits ventilation between the inside and outside of the building structure. The ventilation eave 10 has not been found to be a necessary component of the building structure but its use is recommended. A similar ventilation strip near the upper edge of roof 2 is also desirable and may be used in lieu of the roof ventilator 37.

In the illustrated embodiment, roof 2 consists of a plurality of overlapping metal sheets which are supported and fastened to a number of transverse roof members 12 which run lengthwise across the entire upper portion of the building structure. The roof supporting members 12 are shown as being supported by the upper edge of I-shaped beams 13. Beams 13 are firmly anchored at their lower extremities in a suitable foundation, preferably concrete. The number of I-shaped beams which are used in any given building structure will depend upon the size of the building structure and upon the size of each of the movable thermal barriers 3 to be used within the building structure. The lower or inner edge of I-shaped beam 13 is adapted to serve as a base or anchoring point for one or more trackways within which rollers attached to any desired portion of thermal barrier 3 are adapted to travel.

As shown, movable thermal barrier 3 consists of a plurality of elongated and essentially rigid string of lightweight insulation material or frames of supported non-rigid insulation material 16. The strips of insulation material 16 may be joined to form barrier 3 in a number of ways readily recognized by those skilled in the art. For instance, the individual insulating panels 16 may be joined by suitable receiving brackets 17 and piano type hinges 18 (see FIGURE 5) or panels 16 may be made to adhere to a continuous flexible backing of fabric or metallic material 19, as for instance sheet aluminum (see FIGURE 3) by use of an adhesive. Alternatively insulating panels 16 may have their faces joined to a continuous facing fabric or flexible metallic material and the backs of said insulating panels (i.e. that surface of the panel nearest the outside of the building structure) may be provided with non-continuous aluminum foil which serves a reflective insulation function.

As shown in FIGURE 6, the rollers 15 are preferably mounted directly in the end sections of insulating panels 16 by any suitable mounting means. Rollers 15 could just as well be mounted either on backing material 19 of FIG. 3 or on a portion of insulation supporting brackets 17 of FIGURE 5.

If so desired, lighting means may be arranged below trackway 14. This is best illustrated in FIGURES 1 and 6 by the numeral 20 representing a light source and numeral 21 representing a light shade or diffusor. Other lighting arrangements can of course be employed.

The upper horizontal edge of the upper insulation panel 16 preferably contains a flexible sealing element 22 (as is best shown in FIGURE 3); the purpose of element 22 is to provide, in conjunction with stationary wall seal 23, an effective seal when movable thermal barrier 3 is in its lower position so that air contained between thermal barrier 3 and high thermal capacity wall 1 cannot move from this area into the interior of the building structure by convection or otherwise. Wall seal 23 is preferably permanently fixed at a position either near the top of wall 1 or near the lower portion of roof 2, and as best shown by FIGURE 3, wall seal 23 may be maintained in position by one or more brackets 24 attached to I-shaped beam 13 or to the walls. Seal 22 preferably consists of a flexible fold of plastic, leather, rubber, or similar material. More elaborate and equivalent sealing means will suggest themselves to those skilled in the art (e.g. foam rubber bumpers, etc.).

Referring now to FIGURE 4, a similar sealing means 25 is shown on the lower horizontal edge of the lowest panel member 16. When movable thermal barrier 3 is in its uppermost position and essentially parallel to the roof 2, the seal 25 in conjunction with permanent wall seal 23 serves to restrict movement of air between thermal barrier 3 and roof 2 into the interior of the building structure.

Referring again to FIGURE 1, it will be seen that the I-shaped beam 13 can be considered as dividing the building structure into right-hand and left-hand portions. Movable thermal barrier 3 shown on the left side of beam 13 is in its lowermost position. By examining the area to the left of I-shaped beam 13 near the point where the beam joins the upper portion of roof 2, it will be seen that there are a number of permanently positioned insulating panels 30 which extend across the building structure in a generally (but not necessarily) parallel relationship to the upper part of the roof 2. The purpose of fixed panels 30 is to form an extension of the thermal barrier between the roof and the interior of the building structure when the area of movable thermal barrier 3 is not great enough to adequately cover the entire roof area. The manner in which panel 30 and panel 16 cooperate to cover the entire roof area is best seen by observing the area to the right of beam 13. Of course, if the roof area is exactly the same as the area of the high thermal capacity wall, there would be no need for employing stationary panel members 30.

While panels 30 are shown in FIGURE 1 to be fixed, they may also be movable toward the wall opposite that indicated as wall 1 or panels 30 may be hinged independently but operated as a unit to change from a position approximately parallel to the roof (or floor) to a position approximately parallel to the walls, thus exposing the under portion of roof 2 in the area of panels 30.

FIGURE 1 shows that roof 2 may be constructed of more than one material. For example, the roof may contain in addition to the metallic sheets, one or more areas of glass or transparent or translucent materials such as plastics (e.g. skylights) 35 which permit sunshine to enter the interior of the building structure when movable thermal barrier 3 is in its lowermost position. Also the roof may contain one or more ventilating cowls 37 which permit ventilation of the entire building structure or merely of the closed-off area between the roof and the thermal barrier 3 when barrier 3 is in its uppermost position. Alternatively, a ventilation strip of the type 10 at the eaves may be located at the higher edge of the roof or louvres may be provided in the end walls between roof 2 and the position of fixed panels 30 or thermal barrier 3 in its uppermost position. It will further be noted that the I-shaped beam 13 of FIGURE 1 contains a number of circular holes 39 which in some instances have been found desirable to permit cross circulation of air when the movable thermal barriers are in their uppermost positions.

The movable thermal barrier 3 may be either manually or automatically raised and lowered. Said barrier may be maintained in any raised position by means of counterweights or by merely inserting a pin, lug or spike into a hole in a portion of trackway 15 so that the pin, lug or spike 40 (see FIGURE 4) obstructs the downward movement of roller 15 within trackway 14. Other equally suitable means for regulating the position of the movable thermal barrier will readily suggest themselves to those skilled in the art. Said thermal barrier 3 may be raised by either lifting the lowermost insulating panel of the thermal barrier or by pulling on a rope, cable or chain attached to the uppermost panel of the thermal barrier, said rope or chain preferably passing over appropriate pulley arrangements located near the top of the roof so as to minimize effort involved in raising the thermal barrier. Counterweights or spring arrangements and lockable sprockets or other fastening means may be suitably employed.

While the foregoing description has set forth one particular embodiment for carrying out the broad invention herein disclosed, it will be appreciated by those skilled in the art that numerous other and different ways can be devised for carrying out this same basic inventive concept. For example, the thermal barrier could consist of a single large rigid panel hingeably mounted near the junction of the high density wall and the roof. The thermal barrier would then merely swing between its lower position adjacent to the high thermal capacity wall and its upper position adjacent to the roof, the thermal barrier being fastened or otherwise attached to the roof members or to the wall by any suitable fastening means. It is apparent, however, that if the movable thermal barrier consists of a single rigid panel hinged at the juncture of the high thermal capacity wall and the roof, the raising and lowering of the panel would be cumbersome and would sweep much of the internal volume of the room, thereby interfering with the placement of the furniture in the room. This objection could be reduced by utilizing two or three panels hinged so as to fold against one another during the lowering process, but this also is somewhat cumbersome. It is therefore preferred that the movable thermal barrier consists of a plurality of subdivided insulating members which can be readily moved along curved or angled paths.

Also, one might employ an entirely different means for moving the thermal barrier from one position to another. For example, one might use a thermal barrier having ball bearing mountings, or a sprocket and chain arrangement or an arrangement involving a plurality of gears or pulleys, etc.

In summertime, the method of using the thermal valve means to obtain internal temperature modulation involves positioning movable thermal barrier 3 near roof 2 during the daytime and adjacent high thermal capacity wall 1 during the nighttime. In this manner, the heat from the sun which penetrates the roof during the daytime will be blocked by the movable thermal barrier from entering the room. Also, during the day the sun's heat will start penetrating high thermal capacity wall 1 but owing to the twelve hour lag preferably provided in the wall, this heat will not reach an excessive temperature at the interior surface of the wall until after sunset. At this time the movable thermal barrier is lowered and the insulating properties of the thermal barrier prevent heat stored in the high heat capacity wall from passing into the room at night, thereby avoiding an undesirable temperature in the room. Simultaneously, the lowering of the movable thermal barrier from the overhead position adjacent the roof permits heat radiation from the room through the roof to the cold night sky. Thus the heat of day is excluded from the room while the interior of the room is allowed to cool to night temperatures through internal convection and without the necessity of opening doors, ventilators and windows as is usually practiced with only partial effectiveness if house design, orientation or external wind velocity are not optimum.

The flow of heat stored in the high thermal capacity wall during daytime is blocked by the presence of the movable thermal barrier at night and is caused to reverse its direction and to dissipate heat to the night sky by radiation. During daytime the interior surface of this wall will then be cool, exposed and able to absorb from the room a good portion of the heat leakage through doors and windows since the movable thermal barrier has then been removed from the wall and is positioned near the roof.

During wintertime, the method of obtaining optimum thermal modulation by means of the movable thermal barrier consists of reversing the relative position of the movable thermal barrier as compared to its position in the summer. Thus during the day the movable thermal barrier would be positioned against the high thermal capacity wall so that heat in the room is not absorbed into this high thermal capacity wall which has cooled off during the night. Simultaneously, the roof which is exposed to the sun rapidly heats during the day and radiates this solar heat into the room thereby raising the temperature to or nearer the optimum comfort range. At night the movable thermal barrier is raised thereby preventing heat loss from the room through the roof and simultaneously the stored solar heat acting with a twelve-hour heat lag through the high thermal capacity wall enters the room maintaining comfortably warm temperatures throughout the night despite heat loss through leakage at the doors, ventilators and windows.

FIGURES 7 and 8 are presented to illustrate the great degree of temperature control achieved by employing the novel thermal valve means of this invention in conjunction with a high thermal capacity wall and other elements of the building structure. FIGURE 7 graphically illustrates the striking temperature variations achieved during summertime operation of the movable thermal barrier while FIGURE 8 graphically illustrates the temperature control achieved during wintertime operation when using the movable thermal barrier. The solid lines in these graphs represent the official Weather Bureau shade temperature at a distance of approximately five miles from the experimental house. The curve defined by x's represents the observed temperature in an adjacent room not provided with a movable thermal barrier, the adjacent room being used as a control. The curves defined by a series of small circles represent the observed temperature in the room of a building structure provided with a movable thermal barrier.

Referring to FIGURE 7, it will be seen that the Weather Bureau shade temperature, the temperature in an adpacent room and the temperature in the room provided with a movable thermal barier are all approximately the same at about 6 a.m. Between about 6 a.m. and 10 a.m. the temperautre in the room provided with a movable thermal barrier operated under the conditions indicated, rises somewhat above the other two temperatures, but at about 10 a.m. the temperature in the room provided with the movable thermal barrier begins to level off and does not exceed a maximum of about 88° while the other two temperatures continuously increase to a maximum of between 92° and 96° at about 2 to 4 p.m. as a result of the uncontrolled effects of the sun. After about 4 p.m. the Weather Bureau temperature and the temperature in the adjacent room begin to drop and at about 10 p.m. the three temperatures approximate each other again and then drop together until about 6 a.m. the next day. It is thus seen that by proper placement of the movable thermal barrier one is able to lower the peak interior temperature during the day so that the average temperature within a room is considerably below the temperature which would exist in the room if there were no movable thermal barrier. It is apparent that the peak with the thermal barrier is approximately one-half that of the outdoor temperature in this example where a 16 to 18 degree diurnal variation was recorded. In cases where a 40 degree variation is common, the benefit of comparably reducing the peak temperautre is of much greater value.

Referring now to FIGURE 8 which illustrates wintertime operation in accordance with this invention, the movable thermal barrier is raised between the hours of about 6 p.m. and 8 a.m. While the movable thermal barrier is in the raised position it prevents loss of the heat from the interior of the building structure through the roof and permits the heat stored in the high thermal capacity walls to flow into the room. Therefore between the hours of 6 p.m. and about 8 a.m. the temperature within a room provided with a thermal barrier will be much higher than either the Weather Bureau shade temperature or the temperature in an adjacent room not provided with a thermal barrier. Between the hours of about 8 a.m. and 6 p.m. the movable thermal barrier is in its lowered position and while in this position it permits solar heat to flow into the building structure through the roof while at the same time it prevents loss of heat from the room into the night-cooled high thermal capacity wall. By using a movable thermal barrier and a high thermal capacity wall one is thereby able to maintain the temperature within a building structure during the wintertime at a level considerably above that which would otherwise be possible if no thermal barrier means were used.

The results shown in FIGURES 7 and 8 were obtained in successive weeks during the month of September when the day and night temperature differential was minimal in the area. A much more pronounced effect would be shown in results when the winter range is 30 to 70° F. and the summer range is 70° to 110° F.

In mentioning the foregoing examples of materials from which the thermal barrier, the high thermal capacity wall and the roof may be constructed, it is not the intent to limit the invention to these materials or forms. Other materials known to the art which will yield essentially the same effect as the disclosed materials are also to be considered as within the purview of this invention.

Likewise, many minor design details are contemplated, such as (a) interposing a grill of metal, plastic, wood or other material between the view of a person in the room and the movable thermal barrier so as to improve the aesthetic appearance of the room; (b) providing either or both manual or electrical means for changing the position of the movable thermal barrier, including possible use of automatic controls regulated by external temperature or light intensity; (c) providing windows in the roof so that during winter, light will enter the room when the thermal barrier is positioned adjacent the wall but will be excluded during the summer when the intense glare would be objectionable, since at that time the thermal barrier is near the roof; (d) by the provision of one or more fixed or adjustable ventilators between the roof and the thermal valve in position near the roof; or (e) by special treatment of the surfaces of the wall, the roof or the panel so as to alter the reflectivity or diffusivity of the materials contained therein. Similarly it is anticipated that this invention can be used with equal or greater effectiveness with walls of metal, plastic or other materials which can retain water or other liquids of high heat capacity and which may be stored or pumped to other walls, to heating or cooling systems embedded in floors or the like. The principles of the invention may also be embodied in combination with other solar heat devices, such as solar heat collectors of the liquid or air circulation type and the thermal barrier may even serve to replace a part of a solar heat collector as for example in the chemical type calling for a curtain or closing screen to be interposed between the thermal collector and the solar heat source but this invention would be an improvement over the previously described curtain or closing screen in that it has greater insulating characteristics and acts favorably not only with respect to the heat collector but also with respect to the heat transfer in the high heat capacity wall—a dual benefit not heretofore conceived.

Because the material of the movable thermal barrier and the means for moving it are important aspects of this invention, it is desirable to describe another thermal barrier means which constitutes an alternate to the rigid panels mounted with rollers and trackway as illustrated in FIGURES 1 through 6. As shown in FIGURES 10, 13 and 14, movable thermal barrier **303** may consist of flexible polyurethane **334** fastened by means of adhesives to a more weather resistant, flexible backing strip material **319** (which corresponds to **19** of FIGURE 3) and having a plurality of horizontal stiffening I-shaped members **332** attached to said backing strip **319** which transfer the weight of said thermal barrier **303** onto a knife-edge runner **327** a portion of which **336** engages said I-shaped member while the knife-edge portion is mounted to engage in a grooved trackway **228** suitably mounted on the I-section arched rigid frame **213** of FIGURE 10 which is a part of the enclosure of this invention.

Stiffening members **332**, of FIGURES 13 and 14, may be made of aluminum; knife-edge runner **327** may be made of Delrin; grooved trackway **228** may be formed from nylon resin fastened by any suitable adhesive to arched frame **213** which may be made of steel, aluminum, wood or other appropriate material. FIGURE 13 shows grooved trackway **228** formed with projections **229** partially surrounded by lip member **331** formed as a part of knife-edge runner **327**. An enlarged view of continuous grooved trackway **228** with projections **229** is shown in FIGURE 16.

FIGURE 17 shows a dual knife-edge runner **27** and **27a** having a shape substantially as in FIGURES 13 and 14 except for the portion to be attached to the movable thermal barrier. In FIGURE 17, side projections **52** and **52a** provide a wide base for fastening the knife-edge runners **27** and **27a** to panels of insulation, such as panels **16** of FIGURE 1, at points suitably oriented on said panels to transfer their weight onto structural member **13** of the enclosure. The two knife-edge runners **27** and **27a** of FIGURE 17 are interconnected by a thin, flexible section **38**, of the same plastic from which said runners are formed, which can serve as a hinge when **27** and **27a** are fastened to separate but abutting panels **16** of FIGURE 1. The lip projections **31** and **31a** of FIGURE 17 are designed to engage projections **229** of the trackway shown in FIGURE 16 so that knife-edge runners **27** and **27a** do not become disengaged from said grooved trackway when the latter is mounted onto a vertical portion of a frame member such as **213** of FIGURE 13.

It is apparent that the knife-edge runner of FIGURE 17 could be extended from the dual form illustrated to include any number of knife-edge runners of the type of **27** separated by one less flexible hinge of the type of **38**. It is equally obvious that parallel rows of these knife-edge runners could be made with projection **52a** shared in common by said parallel rows and thus integrated into a single unit comprising a plurality of rows of individual knife-edge runners of the type of **27** and **27a**.

The advantages to this invention of the use of knife-edge runners of the type described above and of continuous, movable thermal barriers also described above are the following: The continuous insulation eliminates the need for forming and mounting a plurality of panels and hinges such as **16** and **18** of FIGURE 5, also shown in FIGURE 1. Likewise, the cost, installation and maintenance expense of the more elaborate trackway and roller moving means of FIGURES 1 to 6 are eliminated and the problems of lubrication and squeaks are reduced. It is precisely to minimize friction and noise that the grooved trackway and knife-edge runner are made of nylon resin and Delrin respectively. Additionally, the movable thermal barrier may now be formed so that the flexible polyurethane **334** constitutes its own sealing means thereby eliminating the need of sealing elements **22** and **25**, such as are used in FIGURES 1 to 6.

It is obvious that the knife-edge runners may have to be variously mounted on the structural framing of the enclosure in different embodiments of this invention. FIGURE 15 shows the details for mounting two thermal barrier means **103** and **103a** on a common frame element **113** of the enclosure made by roof **102** supported by purlin **112** fastened to structural frame element **113** to form a structure of the type of FIGURE 1. In FIGURE 15, panels **116** bear on knife-edge runners **127** which transfer the load to grooved trackway **128** supported by said structural member **113**. The movable thermal barrier **303** of FIGURES 13 and 14 has been previously described and is supported by structural member **213** so as to be outside of the enclosure made in part by roof **202** which is composed of transparent material such as glass or suitable plastic affixed to said structural member **213** by bolts **250** which effect a sealing pressure on the plastic or fibrous roof-framing material **248**. The exterior mounting of the movable thermal barrier illustrated in FIGURE 13 and 14 can suitably be used for an embodiment of this invention shown in FIGURE 10 which will be described in greater detail.

While this invention has been described primarily for a structure of the type shown in FIGURE 1, it is apparent that the movable thermal barrier, if made of weather-resistant materials or suitably protected from the weather, may be made positionable against the ouside of the high thermal capacity wall and the roof of a building structure and may be of such size as to cover both simultaneously. FIGURE 10 illustrates this embodiment of the invention in the form of a greenhouse comprising a hot-house portion to the left for growing plants and a cold-storage portion to the right for the storage of seeds or bulbs and for retarding the growth of plants kept therein until periods of greater demand.

In this embodiment, thermal barrier **303** has been shifted from a southerly exposed room or compartment in the northern hemisphere over a ridge at position marked C to the northerly side of the building. During the winter day the southerly side is heated through roof **202** which comprises high heat transfer materials of transparent types also forming a substantial portion of the south wall. During this period floor **205** and the other walls **204** in addition to the high heat storage south wall **201** absorb and store heat and consequently said floor, other walls and south wall all may be considered as high heat storage portions of the enclosure and therefore may be considered in common as the high heat storage component of this embodiment of the invention These elements absorb heat from both direct external solar radiation and indirect internal radiation from the roof and wall. At night, in this embodiment, the thermal barrier is moved from the northerly side of the building structure to the external southerly portion and is disposed to insulate both the wall and the roof of the southerly side. This not only has the advantage, previously described in relation to a building structure comprising an entirely southerly exposed roof as in FIGURE 1, of preventing heat loss through the southerly exposed roof during the nighttime, but it also has the added advantage of retaining within the newly defined building structure all the solar heat stored in the southerly exposed high thermal capacity wall **201** during the day and directs radiation from said wall inwardly during the night. In contrast, the earlier described embodiment permits radiation of a portion of the stored heat to be directed both inwardly to the room and outwardly to the night sky.

By dividing the building structure into a plurality of rooms or compartments, as illustrated in FIGURE 10, the novel features of this invention produce opposite thermal effects in the rooms or compartments southerly exposed and those northerly disposed. Thus, while in wintertime the temperature within the southerly exposed room is being raised during the daytime and held at an elevated temperature by internal radiation from the high thermal capacity wall during nighttime, the northerly disposed rooms are prevented by the thermal barrier from increasing in temperature during daytime and are cooled to night temperature during nighttime. This provision of dual thermal control provides comfort in the southerly exposed rooms for living things and prevents damage to materials or goods deleteriously affected by low temperatures while it provides low temperatures corresponding to cold storage conditions in the northerly disposed rooms. Similarly in the summertime the dual thermal control may be used to lower the temperatures in the southerly exposed room while maintaining an elevated temperature in the northerly disposed rooms, this elevated temperature being desirable in some building structures for the drying of seeds, fruits, and the like or for forcing faster growth of plants in a greenhouse structure, or for the fermentation of fodder in a farm structure or for other purposes.

It is also apparent that the movable thermal barrier of the embodiment illustrated in FIGURE 10 may, under other circumstances, create desirable temperature conditions within the building structure by being positioned part of the day so as to insulate all or a portion of the southerly exposed roof or all or a portion of the northerly disposed roof while leaving another portion of the external walls uninsulated. This is clear from FIGURE 10 where the length of movable thermal barrier **303** is defined as the area between points D–F and leaves an area of roof **302** exposed between limiting points C and D. If, however, the C–D area of said roof should be covered by the thermal barrier, a corresponding section of high heat storage wall **301** will be exposed (as indicated for example between points E and F). Similarly, if D–F equals C–B on the structure and the insulation is positioned to cover the roof area **202** between points C–B, the wall portion **201** between points B–A will be exposed, but if the same thermal barrier is moved down to A, a portion of the roof **202** near the ridge at C will be left exposed. In this manner it is possible to obtain controlled temperatures within the compartments ranging substantially from the maximum to the minimum of the daily diurnal variation.

In the embodiment of FIGURE 10, the common wall of the two compartments includes an insulating material **226** to reduce thermal flow between the compartments. The roof **302**, walls **304**, floor **305** and wall **301** all become the high heat storage portion of this compartment in which the movable thermal barrier is positioned by means of a knife-edge runner assembly indicated generally by **328**. Knife-edge runner assembly **328** comprises a knife-edge runner fastened to said thermal barrier by means illustrated in FIGURES 13 and 14, and a trackway such as that illustrated in FIGURE 16 which in FIGURE 10 is shown as being fastened by suitable means directly to the concrete roof and wall portions **302** and **301** respectively. The trackway of knife-edge assembly **328** continues over the ridge C and onto the structural frame member **213** where it is indicated as **228** and a corresponding trackway at the end of the structure is indicated as **228*a***. The roof framing material **248** of roof **202** may be made of plastic, wood or metal and the transparent portions **249** of the roof may be of plastic, such as Teflon, Tedlar, Aclar, Kel-F and Mylar, or it may be of glass.

An alternative arrangement (not shown) with rooms of similar size and shape disposed side by side with identical orientation, permits insulation covering both the sides and the roof of one room to be laterally shifted on rollers bearing on a foundation common to both rooms so that the insulation covers, during a different portion of the day, the second room.

In another embodiment illustrated in FIGURE 11, which shows only a portion of the upper part of a building structure, this invention encompasses the use of a movable thermal barrier **403** positioned during a portion of the day substantially parallel to the floor (not shown) and at a considerable angle to and distance from a roof **402** supported by framing member **413**. In this instance, trackway **414** on which the movable thermal barrier is mounted in a manner comparable to that of FIGURES 1 to 6 is parallel to the high heat storage wall **401** until it approaches roof **402** whereupon it becomes parallel to the floor (not shown) and is fastened at **442** to the other wall **404**. When the thermal barrier is used as illustrated in FIGURE 11, it is apparent that a considerable distance may exist between the major portion of thermal barrier **403** and the major portion of roof **402**. The space between said roof and said thermal barrier (when disposed parallel to the floor) has a tendency to build up high temperatures during a summer day. While the high temperatures are useful in greenhouses, grain or lumber driers and in solar stills as will be described in section B, the effect is not desirable in houses since it results in excessive heat storage in the portion of wall **404** extending upwards from the level of thermal barrier **403** when said barrier is positioned parallel to the floor. Consequently, it is advisable to have louvres **441**, or other means (such as are shown in FIGURE 1), which will reduce the build-up of heat in this enclosed area. The usefulness of this embodiment of the invention which positions the movable insulation **403** substantially parallel to the floor and at an appreciable distance from the roof is evident from the data of FIGURES 7 and 8 which were obtained in a house built according to this embodiment.

In another embodiment illustrated in FIGURE 12, movable insulation 503 is mounted by any suitable means heretofore described to move on trackway 514 which is continuous over exterior wall 501 and roof 502, passes through aperture 545 in said roof and continues along the interior surface of said roof and said wall in a manner which permits movable thermal barrier 503 to be positioned inside of or outside of the enclosure substantially formed by said roof and said wall. A ridge-roll 543 and a suitable hinged sealing device 544 is supported adjacent aperture 545 by support 559 mounted at the upper ends of wall 504.

It is apparent that in the embodiment illustrated by FIGURE 12, the insulation may be positioned totally within the structure during the day in which case the exposed wall 501 and roof 502 become heated and much of this stored heat can be caused to radiate into the room when the movable thermal barrier is put into a nighttime position exterior to said roof and said wall. Instead of thus warming this portion of the enclosure, it is possible to cool it by the same thermal barrier means by merely reversing the daytime and nighttime positioning of said thermal barrier.

In an additional embodiment of the invention which can be made sufficiently clear to those versed in the art by FIGURE 12, one can arrange a switching device, similar to those used in railroad tracks, above wall 504 so as to interconnect the trackways both internal and external on the portion of the structure to the right of said wall 504 with trackways 514*a* shown broken attached to roof 502*a* to the left of wall 504. By means of such switching mechanism it is possible to cause movable thermal barrier 503 to pass through aperture 545 to a position either on the interior or on the exterior side of roof 502*a* and other possible components of a compartment to the left of wall 504, such as a high heat capacity wall (not shown), and thereby provide a means for controlling the temperatures in the two compartments partially indicated to the left and to the right of wall 504 of FIGURE 12. In another embodiment not shown, the aperture through which the movable insulation passes could be located at the eaves by removing eave ventilator 10 shown in FIGURES 1, 3 and 4. At this location of the aperture, the movable insulation might be caused to take various positional relationships with the wall 1 and the roof 2 of FIGURE 1. With suitable trackway systems and apertures at both the eaves and the ridge the number of positionings greatly increases as does the degree of control of the temperature within the enclosure or within different compartments of the enclosure.

While it is preferable that, in the embodiment of FIGURE 1, the roof of the building structure shall be of thin material of rapid thermal transfer, in other circumstances the roof may be of thick concrete construction, as indicated by 502 of FIGURE 12 or of varying thickness as indicated by 302 of FIGURE 10 and also the roof, of any type, may be integrated with all or a portion of the side wall and indistinguishable therefrom as in FIGURES 10 and 12. Likewise the high heat capacity material may be a material liquifiable below 160° F. such as water 147 of FIGURE 9, or the heat collecting chemicals previously mentioned, and it will hereinafter be disclosed in detail how it also can be water or other distilland or distillate in a distillation process. Moreover, it may be water contained within grain or lumber which is being dried in a solar drier.

It will now be evident that the movable thermal barrier of this invention does not need to be co-extensive with any particular element of the structure nor does it need to be located close to any porticular element, and neither does it have to be positioned so as to make heat flow through a first portion of the enclosure independent of heat flow through a second portion of the structure where said first and second portions do not include the thermal barrier means. The criterion for the movable thermal barrier means of this invention is that it shall be effective in controlling or modulating the temperature within an enclosure partially comprising material of high heat storage capacity.

It is also evident that while the movable thermal barrier is preferably of low density with low heat capacity and low heat transfer, said barrier could be effective if made of high heat capacity and high thermal storage materials such as thick metal, concrete, confined water, and the like having a suitable time lag for heat transfer similar to the construction of wall 1 of FIGURE 1. Movement of such a high heat capacity thermal barrier has obvious limitations in a building structure and costs would be high. These limitations do not apply, however, when the high heat capacity thermal barrier is distilled or distillate in a movable basin floating within a solar still *

The essential consideration of this invention is that a thermal barrier of whatever type forming a part of an enclosure be moved in consonance with the daily diurnal variation of temperature and modulate, in a novel manner, the temperature which would otherwise exist within said enclosure.

B. THERMAL MODULATION OF PROCESS TEMPERATURES

The modulation of temperatures within enclosures inevitably affects many thermally sensitive objects and processes which may be operating within said enclosures. Temperature modulation in a house has a desirable effect upon inhabitants through affecting their physiological processes. This results even though the enclosure may not always be intact—at times doors and windows may be open. In the case of a greenhouse, and in the cold storage of vegetables, fruits, bulbs, and the like, this invention was applied in Part A to modulate temperatures specifically affecting physiological processes such as growth, blooming, and rotting. In all such cases involving life within the enclosures of Part A of this application, thermal modulation has an effect upon the heating and evaporation of water constituting a part of that life. My invention can, in other ways, modulate temperatures within enclosures so as to affect processes of evaporation, distillation and drying. Moreover, I can apply my invention to the heating and cooling of water for household or industrial uses. Such applications will now be described.

A solar still may be constructed in which at least one of my movable thermal barriers is in the form of a distillate basin which floats on and laterally moves over a reservoir of distilland confined by concrete side walls of the still and a plastic bottom liner the major portion of which rests on the ground. At least one rigid stationary brine tray made of plastic, metal or asbestos cement supported by side walls is suspended across the width of the still. Distilland introduced into said stationary tray through a conduit through the side wall overflows through a second conduit and falls into the underlying brine basin and is discharged from said underlying basin and from the solar still through a third conduit and a valve and piping means. Distillate which condenses on the plastic film cover, which may be of any type transmitting solar radiation, is collected in peripheral troughs or in troughs suspended from the cover by means of a recess and spline adapted to clamp a portion of said cover. The collected distillate is conducted to a conduit connected through flexible tubing to a distillate reservoir which may be within the floating thermal barrier basin which may be variously positioned by means of a drawline cord connected to said movable basin and passing out through the two ends of the solar still. The distillate conduit is also connected to a piping and valve means for removing distillate from the solar still.

The cover support is suspended across the width of the

still on columns located beyond the edges of the still where said cover is clamped to the side walls; the cover is similarly clamped at the ends to form an enclosure. Materials of this embodiment are well known to those practicing the art and are fully described in my co-pending application.

In this embodiment, to be described with distillate in the movable basin, the daytime position of the movable thermal barrier basin is beneath the stationary brine tray and extends slightly beyond the bottom edges thereof by virtue of greater width of the movable basin. Brine over the bottom liner, which must resist actinic rays and high temperatures, is then exposed to solar radiation but distills somewhat slower than brine similarly exposed in the stationary tray owing to the necessity to indirectly heat brine underlying the movable basin by conduction and convection.

At sunset, the movable basin is positioned mostly outside the area underlying the stationary tray and in the new position distillate which entered it during the day through troughs, conduit and tubing is cooled to the night sky. Brine in the basin made by the bottom liner then continues to distill at night and vapors condense on the sloping underside of the stationary tray giving up latent heat thereto and causing further distillation of brine therein. Condensate on the underside of the stationary tray drips from bottom edges into the wider movable distillate basin except at one end of the still where a special collecting trough is provided to conduct distillate to the conduit connected with the movable distillate basin.

In the morning, brine contained above the bottom liner, as well as that in the stationary tray will be warmer than distilland in basins of prior art in which movable insulation is not used and said brine in the present embodiment will start distilling earlier. The cold distillate can then be withdrawn from the movable basin through tubing and a conduit or it may be left in the movable basin to serve as an internal condensing surface. If it is not desired to cool the distillate, nor to use it as a condenser, the movable thermal barrier need not be formed as a basin but can be a flat sheet of water-impervious insulating material such as expanded polystyrene in which case the distillate conduit and tubing passing distillate to the previously described movable distillate basin are not needed but the special collecting troughs are required at each bottom edge of the stationary trays.

In the foregoing embodiment of my invention, a movable thermal barrier within the meaning of this invention was used within a solar still to effect distillation by modulating the temperature of distilland and distillate. However, these processes are understood to be distinct from simple thermal control within a building structure. Clearly, the invention is equally applicable for modulating the temperature of water not involved in a distillation process. In the embodiment now to be described it is used to modulate the temperature of water in a water supply system.

Solar water heaters of various designs are in use in fairly large numbers in the United States and in other countries. All designs involve a relatively large black collector which receives solar radiation to heat water and which is faced toward the equator. A separate well-insulated storage tank has been used in prior art for overnight storage and is frequently placed at a higher level to take advantage of the thermosiphon principle of natural circulation brought about by less dense hot water rising through a conduit from the heater to the higher-level storage tank and replacement by colder water from said storage tank.

In regions of high solar intensity where solar water heaters are advantageous, the natural temperature of a surface water supply may be at the average of day and night temperatures, or higher, and not be as refreshing for drinking purposes as water at or near the lowest night temperature. Ice or refrigeration is not always available for cooling the drinking water and in such areas I apply my invention in the following manner.

The hot water heater of this embodiment is in the form of two rectangular tanks made of galvanized iron, copper, or aluminum fastened to the southerly sloping portion of a roof of a house or similar structure in the northern hemisphere. Both tanks are fastened to roof members by bolts, screws, or nails passing through tabs or projecting portions on the tanks. Insulation encloses all sides of the tanks except the upper surface inclined to absorb solar radiation; this upper surface is painted dull black or chemically coated by electroplating a black deposit thereon. A pipe conducts cold water into the lower portion of the lower tank; a plurality of tubes interconnect the two tanks and reduce any tendency for water passing from the lower tank to the upper tank before it has been heated; and another pipe which allows hot water to be withdrawn from the upper portion of the upper tank. If the tanks are not to be kept constantly under the usual pressure of a water supply system, the hot water pipe in the upper tank must be at a somewhat lower level and said tank must be vented at its highest level.

Solar radiation during the daytime will heat water in both heating tanks but as hot water is drawn off from the upper tank it will be replaced by the hottest water present in the lower tank rising through the interconnecting conduits.

At one side of the two water heating tanks, I fasten two cold water tanks constructed almost identical to the water heaters described above. Cold water is withdrawn from a pipe leaving the bottom of the lower tank and is replaced by water from the upper tank passing through the interconnecting plurality of tubes. Warm water enters the upper tank through an inlet near the top of said upper tank. A vent may be provided if the water cooling tanks are not to be under the pressures normal to urban water systems.

Across the upper ends of the upper hot and cold water tanks and across the lower ends of the lower hot and cold water tanks, I mount and fasten a trackway similar to the trackways of FIGURES 3 and 6 or of FIGURES 13 to 16 inclusive. A sheet of thermal insulation, preferably expanded polystyrene covered with reflective aluminum sheet, is mounted to said trackway and is moved in a manner similar to the movement of the movable thermal barriers described in Part A of this application. The area of the external movable thermal barrier of this embodiment is essentially equal to the combined upper surface of the pair of water heating tanks or of the pair of equal-size water cooling tanks.

During the daytime, I maintain the movable insulation over the water cooling tanks to protect said tanks from solar radiation while exposing the upper surface of the water heating tanks thereto. At sunset, I move the insulation to a position over the water heating tanks to prevent said tanks from radiating heat to the night sky while simultaneously exposing the upper surface of the water cooling tanks to the cooling effect of the night sky. In this manner, hot water may be drawn from the water heating tanks at any time of the day and cold water may similarly be drawn from the water cooling tanks within the capacity limitations of said tanks. To obtain the hottest and coldest water, the heating and cooling tanks should not have a depth of much more than four inches.

My invention may be applied to the heating and cooling of water in a cylindrically shaped storage tank formed from two adjacent metal semi-cylindrical tanks separated by a layer of insulation but joined by bolts and painted black on the curved exterior surfaces. The half cylinder oriented toward the north in the northern hemisphere is for water cooling and has the necessary pipe connections while that oriented toward the south, and also having the necessary pipe connections, is for heating water. Movable insulation of adequate size and shape to externally cover one of the semi-cylindrical tanks is mounted to a trackway running around the assembly of the two semi-cylindrical tanks at the upper and lower ends thereof. In a manner previously made clear herein, the movable insulation may be easily positioned around the northerly exposed surface of the water cooling tank during the daytime and around the southerly exposed surface of the water heating tank during the nighttime. Such positioning of the movable insulation provides means to obtain hot and cold water throughout the day and night.

Lumber driers are being developed by the United States Forest Products Laboratory to utilize solar energy. A black metal absorber and fans actuated by electricity or by wind are used to circulate hot air to dry lumber covered by a low-cost plastic film. Grain, fruit, and tobacco driers have also been built to utilize solar energy. In all cases, there is considerable heat loss at nighttime which may be avoided by using movable insulation to modulate temperatures within the driers. Such insulation may be formed from reflective materials in the shape of a solar radiation concentrator which, during the daytime, reflects radiation onto the product being dried or onto a collector which may be of the high thermal capacity type. The movable insulation may be positioned at nighttime to prevent radiation of heat to the night sky either from the product being dried or from the high thermal capacity collector and the heat so saved may be used to continue drying the product during the nighttime.

Thus the advantages of the present invention of movable thermal barriers are many and cannot all be related here. It is in common with all, or nearly all, of the embodiments of this invention that the movable thermal barriers effective for controlling the temperatures within the enclosures are utilized and effectively modulate temperatures within the enclosures when in different positional relationships with respect to various portions of the enclosure during different portions of the heat cycle and are frequently serving somewhat different or additional functions in the different positionings though it is not essential that the movable insulation performs in all of these manners in order to fall within the scope of this invention. *

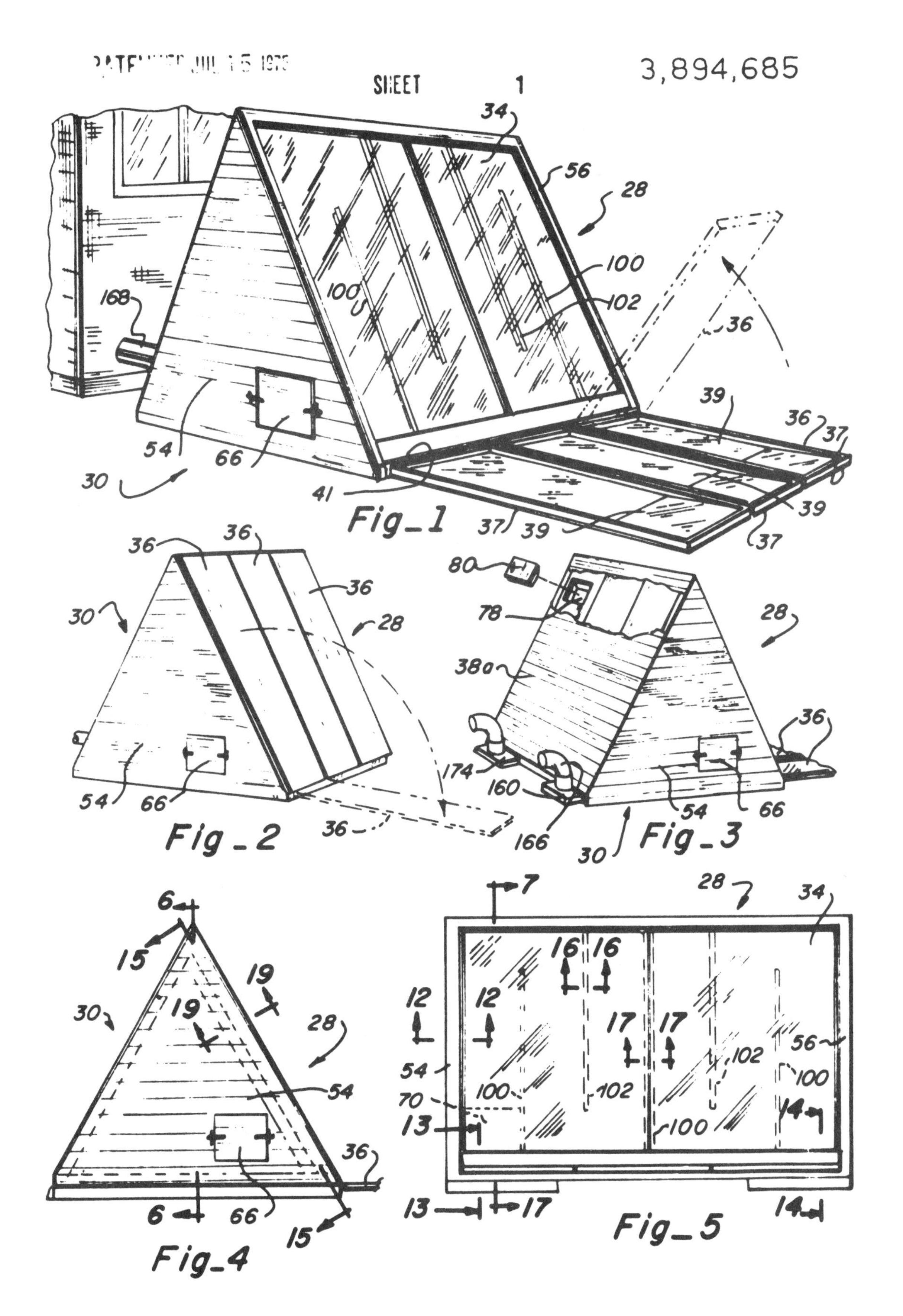
SHEET 1
3,894,685
Fig_1
Fig_2
Fig_3
Fig_4
Fig_5

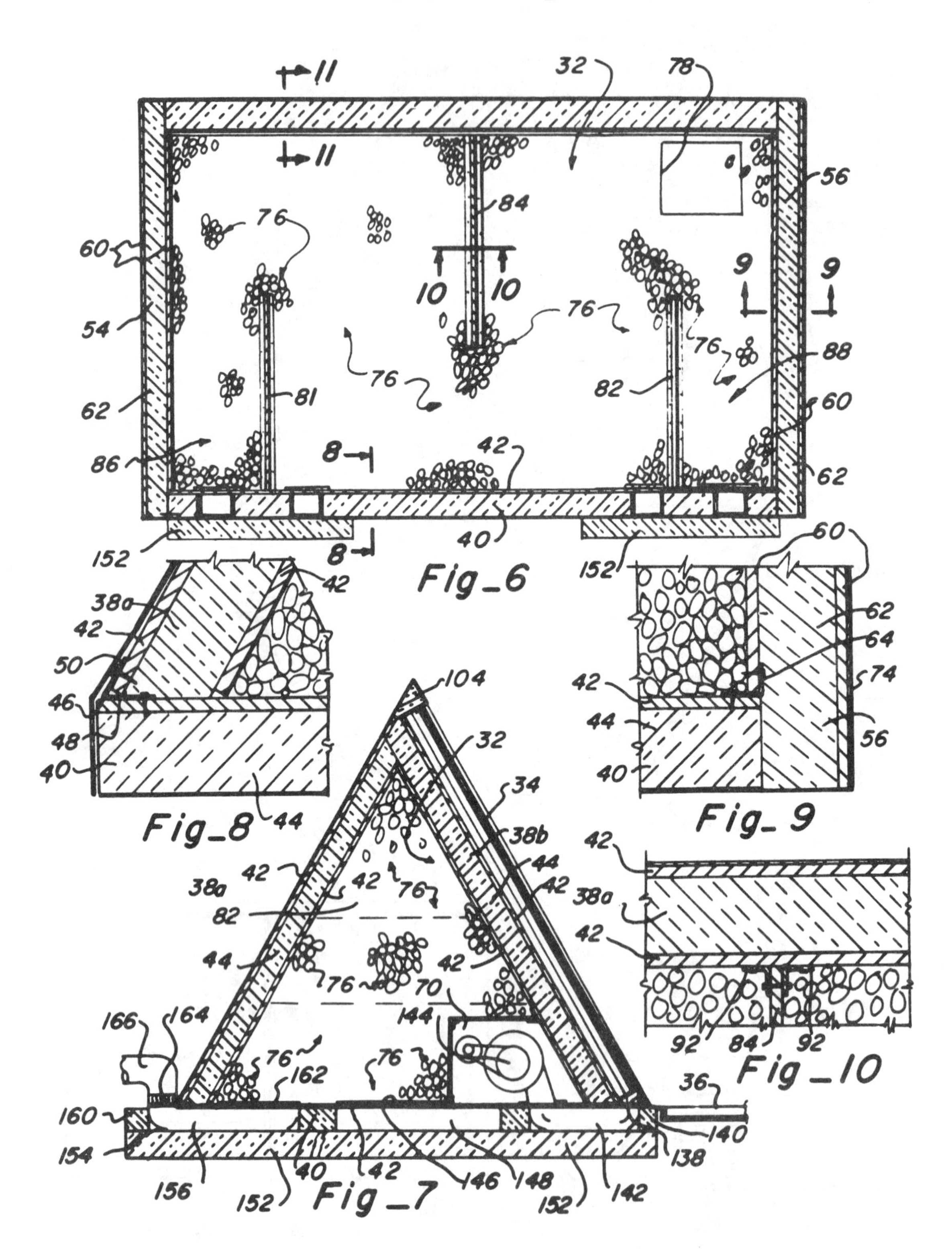
3,894,685
SHEET 2
Fig_6
Fig_7
Fig_8
Fig_9
Fig_10

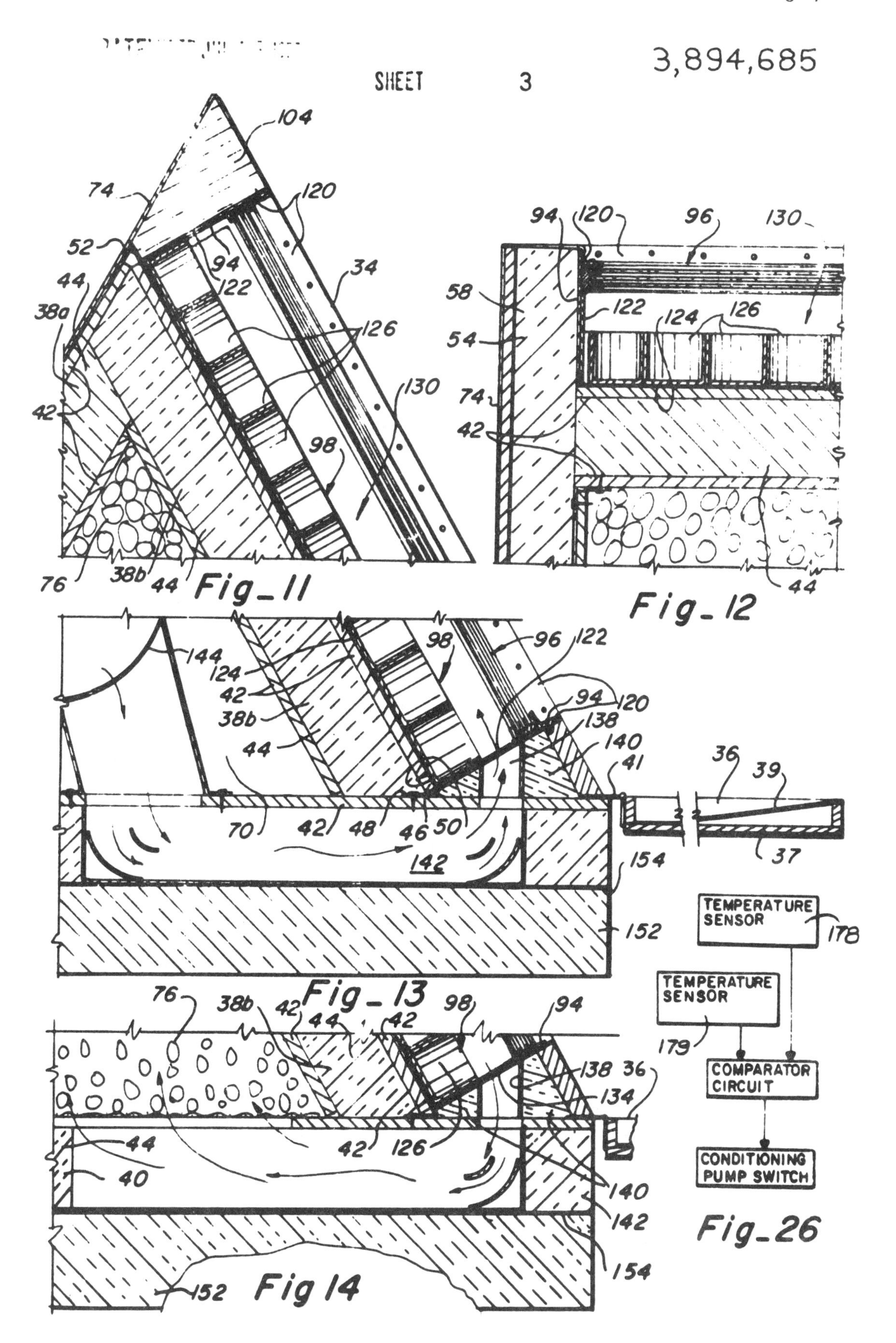

Fig_11

Fig_12

Fig_13

Fig 14

Fig_26

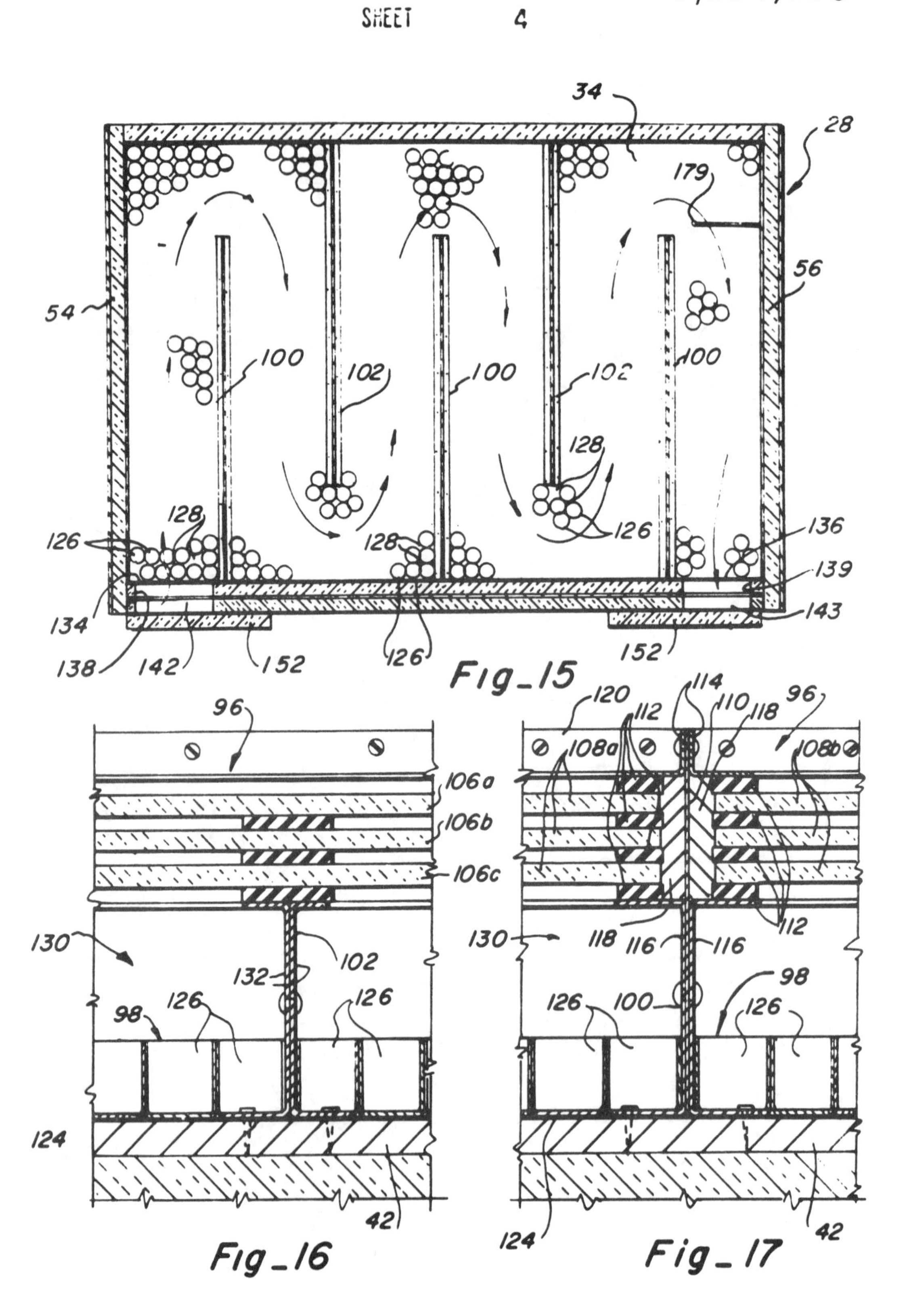
3,894,685
SHEET 4
34
28
179
56
54
100
102
100
102
100
128
128
126
126
128
136
139
143
134
138
142
152
126
152
Fig_15
96
120
112
114
110
118
96
108a
108b
106a
106b
106c
130
102
132
98
126
126
124
42
Fig_16
130
118
116
116
112
98
126
100
126
124
42
Fig_17

3,894,685

SHEET 5

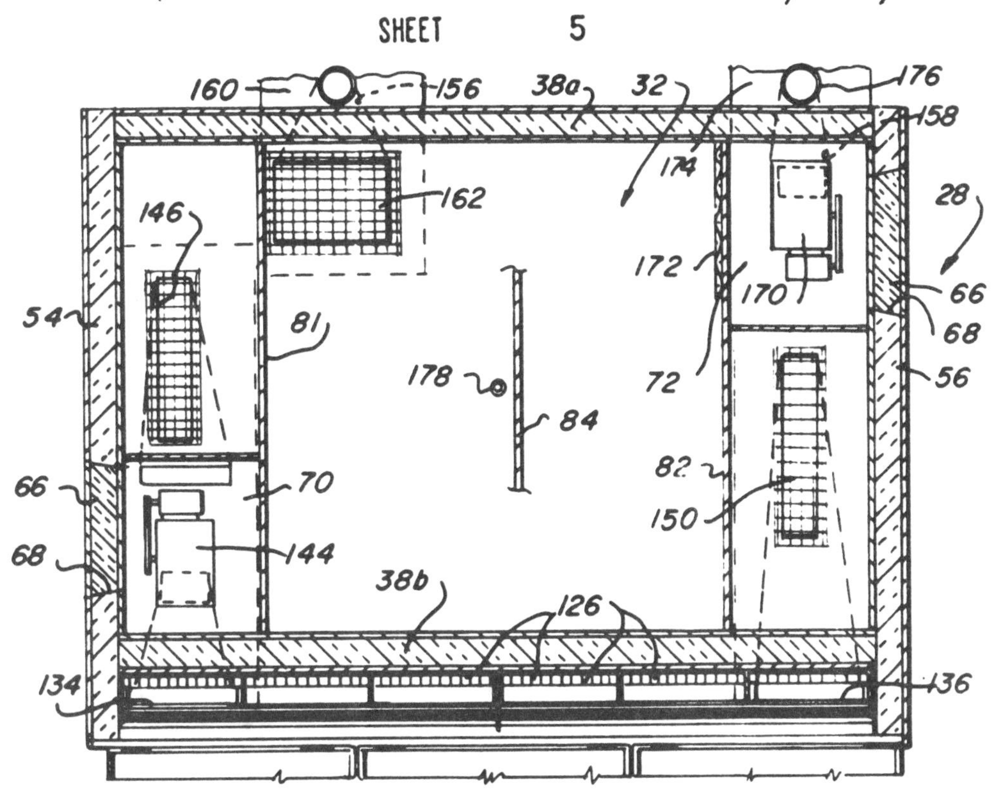

Fig_18

Fig_19

Fig_20

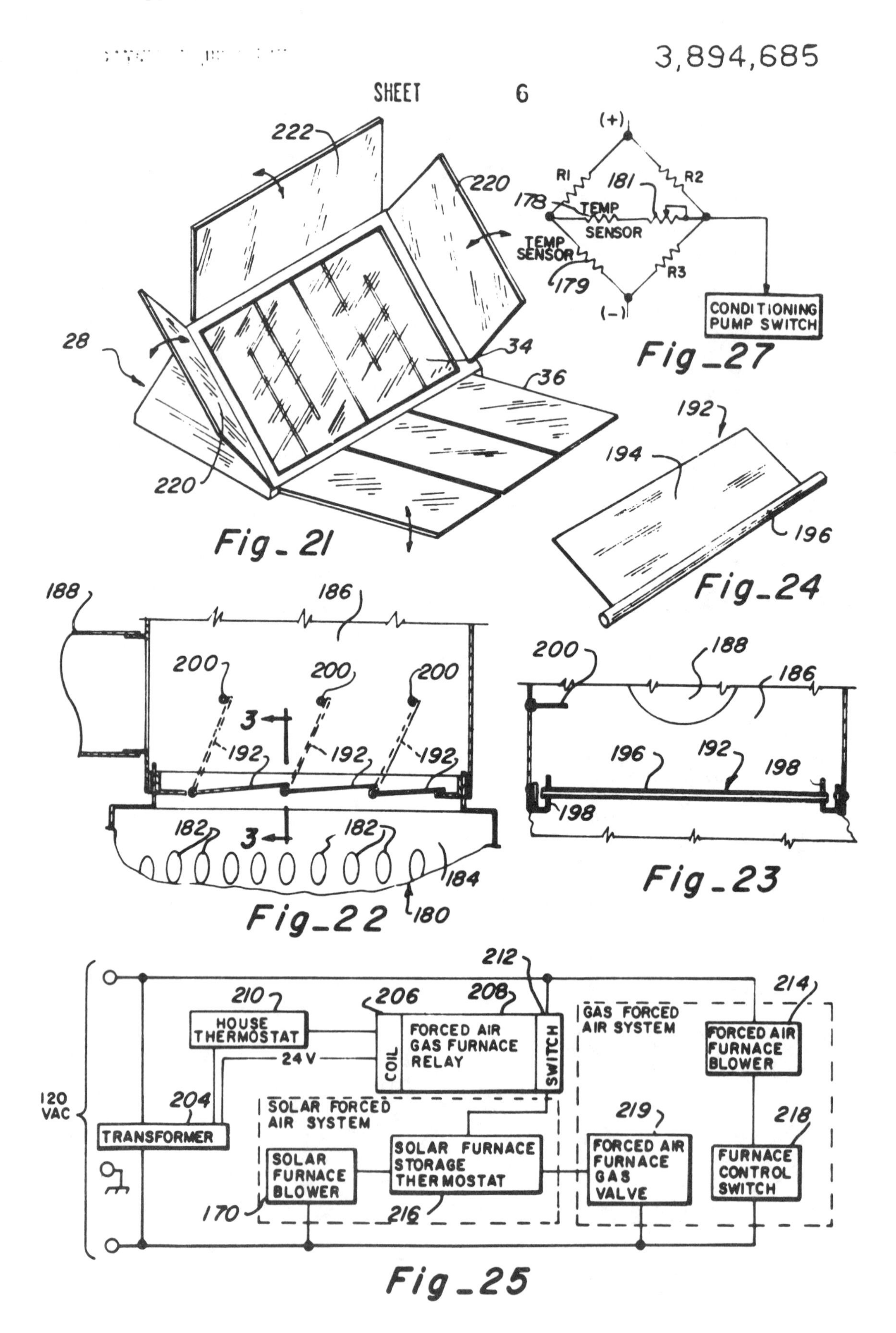
3,894,685
SHEET 6
(+)
R1
181
R2
178
TEMP
SENSOR
TEMP
SENSOR
179
R3
(-)
CONDITIONING
PUMP SWITCH
Fig_27
222
220
28
34
36
220
Fig_21
192
194
196
Fig_24
188
186
200
200
200
3
192
192
192
182
3
182
184
180
Fig_22
200
188
186
196
192
198
198
Fig_23
120
VAC
212
214
210
206
208
HOUSE
THERMOSTAT
COIL
FORCED AIR
GAS FURNACE
RELAY
SWITCH
24 V
GAS FORCED
AIR SYSTEM
FORCED AIR
FURNACE
BLOWER
204
SOLAR FORCED
AIR SYSTEM
219
218
TRANSFORMER
SOLAR
FURNACE
BLOWER
SOLAR FURNACE
STORAGE
THERMOSTAT
FORCED AIR
FURNACE
GAS
VALVE
FURNACE
CONTROL
SWITCH
170
216
Fig_25

* ABSTRACT

A self-contained apparatus for collecting, storing and transmitting solar heat includes an elongated insulated housing in which a quantity of heat retaining material is confined and a collector on one face of the housing which has a multi-layered glass face through which solar heat may pass and be collected upon a unique heat-collecting bed which is insulated from the ambient environment by the glass face. Conditioning pump means are provided within the housing to circulate conditioning air through the collector and the heat retaining material in the housing so that heat is transferred from the collector to the material in the housing. Specially designed and positioned ducts connect the collector to the interior of the housing in a manner such that air interchange between the collector and the interior of the housing is prevented except during operation of the conditioning pump. Both the collector and the interior of the housing are provided with appropriately positioned baffles to optimally expose the conditioning air to the heat collecting bed and to heat retaining material in the housing. Reflective solar amplifiers are pivotally connected to the housing in a manner such that they are movable from an open operative position wherein they reflect solar radiation into the collector and a closed protective position overlying the glass face of the collector. Utility pump means are also provided in the apparatus for withdrawing air from the interior of the housing and circulating it through a building structure to be heated thereby.

The method of collecting, storing and transmitting solar heat includes the steps of absorbing solar heat on a collector surface wherein the collector surface is insulated from the ambient environment, passing air across the collector surface in a heat transfer process whereby the heat absorbed by the collector surface is transferred to the air, passing the hot air leaving the collector surface through a horizontal duct disposed at a lower elevation than the collector surface, and passing the hot air flowing from the duct into an elevated storage chamber containing material with heat absorbent and heat retaining characteristics whereby the heat in the hot air is transferred from the hot air to the material and retained by said material until it is removed therefrom by a relatively cool air flow. *

SOLAR HEATING SYSTEM

*

BACKGROUND OF THE INVENTION

1. Field of the Invention

The present invention relates generally to a method and apparatus of collecting, storing and transmitting solar heat and more particularly relates to a method and apparatus for heating building structures and the like.

2. Description of the Prior Art

The tremendous energy output of the sun has been recognized for many years and numerous attempts have been made at harnassing this energy so that it can be converted into a useful state. For example, the sun's energy has been successfully converted into electrical energy with solar batteries and similarly, the sun's energy has been converted into heating systems by so-called solar stoves, furnaces and the like. The solar furnace apparatusses, however, have been typified by extremely large collector plates covering large portions of the roof structure of a building to be heated with the apparatus and large storage chambers usually in the substructure of the building wherein the heat is stored after having been transferred from the collector by a liquid fluid medium. The heat in the storage chamber is then circulated through the building structure by a separate fluid flow.

These systems, which have not only been unwieldly and very expensive to install, have proven to be very inefficient in that there is an excessive heat loss when transferring the solar heat from the collector to the removed storage chamber. Furthermore, these systems have not been capable of being easily installed in existing building structures and have not been devised to cooperate as an auxiliary heating unit to the conventional forced air heating systems commonly found in building structures.

Typical examples of prior art solar heating systems may be found in the June, **1973** and October, **1973** issues of Popular Mechanics magazine and in the May, **1973** issue of Popular Science magazine.

OBJECTS OF THE INVENTION

The present invention has for its primary object the provision of a new and improved method and apparatus for collecting, storing and transmitting solar heat.

It is another object of the present invention to provide a compact, self-contained solar heating unit which can be positioned exteriorly of a building structure and with minimum time and expense connected to the building structure so as to convert solar radiation into heat for maintaining a desired temperature within the building structure.

It is another object of the present invention to provide a new and improved solar heating system which is readily connected into an existing forced air heating system so as to serve as an auxiliary heating system with minimum alteration to an existing building structure.

It is still another object of the present invention to provide a new and improved solar heating system which can also serve as a cooling system with minimal physical or mechanical alterations.

It is another object of the present invention to provide a solar heating unit which utilizes a small and compact heat collector yet has the capacity for adequately heating typical residential building structures.

It is another object of the present invention to provide a solar heating apparatus having a reflective panel to increase captured solar radiation and which can also serve as a protective covering for the collector portion of the apparatus in inclement weather conditions.

It is another object of the present invention to provide a solar heating method and apparatus wherein conventional valve means between a collector and storage chamber of the apparatus are eliminated through the unique positioning and types of air transfer ducts and baffles.

It is another object of the present invention to provide a hot air solar furnace in which baffle members are positioned on the collector and in the heat storage chamber to desirably circulate air in obtaining optimum temperature outputs from the unit.

It is another object of the present invention to provide a hot air solar furnace in which air is transferred from a solar heat collector to a storage chamber with a minimum of heat loss and removed from the storage chamber and transmitted into a building structure with a minimum heat loss.

It is another object of the present invention to provide a hot air solar furnace which has above ground heat storage eliminating the need for costly and disfiguring excavation.

It is another object of the present invention to provide means to containerize heat storage with a new and simplified framing technique.

SUMMARY OF THE INVENTION

The foregoing and other objects are obtained in accordance with the present invention whereby solar heat is collected and stored in an integrated compact unit which is capable of generating a heat flow equal to or surpassing those of much larger unwielding units which have been typical of prior art solar heating units. The solar heating apparatus of the present invention is self-contained in an elongated housing preferably of triangular transverse crosssectional configuration. This configuration has been found to allow a maximum quantity of heat retaining material, such as gravel, to be stored in the apparatus with a minimum of structural reinforcement. The housing is basically constructed of two rectangular top panels, a rectangular bottom panel, and two triangular end panels which are interconnected to define an enclosed storage chamber for the heat retaining material. The panels are each laminated in such a manner as to give both structural strength and the required insulating qualities for maintaining the temperature of the heat retaining material in the storage chamber. A collector unit is mounted upon one of the top panels of the housing so as to be inclined relative to the vertical in a position to receive the maximum heat from the Winter sun.

The collector unit is uniquely designed to absorb solar radiated heat and retain the heat by converting the heat waves, which will readily pass through transparent glass or plastic panes on the collector face, into long wave heat radiation which will not readily pass back through the glass or plastic panes on the face of the collector. The solar heat is absorbed on a base panel of the collector which emits relatively long wave heat radiation that becomes trapped in the collector. The base panel of the collector has a plurality of forwardly opening cups which serve to increase the heat absorption and emission capability of the collector. Depending upon the material from which the cups are made, they usually will not retain the heat imparted thereto by the solar radiation for extended periods of time; accordingly, air is circulated through the collector to transfer the heat absorbed by the cups into the storage chamber of the apparatus wherein the gravel material not only absorbs the heat carried by the air but also retains the heat for extended periods of time due to inherent heat retaining characteristics of gravel and its inherent restriction of convection. The air which passes through the collector and into the storage chamber is re-circulated through the collector so as to continuously transfer heat, when desired, from the collector to the storage unit. For purposes of the present disclosure, this circulating air will be referred to as conditioning air. Since it is important to the optimum operation of the unit that the conditioning air be equally exposed to the entire base of the collector, a series of baffles are provided in the collector to direct the air stream through a series of reversing bends. Similarly, baffles are provided in the storage chamber to direct the conditioning air throughout the entire quantity of gravel in the storage chamber.

A conditioning air pump is positioned within the storage chamber to effect the desired conditioning air flow. The air is passed from the storage chamber to the collector and back into the storage chamber through inlet and outlet ducts which are positioned at an elevation below both the storage chamber and the collector so that when the pump is not in operation, the hot air which is lighter than cold air, and therefore urged to the top of the respective components of the apparatus, will not be able to freely flow between the components so that the ducts establish thermal traps that avoid the necessity of relatively expensive valve means to accomplish the same purpose.

A reflector panel is hinged to the framework of the housing along an edge of the collector unit so that by opening the reflective panel, the solar heat radiation being absorbed by the collector unit is increased. This reflective panel is designed so that in a closed position it overlies the collector unit and thereby protects the relatively fragile glass from detrimental environmental elements such as hail, sunlight in Summer months, and the like.

The heat retained by the heat retaining material in the storage chamber is transferred into an adjacent building structure or the like by a utility pump which may also be positioned within the storage chamber and connected to the building structure by suitable insulated duct work having outlets for selectively distributing the hot air through the building structure. This air flow, which will be hereinafter referred to as the utility air flow, is circulated back through the storage chamber in a manner so as to obtain a maximum heat transfer from the heat retaining material to the air and in a manner such that the utility air is not short circuited and directed through the collector with the conditioning air unless both pumps are operating simultaneously. As will be explained in more detail hereinafter, this is accomplished by positioning the inlet and outlet ducts for both the conditioning air circuit and the utility air circuit on appropriate sides of the baffle members within the storage chamber..

As will be more fully appreciated hereinafter, the unit is ideally suited for connection to an existing forced air heating system in a building structure so as to serve as an auxiliary unit to the forced air heating system even though in many instances, the solar heating unit is sufficient in itself to provide the necessary heat for the building structure.

According to the method of the present invention,

heat is first absorbed from the sun on a collector surface wherein the collector surface is insulated from the ambient environment and internal air is passed across the collector surface in a heat transfer process so that the heat absorbed by the collector surface is transferred to the internal air. The air is then passed through a duct which is lower than the collector surface into a raised storage chamber wherein it is directed through heat absorbent and heat retaining material in the storage chamber so that the heat in the hot air is transferred to the material in the storage chamber. The heat retained by the material in the storage chamber is transferred into a building structure by directing a utility stream of air through the material in the storage chamber and into the building structure wherein it is distributed as desired throughout the structure.

Other objects, advantages and capabilities of the present invention will become more apparent as the description proceeds taken in conjunction with the accompanying drawings.

DESCRIPTION OF THE DRAWINGS

FIG. 1 is a perspective view of the solar heating apparatus of the present invention with the reflector panel shown in an open position.

FIG. 2 is a perspective view of the solar heating unit of FIG. 1 with the reflector panel in a closed position.

FIG. 3 is a perspective view of the solar heating unit of the present invention as viewed from the reverse side of FIG. 1.

FIG. 4 is an end elevation of the solar heating unit of FIG. 1.

FIG. 5 is a side elevation of the solar heating unit of FIG. 1 showing the collector unit.

FIG. 6 is an enlarged vertical section taken along line 6—6 of FIG. 4.

FIG. 7 is an enlarged vertical section taken along line 7—7 of FIG. 5.

FIG. 8 is an enlarged fragmentary vertical section illustrating the connection of a top panel of the solar heating unit to the bottom panel.

FIG. 9 is an enlarged fragmentary section illustrating the connection of an end panel of the solar heating unit to the bottom panel.

FIG. 10 is a section taken along line 10—10 of FIG. 6.

FIG. 11 is an enlarged fragmentary vertical section taken along line 11—11 of FIG. 6.

FIG. 12 is an enlarged section taken along line 12—12 of FIG. 5.

FIG. 13 is a vertical section taken along line 13—13 of FIG. 5.

FIG. 14 is a vertical section taken along line 14—14 of FIG. 5

FIG. 15 is a section taken along line 15—15 of FIG. 4.

FIG. 16 is a section taken along line 16—16 of FIG. 5.

FIG. 17 is a section taken along line 17—17 of FIG. 5.

FIG. 18 is a diagrammatic horizontal section illustrating the floor plan of the solar heating apparatus of the present invention.

FIG. 19 is an enlarged section taken along line 19—19 of FIG. 4.

FIG. 20 is a diagrammatic perspective view illustrating the air currents through the storage chamber of the solar heating apparatus of the present invention.

FIG. 21 is a diagrammatic perspective view showing a modified form of the solar heating unit of the present invention.

FIG. 22 is an enlarged vertical section taken through an upper portion of a forced air furnace illustrating the connection of the solar heating apparatus of the present invention to the forced air furnace.

FIG. 23 is a section taken along line 23—23 of FIG. 22.

FIG. 24 is a perspective view of a valve plate shown in FIGS. 22 and 23.

FIG. 25 is a circuit diagram of the connection of the solar heating apparatus of the present invention to a conventional forced air furnace system.

FIG. 26 is a diagrammatic representation of the dual switch control for the conditioning pump of the apparatus of the present invention.

FIG. 27 is an electrical schematic of the dual switch control of FIG. 26.

DESCRIPTION OF THE PREFERRED EMBODIMENTS

The solar heating apparatus 28 of the present invention includes a housing 30 defining an internal storage chamber 32, a collector unit 34 mounted upon one face of the housing 30, and a reflector panel 36 pivotally connected to the housing so as to be movable between an open position exposing the collector unit 34 to the ambient environment and a closed protective position overlying the collector unit.

The framework for the apparatus includes three insulating rectangular panels of substantially the same size which are interconnected along their longitudinal edges to form an elongated housing of triangular transverse cross-section. The three rectangular panels consist of two inclined top panels 38*a* and 38*b* and a floor panel 40 with the top panels 38*a* and 38*b* forming an angle of approximately 60° with horizontal. Each of the top panels and bottom panel are laminated with conventional plywood sheets 42 on opposite faces and an inner relatively thick core 44 of an insulating material such as a rigid polyurethane foam. The plywood panels are preferably painted or coated with a reflective paint such as a silver paint to better retain heat within the storage chamber.

The panels 38*a*, 38*b*, and 40 are connected along their edges with a relatively thin gauge angled metallic strip which is positioned to be self-tightening. Referring to FIG. 8, it will be seen that the lower edge of each top panel is tapered to fit flush against the horizontal top surface of the bottom panel 40 and an angled metallic strip 46, FIGS. 8 and 13, is positioned along the outer edge of the top and bottom panels 38*a* and 38*b* so as to have a horizontal leg 48 which lies between the panels and an upwardly inclined leg 50 which is flush with the outer surface of the top panel. Conventional fasteners, such as of the screw type, connect the horizontal leg with the bottom panel and the upwardly inclined leg with the top panel. These fastening strips 46 extend along the length of the bottom of the panels to securely and reliably interconnect the panels. The bottom panel extends beyond the lower edge of the top panel **38*b*** for a reason which will become clear later.

At the juncture of the upper edges of the top panels **38*a*** and **38*b***, one of the top panels **38*a*** extends across the upper end of the other top panel **38*b*** and is bevelled at its outer end so as to form a **60°** angle therewith and establish a smooth juncture of the two panels. The plywood laminate **42** on the outer surface of each of the top panels extends upwardly to the uppermost point of the housing and an angle iron strip **52** is placed downwardly over the juncture of the two outermost plywood sheets to extend along the length of the panels. This angle iron strip **52** is suitably fastened to the respective top panels, such as with screw type fasteners, to reliably secure the panels along the top edges thereof.

Triangular shaped end panels **54** and **56** are secured to the end edges of the top and bottom panels **38*a*** and **38*b*** of the housing in a manner which is best illustrated in FIG. **9.** There it will be seen that the end panels **54** and **56** extend downwardly to the lower edge of the bottom panel **40** and likewise extend outwardly to the outer edges of the top panels **38*a*** and **38*b*** to completely cover the end edges of the top and bottom panels. The end panels actually extend beyond the top panel **38*b*** at **58,** FIGS. **12** and **19,** for a purpose to be described later. The end panels are constructed identically to the top and bottom panels in that they are laminates having outer layers **60** of a rigid material such as plywood and an inner insulating rigid foam core **62.** The end panels are connected to the top and bottom panels by angled metallic strips **64,** FIG. **9,** which extend along the junctures of the panels and are fastened thereto as with screw-type fasteners in a self-tightening manner. Each end panel has a removable door **66** closing an opening **68** therein which provides selectable access to pump containing compartments **70** and **72** in the storage chamber **32** which will be described later.

A water-repellant sheet metal covering **74** is provided over the top panel **38*a*** and the end panels **54** and **56** so that these panels will be protected from deterioration by moisture in the ambient environment.

The top, bottom and end panels cooperate in confining a heat retaining material **76** such as gravel in a manner such that the weight of the gravel does not place excessive outward pressure on the housing. In other words, since gravel is naturally piled with inclining sides, the pressure on the top walls **38*a*** and **38*b*** of the housing, since they too are inclined, is minimal. In the preferred form, the heat retaining material **76** is a granite rock of approximately 1½ inches in diameter so that the spaces between the rock particles are sufficient to allow the flow of air through the storage chamber. A fill opening **78,** FIGS. **3** and **6,** is provided near the top edge of one of the top panels so that gravel can be poured through the opening to fill the storage chamber. An insulated door **80** removably seals the opening **78** during operation of the apparatus.

The storage chamber **32** of the apparatus has a plurality of baffles or barrier plates **81, 82** and **84** positioned therein to encourage the desired circulation of air through the gravel material as will be described in more particularity later. The baffle members include two upstanding baffle members **80** and **82** of trapezoidal configuration which are flush with the bottom wall and extend slightly over half the height of each of the top panels thereby separating the lower portion of the storage chamber into two end sections **86** and **88** and a central section **90,** FIGS. **6** and **20.** The third depending baffle member **84** is suspended from the upper portion of the top panel members at approximately their longitudinal center and is of triangular configuration to fit flushly against the inner surfaces of the top panel members and extend slightly over half the height of the top panel members so as to overlap the upward extent of the upstanding baffles. Each of the baffle members is secured to the abutting top and bottom panel members by suitable fasteners **92,** FIG. **10,** which could be angle iron strips.

The reflector panel **36** in the preferred form includes a framework **37** in which three highly reflective sheets **39** of aluminum or the like are retained. The sheets may follow a modified parabolic curve to concentrate solar radiation on the collector unit **34.** The framework **37** is pivotally mounted as by a hinge **41** to the floor panel **40** of the apparatus. The reflective sheets, of course, could be other suitable materials such as mirrors, or the like, and if the mirrors were readily susceptible to breakage, a large number of relatively small mirrors could be mounted in the framework **37** so that replacement of damaged or broken mirrors would not be a great economical burden.

The collector unit **34** which is probably best illustrated in FIGS. **1, 5, 7** and **11–14,** is of a size substantially the same as the top panels of the housing and is mounted directly on the outer face of the top panels **38*b*.** The collector unit includes an outer peripheral rigid frame **94,** a front insulating glass portion **96,** and a back heat accumulator portion **98.** The insulator glass portion and heat accumulator portion are separated by a plurality of baffle members **100** and **102** which, as will be explained hereinafter, serve to circulate air uniformly through the collector.

The peripheral frame **94** abuts the inner surfaces of the extensions **58** of the end panels beyond top panel **38*b*** so as to be insulated along the associated two sides from the ambient environment and an elongated wedge shaped insulating block **104** lies across and is attached to the top portion of the peripheral frame to insulate the top portion from the ambient environment.

The insulating glass portion **96** of the collector unit consists, in the preferred form, of three spaced layers **106*a*,** 106*b* and **106*c*** of glass with each layer of glass having two coplanar glass or plastic panels **108*a* 108*b*** separated at the longitudinal center of the collector by a center plate **110.** Each glass or plastic panel is separated from the glass panel in the next adjacent layer by a rubber sealant strip **112** which extends around the periphery of the panel. Referring to FIG. **17,** the rubber sealant strips extending along the adjacent ends of the glass panels at the longitudinal center of the collector are seen sandwiched with the glass panels between an outer angle iron strip **114** which is secured as by a rivet to the center plate **110** and an inner channel member **116** which is also secured to the center plate as by a rivet. The periphery of each glass panel is embedded along with the rubber sealant strips **112** in a caulking compound **118,** FIG. **17,** to hermetically seal the perimeter of the insulating glass portion of the collector so that heat accumulated in the heat accumulator portion of the collector cannot escape back to the ambient environment around the periphery of the glass panels. In FIGS. 11–13, the top, bottom and side edges respectively of the glass panels are seen similarly sandwiched between an outer angle iron strip 120 and an inner channel member 122 each of which are affixed in any suitable manner to the outer frame 94 of the collector unit. Accordingly, the glass panels 108*a* and 108*b* on each half of the glass insulating portion of the collector unit are retained in parallel spaced relationship and are sealed around their periphery to prevent heat loss.

The heat accumulator portion 98 of the collector unit includes a planar back plate 124, preferably a sheet of black coated metallic coil or the like which lies against or is affixed to the outer plywood sheet 42 of the top panel 38*b*. A plurality of forwardly opening cups 126, preferably of cylindrical configuration and made of aluminum and coated black, are positioned upon the black aluminum back sheet and define spaces 128 therebetween which expose the back sheet 124. Again, preferably the cups are coated or annodized in a black color as black is known to be the best heat absorbent color. The cups may be loosely disposed upon the back plate 124 or could be secured thereto if desired. It will be appreciated that the cups enlarge the surface area of the heat accumulator 98 and thus the solar thermal energy capturing ability of the apparatus. In fact, by using cups which are approximately 2 inches in length and 2¾ inches in diameter, the surface area of the heat accumulator will be increased approximately 4.75 times over that of a planar heat accumulator. As clearly seen in FIGS. 11–13, the forward extent of the accumulator cups 126 is rearwardly spaced from the insulator glass 96 defining an open space or passage 130 therebetween through which air can freely pass. The baffle members 100 and 102 are positioned within this space to direct the conditioning air currents along a predetermined path which fairly uniformly covers the entire array or matrix of accumulator cups whereby a complete and effective transfer of heat from the accumulator cups to the air can be effected.

As best illustrated in FIG. 15, in the preferred form, there are three rising baffle members 100 which extend upwardly from the lower edge of the collector unit in uniformly spaced relationship and two depending baffle members 102 which extend downwardly from the top edge of the collector unit into the centralmost spaces between the three rising baffle members. Each of the baffle members extend approximately three-fourths of the height of the collector. Referring to FIGS. 16 and 17, these baffle members can be seen to be comprised of the back-to-back channel members 132 and 116 with the channel members 116 on the center baffle 100 being those at the longitudinal center of the collector unit which support the adjacent center edges of the glass panels 108*a* and 108*b*. The remaining baffle members, as shown in FIG. 15, serve to support the glass panels and additional rubber spacer sealant strips at intermediate locations so that the glass insulating portion 96 of the collector unit is adequately supported and less prone to damage. Of course, each of the baffles are secured to the back plate and the underlying plywood sheet of the top panel by suitable fasteners.

Referring now to FIGS. 13–15 and 20, it will be seen that the lower horizontal portion of the frame 94 of the collector unit has rectangular openings 134 and 136 at opposite ends thereof which communicate with the space 130 between the glass insulator section and the heat accumulator section of the unit. The opening 134 is the inlet opening to the collector while the opening 136 is the outlet opening. Air entering the collector through the inlet opening 134 is confined in the space 130 between the glass insulator portion 96 and heat accumulator portion 98 and is directed along a path defined by the baffle members which passes through a series of reversing bends as indicated by the arrows in FIG. 15, thereby forcing the air to pass across all of the accumulator cups in the collector. Turbulence created by the configuration and positioning of the cups assists in the more efficient transfer of heat.

Referring now to FIGS. 7, and 13–15, it will be seen that the inlet and outlet pressure 134 and 136 respectively of the collector unit are connected through rectangular passages 138 and 139 in an insulating foam block 140 to insulated ducts 142 and 143 which are cut or otherwise formed in the floor panel 40 of the housing. The ducts 142 and 143 open into the storage chamber 32 of the apparatus. The duct 142 communicating with the inlet opening 134 of the collector unit is in fluid communication with a conditioning air pump 144 mounted within the enclosed compartment 70 in the storage chamber. The pump 144 is also in fluid communication with an outlet 146 from the storage chamber via a duct 148. The ducts 143 and 148 each have screens covering their openings into the storage chamber 32 and each screen has a mesh size less than the size of the rock material stored in the storage chamber so that the rock material cannot pass into the ducts. The screened opening 150 connecting the duct 143 to the storage chamber, will hereafter be referred to as the conditioning air inlet to the storage chamber while the screened opening 146 will be referred to as the conditioning air outlet from the storage chamber.

It will, therefore, be seen that a circulating path is established through the collector and the storage chamber with the conditioning air pump serving as the means for effecting the desired circulation of the conditioning air. The conditioning air pump draws the air from the storage chamber through the duct 148 which again is cut or otherwise formed in the bottom panel of the housing so as to be at a level beneath both the collector and storage chamber and open into the conditioning air pump compartment as well as into the end section 86 of the remaining open area of the storage chamber so that air which has passed through the storage chamber is drawn downwardly into the duct 148 before passed through the conditioning air pump and subsequently into the collector unit. The purpose for the three under-the-floor ducts 142, 143 and 148, is to prevent the free flow of air between the spaces connected by the ducts eliminating the need for conventional fluid flow valves.

It is important that once the heat has been transferred from the collector into the storage chamber that it not be allowed to escape from the chamber by convection during non-operation of the circulating pump. Since hot air rises to the top of the storage chamber and will not pass downwardly through any of the ducts connecting the storage chamber to the collector unit and thereby allow heat to escape from the storage chamber. Accordingly, by placing the ducts at a level beneath both the storage chamber and the collector unit, the hot air is prevented from escaping from the storage chamber and the use of conventional and relatively expensive valves are avoided. To insulate the ducts from the underlying terrain on which the apparatus is supported, insulated pads **152** are positioned beneath the ducts, even though a complete insulating panel approximately the size of the bottom panel could be used. Preferably, a vapor barrier **154** in the form of a corregated metal or plastic sheet would separate the insulating panel from the bottom panel and the ducts to prevent the ingress of moisture.

The flow of conditioning air through the storage chamber of the apparatus is best illustrated in FIG. **20** wherein it is seen that hot air leaving the collector unit through the outlet opening **136** emerges through the screened opening **150** at the inlet end of the storage chamber and is forced to pass unwardly over the baffle member **82** into the heat retaining gravel and then follow a downwardly and upwardly reversing path below and above the three baffle plates **80, 82** and **84** in the storage chamber until it is drawn downwardly through the screened outlet opening **146** at the opposite end of the storage chamber and subsequently blown by the conditioning pump into the collector unit through the inlet opening **134.** In this manner, the hot air being directed into the storage chamber from the collector unit is forced to pass through the storage chamber in such a manner as to come into contact with substantially all of the heat retaining gravel material in the storage chamber. It should be realized that the inlet end of the storage chamber will normally be substantially hotter than the outlet and during operation of the conditioning pump since the hot air entering the storage chamber will lose its heat to the gravel material as it passes through the storage chamber (provided that circulated air temperature is higher than storage temperature) so that by the time the air reaches the outlet end of the storage chamber it is somewhat cooler than when it entered the storage chamber.

In addition to the three aforedescribed underthe-floor ducts **142, 143** and **148,** the apparatus has two additional under-the-floor ducts **156** and **158** defining inlet and outlet ducts respectively of the utility air circuit so that the heat retained by the material in the storage chamber can be transferred via a flow of utility air through an adjacent building structure. The inlet duct **156** for the utility air is seen in FIG. **7** to comprise an elongated channel cut or otherwise formed in the floor panel **40** of the apparatus and sealed by an insulating block **160** so as to extend beneath the lower edge of the top panel. The inner end of the inlet duct opens upwardly through the floor of the unit and has a screen **162** covering thereover of a smaller mesh than the particle size of the gravel heat retaining material so as to prevent the gravel material from falling into the duct. The outer end of the duct opens upwardly and extends above the floor of the storage chamber and is connected through a conventional air filter **164** to an elbow conduit **166** which is connected via an air flow conduit **168,** FIG. **1,** to a circulating duct system in the building structure (not shown). The circulating duct system in the building structure could be in an existing forced air furnace duct system and the heating apparatus of the present invention could be connected thereto in a manner to be described in detail later. However, the solar system could have its own circulating duct system.

Similarly, the outlet duct **158** of the utility air circuit is formed in the floor panel the same as the the inlet duct and has its inner end opening upwardly in fluid communication with a utility pump **170,** FIGS. **18** and **20,** which is housed in the enclosed compartment **72** in the storage chamber at the diametrically opposite corner from the conditioning pump **144.** The inlet of the utility pump opens through a screened opening **172** in the adjacent upstanding baffle plate **82** so as to draw air from the central section of the storage chamber. The outlet duct **158** of the utility system also opens at its outer end through an insulated block **174** and may be connected through an air filter (not shown) to a second elbow conduit **176** and subsequently through an air flow conduit (not shown) to the circulating duct work in the building structure. It can, therefore, be appreciated that a circulating utility air flow circuit is established through the storage chamber and the heating duct work in the building structure whereby hot air can be drawn from the storage chamber and blown into the building structure wherein it may be selectively diverted through various vent openings into desired locations in the building structure.

As mentioned previously, the heat retaining gravel material **76** in the storage chamber is hottest at the inlet end of the storage chamber with respect to the conditioning circuit and progressively becomes relatively cooler toward the outlet end. It is, therefore, desirable that the utility air flow, or that air which is directed into the building structure, is withdrawn from the storage chamber at the hot end or the inlet end thereof and for this reason, the utility pump which withdraws air from the storage chamber and directs it into the building structure is positioned at the hot or inlet end in the section **88** of the storage chamber. However, to prevent air entering the storage chamber from the collector unit through opening **150** from being withdrawn directly by the utility pump **170,** the inlet **172** to the utility pump is positioned on the opposite side of the upstanding baffle plate **82** from the opening **150** so that the hot air entering the storage chamber is forced to begin circulating and thereby transferring its heat into the gravel material whereby this heat will be retained by the gravel material and can be readily withdrawn when the utility pump is in operation. In other words, by positioning the inlet **172** to the utility pump on the opposite side of the baffle plate **82** from the outlet of the collector, a short circuit in both the utility and conditioning air flows is avoided.

So that the utility air entering the storage chamber will have adequate time to absorb heat from the gravel storage material before it is withdrawn from the storage chamber by the utility pump, it is desirable that the inlet **162** to the storage chamber in the utility circuit be positioned as far away from the utility pump as possible. However, the inlet in the utility circuit is preferably not placed closely adjacent to the outlet **146** from the storage chamber in the conditioning circuit so that the air does not flow directly into the outlet of the conditioning circuit but rather flows toward the utility pump **170** and thus toward the hot end of the storage chamber in a counter-flow direction relative to the conditioning air circuit except when both pumps are in simultaneous operation. For this reason, the inlet **162** of the utility circuit has been positioned on the opposite side of the upstanding baffle plate **80** so that this air will migrate toward the hot end of the apparatus beneath the center baffle plate **84** and will not rise and pass over the upstanding baffle plate **80** and thereafter pass into the outlet **146** of the conditioning circuit. Accordingly, this relative relationship of the inlet **162** in the utility circuit to the outlet **146** in the conditioning circuit prevents short circuiting of the utility air flow and encourages the air to flow in the desired direction.

It should be appreciated that the apparatus is designed so that if desired, the storage chamber can be essentially by passed whereby hot air can be circulated through the collector and the building structure with minimal contact with the heat retaining material. In this manner heat from the collector is transferred substantially directly into the building structure. This can be best understood by reference to FIG. **20** wherein it will be seen that if both the utility pump **170** and the conditioning pump **144** are operated simultaneously, air leaving the collector and entering the storage chamber through opening **150** will pass upwardly over the baffle member **82** and will be immediately drawn into the inlet **172** of the utility pump wherefrom it will be circulated through the duct work in the building structure. In other words, when the hot air enters the storage chamber and passes over the baffle member **82**, the low pressure existing at the inlet **172** to the outlet pump during operation of the utility pump attracts the hot air so that it does not take its normal circulating path through the heat retaining material in the storage chamber. After the air has circulated through the duct work in the building structure it enters the storage chamber through inlet **162** and is drawn over baffle member **80** into outlet **146** from the storage chamber whereby it is cycled into the conditioning pump **144** and into the collector through the inlet **134** to the collector. Thus it will be seen that a closed circulating path directly connecting the collector to the duct work in the building structure, with minimal contact with the heat retaining material **76**, is established by simultaneous operation of the conditioning and utility pumps.

The conditioning pump **144** in the preferred form is automatically controlled by a dual control system illustrated in FIGS. **26** and **27**. A resistant temperature detector in the form of a probe **178**, FIG. **18**, is positioned in the storage chamber near the center thereof and a second resistant temperature detector in the form of a probe **179**, FIG. **15**, is mounted in the collector near the outlet from the collector so that each is disposed to sense the temperature at the respective locations. The temperature detectors are connected through a comparator circuit, illustrated in FIG. **27**, to the control switch of the conditioning pump. The comparator circuit, as will be explained hereinafter, is used to compare the temperatures of the detectors **178** and **179** and to switch the conditioning pump on when the temperature of the detector **179** equals or succeeds by a predetermined amount the temperature of detector **178**. By so controlling the operation of the conditioning pump, breakage of the collector glass panels by thermal shock is alleviated, the use of less insulation at the collector glass panels is allowed since heat is extracted rapidly from the collector cutting heat loss through the glass panels, and the life of the conditioning pump is extended due to less cycling. While other comparator circuits could be utilized, in the preferred form, the comparator circuit is in the form of a conventional wheatstone bridge where identical resistors **R1** and **R2** are connected in the bridge with a third resistor **R3**, the detector **178**, the detector **179**, and a rheostat **181**. The operation of the wheatstone bridge circuit is conventional with the rheostat **181** serving to adjust or regulate the temperature differential between detectors **178** and **179** desired for operation of the conditioning pump. It will, therefore, be seen that with the dual control system, the temperature in the storage chamber is automatically maintained or raised during normal weather conditions.

As mentioned previously, the aforedescribed heating apparatus can be easily connected into an existing forced air furnace system in a building structure. Referring to FIGS. **22–25**, the manner in which the heating apparatus can be connected to a forced air furnace system is illustrated. Looking first at FIG. **22**, the upper end of a typical forced air furnace unit **180** is illustrated having heat exchangers **182** in a heat exchange portion **184** of the unit and a plenum chamber **186** above the heat exchange portion **184** wherein the hot air emitted from the forced air furnace unit is directed into the circulating duct work in the building structure for desired distribution through the building structure. An outlet conduit **188** in the utility circulating system of the solar heating apparatus **28** of the present invention is connected to the plenum chamber **186** of the forced air heating unit through an opening **190** in one side thereof so that the air entering the plenum chamber from the solar heating apparatus will pass into the plenum chamber wherefrom it can be directed into the circulating duct work in the building structure for desired distribution throughout the structure. To prevent this air from passing downwardly into the forced air furnace when the forced air furnace is not in operation, a series of valve plates **192** are pivotally mounted across the open upper end of the heat exchange portion **184** of the forced air furnace apparatus so that in normal conditions when the forced air furnace is not in operation, these valve plates lie in the closed solid line positions of FIGS. **22** and **23**. The valve plates include a rectangular planar section **194** with a pivet rod **196** along one longitudinal edge. The pivot rod extends beyond the ends of the rectangular planar section so that the ends of the rod can be journalled in suitable bearing members **198** shown as U-shaped brackets in FIG. **23**, to pivotally support the valve plates in a horizontal disposition. The width of the rectangular planar section of each plate is such that the plate overlie the pivot rod of the next adjacent plate whereby when the plates are in their closed positions, the outlet from the heat exchange portion of the forced air furnace is blocked. Accordingly, air entering the plenum chamber from the solar heating apparatus **28** through the conduit **188** cannot flow downwardly but must flow upwardly and into the circulating duct work for desired distribution through the building structure.

When the forced air heating apparatus is in operation, however, the air being blown upwardly through the heat exchange portion **184** and into the plenum chamber **186** is sufficiently strong enough to pivot the valve plates **192** about their pivot rods so that they open into the dotted line position of FIG. **22** thereby allowing the air to pass into the plenum chamber and subsequently into the circulating duct work of the building structure. Pin stops **200** are provided for each valve plate to limit the pivotal movement of the plate. In this manner, the solar heating unit can be connected directly into the forced air heating unit and neither system will inhibit proper functioning of the other. Accordingly, when it is desired to operate the forced air furnace apparatus, it will operate independently of the solar heating unit and when the solar heating unit is operated, it can operate independently of the forced air heating apparatus.

Referring to FIG. **25**, a schematic control circuit diagram is shown with the solar furnace system and a conventional forced air furnace system connected in a complementary fashion. It will be seen that as is conventional, a step-down transformer **204** converts the **110** volt A.C. input into a **24** volt potential which is placed on the coil **206** in a forced air gas furnace relay **208**. The thermostat **210** in the house or building structure is also connected between the transformer **204** and the coil **206** so that the coil is not energized unless the house thermostat is closed, such has when the temperature in the house is below a preselected temperature. When the coil in the forced air gas furnace relay is energized, it closes a switch **212** which places a potential on the forced air furnace blower **214** and on a thermostat **216** in the solar furnace storage chamber. The forced air furnace blower, however, will not operate unless a furnace control switch **218** which is also temperature controlled and which is positioned within the forced air furnace is closed. This furnace control switch, however, does not close until the temperature within the forced air furnace is above a preselected level. The solar furnace storage chamber thermostat **216** is a double-throw switch so that when the temperature in the storage chamber is below a preselected temperature, the forced air furnace gas valve **219** is energized thereby causing the forced air furnace to heat and once the temperature of the furnace unit is above a preselected level, the furnace control switch closes thereby energizing the forced air furnace blower so that the hot air from the forced air furnace will be circulated through the building structure. However, if the temperature within the solar furnace storage chamber is above a preselected level, the solar furnace storage thermostat rather than energizing the forced air furnace gas valve **219** energizes the solar furnace blower or utility pump **170** so that the utility circulating air in the solar furnace is operated to heat the building structure. It will be appreciated, that in this manner, the conventional forced air heating system and the solar heating system of the present invention are used to supplement each other and depending upon the solar radiation in the particular area in which the unit is in operation, the solar furnace system can be predominately used with the forced air furnace system only as a backup during unusual weather conditions. The operaton of the conditioning pump **144** is automatically controlled by a dual sensor thermostat.

Referring to FIG. **21**, it is seen that additional reflector panels have been mounted upon the solar heating unit **28** to increase the solar radiation received by the collector unit **34**. As illustrated, reflector panels **220** are pivotally mounted along each side of the collector unit and a reflector panel **222** is mounted along the top edge of the collector unit to cooperate with the reflector panel **36** previously described as being connected along the bottom edge of the collector unit. Of course, during inclement weather conditions, when it is desirable that the glass or plastic insulator **96** on the collector unit be covered, each of the reflector panels can be folded inwardly into protective overlying face-to-face relationship with the collector unit.

It has been found by building the solar heating unit of the present invention in accordance with the previous description that the units can be made in a very compact manner and of a size to be positioned in a fairly inconspicuous manner adjacent to a building structure, such as a home, without materially detracting from the appearance of the home. In fact, it has been found that the unit can be placed in a normal sized backyard without taking up unreasonable ground space.

In a test unit, which was not placed in an optimum position for receiving maximum solar radiation, each of the top and bottom panels of the unit, the reflector panel, and the collector unit were approximately **8** feet by **12** feet as oppostcd to the prior art arrangements wherein substantial portions of the roof of the building structures were needed to collect adequate solar radiation to heat the building structure. By utilizing the thermal cups in the collector unit, it was found that the solar heat absorbed by the unit was equivalent to a conventional planar collector unit that was **16** feed by **28** feet, or the solar absorbing capacity of the collector of the present unit was found to be approximately **4.75** times that of a conventional planar collector not utilizing the accumulator cups. When using gravel of approximately **1½** inches in diameter particle size, the unit has been found capable of obtaining temperatures at the hot end of the storage chamber of around **300°F**, a mean storage chamber of approximately **250°F**, and was found to lose only **1½°** to **5°** (depending upon outside ambient temperature) per day when the conditioning and utility pumps were not operated. Since typical forced air furnace systems only obtain mean temperatures of about **130°** in the plenum chamber, it will be appreciated that due to higher operating temperatures, the solar unit utility pump does not require as long a duration of operating cycles as a forced air furnace to maintain a given temperature in the building structure with the same outside ambient temperatures. Since a particular storage material inherently absorbs and emits heat at approximately the same rate, and since

the rate at which heat is exposed to the storage material is excessive in the present apparatus of the absorptive capability of the storage material, the rise and fall of the storage material temperature occurs at the same rate given similar pump capacities of the utility and conditioning pumps, and not unusual temperature differentials in the building structure being heated and exclusive of simultaneous conduction losses through the walls of the apparatus.

While the foregoing description has been directed to the heating capability of the apparatus of the present invention, it should be appreciated that the apparatus is also capable of cooling building structures and therefore has a dual capability. When using the apparatus to cool a building structure, it is connected to the building structure in the same manner as previously described but instead of storing solar heat during daylight hours, the unit is closed during the daylight hours with the reflector panel 36 lying over the collector unit 34 to prevent solar heat from being absorbed by the collector unit. Then, when the sun is not shining, the conditioning pump is then operated to circulate air through the collector and the storage chamber wherein heat is removed from the storage material 76 or gravel in the storage chamber. After the gravel has been adequately cooled, and before the ambient air begins to warm up during daylight hours, the conditioning pump 144 is turned off thermostatically. When cool air is desired in a building structure, the utility pump 170 is operated to circulate air through the relatively cool storage material to thereby remove heat from the building structure.

*

Chapter 5

House Cooling Systems

Feb. 11, 1936. A. T. BREMSER **2,030,350**

SOLAR OPERATED REFRIGERATING SYSTEM

*

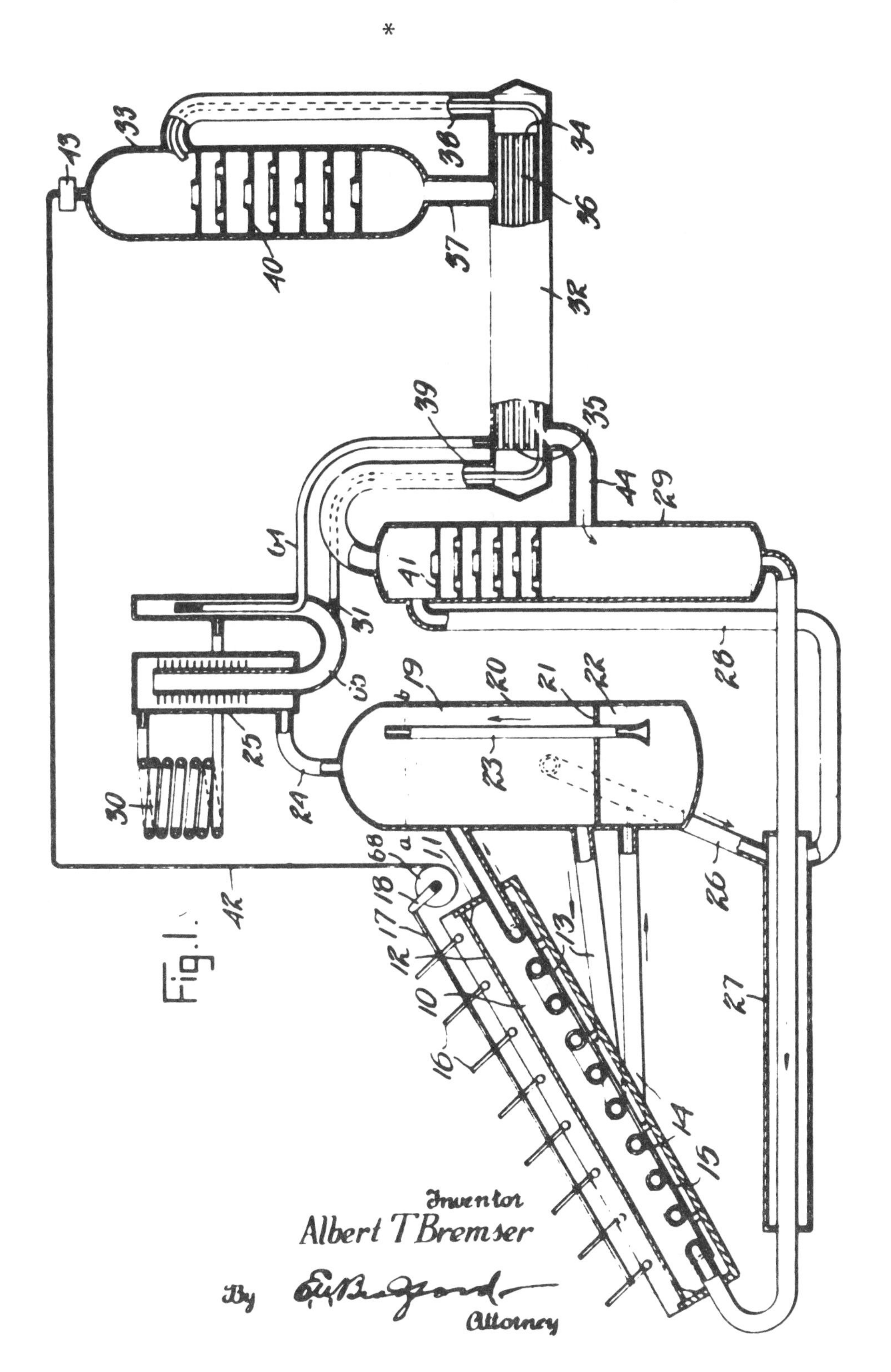

Feb. 11, 1936. A. T. BREMSER **2,030,350**

SOLAR OPERATED REFRIGERATING SYSTEM

*

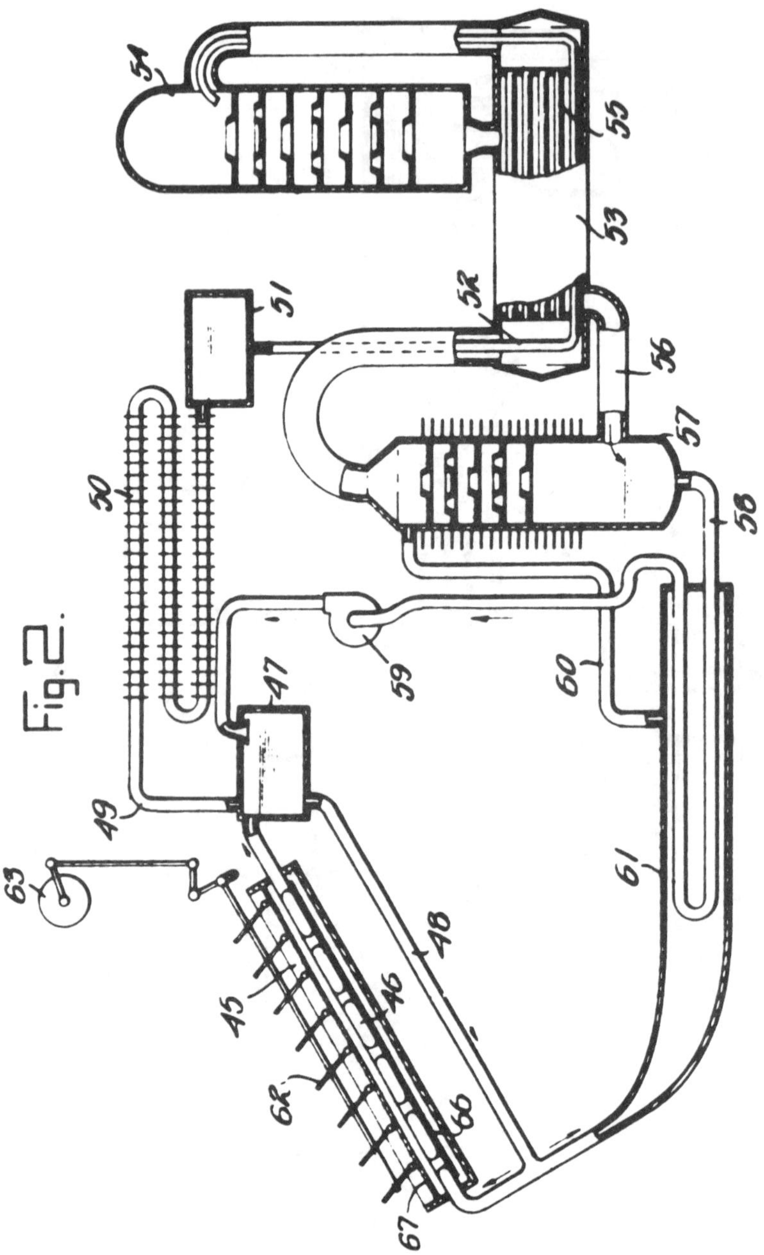

Fig. 2.

Inventor

Albert T. Bremser

By [signature]

Attorney

UNITED STATES PATENT OFFICE

2,030,350

SOLAR OPERATED REFRIGERATING SYSTEM

Albert T. Bremser, Westmont, N. J., assignor of fifty-two per cent to Carl G. Fisher, Miami Beach, Fla.

*

My invention provides a system of cooling by utilizing the heat energy of the sun's rays. The invention therefore relates to a cooling or refrigerating system operated by solar heating means. The invention comprises a combination of some form of absorption type of cooling system with a solar heater.

The object of the invention therefore is to provide a cooling system which may be operated without mechanical heat and which may be operated without fuel cost and in sections having no available mechanical heat source other than the sun's rays.

A further object is to provide a cooling system which will respond automatically to changes in temperature to keep the temperature within desired limits.

Referring to the accompanying drawings, which are made a part hereof and on which similar reference characters indicate similar parts,

Figure 1 is a view in elevation with parts shown in section of my cooling system, and

Figure 2, a view in elevation of a modified form of cooling system adapted particularly for the cooling of rooms or compartments.

In the drawings numeral 10 indicates a solar heater which comprises an insulated box 11 having preferably a glass cover 12 and having coils 13 and 14 therein. These coils are made of metal having a high co-efficient of heat conductivity. The coils are mounted upon a sheet of metal 15 which likewise is of a high heat conductive material such as copper, aluminum or other suitable metals. Shutters 16 are pivotally mounted upon the box and are connected by an operating link 17 which in turn is connected to an arm 18. The purpose of the shutters is to control the amount of sun rays permitted to strike the coils within the box and thus control the temperature of the solar heater. The box is set at a suitable angle to the horizontal in order to afford a better absorption of heat throughout the day. Two sets of coils 13 and 14 are positioned within the box 10. The coil 13 communicates at its upper end with the upper portion of a container 20. This container is divided by a horizontal partition into upper and lower chambers 19 and 22. The lower end of the coil enters the chamber 19 just above the partition 21. One or more riser tubes 23 are positioned with their lower ends extending well down into the chamber 22 and the upper ends above the normal level *a*—*b* of liquid in the chamber 19. The upper end of the coil 14 enters the lower chamber 22. The upper portion of the chamber 19 is connnected by an outlet tube 24 with a rectifier 25 of known construction. The lower section of the upper chamber 19 is connected by a tube 26 which communicates with a jacket 27 surrounding the lower portion of the coil 14. A second tube 28 passes from the jacket 27 to the upper portion of an absorber drum 29. The upper portion of the rectifier is connected to a condenser coil 30 which may be cooled in any suitable way, either by water or by air. The lower portion of the U-tube 65 which forms part of the rectifier 25 is connected by a pipe 31 which passes through a liquid cooler 32 and enters the evaporator 33. The evaporator is filled with hydrogen gas and operates in a well known manner. The lower portion of the coil 14 communicates with the lower portion of the absorber 29. The liquid cooler 32 consists of a drum having plates 34 and 35 in which are fixed tubes 36. The lower portion of the evaporator communicates through a pipe 37 with the space surrounding these tubes. The chambers formed at the ends of the partitions are connected by jackets 38 and 39 with the upper portion of the evaporator 33 and the upper portion of the absorber 29. The evaporator has baffle plates 40 positioned in staggered relation therein and the absorber has similar parts 41. The space surrounding the tubes 36 communicates through pipe 44 with the absorber 29. A riser tube 64 also connects the space about the tubes 36 with the space above the liquid in the U-tube 65.

Before starting operation the container 20 is filled with water and ammonia. This is a strong ammonia liquid. The lower chamber 22 of the container 20 is also partially filled with ammonia liquid. The evaporator 33 and the upper portion of the absorber 29 are filled with hydrogen gas. The shutters 16 are positioned at a suitable angle and are operated by lever 18 which is operably connected with a thermostat 68 which is actuated by a heat responsive device 43 of any suitable construction. Thermostat 43 may be positioned to respond to changes of temperature in the evaporator or the chamber surrounding it. The ammonia liquid in the coils 13 and 14 is heated by rays from the sun. It is well known that the sun's rays may be controlled so as to raise the temperature of water to and even above the boiling point. The heat imparted to the liquid in the coils 13 and 14 therefore will vaporize the ammonia and also will cause circulation of the liquid in these coils. The circulation of the liquid through the upper coil 13 will be from the low portion of the chamber 19 to its upper portion. The ammonia gas and steam will be driven off from the surface of the liquid in the chamber 19. This gas will pass up through the tube 24 into the rectifier 25. Some of the liquid in the rectifier will pass immediately into the rectifier U-tube 65 and the gas will pass over into the condenser 30 where it is liquefied and returns to the right hand side of the U-tube and down through the tube 31, thence through the liquid cooler 32, and into the evaporator 33. The evaporator is filled with hydrogen gas into which ammonia freely evaporates to produce a lower temperature in the medium surrounding the evaporator. The circulation through the coil 14 is from the bottom of the absorber tank 29 through the coil 14 into the chamber 22 in the lower portion of the container 20. As this coil is heated the ammonia therein will be driven off from the water and this gas will be trapped in the space below the partition 21 and the surface of the liquid in the chamber 22. When the pressure in the chamber 22 reaches a high enough point to balance the column of liquid in the tube 23 the liquid will be forced up through this tube into the chamber 19 until the level of the liquid in the chamber 22 reaches the bottom of the tube 23 after which gas in the chamber 22 will rush up through the tube 23 carrying with it the liquid in the tube. This portion of the apparatus operates not altogether unlike a coffee percolator. Weak ammonia liquid from the lower portion of the chamber 19 will pass down through the tube 26 and through the tube 28 into the upper portion of the absorber 29. Strong ammonia liquid from the lower portion of the absorber 29 will pass into the lower portion of the coils 14, the circulation being caused by heating of the coils in the solar heater. The ammonia gases in the evaporator together with the hydrogen gases into which the ammonia has evaporated will pass down through the tube 37 and through the tube 44 into the absorber 29, where the ammonia will be absorbed by the water in the absorber and the hydrogen gases will rise to the top of the absorber to return through the jackets 39, the tubes 36 and the jacket 38 into the evaporator again. The hydrogen and ammonia gases as they leave the evaporator have been greatly lowered in temperature and these serve to pre-cool the ammonia liquid as it passes through the pipe 31 through the liquid cooler 32. After starting, the operation is continuous so long as heat is applied to the coils 13 and 14. The thermostat 43 may be set to maintain the temperature at any desired point in the evaporator. When the temperature falls below a predetermined degree the shutters 16 will be closed to reduce the amount of coils exposed to the rays of the sun so that the device will operate automatically to maintain the temperature at the desired low level.

In the system shown in Figure 2 the heating chamber 45 contains only a single coil 46. This coil at its upper end communicates with the upper portion of a chamber 47 and the liquid returns from chamber 47 through return pipe 48. The coils 46 are mounted upon a metallic plate 66. The chamber is covered by a glass plate 67. When the ammonia in the coils 46 has been heated circulation is set up through the chamber 47. As the temperature of the ammonia is raised the ammonia gas will pass off and out through the tube 49. This ammonia vapor is liquefied by the cooler 50 and passes into a receiver 51. From this receiver liquid ammonia passes through the tube 52 and the liquid cooler 53 where it evaporates into the hydrogen filled evaporator 54. Hydrogen and ammonia gas return from the evaporator through the spaces about the tubes 55 and return through the tube 56 to the absorber 57. The lower portion of the absorber 57 is connected by a coil 58 which is connected with the upper portion of the chamber 47. A pump or other fluid impeller 59 may be positioned in the pipe 58 to force circulation from the absorber into the chamber 47. The upper portion of the absorber 57 is connected by a pipe 60 with a chamber 61 into which chamber the coil or pipe 58 extends. The absorber 57 may be cooled in any suitable way either by air or water as desired. Shutters 62 may be pivotally mounted on the heater 45 and operated by a thermostat 63 which may be positioned in the chambers or rooms to be cooled so that the amount of heat imparted to the ammonia liquid will be controlled in response to the temperature in the rooms which are cooled. *

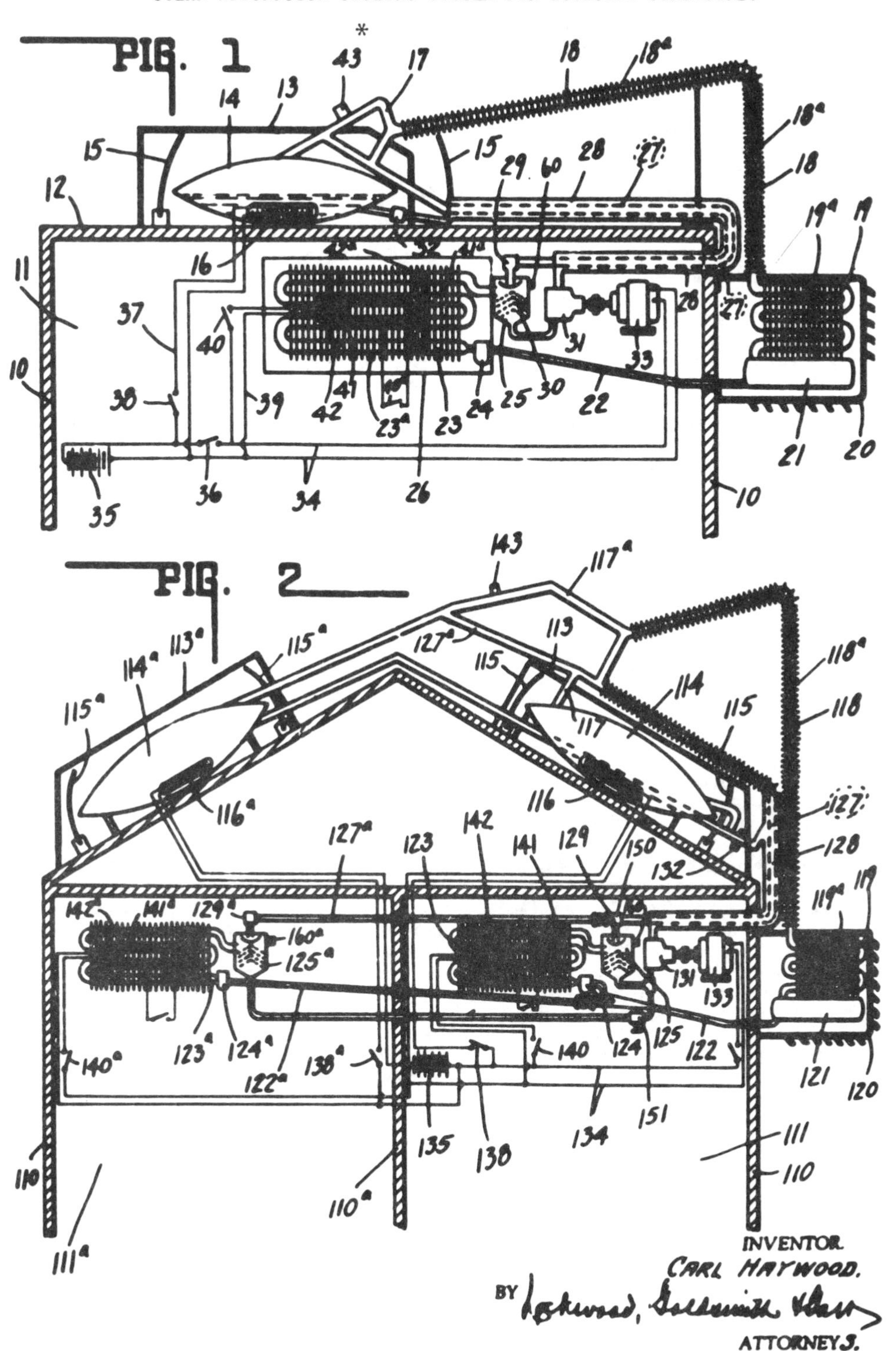
Nov. 19, 1940.
C. HAYWOOD
2,221,971
SOLAR-ABSORPTION COOLING SYSTEM FOR BUILDING STRUCTURES
FIG. 1
FIG. 2
INVENTOR
CARL HAYWOOD.
BY Lockwood, Goldsmith & Galt
ATTORNEYS.

UNITED STATES PATENT OFFICE

2,221,971

SOLAR-ABSORPTION COOLING SYSTEM FOR BUILDING STRUCTURES

Carl Haywood, Indianapolis, Ind.

*

This invention relates to a solar system operated continuous absorption type air cooling system.

The chief object of this invention is to provide a cooling system for a building structure or compartment which is subject to the rays of the sun for relatively long periods during the day and more especially in localities where the normal daily temperature is relatively high so that the sun's heat responsible for such high temperatures serves as a source of energy for operation of a cooling system to eliminate or reduce the suffering or unpleasantness due to such heat.

The chief feature of the invention consists in the application to a refrigerating system of a solar furnace and associating therewith other apparatus, such as hereinafter described, for accomplishing the foregoing object and other purposes set forth hereinafter.

This invention, as stated, may be applied to a stationary structure such as a building having one or more rooms, or a house type trailer or the like, although not necessarily restricted thereto. It may be utilized where central station electric power is not available, or whenever for reasons of economy, power line connection is not desired.

The full nature of the invention will be understood from the accompanying drawing and the following description and claims:

In the drawing,

Fig. 1 is a vertical sectional view of a compartment with the invention diagrammatically illustrated as applied thereto.

Fig. 2 is a similar view of a modified form thereof.

In Fig. 1 of the drawing, **10** indicates a building structure having at least one room or compartment **11** therein and a relatively flat roof **12**. The same supports a glass compartment **13** to eliminate as much as possible the circulation or passage of air should there be a slight breeze.

Mounted within compartment **13** is a generator **14** of an absorption type refrigerating system. If it be assumed the plane of the section is latitudinal, then there may be, if desired, provided mirrors **15** to the east and west of the generator which in the early morning and late evening will reflect the sun rays onto the generator **14**.

If desired a source of heat such as an electric heating element or a flue gas heating arrangement, may be provided, but either of these, if employed, is solely utilized as an auxiliary source of heat. Herein such an auxiliary source is indicated by numeral **16**.

The numeral **17** indicates an analyzer which automatically separates water vapor from the ammonia vapor liberated by the generator. Element **18**, connected at one end to the analyzer, serves as a rectifier and traps out of the gas the remaining moisture. This may be finned as shown at **18a**. The other end of the rectifier is connected to the condenser **19** which may be similarly finned as at **19a** and enclosed in a louvred compartment **20**, preferably mounted in the shade.

Solar heat evaporates ammonia gas and water vapor from the aqua ammonia in the generator. The dry gas following analysis and rectification is liquefied in the condenser located on the shaded side of the building.

The condenser discharges to a receiver **21** in the same compartment **20** which in turn is connected to the expansion line **22** discharging to one end of the evaporator **23** through the automatic expansion valve **24**. The evaporator is finned as at **23a**. The evaporator is illustrated as a sinuous conduit and its other end is connected to the absorber **25**.

The condenser changes the vapor ammonia to liquid ammonia, and the evaporator reverses this change of state thereby abstracting heat from chamber **26** which includes the evaporator. The receiver serves as a storage receptacle for liquid ammonia and its capacity may be so arranged relative to the evaporator capacity that an appreciable "carry-over" is possible, in some instances, the device storing sufficient liquid ammonia for use during the entire night when solar heat is not available for vaporization.

In the absorber **25** the heated ammonia vapor is absorbed by the weak aqua ammonia which is supplied thereto by the weak liquor line **27** enveloped by the heat exchanger **28**. Such supply is controlled by the automatic throttling valve **29** and is diverted by baffles **30** in the absorber **25**.

The weak liquor upon absorbing the ammonia gas in the absorber becomes strong liquor and is drawn from the bottom of the absorber by the pump **31** and supplied by line **28** (previously designated as heat exchange) to the generator through the check valve **32**. The pump **31** may be driven by an electric motor **33** supplied by lines **34** from a conventionally illustrated source of electrical energy **35** and controlled by switch **36**. The auxiliary heating unit **16** may also be connected to the source of energy **35** by lines **37** and controlled by switch **38**.

Lines **39** connected to said source of energy and controlled by switch **40** are connected to an auxiliary or a circulating fan operating motor **41** operating fan **42**. This fan circulates the air through the finned sinuosities of the evaporator which is protected by a suitable grill arrangement **26**. An additional motor **41a** and **42a** controlled by switch **40a** may be provided if desired.

Plug **43** is provided for filling the system. Switches **36**, **38** and **40** are of conventional type that is, may be thermostatically controlled or manually controlled, as described.

Whenever desired, there may be provided in each room of the building and which is to be cooled an evaporator with its expansion valve and a circulating fan. All evaporators would be supplied by line 22 and all evaporators would discharge to a common absorber 25.

As herein illustrated, the pump motor 33 is usually less than $\frac{1}{16}$ horsepower and the fan motor 41 may be as small as desired or as large as required. An automobile type storage battery, therefore, normally provides sufficient energy for motor operation for a reasonable period of time. Whenever central station power is available, the auxiliary heat source 18 may be utilized as often as required or desired, and in such event the system receiver 21 need not be of such large capacity since the element 18 could be automatically cut in, whenever the room temperature exceeded the predetermined maximum desired, irrespective of whether the solar heating portion of the system was operative or not.

Many individuals are not much affected by heat during their waking hours but experience difficulty in getting to sleep during hot nights. Where this is the case and where central station power is not available for auxiliary heating, the receiver should be constructed of large size to enable sufficient liquor to accumulate therein during the day to permit of operation of the system during the night. While continuous operation of all parts of the system is possible, and in fact is the usual method of operation, it is apparent that continuous day and night operation is not possible. It is to be noted, however, that day and night cooling may be had with two separate systems.

Where only night operation is required, the switch 36 is open during the day preventing operation of the pump and evaporator. This permits the accumulation of strong liquor in the receiver. Also, during the day automatic throttling valve 29 is kept closed and weak liquor from the generator is stored in the tube 27. In the evening switches 36 and 40 are closed and valve 29 opened whereby the system functions as in continuous daytime operation, the pump returning the fortified liquor from the absorber 25 to the generator where it awaits the action of the sun the following morning. The generator, in other words, acts as a storage tank during night operation.

In Fig. 2 of the drawing, there is illustrated a modification of the form of the invention shown in Fig. 1. This modification only differs therefrom by providing two generators connected in parallel into the system in place of a single generator, said dual generators being positioned on both sides of a hip roof instead of flat roof. Parts in Fig. 2 like or corresponding to parts in Fig. 1, bear similar numerals of the one hundred series and the subscript *a*.

In this modification the two evaporators while connected in multiple, are each provided with an absorber. Valve 150 between line 127 and 127*a* and valve 151 in the connection between absorber 125*a* and pump 131 provide a control for isolating the portion of the system in room 111*a* from the remainder of the system. Similar valves may be provided ahead and behind absorber 125, if desired.

To facilitate filling of the system, the absorber may be provided with a filling plug. Thus, in Fig. 1 absorber 25 is shown provided with plug 60 while in Fig. 2 absorber 125 is shown provided with filling plug 160 and absorber 125*a* is shown provided with filling plug 160*a*. *

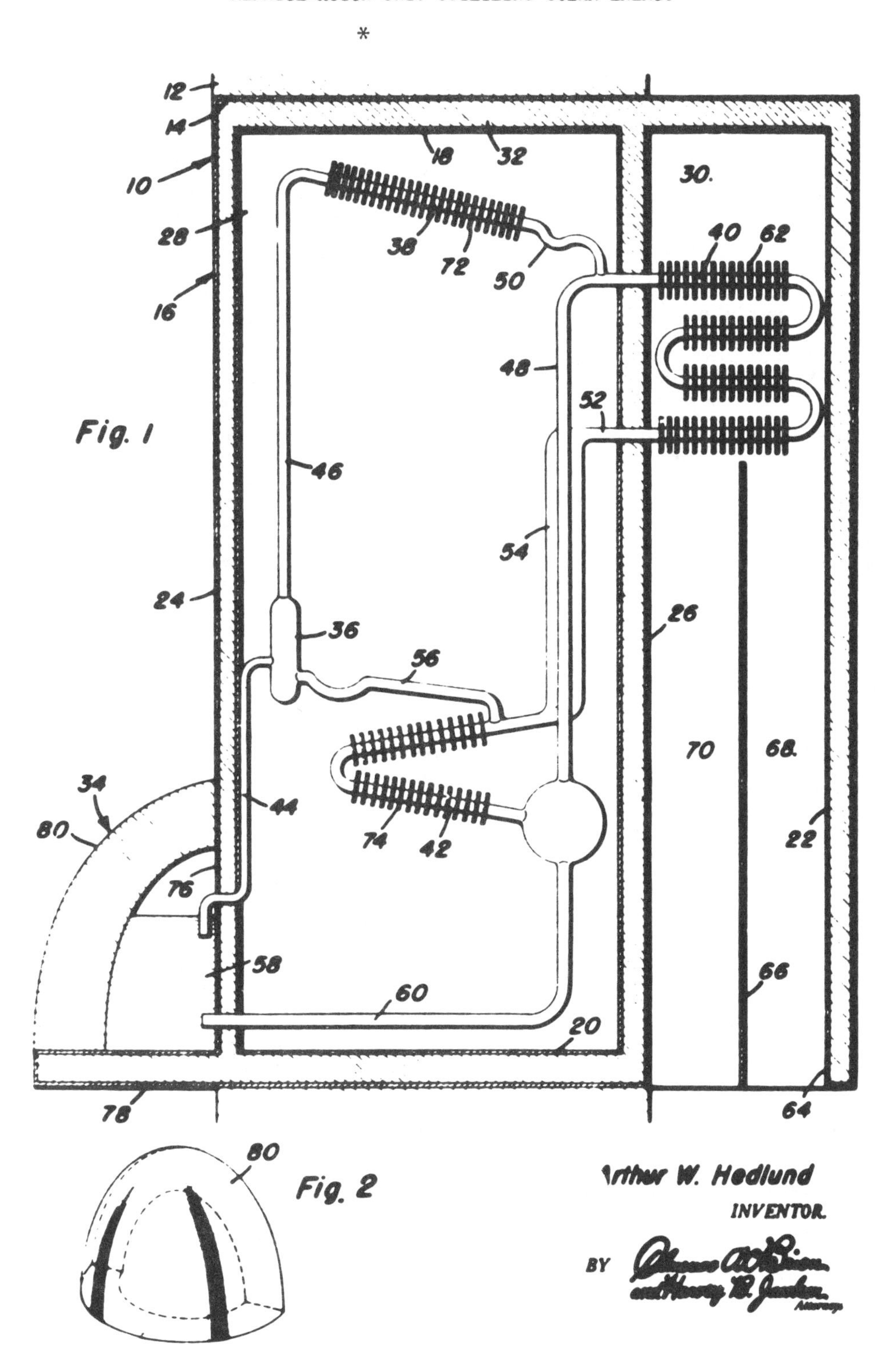

Oct. 26, 1954
A. W. HEDLUND
2,692,483
REFRIGERATION UNIT UTILIZING SOLAR ENERGY
*
Fig. 1
12
14
10
28
16
18
32
38
72
50
30.
40
62
48
52
46
54
24
36
56
26
70
68.
34
80
44
74
42
22
76
58
66
60
20
78
64
80
Fig. 2
Arthur W. Hedlund
INVENTOR.
BY

UNITED STATES PATENT OFFICE

2,692,483

REFRIGERATION UNIT UTILIZING SOLAR ENERGY

Arthur W. Hedlund, Minneapolis, Minn.

*

This invention pertains to new and useful improvements in refrigerating apparatus, and relates particularly to apparatus uniquely adapted to utilize solar energy for the purpose of either refrigerating or air conditioning an enclosed space.

The primary object of this invention is to utilize solar energy for the purpose of producing a refrigerating effect, and to provide an apparatus which will operate with at least as great efficiency in hot climates as in cool climates.

Another important object of this invention is to provide an apparatus of this character which will operate at optimum efficiency throughout the day, that is, an apparatus in which the relative angular movement of the sun during the day will not materially effect the efficiency of the apparatus.

Yet another important object of the present invention is to provide an apparatus of this character which will occupy a minimum of otherwise useful space, and in which the housing therefor will constitute a part of the insulation surrounding the space being refrigerated thereby.

Still another important object of the present invention is to provide an apparatus of this character which will afford an excellent heat exchange with the medium being cooled thereby.

A meritorious feature of the present invention resides in the provision of a concentrator for collecting and directing the solar energy striking the same to the generator, which will operate at optimum efficiency irrespective of the declination of the sun or the hour of the day.

Another important feature of the present invention resides in the positioning of the apparatus almost entirely within a wall enclosing the refrigerated space, so as to constitute a portion of the insulation therefor.

A final important feature of the present invention to be specifically enumerated herein resides in the positioning of the evaporator and the structure surrounding the same that is adapted to induce air circulation to afford better heat exchange by conduction, and which construction will still avoid the creation of excessive cold drafts that would be objectionable when the device is used for air conditioning in a home or office.

These, together with various ancillary objects and features of the invention which will become apparent as the following description proceeds, are attained by the present invention, a preferred embodiment of which has been illustrated by way of example only in the accompanying drawings, wherein:

Figure 1 is a vertical transverse sectional view of a suitable embodiment of the present invention; and

Figure 2 is a perspective view of the solar energy concentrator.

Reference is now made more specifically to the accompanying drawing, wherein like numerals designate similar parts throughout the various views, and in which a wall section is designated generally at 10. It will be understood that the wall section 10 constitutes only a portion of a wall construction, not shown, built to enclose a refrigerated space that appears to the right of the wall section 10 as shown in Figure 1.

The wall section 10 includes a wall 12 having an opening 14 therethrough in which is positioned a housing designated generally at 16.

The housing 16 includes top and bottom walls 18 and 20, respectively, and inner and outer walls 22 and 24, respectively. It will be noted that the walls 22 and 24 are preferably parallel to the wall 12, and that in addition the interior of the housing 16 is provided with a partition 26 that is also parallel to the walls 22 and 24 so as to divide the interior of the housing 16 into chambers 28 and 30. In the preferred construction, the walls 18, 20, 22 and 24, as well as the partition 26 are hollow, and are filled with a suitable heat insulating material 32.

The present invention includes an absorption-type refrigeration system which includes a generator designated generally at 34, a separator 36, a condenser 38, an evaporator 40, and an absorber 42. A conduit 44 communicates between the generator 34 and the separator 36, the upper end of the latter in turn communicating with the condenser 38 through a conduit 46. The upper end of the evaporator 40 is connected to the lower end of the absorber 42 by a conduit 48 and to the discharge end of the condenser 38 by a lateral conduit 50. The lower end of the evaporator 40 communicates with the upper leg of the absorber 42 through a conduit 52, it being noted that its intermediate portion 54 of the conduit 52 surrounds a portion of the conduit 48 so as to be in heat exchange relation therewith. Finally, the absorption refrigeration circuit includes a conduit 56 which communicates between the lower end of the separator 36 and the upper leg of the absorber 42.

As will be understood, the showing of the absorption refrigeration circuit is substantially diagrammatic, and since in itself it does not constitute the claimed subject matter of the present invention, it is believed that a brief description of the operation of the same will suffice since the operation of such devices is well understood by those skilled in the art. The system is, of course, of the type operating with water, ammonia, and hydrogen, of which only a concentrated mixture, or solution of ammonia in water 58 is present in the generator 34. Upon the application of heat to the solution 58 in the generator 34, vapors consisting primarily of ammonia are driven upwards through the conduit 44 to the separator 36, where portions of the vapors which have condensed in the conduit 44 and the separator 36 drain from the separator 36 into the upper leg of the absorber 42 through the conduit 56, the uncondensed portions of the vapors (substantially pure ammonia) passing on upwardly through the conduit 46 to the condenser 38 where they are cooled sufficiently to pass into the liquid phase. The ammonia condensed in the condenser 38 then passes into the upper end of the evaporator 40 through the conduit 50 to pass downwardly therethrough where the same meets a counter-current flow of upwardly moving hydrogen, so that by virtue of the reduction of the partial pressure of the ammonia vapor in the evaporator 40 due to the presence of the hydrogen gas in the vapor phase, the ammonia evaporates to move upwardly with the hydrogen gas and then downwardly through the conduit 48 to the lower leg of the absorber 42. The mixture of ammonia vapor and the hydrogen gas then moves upwardly through the absorber 42 counter-current to the flow of water passing downwardly through the absorber 42 from the conduit 56, so that the mixture of ammonia vapor and the hydrogen gas is stripped of the ammonia due to the extreme solubility of the ammonia vapor, and the concentrated water solution of ammonia vapor passes downwardly from the lower end of the absorber 42 through the conduit 60 to return to the generator 34, the stripped hydrogen gas passing upwardly through the conduit 52 from the upper end of the absorber 42 to the lower end of the evaporator 40.

It will be noted that the entire absorption refrigeration circuit is disposed within the compartment 28 with the exception of the generator 34 and the evaporator 40, the generator 34 being disposed outside of the wall section 10, while the evaporator 40 is disposed within the compartment 30. Inasmuch as it is desired that the evaporator 40 have good heat exchange with its surroundings, the evaporator 40 is provided with a plurality of heat exchange fins 62. In order to further enhance the heat exchange of the evaporator 40 with its surroundings, the bottom of the compartment 30 is open as at 64, and a baffle 66 is disposed within the compartment 30 to extend in parallel relation with the walls 22 and 24 in spaced relation with the wall 22 and the partition 26 below the evaporator 40. The purpose of this arrangement is that warm air will rise in the space 68 between the baffle 66 and the wall 22 to pass in intimate contact with the evaporator 40 to become cooled and descend in the space 70 between the baffle 66 and the partition 26.

In order to facilitate the heat exchange of the condenser 38 with its surroundings so as to compensate for the heat of vaporization of the ammonia, the condenser 38 is provided with a plurality of heat exchange fins 72, and in a similar manner, the absorber 42 is provided with a plurality of heat exchange fins 74 in order to compensate for the heat of solution of ammonia in water. Since both the condenser 38 and the absorber 42 liberate heat within the compartment 28, the compartment 28 is vented by means, not shown, through the wall 28 to permit the escape of such liberated heat.

The generator 34 comprises a portion 76 of the wall 24 and outwardly extending portion 78 of the bottom wall 20, and a radiant energy concentrator 80. The concentrator 80 in conjunction with the wall portions 76 and 78 constitute a housing for the fluid 58, the concentrator 80 being substantially a shell that rests upon the wall portion 48 in sealing engagement with both of the wall portions 76 and 78. As best shown in Figure 2, the concentrator 80 is concavo-convex in shape, and is substantially semi-cylindrical in horizontal section throughout its vertical extent, and is substantially semi-cylindrical in vertical section taken parallel to the wall portion 76. In addition, the concentrator 80 is formed of transparent material, and is preferably of a material particularly high in transparency as to heat or infrared radiation. Further, the shape of the concentrator 80, and its index of refraction are preferably such that radiant energy emitted from any source disposed within the dihedral angle defined by the wall portions 76 and 78 striking the same will be collected and directed to the fluid 58 within the generator 34 so as to heat the fluid 58. It will be noted that both the wall portions 76 and 78 are insulated to prevent the escape of heat from the fluid 58, and in addition it is preferred that the material of which the concentrator 80 is formed be also of a material possessing low thermal conductivity to prevent the escape of heat through the concentrator 80 by conduction.

The use of the present invention will be readily appreciated. The housing 16 will be disposed in a wall 12 lying in an east-west direction with the concentrator 80 facing toward the equator, so that in temperate zones the concentrator 80 will be exposed during the hours of daylight to the radiations of the sun. Of course, when the present invention is to be utilized in the tropics, it will be preferred that two of the constructions shown in Figure 1 will preferably be employed, one of which faces towards the equator with the other facing away from the equator, so that throughout the seasons at least one of such units will be exposed to the sun's radiation.

Obviously, the apparatus will be charged with the proper quantities of water, ammonia, and hydrogen for optimum refrigerating performance, such quantities being dependent on the volumetric capacity of the entire apparatus and the relative size of the components thereof. It is contemplated that the charging of the apparatus and the installation thereof may be facilitated by an alternative construction of the same, not shown, in which a separate container will be provided for the liquid contained in the heat concentrator and placed therein, such container being provided with couplings for detachably connecting to the conduits 44 and 60. *

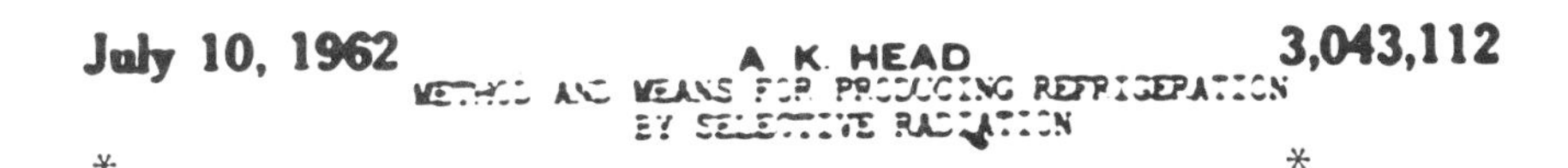
July 10, 1962 A. K. HEAD 3,043,112
METHOD AND MEANS FOR PRODUCING REFRIGERATION
BY SELECTIVE RADIATION

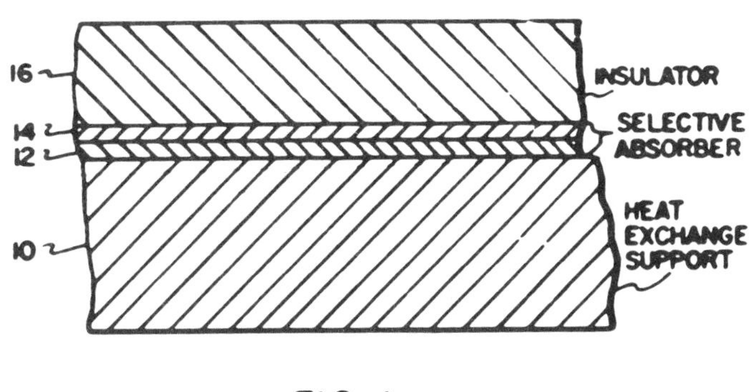

FIG. 1

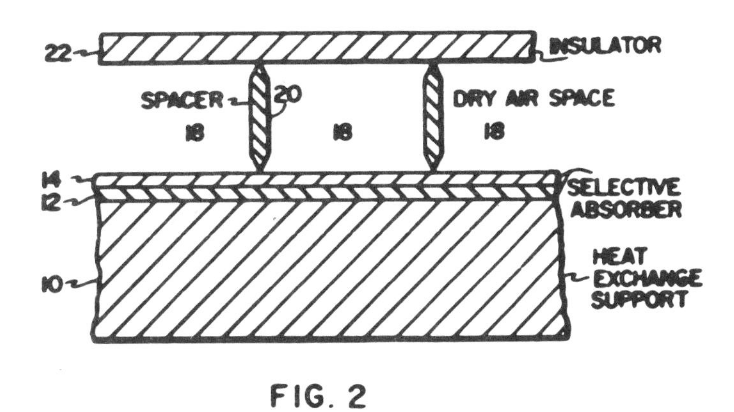

FIG. 2

July 10, 1962 A. K. HEAD **3,043,112**

METHOD AND MEANS FOR PRODUCING REFRIGERATION
BY SELECTIVE RADIATION

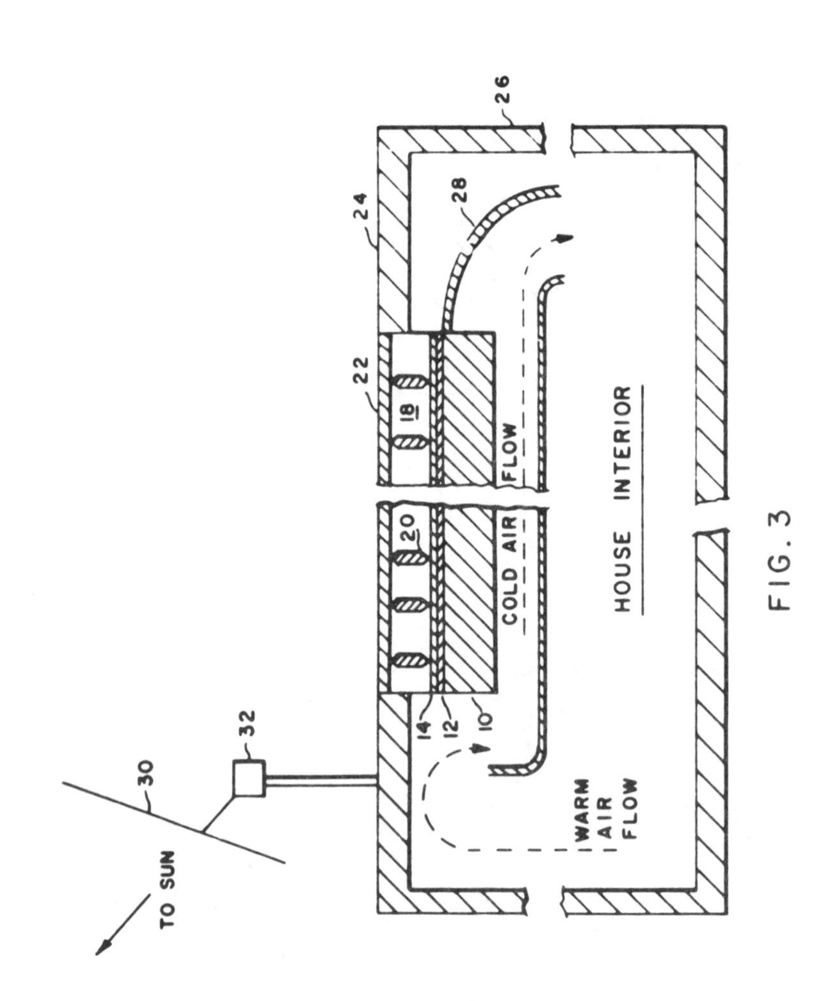

FIG. 3

INVENTOR.
Alan K. Head
BY
Oliver W. Hayes

3,043,112
METHOD AND MEANS FOR PRODUCING REFRIGERATION BY SELECTIVE RADIATION

Alan K. Head, Toorak, Victoria, Australia, assignor to Commonwealth Scientific and Industrial Research Organization, Victoria, East Melbourne, Australia, a body corporate of Australia *

This invention relates to refrigeration and more particularly to devices for producing refrigeration.

It is common practice to effect refrigeration by expansion or absorption of gases and vapors, and use has also been made of chemical and electro-magnetic means of cooling. However, all of these means require the supply of energy whether mechanically, as heat, or in some other form.

Accordingly, it is a principal object of this invention to provide a simpler method and means by which the natural heat loss by radiation can be made greater than the total heat gain by radiation, conduction and convection thereby resulting in a net loss of heat and consequent lowering of temperature.

Another object of the invention is to provide a method and apparatus for producing temperatures below ambient without utilizing a source of power.

The method of this invention requires no supply of energy, heat abstracted from the refrigerated substance being radiated to outer space or to clouds in the sky if they are present.

As clouds have an ambient temperature, it is accordingly a further object of the invention to provide means to refrigerate a surface to the temperature of the clouds present at the time.

Other objects of the invention will in part be obvious and will in part appear hereinafter.

The invention accordingly comprises the product possessing the features, properties, and the relation of components and the process involving the several steps and the relation and order of one or more of such steps with respect to each of the others which are exemplified in the following detailed disclosure and the scope of the application of which will be indicated in the claims.

For a fuller understanding of the nature and objects of the invention, reference should be had to the following detailed description taken in connection with the accompanying drawings wherein

FIGURE 1 is a sectional schematic illustration of the invention,

FIGURE 2 is a sectional schematic illustration of an alternate form of the invention; and

FIGURE 3 is a diagrammatic, schematic illustration of the use of the invention for cooling a house.

In the following description, radiation is specified by its wave lengths in microns, one micron being a thousandth part of a millimetre.

According to this invention, a method for producing temperatures below ambient consists in arranging a layer of material which emits or absorbs radiation within the range of about 8 to 13 microns, in contact with a surface which is relatively reflective to radiation outside this range. The selective absorber so produced, and hereinafter called the selective absorber for the purposes of the specification and claims can radiate more energy to the sky than it absorbs from the atmosphere and other sources whereby temperature of the selective absorber is caused to fall below ambient. Normally these conditions are met by setting up the selective absorber in a position where it can emit radiation to the sky and covering it with a layer of material which is a poor thermal conductor but which is substantially transparent to all wave lengths of light incident thereon.

According to a further feature of the invention the refrigerating means comprises a selective absorber, as referred to above, arranged in heat exchange relation with a body to be cooled and positioned so that it can radiate to the sky.

In one preferred embodiment of the invention, the refrigeration device of the present invention is preferably formed by coacting a heat exchange support 10 with a highly reflective layer 12 of silver, gold, aluminum or other suitable metal, and applying on top of this highly reflective layer a thin layer 14 of a substance which is transparent to all wave lengths except between 8 and 13 microns where it absorbs strongly. If desired, the heat exchange support 10 and the reflective layer 12 may, for example, be provided for by a single highly polished metal being substantially reflective outside the 8 to 13 microns range. The combination of the reflective surface and the layer of high absorption in the 8 to 13 micron range thus forms the "selective absorber." To prevent conductive and convective transfer of ambient heat to the selective absorber an insulating layer, schematically indicated at 16, is provided on the front surface of the selective absorber. Layer 16 can be transparent to radiation in the range of 3 to 40 microns but is preferably transparent to all wavelengths of light incident thereon. One suitable material for the insulating layer 16 is polyethylene.

In a preferred embodiment of the refrigerating device according to this invention the selective absorber preferably consists of a vacuum vaporated reflective aluminum layer covered with a vacuum evaporated layer of silicon monoxide having a thickness in the range of 0.9 micron to 1.5 microns and preferably on the order of 1.2 microns. The term "silicon monoxide" as used in the specification and claims consists of the compositions SiO and SiO_1+X. Alternatively other substances containing a silicon-oxygen bond (such as silica, silicones and silicates), or a carbon-fluorine bond (such as polytetrafluorethylene), or a carbon-carbon bond, or a carbon-nitrogen bond, or a carbon-oxygen bond, or a nitrogen-hydrogen bond such as ammonia or its compounds, can be used to give absorption of radiation between 8 and 13 microns.

In a further embodiment of the invention as illustrated in FIG. 2, the layer of poor thermal conductivity which covers the selective absorber is formed of a plurality of air spaces 18 which are preferably free from water vapor and carbon dioxide. Suitable thermal insulators 20 are used to form the columns and support a sheet of insulation 22 which protects the interior of the column from mixing with ambient air. Insulator 22 can be transparent to radiation in the range of 8 to 13 microns but is preferably transparent to all wavelengths incident thereon.

It is to be understood that the insulating layer 16 of FIG. 1, which is in thermal contact with the selective absorber, will be cooled below ambient by conduction and so must not absorb substantial amounts of incident radiation. In FIG. 2 the true insulator is the air space which is transparent in the range below 40 microns. As stated above the purpose of the insulator 22 is to keep the air in the space stagnant. Since insulator 22 is only in "radiant contact" with the selective absorber, it need only be transparent to radiation in the range of 8 to 13 microns. A single column of air may be used where such would be more suitable. Alternative protective insulation means can be a mass of infra-red (8 to 13 microns) transparent material containing pockets of air or other suitably transparent gas.

With the selective absorber mounted horizontally in the open, the heat that it emits is in the far infra-red with the majority of the radiation between wavelengths of 8 and 13 microns. However, in this wavelength range the cloudless atmosphere emits or absorbs very little radiation, while outside this range (due to the presence of water vapor and carbon dioxide) the atmosphere is essentially opaque and emits and absorbs radiation.

Due to the selective properties of the absorber it can only emit or absorb radiation in the range of 8 to 13 microns. Due to the fact that the atmosphere is not emitting at these wavelengths there is very little radiation falling on the selective absorber. The selective absorber thus emits more radiation than it absorbs and so its temperature will fall.

The heating effect of sunlight is minimized by the reflecting surface of the selective absorber because the majority of the energy in sunlight is in the visible, near infra-red and ultra-violet range of wavelengths. The provision of a thin layer of a material such as germanium or silicon, which is opaque to radiation outside the range of 8 to 13 microns, on the outer face of the insulating layer (16 of FIG. 1 and 22 of FIG. 2) further limits heating by solar radiation. This layer will get warm due to the energy it absorbs but being in contact with the outside air it will not get too warm.

A sunshade (indicated at 30 in FIG. 3) of suitable size and shape can also be added so that the surface of the selective absorber is in shade at all hours of the day. For example, a vertical sunshade of sufficient height and width and having its upper portion forming an obtuse angle over the selective absorber surface will provide shade for the absorber surface. This sunshade is preferably mounted so that it is freely movable to permit convenient orientation to the sun. Since the sun is continually moving, suitable automatic means 32 may be provided to permit the shade to be oriented to the sun at all times. The surface of the sunshade presented to the selective absorber should be a good reflector so that it will not emit heat radiation to be absorbed by the selective absorber, and should preferably be placed at such an angle that it reflects the sky into the selective absorber.

The performance of this system can be calculated from the Planck radiation law and measurements of the infrared radiation emitted by the atmosphere. For a cloudless sky, it is found that the net loss of heat by radiation from one square metre of surface (having an emissivity of 0.5) at 0° C. in one day is 1,600,000 calories. This is equivalent to the heat absorbed in melting 20 kilograms of ice. If a lower temperature is desired then less "cooling power" is available, or if a higher temperature is desired then more "cooling power" is available. The lowest temperature which can be reached and at which no "cooling power" is available appears to be about −80° C.

If the sky is covered completely with clouds, the lowest temperature which can be reached is the temperature of the clouds and the amount of heat energy which can be transferred from the selective absorber is limited accordingly. If the rear of the selective absorber is effectively insulated, the active surface will cool to the temperature of the clouds, say, 0° C. If the cloud cover is partial the active surface will cool to a temperature between −80° C. and 0° C., in proportion to the amount of cloud cover. Thus measuring the temperature of the active surface gives a measure of the amount of cloud cover.

From the above performance figures it can be calculated that if the roof 24 of a single storied house 26 is made of active surface then the cooling available should be sufficient to air condition the house. As the source of cold is above the rooms to be cooled, suitable ducting 28 gives automatic circulation of air.

In some cases it would not be necessary for the active surface to cool below 10° C. If this is so, then, besides absorbing between 8 and 13 microns, no harm, and a small amount of good, would come if the active surface also absorbed between 4 and 8 microns. This is because the back radiation from the sky between 4 and 8 microns has an average equivalent temperature of about 5° or 10° C.

If the active surface cools below the dew point of the air, then water will condense. It appears that a square metre of active surface could condense a few pints of water from the air per day. The exact amount depends on the dew point of the air and the efficiency of the heat exchanger through which the warm incoming air and cold dry exhaust air pass. Once again its should be possible to circulate the air automatically by thermal syphon action.

The efficiency of a heat engine depends on the temperature difference available. By using a sink below ambient temperature produced by means of the present invention, the efficiency of heat engines, and particularly of engines operating by means of solar radiation could be raised.

While the invention has been described with respect to particular embodiments thereof wherein the layer of high absorption in the range 8 to 13 microns preferably consists of silicon monoxide, other materials can be used in combination with a reflective surface to form the "selective absorber," the principal requirement being that the layer be transparent to all wavelengths except between 8 and 13 microns where it absorbs strongly. In addition to the materials discussed previously, certain metallic oxides such as zinc oxide are equally suitable.

*

March 21, 1967 F. TROMBE 3,310,102
DEVICES FOR LOWERING THE TEMPERATURE OF
A BODY BY HEAT RADIATION THEREFROM

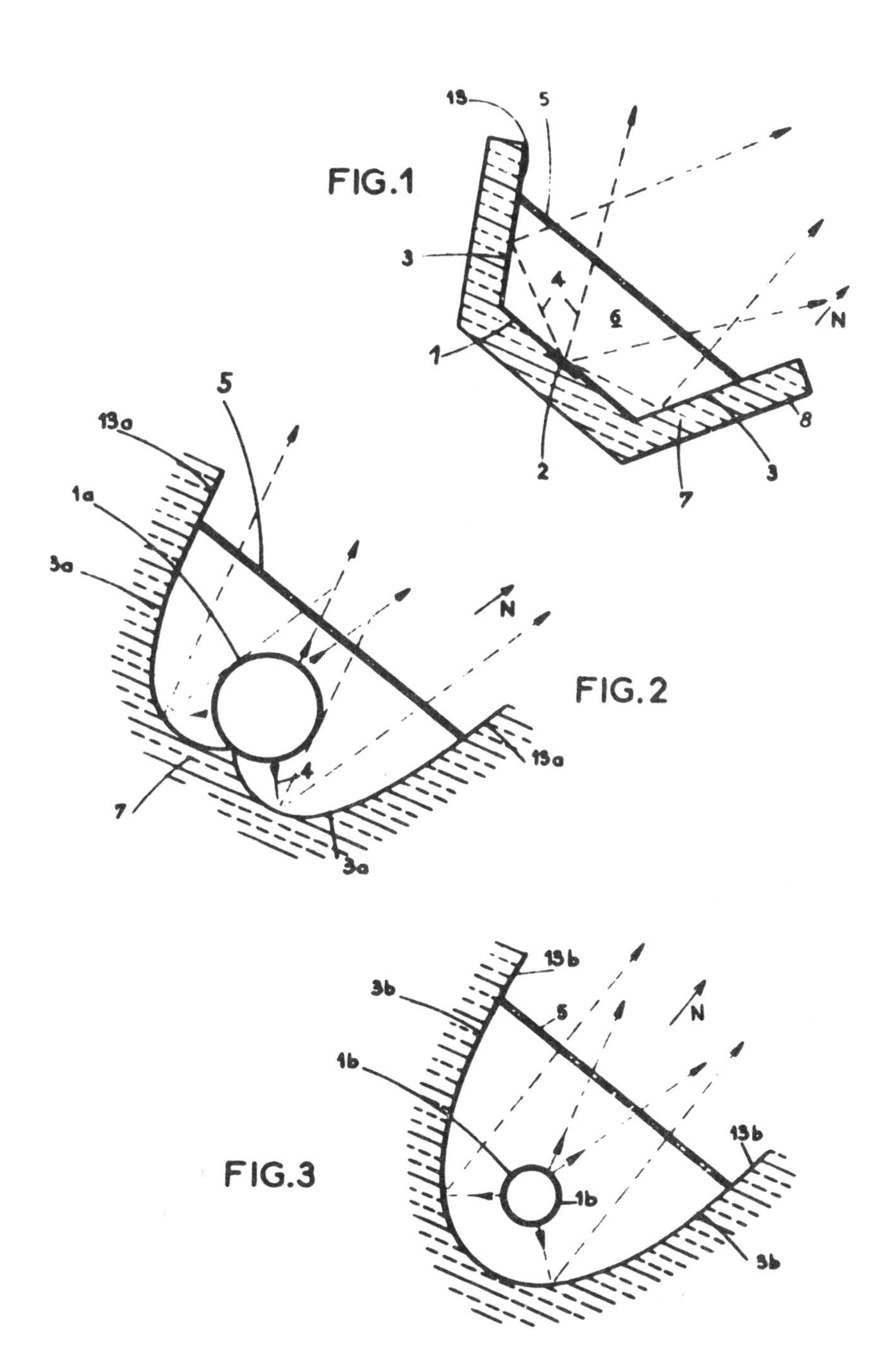

March 21, 1967 F. TROMBE **3,310,102**

DEVICES FOR LOWERING THE TEMPERATURE OF
A BODY BY HEAT RADIATION THEREFROM

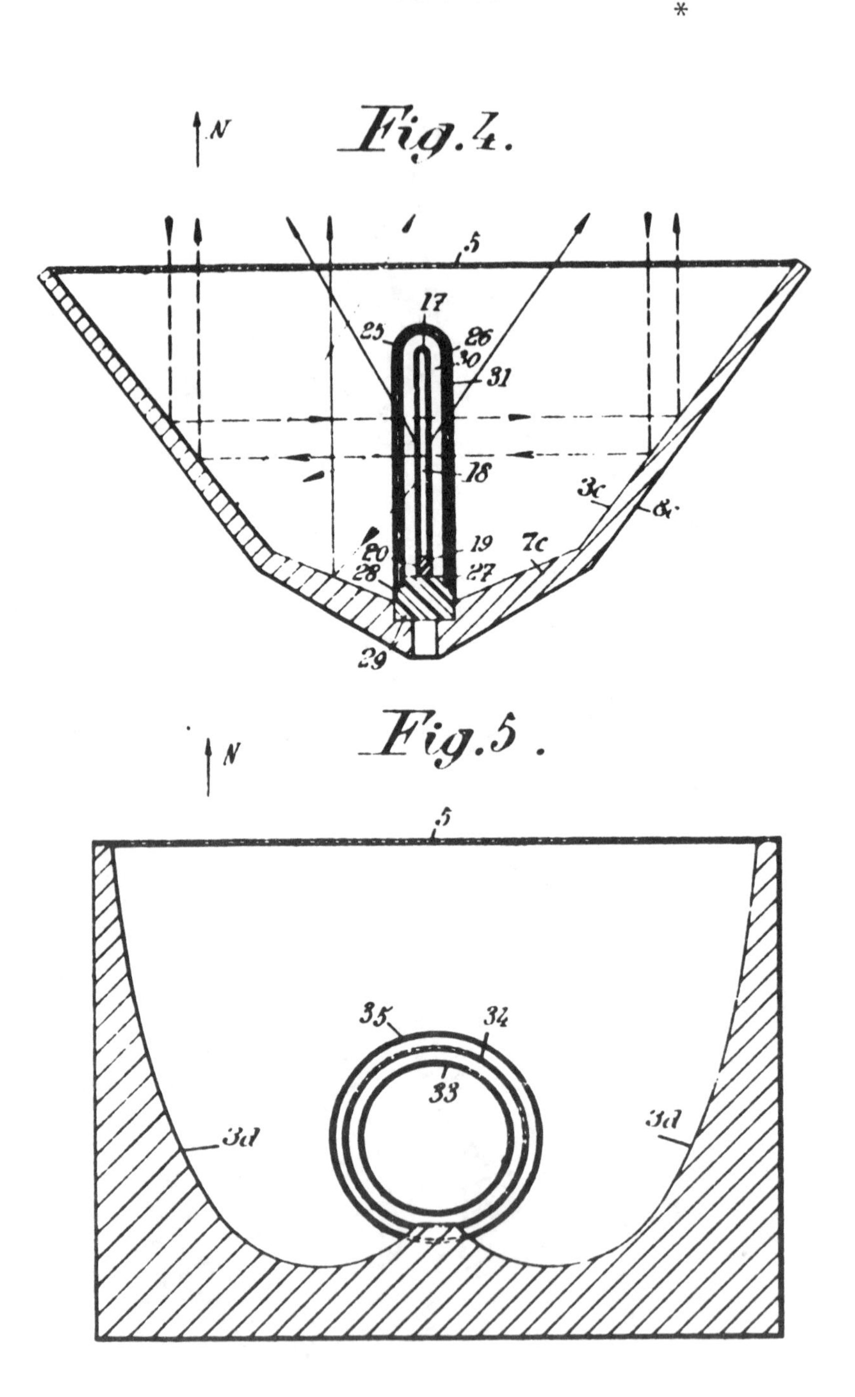

March 21, 1967 F. TROMBE **3,310,102**
DEVICES FOR LOWERING THE TEMPERATURE OF
A BODY BY HEAT RADIATION THEREFROM

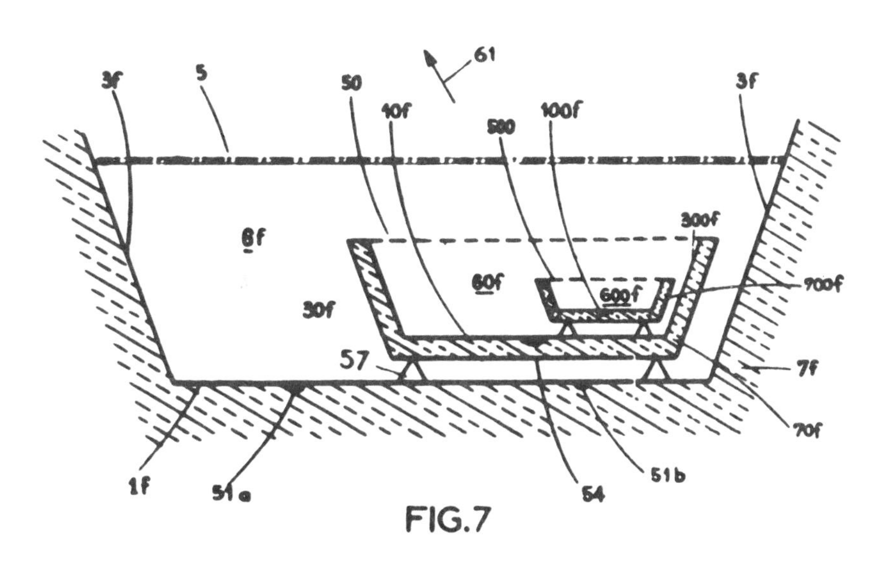

FIG.7

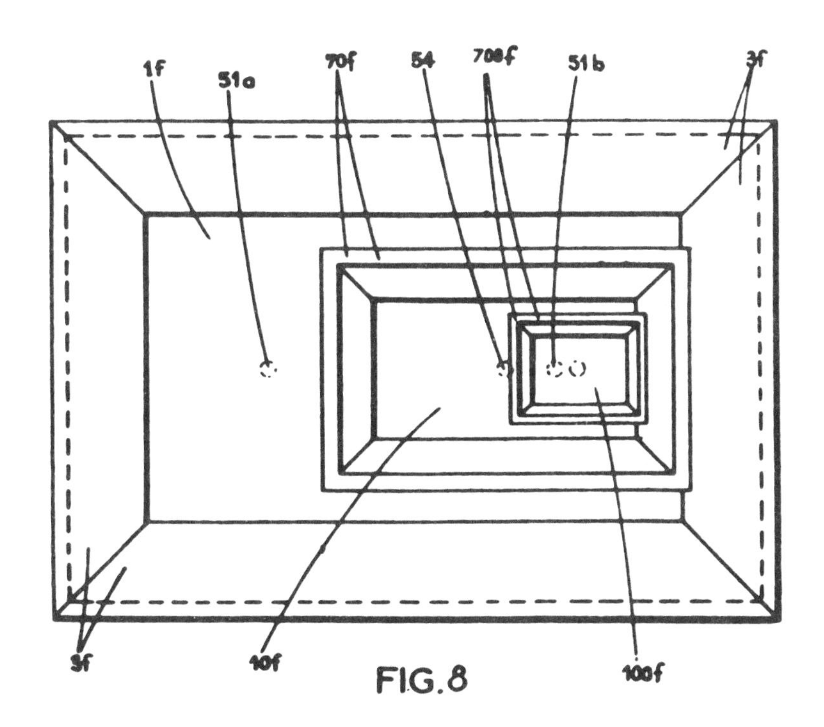

FIG.8

March 21, 1967 F. TROMBE **3,310,102**

DEVICES FOR LOWERING THE TEMPERATURE OF A BODY BY HEAT RADIATION THEREFROM

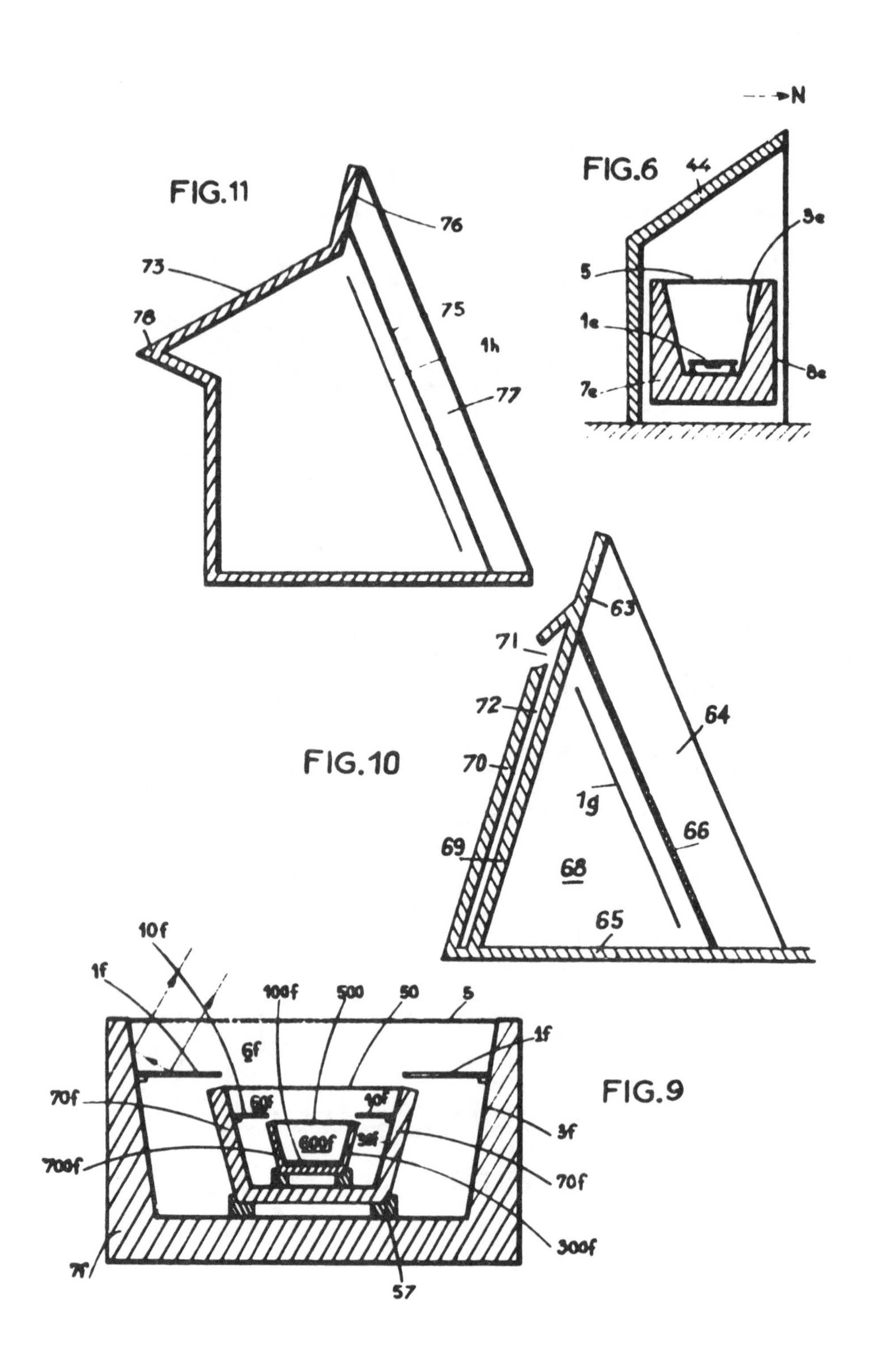

March 21, 1967 F. TROMBE **3,310,102**

DEVICES FOR LOWERING THE TEMPERATURE OF A BODY BY HEAT RADIATION THEREFROM

* *

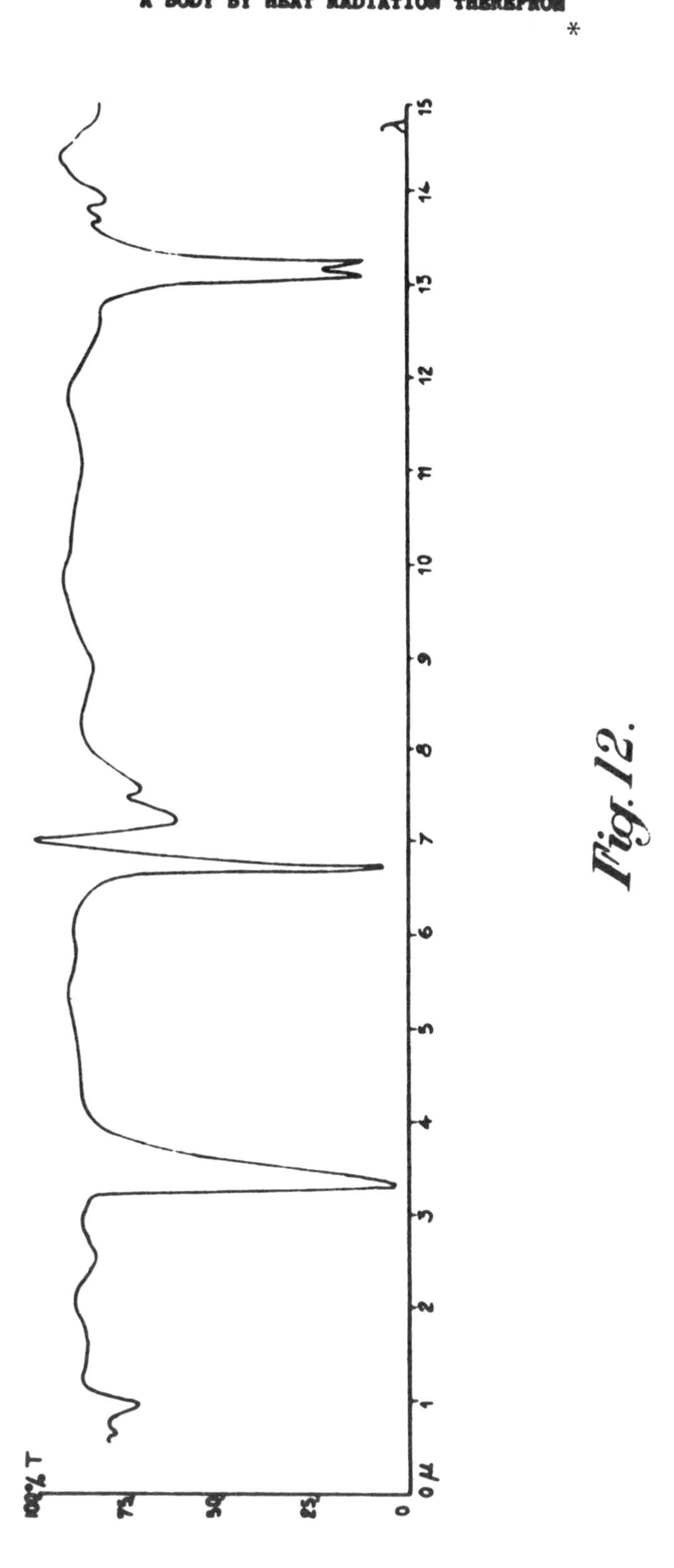

Fig. 12.

March 21, 1967 F. TROMBE **3,310,102**

DEVICES FOR LOWERING THE TEMPERATURE OF A BODY BY HEAT RADIATION THEREFROM

* *

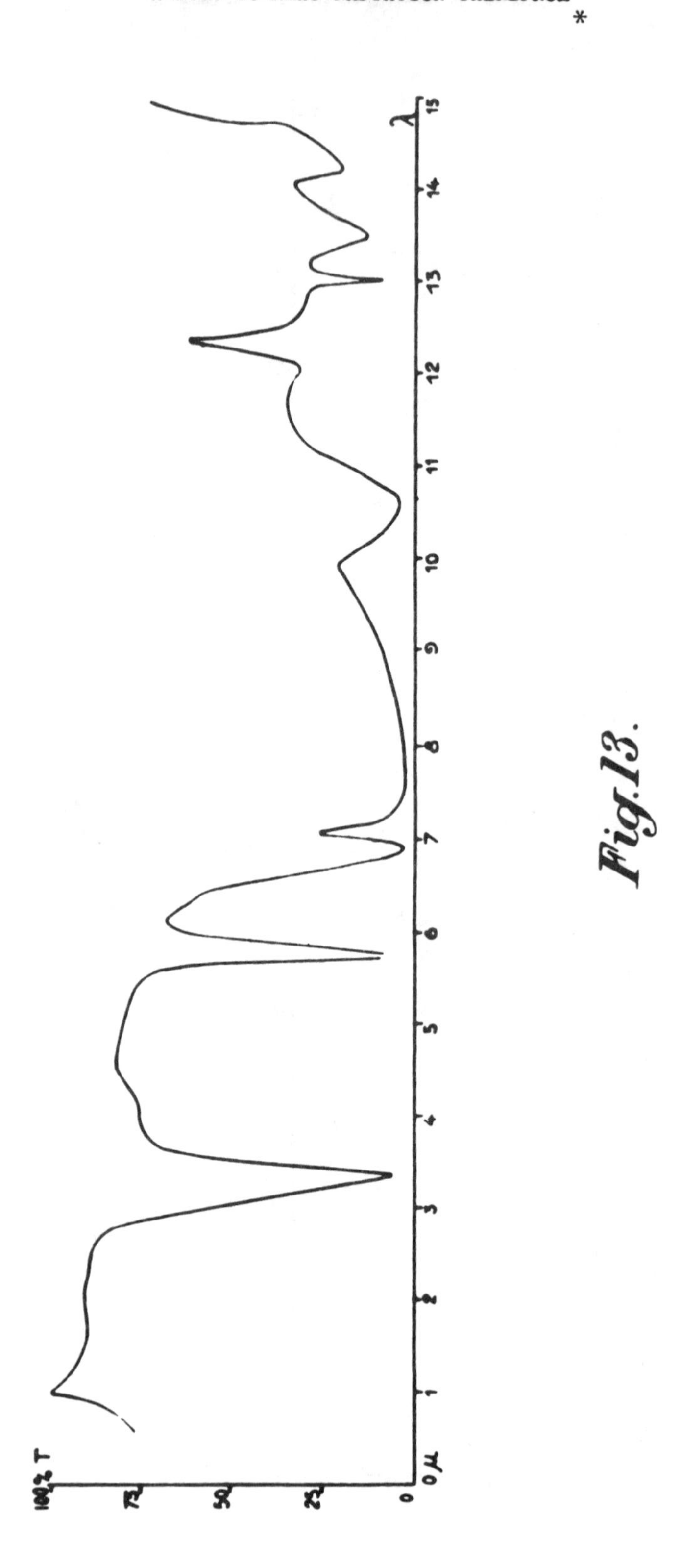

Fig.13.

March 21, 1967 F. TROMBE 3,310,102
DEVICES FOR LOWERING THE TEMPERATURE OF
A BODY BY HEAT RADIATION THEREFROM

* *

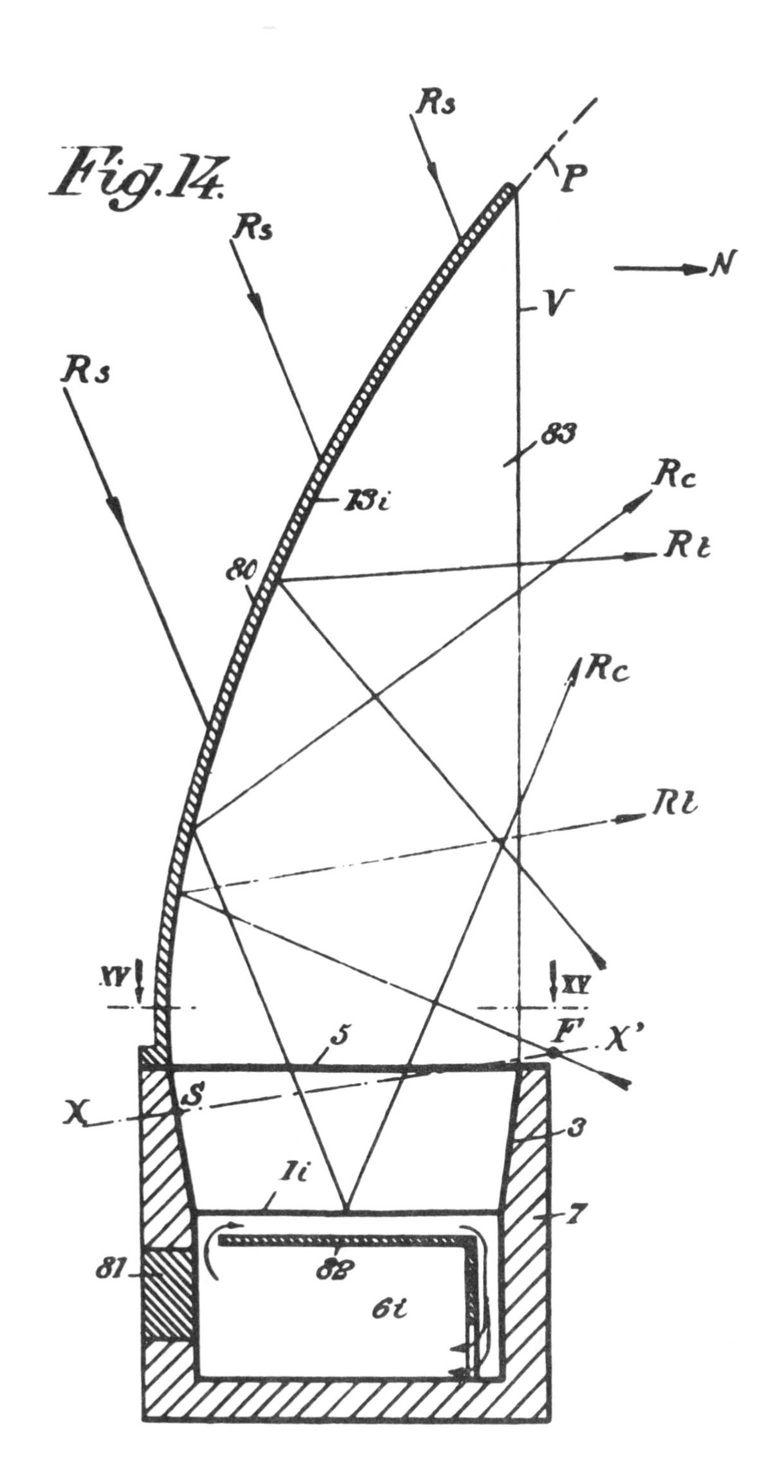

March 21, 1967 F. TROMBE **3,310,102**
DEVICES FOR LOWERING THE TEMPERATURE OF
A BODY BY HEAT RADIATION THEREFROM

* *

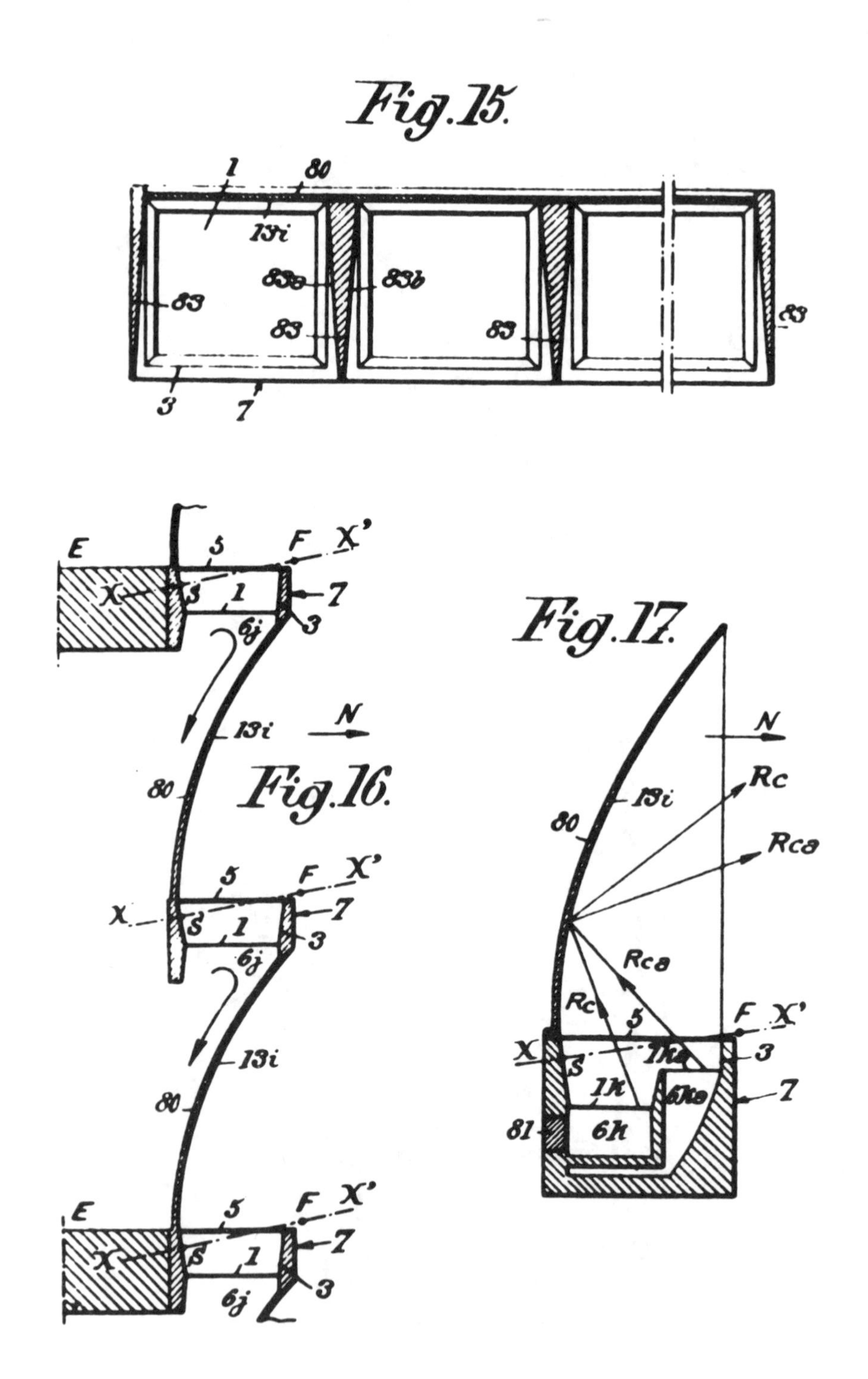

March 21, 1967 F. TROMBE 3,310,102
DEVICES FOR LOWERING THE TEMPERATURE OF A BODY BY HEAT RADIATION THEREFROM

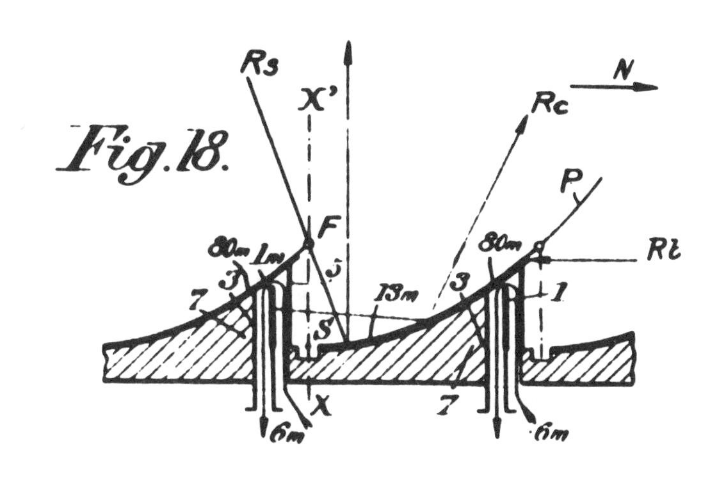

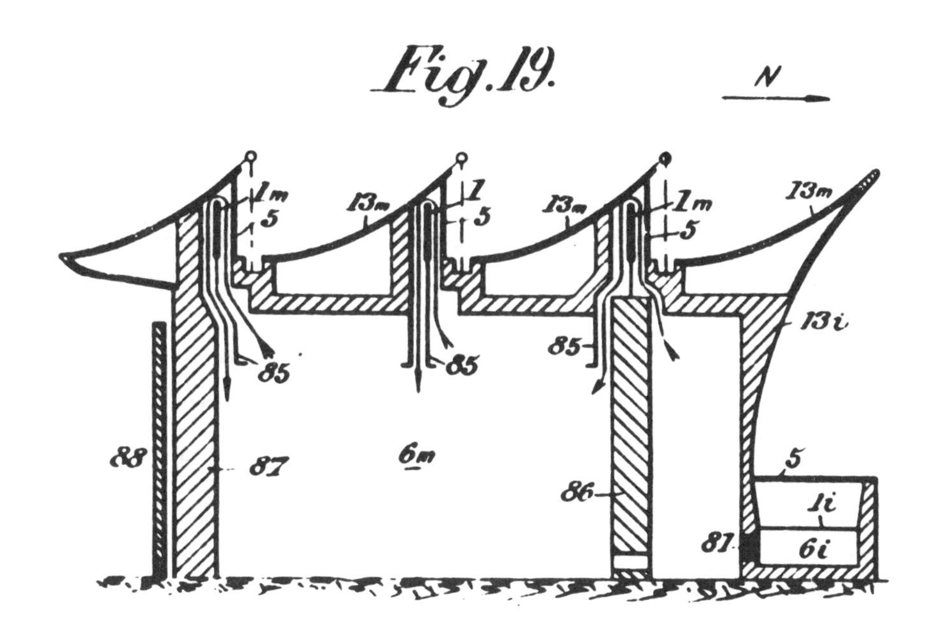

3,310,102
DEVICES FOR LOWERING THE TEMPERATURE OF A BODY BY HEAT RADIATION THEREFROM

Felix Trombe, Paris, France, assignor to Centre National de la Recherche Scientifique, Paris, France

*

It is known that, in thermodynamics, the term "black body" designates a body which radiates an energy proportional to the fourth power of its absolute temperature. This radiated energy is still considerable at ordinary temperature and even well below 0° C., as shown by the following table:

TABLE I.—ENERGY RADIATED BY THE BLACK BODY

Temperature		Total energy radiated per m.^{2} (Stefan's law), watt/m.^{2}
° C.	° K.	
90	363	1.000
50	323	625
40	313	546
20	293	419
0	273	316
−20	253	233
−50	223	130

On the other hand, within the above mentioned temperature ranges, the radiated energy is wholly within the infra-red range, extending practically from 4 to 25 microns. The maximum energy emission wavelength λ_m (the value of which, as it is known, is proportional to the reverse of the absolute temperature) ranges from 9.5 microns (when the temperature of the black body is +40° C.) to 13 microns (when the temperature of the black body is −50° C.).

The emission of energy from the black body, if the latter received no external energy, in particular by radiation, would take place at the expense of its own thermal reserve. It would therefore theoretically come, after a time depending upon its calorific capacity, close to the absolute zero.

As a matter of fact, at the level of the earth ground, the loss of energy by radiation of the black body is partly compensated for by radiations received from the atmosphere and, in the absence of insulation, by heat transmitted, on the one hand, by conversion from the surrounding mass of air and, on the other hand, by conduction from the earth surface. To the radiation of the atmosphere within the infra-red range are added the sun rays diffused by the atmosphere during the daytime and the wavelengths of which range chiefly from 0.3 micron (ultra-violet) to 3–4 microns.

However, it has been noted that the infra-red radiation of the atmosphere has a noncontinuous spectrum, most of this radiation taking place within the wavelength ranges corresponding to the absorption bands of steam, carbonic acid gas and ozone, and consequently there remain wavelength bands within which the atmosphere does not radiate and for which it is practically nonabsorbing. In what follows, these bands will be designated by the term "windows of the atmosphere." The radiations from the black body taking place within the wavelength bands corresponding to said "windows of the atmosphere" can therefore (especially when the weather is clear) pass through the atmosphere without being absorbed and go off to the space beyond said atmosphere. The most important of these windows of the atmosphere ranges from 8 to 13.5 microns (with only an ozone absorption band from 9.4 to 10 microns). Other windows can also be cited, in particular a very small one near 6 microns and another one ranging from 16 to 24 microns. It will be noted that the energy emission maximum wavelengths λ_m of the black body at the temperatures considered in the above table are in fact located within the said windows of the atmosphere.

From what precedes it follows that, if account is not taken of the exchanges of energy by radiation between a black body and the external medium, the energy lost by said terrestrial black body into space may be greater than that it receives from the outside.

The energy finally lost by a terrestrial black body radiating into space by clear weather and without any mask into a solid angle of 2π steradians is about equal to ⅓ of the total theoretical radiated energy such as indicated in the above Table I. Therefore, in the best possible conditions, this lost energy would be that indicated in the following Table II as a function of the temperature.

TABLE II.—ENERGY RADIATED IN THE BEST POSSIBLE CONDITIONS ON THE SURFACE OF THE EARTH

Temperature in ° C.:	Energy radiated toward space per m.^{2} of black body, watt/m.^{2}
90	333
50	208
40	182
20	130
0	105
−20	78
−50	43

These values are still very great and should enable bodies having a high coefficient of emission (black bodies) and suitably protected against thermal transfer from the earth surface, to reach very low temperatures, merely as a consequence of their outward radiation.

However, experience teaches that the result that is obtained is relatively small, as compared with the importance of the radiated energy.

In particularly favorable conditions, a flat surface having the characteristics of a black body and thermally insulated from the ground reaches, with a very clear sky, in the absence of wind, with dry weather, in the absence of any terrestrial mask, a temperature lower by about 9° C. than the temperature of the ambient air ($\Delta t=9°$ C.). In the presence of wind, even very small, the convection exchanges are increased and the temperature difference Δt decreases considerably. Likewise, in the presence of moist air, the radiating black body acts as a water or ice condenser and this temperature difference Δt is only from 3 to 5° C.

The object of the present invention is to provide arrangements for obtaining black body temperatures much lower than that of the surrounding air, such temperatures permitting practical applications, for instance for the production of cold air or even of ice.

The present invention consists in a cold producing device which comprises, in combination, an infra-red rays radiating body capable of giving off rays within the wavelength bands for which the atmosphere is transparent thereto, means partly surrounding said radiating body for thermally insulating it from the earth and for preventing the radiations from the sun and from earth objects from reaching said radiating body, reflecting means inside said means shaped and positioned to reflect the radiations emitted by said body into the atmosphere within a substantial solid angle, and a screen of a material transparent to radiations of the wavelengths for which the atmosphere is transparent, out of contact with said radiating body and forming a partition between it and the atmosphere.

Such a device enables a radiating body having the characteristics of a black body to cool down more than in the case above considered where a black body flat surface thermally insulated from the ground takes, under the best possible conditions, a temperature lower by about 9° C. than the temperature of the surrounding air.

The device according to the present invention permits, in all cases, of obtaining a much greater lowering of the temperature of a radiating black body by reducing, and possibly practically eliminating, all external causes of heating of said radiating body.

By interposing a transparent screen between the radiating body and the atmosphere, air is prevented from flowing along the surface of said radiating body, but this transparent screen further has the advantage of avoiding condensation of atmospheric moisture on the radiating body.

As for the heat transmitted to the radiating body by the radiations from the atmosphere, it is very substantially reduced by the provision of opaque walls which prevent any direct radiation from the sun or from earth objects from striking the black body. The only rays diffused by the atmosphere that reach the radiating body correspond, from the point of view of energy, to only some units percent of the direct sun radiation.

If the radiating body that is chosen as above stated consists of an integral black body (this term designating any body having a continuous spectrum of emission in the infra-red range and a coefficient of absorption close to 100% for all radiations), such as a support coated with soot or lamp black, all radiations, including the sun rays diffused by the atmosphere, will be absorbed by said radiating body.

However, it is possible substantially to increase the ratio of the loss of energy of the radiating body by radiation to its absorption of radiated energy, at least during the daytime, by making use of a body which behaves like a black body for infra-red radiations of a wavelength greater than 3 microns (and in particular within the range from 3 to 15 microns which includes the most important "windows of the atmosphere") and as a reflector for radiations of lower wavelengths down to ultra-violet radiations. Such a body will be called "selective radiating body."

These radiations, in particular the sun rays, of wavelengths lower than 3 microns, will consequently produce practically no heating of the radiating body whereas said body keeps all its possibilities of radiation toward space within the infra-red range. For instance such a radiating body may consist of an aluminum surface coated with a layer of alumina 10 microns thick or still of oxides or salts such as CaO, MgO, CO_3Ca, TiO_2, ZnO_2 either associated or not with a pigment.

A body such as glass, which is transparent to radiations of wavelengths ranging from the ultra-violet to 2.5 and 3 microns and which behaves as a black body for infra-red radiations, would lead to the same results, provided that the above mentioned opaque walls are located on the internal reflecting surface in such manner that the sun rays diffused by the atmosphere which pass through the radiating body are subsequently returned directly into the atmosphere.

The lowerings of temperature of selective radiating bodies of this kind are substantially greater during daytime than those obtained with integral black bodies of the same shape arranged in the same manner.

The absorption coefficient of a selective radiating body (averaging from 90 to 95%) being a little smaller than that of an integral black body, it follows that, during night time, the energy emission of said selective radiating body will be a little lower than that of an integral black body. The temperature thereof will therefore tend to drop a little less rapidly than that of an integral black body. However, the total energy balance resulting from the addition of the losses of energy by radiation both during daytime and during night time is very much in favor of the selective radiating body.

The ideal selective radiating body would be one capable of absorbing and therefore emitting radiations within wavelength ranges corresponding to the above mentioned windows of the atmosphere and wholly transparent to all other radiations.

If account were taken only of the thermal exchanges by radiation of such a body with the atmosphere, said body would cool down very quickly. The radiations from the atmosphere would pass through it without being absorbed, that is to say without yielding energy thereto, whereas said body would give off into space the radiations not absorbable by the atmosphere.

Polyvinyl chloride is very close to this ideal body since it is characterized by a strong absorption of the radiations the wavelengths of which range from 8 to 14 microns, with respect to which it therefore behaves as an opaque body. It is transparent to radiations of wavelengths lower than 4 microns, in particular to most of the sun rays, and semi-transparent to radiations of wavelengths of a value higher than 14 microns.

The radiating body should of course have a shape enabling it to radiate within a solid angle as great as possible.

It will therefore be made of a flat, curved, cylindrical or spherical shape, either solid or hollow, according to the material of which it is made, to the kind of apparatus to which the device according to the invention is to be applied and also according to the shape of the internal surface which is to reflect infra-red radiations from said opaque wall.

Concerning now the means for insulating said radiating body from the earth surface and from the opaque wall partly surrounding said body to protect it against direct rays from the sun or from earth objects, they preferably consist of a heat insulating envelope the inner surface of which has a high reflective power both for the infra-red radiations emitted by said body and for the sun radiations. The external surface of this envelope is advantageously coated with paint capable of reflecting sun rays. This envelope should be positioned in such manner that the radiating body never receives direct rays from the sun.

Finally, the inner surface of this envelope must have a shape such that, on the one hand, most of the infra-red rays issuing from the radiating body that impinge upon said inner surface are reflected toward space without possibility of returning to the radiating body and that, on the other hand, the radiations diffused from the atmosphere which penetrate into the inside of the envelope are returned by reflection to the outside as quickly as possible.

The inner surface of this envelope advantageously consists of non-oxidized aluminum which reflects 99% of the infra-red rays, this surface having a shape adapted to that of said radiating body so that said body can radiate outwardly within a solid angle of maximum value, the rays inside said solid angle being reflected toward space without possibility of returning to said black body.

Said surface will have for instance one of the following forms: frustum of a cone, frustum of a pyramid, surface having involute-shaped cross sections limited by plane or cylindro-parabolic surfaces, cylindro-parabolic surfaces limited by parabolic surfaces or by plane surfaces, and elliptical surfaces with various limited profiles.

The external surface of this envelope is preferably coated with a selective paint capable of reflecting sun rays, for instance a titanium oxide paint, of the rutile type.

Of course, there may be provided, about said heat insulating envelope, supplementary envelopes made of panels the inner surfaces of which are capable of reflecting the infra-red rays radiated by said radiating body and the external surfaces of which are coated with a paint, for instance a titanium oxide paint of the rutile type, for reflecting sun rays in such manner as further to increase the protection of the radiating body located inside said heat insulating envelope.

Furthermore, concerning the above mentioned transparent screen interposed between the radiating body and the atmosphere, it should be as transparent as possible within all wavelength bands, in particular within the band corresponding to the wavelengths of the sun rays diffused by the atmosphere and within the interval of the wavelengths ranging from 3 to 25 microns which, as above indicated contains the most important "windows of the atmosphere," so that said screen cannot have any influence upon the thermal exchanges by radiation between the radiating body and space.

As a matter of fact, if this screen had a substantial absorption for some wavelength bands, in particular for those corresponding to the windows of the atmosphere, its own temperature would be lowered and it would constitute a zone of condensation of atmospheric moisture, this condensed water then forming a screen preventing the passage of the rays emitted by the radiating body. This would very quickly limit the drop of temperature of said body.

Advantageously this screen consists of at least one polyethylene sheet.

According to an advantageous feature of my invention, the heat insulating envelope having an internal wall capable of reflecting infra-red rays and the transparent screen will constitute together, about the radiating body, a practically closed structure, the frigories produced by the radiation of said radiating body being then either used directly within this structure or collected in any suitable manner, in particular by circulation of gas about the radiating body, apertures being for instance provided in said practically closed structure for introducing the gas to be cooled and for collecting the gas cooled by contact with the radiating body.

The thermal insulation of the radiating body may be increased by superposition of several thin sheets permitting the passage of the infra-red radiations.

In order to obtain the best possible thermal insulation a distance of from 4 to 5 centimeters should be provided between the radiating body and said sheet.

In a likewise manner, a distance of the same order of magnitude should be provided between two such sheets, so as to imprison cooler and cooler air layers between them.

It should be noted that only the external transparent wall must have a substantial resistance to atmospheric agents such as wind and moisture. The other sheets may be thinner and consequently more transparent to the infra-red rays radiated by the radiating body.

Preferred embodiments of the present invention will be hereinafter described with reference to the appended drawings, given merely by way of example, and in which:

FIGS. 1 to 6 inclusive are sectional views of embodiments of the present invention;

FIG. 7 is an elevational sectional view of a plant comprising several cooling devices placed within one another, according to the invention;

FIG. 8 is a plan view of the plant of FIG. 7;

FIG. 9 is an elevational sectional view of another embodiment of a cooling plant of the kind of that shown by FIGS. 7 and 8;

FIGS. 10 and 11 are diagrammatic vertical sections of devices according to the invention serving to cool down the air of a building;

FIGS. 12 and 13 show curves indicating, in ordinates, the transparency to radiations respectively of a polyethylene sheet of a thickness equal to 50 microns and of a polyvinyl chloride sheet of a thickness of 100 microns, the wavelengths of the incident radiations being plotted in abscissa;

FIG. 14 is a longitudinal section of a cold producing device made according to still another embodiment of the invention;

FIG. 15 is a section on the line XV—XV of FIG. 14;

FIG. 16 is a longitudinal section on a smaller scale of a device such as shown by FIG. 14 in one application thereof;

FIG. 17 shows in longitudinal section a modification of the device of FIG. 14;

FIG. 18 is a longitudinal section of still another embodiment of the invention;

FIG. 19 is a longitudinal section of a device according to the invention applied to the air conditioning of a building.

FIG. 1 shows a cooling device according to the present invention including a flat radiating body 1 the temperature of which can be measured at 2.

This radiating body 1 may be either an integral black body or a selective black body as above described. It may consist for instance of a sheet of aluminum covered by oxidation with a 10 micron thick layer of alumina.

About this radiating body is provided a reflecting lining 3 forming a frustum of a pyramid. This lining is so shaped and so disposed about the radiating body that direct rays from the sun and from earth objects cannot strike said radiating body. The whole should therefore be directed toward the north, indicated by arrow N. Said lining is made of nonoxidized aluminum. Such an arrangement therefore enables the radiating body to radiate freely within an angle of 2π steradians, any ray 4 emitted by said radiating body within this solid angle passing into space either directly or after one reflection.

Across said lining 3 there is provided a polyethylene screen 5 transparent to all radiations. The thickness of this screen can be as low as 5 microns. For practical purposes, its thickness is, for instance, 50 microns. With this arrangement radiating body 1 is located inside a closed chamber 6 heat insulated from the surrounding air and from the earth surface and which imprisons a mass of air cooled down by its contact with said radiating body 1.

Along said lining 3 there is provided a heat insulated envelope 7 consisting, in a known manner, of any suitable material such as glass wool, slags, organic masses, expanded cork, felt, down, and so on. Said heat insulating envelope 7 is provided, on its external surface 8, with a paint consisting chiefly of titanium oxide of the rutile type reflecting sun rays and radiating in the infra-red range.

FIG. 2 shows an analogous device but wherein the radiating body *1a* has a cylindrical surface and cooperates with a lining *3a* capable of reflecting infra-red rays and having the shape of an involute of said cylindrical radiating body *1a*, the end portions *13a* of this lining located on the outside of screen 5 being flat.

The side walls of this device on either side of the plane of the figure consist of reflecting planes inclined with respect to each other at about 30°, the apex of the dihedral angle thus formed being directed toward the south. Thus practically all the rays 4 issuing from the radiating body *1a* are sent into space without possibility of returning onto said body *1a*, either directly or by reflection upon lining *3a–13a*.

The radiating body is, as in the case of FIG. 1, insulated from the surrounding air by a screen 5 and envelope *3a* is likewise heat insulating.

FIG. 3 shows a device analogous to that of FIG. 2

with a radiating body 1a of cylindrical shape cooperating with an infra-red rays reflecting wall 3b which in this case has a cylindro-parabolic shape. The side walls of the apparatus on either side of the plane of the figure consist of reflecting plane making with each other an angle of 30°. This wall shape also gives very satisfactory results concerning the radiation of the radiating body within a solid angle as great as possible.

Of course the device of FIG. 3 might be modified and made of revolution, cylinder 1a being replaced by a sphere and cylindro-parabolic reflector 3b being replaced by a paraboloid of revolution. The efficiency of the device thus obtained would be slightly higher but its construction would be somewhat more difficult.

With devices such as shown by FIGS. 1 and 3 it is possible to obtain, with a sky of medium clarity and with a relatively high hygrometric state of the atmosphere, black body temperatures lower by more than 16° C. than those of the surrounding air. It is important to note that this result was obtained both during daytime and during night time. With a clear sky and a dry atmosphere, the temperature difference should be of the order of 20° C.

The radiating bodies of FIGS. 2 and 3 might have been made of polyvinyl chloride the selectivity of which is still greater than that, for instance, of aluminum covered by oxidation with a layer of alumina.

The use of polyvinyl chloride will be described in a more detailed fashion with reference to FIGS. 4 and 5 which show supplementary improvements of the devices according to the invention in order to obtain a still greater lowering of the temperature of the radiating body, these improvements, consisting in providing several chambers juxtaposed about the radiating body, these chambers containing limited volumes of air which are cooler and cooler when getting nearer to said radiating body.

In FIG. 4 the radiating body therefore consists of a sheet 17 of polyvinyl chloride folded upon itself in such manner as to leave, between its two parallel portions, a limited air volume 18 which forms a kind of cold chamber.

The opposed edges of said sheet 17 are applied against the wall 19 of a parallelepipedal piece 20 made of a thermally insulating material.

As in the constructions of FIGS. 1 to 3, heat insulating envelope 7c is provided, on its inner surface, with a layer 3c of nonoxidized aluminum and, on its external surface, with a layer 8c of a paint capable of reflecting the sun rays, envelope 7c being limited, on either side of the plane of the drawings, by inclined reflecting planes making with each other an angle of 15° opening toward space.

On the ends of said walls 7c there is fixed a screen 5 of polyethylene thus separating the radiating body 17 from the surrounding air.

Insulation of the radiating body from the external medium is further increased by the use of two supplementary transparent screens of polyethylene consisting of sheets 25 and 26 which surround the radiating body 17 and the opposed edges support 29 which also carries piece 20.

The lateral faces of the volumes thus limited respectively by sheets 25 and 26 are closed for instance by pieces of polyethylene welded on their edges to the side edges of said sheets 25 and 26.

Thus, two supplementary juxtaposed gastight chambers 30 and 31 are formed about radiating body 17. The temperature therefore decreases when passing successively from the chamber limited by lining 3c and transparent screen 5 to chambers 31, 30 and 18.

The radiating body 17 is advantageously made of a sheet of polyethylene chloride 100 microns thick, and screens 25 and 26 consist of sheets of polyethylene 50 microns thick. The curves of FIGS. 12 and 13 serve to illustrate the cooling of the radiating body.

FIG. 13 shows the transparency to incident radiations of a sheet of polyvinyl chloride 100 microns thick (this transparency being plotted in percentage values in ordinates) as a function of the wavelengths of said radiations (the wavelengths being plotted in microns in abscissas). It will be noted that this sheet of polyvinyl chloride behaves substantially as a black body for the radiations within the band of wavelengths ranging from 7 microns to 14.5 microns, that is to say within the band corresponding substantially to the chief window of the atmosphere (from 8 to 13.5 microns), whereas, with the exception of very narrow absorption bands, polyvinyl chloride is substantially transparent to radiations of wavelengths lower than 5.5 microns, that is to most of the sun rays diffused by the atmosphere. It results from what precedes that the polyvinyl chloride radiating body 17 will emit radiations preferentially in the above mentioned windows of the atmosphere, these radiations being lost into space.

FIG. 12 shows the curve of transparency to incident radiations of a polyethylene sheet 50 microns thick as a function of the wavelengths of said radiations in the same conditions as in FIG. 13. It will be found that this polyethylene sheet is transparent to more than 80% for all wavelengths ranging from ultra-violet to 15 microns, with the exception of some very narrow peaks of absorption near 3.3 microns, 6.8 microns and 13.2 microns.

Consequently, in the device shown by FIG. 4, the radiations from radiating body 17 will pass into space after travelling successively through transparent screens 25, 26 and 5 either directly or with reflection on the internal surface 3c of wall 21.

On the contrary the diffused rays from the atmosphere which fall upon reflecting lining 3c and the wavelengths of which chiefly range from the ultra-violet to 3 microns, will pass without being absorbed through screens 25 and 26 and radiating body 17 itself without heating said body before being returned into space. In view of the fact that the transparency of these obstacles is not perfect, it will be, of course, advisable to avoid as much as possible parasitic reflection which would cause the rays from the atmosphere to pass several times through the system consisting of radiating body 17 and screens 25 and 26.

The following table shows the lowering of temperature obtained in the inner chamber 18 of radiating body 17 in a device according to FIG. 4 making use of sheets of polyethylene and of polyvinyl chloride of the respective thicknesses above mentioned, the temperature being measured in this chamber 18 for instance at the bottom thereof (this measurement being made at successive time intervals over a total duration of 36 hours on Dec. 3 and 4, 1952, at Montlouis, Pyrenees-Orientales, France).

Times of the measurement	Ambient temperature	Temperature in space	Δt
4	−5	−26	−21
10	+2	−24	−26
12	+10.5	−20.5	−31
16	+7	−19	−26
20	−3	−24	−21
24	−6	−25.5	−19.5
4	−6.5	−25	−18.5
10	0	−24.5	·24.5
12	+2.5	−21	−23.5
16	+1	−18	−19

In the third and second columns of this table are indicated the temperatures of the ambient air and the temperature in chamber 18, respectively, at the times indicated in the first column. It will be noted that the difference between the temperatures existing respectively in cold chamber 18 and on the outside increases with the external temperature, the maximum value of this difference being 31° C. These differences, which are given in the fourth column of the table, bring into evidence the efficiency of cold producing devices according to the invention.

The device shown by FIG. 5 is based upon the same principle as that of FIG. 4. The only difference is concerned with the shapes of the different parts of the device, in order to improve the results obtained.

The radiating body 33, preferably made of polyvinyl chloride, consists of a cylindrical sheet surrounded by a transparent screen consisting of two cylindrical sheets 34 and 35, preferably made of polyethylene, closed at their lower ends by walls, also made of polyethylene, assembled by welding. The whole is associated with an infra-red rays reflecting lining 3*d* preferably associated with a supplementary polyethylene screen 5 stretched across the edge of lining 3*d*. Said lining 3*d* has the shape of an involute of a cylinder. Owing to this arrangement, all the rays emitted by the radiating body are sent to the outside and furthermore all the diffused rays from the atmosphere are allowed to pass at most only one time through the system consisting of said radiating body and of the two screens 34 and 35.

It is also possible to obtain a device having a better efficiency by improving the insulation of the body radiating the rays diffused by the atmosphere.

Such a device is shown by FIG. 6, which discloses the provision about a cooling device, made practically in accordance with the disclosure of FIG. 1, of supplementary walls 44 surrounding, on the east, on the south and on the west, above and below, the heat insulating envelope 7*e*, the inner surface 3*e* of which is adapted to reflect infra-red rays and the outer surface of which is coated with a layer 8*e* of a paint capable of reflecting sun rays, this envelope containing a radiating body 1*e*.

A transparent screen 43 stretched across the edges of envelope 7*e* forms a partition separating said radiating body from the ambient air.

The east and west vertical walls form with the south wall (which is shown in section by FIG. 6) angles which are advantageously of 105°.

The portion of wall 44 provided about envelope 7*e* is inclined on the horizontal so as to permit the radiations issuing from said envelope 7*e* to be reflected toward the north, indicated by arrow N.

Envelope 7*e* and walls 44 have their inner surfaces capble of reflecting infra-red rays, advantageously made of nonoxidized aluminum, and their external surfaces coated with a paint which reflectes sun rays, advantageously consisting chiefly of titane oxide.

With a radiating body 1*e* made of a flat surface of aluminum covered by oxidation with a layer of alumina and a screen 5 made of polyethylene 50 microns thick, the following results were obtained.

Date of the experiments	Time	External temperature	Temperature of the black body 1*e*	Δ*t*
11/18/62	1	−3.5	−21.5	−18
11/28/62	14	+5.5	−16.4	−21.9
12/1/62	4	+3	−18	−21
12/1/62	12	+6.5	−17	−23.5
12/2/62	4	−2	−23.5	−21.5
12/2/62	12	+2	−18	−20
12/3/62	4	−5	−25.5	−20.5
12/3/62	12	+7.5	−22	−29.5

These experiments were made at Montlouis, Pyrenees-Orientales, France, the atmosphere having a relative moisture of 40%.

In this case also there is noted an increasing efficiency of the devices according to the invention when the external temperature rises.

FIGS. 7, 8 and 9 show arrangements including several of the devices above mentioned placed in one another, as hereinafter described, such arrangements making it possible to obtain very important lowerings of the temperature of the radiating body.

Referring to FIGS. 7 and 8, which show in section and in plane view, respectively, a system according to the invention, there is provided a first device of the kind illustrated by FIG. 1 comprising a flat radiating body 1*f* disposed at the bottom of a heat insulating envelope 7*f* the inner side surfaces 3*f* of which advantageously have the shape of a frustum of a pyramid and consists of nonoxidized aluminum. A transparent screen 5 made of polyethylene is stretched between said side walls, thus limiting a closed space 6*c* in which is imprisoned a limited volume of air in contact with radiating body 1*f*, the temperature of which may be measured for instance at two points 51*a* and 51*b*.

On the inside of this space 6*f* there is provided a second structure made exactly as the above mentioned one, that is to say comprising a heat insulating envelope 70*f* having reflecting inner faces 30*f*, a radiating body 10*f* the temperature of which can be measured at 54, a polyethylene screen 50 limiting inside said second structure a space 60*f* containing a smaller volume of air in contact with radiating body 10*f*.

In view of the fact that this second structure is placed in an atmosphere 6*f* already cooled with respect to the external atmosphere, a still more important lowering of the temperature of radiating body 10*f* with respect to the external air than for radiating body 1*f* will be obtained.

Of course, the contacts between the first and second structure must be limited as much as possible in order to avoid heat transfer by conduction between them. This is obtained by using, for the second structure, insulating supports 57 resting upon the bottom of chamber 6*f*. These insulating supports 57 have a cross section as small as possible to enable the circulation of cold air.

A third structure similar to the preceding ones is provided inside the second space 60*f*. The temperature of the radiating body 100*f* of this third structure, measured at 60, is still lower than that of the radiating body 10*f*. The polyethylene screen is shown at 500, and the heat insulating envelope at 700*f* with its inner walls 300*f*.

The system illustrated by FIG. 7 is inclined toward the right and toward the north, arrow 61 indicating the vertical direction. Thus the cold air produced in the respective stages has a tendency to flow from the left toward the right.

The performance of such a system is still further improved by locating, as shown by FIG. 9, radiating bodies 1*f* and 10*f* in spaces 6*f* and 60*f*, respectively, no longer at the bottoms of said spaces but at a small distance under the respective screens 5 and 50, so as to avoid that a portion of the rays that are emitted is stopped by the respective lower walls of envelopes 70*f* and 700*f*.

The total solid angle for the radiations from every radiating body 1*f* and 10*f* thus remains practically equal to the value it would have in free air. The radiating body 1*f* of the first chamber arranged in this manner further permits of more efficiently cooling the polyethylene screen 50 of the second structure. Likewise, the transparent screen 500 of the third structure or stage is more efficiently cooled. The following table shows the temperature drops that have been obtained in contact with the radiating body 100*f* (each of the radiating bodies 1*f*, 10*f* and 100*f* consisting of an aluminum sheet covered with a layer of alumina) inside the third space 600*f*, in a system as shown by FIG. 9.

Experiments performed between December 1 and 4 at Montlouis, Pyrenees-Orientales, France, at the altitude of 1600 meters with a dry clear weather and a relative moisture averaging 40%.

Date	Time	External temperature	Temperature of the radiating body, 100f	Δt
1/12/62	21	−2.5	−24	21.5
2/12/62	2	−2	−27.2	25.2
	6	−1.8	−27.9	26.1
	12	+4.5	−17	21.5
	16	+2.5	−18	20.5
	23	−4	−27	23
3/12/62	4	−5	−30	25
	8	−6.5	−33	26.5
	12	+10.5	−19.5	30
	16	+7	−17	24
	24	−6	−29	23
4/12/62	5	−6.2	−29	22.8
	9	−5	−29.5	24.5
	11	+1.5	−27	28.5
	15	+2.5	−21	23.5
	17	−1	−22	21

It goes without saying that, in all the embodiments of the devices according to the invention which have been above described, the frigories produced in the radiating body and in contact therewith may be used or recuperated as above considered, the means to be used for these purposes having not been shown in FIGS. 1 to 9.

A very interesting application of the devices according to the present invention is illustrated by FIGS. 10 and 11, this application concerning the air conditioning of buildings.

FIG. 10 diagrammatically shows a vertical section by a north-south plane of a building made according to the present invention. This building comprises heat insulating walls turned toward the west, the south and the east (64 being the east wall and 63 the south wall) and a heat insulated floor 65 insulated from the ground. The north wall of the building is at least partly constituted by a screen 66 transparent to radiations of all wavelengths, the envelope having the shape of a tent. The flat radiating body 1g is provided behind screen 66. Walls 63 and 64 and floor 65 have inner lining capable of reflecting infra-red rays. This structure constitutes, on the scale of a building, a device having all the characteristics of the invention, the limited volume of air being imprisoned in a space 68 in contact with the radiating body 1g, the circulation of cold air in this space being obtained by the mere effect of gravity.

Insulation of the side walls of the building may be further provided by making them, as shown by FIG. 10 for the south wall 63, in the form of double panels 69 and 70 opening at the top at 71 to permit the accumulation of cold air in the intermediate recess 72. The external panel 70 has an inner surface capable of reflecting infra-red rays and an outer surface capable of reflecting sun rays.

FIG. 11 shows a building of the same kind as that of FIG. 10 but provided with a roof 73. A flat radiating body 1b extends nearly to the top of said roof and is protected by a transparent screen 75 and by reflecting surfaces such as 76 and 77. Roof 73 preferably has a projecting portion 78 acting as a sun protection for the side walls of the building.

By way of example here are the results obtained with the device of FIG. 10. The radiating bodies (aluminum covered with a layer of alumina) have an area of 6 m.² and serve to cool down a cavity in the form of a tent having an area of 3 m. × 3 m. at the basis and 3 m. high. Date: Sept. 24, 1962. Experiments made in Montlouis, Pyrenees-Orientales, France. with a dry and clear weather, the relative moisture averaging 40%.

Time	Ambient temperature	Temperature of the radiating body 1g	Temperature of the air in the building
0	+7	−6	−3
2	+6.5	−6.5	−3.5
4	+6.5	−7.7	−4.5
6	+8	−8.5	−5
8	+15	−7.5	−4.5
10	+20	−3.5	−0.3
12	+22	+0.3	−4
14	+23	+2.5	+6.5

When the radiating bodies 1g and 1h of FIGS. 10 and 11 respectively consist of one or several sheets of polyvinyl chloride, said sheets permit, while producing cold in the room to be conditioned, of allowing light diffused from the sky to penetrate into said room. This light should be reflected toward the outside either again through the polyvinyl chloride sheets or through other windows provided in other walls of the building. These last mentioned windows must be protected as much as possible through external reflectors (not shown) disposed in such manner as to reflect into the atmosphere the maximum of direct external radiations that would fall on said windows.

It is also possible to make use, in a row of buildings extending in the north-south direction, on the surfaces of their roofs turned toward the north, of cooling radiators associated with transparent and insulating screens as shown for instance by FIG. 11, the surfaces of said roofs turned toward the south forming reflectors for the infra-red rays radiated by the radiating bodies disposed on the surfaces turned toward the north.

FIG. 14 shows another embodiment of a cold producing device according to the invention, for cooling a chamber 6i.

This device comprises in particular the means above disclosed, that is to say:

A radiating body 1i emitting infra-red radiations, in particular in the wavelength bands for which the atmosphere is transparent (windows of the atmosphere), said radiating body being, for instance, an aluminum surface coated either with a layer of alumina about 10 microns thick or with a paint the main component of which is titanium oxide, the shape of said radiating body being for instance plane, curved, cylindrical or spherical, etc.;

A heat insulating envelope 7 made of a suitable insulating material, partially surrounding said radiating body 1 and isolating it from contact with the earth, the inner surface of said envelope 7 carrying a lining 3 highly reflective in particular for the radiations emitted by the radiating body 1 as well as for the sun and earth rays;

A protection screen 5 closing said envelope and defining therewith a closed space containing the radiating body 1i and isolated from the atmosphere, this protection screen, advantageously constituted by a sheet of polyethylene, being more particularly transparent in the wavelength bands corresponding to the windows of the atmosphere;

Cold chamber 6i located, preferably, below the radiating body 1i.

The present description is concerned with devices established in the northern hemisphere of the earth, where the sun rises in the east, passes through the zenith in the south direction and sets in the west.

If such devices were to be provided in the southern hemisphere of the earth it would of course be necessary to take into account the corresponding changes of orientation.

According to the invention, there is provided on the outside of the envelope 7, closed by protection screen 5, a reflecting surface 13*i* having a high reflective power for the radiations emitted by the radiating body 1 as well as for the solar and earth radiations, said reflecting surface 13*i* being constituted by the concave face of a wall 80 shaped substantially as a cylinder the generatrices of which are perpendicular to the plane of FIG. 14 and the directrix of which is a parabola located in this plane, this reflecting surface 13*i* being so positioned that, on the one hand, it reflects the radiations emitted by the radiating body 1 in directions above the horizon and on the other hand it prevents, by reflection and or interception, the direct sun radiations and the earth radiations from striking the radiating body.

According to the embodiment of the invention shown by FIGS. 14 and 15 the radiating body 1*i* is of flat shape and is positioned horizontally in a parallelepipedic envelope 7, having a rectangular horizontal section, which opens at its upper part and is provided with insulating walls, the inner faces 3 of which are highly reflective for the radiations emitted by said radiating body 1*i*.

A protection screen 5 is stretched across the upper edge of said envelope to define therewith a space containing said radiating body 1*i* and insulated from the atmosphere, the portion of this space located below the radiating body 1*i* constituting the cold chamber 6*i* which is advantageously provided with a gate 81. This cold chamber 6*i* may also be advantageously provided, as shown in FIG. 14, with at least one screen plate 82 which, on the one hand, prevents the radiating body 1*i* from radiating toward chamber 6*i* and, on the other hand, favors convection movements within said chamber 6*i*. Moreover the wall surfaces 3 located immediately above said radiating body 1 are slanted with respect to the vertical to form therewith an angle of about 10 to 15° so as to give to the upper portion of the envelope 7 a form diverging slightly in the upward direction.

The dimensions of this parallelepipedic envelope 7 are chosen such that the minimum angle of incidence of any radiation emitted by body 1*i* and striking said protection screen 5 is 25°, so as to limit the partial reflection of said radiations by said protection screen 5. In the case of the construction of cold chamber 6*i* of important sizes, it will be advantageous to provide a plurality of contiguous envelopes 7 as illustrated by FIG. 15, the use of several envelopes 7 involving also other advantages pertaining to the easy positioning and the mechanical resistance of such screens 5, the thickness of which is relatively low (advantageously of about 1/10 mm.).

Envelope 7 (or the series of envelopes 7) is then disposed so as to have one of its longest sides turned toward the south.

The external wall 80 having a concave reflecting surface 13*i* is mounted on the south side of envelope 7, said reflecting surface 13*i* substantially forming an extension of the internal wall surface 3 which is turned toward the north.

The wall 80 extends along the whole length of the south side of envelope 7 and, advantageously, it has the following characteristics:

(1) The focus F of the parabolic directrix P of said surface 13*i* is located on the outside of said envelope 7, slightly above the north side thereof;

(2) The axis XX' of said parabola P is advantageously slightly oblique to the horizontal direction (by about 10 to 15°) upward from south to north, the vertex S of said parabola P being substantially located inside of said envelope 7 and on the south wall thereof, and

(3) The portion of said parabola P that is used extends between the south side of envelope 7 and a vertical plane V passing approximately through the north side of said envelope 7, its exact position depending in fact upon the position of the sun at its zenith in the area of the earth where the device is to be located.

Owing to the fact that, in these conditions, the surface of the radiating body 1 is located in the area between the focal line of reflecting surface 13*i* and said surface itself, the rays R_e emitted by the radiating body 1 are reflected by the reflecting surface 13*i* above the horizon; the direct rays R_s of the sun are intercepted by the external face of the wall 80 and thus cannot strike the radiating body 1 and the earth rays R_t are reflected by the reflecting surface 13*i* and also not allowed to strike the radiating body 1.

The protection of the radiating body 1 can be further improved, in particular against the direct rays of the sun when the latter is low above the horizon (sunrise and sunset) by providing, at least on the east side and the west side of said device, vertical screens 83 the opposed faces 83*a* and 83*b* of which are reflective for the sun rays and advantageously inclined with respect to each other (see FIG. 15) so as to eliminate by either direct or successive reflections, the direct sun rays at sunrise and at sunset.

In the case of a device comprising several envelopes 7 intermediate vertical screens of this type can be provided as partitions between the respective contiguous envelopes as shown in FIG. 15.

FIG. 16 shows a combination of devices according to the invention provided in the north wall of a building comprising several stories E. The devices, comprising envelopes 7 and walls 89, are advantageously given such a size that the height of two of them corresponds to the height of a storey. In this embodiment the cold chambers 6*i* communicate, at the bottoms thereof, with the rooms of the building and permit a circulation of cooled air along the inner faces of the walls 80.

Of course, a portion of the cold produced by such devices might be used for the cooling of refrigerating chambers.

It must be noted that in the case where these devices are used in connection with buildings having several stories it may be necessary to take into account the possible presence of neighbouring buildings which constitute sources of earth rays.

Another embodiment of the invention is shown in FIG. 17 wherein the elements similar to those of FIG. 14 have been designated by the same reference numbers.

According to this embodiment, there is provided a primary cold chamber 6_{ka} partly surrounding the main cold chamber 6_k, said primary cold chamber 6_{ka} being located on the north side of main cold chamber 6_k and having its radiating body 1_{ka} located at a higher level than the radiating body 1_k of said main cold chamber (therefore nearer to screen 5 than it).

With such an arrangement, the main radiating body 1_k radiates in a more favorable direction than the primary radiating body 1_{ka}, since the rays R_e from the main radiating body 1_k are reflected more upwardly than the rays R_{ea} from the primary radiating body 1_{ka}. It is thus possible to obtain in main chamber 6_k a temperature lower both than that in primary chamber 6_{ka} and also than that which would be obtained with a single chamber arrangement such as illustrated by FIG. 14.

In the foregoing it has been assumed that the radiating body had a flat or stepped shape and that the envelope 7 had a substantially parallelepipedic form with side internal walls inclined with respect to the vertical.

Of course it would be possible to modify these devices for instance by giving the radiating body a cylindrical shape and associating therewith an envelope 7 having the form of an involute of a circle or of a parabola, the reflecting surface 13*i* being however always positioned with respect to the envelope 7 in a manner such that the radiating body 1 is entirely located in the space defined between the focal zone of reflecting surface 13*i* and this surface itself.

Another embodiment of the cold producing device according to the invention is shown in FIG. 18.

In this embodiment, the radiating body 1_m has a flat shape, is vertical and extends in the east-west direction. It is located between:

On the south side, heat insulating envelope 7 the wall surface 3 of which is highly reflective for the radiations emitted by said body 1_m;

On the top, a reflective portion of the under face of wall 80_m forming a lining for heat insulating envelope 7; and

On its north side, screen 5;

The space where body 1_m is located advantageously communicating, at its lower end, with a cold chamber 6_m.

Advantageously, in order to facilitate the circulation of air around radiating body 1_m, a passage is left between the top of said radiating body 1_m and the under face of wall 80_m.

Wall 80_m, the upper face 13_m of which is reflective, has the shape of a cylinder the directrix of which is a parabola P, the generatrices of this cylinder extending in the east-west direction over the whole length of radiating body 1_m.

Furthermore:

(1) The focus F of parabola P is located at a short distance above the top edge of wall 80;

(2) The axis XX' of said parabola P is approximately vertical and disposed at a small distance from protection screen 5 on the north side thereof, the vertex S of said parabola P being approximately located at the level of the lowest portion of the radiating body 1_m and on the north side of envelope 7;

(3) The arc of the parabola that is used extends in the north direction substantially from the apex S thereof to the intersection thereof with a horizontal plane passing approximately through the upper part of the space where the radiating body is located, the exact position of said horizontal plane depending upon the importance and the origin of the earth rays emitted around the device.

It will thus be conceived that, in such a device, in which the surface of the radiating body 1_m is entirely located between the focal zone of the cylindro-parabolic surface 13_m and this surface itself, the radiations R_e emitted by the radiating body 1_m are reflected by the reflective surface 13_m above the horizon in the direction of the sky, the direct rays R_s originating from the sun are reflected by the reflective surfaces 13_m and are prevented from striking the radiating body 1_m and the earth rays are intercepted by the walls 80_m and are thus also prevented from striking the radiating body 1_m.

In this embodiment also the rays from the sun when the latter is at a low level above the horizon (sunset or sunrise) can be deflected by vertical screens not shown in FIG. 18.

Such devices can also be placed contiguous to each other as shown by FIG. 19 to constitute for example the roof of a building, the cold chamber 6_m being then constituted by one or several rooms inside said building.

FIG. 19 shows a building using cold producing devices according to the invention on both its north face and its roof, its north face being provided with cold producing devices according to the embodiment shown by FIG. 14 and its roof being provided with devices according to the embodiment shown by FIG. 18.

Cooling by the devices located in the roof is very advantageous; the cooled air produced by contact with the radiating body 1_m goes down into the dwelling rooms through circulation chimneys 85 and cools the interior walls 86 and the exterior walls 87 of the building, said walls having an important thermic mass enabling them to act as accumulators of thermal energy.

In the case of FIG. 19 the building is further provided with a cold producing device at the level of the ground for use either in a cold storage chamber to cooperate with the cooling systems located in the roof for air-conditioning purposes.

In the case of buildings having several stories, cooling through their north wall further permits of providing cooling devices at the level of every story and of the ground, in particular in the case where said north walls are provided with cooling systems made according to the embodiment shown by FIG. 16.

The external faces of the external walls 87 of the building, preferably, reflect the infra-red rays and cooperate with walls 88 characterized by a low themic mass and a high insulating capacity which permit the selective collection of cold air during nighttime and the stabilization of this cold air by gravity during daytime.

In the case where the cold producing devices are to be used in connection with cold chambers or storage spaces, the protection screen 5 may be made of a material transparent for the radiations of the windows of the atmosphere and absorbant for the radiations in the wavelength bands for which the atmosphere is itself absorbant. Such a screen is then likely to act as an inversed glass-house.

If the air surrounding the radiating body in such devices is replaced by carbon dioxide, which is responsible more particularly for the absorption ability of the atmosphere for the wavelength bands ranging from about 13 to about 16 microns, the temperature in the vicinity of the radiating body can become lower by a few degrees, approximately 3 to 5 degrees, than in the case of the same chamber being filled with air. The carbon dioxide between the radiating body and the polyethylene screen 5 acts itself as the above screen transparent for the radiations of the windows of the atmosphere and absorbant for wavelengths bands for which the temperature is absorbant, thereby ensuring said inversed glass-house effect. *

May 17, 1966 D. N. CROSTHWAIT, JR **3,251,407**

REFRIGERATION AND VENETIAN BLIND MEANS FOR CONTROLLING THE ENTRY OF LIGHT AND HEAT FROM A WINDOW OR THE LIKE

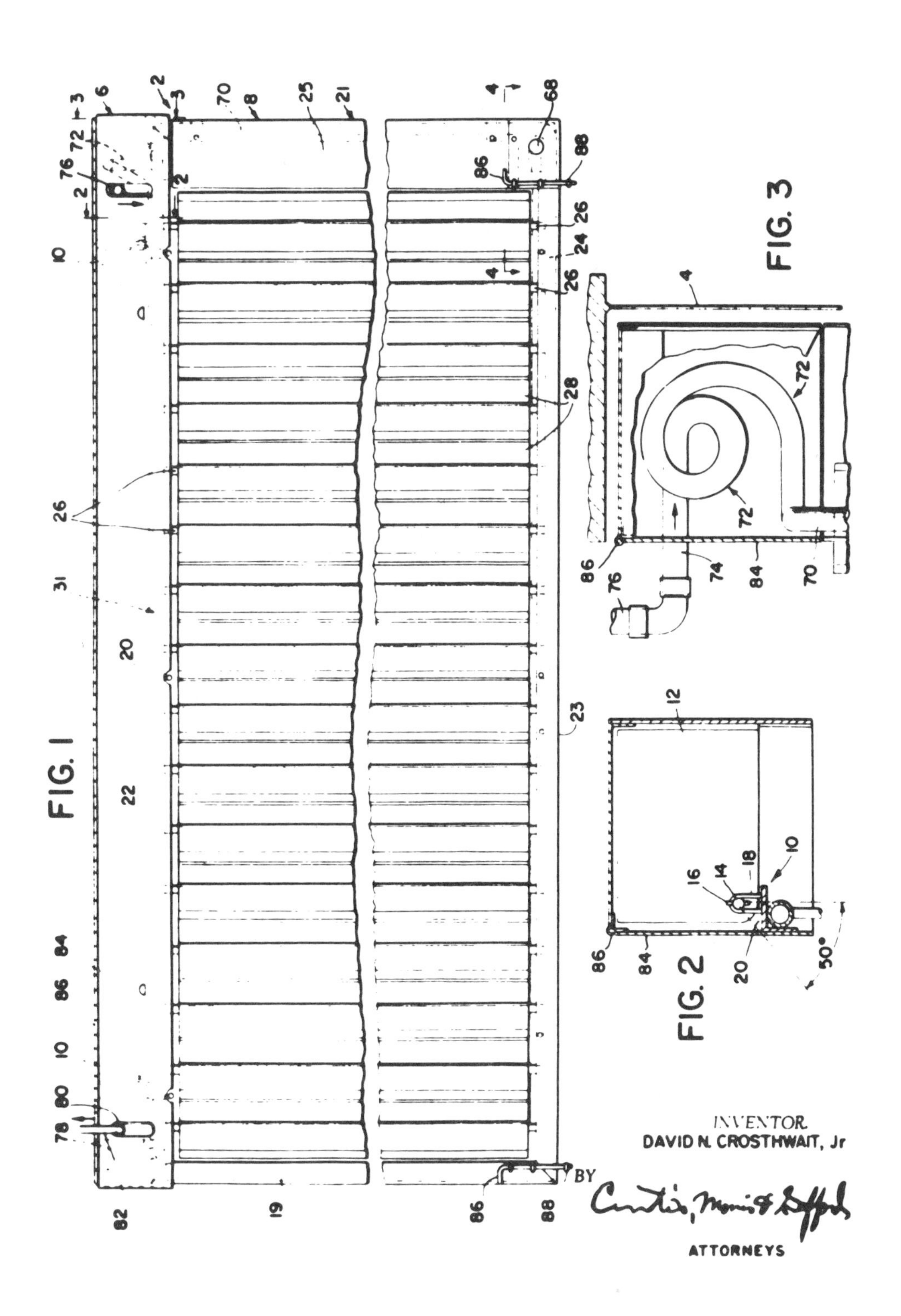

May 17, 1966 D. N. CROSTHWAIT, JR **3,251,407**

REFRIGERATION AND VENETIAN BLIND MEANS FOR CONTROLLING THE ENTRY OF LIGHT AND HEAT FROM A WINDOW OR THE LIKE

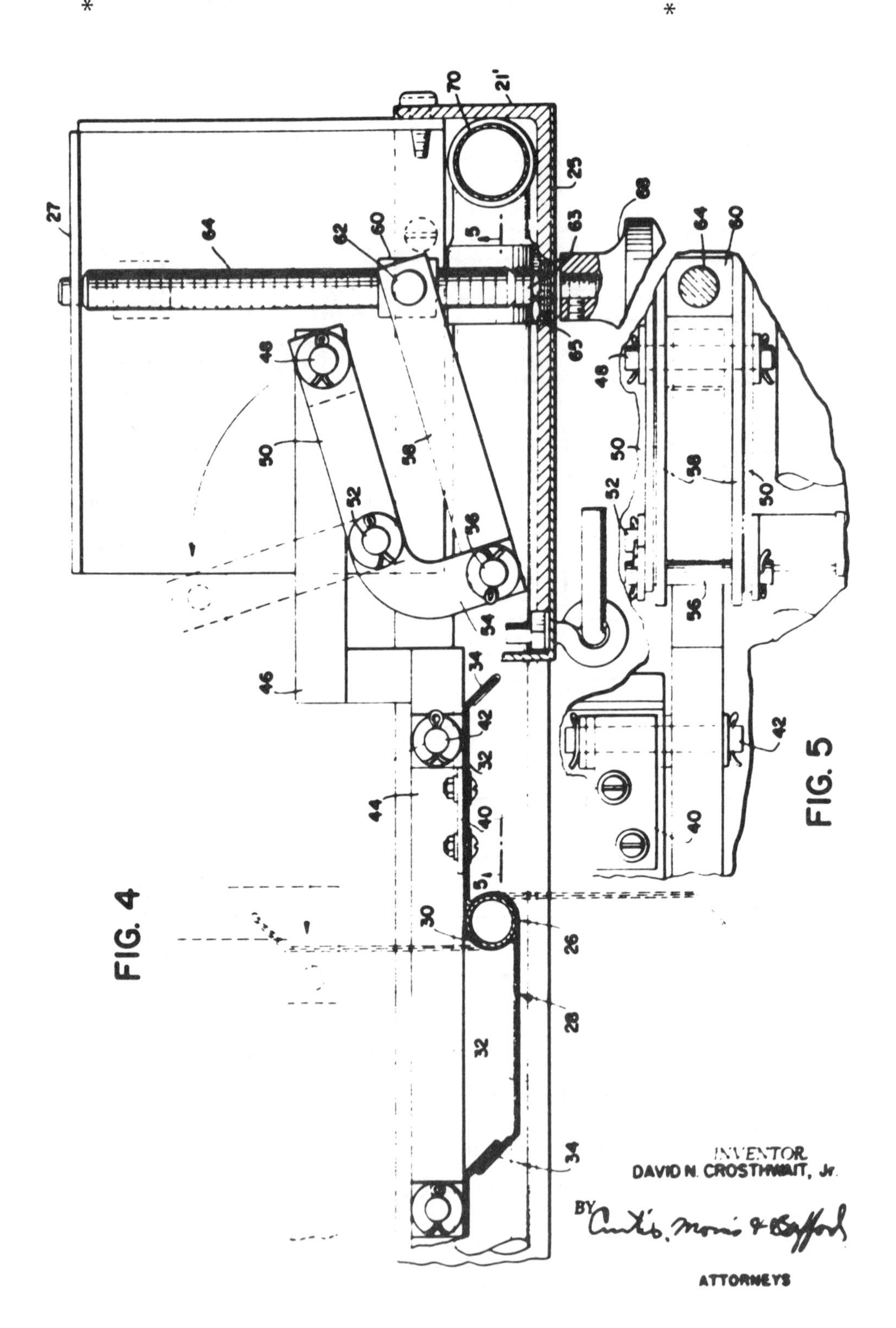

3,251,407
REFRIGERATION AND VENETIAN BLIND MEANS FOR CONTROLLING THE ENTRY OF LIGHT AND HEAT FROM A WINDOW OR THE LIKE
David N. Creethwait, Jr., Michigan City, Ind., assignor to Dunham-Bush, Inc., West Hartford, Conn., a corporation of Connecticut
*

This invention relates to air conditioning and refrigeration, and more in particular to a system which includes a louver assembly in a window which is adapted to absorb or dissipate heat and to control the transmission of light and radiant heat through the window to the room or space, and which is also adapted to provide heat transfer between the occupants and the air within the room or space and a cooling fluid such as water.

An object of this invention is to provide an improved construction for cooling the air in a room or space and for controlling the passage of heat and light thereto. Another object is to provide an improved movable louver construction. Another object is to provide an improved heat transfer assembly having movable heat transfer elements. A further object is to provide an improved system for absorbing and dissipating heat to maintain the desired temperature conditions within a room or space. A still further object is to provide for the above with structures which are sturdy and durable and which are relatively simple, light in weight, inexpensive to manufacture and maintain, adaptable to various conditions of installation and use, and thoroughly practical in every respect. A still further object is to provide for the above with structures which are pleasing in appearance and which are free of the faults and objectionable characteristics of prior similar constructions and systems. These and other objects will be in part obvious and in part pointed out below.

In the drawings:

FIGURE 1 is a front elevation of one embodiment of the invention with the central portion cut away;

FIGURES 2, 3, and 4 are enlarged views on the lines 2—2, 3—3, and 4—4 of FIGURE 1; and,

FIGURE 5 is a fragmentary view on the line 5—5 of FIGURE 4.

Referring to FIGURE 1 of the drawings, a unit 2 is positioned within a window opening parallel to the window pane 4 (see also FIGURE 3). Unit 2 comprises a stationary top assembly 6 rigidly mounted at the top of the window, and a swinging louver assembly 8 (FIGURE 1) which is swingably supported at its top by a pair of hinge assemblies 10 (see also FIGURE 2) mounted in assembly 6. Each of the hinge assemblies 10 comprises a pair of angle brackets 12 with parallel spaced vertical webs and a pivot pin 14 mounted in aligned openings in the webs and held in place by removable pins 16. Positioned between the two vertical webs of each hinge assembly is an eye bracket 18, which hangs on its pivot pin 14 and is welded to a horizontal angle bar 20 which is a frame member of the louver assembly.

Louver assembly 8 comprises a rigid frame and tube assembly 21 and a set of rotatable louvers 28. Assembly 21 includes a rectangular frame of angle bars 19, 20, 21' and 23 around its periphery, a front wall 25 at the right, a rear wall 27 (FIGURE 4), and a tube assembly 31 having horizontal top and bottom header tubes 22 and 24, respectively, and a large number of vertical tubes 26, illustratively sixteen in number. Tubes 26 are rigidly mounted at their ends in the respectively header tubes so as to provide for the flow of a liquid such as water from the bottom header tube through the vertical tubes to the top header tube. Header tubes 22 and 24 are rigidly clamped to their respective angle bars 20 and 23 so as to provide support for the tube assembly.

Swingably mounted upon each of the vertical tubes is a louver 28 (see also FIGURE 4) which is formed of sheet metal with a central sleeve portion 30 snugly received upon the tube 26 and two oppositely extending tangential vanes 32 having angularly disposed edge strips 34. Each of the louvers is formed by forming two strips of sheet metal into the cross-section shown in FIGURE 4 and then welding or otherwise joining the coextensive portions of the sheets together to provide double wall portions. Each of the edge portions or strips 34 is at an angle to the main vane. The snug relationship between the sleeve portion 30 of each louver and its tube 26 is such as to permit turning of the louver upon the tube with an acceptable amount of friction, and there is an excellent heat-exchange relationship between the tube and the louver.

Each of the louvers 28 is adapted to move to any position between the fully open position shown in broken lines, where light and radiant heat passes freely through the window into the room, and the fully closed position shown in full lines, where the edge strips 34 of the adjacent louvers overlap and shut out light and radiant heat completely. In the closed position the angular relationship and the resiliency insure a thoroughly satisfactory light seal so that any light leak is minimal and insignificant.

The louvers are moved between the closed and opened positions by the operating mechanism shown at the right in FIGURES 4 and 5. Bolted to the bottom, right-hand portion of each louver is a bracket 40 which is pivotally connected by a pivot pin 42 to an operating bar 44 which extends horizontally along the louver assembly directly below the level of the bottom of the louvers, and which is supported by the pivot pins 42. Bar 44 has an angular extension 46 which extends at right angles to the bar and thence parallel again and has its extreme end connected through a pivot pin 48 to a pair of flat crank arms 50 (FIGURE 5) positioned respectively above and below the extension 46 or bar 44. Crank arms 50 are mounted upon a fixed pivot pin 52 which projects upwardly from the bottom wall, and the crank arms have right-angle arms 54 connected through a pivot pin 56 to a pair of operating links 58. The other ends of the links 58 extend respectively above and below a nut 60 and are attached thereto by pivots 62, and nut 60 is threaded onto a screw shaft 64. Screw shaft 64 is pivotally mounted in the rear wall 27 and a pivot sleeve 63 extending through the front wall 25. Sleeve 63 is held by a nut 65.

The forwardly projecting end of shaft 64 carries an operating knob 68 by which the shaft may be turned. Clockwise rotation moves nut 60 from the forward full-line position toward the broken line position adjacent the rear end of the screw shaft. This movement of nut 60 carries links 58 with it and swings crank arms 50 through an angle of the order of 90° to the broken line position. This movement of the crank arms is transmitted through pivot pin 48 and swings bar 44 to the broken line position, and that movement of bar 44 turns all of the louvers to the fully open position shown in broken lines. The turning of knob 68 and shaft 64 in a counter-clockwise direction reverses the movements so as to swing the louvers back toward the closed position shown in full lines. Hence, the louvers may be operated readily by the simple turning to knob 68.

It has been indicated above that cold water is passed through the tube assembly 31. The water inlet connection to the lower header 24 is through a tube 70 shown in broken lines at the right in FIGURE 1 and extending upwardly to the top assembly 6 (see FIGURE 3). The upper end of tube 70 is connected to a spiral tube 72 which terminates in a horizontal portion 74 which connects with a water supply tube 76. The water connection to the upper header 22 as shown in broken lines at the upper left-hand portion of FIGURE 1 and is a spiral tube 78 similar to tube 72 and terminating in a horizontal portion 80 which is connected to a water return tube 82. The front wall 84 of the top assembly 6 is hinged along its upper edge at 86 so that it may be lifted, and each of the tubes 74 and 80 extending through a slot which is of sufficient vertical dimension to permit the cover 84 to be raised.

It has been indicated above that the louver assembly is swingably mounted, and, as indicated in broken lines in FIGURE 2, it may be swung out for example through an arc of 50°. As shown in the lower right and left hand portions of FIGURE 1 the louver assembly may be latched in its vertical position in the window frame by latch pins 86 which are slidably mounted upon the louver assembly and projected into eye screws 88 in the adjacent wall. The spiral tubes 72 and 78 flex during the swinging movement of the louver assembly, and are sufficiently flexible to permit free swinging movement without interfering with the liquid connections.

Louvers 28 provide for the transfer of the heat from the air and occupants in the room and they also act to control the entry of light and radiant heat through the window. The louvers are adapted to absorb radiant heat which enters the window, thus to prevent the passing of the radiant heat to the occupants and other objects within the room. Also, the radiant heat which is absorbed by the louvers is carried away by the flowing water so as to maintain the louvers at a reduced temperature. This prevents the louvers from being heated by radiant heat and then acting to radiate heat into the room. When the louvers are in the fully closed position they reflect some of the light and radiant heat which enter the window pane, and the air is cooled so as to maintain a reduced temperature condition between the louvers and the window. Also, the air within the room is cooled by the large exposed louver area so that a satisfactory air temperature condition can be maintained within the room without excessively low temperature water in tubes 26. When the louvers are partially or fully opened, the air within the room is exposed to both sides of the louvers with free circulation of the air along the louvers. Special surface coatings may be provided upon the louvers, for example, to provide increased or decreased reflection of the radiant heat on the window pane side, or increased or decreased heat absorption and dissipation on the room side of the louvers. However, for most installations, the louvers are painted or enameled in accordance with the decor of the building.

It has been pointed out above that the tube assembly with the attached louvers provides an excellent heat transfer relationship between the water or other fluid in tubes 26 and the louver surfaces which are exposed. This permits the maintenance of desirable temperature conditions within the room and comfort conditions for the occupants with a fairly small difference between the temperature of the water or other fluid in the tubes and that of the air. Therefore, the temperature gradient may be sufficiently small to avoid objectionable condensation of moisture from the air. Also, the position of the louvers may be adjusted to permit the entry of the desired amount of light and radiant heat.

During the period of the year when heating is desirable, warm or hot water or other fluid may be passed through the tube assembly so as to provide heating rather than cooling. In many respects the structure has advantages for heating which correspond to those for cooling. The temperature gradient between the exposed louver surfaces and the water or other fluid may be sufficiently low to avoid objectionable drafts or objectionable radiant effects. The heating is by radiation as well as conduction and convection.

Under conditions where there are wide variations in the sun effect, i.e., light and heat radiation, the position of the louvers may be adjusted to provide the desired control of the light as well as the heat radiation or dissipation; for example, when the fluid in tubes 26 is at or near the room temperature the louver assembly will absorb heat only when there is substantial absorption of radiant heat. With such an arrangement, the desired room temperature is maintained primarily by other heating or cooling. *

Feb. 20, 1968 G. MECKLER **3,369,540**

HEAT ABSORBING STRUCTURE FOR AN AIR CONDITIONING SYSTEM

* *

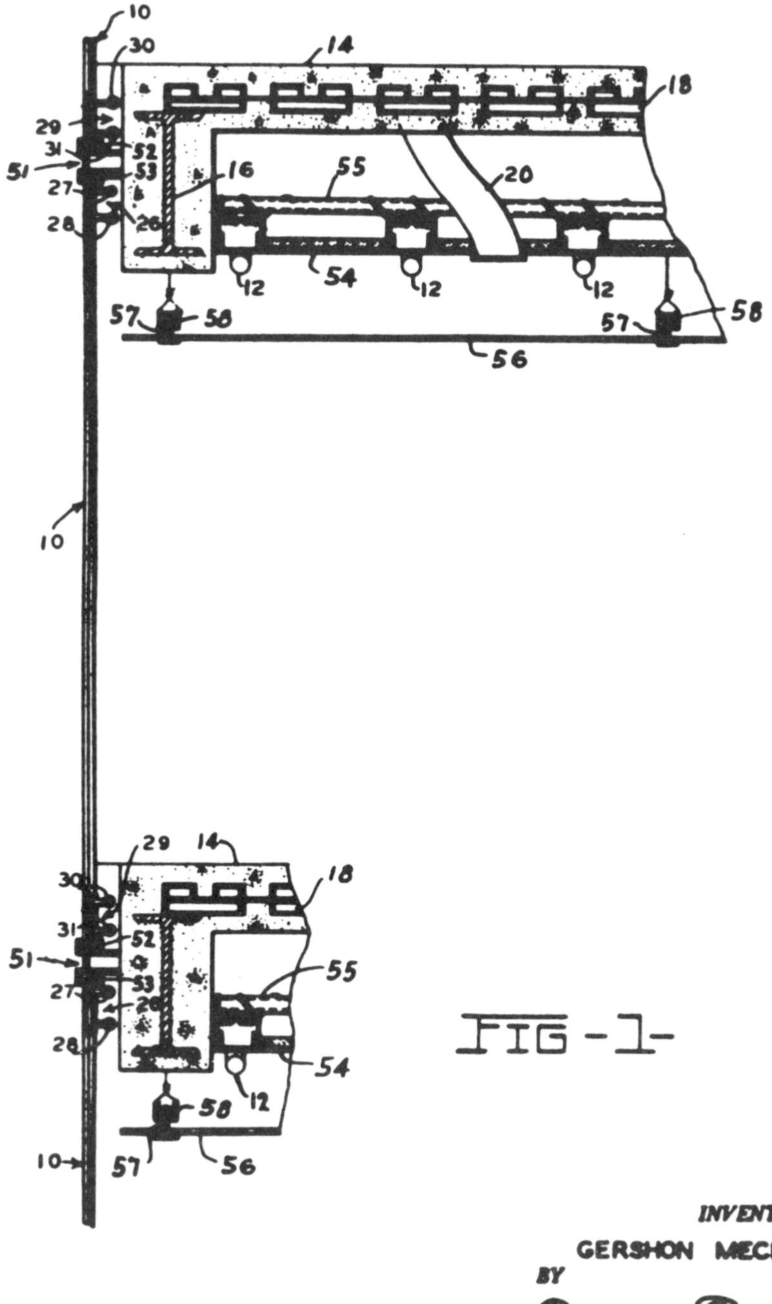

FIG -1-

INVENTOR.
GERSHON MECKLER
BY
Owen & Owen
ATT'YS.

Feb. 20, 1968 G. MECKLER 3,369,540

HEAT ABSORBING STRUCTURE FOR AN AIR CONDITIONING SYSTEM

* *

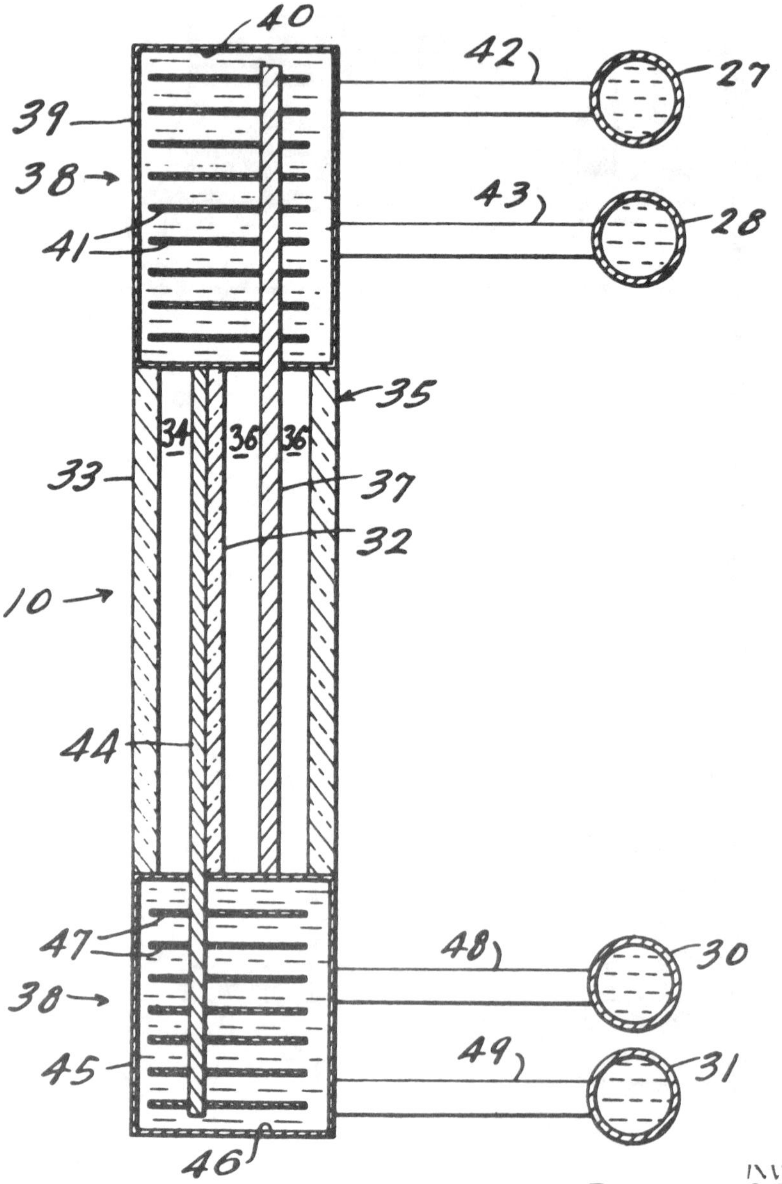

FIG-2-

INVENTOR:
GERSHON MECKLER.
BY
Owen & Owen
ATT'YS.

Feb. 20, 1968 G. MECKLER **3,369,540**

HEAT ABSORBING STRUCTURE FOR AN AIR CONDITIONING SYSTEM

* *

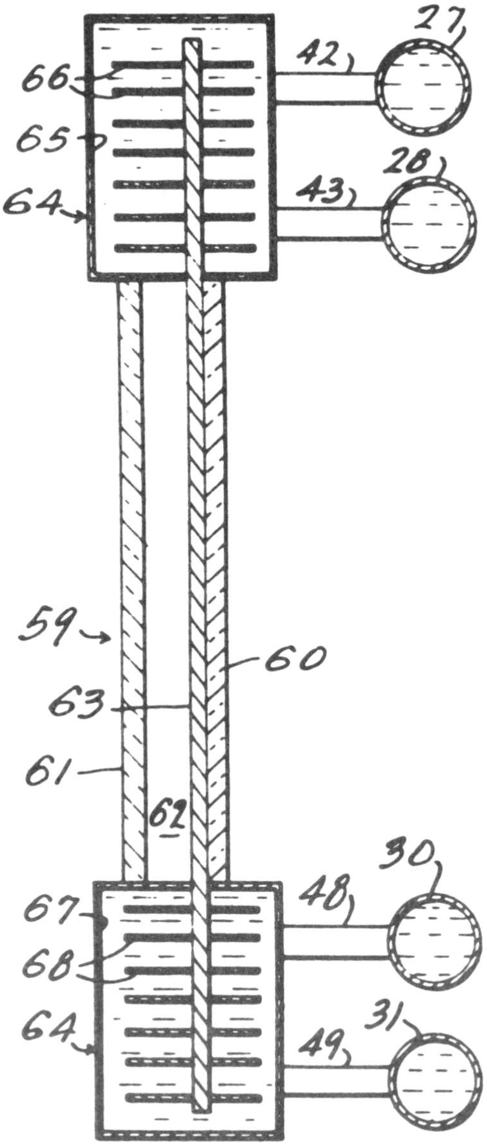

FIG-3-

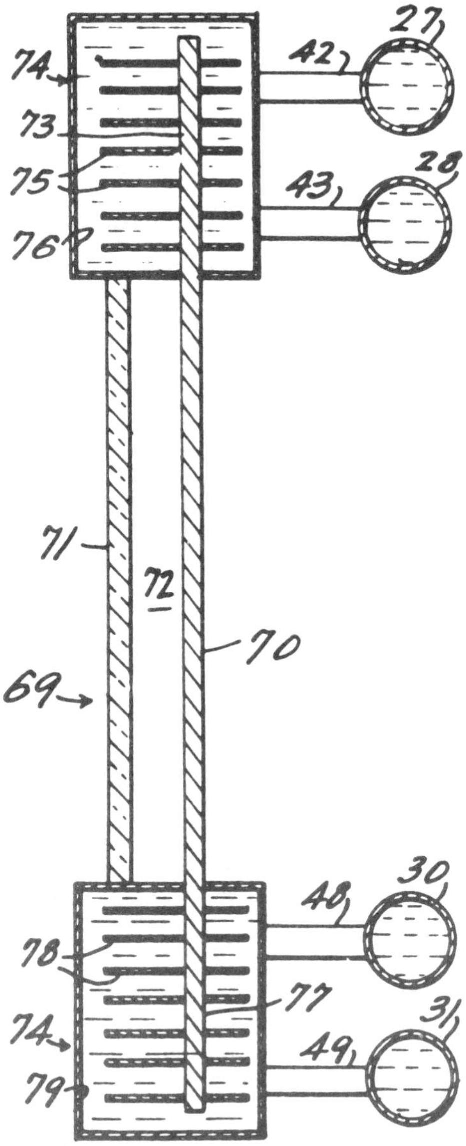

FIG-4-

INVENTOR:
GERSHON MECKLER.
BY
Owen & Owen
ATT'YS.

3,369,540

HEAT ABSORBING STRUCTURE FOR AN AIR CONDITIONING SYSTEM

Gershon Meckler, Atlanta, Ga., assignor to Lithonia Lighting, Inc., Conyers, Ga., a corporation of Georgia

*

The present invention relates to air conditioning the interior of buildings and the like and more particularly to the absorption and dissipation of undesirable heat which is introduced into buildings by natural light from the exterior thereof.

A considerable amount of heat in the form of radiant energy is present in natural light, both in the visible range and in the infrared and the ultraviolet ranges. The presence of this heat in natural light causes numerous problems in the heating and air conditioning of buildings. More particularly, when clear glass is used in building fenestrations, much of the heat is transmitted into the interior of the building. In an attempt to overcome this, heat-absorbing glass has been substituted for clear glass and certain combinations of heat-absorbing glass and clear glass have likewise been utilized. While some heat has been absorbed by the heat-absorbing glass, nevertheless, a substantial amount still has been transmitted into the interior of the building. The transmitted heat has constituted a severe problem for known air conditioning systems because it affects only a portion of the building at any given time, thereby causing a condition of imbalance within the building with certain portions requiring more heating or cooling than others. The problem is further complicated because different portions of the building are subjected to the solar heat load as the position of the sun changes relative to the building. Also, the absorption of some of the solar energy tends to increase the temperature of the glass and may, in some cases, elevate the temperature of the glass to an extent that the glass acts as a hot body from which heat energy is transferred into the interior of the building even after the glass ceases to be exposed to the solar energy. In addition, cracking of heat-absorbing glass panels has occurred, particularly in installations where a part of such a panel has been shaded while another part thereof has received direct sunlight.

The present invention is based upon the discovery of apparatus for preventing or minimizing the thermal load normally imposed upon the air conditioning system of a building due to external, natural light sources. In accordance with the invention, a multi-sheet light-transmitting structure has been effected which is capable of absorbing a substantial amount of solar energy which would otherwise pass therethrough and of dissipating this energy while minimizing the increased heat load in the building. The structure also prevents cracking of heat-absorbing panels used therein.

It is, therefore, a principal object of the invention to provide a light-transmitting panel structure for minimizing the thermal load normally imposed on a building air conditioning system as an incident to the lighting thereof by natural sources.

Other objects and advantages of the invention will be apparent from the following detailed description of preferred embodiments thereof, reference being made to the accompanying drawings, in which:

FIG. 1 is a view in vertical cross section of a building showing the relative positions within the building of heat-absorbing, light-transmitting panel structures in accordance with the present invention;

FIG. 2 is a greatly enlarged, fragmentary view in vertical cross section of the light-transmitting structure shown in FIG. 1;

FIG. 3 is a view similar to FIG. 2 of a slightly modified heat-absorbing, light-transmitting panel structure; and

FIG. 4 is a view similar to FIG. 3 of another slightly modified panel structure.

Referring to FIG. 1 in particular, a typical lighting system is shown which embodies the features of the present invention when installed in an enclosed structure such as a building. More particularly, this lighting system includes a heat-absorbing, light-transmitting panel indicated at **10**, through which natural light is transmitted to the interior of the building. The panel absorbs, from the transmitted light, heat in the visible range of the spectrum, in the ultraviolet range, and in the infrared range. The lighting system also includes a plurality of supplemental sources **12** of artificial light. These sources can be fluorescent units, for example, for selectively augmenting the transmitted natural light.

The building comprises a plurality of concerete and cellular decks **14** supported by beams **16**. Passages **18** are formed in the decks **14** to conduct a fluid medium, such as air, for heating, cooling, or other air conditioning of the structure. This fluid may be conveyed to or from the various rooms within the structure through suitable flexible conduits, one of which is designated **20**, and each of which is in communication with one of the passages **18**.

The building also has a heat transfer system which includes a first stage **26** located near the ceiling of each level of the building and which comprises a supply pipe **27** as well as a return pipe **28** for conveying a heat transfer fluid, such as water, around the periphery of the building. The system also includes a second stage **29** located at the floor of each level of the structure. The second stage is substantially identical with the first in that it comprises a supply pipe **30** as well as a return pipe **31** for conveying heat transfer fluid. The temperature of the water in the first stage can be in the range of 65°–75° F. while the second stage can be somewhat warmer, e.g., having a temperature within the range of 85°–95° F.

According to the present invention, cooling means are provided for the light-transmitting panel **10** for removing heat that is absorbed, or would otherwise be transmitted, by the panel **10**. Heat exchange means (not shown) connected to the building heat transfer system, including both the first stage **26** and the second stage **29**, are provided for removing heat from the cooling means.

Referring to FIG. 2, the panel **10** comprises a plate **32** of heat-absorbing glass located substantially at the center of the panel. A transparent sheet **33** is separated from the heat-absorbing plate **32** by a space **34**, and the transparent sheet **33**, which may be of clear glass or the like, is on the outermost side of the panel **10** which faces outwardly from the building. A second transparent sheet **35**, which can be similar to the sheet **33**, is located on the innermost side of the panel **20** and faces the interior of the building. The sheet **35** is separated from the heat-absorbing plate **32** by an air space **36**.

Cooling means in the form of a heat interceptor **37** is located in the inner space **36** between the heat-absorbing plate **32** and the transparent sheet **35** and serves to cool the transparent sheet **35** and, to a certain extent, the air space **36**. The heat interceptor **37** comprises a plurality of extremely thin, narrow strips of a heat-conducting material such as copper. The strips are parallel to one another and preferably extend vertically, being spaced approximately twenty per foot.

Heat from the heat interceptor **37** is dissipated to heat exchange means within the building structure associated with the panel **10**. Specifically, the panel **10** includes a frame **38** within a portion of which is housing **39** forming a chamber **40** into which upper end portions of the cooling strips **37** extend. The chamber **40** is located within that portion of the frame 38 which extends along the top of the panel 10 and preferably contains water or other heat-transfer fluid. Heat exchange between the cooling strips 37 and the fluid in the chamber 40 is aided by fins 41 which are positioned in the fluid and in thermal contact with the cooling strips 37. The chamber 40 is connected to the supply pipe 27 of the first stage 26 of the building heat transfer system by means of a fluid conduit 42. A spaced portion of the chamber 40 is connected to the return pipe 28 of the first stage 26 of the building heat transfer system by means of a similar conduit 43. The conduits 42 and 43 enable the heat transfer fluid to circulate continuously through the chamber 40.

A high temperature region formed by the heat-absorbing panel 32 between itself and the outer panel 33 is cooled similarly to the lower temperature region formed between the heat-absorbing panel 32 and the inner panel 35. For this purpose, thin metal strips 44, e.g., of film, are located in the higher temperature region and, specifically, on the outwardly-facing surface of the heat-absorbing plate 32. The strips can be formed, at least in part, by vapor deposition. The strips extend into a suitable housing 45 forming a chamber 46 located at the bottom of the panel 10, within the lower portion of the frame 38. The chamber 46 contains water or other heat transfer fluid for heat exchange with the strips 44. The heat exchange is aided by fins 47 which are in contact with the strips and with the fluid. The fluid for the chamber 46 is supplied by means of a supply conduit 48 connected to the supply pipe 30 and a return conduit 49 connected to the return pipe 31.

With the panel structure, the temperature of the outer air space 34 may reach 200° F. while the interior of the inner glass sheet 35 is maintained at 75° F. Heat transfer from the outer space 34 to the inner air space 36 is reduced by the heat-absorbing glass plate 32, heat being transferred to the strips 44 as well as to the strips 37 and dissipated in the chambers 40 and 46.

Referring again to FIG. 1, the panels 10 are secured to the building by means of suitable brackets 51, each of which comprises a lower support section 52 which supports the upper panel along the bottom portion of the frame 38. The bracket also includes a top support section 53 which engages the top portion of the frame 38 of the lower panel.

The artificial light sources 12 can also be associated with water-cooled integrated radiant panels 54 supported overhead by suitable channels 55. Below the light sources 12 are louvered panels 56 which are effective to absorb heat from the sources 12 and transfer this heat through hangers 57 to heat transfer pipes 58. Hence, with this overall system, heat from both natural and artificial light sources is intercepted to minimize the heat load in the building.

Referring now to FIG. 3, the panel structure shown is similar to that of FIG. 2 but, basically, does not include the inner sheet 35. In this instance, a panel structure designated 59 includes a plate 60 of heat-absorbing glass or the like near the center of the panel 59. A transparent sheet 61 is separated from the heat-absorbing plate 60 by an air space 62 and the transparent sheet 61, which may be of clear glass or the like, is on the outermost side of the panel 59 which faces outwardly from the building.

Cooling means is located between the heat-absorbing panel 60 and the transparent sheet 61. The cooling means is in the form of a metal member or plurality of strips 63 of heat-conducting material such as copper. The strips can be formed, at least in part, by vapor deposition or electro-deposition on the outer surface of the panel 60. The strips 63 extend beyond the upper and lower extremities of the panel 60, as shown.

A frame 64 surrounds the panel 60 and the outer sheet 61, the upper portion of the frame 64 forming a chamber 65 containing fins 66 with which the conducting strips 63 are in heat transfer relation. Suitable heat transfer fluid can be supplied to the chamber 65 by the conduits and pipes 27, 28, and 42, 43.

At the lower edge of the heat-absorbing panel 60, the conducting strips 63 again can extend beyond the lower edge and into the frame 64. At the lower edge portion of the panel, the frame 64 forms a chamber 67 in which are heat transfer fins 68 in thermal contact with the metal strips 63. Heat transfer fluid in this instance is supplied by the conduits and pipes 48, 49, and 30, 31. With this arrangement, heat is transferred from the panel 60 at a relatively high rate since the panel is in thermal contact with the cooling fins 66 and 68 at both the upper and lower portions of the panel.

Referring now to FIG. 4, a heat-absorbing panel structure 69 is similar to the panel structure 59 except in this embodiment, no separate cooling means are employed. Instead, a heat-absorbing panel 70 is used in combination with an outermost panel 71, with an air space 72 therebetween. However, in place of the metal strips 63, for example, the heat-absorbing panel 70 is simply larger with an end portion or extension 73 extending into an upper portion of a panel frame 74 and in heat relationship with fins 75 in a chamber 76 to provide direct heat transfer from the panel to fluid in the chamber. Similarly, at the lower edge of the panel 70 is an end portion or extension 77 which extends in heat transfer relation with fins 78 in a chamber 79 formed by a lower portion of the panel frame 74. Suitable seals are provided for the extensions 73 and 77 where they enter the chambers 76 and 79.

It will be appreciated that a primary function performed by a panel according to the invention is to intercept radiant heat energy from the sun (which would be transmitted through a transparent panel and into a space to be air conditioned), and to transfer the heat which results from the interception to a heat transfer fluid. By virtue of transfer of the heat to a heat transfer fluid, cracking of heat absorbing panels is prevented, as is the imposition of excessive solar loads on certain portions of an air conditioned building. The net effect of operation of a panel according to the invention when solar energy is incident thereon is an increase of the temperature of the heat transfer fluid circulated as described above, and as a consequence of the transfer of heat to the fluid. The heat transferred to the fluid can be treated as problem heat, or can be treated as an energy source. When the heat is treated as a problem, the fluid can merely be circulated for cooling by any suitable means. Since a relatively high temperature fluid is capable of performing the desired heat transfer function, the use of an evaporative cooler to perform the cooling function is peculiarly advantageous because of the economic advantage over refrigerating apparatus. When the heat in the circulated fluid is treated as an energy source, this can be to drive a suitable heat pump, as claimed in application Ser. No. 476,236, now Patent No. 3,268,720, or by circulating fluid heated by heat exchange with a given panel according to the invention or a given group of panels according to the invention for heat transfer with a different panel or series of panels according to the invention. The latter procedure is particularly advantageous under conditions of winter operation when there may be a substantial amount of heat available from panels on which sunlight is incident at a given time while a substantial amount of heat is required in other portions of the building where solar energy is not then incident upon the panels.

It will be apparent that various changes and modifications can be made from the details set forth herein and shown in the attached drawings without departing from the spirit and scope of the invention as defined in these appended claims. For example, while fins 41, 47, 66, 68, 75 and 78 are shown, and are desirable for maximum heat transfer, panel structures according to the invention which do not include such fins are sometimes economically preferable. Similarly, while specific temperatures hage been suggested for the circulated heat transfer fluid, these are only exemplary, as the optimum temperatures depend upon many factors, including the climate which is involved and many specific details of the particular air conditioning system with which panels according to the invention are used. Other changes and modifications will be apparent. *

UNITED STATES PATENT OFFICE
CERTIFICATE OF CORRECTION

Patent No. 3,369,540 February 20, 1968

Gershon Meckler

It is hereby certified that error appears in the above numbered patent requiring correction and that the said Letters Patent should read as corrected below.

Column 1, line 18, after "1961" insert -- , now abandoned --; column 2, lines 11 and 12, for "modiged" read -- modified --; line 29, for "concerete" read -- concrete --; column 5, line 9, for "hage" read -- have --.

Signed and sealed this 6th day of May 1969.

(SEAL)
Attest:

Edward M. Fletcher, Jr.
Attesting Officer

Edward J. Brenner
Commissioner of Patents

Chapter 6

House Heating and Cooling Systems

Oct. 11, 1949. W. STELZER 2,484,127

HEAT EXCHANGE SYSTEM

*

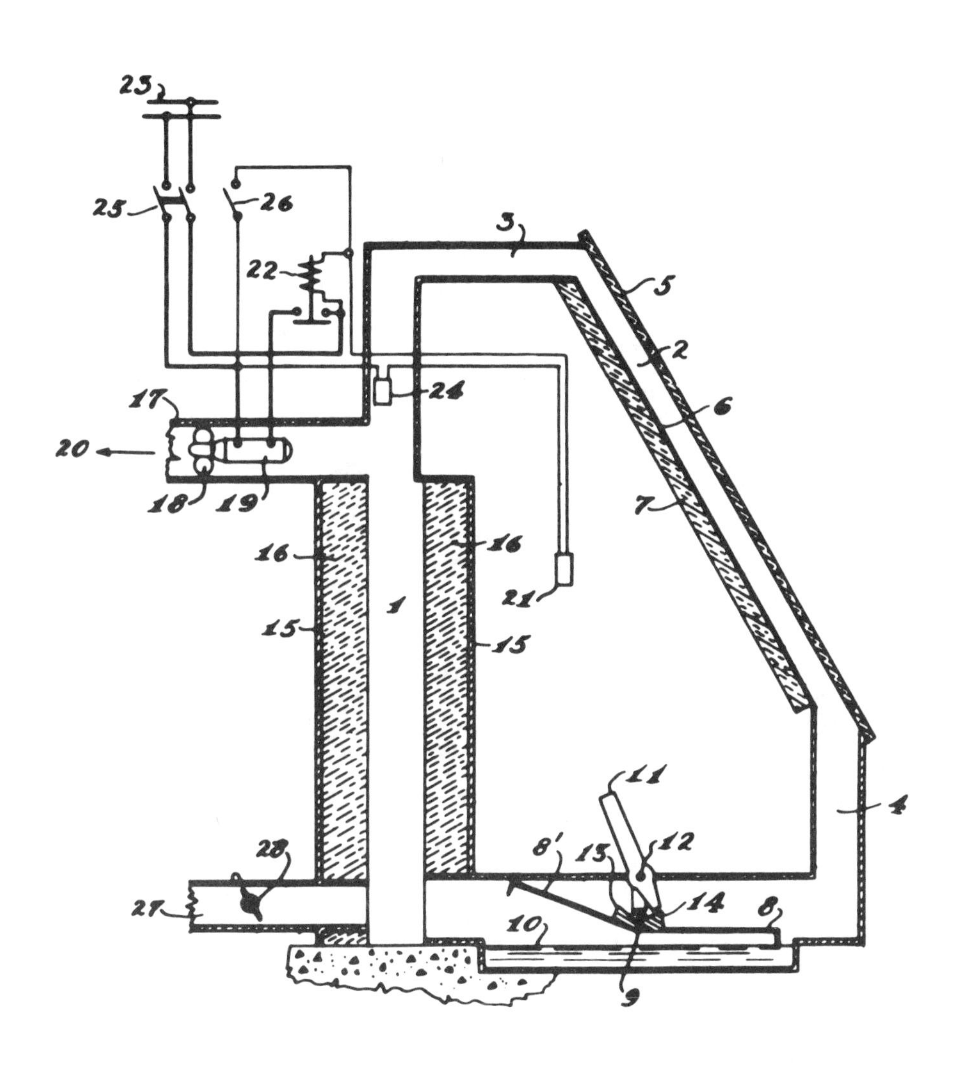

INVENTOR.

William Stelzer

UNITED STATES PATENT OFFICE

2,484,127

HEAT EXCHANGE SYSTEM

William Stelzer, Summit, N. J.

*

The invention relates to a heat exchange system and more particularly to a heating and cooling system where absorption or emission of heat rays is utilized through convection by means of air.

The main object of the invention is to utilize solar heat economically for the heating of dwellings in northern climates by using a heat absorbing surface of a material of low specific heat, from where the heat is transmitted by means of flowing air to an accumulator for storage, and from where heat may be drawn for heating purposes only as required to maintain a desired temperature.

Another object is to produce a simple system where the heat may be transmitted from the heat absorbing surface by free convection to reduce the operating expenses to a minimum.

A further object is to introduce a novel check valve to control the air flow between the accumulator and the heat absorbing surface in such a way as to permit transfer of heat only as desired.

It is also an aim of this invention to use the same system to produce a cooling effect so that the system is adapted to maintain a desired temperature regardless of natural fluctuations in temperature.

Other objects and advantages of this invention will be apparent from the following description considered in connection with the accompanying drawing submitted for the purpose of illustration and not to define the scope of the invention.

* In the drawing, wherein similar reference characters refer to similar parts:

The illustration is a diagrammatic view of the new heating and cooling system where the structural elements are shown in cross-sectional elevation. *

In the preferred embodiment I employ a circulatory system comprising an accumulator 1 in communication with a heating chamber 2 by means of ducts 3 and 4. The heating chamber 2 is separated from the atmosphere by a plate of glass or other transparent material 5 adapted to permit the passage of heat rays, as well as certain ultra violet rays from the sun to keep the passing air fresh. A heat absorbing or emitting surface 6 backed by a heat insulating partition 7 is arranged to be exposed to the solar rays and should be made of a material of very high absorptivity or emissivity but very low specific heat. Thus it is desirable to use a heat insulating material whose exposed surface is covered with a thin coat of black color. The purpose of this is to provide a construction where the heat received from the rays is transferred to the passing air immediately by convection so that nothing is lost if the source of radiant heat is suddenly cut off and the emission of heat becomes greater than the absorption.

In order to prevent the circulation of air through the system when the temperature in chamber 2 is not suitable, a check valve is provided in duct 4 comprising a pair of shutters or flaps 8 and 8' extending from a central portion pivotally supported at 9. The outer edges of flaps 8 and 8' are adapted to come in contact with the surface of a basin of liquid 10 providing a seal in the closed position of the valve. A manually operable lever 11 pivoted at 12 permits the reversal of the valve to check the flow of air in one direction or the other as desired. To control the directional flow of air through the valve I provide stops or abutments 13 and 14 extending from the central portion of the valve and limiting the opening of the valve when engaged by the lower extremity of lever 11, said stops 13 and 14 having sufficient clearance with said lever to allow the check valve to open. The check valve is constructed in such a way that the center of gravity of the movable part is located above pivot 9 whereby the flap nearest the surface of the liquid is urged in a closed position due to gravity because the center of pressure or weight is beyond the dead center. Thus in the illustration shown flap 8 is urged in a closed position until the opposite flap is arrested by the top of duct 4. Since the forces of the fluent stream urging to open the valve are very small, it is necessary that all unnecessary friction is eliminated, which is the reason for introducing the liquid 10. On the other hand, the forces urging the valve in a closed position should be as small as possible and the area of flaps 8 sufficiently large so as to respond to a small difference in static pressure on opposite sides of the valve.

The heating chamber 2 may be incorporated in the roof of a building or it may form the roof itself, while the accumulator 1 is preferably inside of the building and may be constructed of a ceramic material. Walls 15 should be well sealed to house the refractory 16 for storing heat. While hollow tile is ideal for this purpose, bricks stacked loosely may be used effectively and most economically, since due to the cheapness a larger mass may be employed.

The system thus far described permits a continuous circulation according to the thermosyphon principle. A hot air duct 17 extends from duct 3 and houses an axial flow fan 18 driven by an electric motor 19 to blow air in the direction of arrow 20. The motor is controlled by a room thermostat 21 closing an electric circuit to operate relay 22 which in turn closes the power circuit feeding the electric motor from line 23. Thermostat 21 is of the conventional type so that it will not be shown or described in detail. It may be set manually so that the circuit closes as soon as the room temperature drops to a certain point and is broken again when the temperature has risen a certain amount. Another thermostat 24 electrically in series with 21 is located in duct 3 and is of the type that breaks the circuit when the temperature is below a pre-determined value. Numerals 25 and 26 indicate switches for the main or power circuit and the control circuit, respectively. A cold air return duct 27 is provided to lead from the rooms to the lower portion of accumulator 1. A manually operable valve 28 is provided within this duct to be closed when the system is not in use.

In cold weather, when the system is intended to serve as a heating plant the check valve is positioned as shown on the drawing, whereby air is permitted to pass from accumulator 1 through duct 4 to rise in chamber 2. The circulation is induced by the heating of the air in chamber 2 where the surface 6 receives the heat rays from the sun to which it is exposed. The warm air passes through duct 3 from chamber 2 into accumulator 1 where it transmits the heat to the refractory 16. The cooled air descends to the bottom and is drawn again through duct 4 and through the check valve to the heating chamber 2. The passage of the air through the check valve is effected by the air pressure acting on the underside of flap 8 to lift the latter, whereby the sealing edge is raised out of the liquid, the opening obtained depending on the air pressure but being limited by the clearance between the lower end of lever 11 and abutment 14. Thus a continuous circuit of fluent air is produced which gradually warms up accumulator 1. If the radiation of solar energy ceases, or if the temperature produced in chamber 2 is lower than that existing in accumulator 1, the circulation ceases, and is prevented in the opposite direction by the check valve. Supposing the room temperature drops to a point where thermostat 21 closes the electric control circuit and that the temperature in duct 2 is sufficiently high to keep the electric contacts of thermostat 24 closed, relay 22 is energized and closes the power circuit to energize motor 19 so that fan 18 induces a draft in the direction of arrow 20 to blow hot air into the room or rooms to be heated, the return of the air taking place through duct 27.

During hot weather the apparatus may be used for cooling. Since the emissivity of a surface is equal to its absorptivity, it is equally efficient in radiating heat into the sky during the night to lower the temperature. Thus the air in chamber 2 cooled by surface 6 tends to sink downwardly. To permit a circulation where the air in chamber 2 descends due to gravity and rises in accumulator 1 the check valve lever 11 is moved in the opposite direction where the lower end of the lever abuts against boss 13 so that flap 8' is held in the proximity of the surface of liquid 10 to prevent the flow of air from accumulator 1 to the heating chamber. Due to gravity the sealing edge of flap 8' is urged into contact with surface 10, but the cooled air descending from passage 2 via passage 4 produces a slight pressure to lift up flap 8' to permit flow of air into accumulator 1. When the heat exchange has ended due to a change in conditions, the reversal of air flow is prevented as the sealing edge of flap 8' dips again into the fluid and seals off the passage. Thus accumulator 1 becomes a cooler capable of absorbing heat from the rooms to be cooled to make them more comfortable. The transfer of heat may be controlled by closing switch 26 which puts fan 18 into operation. *

July 26, 1966 D. E. HERVEY **3,262,493**

MEANS FOR HEATING AND COOLING A STRUCTURE

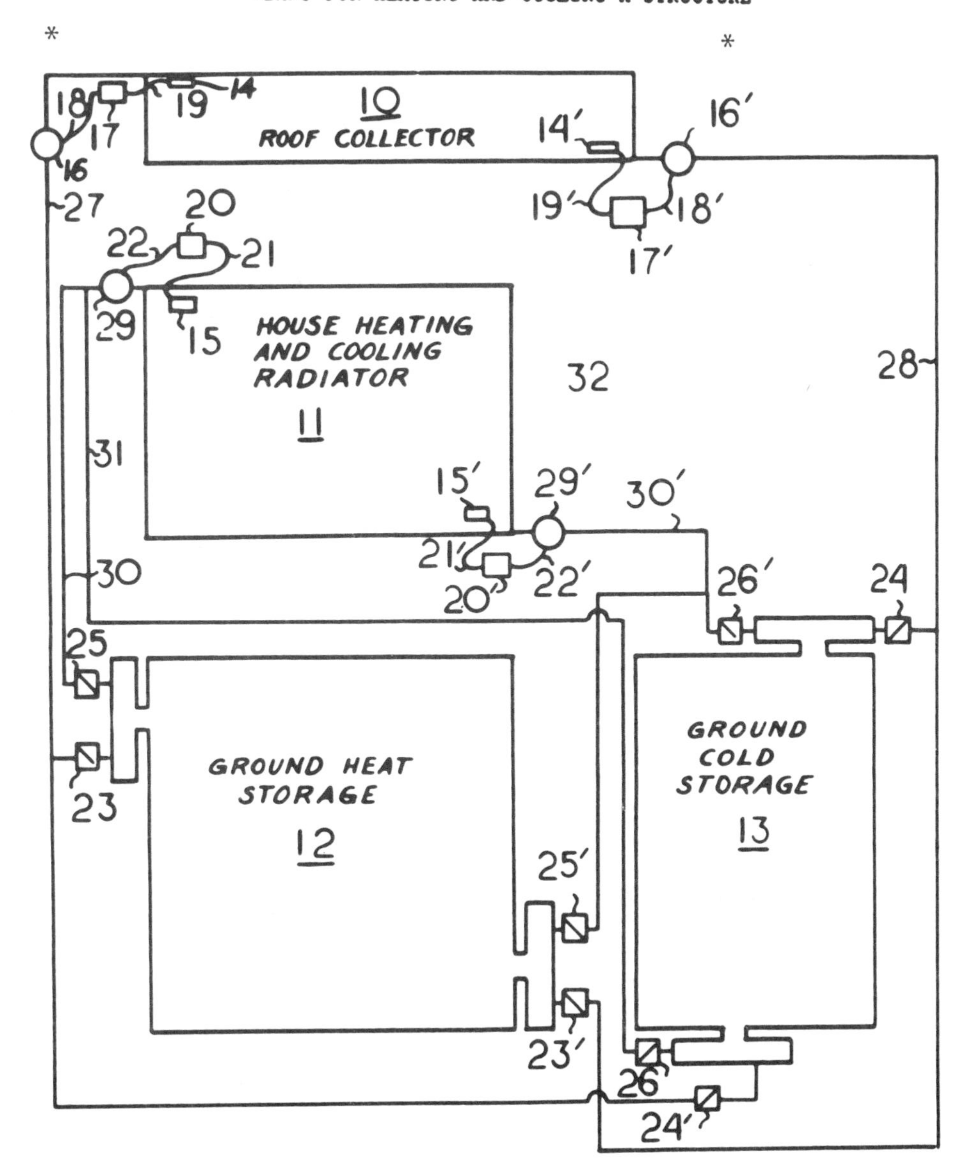

FIG. 1

David E. Hervey

INVENTOR

July 26, 1966 D. E. HERVEY 3,262,493

MEANS FOR HEATING AND COOLING A STRUCTURE

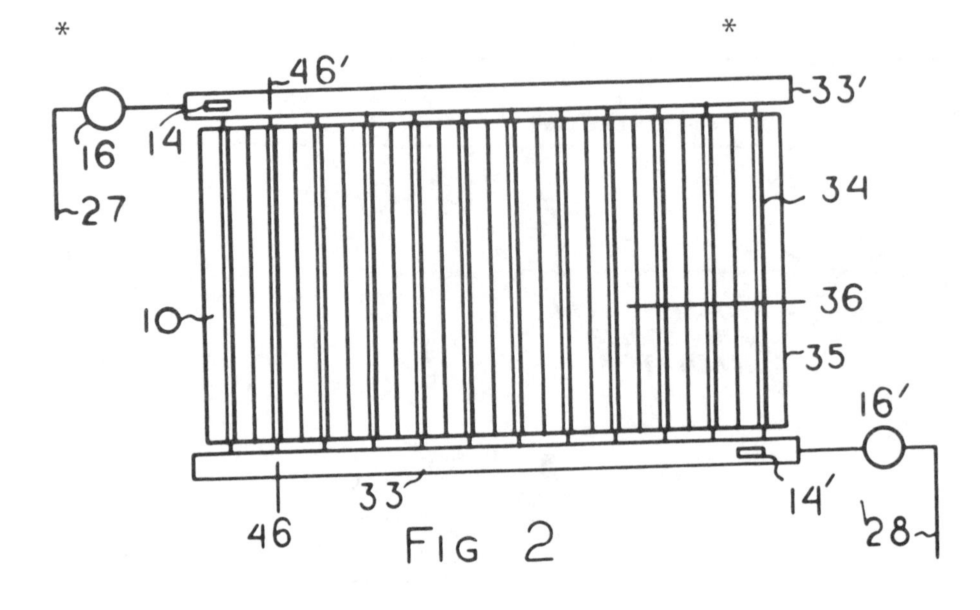

FIG 2

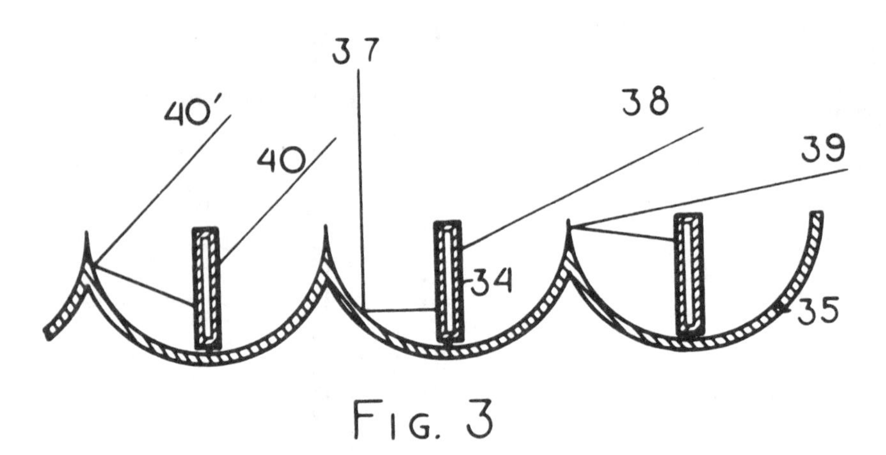

FIG. 3

David E. Hervey
INVENTOR

July 26, 1966 D. E. HERVEY 3,262,493

MEANS FOR HEATING AND COOLING A STRUCTURE

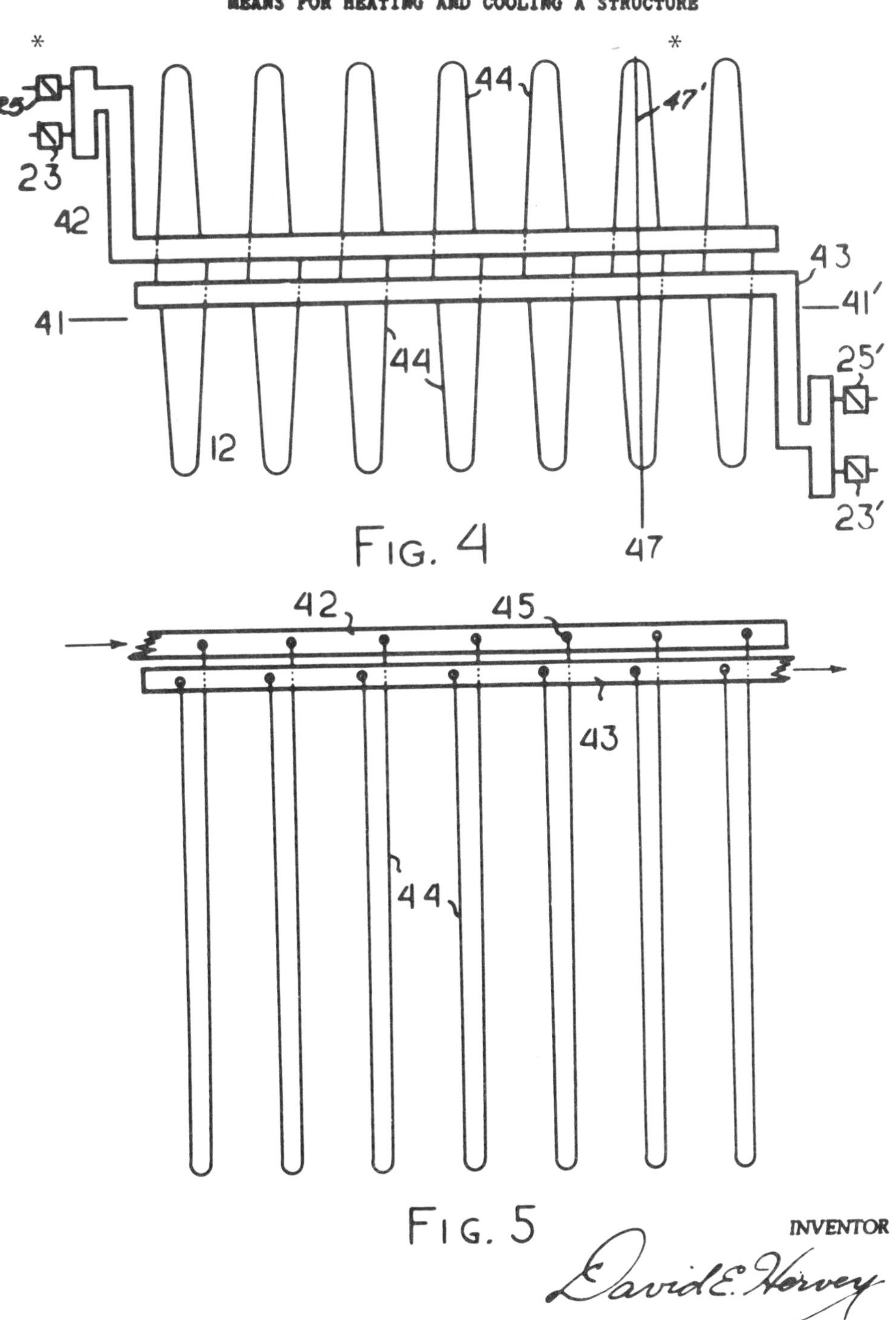

July 26, 1966 | D. E. HERVEY | **3,262,493**

MEANS FOR HEATING AND COOLING A STRUCTURE

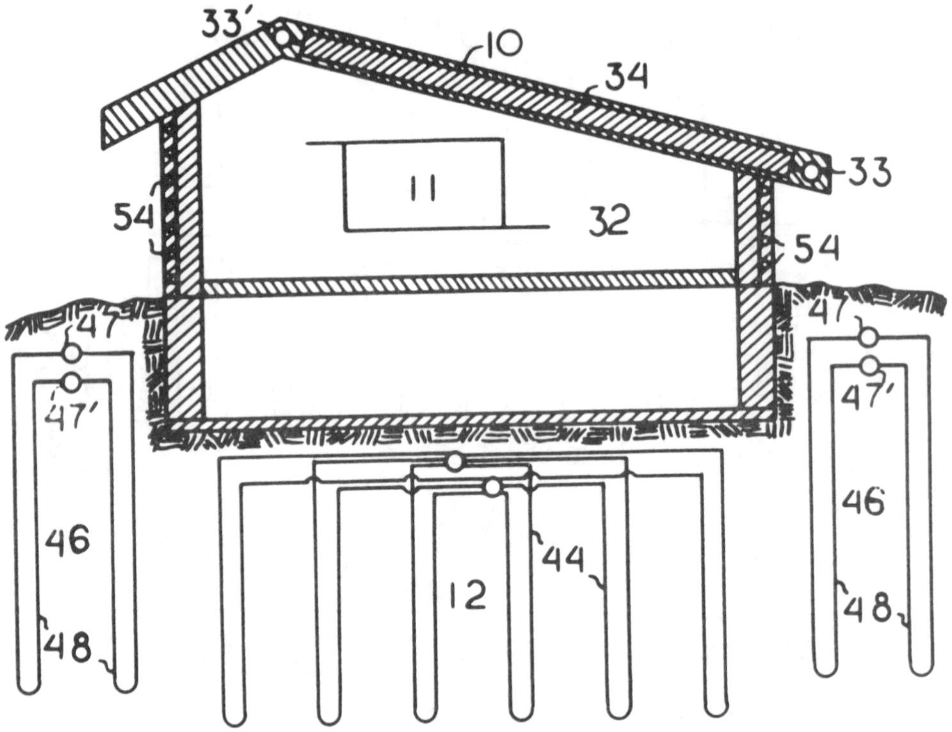

FIG. 6

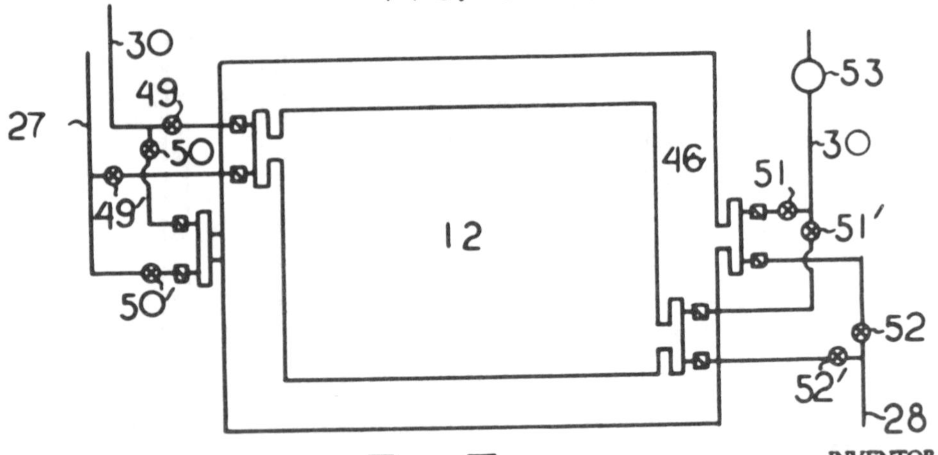

FIG. 7

INVENTOR

David E. Hervey

3,262,493
MEANS FOR HEATING AND COOLING A STRUCTURE
David E. Hervey, Logansport, Ind., assignor to Industrial Institution International, Ltd., Elm City, N.C.

*

This invention relates to heating and cooling a structure by using climatic heat and cold.

More particularly this invention relates to heating and cooling a structure by the use of natural heat and cold ambient to the structure without the use of mechanical, chemical, or other means of increasing said heat or cold for such purposes.

A preferred embodiment of this invention incorporates the improved collection and storage of heat and cold each in one season for use in the opposite season, said storage being in large blocks of undisturbed earth.

Said preferred embodiment also incorporates in certain desired applications the use of a single large block of undisturbed earth for both the storage of cold in the winter time for use in the summer following and for storage of heat that summer for use the next winter.

Also, this invention incorporates a dual purpose method and means of heat removal from a structure for both the cooling of said structure and the storing of said heat for later use in warming the structure. Conversely, this invention incorporates the removal of cold from a structure for the dual purpose of warming said structure and storing said cold in the one process and for later use of said cold for cooling said structure.

In some cases the most efficient application of this invention incorporates the graduated zoning of said heat and cold storage areas with less intensity out from the center of a storage area, so that heat and cold of multiple intensities may be received and stored as available and also to reduce perimeter losses of heat or cold of the storage block.

This invention also incorporates the use of ambient temperatures of soil surrounding a structure to semi heat and cool the exterior walls of a structure to reduce the heating and cooling load of the interior portions of that structure.

This invention also incorporates the provision of an improved system of collecting solar heat and of a basically new concept of storing this heat deep within a large block of undisturbed earth in an extremely efficient and economical manner and one requiring only negligible maintenance and operating costs and astonishingly low installation costs.

As with the heat storage facilities in this invention all prior solar heat collectors and transfer elements are completely inadequate to accomplish what has been accomplished by my present invention by actual construction and use over two entire winter heating periods and summer storage periods.

Heretofore solar heat receptors have either comprised merely flat surface receptors, simple round pipe direct solar ray receptors, or with flat back reflectors, or where curved or semicylindrical reflectors were used the focal plane was disregarded and the small round heat reception tubes received only a small portion of the rays falling on the collector. In addition, my collector serves the dual purpose of collecting cold at night in the winter and transferring it to a cold storing block of earth while simultaneously heating the roof surface of the structure and thereby reducing its heat load.

The structure element in my present invention is without precedence in several ways. Natural heat and natural cold are collected and stored in the ground as such and are brought back to the structure to make it comfortable year round. This is augmented by current climatic heat and cold collection, so that no auxiliary house heating or cooling systems are needed even in relatively severe climates.

Various temperatures of both heat and cold may be stored and then used or used directly in various parts of the structure so as to both utilize lower temperatures of heat and higher temperatures of cold and to conserve the stored heats of higher temperatures and the stored colds of lower temperature.

Thus, the house heating and cooling loads are greatly reduced by using low heat and low cold temperature values in hollow exterior wall zones—said low heat and cold values would otherwise be lost.

Also, each element of the structure heating and cooling system may be used either for collecting heat or collecting cold to be transferred and stored as well as for structure conditioning elements and, in fact with this invention may be performing both functions at the same time.

Thus the colder the winter the better for conditioning the house the next summer and vice versa. Not only is this true, but the act of storing cold warms the structure and the act of storing heat cools the structure, both when needed most. There is no precedent for this system of "having your cake and eating it too."

This invention, therefore, accomplishes the complete task of furnishing all the heat and cold required to heat and cool a structure such as a house year round by employing four basic elements and four only. Namely, One—natural heat and cold collection by adequate means. Two—storing this heat and cold by adequate means. Three—utilizing this heat and cold within a structure by adequate means; and Four—by utilizing adequate fluid transfer elements to transfer adequately the heat and cold as the case may be when it is in excess, to the storage, or as needed to supply the structure.

It is an object, therefore, of this invention, to collect, store, and use natural heat and cold to condition a structure.

Another object of this invention is to provide a three-fold structure conditioning system comprising an improved solar collector, improved and adequate ground storage, and improved structure conditioning means.

A further object of this invention is to provide an improved solar collector which receives every ray of solar energy falling on its area into its heat receptor-transfer tubes.

Another object of the invention is the provision of a solar collector having flattened fluid heat transfer tubes for improved heat reception in cooperation with semi-cylindrical heat reflectors.

Still another object of this invention is the provision of method and means for semi heating and cooling exterior walls of a structure by using natural heat and cold of low intensity ambient or near a structure to reduce the interior heating and cooling load of the structure.

Another object of this invention is to provide a very inexpensive system for large scale storage of heat and cold in undisturbed earth and also the removal and use thereof when needed.

Another object of this invention is to provide multiple zoned earth heat and cold storage blocks for storing various intensities or temperatures of heat or cold.

Still another object of this invention is to provide concentric zones of storage of heat and cold to reduce perimeter losses of heat and cold from that storage by conduction.

A further object of this invention is to collect, store and use natural heat and cold by the combined processes of radiation, conduction and convection to completely temperature condition a structure.

Further objects will be apparent from the specifications and drawings and the more detailed description and illustration of preferred embodiments contained herein must not be construed to limit the scope of the invention.

Referring to the drawings

FIG. 1 is a schematic drawing of basic elements of the invention.

FIG. 2 is a plan view of a collector element.

FIG. 3 is a cross section view of a part of FIG. 2.

FIG. 4 is a plan view of a storage element.

FIG. 5 is an elevation of a section of FIG. 4.

FIG. 6 is cross section of a house and cross sections of various basic elements of the invention.

FIG. 7 is a schematic plan view of the hot central and warm perimeter ground storage areas as illustrated in FIG. 6.

The above mentioned drawings illustrate a typical domestic installation embodying the invention by way of example. Following is a more detailed description of same.

Referring to FIG. 1 of the drawings the various elements are shown as follows, the roof collector **10**, house heating and cooling radiator **11**, ground heat storage block **12**, and ground cold storing block **13**.

On a typical summer day when the fluid in solar collector **10** reaches a temperature of say 180° F. aquastat **14** with capillary **19** activates electric switch **17** which activates electric motor circulator **16** by way of electrical line **18** causing the hot fluid to pass from collector **10** out through pipe line **27** thence through check valve **23** into ground storage coil **12** and being a closed fluid system, this causes a counter flow of fluid of the temperature ambient coil **12** of say 70° F. to flow out through check valve **23'** through line **28** and collector **10** to probe **14** said cooler 70° F. temperature then causing probe **14** to break the circuit from switch **17** by way of line **18** to circulator **16** and causing it to stop until solar heat again raises the temperature of the fluid in collector **10** to the preset temperature of say the 180° F. at which time the foregoing process is repeated. By this process fluid of higher heat is transferred repeatedly from collector **10** to ground heat storage coil **12** and the heat thereof flows by conduction into the earth block ambient coil **12**.

Likewise, in the wintertime at night when the temperature of the fluid in roof collector **10** drops to a preset point say 35° F., aquastat **14'** by means of capillary **19'** activates switch **17'** which makes on the fall to activate motor circulator **16'** by way of electric line **18'** which causes flow out of collector **10** by means of line **28** through check valve **24** into cold storage coil **13** causing thereby counterflow from coil **13** through check valve **24'** and line **27** into collector **10** of fluid from cold storage coil **13** of say 45° F. until it reaches aquastat **14'** causing its temperature to rise thereby opening switch **17'** by means of capillary **19'** and stopping electric motor circulator **16'**.

When the structure **32** needs to be heated by structure radiator **11**, as sensed by thermo probe **15** which may be inside or outside radiator **11**, switch **20** activated by capillary **21** conducts electricity via line **22** to motor fluid circulator **29** causing fluid in radiator **11** to flow through line **30** and check valve **25** into ground storage coil **12** and being a closed circuit this causes heated fluid in coil **12** by counter flow action to flow through check valve **25'** and line **30'** into house heating radiator **11** thus heating it and heating the structure. By repeated exchanges of fluid in radiator **11** (which has dissipated its heat to the structure **32**) with the fluid in heat storage coil **12** which has absorbed heat from the ground storage block of earth surrounding coil **12** the structure is heated.

When the structure **32** needs to be cooled a similar exchange takes place between house radiator coil **11** and cold storage coil **13** activated by thermo probe **15'**, capillary **21'**, switch **20'**, line **22'** and motor fluid circulator **29'** through line **30'** check valve **26'** into coil **13** with counter flow of the cold fluid in coil **13** passing through check valve **26** and line **31** into house coil **11**. The cold fluid in coil **11** then absorbs heat from the structure because of the differential of temperature between the two and when it becomes sufficiently warm thermo probe **15'** again activates a similar exchange of fluids between coil **11** and coil **13** so that the warmed fluid is transferred to coil **13** where the heat in said fluid is absorbed by the cold block of earth ambient coil **13**, slowly but gradually warming said earth ambient coil **13**.

The following winter at night when the fluid in the roof collector **10** reaches a predetermined low temperature below that of coil **13** and the surrounding earth, said coil **13** is again cooled by the fluid from collector **10** as previously described but in doing so the heat stored in earth block ambient coil **13** from the summer cooling operations of the structure **32** and stored in earth block ambient coil **13** now is sent to the roof collector coil **10** to be dissipated, but in so doing the roof of the structure **32** containing roof collector coil **10** is heated to say 40° F. thereby reducing the heating load of the structure **32** by this semi heating of its exterior surface. This reduction of heat loss from a house for instance may be very substantial, especially in a severe climate or on very cold days and nights since the temperature differential from inside to outside the structure **32** may be as from 70° F. to 40° F. instead of from 70° F. to say 10 below zero F. Thus as far as the roof is concerned it is as though the structure was built in a semi tropical region. Power is furnished to electric switches **17** and **17'**, and **20** and **20'** by regular house electric circuits not shown.

In order to achieve an object of the invention i.e. to heat and cool a structure year round without auxiliary means, highly efficient elements and methods for heat and cold collection, storage, and use are required. FIGURES 2 and 3 show the structure of a preferred type of heat and cold collector. In FIG. 2 fluid circulators **16** and **16'**, sensing probes **14** and **14'** and flow lines **27** and **28** may be the same as in FIG. 1. The electrical elements of FIG. 1 are not shown to avoid too much duplication. In FIG. 2 fluid transfer from heat storage coil **12** (FIG. 1) and cold storage coil **13** (FIG. 1) enter roof collector coil **10** by way of pipe line **28** and leave by way of pipe line **27** as previously described in the functioning of the system FIG. 1. Parts of collector **10**, a preferred embodiment of same, are shown in more detail to more adequately describe the exact functioning of collector **10**. When relatively cool fluid say 70° F. from heat storage ground coil **12** enters collector **10** it does so by entering manifold **33** thence passes through manifold tubes **34** (which transverse the vertical radius of semicylindrical heat reflectors **35** bisecting same) until said fluid enters manifold **33'**, whence it leaves manifold **33'** by way of pipe line **27**.

On a day when solar heat is available, the solar rays impinge on tubes **34** directly or are reflected to same by semicylindrical reflectors **35** and the resultant heat received by the tubes **34** is transmitted by conduction to the fluid contained by them thus raising its temperature to a predetermined level of say 180° F. These tubes and also the manifolds are colored to a heat receptive color such as dark brown or soot black. The heat in the manifold **33'** is also warmed by direct solar rays and while the tubes reach a temperature of 180° F., the manifold reaches a temperature of say 160° F. and when this situation obtains the aquastat temperature probe **14** activates fluid circulator **16** as previously described and moves the fluid from collector **10** to ground heat storage coil **12** (FIG. 1) with counter flow from storage coil **12** filling collector

10 with cool fluid.

This novel collector is so scientifically constructed that all of the solar rays falling on the face of said solar collector fall either directly onto said collector tubes 34 or are reflected to same by semicylindrical reflectors 35. Thus not only 100 percent of the sun's rays enter the fluid transfer tubes 34 of the collector 10, but the surface of said tubes 34 is reduced to about one half that of a flat collector by their being vertical in cross section and of their relative position within reflectors 35 so that virtually the entire surface receives heat. There are thus no moving parts needed to orient the collector to the incidence of the sun's rays. This results in almost double heat reception on the surface of collector tube 34 formerly obtained resulting in very high heat receptivity for collector 10.

This is more clearly shown in FIG. 3, vertical cross section of part of FIG. 2 taken on line 36 of FIG. 2 where 37, 38, 39, and 40 and 40' represent solar radiant heat rays entering collector 10 and either entering tubes 34 directly or by reflection from reflectors 35.

Conversely, when at night in the winter the collector 10 is acting to collect cold instead of heat it does so by removing heat from cold storage block 13 FIG. 1 by means of fluid passing through pipe line 27 and filling collector tubes 34. Again referring to FIG. 3 tubes 34 are now the source of radiant energy and in addition to radiating directly into space as represented by rays 40 and 38 this heat is radiated into space by first being reflected by reflectors 35 as represented by rays 37, 39, and 40'. There is also heat exchange in both collection and dissipation by the usual processes of conduction and convection with the atmosphere.

Ground heat storage unit 12, FIG. 1 will now be more completely described in a preferred embodiment by describing plan view FIG. 4 wherein check valves 25 and 23 and 25' and 23' correspond to those of like numerals in FIG. 1. In the case of heat storage, hot fluid enters the coil 12 by way of check valve 25 from roof collector 10 and enters manifold 42 from whence it passes outwardly and downwardly through U exchange tubes 44 at spaced intervals in heat storage coil zone 12, from whence said fluid also rises through the latter half of said U returns 44 upwardly and inwardly to manifold 43 where it comes to rest and loses its heat to the earth, ambient coil 12. Heat storage coil zone 12 should be of sufficient size to heat the house for a full winter when subjected to to a full summer's heat, and under average conditions the area underneath a house and 30 feet deep from below the basement floor will suffice in average soil where there is a reasonable amount of solar heat collection in the winter on sunny days. In more extreme conditions and requirements a larger block and added features are necessary to completely heat the house. To insert said U returns 44 holes are first bored into the earth block 12.

FIG. 5 is a longitudinal elevation taken on line 41–41' of one row of U return tubes 44 in their corresponding relationship and connection to manifolds 42 and 43, FIG. 4, by way of orifices 45.

When heat is taken from heat storage coil zone 12 to heat the house by means of radiator coil 11, FIG. 1 cool fluid from coil 11 enters coil 12 by way of check valve 25, FIG. 4 and manifold 42, then passes through U returns 44 and into manifold 43 causing a counter flow of fluid in coil 12 (which has been warmed by contact with warm ambient earth) into the house radiator 11, FIG. 1 by way of check valve 25' and line 30' which in turn warms the structure.

In like manner cold fluid is taken from cold storage area 13, FIG. 1 which is the same or similar in structure and operation to FIG. 4, and delivered to house coil 11 in exchange relationship with fluid from coil 11, said cold fluid then cools said house structure 32 by absorbing heat from same through the processes of radiation from said structure 32 and convection air currents and conduction into radiator 11. This then heated fluid is then exchanged with fluid in said cold storage coil 13 where it comes to rest and deposits said heat in said cold storage area 13 ambient earth, in a repetitive process all summer depositing considerable quantities of heat in millions of B.t.u.'s. This heat is then transferred to roof collector 10 the following winter while cold is being stored in cold storage area 13, heating said roof and thereby partially heating said house.

FIGURE 6 is a diagrammatic cross section of a house showing the relationship of elements of the heating and cooling system as used in this illustrative embodiment of the invention. Roof collector 10 is shown in cross section on line 46–46' of FIG. 2 and corresponding parts have like numbers. Subbasement hot storage coil zone 12, FIGS. 1 and 4, is shown in diagrammatical cross sectional elevation taken on line 47–47', FIG. 4. House radiator coil or temperature conditioning coil 11, FIG. 1, is shown in living area of the house 32, connected relationship being shown in FIG. 1. In FIG. 6 and FIG. 7 is also shown perimeter warm and cool storage zone coil 46 with manifolds 47 and 47' and U return coils 48. This warm and cool storage zone 46 is operated in conjunction with roof coil 10 in the same manner as the hot storage coil 12, but in this case coil 46 is substituted on occasion for hot coil 12 by manually operated valves as illustrated in FIG. 7. When solar energy available in collector 10 is not sufficient to make a profitable exchange with hot zone 12, then hand valve 49' is closed and valve 50 is opened and warm storage zone 46 is automatically substituted for hot zone 12. Thermal probe 14 in roof collector 10 is adjusted downward to say 120° F., for example, to make a more efficient collection of available heat. In the fall and spring also, fluid from warm storage area 46 may be valved through house radiator 11, FIGS. 1 and 7, by closing valve 49 and opening valve 50 and leaving open valve 51 thermoprobe 15, FIG. 1 is in this case also wired to fluid circulator 53 in line 30, FIG. 7, which then makes fluid exchange between house coil 11 and warm storage coil 46.

In the same manner house warming auxiliary coil as shown within the exterior wall in cross section as tubes 54 plying between manifolds not shown but operating as a standard manifold coil similar to roof coil 10 is used to warm the exterior walls of said house 32 FIGS. 1 and 6 being valved by hand valves in substitution for interior house warming coil 11 so that hot fluid from coil 12 or warm fluid from coil 46 may be exchanged with the fluid in exterior wall coil 54 either on a continuous basis or as called for by a thermoprobe in the same manner as used in coil 11. Thus when heat from coil 54 is transferred to ground coil 46 to cool said wall, said heat is stored in coil storage block 46 in the process. Then when the wall needs to be warmed in the winter this same heat is brought back from coil storage block of earth 46 into coil 54 and warms said wall. Conversely, the same cold is transferred from coil 54 to coil storage 46 and then brought back to cool said wall in the opposite season.

The collector in my present invention collects every ray of the sun which falls on it, winter and summer, from sun-up to sun-down either directly or by reflection into its heat transfer tubes of greatly reduced surface and has no moving or mechanical parts. The focal plane of parallel rays falling on the inside of a semicylindrical reflector is the mid radial plane of that semicylinder regardless of the direction of the parallel rays falling on the inside of said semicylinder. For this reason the heat transfer tube of my collector is made as a flattened tube and is made to transverse the semicylindrical reflector in this radial focal plane, thus reducing by one half the total surface area of said tube while at the same time receiving every ray of the sun falling on the roof of the solar collector.

At night, in the winter, when my collector is collecting cold to be stored in a large block of undisturbed earth it does so by dissipating heat from this block of earth which comes up and out through this flattened collector tube which now has become a heat dissipator tube or radiator tube in the roof, radiating heat directly to the atmosphere above and also indirectly by radiating it toward the semicylindrical heat reflector which in turn reflects all that heat to the atmosphere because of its shape. Double reflective surfaces are thus obtained by having both sides of the flattened tube exposed to the atmosphere for dissipating conducted heat and exposed to the semicylindrical reflector on each side of it for dissipating the radiant heat by reflection.

Thus it is seen that by using a flattened fluid bearing tube that completely or substantially encloses the bisecting radial plane of the semicylindrical reflector in a solar collector, substantial improvements in efficiency are achieved. First, a low volume-high direct contact, ratio is established between the volume of the fluid in the tube and the surface of the tube. This provides quick direct heating of the fluid overcoming natural insulation properties of the fluid as disposed in a round tube. It also overcomes the high reradiation losses of heat inherent in a fin type collector tube. It also has the tremendous advantage of intercepting every ray of the sun's heat falling on the collector from morning till nite and of giving total radiation at nite in the cooling process.

The heat and cold from this highly efficient collector is then alternately transferred into highly efficient and now adequate storage means. In order to provide adequate heat and cold storage in the earth a large volume of the right condition of the earth is necessary. By the method of boring inexpensive holes into the earth (in actual practice 40 feet are bored in 4 minutes), in checker board fashion, and inserting therein U-return tubes which are connected on opposite ends to manifolds, large storage blocks of readily conductive undisturbed earth are provided. The larger the block thus constructed the less is the loss of heat or cold by conduction to outer areas. Thus a point in size is reached where the economical complete heating or cooling of a structure is made possible entirely from natural sources without the necessity of increasing their intensity or without the necessity of using auxiliary means.

Since the perimeter heat losses through the surface on all sides of a storage block, or of a structure, is directly proportional to the temperature of the block or structure on the one hand and of ambient areas on the other my design and invention of zoning the block and the structure as to temperature gradient greatly reduces these perimeter heat losses. Also these individual temperature storage zone gradations provide storage zones for the temperatures of heat and cold of a lower magnitude not possible to store in a central block of intensive heat or cold. Also these perimeter zones recover conducted perimeter losses of heat or cold from the central block.

These moderate temperatures of heat and cold are then used to modify the temperature of the structure during periods of low requirements and for zoned conditioning. Also temperatures ambient to the collector and structure coils provide moderate heat and cold for transfer and storage in these perimeter zones.

These improvements improve and increase the efficiency of heating and cooling by natural means over former constructions manyfold. *

Feb. 22, 1944. A. B. NEWTON **2,342,211**

UTILIZATION OF NATURAL HEATING AND COOLING EFFECTS

*

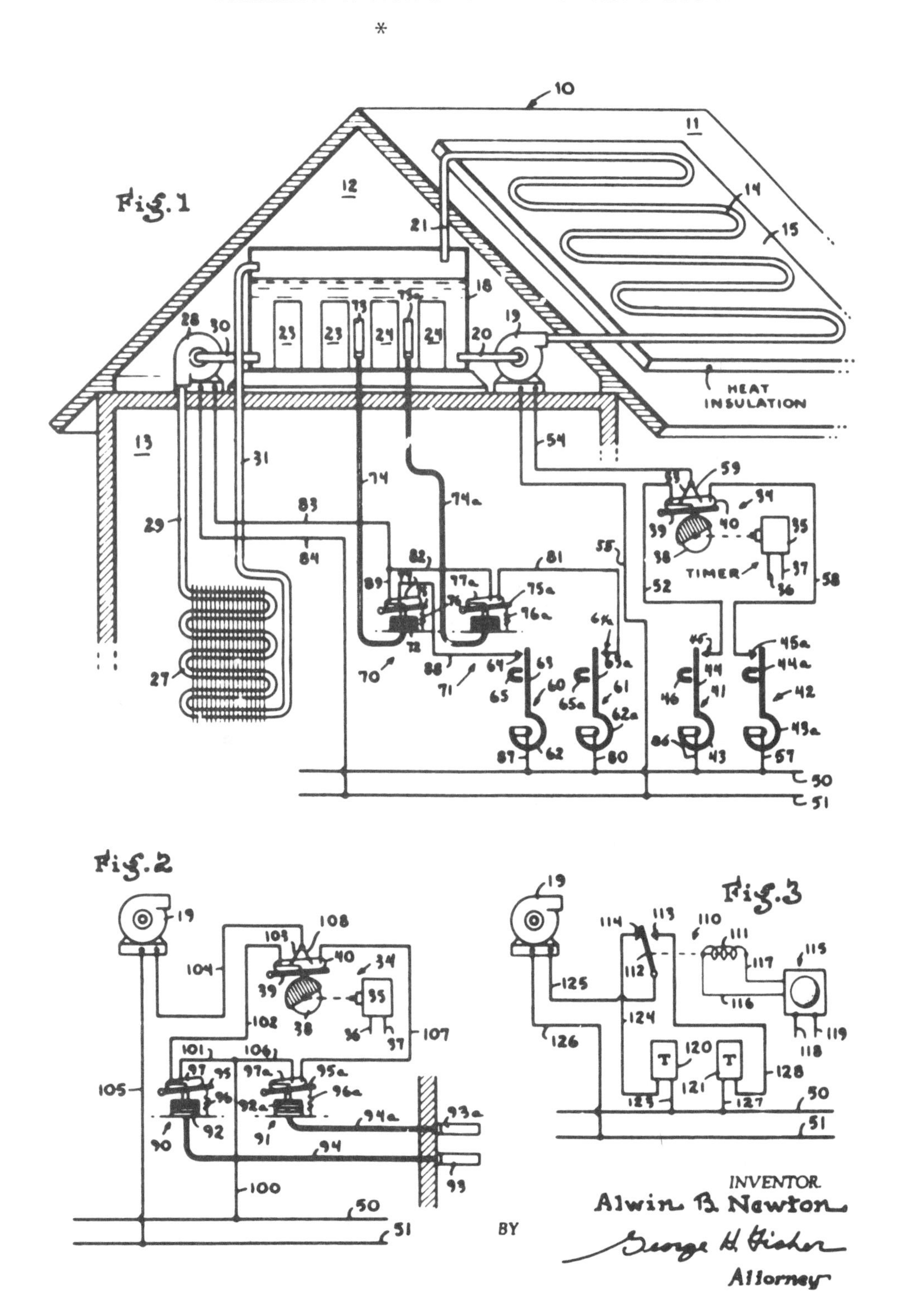

UNITED STATES PATENT OFFICE

2,342,211

UTILIZATION OF NATURAL HEATING AND COOLING EFFECTS

Alwin B. Newton, Minneapolis, Minn., assignor to Minneapolis-Honeywell Regulator Company, Minneapolis, Minn., a corporation of Delaware

*

This invention relates to methods and means for utilizing natural heating and cooling effects by storing these effects when they are available by means of heat storers and cold storers, and utilizing the stored heat or stored cooling effects when necessary to control the temperature of a given objective. The natural heating and cooling effects which the invention primarily takes advantage of, are those occasioned by radiation of heat from the sun to a heat absorbtive body and by radiation of heat from a radiating body to space. By utilizing the radiant heat effects, much greater temperature differentials are produced between different bodies or mediums than can be produced by conduction or convection methods of heat transfer under similar circumstances. By reason of these greater differentials, the heating effect of the sun and the cooling effect of radiation from a hot body to space are made more available and greater advantage can be taken of them.

My invention comprehends cooling a medium by allowing its heat to be radiated from a radiating body to space at night. The principle upon which this effect is based is the same as that which is operative when frost forms on the surface of the earth even though the temperature of the air does not fall to the freezing point. That is, the earth is a body having good heat absorptive and radiating properties, and after the earth has been heated during the day by radiation from the sun it is cooled at night when it radiates this heat back to space. This cooling effect of the earth by reason of the radiation of its heat to space lowers its temperature to a value lower than the temperature of the air at the surface of the earth. Thus the moisture is condensed out of the air and is formed as frost on the surface of the earth. Temperatures may be produced by radiation in this manner which are considerably lower than the lowest air temperature which may have existed during the night.

My invention also comprehends heating a medium by means of direct radiation from the sun, and likewise temperatures may be reached in this manner which are considerably higher than the temperature of the air ambient to the body which is being heated by radiation. These cooling and heating effects produced by radiation are stored, according to my invention, during the time the effect is being produced, and at other times when temperature change of a given objective is needed advantage may be taken of the stored heating and cooling effects as needed.

My invention finds an ideal application in air conditioning systems for buildings, particularly in regions having a relatively mild climate. In such climates, the weather conditions are such during a good part of the year that cooling may be required during the day while the nights are cool enough so that heating is perhaps not required but nevertheless natural cooling effects can be stored up for use in cooling on the following day. Also in regions having mild climates, the weather conditions are often such during a part of the year that while some heating may be required at night, usually the days are warm enough so that heating is not required but natural heat can be stored up during the day for use at night. My invention and its principles could of course also be employed for air conditioning under weather conditions such that cooling is actually required during the day and heating at night.

One of the principal objects of my invention is to provide novel means for storing natural heating and cooling effects so that they may be used when necessary to control the temperature of a given objective.

Another primary object of my invention is to provide methods and means of making use of the natural heating and cooling effects of radiation from the sun and radiation from a body to a space.

Another object of my invention is to provide novel means and arrangements for storing heat and cold, that is, heating and cooling effects, produced as a result of transfer of heat by radiation.

Another object of my invention is to provide a novel method and means for storing heat wherein a substance which is normally a solid is melted when the heat is available and is allowed to solidify again when it is desired to make use of the heat.

Another object of my invention is to provide a means for cooling a medium by direct radiation of its heat to space at night and for heating the medium by direct radiation of heat from the sun during the daytime.

Another object of the invention is to provide control means for controlling the heat and cold storing apparatus so that the heating or cooling effect is utilized at a time when it is necessary to do so for maintaining desired temperature conditions of a given objective.

In accordance with my invention, means are provided for circulating a fluid medium through a device adapted to be heated by direct radiation from the sun or to be cooled by radiation from the device to space at night.

Another object of my invention is to provide time and temperature responsive control means for controlling the circulation of medium through the device both at night and in the daytime so that the fluid medium is circulated so as to cause either a heating effect or cooling effect to be stored up depending upon whether or not the temperature is indicative of an expectancy of heating or cooling requirements of an objective at a later time.

Fig. 1 represents diagrammatically a portion of a building structure having a form of my invention associated therewith,

Fig. 2 represents a modified form of control arrangement, and

Fig. 3 represents another modified form of control arrangement.

Referring to Fig. 1 of the drawing, numeral 10 represents diagrammatically a building structure having a roof 11, an attic 12, and another enclosed portion or space 13. Mounted on the roof of the building is a heat exchange coil 14 of the serpentine type, there being heat insulating material 15 disposed between the roof of the building and the coil 14 to insulate against transfer of heat between the roof and the coil by conduction and radiation. The insulating material and the exchanger may be fastened to the roof in any suitable manner.

In the attic of the building 10 is a tank 18 which may contain either water or under some circumstances it may contain a solution which freezes at temperatures below 32° F. My invention comprehends cooling the water in tank 18, and when the operation is arranged such that the water may be cooled below 32° F., a solution which freezes at a temperature lower than the freezing point of water is used instead. The tank 18 is preferably insulated to minimize transfer of heat between the water in the tank and the air in the attic.

One end of the heat exchanger 14 is connected to the discharge of a circulating pump 19 which is driven by an electric motor, the inlet of the pump being connected to the lower part of the tank 18 by a pipe 20. The other end of the heat exchanger 14 is connected to the upper part of the tank 18 by a pipe 21.

The heat exchange coil 14 forms a device which acts as a radiator which radiates heat to space at night so as to lower the temperature of the water in the coil and which acts as an absorber of heat in the daytime to absorb radiant heat from the sun so as to heat the water in the heat exchanger. Objects that are good radiators of heat are also good absorbers and vice versa.

The primary objects of my invention are to cool the water in the tank 18 by means of radiation from the coil 14 and at other times to heat the water in the tank 18 by means of absorption of radiant heat at the coil 14. As will be presently pointed out, my invention provides means for storing the heating and cooling effects which can be produced by the system as so far described and utilizing these effects for maintaining the temperature of a space at desired values at times when the temperature deviates from these values.

Thus when it is desired to cool the water in the tank 18 and store up a cooling effect which may be subsequently utilized for cooling, circulator 19 is operated at night to circulate the water through the heat exchanger 14 and back to the tank 18. During the night heat will be radiated from the coil 14 to space in substantial amounts, or in other words at a relatively high rate, this effect being particularly pronounced on a clear night. The heat given up by the coil 14 by radiation in this manner will lower the temperature of the water in the coil to a value considerably below the lowest temperature to which the air falls during the night. The principle underlying this temperature fall of the water in the coil is the same as that involved when frost forms on the ground or on other objects which radiate heat at night even though the air temperature is above freezing. That is, the ground is heated by radiation from the sun in the daytime. At night when the sun is not shining, there is a considerably greater proportion of radiation of heat from the ground to space, which radiation causes the temperature at the surface of the earth to fall to a value lower than the temperature of the air, the temperature of the air being governed primarily by convection and conduction. The surface of the earth thus being at a lower temperature than the air condenses moisture out of the air, and it forms on the ground as frost or dew. It is known that ice can be produced on water by digging a hole in the ground and letting water remain in the hole overnight. The water will be cooled by radiation during the night causing ice to form on it. It is known that ice has been formed in this manner by the radiation of heat when the temperature of the air did not fall lower than 56° F. during the night.

From the foregoing, it is to be seen that relatively low temperatures of the water in the tank 18 can be produced at night in the manner above described, these temperatures sometimes being as low as or below the freezing point of water. The heat insulating material 15 prevents the coil 14 from being heated at night by radiation and conduction of heat from the roof of the house itself. When the temperature of the water in tank 18 has been lowered to a relatively low value, the tank of water, as a whole, represents a substantial amount of cooling effect which can be utilized subsequently.

If it is desired to store up heat, that is heating effect, in the water in the tank 18, the circulator 19 is operated in the daytime when the sun is shining. Under these circumstances the coil 14 and the water therein will absorb a great deal of radiant heat from the sun and the water in the coil on a warm sun-shiny day may be heated to temperatures as high as 160° F. and the entire body of water in tank 18 may be brought up substantially to this temperature. In the daytime the temperature of coil 14 may be higher than the temperature of the roof 11 of the house, and under these circumstances transfer of heat from the coil to the roof is substantially prevented by the heat insulating material 15. It is to be seen therefore that in the daytime the temperature of the coil 14 may be raised to a value considerably higher than the temperature of the surrounding atmosphere.

From the foregoing description of the invention as so far made, it is to be seen that a heat transfer system is provided having means whereby heating effect or cooling effect may be stored.

My invention provides means for augmenting the cold storing and heat storing properties of the system so that greater amounts of cooling effect or heating effect can be stored and preserved for longer periods of time. Within the tank 18 are containers 23 which are filled with a fluid which freezes at a temperature of approximately 50° F.

A list of suitable substances is given below:

Acetaldehyde	Penta decane
Creosol	Phenyl-cyclo-hexane
Cyclo hexane	Silico iodoform
Ethyl diamine	Undecyl alcohol
Nitro styrene	

Any number of containers, such as the containers 23, may be provided, and when the temperature of the water in tank 18 is lowered to a point below 50° F., the substance in containers 23 freezes, thereby giving up a substantial amount of additional heat depending on the heat of fusion of the substance used and thereby increasing the amount of cooling effect stored. Subsequently the water in tank 18 is used for cooling purposes so that its temperature is raised above 50° F. so as to melt the substance in containers 23 and this substance then takes up an amount of heat equal to that which it gave off when it froze. Thus while the substance in containers 23 is melting, the temperature of the water in tank 18 is kept near the melting point of the substance.

Also within the tank 18 immersed in the water therein are containers 24 containing a substance which is a solid at ordinary temperatures and which has a melting point of around 130° F. One substance suitable for use in the containers 24 is a substance known as Wood's metal, which melts at a temperature of around 130° F. The purpose of containers 24 and the substance therein is to augment the heat storing properties of the system. Thus during the daytime the temperature of the water in tank 18 may be raised to a relatively high value of perhaps 150° F. or 160° F. at which temperature the substance in containers 24 melts so as to take up a substantial amount of heat determined by the heat of fusion of the substance. At a subsequent time when the water in tank 18 is used for heating purposes, its temperature will be lowered to a value below the melting point, that is, the solidifying point of the substance in containers 24, causing the substance to again solidify and to thus give off an amount of heat equal to that which it took up when it melted. Thus the heat storing properties of the system are augmented by reason of the containers 24 and the substance therein. When this substance solidifies it tends to cause the temperature of the water in tank 18 to remain at the solidifying temperature of the substance while it is solidifying.

For cooling or heating the space 13, my invention provides a finned heat exchange coil 27 through which water may be circulated from the tank 18 by a circulator 28 driven by an electric motor. The discharge of the circulator is connected to the coil 27 by a pipe 29, and the inlet of the circulator is connected to the tank 18 by a pipe 30. The outlet of the coil 27 is connected to the tank 18 by a pipe 31.

My invention provides automatic controls for circulating the hot water through the heat exchange coil 27 when heating of the space is required and for circulating cold water through the coil 27 when cooling of the space is required. These controls will be presently described.

In practicing my invention I prefer to provide control means to provide that a cooling effect or a heating effect will be stored up in the system at such times that the required effect will be available when necessary. To accomplish this, I provide controls for operating the circulator 19 at night depending upon whether or not it can be reasonably expected that cooling will be needed on the following day, and for operating the circulator 19 during the day depending upon whether or not it can be reasonably expected that heating will be required that night. Of course the circulator 19 can be operated at night if cooling is needed at the time or it can be operated in the daytime for heating at the time.

The controls for circulator 19 including a timing device 34 comprising an electric timing motor 35 supplied with power by wires 36 and 37. The timing motor 35 drives a twenty-four hour cam 38 which is mounted on the shaft of the timing motor. The cam 38 makes one revolution in twenty four hours and has a single dwell which is preferably of an extent adjustable between something more and something less than 180° of circumferential extent of the cam. The cam 38 has a cam follower in the form of a pivoted lever 39 carrying a double-ended mercury switch 40 having a pair of electrodes at each end. The cam is arranged to cause the electrodes at one end of the mercury switch to be bridged at night and the electrodes at the other end of the mercury switch to be bridged during daylight hours. The cam 38 may be made manually adjustable so as to make closure of the opposite ends of the mercury switch correspond to hours of daylight and darkness or a so-called astronomical disk may be used which is part of a timing mechanism which automatically adjusts the cam throughout the year so that the closed periods of each end of the mercury switch always correspond to the hours of daylight and darkness.

The controls additionally include a thermostat 41 in the space 13 and a similar thermostat 42 also in the space. The thermostat 41 comprises a bimetal element 43 arranged to actuate a movable switch blade 44 in a manner to cause the switch blade to engage a fixed electrical contact 45 at a temperature which may be 75° for example, the blade 44 moving toward its associated contact upon a rise in temperature. Associated with the blade 44 is a permanent magnet 46 which causes the thermostat to operate with a snap action. The thermostat may have a one degree differential for example. The thermostat 42 corresponds to the thermostat 41, its elements being numbered the same with the identifying letter *a*. The thermostat 42 however is set to close its contacts at a temperature which may be 70° for example and this thermostat closes its contacts upon a fall in temperature rather than a rise in temperature.

During the nighttime the left end of mercury switch 40 will be closed as shown in Fig. 1. If during the night the temperature within the space 13 rises to 75°, it can reasonably be expected that cooling of the space will be required on the following day because it is usually warmer in the daytime than during the night. Thus if the temperature in the space rises to 75° or above, the thermostat 41 will close its contacts thereby energizing the motor of circulator 19 through the following circuit: from line conductor 50 through wire 86, element 43, blade 44, contact 45, wire 52, the left end of mercury switch 40, wire 53, wire 54, the motor of circulator 19 and wire 55 back to line conductor 51, the line conductors 50 and 51 being connected to a suitable source of power not shown. As long as the circulator 19 operates, water from the tank 18 will be circulated through the coil 14 and will be cooled in the manner above described, so as to build up a substantial cooling effect in the tank 18.

If the temperature in the space 13 does not rise to 75° at night, it is not expected that cooling will be needed on the following day and so the circulator 19 is not operated.

During the daytime the right end of mercury switch 40 will be closed placing thermostat 42 in control of the circulator 19, and if during the daytime the temperature in the space 13 falls to 70° or lower, it can be reasonably expected that heating will be required that night because it is ordinarily cooler at night than in the daytime. Thus if the temperature falls to 70°, thermostat 42 will close its contacts energizing the motor of circulator 19 through the following circuit: from line conductor 50 through conductor 57, element 43a, blade 44a, contact 45a, wire 58, the right end of mercury switch 40, wire 59, wire 54, the motor of circulator 19 and motor 55 back to line conductor 51. As long as the circulator 19 operates during the day, water from tank 18 will be circulated through the coil 14 and it will be heated so as to store up a substantial amount of heat in the tank 18 in the manner above described.

The controls which control the temperature in space 13 will now be described. These controls include a pair of thermostats 60 and 61 responsive to the temperature in the space 13. The thermostat 60 includes the bimetal element 62 arranged to operate a movable switch blade 63 which cooperates with a fixed electrical contact 64. The blade 63 is moved to the left upon fall in temperature and is brought into engagement with the contact 64 at a temperature which may be 68° F., for example. Associated with the blade 63 is a permanent magnet 65 which causes the thermostat to operate with a snap action. The thermostat may have a one degree differential for example. The thermostat 61 corresponds to the thermostat 60, its elements being numbered the same and having an identifying letter a. However the thermostat 61 makes its contacts upon a rise in temperature and preferably is so set that it closes its contacts at 80° F. for example.

Connected in series with the thermostat 60 is a thermostatic switch 70 and connected in series with the thermostat 61 is a thermostatic switch 71. The thermostatic switch 70 comprises an expansible and contractible bellows 72 connected to a thermal bulb 73 disposed in the water in tank 18, by means of a capillary tube 74. The bulb 73 is filled with a volatile liquid which vaporizes and causes a pressure to build up in the bulb and bellows 72 dependently upon the temperature in the water in tank 18 so that the bellows 72 expands and contracts accordingly. The bellows 72 has an operating stem into engagement with which a switch operating lever 75 is normally urged by a coil spring 76. The lever 75 carries a mercury switch 77 having electrodes at its left end which are bridged when the bellows 72 expands in response to the existence of a predetermined pressure therein which may be a pressure corresponding to a temperature of the water in tank 18 of 69° F., for example. The temperature responsive switch 70 may have a differential of one degree for example; that is, the switch 77 may open at a temperature of 68° of the water in tank 18.

The thermostatic switch 71 corresponds to the thermostatic switch 70, the elements being similarly numbered with the identifying letter a. However the electrodes of mercury switch 77a are at the right end of the switch so that the switch is closed upon a fall in temperature rather than upon a rise in temperature, the mercury switch 77a closing at a temperature of the water in tank 18 which may be 78° F., for example. The thermostatic switch 71 may also have a differential of one degree, the mercury switch 77a opening at a temperature of 79° F. The thermostats 60 and 61 and the temperature responsive switches 70 and 71 control the motor of circulator 28, the purposes of switches 70 and 71 being to prevent operation of the circulator for heating unless the water in tank 18 is at a temperature high enough for heating purposes and to prevent operation of the circulator 28 for cooling unless the temperature of the water in tank 18 is low enough for cooling purposes.

If at any time the temperature in the space 13 rises to 80° F., thermostat 61 closes its contacts. If at this time the temperature of the water in tank 18 is at 78° or below so that cooling can be affected, a circuit is completed for the motor of circulator 28 as follows: from line conductor 50 through wire 80, element 62a, blade 63a, contact 64a, wire 81, mercury switch 77a, wire 82, wire 83, the motor for circulator 28, and wire 84 back to line conductor 51. Completion of this circuit will cause the circulator 28 to operate and the water from the tank 18 will be circulated through the heat exchange coil 27 for cooling the space 13. As long as cooling is available by the water in tank 18, the thermostat 61 will control the circulator 28 to prevent the temperature in the space from rising above 80° F.

It is to be seen that the thermostat 61 can control the circulator 28 in the manner just described for cooling the space 13 either at night or in the daytime. Obviously if the thermostat 61 operates the circulator 28 at night, the circulator 19 will be operating at the same time in response to thermostat 41 to keep the water in tank 18 cold and to build up the cooling effect stored in the tank.

If at any time the temperature in the space 13 falls to 68° F., thermostat 60 will close its contacts. If at this time the temperature of the water in tank 18 is at or above 69° F., such that heating can properly be affected by the coil 27, a circuit will be completed for the motor of circulator 28 as follows: From line conductor 50 to wire 87, element 62, blade 63, contact 64, wire 88, mercury switch 77, wire 89, wire 83, the motor of circulator 28 and wire 84 back to line conductor 51. In this manner the thermostat 60 will control the circulator 28 to prevent the temperature in the space 13 from falling below 68° F.

If the thermostat 60 calls for heating during the daytime, the circulator 19 will of course be in operation at the same time because thermostat 42 will at this time be closed so that water is being circulated through the coil 14 for heating it and for building up heating effect in the tank 18.

From the foregoing, it is to be seen that the arrangements of my invention provide for utilizing natural heating and cooling effects by storing these effects and using them when required to maintain the temperature of the space at desired values. By reason of my particular arrangement, sufficiently great temperature differentials can be produced between the temperature changing agency and the temperature of the space such that substantial cooling and heating effects can be stored and preserved to be subsequently used as required. The temperature differentials produced by my arrangements are considerably greater than can be produced by ordinary conduction or convection heat transfer methods and, by reason of the substances which I use which melt and solidify, the amounts of cooling effect and heating effect which can be stored are considerably augmented. The controls provide for selective operation of the heat and cold storing system dependent upon whether or not it is to be reasonably expected that heating or cooling of the space will subsequently be required within the length of time that the stored heating and cooling effects can be preserved.

From the foregoing, it is to be observed that my invention is ideally adapted for use in air conditioning in milder climates, particularly in climates wherein during some seasons the days are warm enough and the nights relatively cool, such that heat can be stored during the day for use at night. During other seasons in such climates the nights are cool enough but the days relatively warm so that cooling effect can be stored at night for use during the day.

For selectively determining whether or not the circulator 19 should be operated, outdoor temperature rather than indoor temperature may be utilized. Thus in Fig. 2 of the drawing, I have shown a control arrangement for circulator 19 which is similar to that of Fig. 1 of the drawing wherein the timer shifts control between two controllers designated 90 and 91 which are responsive to outdoor temperature rather than indoor temperature. Thus if the outdoor temperature rises above a value which may be 55° or 65° F., for example, at night it may be reasonably expected that on the following day the outdoor temperature will be high enough so that cooling of the space will be required. Thus the arrangement of Fig. 2 provides for operating the circulator 19 at night when the outdoor temperature rises above a specified value which may be 55° or 65° for example, as pointed out above. The controller 90 comprises an expansible and contractible bellows 92 connected to a thermal bulb 93 disposed outdoors by means of a capillary tube 94; the bulb 93 is filled with a volatile liquid which causes the bellows 92 to expand and contract in accordance with the amount of vaporization of the liquid as determined by outdoor temperature. The bellows has an operating stem into engagement with which a switch operating lever 95 is normally urged by a coil spring 96. The lever 95 carries a mercury switch 97 having electrodes at its left end which are bridged when the outdoor temperature rises to the above mentioned value of 55 or 65° F. The controller 90 may have a one degree differential.

The controller 91 corresponds to the controller 90, its elements being numbered the same and having an identifying letter *a*. However the electrodes of mercury switch 97*a* are at its right end, and this switch closes upon a drop in outdoor temperature to a value of 65° F. The timing mechanism places controller 91 in control in the daytime and the circulator 19 is operated in the daytime if the outdoor temperature is below 65° F., it being reasonable to expect that if the temperature is below 65° in the daytime it will be low enough at night to require heating of the space.

During the night time when the left end of mercury switch 40 is closed if mercury switch 97 closes, a circuit is completed for the motor of circulator 19 as follows: from line conductor 50, through wire 100, wire 101, mercury switch 97, wire 102, the left end of mercury switch 40, wire 103, wire 104, the motor of circulator 19 and wire 105 back to line conductor 51. Thus the system is operated for storing cooling effect at night when the outdoor temperature is above a predetermined value.

During the daytime the right end of mercury switch 40 is closed, and if the mercury switch 97*a* closes, a circuit is completed of the motor of circulator 19 as follows: from line conductor 50, wire 100, wire 106, mercury switch 97*a*, wire 107, the right end of mercury switch 40, wire 108, wire 104, the motor of circulator 19 and wire 105 back to line conductor 51. Thus in the daytime the system is operated for storing heat when the outdoor temperature is below a predetermined value.

Of course the system can operate to heat the space in the daytime or cool the space at night as in the previous embodiment.

In Fig. 3 of the drawing, I have shown a modified form of the invention wherein instead of using a timer to control the day and night operation of the circulator 19 I utilize a photoelectric cell which shifts control from one thermostat to the other. In Fig. 3 numeral 110 designates a relay comprising a winding 111 having an armature associated therewith attached to the switch blade 112 of a single-pole, double-throw switch, the armature moving the blade 112 into engagement with a fixed electrical contact 113 when the winding 111 is energized, the switch blade 112 engaging a fixed contact 114 when the winding 111 is deenergized. The winding of relay 110 is controlled by a photo-electric cell 115 through wires 116 and 117, power being supplied to the photo-electric cell through wires 118 and 119. The sensitivity of the cell 115 is such and it is so arranged as to energize the relay 110 in the daytime and to deenergize it at night.

Figure 3 includes two thermostats 120 and 121 which may be like the thermostats 41 and 42 of Fig. 1 or the thermostatic controllers 90 and 91 of Fig. 2. Thus at night the thermostat 120 is in control, and if it closes its contacts the motor of circulator 19 is energized through the following circuit: line conductor 50, wire 123, thermostat 120, wire 124, fixed contact 114, switch blade 112, wire 125, the motor of circulator 19 and wire 126 back to line conductor 51. Similarly, in the daytime the thermostat 121 is in control of the circuit, and if it closes its contacts a circuit is completed for energizing the motor of circulator 19 as follows: from line conductor 50, wire 127, thermostat 121, wire 128, contact 113, switch the restricting orifice 128, the pipe 128 and the pipe 127 to the lower end of the radiation portion 123. Also, since valve 145 is open, the major portion of this hot liquid will flow from the upper end of radiation portion 123 by way of pipe 147, pipe 146, valve 145, and pipe 144 to the heat exchanger 142. It will flow from the heat exchanger by way of pipes 148, 149 and 127 back to the lower end of the radiation portion 123. In this manner, the liquid in the tank 130 will be heated. In order to increase the heat storage capacity of the tank 130, containers 155 may be provided therein filled with a suitable substance as explained in connection with the containers 17 of Figure 1.

The valve 145 may be controlled in any desired manner. I prefer to control it by temperature and for this purpose provide a temperature responsive means 156. This temperature responsive means may take the form of a straight temperature thermostat but preferably takes the form of a differential temperature thermostat. It includes a switch operating arm 157 pivoted at 158 which carries a mercury switch 159. The arm 157 is operated by a bellows 160 connected to a temperature controlling bulb 161 by a tube 162. The bulb 161 is secured in any usual manner to the pipe 125 so that it responds to the temperature of the liquid flowing therethrough. With as much of the apparatus 156 as thus far described, the mercury switch 159 will be operated entirely by the temperature of the fluid or liquid flowing through the pipe 125. When the temperature of this liquid is high enough, say 90 degrees, the mercury switch 159 will be moved to the closed circuit position in which it is shown so as to open the valve 145, whereupon heating of the liquid in the tank 130 will take place. I prefer however to operate mercury switch 159 in accordance with the temperature differential between the liquid in tank 130 and the temperature of the fluid flowing through pipe 125. To this end, the arm 157 is provided with an extension 163 which extends to the left of pivot 158. A bellows 164 operates upon the extension 163 in opposition to the bellows 160. The bellows 164 is connected to a temperature controlling bulb 165 by a tube 166. The temperature differential instrument is set so that mercury switch 159 is only closed when the temperature of the liquid flowing through the pipe 125 is a predetermined amount higher than the temperature of the liquid in the tank 130. In this manner, whenever the temperature of the fluid is sufficiently high to raise the temperature of the liquid in tank 130, it is used for this purpose. This is better than having the plain thermostat since, under conditions where there has been no appreciable heating of the radiating portion 123 for a considerable length of time, the fluid in tank 130 might be cold enough that there would be no utility in waiting until the temperature of the liquid passing through pipe 125 has been raised to 90 degrees. Under such conditions, the liquid in tank 130 might well be heated even though the temperature of the liquid passing through pipe 125 were only 75 or 80 degrees.

Assume now that it becomes night and it is a clear night so that heat is radiated from the radiation portion 123 to the universe. Let us assume then that the temperature of such fluid in the radiating portion 123 becomes reduced to 65 degrees. Under these conditions, the liquid in tank 130 will be higher than 65 degrees so that the valve 145 is closed. However, let us assume that the valve 151 remains closed likewise. Now, since the temperature of the liquid in pipe 125 is higher than that in the radiation portion 123, the flow in the closed loop will be reversed. In other words, the warm water in pipe 125 will flow upwardly and enter the radiating portion 123 at the top. It will then flow downwardly through the radiating portion 123, where it will lose heat to the universe. It will then flow from the lower portion of radiating portion 123 to the lower end of pipe 126 by way of pipe 127. Let us now assume that the temperature of the water flowing through the closed loop is thus reduced to 60 degrees. At this time, let us assume that valve 151 is open. The flow of water through the closed loop of course is restricted by the orifice 128 and, with valve 151 open, the major portion of such cold water will flow from the lower end of radiation portion 123 through pipe 127, pipe 149, and pipe 153 to the lower end of heat exchanger 143 located in the cold storing means or tank 136. This flow of liquid will result in the lowering of the temperature in the tank 136. At the same time, such liquid flowing through the heat exchanger 143 will pick up heat and rise in temperature. This will help the liquid to continue its flow back to the upper end of the radiating portion 123 by way of pipe 150, valve 151, and pipe 152.

The valve 151 is automatically controlled by a temperature responsive mechanism 170. Here again, this temperature responsive mechanism 170 could comprise a simple thermostat. This mechanism includes an arm 171, pivoted at 172, which supports a mercury switch 173. The arm is operated by a bellows 174 connected to a temperature bulb 175 by a tube 176. The bulb 175 responds to the temperature of the liquid flowing through the pipe 126. If only a simple thermostat as thus far described is used, it could be set for example at 60 degrees so that mercury switch 173 would close whenever the temperature of the liquid flowing through pipe 126 fell to 60 degrees or lower. Under such conditions then, the valve 151 would be opened and the operation by which the liquid in tank 136 is lowered in temperature would take place as outlined above. Here again, however, I prefer that the temperature responsive mechanism 170 be a differential temperature type of apparatus so that cooling of the liquid in the tank 136 may take place even at temperatures of 75 or 70 degrees where no cooling action has been available for a substantial period, as for example due to the sky being cloudy for one or more nights. Arm 171 is therefore provided with an extension 177 against which a bellows 178 bears. The bellows 178 is connected to a temperature bulb 179 by a tube 180. The bulb 179 is located in the tank 136. This differential temperature responsive mechanism is set so that mercury switch 173 is closed whenever the temperature of the liquid flowing through pipe 126 is below that of the liquid in the tank 136 by a predetermined amount. In order to increase the storage capacity of the cold storing means 136, containers 181 may be placed therein filled with a suitable substance for storage purposes as explained in connection with the containers 23 in Figure 1.

The supplies of hot and cold liquid are utilised to cool the space 120 in the same manner as explained in connection with Figure 1. To this end, a room thermostat 182 is provided with hot and cold contacts 183 and 184 which respectively energize relays 185 and 186. Upon energization of relay 185 by reason of thermostat closing hot contact 183, the cooling pump 139 is operated by a circuit as follows: line wire 187, wire 188, wire 189, switch arm 190, contact 191, wire 192, cooling pump 139, wire 193 and wire 194 to the other line wire 195. On the other hand, when the room thermostat 182 engages its cold contact 184, the heating pump 135 is energized as follows: line wire 187, wire 188, wire 196, switch arm 197, contact 198, wire 199, heating pump 135, wire 200, and wire 194 to the other line wire 195.

From the foregoing, it will be seen that I have provided novel systems of heating and cooling by the use of heat and cold storing means that are respectively heated and cooled through the use of a radiation element or device that receives heat from the sun by radiation during the daytime and gives up heat to the universe by radiation during the night. Further, I have provided automatic control systems by means of which the radiation element selectively heats and cools the heat storing means and cold storing means and that further automatically control the application of such stored heating capacity and cooling capacity to the room or space to be controlled so as to maintain it within desired temperature limits. It will be obvious to those skilled in the art that many changes and rearrangements of the parts can be made, as well as variations in the systems of control, without departing from the spirit of my invention and it is therefore my intention to be limited only by the scope of the claims appended hereto. *

March 12, 1946. A. B. NEWTON 2,396,338

RADIATION HEATING AND COOLING SYSTEM

*

Fig. 1.

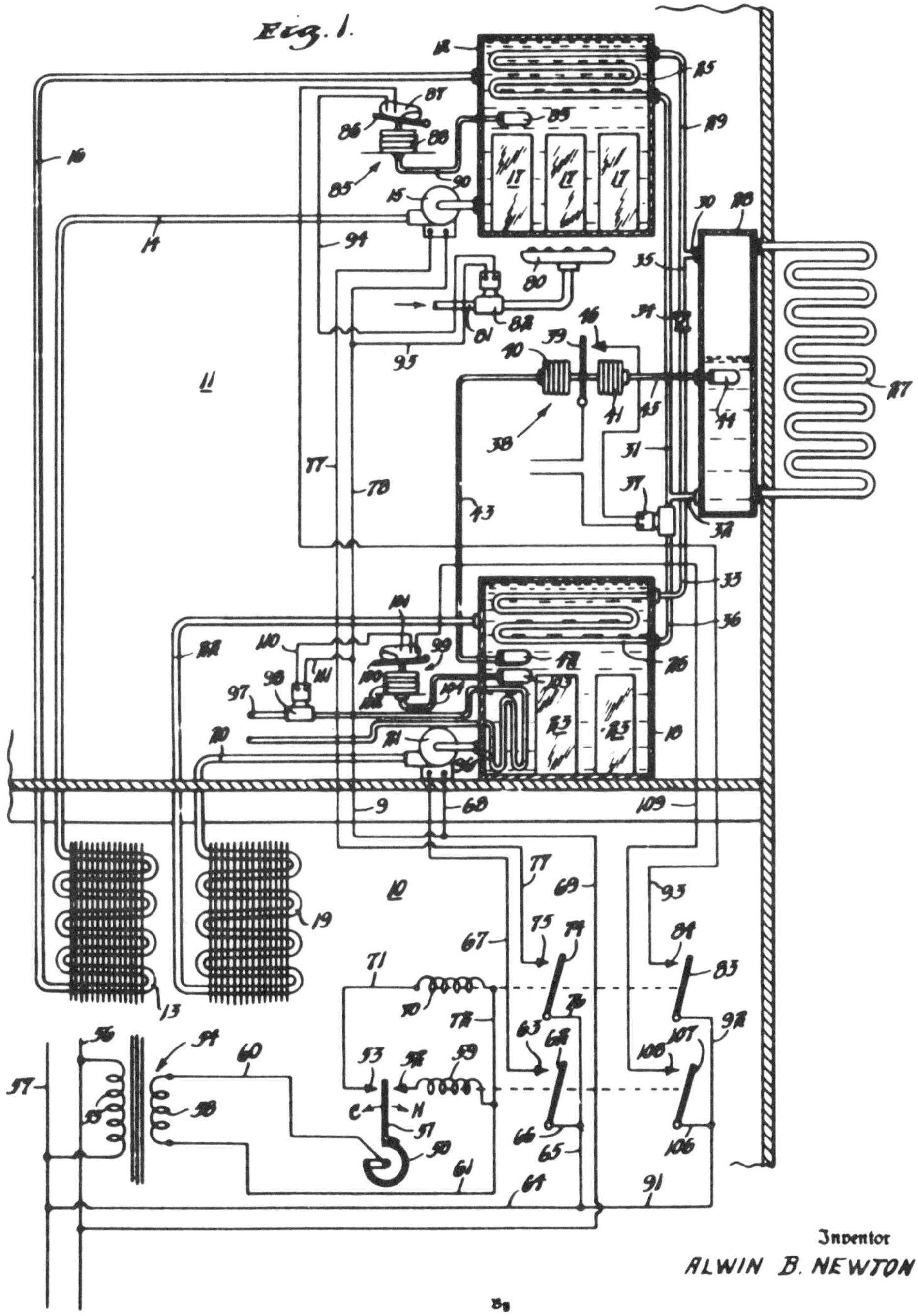

Inventor
ALWIN B. NEWTON

By

George H. Fisher
Attorney

March 12, 1946. A. B. NEWTON **2,396,338**

RADIATION HEATING AND COOLING SYSTEM

*

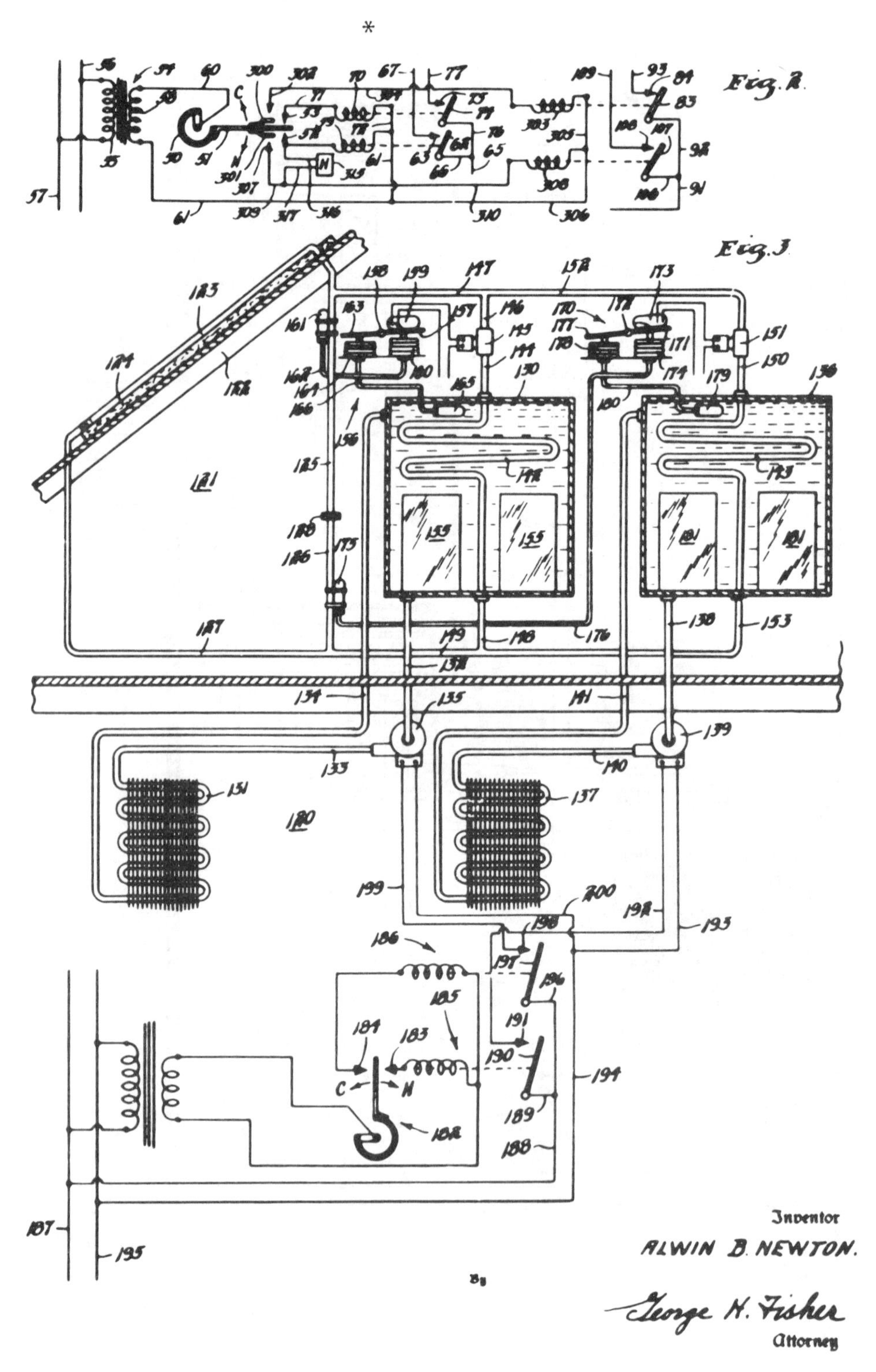

UNITED STATES PATENT OFFICE

2,396,338

RADIATION HEATING AND COOLING SYSTEM

Alwin B. Newton, Minneapolis, Minn., assignor to Minneapolis-Honeywell Regulator Company, Minneapolis, Minn., a corporation of Delaware

*

The present invention relates to heating and cooling by the transfer of heat from and to the universe by means of a radiation unit and constitutes an improvement upon my
Patent No. 2,342,211, issued February 22, 1944,
and entitled "Utilization of natural heating and cooling effects."

It is an object of my present invention to heat and cool a space, according to the requirements of such space, by providing independent heat and cold storing means which are respectively heated and cooled by a single radiation device so arranged as to permit the transfer of heat between such device and the universe by radiation so that the device is heated by radiation from the sun during the daytime and is cooled by radiation from the device to the universe at night.

It is a further object of my invention to provide means, preferably in the nature of automatic means, for selectively permitting the radiation device to heat the heat storing or cool the cold storing means, depending upon the relative temperatures of some or all of the heat and cold storing means and the radiation device.

In one form of my invention, the heating or cooling of the heating and cold storing means is controlled by the temperature differential between the radiation device, or the fluid therein, and the temperature of one of the storing means. It is therefore a further object of my invention to control the effect of the radiation device in respect to the heat and cold storing means in accordance with such differential temperature.

In another form of my invention, the effect of the radiating means or device upon the heat and cold storing means is controlled by the temperature of the fluid flowing through the radiation device. It is therefore a further object of the present invention to permit heating of the heat storing means by the radiation device when the temperature of the fluid flowing through such device is at or above a predetermined temperature, and to permit cooling of the cold storing means by the radiation device when the temperature of the fluid flowing therethrough is at or below a predetermined temperature.

A further object of the present invention is to control the effect of the heat and cold storing means upon the space in accordance with fluctuation in the space temperature.

Additionally, it is an object of my invention to supplement the action of the heat and cold storing means by additional heating and cooling means for heating and cooling such storing means.

Another object of the present invention is to control such additional heating and cooling means by the temperatures of the heat and cold storing means. Preferably, such additional heating and cooling means are placed in operation upon a further fall or rise in space temperature, as the case may be.

It is another object of my invention to place the additional cooling means into operation before the space temperature rises to a high value if the humidity is high when an intermediate rise in space temperature occurs.

Another object of the present invention is to provide a closed fluid system having a first heat exchange portion for heating a heat storing means and a second heat exchange portion for cooling a cold storage means together with a radiation portion exposed to the universe, the fluid system being charged with a volatile fluid, as distinguished from being completely filled with a heat transfer liquid.

Other objects of the invention will become apparent from the following detailed description and the accompanying drawings, in which:

Figure 1 discloses one type of system constructed in accordance with my present invention wherein the closed fluid system is charged with a volatile fluid,

Figure 2 is a modification of the system of Figure 1 employing a two-stage type space thermostat, and

Figure 3 is a modified system in which the radiation device and associated heat transfer means are completely filled with a liquid.

Referring to Figure 1, a portion of a building is shown therein which includes a space 10 to be heated and cooled and a further space 11 which may, for example, be the attic or top floor of the building. Located in the attic 11 is a heat storing means shown in the form of a tank 12 filled with a suitable heat transfer medium, preferably one having a relatively low freezing point. The lower portion of the heat storing means 12 is connected to a heating coil 13 located in the space 10 by a pipe 14. The pipe 14 may contain any desired type of flow controlling means and such a means is herein shown as an electrically operated pump 15. The other end of the heating coil 13 is connected to the top of the heat storing means 12 by a pipe 16. In order to increase the heat storing capacity of the heat storing means 12, it may be provided with containers 17 which contain a substance, such as Wood's metal, as mentioned in the aforesaid patent, that solidifies at or about the temperature which it is desired to maintain in the heat storing means 12 in order that a larger amount of heat may be stored therein for a given capacity of the tank forming the heat storing means.

Also located in the attic 11 is a cold storing means 18 in the form of a tank which is likewise filled with a liquid. The bottom of the cold storing means 18 is connected to a cooling coil 19 by a pipe 20. The pipe 20 may be provided with any suitable flow controlling means herein shown as an electrically operated pump 21.

The other end of the cooling coil 19 is connected near the top of the cold storing means 18 by a pipe 22. The cold storing means 18 may likewise be provided with containers 23 having suitable substances therein, such as listed in my aforesaid patent and including acetaldehyde, so as to increase the storage capacity of the cold storing means 18.

The heat storing means 12 and cold storing means 18 are arranged to be heated and cooled respectively by means of a closed fluid system that includes a first heat exchange portion 25, a second heat exchange portion 26, and a radiation portion 27. The heat exchange portion 25 takes the form of a coil located within the heat storing means or tank 12. Similarly, the heat exchange portion 26 comprises a pipe coil located within the cold storing means or tank 18. The radiation portion 27 also takes the form of a pipe coil but such radiation portion 27 is so located as to permit the radiation of heat to it from the sun as well as to permit the radiation of heat from the radiation portion 27 to the universe at night when the sun is not shining. To this end, the radiation portion 27 has been shown as located outside of the building. Although the radiation portion 27 in this diagrammatic showing is entirely exposed, it should be understood that it could be enclosed by some suitable means, such as one of the forms of Lucite, which permits the radiation both of high and relatively low temperatures so that the heat from the sun can be radiated to the radiation portion 27 during the daytime and at night the relatively higher heat of the radiation portion 27 may be radiated to the universe.

In addition, this closed fluid system includes a header 28, to the top of which the upper end of the radiation portion 27 is connected. Also, the lower end of the radiation portion 27 is connected to the lower portion of the header 28. The heat storing means 12 is located above the header 28 and the heat exchange portion 25 located therein has its upper end connected to the upper end of the header 28 by means of pipes 29 and 30. The lower end of heat exchange portion 25 is connected to the lower end of header 28 by pipes 31 and 32. The cold storing means 18 is located below the header 28 and the upper end of the heat exchange portion 26 is connected to the upper end of header 28 by means of a pipe 33, a check valve 34, a pipe 35, and pipe 30. The check valve 34, as indicated, permits the flow of fluid upwardly through the pipes 33 and 35 but prevents downward flow therethrough. The lower end of heat exchange portion 26 is connected to the lower end of header 28 by a pipe 36, electrically operated valve 37, and the pipe 32. This complete fluid system, which is entirely closed, is charged with a volatile fluid. This fluid may, for example, be methylchloride or any of the various Freons. The system is not completely filled with the fluid so that there is always a certain amount of liquid as well as a certain amount of gas or vapor, the liquid level being shown in the header 28 which is in cross-section.

The electrical valve 37 is herein shown controlled by a differential temperature responsive device 38 which responds to the difference in temperature between the liquid in the header 28 and the heat exchange fluid in the tank or cold storing means 18. This differential temperature responsive device 38 includes a pivoted arm 39 actuated by a pair of bellows 40 and 41. The bellows 40 bears on the left-hand side of the arm 39 and is connected, by means of the usual tubing 43, to a temperature controlling bulb 42 located in the tank 18. The bellows 41 bears on the right-hand side of arm 39 and is connected to a temperature responsive bulb 44, located in the header 28, by a tube 45. When the temperature of the fluid in the header 28 is substantially equal to the temperature of the liquid in the cold storing means, the arm 39 is substantially vertical, as shown, wherein it is disengaged from a contact 46. On the other hand, when the temperature is less in the header 28 than in the tank 18, the arm 39 swings to the right and engages contact 46 so as to energize and open the electrical valve 37 by a circuit which is obvious upon an inspection of the drawings.

With the parts in the position shown and assuming that it is in the daytime and the sun is shining, then the temperature of the radiation portion 27 will be relatively high due to the radiation of heat thereto from the sun. The volatile liquid contained in the radiation portion 27 will therefore be vaporized and this vapor will pass into the upper end of header 28 and then, by way of pipes 30 and 29, will pass to the head exchange portion 25. Since the temperature of the liquid in the tank 12 will not be as high as the temperature of the volatile fluid in header 28 under the action of the sun, the vapor or gas passing to the heat exchange portion 25 will be condensed therein until such time as the vapor pressure is commensurate with the temperature of the liquid in the tank 12. This condensed liquid will flow back to the header 28 by way of pipes 31 and 32. So long as the temperature of the radiation portion 27 is higher than the temperature of the liquid in the tank 12, this action will continue even though these temperatures vary. This is true since the vapor or gas will only be condensed by the heat exchanger 25 to an extent depending upon the temperature of the liquid in the tank 12. However, so long as the temperature of the radiation portion 27 is higher than the temperature of the liquid in the tank 12, further evaporation will take place in the radiator portion 27. On the other hand, if the sun should be so obscured as to reduce the temperature of the radiation portion 27 or if the temperature thereof becomes reduced by reason of night falling, then the radiation portion 27 will become the condenser. As soon as all the liquid within the heat exchanger 25 has been evaporated due to the higher temperature therein, and flows down to the header 28, there no longer will be vapor or gas present and, since the liquid cannot flow up to the heat exchanger 25, no further exchange of heat from the liquid in the tank 12 to the radiation portion 27 will take place. In this manner, heat exchange can take place in only one direction between the radiation portion 27 and the liquid in the tank 12 and this is in a direction to heat the liquid in the tank 12 when the radiation portion 27 is at a higher temperature than said liquid.

Let us now assume that the night is very clear and conditions are such that the liquid in the header 28 becomes cooler than the liquid in the tank 18. Under such conditions, the arm 39 will engage contact 46 and valve 37 will be energized. There is now free communication between the bottom of header 28 and the heat exchanger 26. Liquid will therefore flow through pipes 32 and 36 to the heat exchanger 26. Since the heat exchanger 26 is at a higher temperature than the liquid in the header 28, such liquid will be evaporated and will flow to the top of the header 28 by way of pipe 33, check valve 34 and pipe 35. Such evaporation of the volatile fluid removes heat from the liquid in the tank 18 so as to cool such liquid. In this manner, the cold storing means is cooled.

Thus, by the use of a volatile fluid and a single electrical valve together with a check valve, the radiation portion 27 is utilized to selectively cool the cold storing means and to heat the heat storing means. These stored heating and cooling capacities are then utilized to heat and cool the space 10 in accordance with demands in the following manner. The space 10 is provided with a room thermostat comprising a coiled bimetal element 50 having one end relatively fixed and supporting a contact arm 51 at its other end. The contact arm 51 is adapted to selectively engage hot and cold contacts 52 and 53. Power is supplied to the room thermostat by a transformer 54 of the step-down type having a high voltage primary 55, connected to suitable line wires 56 and 57, and the usual low voltage secondary 58. Upon a demand for cooling by the room thermostat so that the contact arm 51 engages the hot contact 52, a relay coil 59 is energized as follows: from the upper end of secondary 58, wire 60, room thermostat 50, contact arm 51, hot contact 52, relay coil 59, and wire 61 back to the lower side of secondary 58. Relay coil 59, when energized, moves a switch arm 62 into engagement with a contact 63. This energizes the electrical pump 21 by a circuit as follows: line wire 57, wire 64, wire 65, wire 66, switch arm 62, contact 63, wire 67, pump 21, wire 68, and wire 69 to line wire 56. The pump 21 thereupon forces the cold liquid in the tank 18 to the cooling coil 19 so as to reduce the temperature of the space 10.

If, on the other hand, the temperature of the space 10 becomes too cool, the arm 51 of the thermostat engages the cold contact 53. This energizes a relay coil 70 as follows: from the upper end of secondary 58, wire 60, room thermostat coil 50, contact arm 51, cold contact 53, wire 71, relay coil 70, wire 72, and wire 61 to the lower end of secondary 58. Energization of relay coil 70 moves a switch arm 74 into engagement with a contact 75 to thereby energize the electrically operated pump 15 by a circuit as follows: line wire 57, wire 64, wire 65, wire 76, switch arm 74, contact 75, wire 77, pump 15, wire 78, wire 9, and wire 69 to the other line wire 56. In this manner, when the room 10 is too cold, the pump 15 forces the heated water in the tank 12 to the heating coil 13 so as to raise the space temperature.

Under certain conditions, it may be impossible to store sufficient heat in the heat storage means 12 to adequately heat the space 10 and likewise it may be impossible to store sufficient cooling capacity to adequately cool the space 10. The present invention therefore contemplates providing an additional source of heat for the heat storing means 12 and an additional source of cooling for the cold storage means 18. To this end, a heating means in the form of a burner 80 is shown located under the heat storing means 12. This burner is supplied with fuel by a fuel supply pipe 81 in which is located an electrically operated valve 82. This valve is controlled in part by a switch arm 83 and associated contact 84 operated by the relay coil 70 and also in part by a thermostat 85 which responds to the temperature of the liquid in the heat storing tank 12. The thermostat 85 includes a pivoted arm 86 which supports a mercury switch 87 and is positioned by a bellows 88 that is in turn connected to a temperature responsive bulb 89 by a tube 90. The temperature responsive bulb 89 is located within the tank 12 so as to respond to the temperature of the liquid therein. When the temperature of this liquid is too low, the bellows 88 contracts permitting counterclockwise movement of switch supporting arm 86 about its pivot, whereupon mercury switch 87 moves to its closed circuit position. Whenever the mercury switch 87 moves to its closed circuit position, and provided relay coil 70 is energized as a result of a demand for heat by the room thermostat, a circuit for the fuel valve 82 is established as follows: line wire 57, wire 64, wire 91, wire 92, switch arm 83, contact 84, wire 93, mercury switch 87, wire 94, fuel valve 82, wire 95, wire 78, wire 9, and wire 69 to the other line wire 56. Therefore, whenever the room thermostat demands heat, if the liquid in the tank 12 is not sufficiently hot as determined by the thermostat 85, then auxiliary heat is furnished to the heat storing means 12 by the burner 80.

In a similar manner, the cooling tank 18 is provided with a cooling coil 96 that is supplied with any suitable type of cooling means by a pipe 97. The flow through pipe 97 is controlled by an electrically operated valve 98, which is controlled in part by the relay coil 59 and in part by a thermostat 99. The thermostat 99 includes a switch arm 100 that carries a mercury switch 101 in turn positioned by a bellows 102 that is connected to a controlling bulb 103 by a tube 104. The bulb 103 is located within the tank 18 and the arrangement is such that when the temperature of the liquid in the tank 18 is too high, bellows 102 expands thereby tilting switch arm 100 so as to move mercury switch 101 to closed circuit position. When this occurs, the cooling valve 98 is opened provided the room thermostat is demanding cooling at such time. This circuit is as follows: line wire 57, wire 64, wire 91, wire 106, a switch arm 107 operated by relay coil 59, a cooperating contact 108, wire 109, mercury switch 101, wire 110, cooling valve 98, wire 111, wire 9, and wire 69 to the other line wire 56. In this manner, whenever there is a demand for cooling, and if the liquid in the cold storing means 18 is not sufficiently cold as determined by the thermostat 99, the cooling valve 98 is opened so as to further reduce the temperature of such liquid.

Figure 2 shows a modification of the control system of Figure 1 wherein the auxiliary heating and cooling means are normally brought into operation only upon a further fall or rise in the space temperature, as the case may be. Since many of the circuits are the same as those previously described in Figure 1, similar reference characters have been used on such circuits in Figure 2.

This action is accomplished by placing the control of switch arms 83 and 107 under additional relays operated by additional contacts on the space thermostat instead of operating such switch arms by the relay coils 70 and 69. To this end, the contact arm 51 of the room thermostat 50 is made relatively flexible. On one side of the contact arm 51 and at an intermediate point, a further contact arm 300 is attached. A similar contact arm 301 is attached to the other side of the contact arm 51 and at an intermediate point thereon. When the room temperature becomes somewhat lower than that value at which contact arm 51 engages contact 53, then the contact arm 300 engages a contact 302 and thus energizes a relay coil 303 by a circuit as follows: upper end of secondary 58, wire 60, element 50, contact arm 51, contact arm 300, contact 302, wire 304, relay coil 303, wire 305, wire 306, and wire 61 to the lower end of secondary 58. Energization of relay coil 303 moves switch arm 83 into engagement with contact 84 to establish the previously traced circuit for the valve 82 of the auxiliary heating means, provided the thermostat 85 which responds to the temperature of the stored heating fluid is closed.

When the temperature rises sufficiently above that value at which contact arm 51 engages contact 52, then contact arm 301 engages a contact 307 to energize a relay coil 308 as follows: upper end of secondary 58, wire 60, element 50, contact arm 51, contact arm 301, contact 307, wire 309, wire 310, relay coil 308, wire 306, and wire 61 to the lower end of secondary 58. Energization of relay coil 308 moves switch arm 107 into engagement with contact 108 to thereby energize the valve 98 of the auxiliary cooling means provided the temperature of the stored cooling fluid is sufficiently high that mercury switch 100 of the stored cooling fluid responsive thermostat 99 is closed.

Thus, with the arrangement of Figure 2, upon a first temperature fall the space will be heated by the stored heating fluid if such fluid is sufficiently high in temperature. However if this heating fluid is not at a high enough temperature so that the room temperature falls further, then the auxiliary heating means is brought into operation. This conserves upon the auxiliary heating means since it is obvious that it will not always be necessary to utilize auxiliary heat in order to maintain desired room temperatures. Similarly, during warm weather, upon rise in room temperature it is first attempted to reduce the room temperature by the stored cooling fluid without the use of any auxiliary cooling. However, if the stored cooling fluid is too high in temperature and the room temperature rises further, then and only then is the auxiliary cooling means brought into operation.

It is conceivable that the temperature of the stored cooling fluid may be sufficiently low to prevent excessive rise in room temperature and engagement of contact arm 301 with contact 307 but still not be low enough to cause any appreciable dehumidification. A space humidity controller 315 is therefore arranged in Figure 2 in such manner as to energize relay coil 308 and bring on the auxiliary cooling means upon high humidity even though the room temperature is not excessive. This circuit is as follows: upper end of secondary 58, wire 60, element 50, contact arm 51, contact 52, wire 316, humidity control 315, wire 317, wire 310, relay coil 308, wire 306, and wire 61 to the lower end of secondary 58. In this manner, upon an intermediate rise in room temperature and if the humidity is excessive, then the auxiliary cooling means is brought into operation so as to lower the temperature of the stored cooling fluid, under the control of thermostat 99, to reduce the temperature of the cooled fluid sufficiently to bring about a dehumidifying action.

Turning now to Figure 3, a further form of apparatus is disclosed which uses a closed liquid system. A room or space 120 to be heated and cooled comprises a portion of a house having an attic 121 and a roof 122. Located on the roof 122 is the radiation portion 123 of the closed liquid system. This radiation portion 123 is shown as being suitably insulated from the roof by insulating material 124. The liquid circuit through the radiation portion 123 is closed so as to form a complete or closed loop by means of pipes 125, 126 and 127. An orifice 128 is located between the pipes 125 and 126 so as to restrict the flow through this closed loop. In order to provide for expansion and contraction of the liquid in the closed liquid system, it may be provided with an expansion tank, if desired, as is usual practice in the heating art.

Located in the attic 121 is a heat storage means 130 in the form of a tank filled with liquid. This tank is connected to a heating coil 131 located in the room 120 by means of pipes 132, 133 and 134, there being an electrically operated pump 135 connected between pipes 132 and 133. Similarly, a cold storing means in the form of a tank 136 is likewise located in attic 121. This tank is filled with liquid and is connected to a cooling coil 137 located in the room 120 by a pipe 138, a pump 139, a pipe 140, and a pipe 141. The tanks 130 and 136 may also be provided with the usual expansion tanks if desired.

The closed fluid system, in addition to the closed loop, further includes a first heat exchange portion 142 located in the heat storage tank 130 and a second heat exchange portion 143 located in the cold storing tank 136. The upper end of heat exchange portion 142 is connected to the upper end of pipe 125 by pipe 144, an electrical valve 145, a pipe 146, and pipe 147. The lower end of the heat exchange portion 142 is connected to the junction of pipes 126 and 127 by pipes 148 and 149. Likewise, the upper end of heat exchange portion 143 is connected to the upper end of pipe 125 by a pipe 150, an electrical valve 151, a pipe 152, and pipe 147. The lower end thereof is connected to the junction of pipes 126 and 127 by a pipe 153 and pipe 149.

Assuming that the valve 145 is open and the valve 151 is closed and that it is daytime and the sun is shining, the radiation portion 123 will be at a relatively high temperature due to radiation from the sun. As mentioned above, this system is a liquid system which is completely filled with liquid as distinguished from a volatile fluid system. The liquid in the radiation portion 123 upon being heated will flow upwardly and part of it will flow continuously through the pipe 125, blade 112, wire 125, the motor of circulator 19 and wire 128 back to line conductor 51.

My disclosure is intended to make clear the operating principles of my invention and to explain and describe a concrete form of practicing the invention. It is to be understood however that a great number of variations may be made in the invention without departing from its spirit and scope. For example, the radiating and absorbing coil 14 need not necessarily be in the form of a heat exchanger nor does it have to be mounted on the roof of a building. Also different types of cold storing and heat storing mechanisms may be utilized and different manners of controlling the utilization of the stored heat and cold may be employed.

It is to be understood also that my invention embraces the concept of using an ordinary heat exchanger exposed to atmospheric conditions and affecting heat transfer by well known conduction and convection methods. Using such a heat exchanger, the heat and cold storing mechanism of my invention and the controls take the same form and operate in the same manner as described. *

PATENTED JUL 8 1975 LAING, N. 3,893,506

*

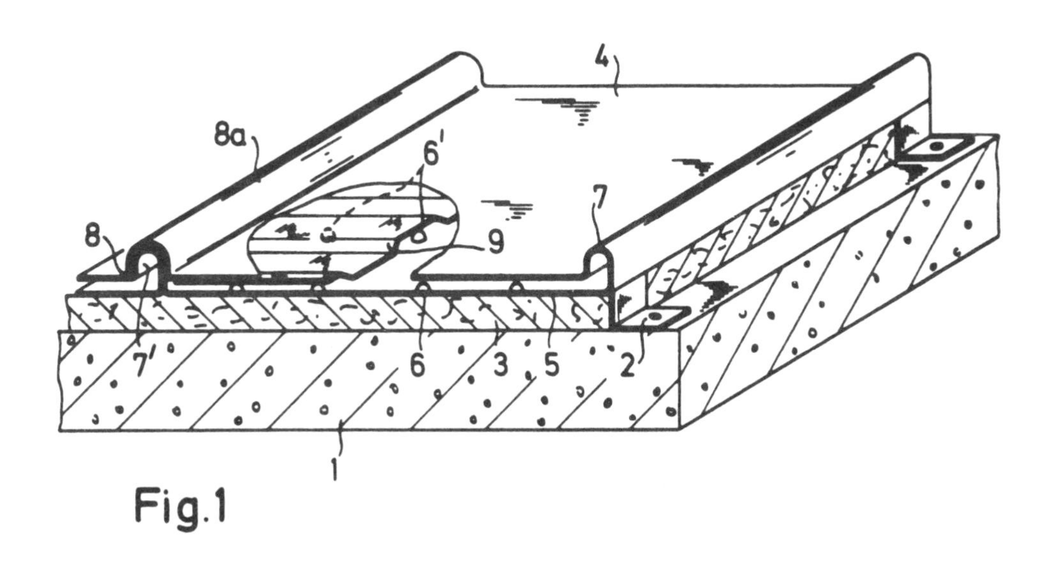

Fig.1

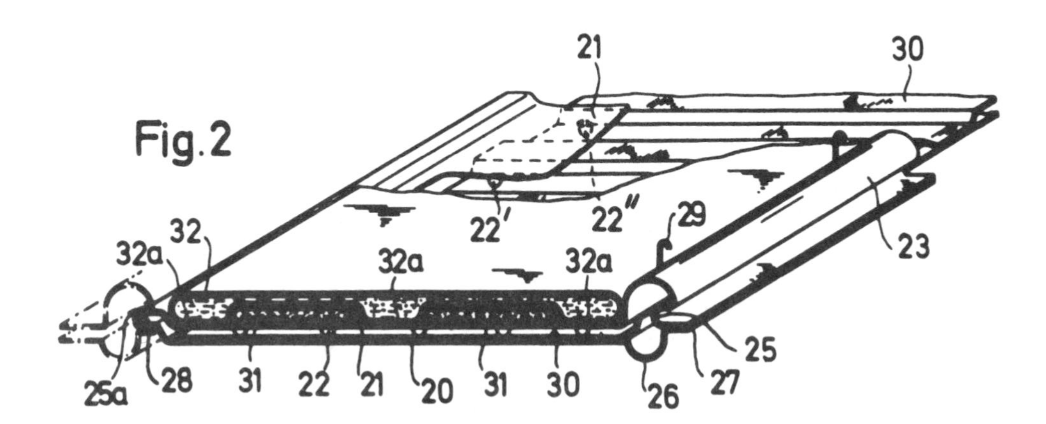

Fig.2

Nikolaus Laing

PATENTED JUL 8 1975 LAING, N. 3,893,506

*

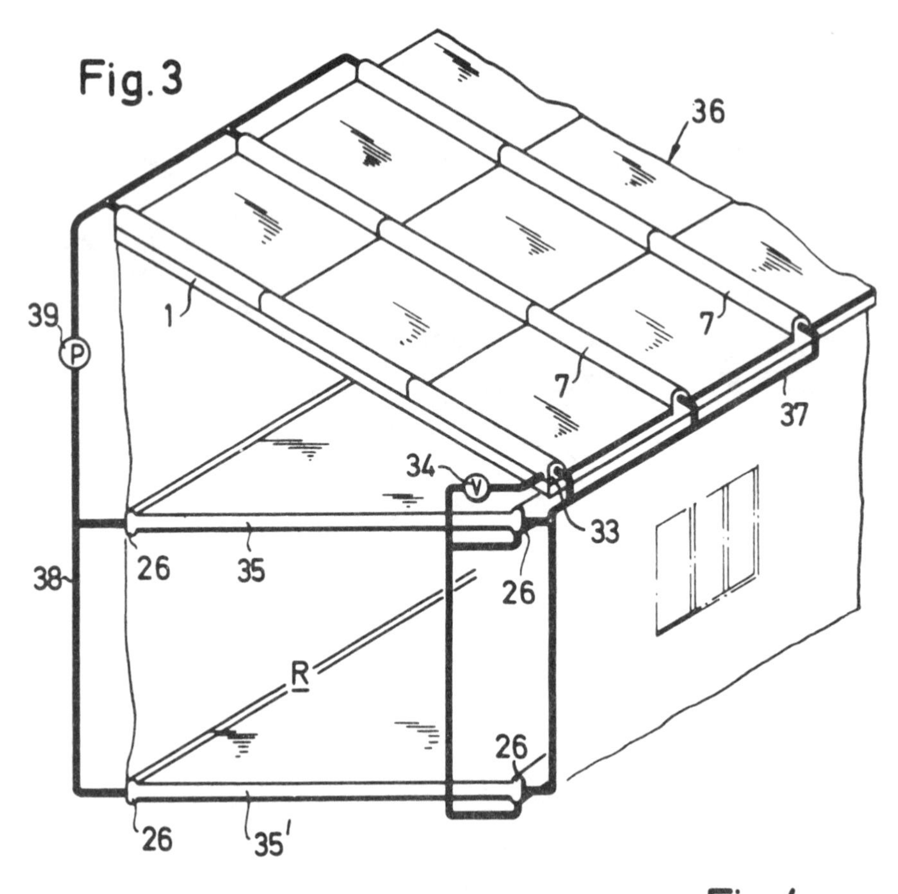

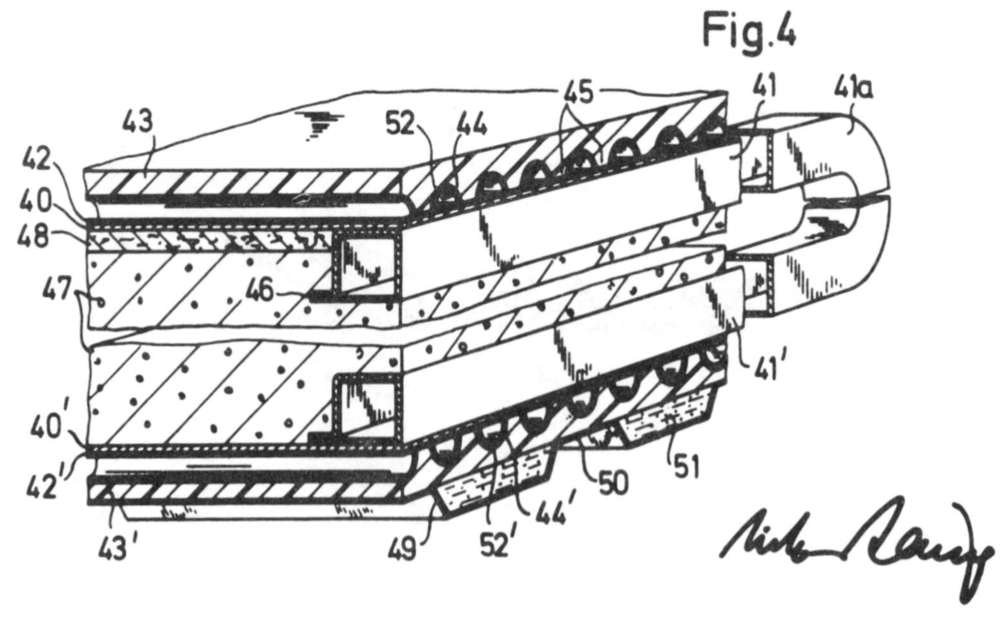

PATENTED JUL 8 1975 LAING, N. 3,893,506

*

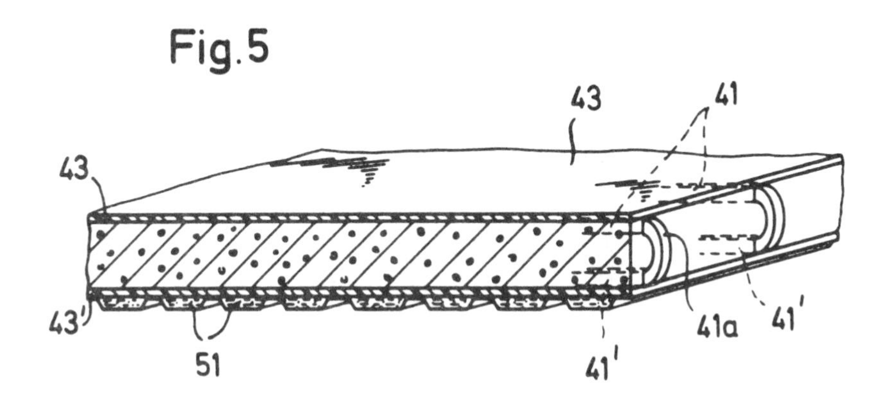

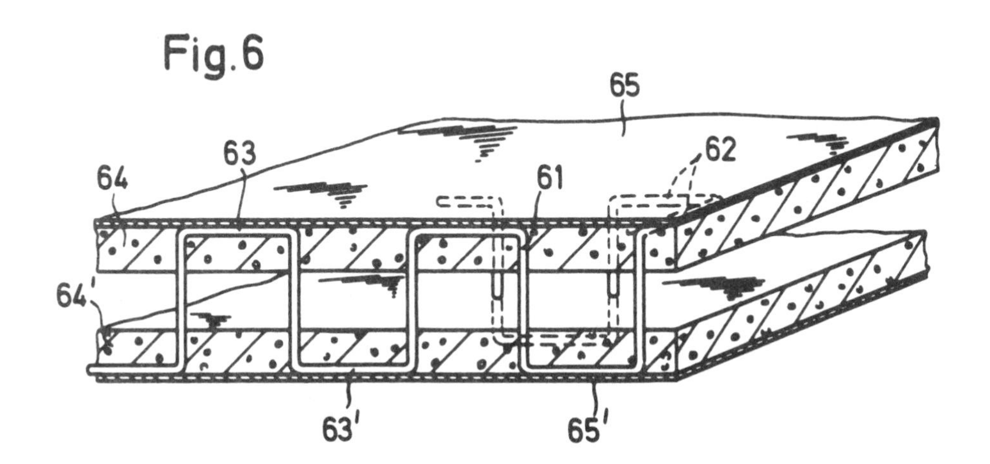

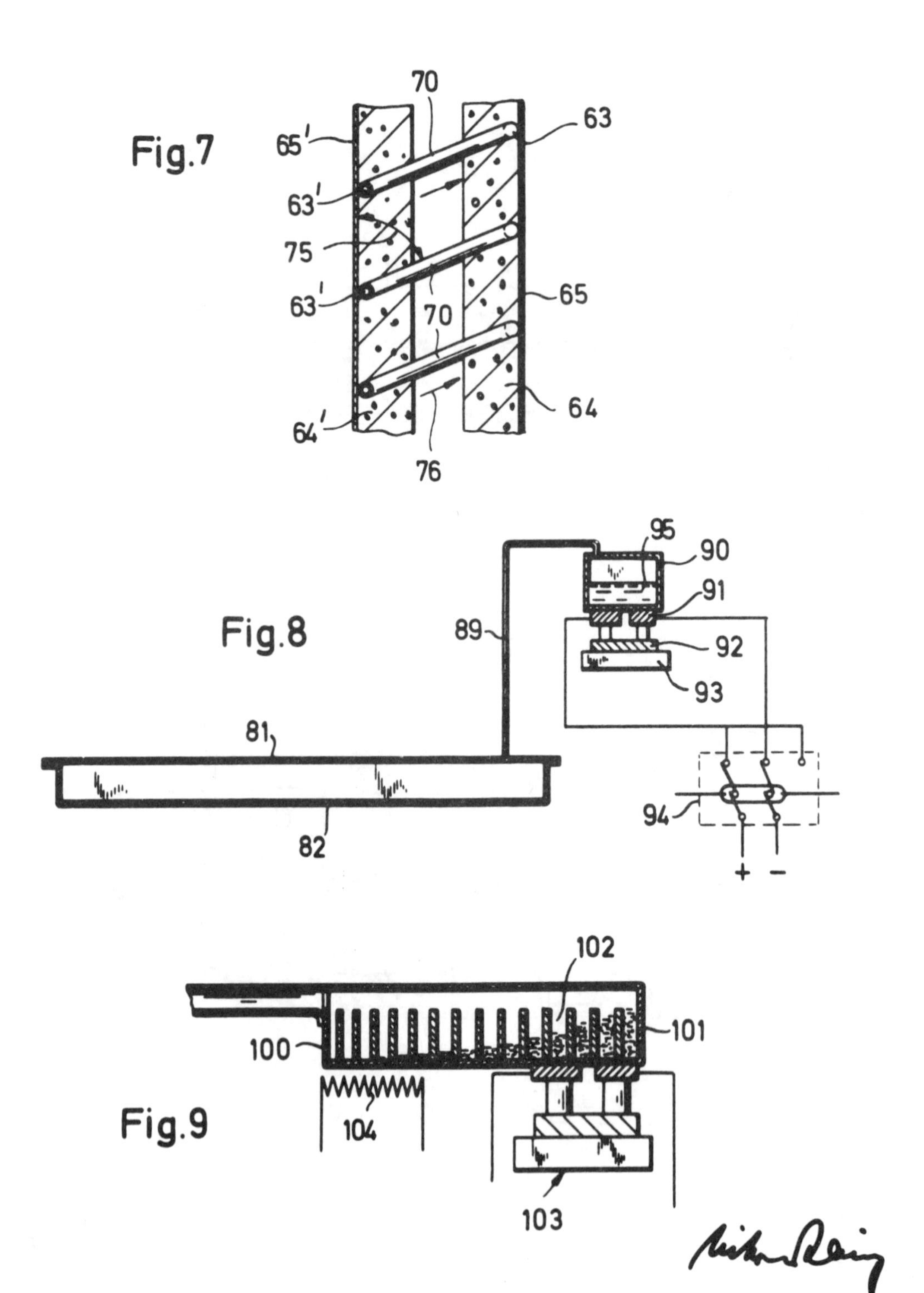
LAING, N.
3,893,506
Fig.7
70
63
65'
63'
75
63'
65
70
64
64'
76
Fig.8
95
90
91
89
92
93
81
94
82
+ –
Fig.9
102
100
101
104
103

PATENTED JUL 8 1975 LAING, N. 3,893,506

*

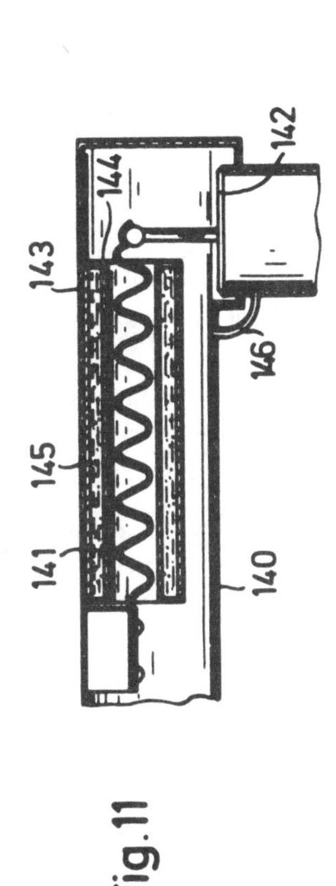

Fig.11

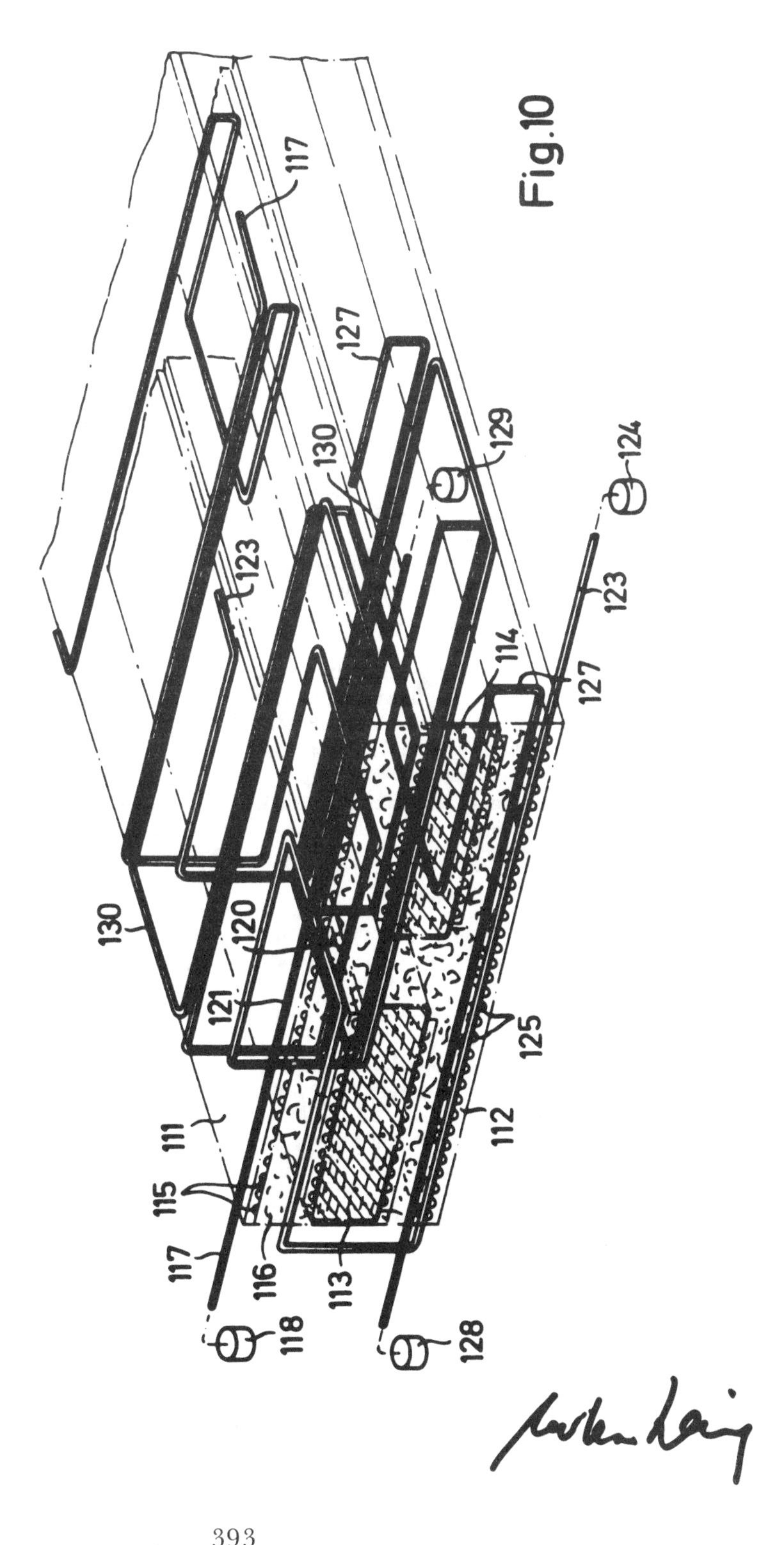

Fig.10

* **ABSTRACT**

In a device for the absorption and release of heat, two large-surface elements are provided, of which one emits the heat and acts as a heat source and the other absorbs the heat and acts as a heat sink. These two large-surface elements are joined to each other with pipes connected in parallel which are in good heat conducting contact with the large-surface elements. The internal space of the pipes is closed and filled with a heat carrier in a state of saturated vapour within the operating range. *

DEVICE FOR THE ABSORPTION AND EMISSION OF HEAT

BACKGROUND OF THE INVENTION

All construction materials have three thermal properties, the magnitude of which is of decisive significance in heat engineering and climatic conditioning, namely:

a. Heat conductivity
b. Heat capacity
c. Radiation behaviour

It is known that, for example, aluminium rods, at least so long as they are clean, are hotter than the ambient air by only a few degrees whilst bitumen roofs may be 50° hotter. Furthermore, it is known that rooms in light-weight buildings with walls of high specific strength material are subject to large daily temperature fluctuations, whilst the temperature in rooms with walls and roofs of large thickness have only a small temperature variation.

On the other hand, it can be stated that a high-quality insulation does not always have beneficial effects. For example, the inside temperature of houses in southern regions is often uncomfortably low because, during the cold season, the walls do not permit solar heat to penetrate inside. Conversely, the room temperature in such houses does not sink at night during the summer, as desired.

STATE OF THE ART

Building panels have already been proposed which enclose a hollow space bounded on all sides, containing the saturated vapor of a heat carrier, wherein the return circulation of the condensate from the heat source to the heat sink is possible only in one sense. These building panels are suitable for the insulation and climate control of rooms which are separated, for example, from the free outside space only by this building board. However, it is not possible with this known arrangement to place the heat source and the heat sink at a large distance from each other or even structurally independently of each other. In addition, it has been found impractical for many purposes to make building panels as gas-tight hollow bodies.

THE OBJECTS OF THE INVENTION

The invention has, therefore, the aim of providing building construction elements the load carrying parts of which are made, for example, of concrete, applicable in structures above and below ground, e.g. shells for covering buildings, coverplates for underground railway tunnels, pavements for roads, steps for staircases, wall elements for dwelling houses and others, which are provided with devices to conduct heat flows through the construction material from one surface to the other. With this approach, the invention has the purpose of combining panels such as building boards, shells, wall elements, walls, roofs, walkway coverings etc., (for convenience hereafter called panels) with thermal conduction elements in such a way that, with the help of additional means, heat flow between the surfaces can be controlled as to heat flow direction and/or heat flux magnitude. Thus, for example, it is desirable, in warm regions, to control the heat flow originating from the sun as to penetration, through the roof and the walls, whilst conversely controlling the escape of the heat accumulated inside as to its escape to the outside during the cool hours of the night.

For convenience of description, the word 'panel' as used herein is intended to include boarding, sheet material as for roofing, and other construction elements which are of a fundamentally flat form, i.e. superficial area on two opposite sides which is large as compared to the thickness of the element. Further the term 'outer' is used to indicate that surface of such an element which is normally exposed to the sky, whilst 'inner' conversely indicates the side which is normally exposed within the building structure.

DESCRIPTION OF THE INVENTION

According to the invention, in a device for the absorption of solar energy and/or for the emission of heat into free space, wherein a large-surface element faces this free space and another surface element is exposed to an exchange of heat with a medium to be heated and/or to be cooled, so that one element acts as a heat absorbing sink and the other element as a heat emitting source, several pipes connected in parallel are provided between the two large-surface elements, which pipes are filled with a fluid heat carrier present both in the gaseous and the liquid phases. The large-surface elements are preferably embodied in the form of sheets of high thermal conductivity and the pipes are preferably arranged at equal spacings parallel, to each other and are firmly joined or integrated in the elements in good thermal contact therewith. In an advantageous embodiment, the pipes are so installed that the fluid heat carrier condensing at the heat source, i.e. the element which emits heat to the outside, flows back under gravity through the pipes towards the element which forms the heat sink and so constitutes the boundary of the room to be cooled. If, for example in a cold climate, it is desired that the solar heat is always conducted from the free outer space towards an inside room without permitting the heat from the inside room to flow towards the outside, and considering the case when, for example, vertical wall elements are concerned, the pipes which enclose the heat carrier fluid (saturated vapour) are so installed between the two wall elements that the condensate liquid can flow by gravity towards the heat sink, i.e. towards the large-surface element which faces the free outer space.

If, finally, e.g. in temperature climates, the heat flow sense is occasionally to be reversed and the converse effect is required, the invention provides that the insides of the vapour pipes be lined in a manner known per se, with a coating which conveys the heat carrier condensate in the vapour pipe by capillary forces. In this instance, the coating acts as a conveying device. In one embodiment, the inside of each pipe is connected, according to the invention, with a condensate space, the temperature of which can be varied through a range larger than the operating temperature range. If an interruption of the heat conduction is desired, the condensate space is cooled sufficiently to ensure that virtually the entire heat carrier contents of the pipe enters into the condensate space, whereby the heat transfer by latent heat effect is interrupted. By suitable means described below, a range of control of rate of heat transfer can be accomplished. In order to control the heat conduction, the invention includes the provision of external thermostats. An even more effective method is one in which the meteorological variables, e.g. the pressure gradient or the forecasting data, are used to monitor or perform the control. The application of this method permits the optimum utilisation of the natural heat source and/or heat sink, in other words, solar radiation and space blackness. These free-of-charge heat flows can be utilised not only for the heating and/or cooling of rooms but also for preventing icing on roads, rails, steps of staircases, balconies and roofs. In using heat storage devices, the invention envisages not only the utilisation of the heat storage capacity in concrete and other construction materials by the accumulation of sensible heat but also latent heat storage, which has the advantage, compared with the storage of sensible heat, that the temperature of the storage device does not vary during the storing process. It is therefore envisaged, insofar as the device according to the invention is to be used for modifying the temperature of a room, to provide storage substances on the side exposed to the room or, insofar as the device is to be utilised to ensure freedom from ice, to provide storage substances underneath a pavement, which storage substances are in good thermally conductive contact with the pipes and deliver their heat of crystallization at a specified temperature. Suitable latent heat storage substances are above all metal salt hydrates with inoculation agents and supporting framework additives.

The essential advantage of the device according to the invention lies in the fact that, for heat flow rectification in flat elements of suitable shape, it is no longer necessary to use hollow panels which must be absolutely gas tight; instead there are provided highly thermally conducting sheets exposed to the free outside space and highly thermally conducting sheets facing the inside room or equally, other components serving the exchange of heat, i.e. finned components, interconnected by means of heat pipes which can be made vacuum tight much more easily than large-surface boards, subject to large thermal expansion.

Suitable heat carrier fluids which, in the relevant range of operating temperatures, are chlorine fluoride hydrocarbon, chain hydrocarbons, ketones, azeotropic mixtures of water and water soluble hydrocarbons, trifluoro-trichloro-ethane, tetrafluoro-dichloro-ethane and other similar substances, having the required thermal properties and suitable substances for thermal storage capable of storing latent heat are disodium-phosphate dodecahydrate, sodium sulphate decahydrate, lithium nitrate trihydrate, a mixture of 69 parts by weight of sodium sulphate decahydrate and 31 parts by weight of potassium chloride, a mixture of 77 parts by weight of sodium sulphate decahydrate and 25 parts by weight of ammonium chloride and similar substances.

The invention is described by way of example with the help of figures.

FIG. 1 shows a panel suitable for the construction of a large-surface roof element for a device according to the invention.

FIG. 2 shows a panel suitable for the construction of a large-surface element exposed to an inside room for a device according to the invention.

FIG. 3 shows diagrammatically the arrangement of the large-surface elements in a dwelling house.

FIG. 4 shows a cutaway portion from a building panel with a controllable heat flow rectification effect.

FIG. 5 shows the building panel of FIG. 4 to a smaller scale.

FIG. 6 shows a cutaway portion of a building panel with a meander-shaped heat conduction pipe.

FIG. 7 shows a cross-section through a cutaway portion of a wall panel which is designed similarly to the roof board shown in FIG. 6.

FIG. 8 shows a control device for a heat conduction pipe according to the invention.

FIG. 9 shows a modification of the control device shown in FIG. 8.

FIG. 10 shows a device according to the invention containing several heat conduction circuits in a cutaway portion.

FIG. 11 shows a control valve for a device according to the invention.

FIG. 1 shows a panel for use preferably as a roof covering which acts as the large-surface element of a device according to the invention. Metal sheets forming panels are mounted with brackets 2 on a concrete baseplate 1, so that the panels assume the positions shown in FIG. 3. An insulating layer 3 is placed between the concrete baseplate 1 and the panel. The panel itself is designed as a double wall and is built up of sheet metal, the outer facing surface 4 and inner facing surface 5 of which are smooth. A large number of buttons 6 serve as spacers to maintain the distance between the sheets 4 and 5. The sheets 4 and 5 enclose between them along one margin a tubular section 7 which serves as a fluid channel. At the other parallel margin the sheets 4 and 5 are bent over at 8a as a U-section 1 and are seam welded along the seam 8. The margin 8a meshes with the tubular edge 7' of the next plate. A lamina 9 of absorbent paper is arranged between the sheets 4 and 5. The paper hangs between adjacent rows of buttons 6 and 6' so that it touches both the upper wall 4 and the lower wall 5 between the rows of buttons. The metal sheet 4 is provided externally with a surface which, in the range of heat radiation of 9 microns, has the highest possible thermal emissivity. In the range of about 0.5 microns, in applications where the main purpose is cooling, the emissivity should be as low as possible which can be achieved, for example, by applying a coating of titanium dioxide enamel, whilst in applications in which preferably heat is to be won the radiation is below **0.5** microns, there will preferably be used carbon black matt paints. In principle, however, lamina synthetic resin is also suitable as a material for the surface, particularly when this is to be made vacuum tight by lamination with an aluminium foil. Finally, sheets for use in the invention can also be extruded; the buttons **6** may be formed whilst the extruded material has not yet solidified.

FIG. **2** illustrates a panel in a second embodiment of the invention, when the panel which is in the form of a large surface element is to be mounted as a partition inside a building, as a ceiling or a wall element. The construction is, in principle, the same as that of a panel according to FIG. **1**. By means of a folded sheet of metal or foil strip, a hollow body is formed resembling the form as described above. In this example the sheet **20** presenting the inner surface is smooth whilst the sheet **21** having the outer surface has the buttons **22**. The pipe section **23** has a profile with a groove-shaped identation **25**. Fluid channels **26** are formed along the margins of sheet **20** in which the liquid heat carrier accumulates when the plate is arranged horizontally. The folded sheet is welded along a seam at **27**.

The folded edge **28** is formed as a projection which dovetails into the groove-ahaped indentation **25*a*** of the adjacent panel. Hooks **29** serve for the suspension of the panel from the ceiling of a room. Between the rows of buttons **22'** and **22''**, which are seen in the cutaway section, a corrugated lamina **30** made of absorbent paper is provided, the corrugations of which touch both the upper sheet **21** and the lower sheet **22**. Pipes **31** and **32**, formed of thin conductive foil or sheet **22** are bonded to the upper sheet. The pipes **31**, closed at their ends, are filled to form a heat storage body having a thermal storage substance with a phase-change temperature which must be above the dew point when the humidity of the air is normal. Temperatures between **17°** and **19°** C. have been found to be suitable as phase-change temperatures for the cooling of rooms. The pipes **32** which touch the sheet **21** in three areas **32*a*** (in the example) contain the latent heat storage substance, the crystallisation or phase-change temperature of which lies advantageously between **27°** and **33°**.

FIG. **3** includes a cross-section through part of a building in which a device according to the invention is installed including panels **35, 35'** which are arranged in two storeys and are according to FIG. **2**, as well panels according to FIG. **1** being arranged as a roof **36**. The pipe sections or channels **7** and pipe sections **23** of laterally adjacent panels are interconnected via pipes **37**. The channels **26** are connected with the inside of the roof panel **36** via a pipeline **38** in which a condensate pump **39** is arranged. A condensate collector **33** is connected with the inside of the panel **35** via a valve **34**. If heat withdrawal (i.e. cooling) is desired from the room R, the valve **34**, which may be thermostatically controlled, is opened. The room heat heats the panels of the ceilings **35** and **35'** which deliver heat to the storage substance in the pipes **31**. The amount of storage substance is so chosen that only the heat quantity due to several days heating is fully taken up latently by the entire storage substance within **31**. During the night, the sheet **36** of the roof which faces space, radiates energy so that this sheet cools down greatly. The inside of the panels and the pipes **37** and **38** are filled with the saturated vapour of a fluid, preferably an azectropic mixture with methanol. Excessive condensate collects in the channels **26**. Condensation takes place due to cooling between the sheets of the element **36**. The saturated vapour pressure reduction caused thereby leads to an evaporation in the hollow panels **35** and **35'** whereby the panels cool down. The stored heat of crystallisation is thereby withdrawn from the storage substance in the pipes **31**. Condensate in the collectors **36** runs back through the valves **34** into the elements **35** and **35'** so that the thermodynamic cycle is closed. The system acts in this mode for emission of heat into free space as heat stored by the storage substance in **31** during the day is radiated into outer space. While the heat of the incident radiation during the day is held back by the insulation **3**, (and possibly further insulations) from penetrating into the inner space. At the end of the summer, the valves **34** are shut. The condensate from the channels **26** of the panels **35** and **35'** is conveyed into the panels **36** by the pump **39**, or in an alternative arrangement by means including squeezable wicks (not illustrated) either of which acts as a conveying device. This condensate is evaporated due to solar heat and flows through the pipes **37** and the pipe sections **23** into the panels **35** and **35'**. Condensation, with consequent heat release, takes place there. The storage substance in **32** is thus charged by the solar heat which also radiates through the inner surface uniformly via the surface sheets **20** into the room. The condensate so formed, is once again, conveyed upwards by means of the pump **39** (or by surface tension) so that the cycle is closed.

When the valve **34** is shut and the pump **39** is not switched on, the system remains ineffective. Heat in any substantial quantity neither enters the internal space nor is withdrawn from it.

FIG. **4** shows diagrammatically a cross-section through a cutaway portion of a device according to the invention. The roof is formed by panelling made of steel sheet or preferably, aluminium sheet **40**. Pipes **41** forming fluid channels are filled with saturated vapour and arranged with regular spacings between them, and parallel to each other and to the roof slope and are in good thermal contact with the sheet **40**. The outer side of the sheet **40** is covered with a coating **42** of a thermoplastic synthetic resin. A synthetic resin sheet **43** which is provided with secondary fluid channels **44** running at right angles to the pipes **41**, is placed above the outer side. The webs **45** between the channels **44** are attached to the coating **42** in a vapour-tight and permanent manner.

The secondary channels **44** are closed at their ends. The inside of a channel **44** is lined with an absorbent layer, and is filled with the heat conveying fluid in the form of saturated vapour and a small amount of the condensate. The pipes **41** are folded of sheet metal and welded along the seam **46**. The seam region forms a recess in the concrete slab **47**. An insulating lamina **48** is arranged between the sheet metal **40** and the concrete **47**. The inner surface facing towards the room is built up in the same way in its essential parts. The inner vapour pipe or channel **41′**, the interior of which communicates via a pipe **41*a*** with the outer vapour pipe or channel **41**, in good heat conducting contact with the inner sheet metal **40′**. The inner sheet metal **40′** is provided with a synthetic resin lining **42′**. Here again, a synthetic resin lamina **43′** is built up in the same way as described to form channels which are provided on their inside with an absorbent layer **52′**. A channelled foil **49** is permanently attached to the synthetic resin lamina **43′** along areas **50**. A latent heat storage substance **51** with a crystallisation or phase-change temperature of preferably 17° t0 19° is introduced in the trapezoidal section channels so provided. The pipes **41**, **41′** and the connecting pipe **41*a*** are connected in parallel to a plurality of pipes of the same construction (not shown).

FIG. **5** serves to explain the device according to FIG. **4** and shows, in perspective, a roof panel according to FIG. **4**. The vapour pipes **41** are connected to the vapour pipes **41′** via the bends **41*a***. During the hours of the day, the storage substance **51** constituting a latent heat sink is charged by the room temperature and thereby withdraws heat from the room or inner space. During the hours of the night, the synthetic resin lamina **43** which provides the roof surface, due to its physical blackness, radiates energy in the **9** micron region and causes the heat carrier fluid to condense in the channels **44** (of FIG. **4**). The condensate in in the inner channel **44′** evaporates as soon as a heat gradient arises between the pipe **41′** and the latent heat storage substance **51** and condenses again immediately below the pipes **41′**. The return of the condensate takes place via the absorbent layer **52′** by surface tension. In the vapour pipe constituted generally by **41′**, **41*a***, **41**, evaporation takes place in the portion **41′** and condensation (heat source) in the portion **41**. The condensate runs back into the pipe **41′**. The amount of storage substance **51** is so chosen that a heat quantity sufficient for a period of several days can be stored so that, even under unfavourable meteorological conditions, e.g. with a fully covered sky, the room cooling effect is not interrupted over such periods.

FIG. **6** shows another form of embodiment according to the invention in which the U-shaped sinuously bent pipes or channels **61** containing saturated vapour, are used for heat transfer. A concrete slab **64** is traversed by a plurality of the pipes **61**, which are interconnected by means of the transverse pipes or channels **62**. Heat flow distributing metal sheets **65**, **65′** are joined in good thermal contact with the pipes **63**. The inside of the pipes **61** is, once again, occupied by saturated vapour and condensate of a fluid heat carrier substance. This arrangement leads to a heat transfer effect from the bottom or inner surface to the top or outer surface and thus, as a rule, from the inside to the outside of a building, whilst heat is not transferred by the fluid in the reverse sense. The pipes between the concrete slab **64** and the concrete slab **64′** may act as reinforcing rods.

FIG. **7** shows diagrammatically a device according to the invention similar to that of FIG. **6** but adapted to vertical walls, in which the connecting sections **70** of a sinuously bent pipe or fluid channels are not vertical but lie at an acute angle **75** to the wall surface. The heat flux is in the direction of the arrow **76** to whichever pipe section **63** lies higher. The condensate flows back to the surface of sheet **65′** via the inclined sections.

The distribution of the heat flow over the surfaces can take place either by means of metal sheet **65**, **65′**, as already shown in the form of the embodiment according to FIG. **1**, or less by means of elements **43** as shown in FIG. **4**.

FIG. **8** shows diagrammatically a panel or large surface element with surface sheets **81**, **82**, which communicates with a condensate container **90** via a pipe **89**. The temperature of the condensate container is controlled by means of a Peltier element of which one set of electrodes **91** is in good heat conducting contact with the condensate container, whilst the other set of electrodes **92** is in good heat conducting contact with cooling fins **93**. The sense of the electric current can be selected by means of a change-over switch **94**. When the electrodes **91** are connected as a heat sink, the heat carrier fluid inside the panel **81**, **82** condenses until gradually the entire heat carrier is liquified as condensate **95** in the condensate container **90**. The thermal conductivity of the panel **81**, **82** is therefore greatly reduced. By changing over the change-over switch **94**, any desirable partial quantity or even the entire condensate can be evaporated back into the circulation, so that every intermediate value of thermal transfer up to the maximum, can be achieved under control. The manner of control of heat transfer as explained with the help of FIG. **8**, is applicable to all devices according to the invention.

FIG. **9** shows a condensate container modified from that of FIG. **8**, in which the amounts of condensate and thereby the heat transfer between the surfaces of **81**, **82**, is controlled by generating a heat flux between two separated regions **100** and **101** of the concensate container. The condensate is collected in a large number of individual chambers **102**. A Peltier element **103** cools one end of the condensate container, whilst the other end is heated by an electric heater **104**. The more powerful the heating by this device, the more of the chambers **102** become fully emptied. This arrangement is especially preferred for proportional control thermostats which, for example, sense the ambient temperature. Devices according to FIGS. **8** and **9** can also be adapted for use for the control of the heat flow between the storage substances and the room ceiling or room walls.

FIG. **10** shows diagrammatically a device according to the invention in which four circuits can be controlled independently of each other in order to bring into good heat transfer relationship the outer surface of sheet **111** and the inner surface **112** as well as a container **114** with low-temperature latent-heat storage substances. The roof at **111** consists of a heat conducting material, advantageously built up as shown in FIG. **4**. The secondary channels **115**, charged with saturated vapour, effect the transfer of the heat flows to the pipes **117** which form fluid channels. The sheet **112** is built up in the same way. An insulating material **116** is placed between the surface sheets. The material **116** insulates the sheet **111** from **112**, and from the storage substance containers **113** and **114**. The heat pipes follow paths sinuous in two planes. The pipe or fluid channel **117** is connected at one end with the condensate container **118**, which corresponds to the container **90** or **101** respectively according to FIGS. **9** and **9**, and at the other end (not shown) the pipe **117** is enclosed. A wick lining is provided inside the pipe **117**. The region **120** (indicated by broken lines) is connected to the bottom side of the storage substance container **113**. When the vapour pipe is charged with saturated vapour by heating of the condensate container **118**, condensate forms in the wick, which may take the form of an absorbent pipe lining. This condensate evaporates in the region **121** which is in good thermal contact with the outer roof sheet. The storage substance with a phase-change temperature of, say **36°** is charged by the latent heat of condensation of the heat carrier fluid in the section **120**.

If heat is required inside the building, the pipe fluid channel **123** leading from the condensate container **124** is charged with saturated vapour. The pipe **123** connects the top side of the storage container **113** with the inner surface sheet **112**, where the heat is uniformly distributed by the channels **125** which contain saturated vapour.

In summer, during the day, heat is supplied along the pipe **127** to the low-temperature storage substance in the container **114** which has a phase-change temperature of, say, **17°**. The heat is withdrawn from the sheet **112** having the inner surface. This process takes place provided that the condensate container **128** has been heated. At night, the condensate container **129** is heated so that the pipe **130**, which is in contact with the top side of the storage substance container **114** and the roof sheet **111**, is charged with saturated vapour and condensate, whereby the heat stored during the day in the storage substance container **114** is supplied the roof sheet **111** and radiated by it. The pipe systems **127** and **130** need no inside lining because the condensate always gravitates back to the heat source.

By means of this device, the heating and cooling of the interior of a building can be accomplished by the utilisation of solar energy. The control can be performed by on-and-off switching thermostats with the help of a device similar to that in FIG. **8** or by modulating thermostats according to FIG. **9**, and can be made fully automatic.

According to the invention, a pump as at **39** in FIG. **3** can be substituted for the capilliary wick or pipe lining capable of suction and a valve according to **34** in FIG. **3** for the condensation in the containers **118**, **124**, 128, 129 and vice versa. Furthermore, externally actuated or bi-metal controlled valves may be utilised for the interruption of the vapour flow in the vapour pipe.

FIG. **11** shows a valve according to the invention in a pipe **140** charged with saturated vapour. The valve is actuated by means of a bi-metal strip **141**. In a heat rectifier arrangement, heat is to be conducted, e.g. from [illegible] rooms of a building to the outer surface of the roof only during the hot season of the year. In order to interrupt this effect in winter, the bi-metal **141** is so adjusted that, at a temperature which lies below the desired room temperature, the valve **142** is shut ageinst its seat. In order to prevent shutting during a short temperature drop below the limit, the invention envisages the arrangement of the bi-metal strip formed as a corrugated element inside a double-walled tube, which consists of the walls **143** and **144** the intermediate cavity of which is filled with a heat-storage substance **145**, the phase-change temperature of which is near the desired temperature inside the building. The amount of storage substance is so chosen that undercooling periods of less than **12** hours do not shut the valve **143**, so that the otherwise automatic cycle is interrupted only when the weather cools down to constantly lower level, e.g. autumn. A by-pass pipe line **146** serves for the return of the condensate and has such a small bore that no vapour flow with a disturbing heat content flows past the valve. *

June 7, 1966 H. E. THOMASON **3,254,702**

HEAT (OR COLD) STORAGE APPARATUS

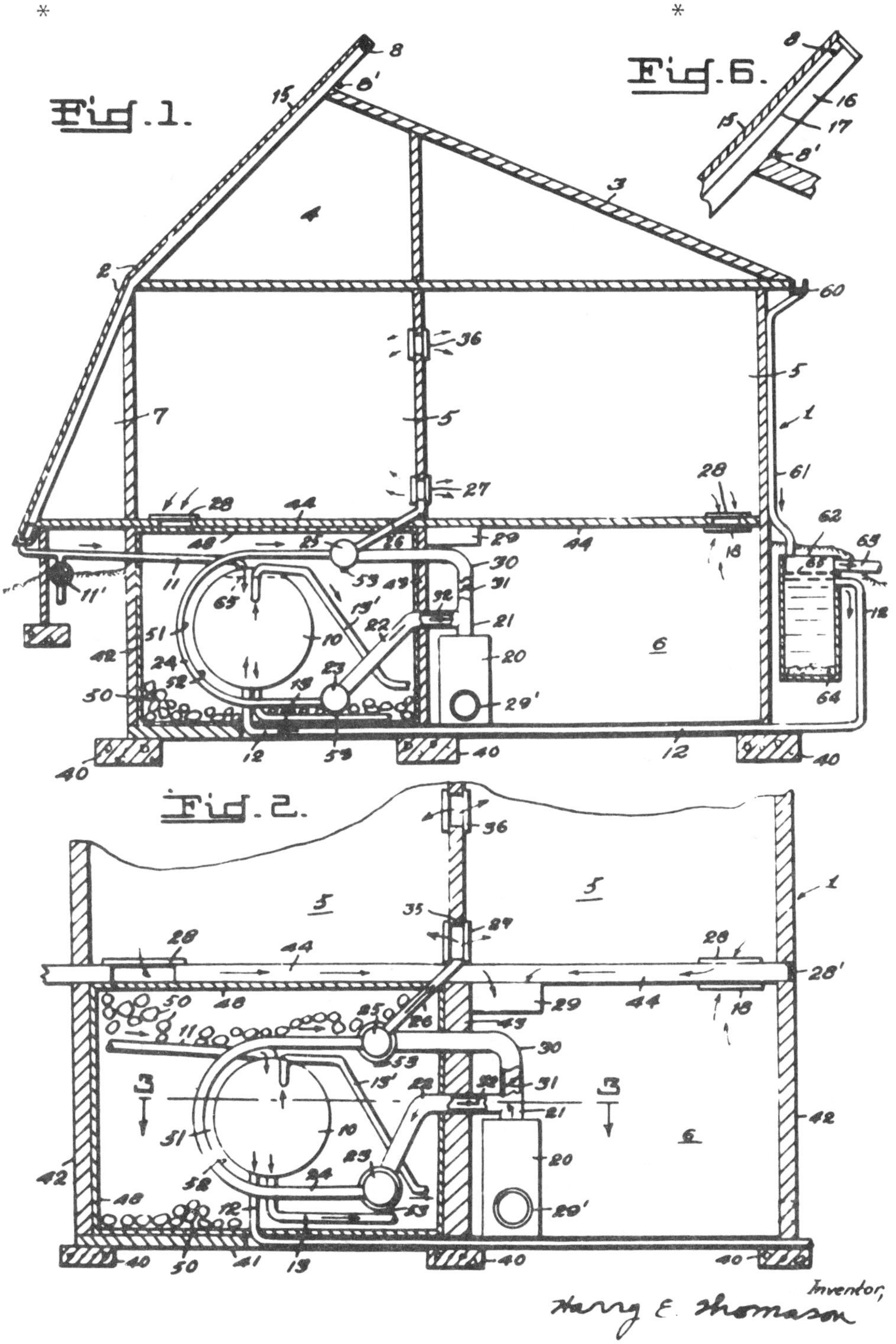

* *

Fig. 1.

Fig. 6.

Fig. 2.

Inventor,
Harry E. Thomason

June 7, 1966 H. E. THOMASON 3,254,702

HEAT (OR COLD) STORAGE APPARATUS

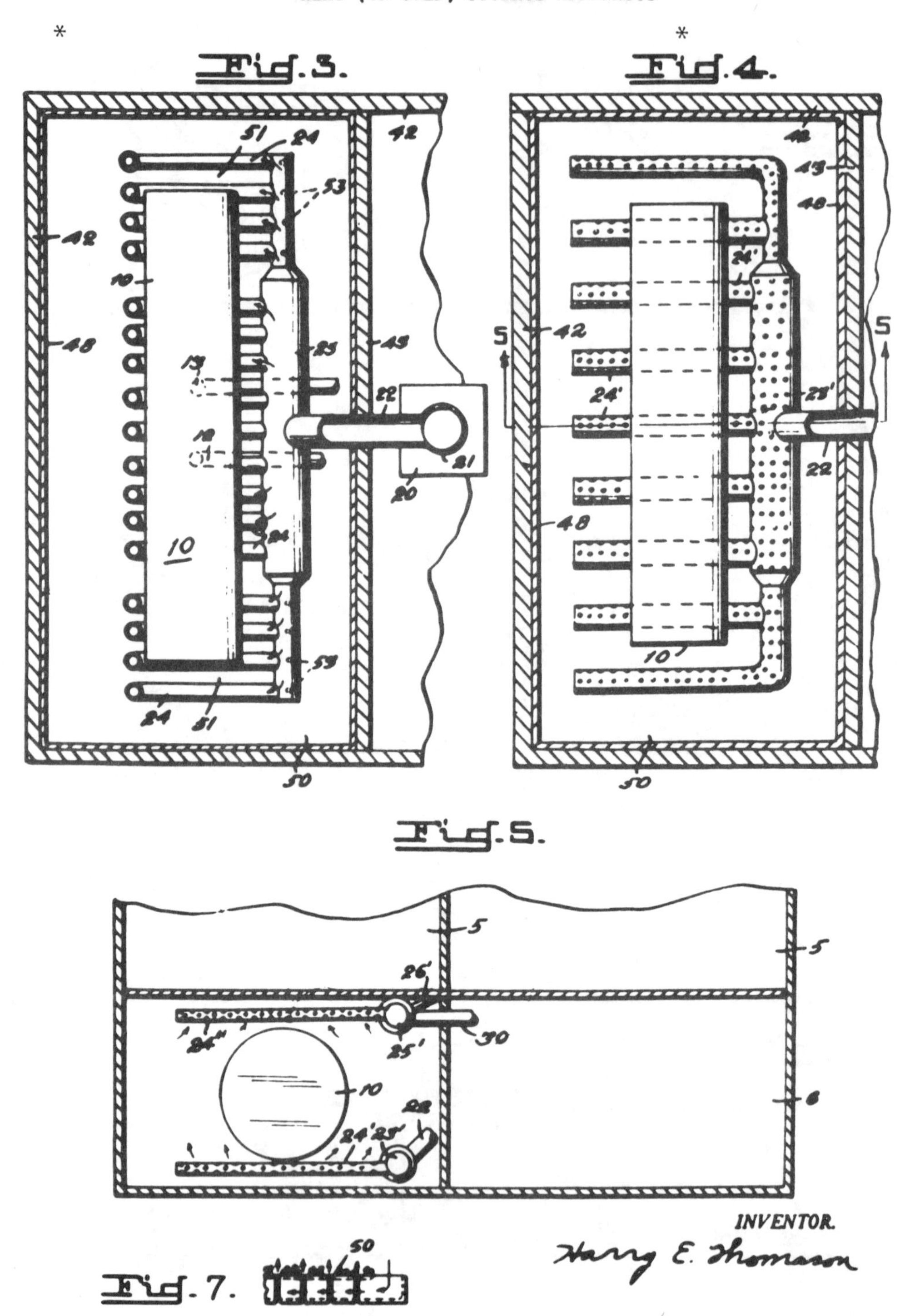

3,254,702
HEAT (OR COLD) STORAGE APPARATUS

Harry E. Thomason, 6911 Walker Mill Road SE.,
Washington, D.C.
*

The present invention relates to storage of heat, or "storage of cold," for use hours or days later. The problem arises in circumstances such as in connection with heating or cooling buildings, particularly where such heating is done by solar heat, and such cooling is done by radiating and evaporating heat dissipators. Obviously heat storage is important in many other instances, but the above conditions will be used as exemplary.

As a pre-requisite to economical use of solar energy for heating, it is necessary to provide a low-cost, highly efficient, and trouble-free solar heat collector to trap solar insolation in the form of heat. Additionally, it is necessary to provide low-cost, trouble-free, and effective heat storage means to hold the heat which has been trapped by the heat collector. Then, it is necessary to provide a simple, low-cost, and trouble-free means for getting the heat back out of the heat storage means in controlled quantities and to the place of desired use. Further, it is desirable that the heating system be capable of reversable operation so as to dispose of heat during hot days, thereby yielding greater value from the system and making it of greater economic value, since the system is then usable the year around.

In my Patent No. 3,145,707 I have disclosed a low-cost, highly efficient, simple and trouble-free solar heat collector. In Patent 3,254,701, I have disclosed a very simple and inexpensive combination solar heat collector and heat dissipator which is very efficient and trouble-free for cooling. Now, the present invention discloses heat (or cold) storage means which is usable together with the aforementioned solar heat collector and the cooling mechanism. The three inventions, when used together, form a system usable, for example, to heat a home by solar heat in winter, including nights and a series of cloudy days, and to air-condition it in summer. The entire system uses low-cost permanent type materials; and construction, operation and maintenance are extremely simple.

In accordance with the above, it is an object of the present invention to provide heat storage means which is simple to construct.

Another object is to provide heat storage means that is low-cost in construction.

A further object is to provide heat storage means that provides for storage of tremendous quantities of heat for use at later times, while retaining the features of simplicity and low cost.

A further object is to provide storage means that is usable reversely, that is, to store heat, or to "store coolness," for use at later times.

A still further object is to provide such storage means, along with low-cost, effective means of getting heat (or of "getting coolness") out of the storage means in controlled quantities.

Another object is to provide a heat (or cool) storage means usable together with conventional air heating system ductwork, and cnventional air heating furnace filter and blower equipment, thereby keeping costs low, while providing auxiliary heating means.

Another object is to provide apparatus to supply fresh air to the system, and to circulate air in the basement.

Another object is to provide storage means which will give up heat as needed by the building heating system as soon as it becomes available from the solar heat collector, and which will then continue to store the excess heat all day long, and day-after-day, until a great reserve is stored.

Another object is to provide clean makeup liquid to keep the liquid (water) automatically replenished in the storage means, and to divert excess liquid from the storage means.

Other objects will become apparent as the description proceeds.

In the drawings;

FIG. 1 illustrates a basic home heating-air conditioning system utilizing the present invention.

FIG. 2 is an enlarged view of a portion of FIG. 1;

FIG. 3 is a cross-section taken along line 3—3 of FIG. 2;

FIG. 4 illustrates a modification of the present invention;

FIG. 5 is a view taken along line 5—5 of FIG. 4;

FIG. 6 illustrates details of the heat collector and dissipator manifolds;

FIG. 7 is a view of a modified form of the distributor ductwork for bringing air into the storage apparatus.

Referring more specifically to the drawings, one typical design for a solar heated-air conditioned building is illustrated in FIG. 1. Such building preferably has a south-facing solar heat collector roof **2**, such as that described in my Patent No. 3,145,707 *
Of course other solar heat collectors, or heat sources other than solar, may be used. The remaining portion of the roof structure, which is illustrated at **3**, is preferably a heat dissipator to cool a fluid, such as in summertime when it is desirable to cool the building. The heat dissipator may be constructed in an inexpensive form, as particularly described and claimed in my co-pending Patent 3,254,701. FIG. 6 illustrates details of a solar heater-heat dissipator construction wherein **8** is a distributor manifold, **15** is glass, **16** is insulation and **17** is black corrugated sheet metal. Distributor manifold **8'** is used to supply liquid to the heat dissipator **3**.

The building has attic space **4**, living quarters **5**, basement **6** and closet space **7**. Closet space **7** acts as a buffer zone against outside cold or hot weather.

A fluid reservoir is shown at **10**, this reservoir preferably being filled with a liquid such as water, which can be heated or cooled. Multiple reservoirs may be provided if desired. If multiple reservoirs are provided, they may be connected in series, or in parallel. Inlet line **11** brings in heated fluid, from solar heat collector **2** for example. Water may be withdrawn via line **13** and recirculated through the heat collector via distributor manifold **8** for further heating. When cooling is desired, cool fluid may be brought in via inlet line **12**, and this cooling fluid may be supplied from an evaporation-radiation type roof cooler as at **3**, a cooling tower, a refrigeration unit, or other. If a refrigeration unit is to be used, the evaporation or cooling coil may be immersed directly in the reservoir **10**, if desired. Outlet line **13'** may be used to withdraw fluid from the reservoir **10**, as by means of a circulating pump, to return the fluid to the cooling apparatus. When used for cooling, line **13'** is preferably brought out near the top of tank **10**, the return being in the bottom thereof, thus taking the warmer fluid out of the top to be cooled.

A valve **11'** may be provided in return line **11** so that heated water may be taken directly from the solar heat collector for a use such as heating swimming pool water, for example.

In order to extract the heat (or coolness) from the storage area near reservoir **10**, I provide a blower unit **20** having a discharge duct **21** and return **29'**. This blower unit may be the conventional blower unit found in a heating furnace for example, having an air filter therein, and the furnace unit being usable as a standby heat source for extremely long periods of cloudy weather, for warming a building quickly if it has been unoccupied and is cold, or for emergency use.

Leading off from discharge duct **21** is a duct **22** which feeds into distributor manifold 23. Distributor manifold 23 extends longitudinally along storage reservoir 10, and ducts 24 extend around said reservoir and come back into manifold 25. From manifold 25, ducts 26 lead to the points of use of the heated (or cooled) air, such as outlet registers 27. Return registers are provided at 28 and ductwork may be provided from 28 via 29 to 29' if desired. However, inasmuch as basement space 6 may be substantially air tight, return ductwork may be dispensed with if desired. If fresh air from outside is desired, such may be drawn in through a damper controlled vent such as at 28'. The damper may be gravity closed and vacuum opened, or may be mechanically or power operated.

At 18 I provide a register with adjustable louvers to admit a predetermined and adjustable amount of fresh air to the system from the basement. This is desirable for several reasons. In winter, fresh air can be brought in from outside of the house by way of register 28', where the air may be extremely cold, or it may be brought in by way of register 18 from the basement where the temperature is from 50° to 60° F., thus requiring little additional heating to come up to room temperature. During the hot summer months, fresh air may be brought in by way of register 28' or by 18 at a basement temperature of about 75° F., instead of at a hot outdoor temperature, thus requiring no cooling. The amount of fresh air taken in by the system per hour will not be great and that extracted from the basement will be replaced by slight leakage which is inherent in building construction. Obviously a supply register may be provided for the basement. This latter arrangement assures circulation of air in the basement, thus warming the basement in winter and keeping the air fresh and less humid in the summer. If dehumidifying is desirable for summertime, a small dehumidifier may be placed in the basement area 6 to keep the humidity low. The dry cool basement air is drawn into the household air supply via 18 and is distributed via 20, 27 thereby helping to cool and dehumidify the living quarters also. A portion of the air from the living quarters may be returned to the basement area by a supply register as mentioned above for cooling, dehumidifying and changing the basement air.

A by-pass duct is provided at 30 extending from discharge duct 21 to manifold 25. A damper is provided at 31, and another damper may be provided at 32. If heat is needed directly from unit 20, damper 31 is opened and heated air will flow, by the path of least resistance, predominantly through by-pass 30 to manifold 25, through lines 26 and registers 27. If desirable, damper 32 may be closed to make certain that all of the heated air goes through by-pass 30. Alternatively, damper 31 may be gravity closed and damper 32 closed and opened by an electromagnet and spring. Then, when the furnace 20 cuts on to supply heat, damper 32 is closed and a buildup of air pressure in outlet 21 will open damper 31.

The building rests on footings 40, the storage bin having a floor 41, preferably of concrete. Foundation walls 42 and storage bin wall 43 support floor joists 44. The storage reservoir is lined with insulation 48 and is preferably provided with additional heat-storage means at 50. This heat storage means may be low-cost stone or gravel, containers of Glauber's salt, or other. In the areas adjacent the ductwork, as at 51, a material such as sand may be provided. These materials have desirable characteristics such as: (1) both gravel and sand are low-cost and permanent materials; (2) the sand adjacent the ductwork yields a uniform pressure upon the ductwork, thereby permitting lightweight, low-cost, thin ductwork to be used; (3) the sand helps to store heat, and transfers same to or from the ductwork readily, heat absorption and transfer being enhanced if a black coating 52 is used on the interior and/or exterior of the ductwork. Drain holes may be provided at 53 to permit escape of condensation when the apparatus is dehumidifying the air in humid weather.

In FIG. 2 a desirable arrangement of non-fluid heat-storing means 50 is illustrated. The bin is substantially filled to the top around the edges so that the stone 50, or similar type material, will absorp more heat at the upper edges of the bin. This also helps to minimize loss of heat near the upper edges. The center area of the bin is not completely filled. Therefore, the uppermost layer of the stone is dished out, i.e. higher at the periphery of the bin and lowered in the central area in a pattern resembling a saucer. This arrangement also provides crawl space in the central area of the bin at the top for work, inspections, repairs, etc inside of the bin. This desirable arrangement of stone may be used in any of the modifications. In the modification wherein a perforated inlet manifold, say of building blocks, is used at the bottom of the bin, the saucer-shaped space at the top of the stone is particularly desirable. Warm air can rise to this warm air pocket and is readily available to supply warm air to the supply ducts for the living quarters.

In FIGS. 4 and 5 I have illustrated modified apparatus for getting heat (or coolness) out of the storage bin. In this apparatus I use reservoir 10, insulation 48 and a material such as stone 50, similar to that used in the previous embodiment. I also use the filter-blower (or furnace) 20 with ductwork 21, 22, etc. However, the manifold 23' may be provided with perforations, and perforated branches 24' may be extended outwardly from manifold 23' below reservoir 10. In this modification, material such as sand may be dispensed with and the air coming into manifold 23' and branches 24' may filter out through the perforations and up through the gravel. Similar perforated ductwork may be provided above reservoir 10 at 24" and 25'. The air re-enters such ductwork to flow to the living quarters 5 which are to be heated or cooled. Or, the return ductwork may be eliminated completely, and warm air may be taken from the pressurized storage bin at any places desired. Instead of round ductwork as illustrated, other forms or shapes may be utilized to conduct the air through the storage bin. For example, concrete or cinder blocks may be aligned as illustrated in FIG. 7 such that the holes therein form the lower manifold and fluid conduits. By spacing the blocks apart slightly, the desired "perforations" are provided in the conduits and fluid can filter out and up through the storage means 50 and past reservoir 10. In this type of construction the air is filtered of dust particles, to a considerable extent, as it drifts slowly up through the stonelike material 50. However, the filter in blower unit 20 will extract substantially all dust.

Use of the roof dissipator 3 and storage drum 10 presents certain problems which are overcome by use of diverter-sediment trap 62. Dust particles from the air will settle on the heat dissipator 3. Water circulated thereover, or rain water, will wash this dust off into gutter 60. If this dust were washed directly from the dissipator, it would tend to settle out as sludge in drum 10, or even worse, it would tend to settle in line 12 and clog same. With the present diverter-trap the sediment will settle out at 64 so it can be readily removed, although removal may not be necessary for many years.

It is desirable to have the water in drum 10 automatically replenished as some of it is lost through evaporation from the heat dissipator. This is achieved by the present system including trap 62. This trap has an inlet line 61, outlet line 12 and overflow 63. The normal water level in tank 10 and in trap 62 is indicated at 65. If the apparatus has been operated for cooling for several days, the water level will be lowered somewhat. However, as soon as it rains, the water level in 10 and 62 will be restored to normal. Then, excess water from rain (snow or ice), will not overfill drum 10 or trap 62 because the excess will drain away via overflow 63. Of course trap 62 may be set at any desired elevation so as to maintain water throughout drum 10 and in pipes 11, 12 at any level desired.

Thus, it is apparent that the trap-diverter 62 performs at least three valuable functions, that is it acts as a sediment trap, and permits only clean water to enter tank 10, it automatically keeps water replenished in tank 10, whether summer or winter, and it automatically diverts excess rain water away from the system. Also, if this trap is not insulated from the cool earth, it can liberate some heat to the earth and help cool the water returning from heat dissipator 3 under some conditions. All of these advantages are obtained with the simple trap-diverter which has no moving parts or mechanical apparatus to give trouble.

When the present apparatus is used in extremely dry climates where evaporation is great and rainfall is slight, then a float-controlled valve may be used in tank 10, or in trap 62, to admit make-up water from a public water supply or well if needed. In such case, if the float-controlled inlet valve should fail to function, the overflow 63 would take care of the excess water automatically and avoid overfilling of the liquid tank and flooding of the storage bin, if tank 10 is of open-top construction. Further, a float-controlled valve may be provided in trap 62 to divert excess rain water from 61, as a substitute for overflow diverter outlet 63.

The present apparatus may be operated as follows. During the wintertime a liquid, such as water, is heated in a solar heat collector, such as collector 2. (This heat collector may be the roof of the building to be heated, may be the roof of an adjoining building, a shed-roof, or other.) The heated water flows into reservoir 10 where it gives up its heat to the stone or air and is circulated from the reservoir back to the heat collector for re-heating. Thus, the water in reservoir 10 is heated to a considerable extent within a few hours and is quickly available for use in heating air flowing through the ductwork in FIG. 1, or around drum 10 and through the stone in FIG. 5. If the heat is not needed or drawn off by air circulating in the ductwork or stone, then the heat passes into the adjacent sand and/or stone bed and is stored for later use. Insulation at 48 substantially blocks exit or heat from the warm gravel bed. Then, at night and on cloudy days, as heat is extracted via the ductwork to warm the building, heat travels back through the gravel bed, as well as from the heated reservoir of water, to the ductwork where it is taken away by air to heat the living quarters.

Now, suppose that the occupants of the home have been away on vacation and the system has not been in operation, or that some emergency arises. To heat the building quickly it is only necessary to open damper 31, and close damper 32, and start furnace 20. This makes hot filtered air available immediately through by-pass 30. Damper 31 (and damper 32) may be operated automatically by a power device when the furnace comes on if desired. Alternatively, damper 32 may be power operated and damper 31 may be gravity closed, so that when damper 32 is closed, air pressure buildup in outlet 21 will automatically force damper 31 open. If damper 32 is eliminated, substantially all warm air will flow via 30 anyway, this being the path of least resistance.

Now, for summertime use, when filtered cool air is needed, operation is as follows. The water in reservoir 10, and the bed of gravel, are cool. Hot air from the living quarters is withdrawn through registers 28 and blower inlet 29'. The air is filtered in unit 20 and expelled via 21, 22, 23, 24 and 25. The heat from the air is given up to the surrounding cool stone and the water in reservoir 10 as the air passes through the ductwork. This filtered cool air moves up through ducts 26 and may exit at 27, but preferably, registers 27 are closed for summertime operation and damper 35 is opened. The cool air then exits at 36 to drift down across the living space and cool the living quarters. Damper 35 is preferably automatically closed by gravity and opened due to pressure buildup in ducts 26 when registers 27 are closed.

When the present apparatus is being used to air-condition a building, during periods of hot weather with very high relative humidity, the moisture-laden air will strike the cool walls of the ductwork and some of the excessive moisture may condense, thus dehumidifying the air. To provide for escape of this condensation, drain holes and pipes may be provided in the ductwork, as at 53, to permit drainage. Thus, the air can be cooled, filtered, and dehumidified. However an extremely high humidity and hot weather condition seldom exists in areas of large populations. Under some conditions of slightly lower humidity and hot weather, a separate small dehumidifier may be used. Of course, in many areas no dehumidifying is needed.

As heated air is circulated through ductwork 22–26 the storage material will be heated slowly. To dissipate this heat, water from reservoir 10 is circulated to a heat dissipator and the cooled water is returned. Such heat dissipator may be a simple roof heat dissipator illustrated at 3, described in detail and claimed in my patent * 3,254,701 *

Such heat dissipator need be operated for only a short time each day or each night, or on occasional or alternate nights, or on the colder nights and the "cold" is stored. (Nighttime operation is preferable inasmuch as more heat is liberated per hour.)

If no cooling is required, the air may be filtered in unit 20 and circulated via by-pass 30 as previously described. Or, the system may be shut down entirely when the weather is neither too hot nor too cold and air circulation is not desired.

Among the advantages of the present invention are, tremendous heat storage capacity, minimum heat loss, low costs for materials, and simplicity and permanence of construction. The main bulk of heat storage material is stone, which is readily available at very low cost almost everywhere. The liquid heat transfer medium may be water, and such will not freeze in the solar heat collector when such collector is constructed as disclosed in my Patent No. 3,145,707 * The storage reservoir 10 is small and therefore inexpensive due to small size and lightweight materials which are usable in small-drum construction. The ductwork at 23, 24, 25 may be of lightweight material inasmuch as the ducts are not large, they are round, and the sand-like material exerts equal pressure on all sides. Blower-filter unit (furnace) 20 and the remainder of the ductwork may be substantially conventional as is used in most homes. The heat dissipator 3 and heat collector 2 replace the conventional roof and insulation, thereby cutting costs of the dissipator and collector.

In this system, both solar heating and air conditioning are achieved at low cost. Most of the equipment is thus usable the year around and does not deteriorate due to non-use. In spring and autumn weather, large quantities of heat are available from the heat collector and may be used for purposes such as heating swimming pool water, etc. Also, hot water may be used for many other domestic purposes. Further, in extremely hot weather, unwanted heat may be dissipated from such places as a swimming pool, etc. by way of heat dissipator **3**, the cooling capacity of dissipator **3** being much greater than required for air-conditioning the home.

The ductwork at **23**, **24**, **25** includes hundreds of square feet of surface area. This is of great value inasmuch as the rate of heat transfer from the heat bin to the air which is circulating through the ductwork is proportional to the surface area of contact. Thus, in the present apparatus, I have provided hundreds of square feet of ductwork surface area, and this "radiator" surface is of simple low-cost construction. The importance of this tremendous "radiator" surface at low-cost is emphasized when it is considered that use of such large surface permits use of heat at a much lower temperature in the storage bin. In other words, the apparatus is still effective to heat the living quarters even when the temperature of the water, stone and sand in the heat bin is only a few degrees higher than the temperature desired in the home.

Conversely, during hot days when air conditioning is required, the temperature in the heat (or cold) storage bin need be only a few degrees below the desired room temperature. The many ducts **24** are not tiny restricted air passages, and air flows freely therethrough, thus the blower unit **20** may be of normal capacity, not requiring extra power to circulate the air.

Inasmuch as temperatures in the heat bin need not be especially high, the solar heat collector is capable of greater efficiency, and more heat is collected from the sun per day, the efficiency of such solar heat collector rising when the temperature of the fluid being circulated therethrough is not required to be high. The heat dissipator efficiency is likewise greater when the heat bin storage materials do not have to be chilled to a low temperature.

The modification of FIGS. 4 and 5 has corresponding advantages, the air being dispersed throughout the heated stone to get maximum surface contact between the warm (or cooled) stone and the air being heated (or cooled). Also, when the construction of the lower ducts is of building blocks, the cost of materials and the skill and manpower required for construction are minimized, and the upper ductwork may be eliminated if desired. The stone and drum surfaces provide thousands of square feet of heat exchange surface. *

June 7, 1966 | H. E. THOMASON | 3,254,703

SOLAR HEATED HOME

*

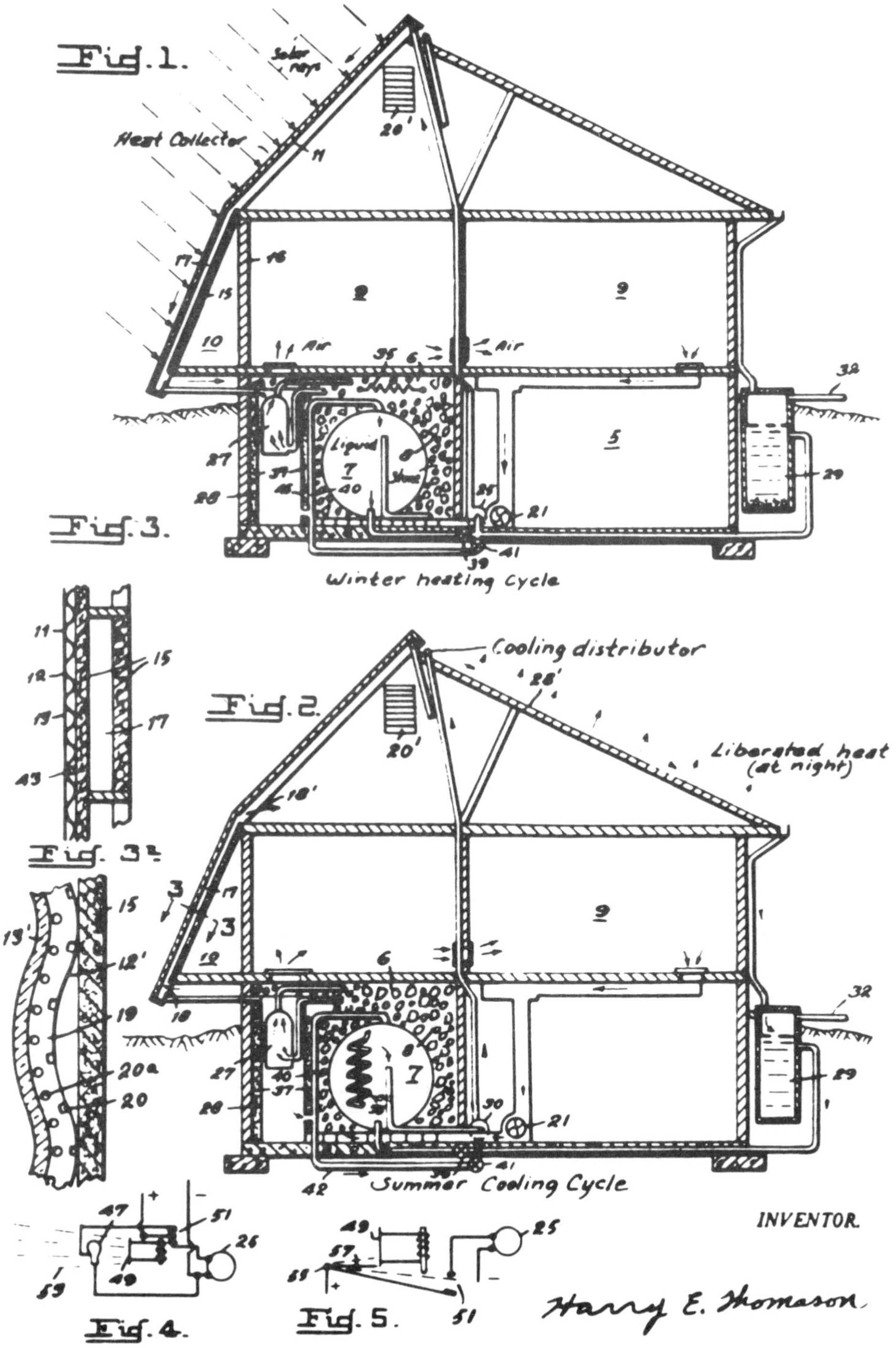

INVENTOR.

3,254,703
SOLAR HEATED HOME
Harry E. Thomason, District Heights, Md.
(7354 Walker Mill Road SE., Washington, D.C.)

*

The present invention relates to solar home heating apparatus. Many problems must be solved in devising a successful solar home. From the standpoint of architecture the problems are great due to a large heat collector set at an angle to the vertical, and it is difficult to avoid "cut-up" living quarters, unnecessary heat losses from the home during the winter and unnecessary overheating during the summer. It is very desirable to minimize the power required to cool the home during the summer and it is desirable to minimize the cost of construction of the solar heat collector, while improving performance of the collector. It is desirable to provide for effective simple heat storage, preferably within the confines of the home so that unavoidable heat losses from the heat storage apparatus will help to warm the home, and so that costs of construction can be minimized. It is desirable to keep control systems as simple and low-cost as possible. The present invention helps to overcome problems in solar heated homes.

In the drawing:

FIG. 1 is a cross section of a solar heated home illustrating wintertime heating.

FIG. 2 is a similar cross section of the same embodiment, illustrating summertime cooling.

FIG. 3 is a view along line 3—3 of FIG. 2 illustrating details of the heat collector and home construction.

FIG. 3*a* is a modification of the construction illustrated in FIG. 3.

FIG. 4 is a schematic diagram of a control apparatus for the heat collector pump.

FIG. 5 is a modification of the control apparatus.

FIGS. 1 and 2 represent the same embodiment but certain elements of FIG. 1 are omitted in FIG. 2, and vice-versa, to simplify the drawing. FIG. 1 includes apparatus necessary for wintertime heating while FIG. 2 includes different elements used for summertime cooling.

In FIG. 1 reference number **5** designates a basement of a solar heated home. It is evident that this space could be the "ground floor" of a home if no basement is provided and if both floors are constructed above earth level. A heat (or cold) storage bin is provided at **6** having a liquid reservoir **7** and solid material **8** such as stone, cans of Glauber's salt, or such. Said storage bin **6** is preferably insulated and substantially air tight such that the warmed (or cooled) air may be taken from the bin at various registers with a minimum of expensive ductwork. Living quarters are provided at **9** and a restricted heat and cold buffer area, usable for a closet or storage space, is designated **10**. Area **10** is important for several reasons. During the wintertime it serves as a buffer zone between inside room temperatures of say 72° F., and outside temperatures of say 0° F. For summertime it serves as a buffer area between scorching outside temperatures and the living quarters which are kept cooler. Due to this construction the framework of the home is strengthened and the interior living quarters **9** are kept of conventional shape with vertical walls and rectangular floor plans. Tremendous closet and storage space are provided in this relatively restricted space.

A solar heat collector is provided at **11** with a heat collecting member at **12** (see FIG. 3), a transparent cover at **13** and preferably two layers of insulation at **15**. Insulation may be provided at other places such as at **16** if desired. An air space is provided at **17** somewhat in the form of a chimney whereby air may enter adjacent the lower portion of the collector at **18** and may rise as it is warmed to come out at a higher point such as **18'** (note FIG. 2). This feature becomes very important during hot summer days when some of the heat from the heat collector gets through the outermost layer of insulation. When such heat encounters the inner layer most of it is stopped and the air in the chimney or chimneys **17** is heated. Convection currents passing up through spaces **17** automatically exhaust the excess heat to the attic where it escapes through louvers **20'** and helps to minimize damage to the collector which would result if internal heat were allowed to build up excessively. Closet space **10** is kept cooler and hence less heat finds its way into the home. Obviously chimneys **17** could extend to the top of the heat collector or to the top of the home if desired so that the heated air could escape at the top of the collector rather than into the attic.

Blower **21** circulates air from the living quarters through the heat bin to warm the air for wintertime or to cool it during the summer. Blower **21** pressurizes bin **6**. However, the blower may be placed near the outlet or outlets of the bin so as to draw air into the bin under a slight vacuum and discharge it into the home.

Pump **25** in FIG. 1 is used to circulate water through the heat collector and the hot water from the heat collector returns through a heat exchanger unit having an inner fresh water tank **27** to heat the household domestic water supply. The inner tank is "bathed" in hot water in drum **28** from heat collector **11**.

Nighttime chilling of water during the summer is illustrated at **28** in FIG. 2. Heat is liberated from water being circulated to the roof by pump **30**. Such water is preferably drawn from the warmer water in the upper portion of the liquid reservoir **7** in the heat storage bin **6**. This water returns from the roof cooler by way of sediment trap and automatic rainwater makeup device **29**. The water returning from **29** to reservoir **7**, at night, passes through valve **41**, line **42**, and line **40** back into reservoir **7**. The water level in reservoirs **7**, **28** and **29** is substantially equal. Water in **28** is heated only during the day, and is drawn from reservoir **28**, as illustrated in FIG. 2 by the arrow near the bottom of reservoir **28** and the arrow to the right of reference number **42**. Pump **25** draws this water through valve **41** and circulates it back to the heat collector. The water in reservoir **28** is in a static condition during the night while the rooftop cooler is operating. The water to be chilled is withdrawn from near the top of reservoir **7**, by pump **30**, as is indicated by the arrow to the right of cooling element **33**. This leaves space in reservoir **7** for the chilled water to return to **7**. Also, water flowing from line **42** to line **40** is flowing straight through the pipe T-connection near the bottom of reservoir **28**. Therefore, there is no appreciable amount of mixing of the returning chilled water with the hot water in reservoir **28**. As an alternative, valve **39** could be opened nightly during the summertime cooling period if desired to permit the chilled water to return to reservoir **7** via valve **39**. Valves **39**, **41** may be operated by reach-rods, solenoid valve actuators, or by any other means well-known to engineers. Rain falling on the roof area **28'** automatically replenishes the water supply in trap **29** and in the liquid reservoirs **7** and **28** in the heat storage bin. Reservoirs **7** and **28** are preferably vented to avoid air locks or vacuum locks. When the water level has been brought up to normal the excess rainwater flows off automatically by way of overflow **32** which is set at the proper elevation to fill reservoirs **7** and **28** to a desired level, or completely full, before excess water overflows via **32**. This simple apparatus provides free automatic rainwater makeup without valves or mechanical apparatus to cause trouble, and provides a trap for sediment to avoid possible clogging of the liquid lines. Inasmuch as valve **39** is open during the winter and valve **41** is open during the summer, makeup water can flow to the reservoirs **7** and **28**. If desired, a valve could be provided in the return line from **29** so that makeup water can be admitted only at selected times.

In some sections of the world nighttime chilling of water at **28'** is not as great as may be desired. In such event a cooling element may be inserted in the liquid reservoir as at **33**. Cooling may be supplied by means of a refrigeration unit, operable at night when the unit is more efficient, and the "coolness" so supplied is stored away to cool the home during the hot day. With this arrangement overall cooling efficiency is greatly increased and a smaller refrigeration unit and less power will produce more "cooling" of the home. If desired the roof cooler may not be used and yet the refrigeration unit will operate more efficiently to chill the water and stone at night when the refrigeration unit is discharging its heat to cool night air rather than hot daytime air. Also, liquid contact with cooling element **33** provides for better heat exchange from the cold element to the liquid, thereby improving efficiency and minimizing the amount of cooling surface required for element **33**.

At times the stored solar heat may not be sufficient to maint.in the desired temperature of the building. To meet this possible condition auxiliary heating means is provided such as at **35** (see FIG. 1). Such auxiliary heating means may be an electric heating element or other conventional heat producing means such as a gas or oil heater. This heat source is preferably placed such that cold air from the living quarters passes first through the heat storage apparatus to be pre-heated, then to the auxiliary heater for a temperature boost, and thence to the living quarters to warm the building.

Preheater drum **28** is preferably insulated from the remainder of the heat bin as at **37**. The suction line from drum **7** has a valve at **39** and the line from drum **28** has a valve at **41**, note FIG. 1. For wintertime operation valve **41** is closed and valve **39** is open. Thus pump **25** draws water from drum **7** and delivers it to the heat collector **11**. Hot water from the heat collector returns to drum **28** and flows from drum **28** to drum **7** via line **40**, thus heating the water in both. However, for summertime operation water in drum **7** is preferably cooled at night to provide home air conditioning yet water in drum **28** is still to be heated on sunny days to supply hot domestic water to the home. To achieve this, valve **39** is closed and valve **41** is opened. Thus chilled water is not drawn from drum **7** but water to be heated comes directly from drum **28** via line **42**. This water is circulated to the collector **11** by pump **25** where it is heated and returns to drum **28**. Insulation **37** minimizes heat losses from hot drum **28** to the chilled stones **6** and drum **7**. Thus, a relatively small quantity of heat is stored in compartment **37**, **28** sufficient to heat the domestic water for a few days, the remainder of the heat bin being used to store chilled water and stone for summertime air conditioning.

In constructing a heat collector as illustrated in FIG. 3 it becomes desirable to bake the heat collecting member **12** at high temperatures to increase the life of the member or of special coatings applied thereto. To bake such member or coatings in a factory with special ovens would be expensive. It has been found that high temperature baking can be achieved at very low cost by use of solar energy baking. For example, a heat conducting member may be coated with a dull black material which must be baked quickly in order to extend the life of the coating manyfold. Using the method herein described, the surface is blackened during a sunny day, or even a cloudy day when solar input is high, and is promptly covered with a transparent or semi-transparent material such as a sheet of plastic. Solar energy is trapped beneath the plastic and the temperature rises so as to bake the coating and thus prolong its life. This sheet of plastic may be removed after the baking is completed, or may be left in place to serve as a permanent transparency as at **13**. Thus, solar energy is used to advantage in constructing the solar heat collector.

The method of heat treating material by solar energy is valuable for curing coatings or paints by baking, thus prolonging the life of the coating or paint manyfold. It has been said that certain coatings, if heat cured promptly after being applied, will last more than five times as long as the same coatings without heat curing. Thus, by the simple solar energy baking method disclosed herein, the life of a coating of paint, for example, may be greatly increased. However, the method may also be used for other purposes such as heat treating thermo-setting plastics, etc. In FIG. 3*a* a heat collector surface layer is illustrated which may be heat cured by solar energy if desired. Such layer preferably comprises a heat collecting porous layer of material **19** having perforations or passages **20**, **20***a*. Layer **19** is preferably attached to an inner base layer of material **12'** which is substantially impervious to a fluid being circulated through the collector and preferably having an external layer of material **13'** which is transparent or reasonably transparent to admit solar energy to or through the material **19**. Material **19** may be darkened to absorb solar energy and to thereby heat fluid passing thereinto or therethrough via perforations or passages **20** or **20***a*. However the material may be transparent or translucent to let solar energy penetrate to inner layer **12'** where it heats said inner layer and fluid coming in contact therewith. The porous material may be of a desired thickness of a suitable material such as a porous metallic foam-like material, or plastic, or such, or may be one or more layers of a mesh-like material. Such material may be treated with dyes or other substances within the porous material itself or may be provided with coatings to render the material dark and more heat-absorbing. Alternatively, the material may be semi-darkened so as to become heated itself or may be transparent or translucent to admit solar energy to the inner surface **12'**, which inner surface may be darkened to collect solar energy to heat a fluid being circulated through the heat collector. Fluid passages **20** are preferably adjacent the heat collecting surface **12'** such as by being embedded in the material **19**. Some materials are porous enough for fluid flow therethrough without additional passages. Fluid may be circulated through passages **20** only, or through passages **20***a* only, or through both. Passages similar to those at **20***a* are found at random in some foam-like preparations. Although the foam-like and transparent layers are illustrated as being applied to a corrugated base **12'** the base may take other forms or shapes as desired, including planar. The method of heat curing described may be utilized, if desired, to heat cure any one or all of the layers or surfaces described herein.

Heat collector pump **25** is preferably controlled by a switch device responsive to temperatures in the heat collector being raised above temperatures of water being pumped to the heat collector. The switching on-and-off operation is preferably achieved by use of a thermocouple device having its hot junction **43** subjected to heat collector temperatures and its cold junction **45** subjected to temperatures of water going to the collector. Thus, if the heat collector temperature exceeds the temperature of the water going to the collector, a current flows in the thermo-couple circuit. This current is used to trip a switch to start circulating pump **25**. The current flowing in the thermo-couple circuit may be amplified to trip a relay switch to cut the pump on. When the heat collector temperature drops, or the temperature of the water to the collector rises, so that these temperatures approach one-another, the flow of current in the thermo-couple circuit ceases or becomes low enough to stop the circulating pump. Although the hot junction 43 is illustrated as being placed in the heat collector it may be placed at other places to be responsive to solar heat, such as in a separate solar heated control box. Also, the cold junction 45 may be placed at a location other than that illustrated in FIG. 1, such as at the inlet to pump 25, or at the outlet of drum 7, or other. Changing the locations of these junctions will affect the operating characteristics of the control system to some extent but the basic pattern will be similar.

As an alternative to the thermocouple switching mechanism to control operation of pump 25 a light sensitive switch unit may be used. However, an ordinary photocell and relay unit often is not sensitive enough to light intensity changes. Hence, if the switch is tripped on when hazy sunlight occurs it will not be tripped off when the light intensity is lowered to a level of bright cloudiness. To overcome this deficiency the present invention provides means to slightly increase the intensity of light falling on the light sensitive element when natural light drops to a predetermined level and the pump is cut off. Attention is directed to FIG. 4 where the light sensing element 49 is exposed to light rays 53 which may be entering a north-facing window for example. As natural light intensity diminishes due to clouds or the approach of night the light sensitive element 49 trips relay switch 51 and cuts off the pump 25. At approximately this same time lamp 47 in the vicinity of the light sensitive element is turned on to thus boost the intensity of the light at the light sensitive element. However, even the increased intensity of light at the light sensiitve element is hardly sufficient to trip the pump switch back on. Thus, the lamp will stay lighted until the intensity of natural light from the window is increased slightly to a point where the lamp light, plus the natural light, will trip the pump switch back on. When the natural light intensity thus rises again, such as due to the passing of a cloud, then the pump is cut on and the lamp is turned off. However, the slightly increased level of natural illumination is sufficient to keep the pump switched on even without the artificial light which was cut off. If the clouds do not pass for the remainder of the day, or if the cutting off of the pump was due to diminishing natural light with the approach of night, the lamp will stay lighted and will provide a night light for the area. When natural light of the desired intensity returns pump 25 is cut back on and the lamp is cut off.

Although the present invention has been explained with reference to a light sensing element exposed to natural light through a window, the unit may be used outdoors instead of inside. In either event the night light is cut on automatically every evening and is cut off each time natural light reaches the desired level to produce solar heating of fluid being circulated by pump 25. Thus, the apparatus described performs at least three functions, (1) it turns pump 25 on and off, (2) it provides an automatic night light, (3) it provides a visual indicator as to when the pump switch is on or off.

The essence of this invention may be embodied in other simple forms if desired. Note FIG. 5 for example where, instead of having a lamp turn on and off as pump 25 is turned on and off, a simple louvre or screen 57 may be moved about pivot 55 to partially shade the light sensing element 49 when the natural light reaches a predetermined level, and pump 25 cuts on such as due to sunshine. When natural light intensity is diminished, such as by clouds, pump 25 is cut off and the light screen is moved to admit more natural light. The increase in natural light is hardly sufficient to cut the pump back on. However the increased natural light plus a small increment of additional light as the sun comes from behind a cloud will be sufficient to cut the pump on and move the screen 57 back to partially shade light sensing element 49.

Instead of feeding current into a nightlight lamp as illustrated in FIG. 4, current may be fed back into the circuit of the light sensing and switching apparatus to aid in reversing the switch. However, in this proposed arrangement the benefits of the automatic nightlighter and the visual indicator are lost.

Under some conditions the apparatus described herein may "cycle" and may open and close the circuit to the light intensifying apparatus rather rapidly. This condition may be remedied in various ways such as by placing a time delay element in the circuit to the light intensifying apparatus to delay the dimming or brightning of the light from the light intensifying apparatus.

If desired a simple time switch may be connected in the pump circuit to limit operation to certain hours of the day. For example, inasmuch as solar input is greater near noon the time switch may be set to limit pump operation to hours such as 9:00 a.m. to 3:30 p.m. or 8:00 to 4:30 p.m. *

Jan. 3, 1967 H. E. THOMASON **3,295,591**

APPARATUS FOR COOLING AND SOLAR HEATING A HOUSE

*

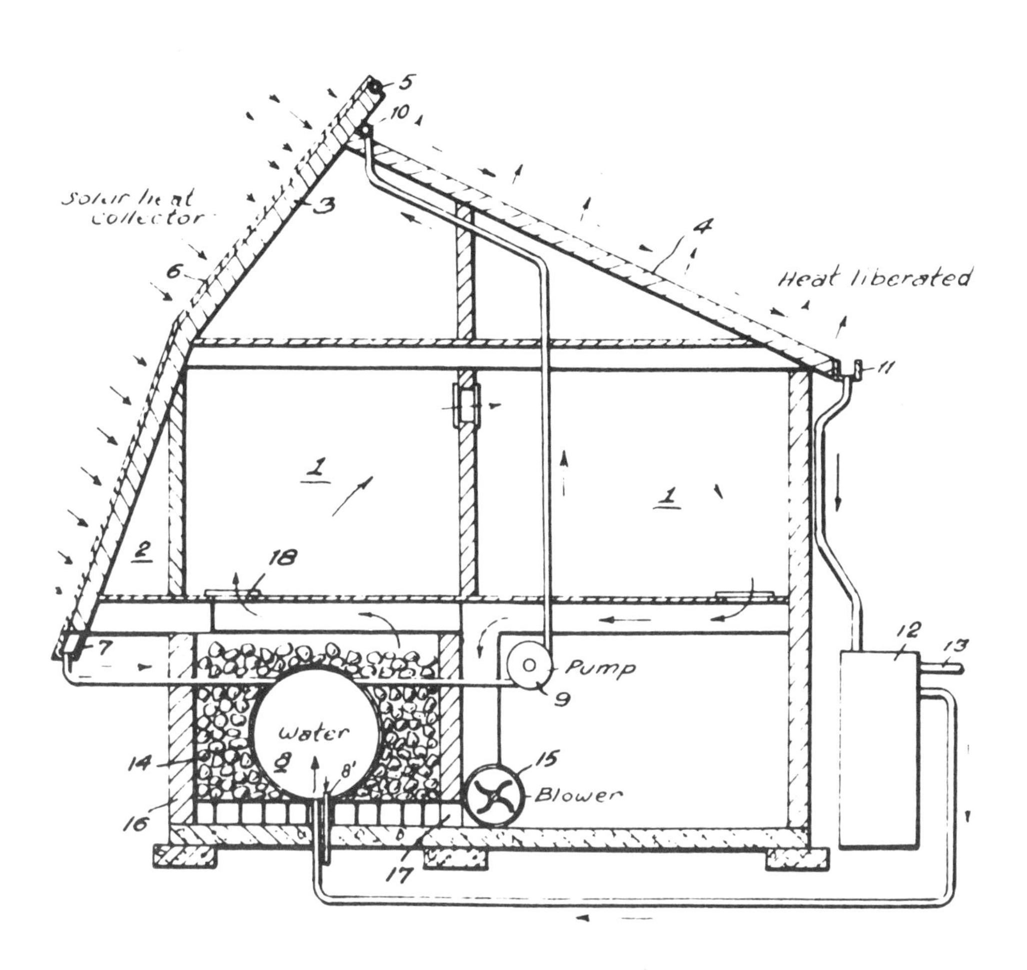

INVENTOR

Harry E. Thomason

3,295,591
APPARATUS FOR COOLING AND SOLAR HEATING A HOUSE
Harry E. Thomason, District Heights, Md.
(7354 Walker Mill Road SE., Washington, D.C. 20027)
*

The present invention relates primarily to cooling apparatus, including means for storing "coolness" (or heat). This permits the discharge of heat, preferably at night, and storage of "coolness" so produced to cool a home during the hot day. The heat may be discharged from the roof of a building, for example. Other uses for the apparatus are apparent.

The storage apparatus may be used in a reverse fashion to store heat produced by a solar heat collector if desired. The solar heat collector warms the storage apparatus on cold sunny days to warm a building, such as a home, on cold nights and during cloudy weather.

In the drawing the single figure illustrates the invention as applied to a home.

The home may have living space **1**, closet area **2**, a solar heat collector **3** and a roof section **4**.

The solar heat collector may be the simple, low-cost and highly efficient type disclosed in Patents Nos. 3,145,-707 and 3,215,134, or may be another type. Such patented collector has a perforated distributor pipe **5** and a transparent covering **6**. Beneath the transparent covering is a blackened sheet (not shown) over which water flows. The sun warms the sheet and as the water flows thereover it becomes heated. The heated water is collected in gutter **7** for return to tank **8** from whence it flows through **8'** and is pumped back to distributor manifold **5** by a pump and piping (not illustrated).

The heated water in tank **8** warms the tank walls and non-fluid material **14**, such as stones, cans of heat-of-fusion salts, or such, in storage bin **16**. The warmed water, tank and non-fluid storage material store large quantities of heat during sunny days to warm the home on cold nights and cloudy days during the winter.

For summertime air conditioning the warmer water from near the top of tank **8** may be pumped to the rooftop by pump **9** and distributed by perforated pipe **10**. As the water flows down the roof, preferably during the cool night, it is cooled by radiation to the night sky, evaporation to the surrounding air or actual contact with cool night air, or by all of these phenomena. The cooled water is collected by gutter **11** from whence it preferably flows through sediment trap-automatic rainwater makeup device **12** back to the bottom of tank **8**. The cooled water in tank **8** cools the walls of the tank and the non-fluid material therearound, thereby storing "coolness" in the water and non-fluid material.

When the air in area **1** becomes too warm a thermostat starts blower **15** to circulate air from area **1** through the cooled non-fluid material **14** and around cooled tank **8**. This cools the air. The cooled air returns to area **1**, by way of opening **18**, to cool area **1**.

Water from rain, snow or the like flows into tanks **8** and **12** until they are filled to the level of overflow **13** through which excess water may flow to the lawn or drainage ditch.

The fluid-filled tank **8** and non-fluid material **14** are preferably supported by a masonry distributor and ductwork system of bricks, building blocks or such as described and claimed in U.S. Patent No. 3,254,702, referred to above. Air from blower **15** is introduced to substantially air-tight, insulated bin **16** through one or more openings **17**. The air passes through the masonry system, across the bin, up and out through cracks between the pieces of masonry. The rising air currents spiral up through the non-fluid material **14** and around tank **8** in heat exchange relationship with the large surface areas of material **14** and **8**. If these materials have been heated, the air is warmed. If they have been cooled, the air is cooled. The air, thus heated for wintertime or cooled for summertime, is returned to area **1** through one or more openings **18**. No refrigeration compressor is required, pump **9** requiring only about ¼ H.P. to bring about the cooling function in a typical installation as described in the "Solar Energy" journal, vol. IV, November 4, October 1960, pages 11–19.

Simplicity and low cost operation, high efficiency and low cost of the apparatus are salient features of the invention. *

Oct. 14, 1947. R. R. HAWKINS 2,428,876

AIR CONDITIONING SYSTEM FOR COOLING OR HEATING

*

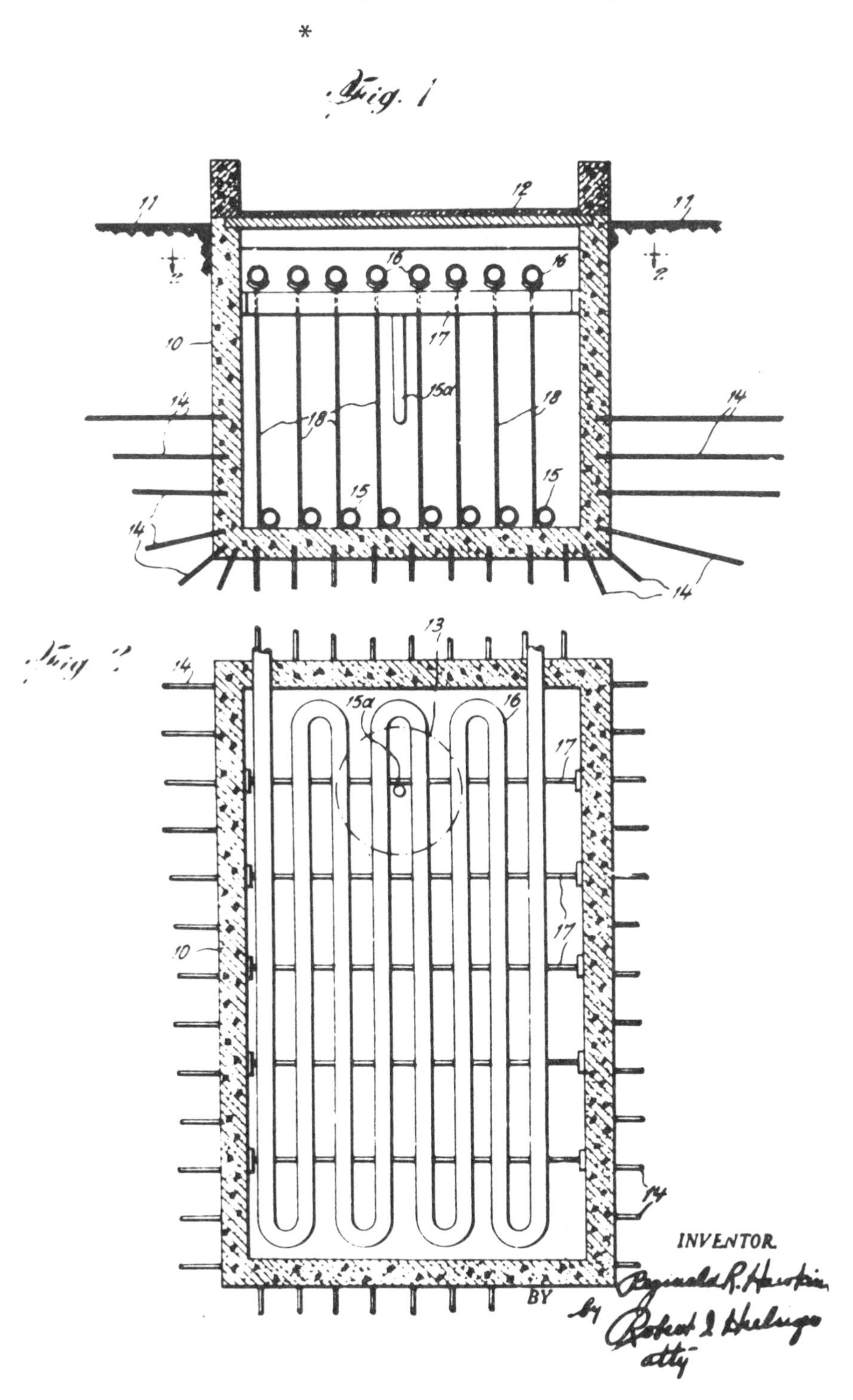

Oct. 14, 1947. R. R. HAWKINS 2,428,876

AIR CONDITIONING SYSTEM FOR COOLING OR HEATING

*

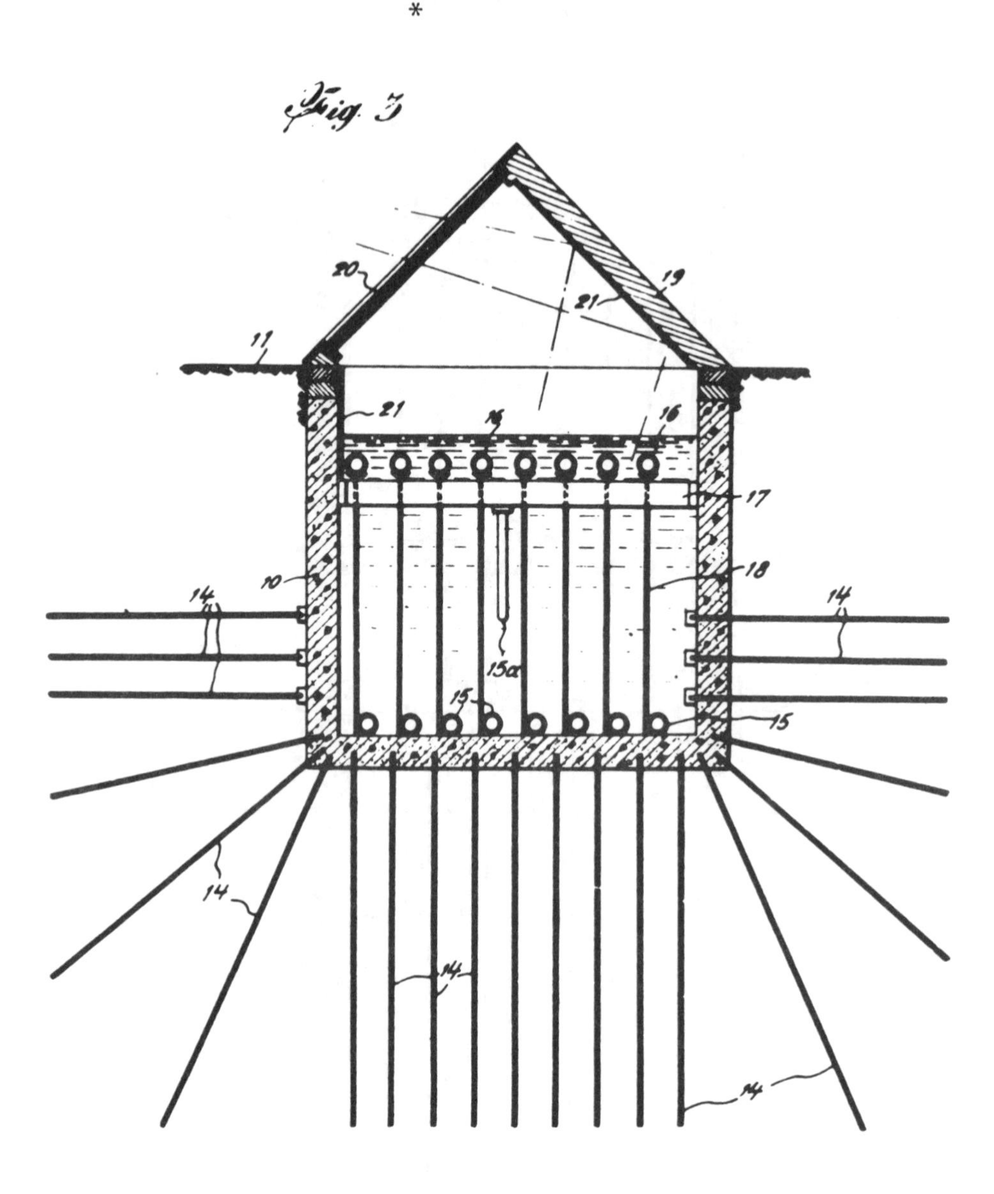

INVENTOR.
Reginald R. Hawkins
BY
Robert I. Hulsizer
atty.

Oct. 14, 1947. R. R. HAWKINS 2,428,876

AIR CONDITIONING SYSTEM FOR COOLING OR HEATING

*

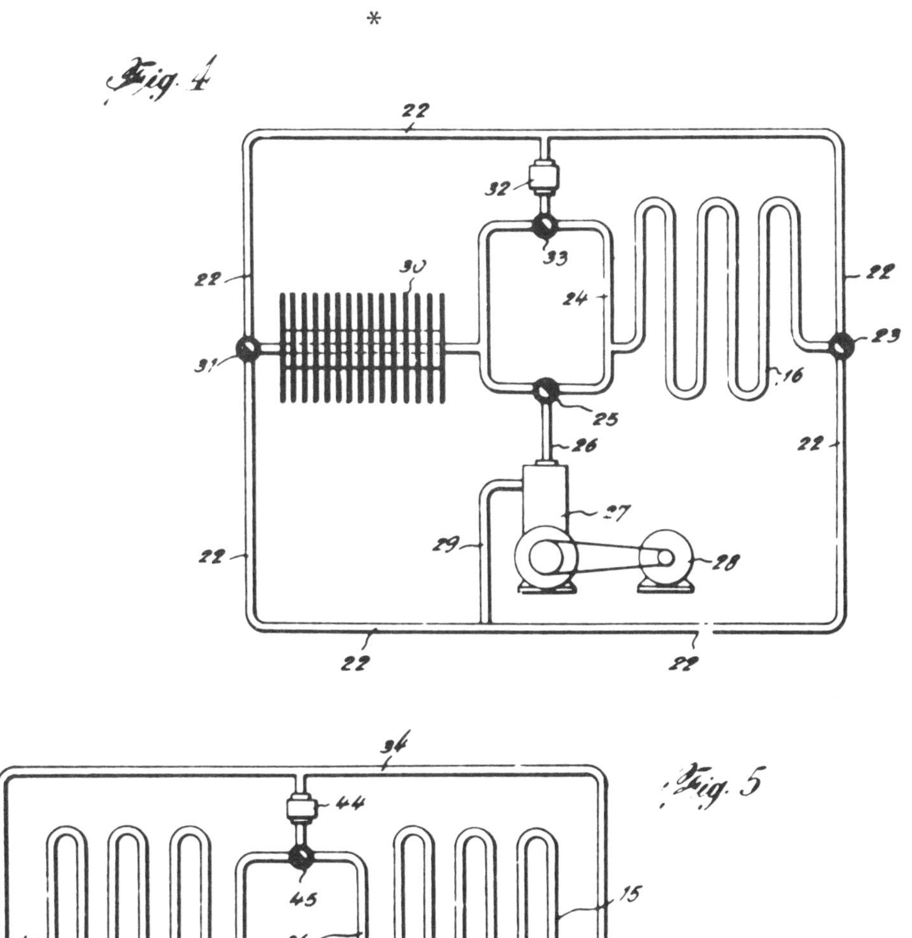

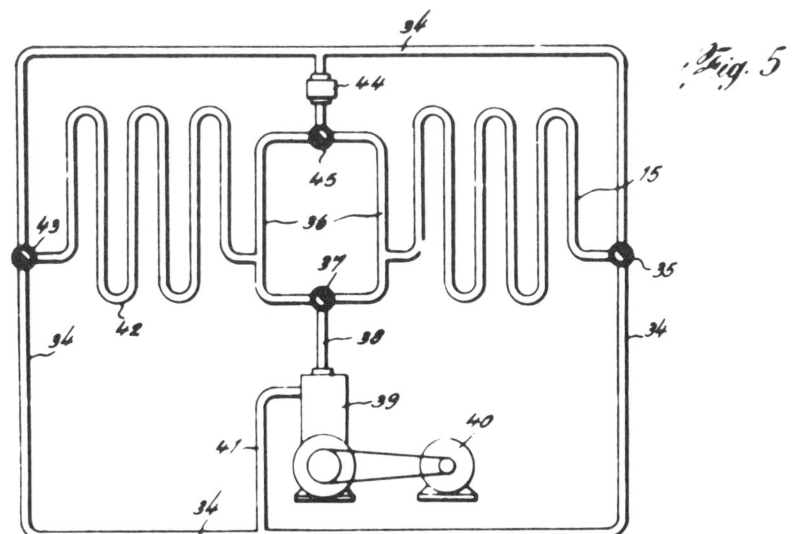

INVENTOR
Reginald R. Hawkins
BY
Robert I. Hulsizer
atty.

Oct. 14, 1947. R. R. HAWKINS 2,428,876

AIR CONDITIONING SYSTEM FOR COOLING OR HEATING

*

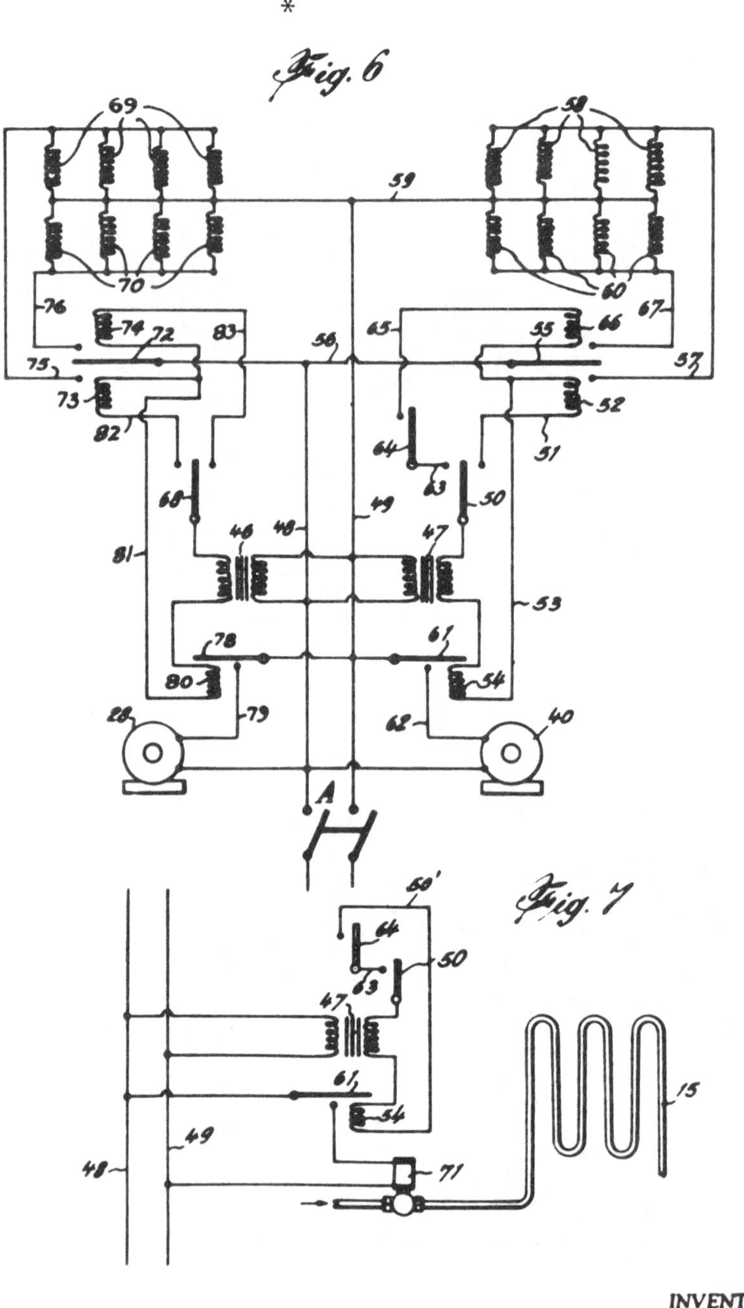

INVENTOR
Reginald R. Hawkins
BY
Robert Mulaiger
ATTORNEY.

UNITED STATES PATENT OFFICE

2,428,876

AIR-CONDITIONING SYSTEM FOR COOLING OR HEATING

Reginald R. Hawkins, Tuckahoe, N. Y.

*

This invention relates to new and useful improvements in heating and, or, air-conditioning systems, and apparatus employed therein. It is especially adapted, but is not limited to, the type of such system that may be used either for heating or cooling, which type is generally known as the reverse-cycle refrigeration, or reverse-cycle air-conditioning type. The main feature of the invention is the provision in such systems of a special type of reservoir containing water or other suitable liquid and adapted to store considerable quantities of heat for use when the system is operating to heat the thing or space it is designed to heat and to absorb and dissipate considerable quantities of heat when the system is operating to cool the space or thing it is designed to cool.

One object of the invention is to provide a reservoir containing water or other suitable liquid, from which useful quantities of heat may be obtained by cooling the liquid, even to the extent of freezing it.

A further object of the invention is to provide an efficient and economical means for warming and thawing the frozen liquid in the reservoir.

A still further object is to provide a reservoir containing water or other suitable liquid, adapted to absorb considerable quantities of heat when the system of which it is a part is operating as a cooling system.

Yet a further object of the invention is to provide means for economically and automatically regulating the temperature of the reservoir including its contained liquid so that it will function as desired when the system of which it is a part is operating to heat, and, or, when it is operating to cool.

Another object of the invention is to provide a form of reservoir into which heat will be conducted readily from the surrounding soil when the temperature of the liquid within the reservoir falls below the temperature of the soil and, or, from which heat will be readily conducted into the surrounding soil when the temperature of the liquid in the reservoir rises above the temperature of the soil.

A further object of the invention is to provide a reservoir of the type described, the liquid which remains in the reservoir and does not circulate in the refrigeration units and tubing of the heating and, or, cooling system.

Yet another object of the invention is to provide a form of reservoir in which the radiation of the sun may be utilized to add heat to the reservoir.

Further and more specific objects, features, and advantages will more clearly appear from a consideration of the following specification especially when taken in connection with the accompanying drawings which form part of the specification and which illustrate present preferred forms which the invention may assume.

It is believed desirable first to describe the drawings and then to describe the preferred forms shown in the drawings to acquaint the reader with what has been constructed to solve the problems, and thereafter to state the problems and ways and means whereby they have been solved to meet the various conditions and requirements encountered in practical systems.

In the drawings, therefore,

Fig. 1 is a vertical cross section through the improved reservoir of a form to be used beneath the cellar of a building;

Fig. 2 is a plan view thereof.

Fig. 3 is a vertical cross section of a similar reservoir modified to take advantage of the heat of the sun;

Fig. 4 is a somewhat diagrammatic representation of the piping and related connections between the upper tank coil and the main conditioning system.

Fig. 5 is a similar view showing the connections between the lower tank coil and an outdoor radiating and, or, absorbing surface;

Fig. 6 is an electric circuit diagram for the system when it is designed for both heating and cooling under automatic thermostatic control and when the lower tank coil is part of a reverse-cycle system which employs outdoor air as a source of heat when the tank contents must be heated and as an absorber of heat when the tank contents must be cooled; and

Fig. 7 is a circuit diagram showing the electric and piping connections for the right hand, or lower tank coil side of Fig. 6, when the lower coil is connected to an outside spring or water main.

One of the basic features of the invention concerns a reservoir shown in Figs. 1 and 2, in the form of a tank 10 with walls of concrete or other suitable material which is sunk into the soil 11 and, in the form shown in these figures, is supposed to be disposed beneath the cellar floor 12 of a building. Preferably in this case, a manhole cover 13 is provided to permit access to the tank from the cellar. At 15a is shown a tube or container of metal or other suitable material adapted to support a thermostat in thermal contact with the contents of the tank.

In order to permit the reservoir to absorb additional heat from the surrounding soil or to dissipate heat thereto depending upon whether the system is working on a heating or a cooling cycle, the tank 10 is provided with heat conductors 14 in the form of metal or other suitable material, preferably as rods which may be embedded in the tank wall or may terminate adjacent to the walls or may extend therethrough to the interior surface thereof as may be desired. These conductors enable the heat of the surrounding soil to be conducted into the liquid of the tank and also permit the heat of the tank liquid to be conducted to the surrounding soil in reverse cycle operation.

Disposed in the tank 10 are two coils 15 and

16 respectively at the bottom and top of the tank. These coils are connected outside the tank to suitable apparatus as will be later described. The lower coil 15 is supported on or near the bottom of the tank and the upper coil 16 is positioned near the top of the tank, preferably on cross bars 17 as shown. The upper and lower coils are connected by heat-conducting elements 18.

In the form of tank shown in Fig. 3, the tank is of the same general type as that shown in the previous figures but the top is open, or at least not covered beneath the cellar floor, and may have a half roof 19 with another half roof 20 of double-paned or heat-insulated glass directed toward the point of maximum average solar radiation so as to permit the rays of the sun to be directed into the tank directly or by reflection from reflecting surfaces 21 on the inner side of the half roof 19 and wall 10 as shown. In this way the tank may be disposed in the yard near the building and the upper and lower coils in the tank may be connected by insulated piping in any suitable manner to the conditioning system.

In Fig. 4 the piping connections between the upper coil 16 and the main conditioning system are somewhat schematically shown and in which the coil is connected at one end to pipe 22 with a two-way valve 23 disposed at the junction of the pipe with the coil as shown. In the figure this pipe 22 extends entirely around the enclosed apparatus as shown. The other end of the coil 16 is connected to the right limb of a closed pipe 24. On the lower limb of the pipe 24 is a two-way valve 25 connected to pipe 26 leading to a compressor 27 driven by a motor 28. This compressor is connected by pipe 29 to the lower limb of pipe 22 as shown. A heat exchange element 30 is disposed between the left limb of pipe 24 and a two-way valve 31 disposed in the left limb of pipe 22. An expansion valve 32 is disposed between the upper limb of pipe 22 and a two-way valve 33 in the upper limb of pipe 24.

Considering Fig. 5, the lower coil 15 is shown connected at one end to a pipe 34 through a two-way valve 35. The pipe 34 extends entirely around the apparatus as shown. The other end of the coil 15 is connected to the right limb of a closed pipe 36. A two-way valve 37 is disposed in the lower limb of the pipe 36 and connects by pipe 38 to a compressor 39 which is driven by a motor 40. The compressor is connected also by pipe 41 to the lower limb of the pipe 34. The left hand limb of the pipe 36 is connected to an outdoor radiator or heat exchanger 42, the other end of which is connected to a two-way valve 43 disposed in the left-hand limb of pipe 34. The upper limb of pipe 34 is connected to an expansion valve 44, the other side of which is connected to a two-way valve 45 disposed in the upper limb of pipe 36.

Referring to Fig. 4 with the four valves set as shown, and understanding that when they are moved, they are moved together by means to be later set forth, the circulation in the system will be from the right end of coil 16, through valve 23 through the lower limb of pipe 22, through pipe 29 and compressor 27, through pipe 26, valve 25, through left limb of pipe 24, through air-conditioning element 30, valve 31, left-hand limb of pipe 22, upper limb of pipe 22, through expansion valve 32, right limb of pipe 24, to the other end of the coil 16.

If the valves are then moved for the reverse circulation, then the circulatory path will be as follows: From right end of coil 16, through valve 23, up through right limb of pipe 22, through upper limb of pipe 22, through the expansion valve 32, through left hand limb of pipe 24, through the air-conditioning element 30, down through left-hand limb of pipe 22, through the lower limb of pipe 22, through pipe 29 to the compressor, through pipe 26, through valve 25, through the right hand limb of pipe 24 to the other end of the coil 16.

Referring to Fig. 5, with the valves set as shown, the circulation will be as follows:

From right end of coil 15, through valve 35, down right limb of pipe 34, through lower limb of pipe 34, through pipe 41, through the compressor 39, through pipe 38, through valve 37, through left limb of pipe 36, through the outside radiator element 42, through valve 43, up left limb of pipe 34, through the upper limb of pipe 34, through expansion valve 44, through valve 45, through right limb of pipe 36 to the other end of coil 15. Movement of the valves for reverse circulation will cause the following path to be taken:

From right end of coil 15, up right limb of pipe 34, through upper limb of pipe 34, through expansion valve 44, through left limb of pipe 36, through the outside radiator element 42, through valve 43, down left limb of pipe 34, through lower limb of pipe 34, through pipe 41, through compressor 39, through pipe 38, through valve 37, through right limb of pipe 36, to other end of coil 15.

In Fig. 6 is shown a complete control circuit for a reverse cycle system where the lower coil is connected as shown in Fig. 5 to an outside radiating surface or the like. In this figure, when the main switch A is closed, it will be observed that two transformers 46 and 47 are disposed across the power lines 48 and 49. The secondary coil of transformer 47 is in series with a thermostat arm 50 which being disposed in tube 15a is in thermal contact with the liquid in the reservoir and swings right and left as the temperature of the liquid goes up or down respectively. When it swings right, it contacts a wire 51 connected to coil 52 of a relay switch connected by wire 53 to another switch coil 54 which in turn is connected back to the other end of the secondary of transformer 47. When coil 52 is energized, switch arm 55 is pulled down, making contact from one side of power line over wire 56 with a wire 57 connected to one set of valve-operating coils 58 which are connected to the other side of the power line by wire 59. These coils 58 are in any suitable manner connected to move the valves shown in Fig. 5 in one direction, and another set 60 are similarly connected to throw the valves in the other direction. When coil 54 is energized as above, it pulls down switch arm 61 to make contact with the power line over wire 62 for the motor 40 of the compressor which then starts up.

When the arm 50 of the tank thermostat swings to the left as the tank temperature drops it will ultimately contact with wire 63 connected to the arm 64 of another thermostat which is disposed in the walls of the building or the soil outside the tank, or at some other suitable point to be influenced by the seasonal outdoor temperature. Therefore, when the tank temperature has dropped sufficiently and the outside temperature has also dropped a predetermined amount, this second thermostat arm 64 will also close a circuit to wire 65 leading to coil 66 which will then pull switch arm 55 upwardly and make contact with power to wire 67 to energize the valve-operating coils 60 and turn the valves to the reverse position and at the same time again over wire 53 cause the operation of the compressor as before. It will be seen that when the tank temperature rises, the valves are operated and the compressor starts to work, but when the tank temperature drops beyond a definite amount, whether the valves are reversed and the compressor started depends not only on the tank temperature but also on the condition of the outside temperature as determined by the position of the thermostat arm 64.

Referring to the left side of Fig. 6, the transformer 46 is connected to an arm 68 of a thermostat which is disposed in the house itself and this arm swings right when the temperature rises, and left when the temperature drops.

When the house temperature rises above a predetermined setting of the thermostat, arm 68 moves to the right and ultimately makes contact with wire 83 connected to coil 74. When coil 74 is energized, switch arm 72 is pulled upwardly making contact from one side of the power line over wire 56 with a wire 76 connected to one set of valve-operating coils 70 which are connected to the other side of the power line by wire 59. These coils 70 are in any suitable manner connected to move the valves shown in Fig. 4 in one direction, and another set of coils 69 are connected to throw the valves in the other direction. The contact of arm 68 with wire 83 also energizes coil 80 by connecting it through the coil 74 and wire 81 to the secondary wiring of the transformer 46. When coil 80 is energized, it pulls down switch arm 78 to make contact with the power line through wire 79 to the motor 28 of the compressor, which then starts up. When the house temperature drops below a predetermined setting of the thermostat, arm 68 moves to the left and ultimately makes contact with wire 82 connected to coil 73. When coil 73 is energized, switch arm 72 is pulled down making contact from one side of the power line over wire 56 with a wire 75 connected to one set of valve-operating coils 69 which are connected to the other side of the power line by wire 59. These coils 69 are in any suitable manner connected to move the valves shown in Fig. 4 opposite to the movement caused by coils 70. The contact of arm 68 with wire 82 also energizes coil 80 by connecting it through coil 73 and wire 81 to the secondary wiring of the transformer 46. When coil 80 is energized, it pulls down switch arm 78 to make contact with the power line through wire 79 to the motor 28 of the compressor, which then starts up.

With reference to Fig. 7, this diagram illustrates the connections for the lower coil 15 when it is connected merely to a well or spring and this water is to be allowed to run through the coil at definite times. In this case, as is apparent, the two thermostats are the same as in the left half of Fig. 6 but the connections now cause the energization of the coil of a magnetic valve 71 to open the connection to the well or spring and allow water to run through coil 15, the other end of which in this case may be connected to a drain or any suitable outlet.

Having thus described in detail several preferred forms of the invention, some of the general problems before the engineer who has to design a reverse cycle refrigeration system for heating and cooling may be discussed in order to illustrate the utility of the invention. There are two main problems when the source of heat is outdoor air. The first one is that as the weather gets colder the demand for heat rises but the heat content of the outdoor air diminishes. The second one is that as soon as the outdoor temperature drops below freezing, ice gradually forms on the surface of the outdoor evaporating element; and of course ice reduces the efficiency of the evaporator. Because of these difficulties, engineers always use ground water as a source of heat if it is available in sufficient quantity at a high enough temperature. Here, again, there are several difficulties. First, warm ground water is not universally available in large enough quantities. Second, there is the problem of disposing of the water after it has been cooled. An isolated plant could discharge its cooled water into the sewer, but if the reverse cycle systems were common, many plants could not thus dispose of waste water unless sewer systems were reconstructed. A third problem is the relatively low amount of heat available in a gallon of ground water. Take water at 50 degrees F. and cool it to 33 degrees F. and only 17 B. t. u. are obtained per pound. However, take water which has been cooled to 32 degrees F. and continue to cool it until it freezes to ice at 32 degrees F. and 80 B. t. u. per pound are liberated. Scientists and engineers have realized for many years that heating systems could be built to utilize the heat obtainable by freezing water if some way could be worked out for economical disposal of the ice thus formed.

My invention provides a means for utilizing the relatively large amount of heat obtainable by freezing water without having to dispose of the ice mechanically; provides means of heat storage which offers a large heat storage capacity at relatively low expense because no insulation against the escape of heat is required; and provides means for employing the heat storage capacity of the soil or rock or ground water in which the heat storage reservoir is built and by which it is partly surrounded. When the reverse cycle system is being used for heating, heat tends to be withdrawn both from the heat storage reservoir proper and from the surrounding medium. When the reverse cycle system is being used for cooling, heat tends to be absorbed by the water in the heat storage reservoir and by the surrounding material.

It is apparent that the heating and cooling system above illustrated in the drawings is of the type in which the compressor and motor unit or units operate at about maximum capacity when they are in operation, the storage reservoir serving to smooth out the peaks of the demand for heating or cooling, as the case may be.

The main part of the invention is a tank designed to hold a sufficient quantity of water in storage to meet, for a predetermined period of time, the heating or cooling demands of the system of which it is a part. Preferably this reservoir or tank will be constructed under the cellar of a house. In building a new house, for example, the excavation for the cellar will be made the required number of feet deeper, the tank will be constructed within the excavation and floored over except for a manhole. Thus, the cellar will have substantially the same appearance as a conventional cellar. However, the tank can easily be constructed under a house which has already been built. Also, the tank may be constructed elsewhere in some suitable spot adjacent the house. In regions where there is considerable winter sun, it may be desirable to build the tank in a location where considerable sun will fall upon it. Such a tank has been shown in Fig. 3 of the drawings. An outside location is feasible for the tank because it can be easily connected with the building to be conditioned by pipes run through insulated conduits in the ground. When the tank is constructed under a building it is not necessary to insulate it thermally because in heating, the water is frozen to remove the heat, hence it may be at any temperature within the range at which it is liquid. It will tend to remain at the temperature of the surrounding soil. When the system is cooling the house rather than heating it, it is necessary only that the water in the tank be at a temperature lower than the temperature of the compressed refrigerant, which temperature may be in the neighborhood of 100 degrees F. Therefore, no thermal insulation is necessary for the tank to carry out its function in weather when the system is cooling rather than heating the house. However, when the tank is built outside the building to take advantage of the sun's heating or for some other reason, it will be desirable to insulate the portions above ground and in the ground above the normal frost line in any suitable way that will reduce heat loss to the atmosphere. In a system designed for summer cooling as well as winter heating, curtains or doors adapted to reflect and retard the ingression of solar radiation and heat may be provided to cover the glass side of the tank roof structure in warm weather.

Another important feature of the tank constituting part of this invention is that it is connected with the surrounding soil or rock together with the ground water in said soil or rock by means of heat conductors. These conducting elements may be metal rods of suitable composition which are driven into the surrounding soil while the tank is under construction. In favorable soil formations these rods increase the heat capacity of the tank to a very substantial extent, hence a smaller tank than usual may be built and yet have the heat dissipating and absorbing capacity of a much larger tank without the rods.

A novel feature of the tank and its furnishings are the supports and conducting rods 18, which are made of metal or other material of good heat-conducting qualities. In addition to wholly or partly supporting the upper coil 16, they provide continuous heat conduction from the upper coil to the lower and vice versa and also distribute heat throughout the fluid contents of the tank, tending to counteract the tendency of undisturbed fluids to lie in layers, a warm layer over a substantially colder one.

Another advantage of the tank is that the liquid therein except for evaporation does not pass into or out of the tank during normal operation of the system. This condition makes it possible to stabilize the tank contents chemically in such ways as to retard the growth of bacteria and the corrosion of the tubing and other fixtures in the tank.

Also under certain conditions, for example in a system installed where true summer cooling load will be approximately equivalent to the winter heating load, the reservoir may be designed to freeze the soil surrounding it while the fluid within the tank remains in a liquid state. This result can be obtained by using in the tank a liquid substance with a freezing point below the freezing point of water, or by dissolving a suitable substance in water and using the solution in the tank. When enough heat is extracted from the tank liquid, heat will be conducted into the reservoir by the heat conducting elements that extend into the soil from the tank. Gradually as heat continues to be extracted from the soil, it will freeze. Then when the system, in response to changed weather conditions, reverses to operate as a cooling system, heat will pass outward from the tank into the soil and gradually thaw it. Auxiliary systems of heating and cooling the liquid in the tank, described elsewhere in this specification, may be used. When the auxiliary system employs water, or waste fluids, as the source of heat, it is designed to discharge it before it has been cooled to the temperature where it would freeze in the coil.

It can be understood that in average installations auxiliary heating or cooling of the tank contents will be necessary only in extremes of weather. The passage of heat along the heat-conducting rods from the surrounding soil into the tank will provide sufficient heat for mild weather conditions. The same is true when the system is cooling the building. The absorption of heat from the tank contents by the surrounding earth will be sufficient except during periods of prolonged hot weather. However, one of the advantages of my tank is that it makes practical economical means of auxiliary heating during times of severe conditions.

The simplest means of auxiliary heating is a coil disposed on or near the bottom of the tank, one end of the coil being connected to a source of water under pressure and the other end being connected to a suitable drain. No harm will be done in situations where water from a spring or artesian well is available at little or no expense by letting the water flow through this coil continually. That is to say, a continuous flow of water through the bottom coil fits in with the normal operation and function of the tank and its contents. The reason is that when the system is heating, the contents of the tank are normally only a little above the freezing point, and along the upper coil in the tank, are actually at the freezing point; and when the system is cooling, the contents of the tank may be at a temperature anywhere between the freezing point of water and a temperature a few degrees lower than the compressed refrigerant circulating in the upper coil 16. Where water must be pumped or purchased, a means of turning the pump on and off, or of opening and closing the valve leading to the supply main is provided as shown in Fig. 7.

In some installations, considerable auxiliary heat may be available in the sewage and other fluid wastes from the building. These wastes may be caused to flow through tubing submerged in the tank in such a way that they will give up a portion of their contained heat before they are discharged into the sewer. Where the temperature of the wastes remains at a suitable low level in hot weather, they may be used as a cooling medium also. In situations where the waste temperature would be too high during the summer, a hand valve and a bypass are used to shunt the wastes around the tank in warm weather. Also, where the temperature of waste waters is likely to vary, and a sufficient quantity of heating or cooling capacity is available to justify some expense in order to utilize it, automatic means of controlling the shunting may be installed. This means of affecting the tank temperature is not shown in the drawings, but the construction is obvious to anyone skilled in the art.

There will be a number of installations, especially when the system is installed in city dwellings, where sufficient auxiliary heating and cooling is not available, either in the form of inexpensive water or in the form of waste waters. In such situations, the outdoor air is used as a source of auxiliary heating and cooling. When the system is heating the building and therefore withdrawing heat from the tank contents, the tank thermostat controls the operation of an auxiliary reverse cycle refrigerator in such a way that when auxiliary heat is needed to keep the temperature of the tank contents above freezing, the auxiliary system goes into operation, removing heat from the outdoor air and adding it to the contents of the tank. It is obvious that in a properly designed system, the auxiliary system can be made small in comparison to the size of the main reverse cycle system because the auxiliary system need not be designed to deliver a large amount of heat per hour but may instead be designed to deliver a relatively small amount per hour and operate over long periods of time when the weather is severe. Since the auxiliary system is relatively small, a proportionately larger outdoor heat radiator or exchanger surface may be used. When a large surface in relation to the capacity of the compressor may be used, there is less loss of efficiency due to ice formation.

In general, a reverse cycle system designed for complete heating of a dwelling is more than large enough to take care of the cooling needs during hot weather because the difference in temperature levels in the winter is greater than in the summer. For the same reason, the tank and its contents will need less auxiliary cooling under average conditions than auxiliary heating. After a winter's operation, the tank, its contents, and the mass of soil adjacent to the heat-conducting rods will normally be at a temperature only a little above freezing. When the outdoor temperature makes it desirable to cool rather than to warm the building, the contents of the tank will then absorb heat from the main reverse cycle plant. This absorbed heat will pass out along the heat-conducting rods until the mass of matter surrounding the rods has reached a temperature level equal to the temperature of the tank contents. After this occurs, auxiliary cooling may be necessary, and it is provided by means of the bottom coil 15. Where cool water is available, it is circulated through the bottom coil. Where cool fluid wastes are available, they are passed through the bottom coil or through a third set of tubing that may be disposed in the tank. Where neither is available, an auxiliary reverse cycle refrigerator absorbs heat from the tank contents and dissipates it to the outdoor air. This latter action is controlled by thermostats and other automatic devices as mentioned above and as shown in the drawings.

It is obvious that when flowing water or waste fluids are used to add or to subtract heat from the tank contents, the lower tank coil 16 may serve to conduct these liquids, but when outdoor air is used as a source and/or an absorber of heat, then coil 16 is either a condenser or an evaporator, depending on whether the reservoir is being heated or cooled, in a refrigeration system.

The general operation of a complete heating and cooling system is set forth and constructively described above with respect to the drawings. When the building interior falls below a predetermined temperature, the thermostatic element 68 swings to the left and closes the contact to the indicated circuit whereby the motor 28 is started and the upper coils 69 are operated to throw the valves (see left side of Fig. 6). This valve circuit need be maintained for only a sufficiently long period of time to place the valves in the desired position, which is the position for heating.

The valves shown in Fig. 4 having thus been set for heating the dwelling, the compressor creates a partial vacuum in coil 16. The refrigerant then passes through the expansion valve 32 into the coil 16. The refrigerant, then absorbs heat through the walls of the coil 16, which heat comes from the water in the tank, especially the portion of it which is in contact with the coil 16 and the heat conducting supports 17 and 18. The gaseous refrigerant, having absorbed heat, is drawn through the compressor 27 where the compression raises the temperature to a suitable degree. From the compressor it passes through the heat exchanger 30 where by means of suitable fans, fins, or other suitable elements, depending upon the heat transfer system used to transfer heat to the air of the building, a portion of its heat is given up and it is cooled to a temperature at which it becomes a liquid.

The temperature of the evaporating refrigerant in the coil 16 causes the water in contact with the coil 16 and in contact with the supporting and heat conducting elements to freeze. However, this ice tends to thaw due to heat reaching it from the heat conducting supports 17 and 18 and from the unfrozen water in the tank. During this process of thawing the ice lowers the temperature of the tank water, which is in contact with the tank thermostat 50, to a predetermined temperature—32 degrees F. in most installations but lower in plants designed to obtain heat by freezing the soil adjacent to the reservoir—the thermostatic element swings to the left and makes circuit through wire 63 with thermostat arm 64. This is another thermostat which is located in a suitable place in the building wall or in the soil. This thermostat is adapted to maintain a closed contact when swung to the left (shown in Fig. 6, right side) during the season when heat is normally required, but to open that contact during the season when cooling is required. Preferably it will be attached to the inner surface of an outer wall which has a moderate degree of heat conductivity and is not exposed to the sun. It can not be exposed directly to the outdoor air because it would then prevent the operation of the auxiliary tank heating system during abnormally warm winter weather, at which times, of course, the auxiliary heating system must nevertheless operate if the temperature of the tank contents is below the predetermined level.

It is clear that if the contact is closed by thermostat arm 64 swinging to the left, then the closing of contact to wire 63 by arm 58 swinging to the left energizes the coils 54 and 66. As is obvious, the energization of these coils starts the motor 40 of the compressor 39 and operates the valves shown in Fig. 5 to correctly position the valves in the auxiliary system so that heat is extracted from the outdoor air and transferred to the contents of the tank by means of the bottom coil 15, which, in this operation, acts as a condenser.

It is believed obvious from a study of the disclosure and the above description how opposite conditions will cause opposite effects in both the main system and the auxiliary system because of the operation of the thermostats described together with their attached electrical circuits. Heating of the tank during summer weather is prevented by the thermostat arm 64 not making its contact. Even if a prolonged spell of cool weather necessitates the use of the main system for heating, under average conditions, the amount of heat withdrawn from the tank and its surrounding mass will not be large enough to make heating of the tank necessary. Therefore the thermostat represented by the arm 64 is employed to prevent the operation of the auxiliary heating system during short spells of cool weather in the summer, electing instead to freeze a larger than usual proportion of the contents of the tank. This thermostat is preferably attached to the inner surface of the outer wall of the building; furthermore, its housing may be constructed of brick or other suitable material in such a way as to provide the right amount of lag behind dropping outdoor temperatures and the right amount of evening of fluctuations in outdoor temperatures. A similar lag could be obtained by the use of a timing element or mechanism in connection with the thermostat represented by the arm 58, or by burying the thermostat represented by the arm 64 in the soil surrounding the tank.

The elements that support the upper coil 18 in the tank are constructed of heat conducting material. They may have conducting fins attached to increase their efficiency. Their purpose, in addition to supporting the upper tube system, is to tend to make the temperature throughout the tank uniform. It is well known that hot water and cold water will lie in layers in a tank if the water is not disturbed or caused to circulate. They will diffuse or mix slowly but the rate is much too slow for efficient functioning of the reservoir herein described. The heat conducting elements tend to distribute the heat evenly throughout the tank. Also, since they are attached to the lower coil 15, they also tend to conduct heat directly from it to the coil at the top of the tank; and in cooling they tend to conduct heat from the latter element directly into the lower coil. *

Nov. 9, 1954 L. MARCHANT ET AL 2,693,939

HEATING AND COOLING SYSTEM

* *

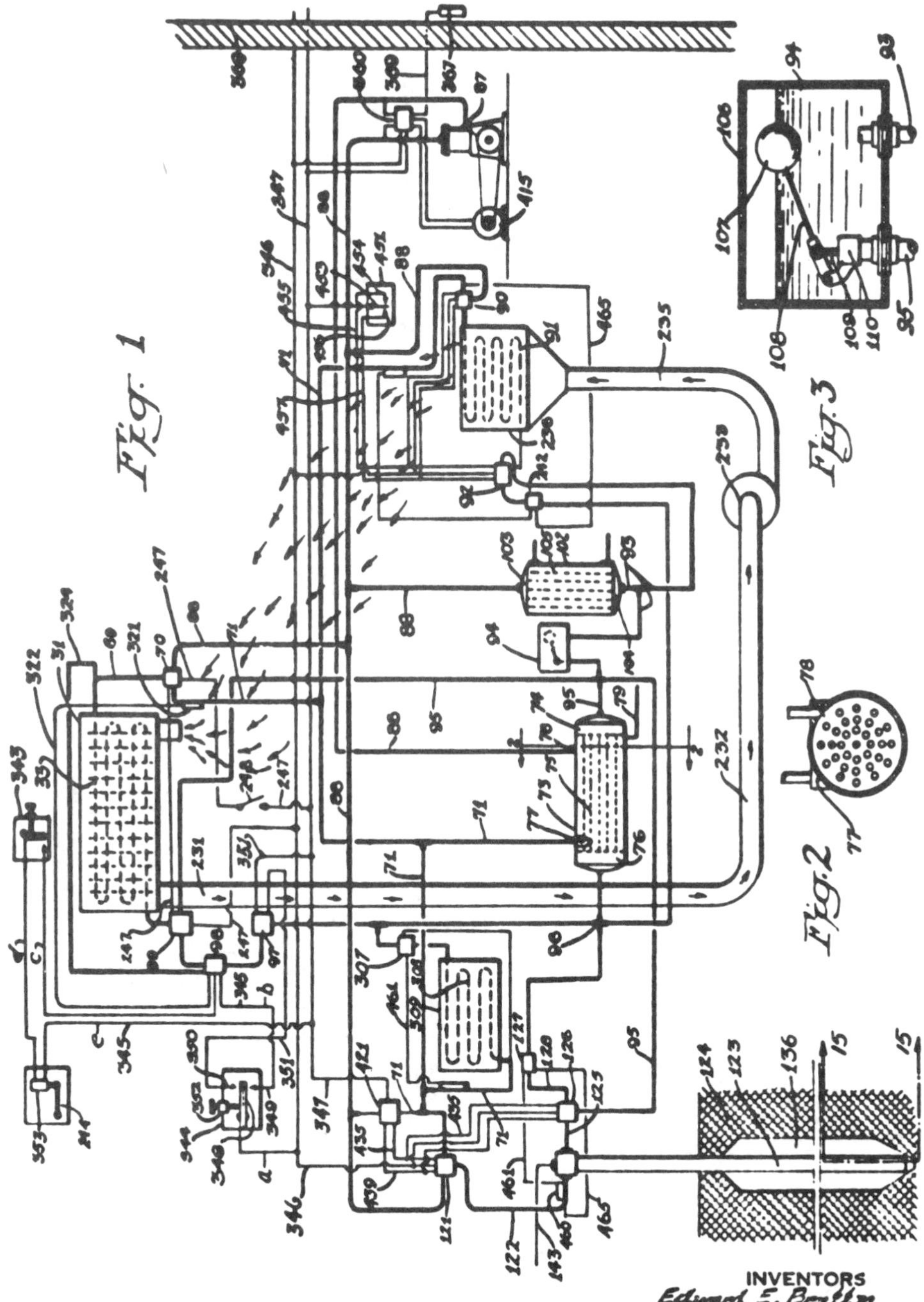

Fig. 1

Fig. 2

Fig. 3

INVENTORS
Edward E. Bratton,
Lewis Marchant
BY
Wm. Steell Jackson and Sons
ATTORNEYS

Nov. 9, 1954 L. MARCHANT ET AL **2,693,939**

HEATING AND COOLING SYSTEM

Fig. 4

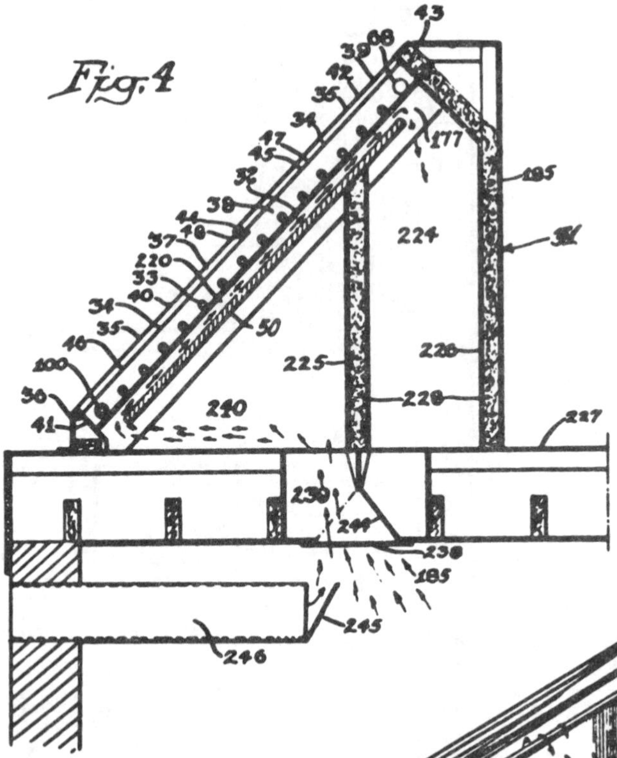

Fig. 5

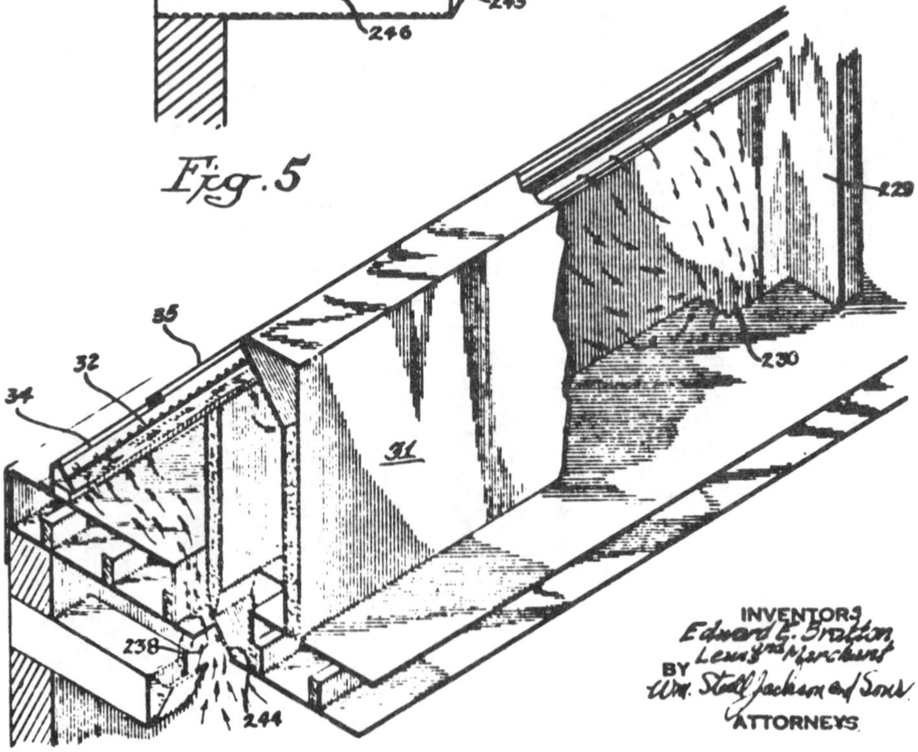

INVENTORS
Edward E. Bratton,
Lewis 3rd Marchant
BY
Wm. Steell Jackson and Sons
ATTORNEYS

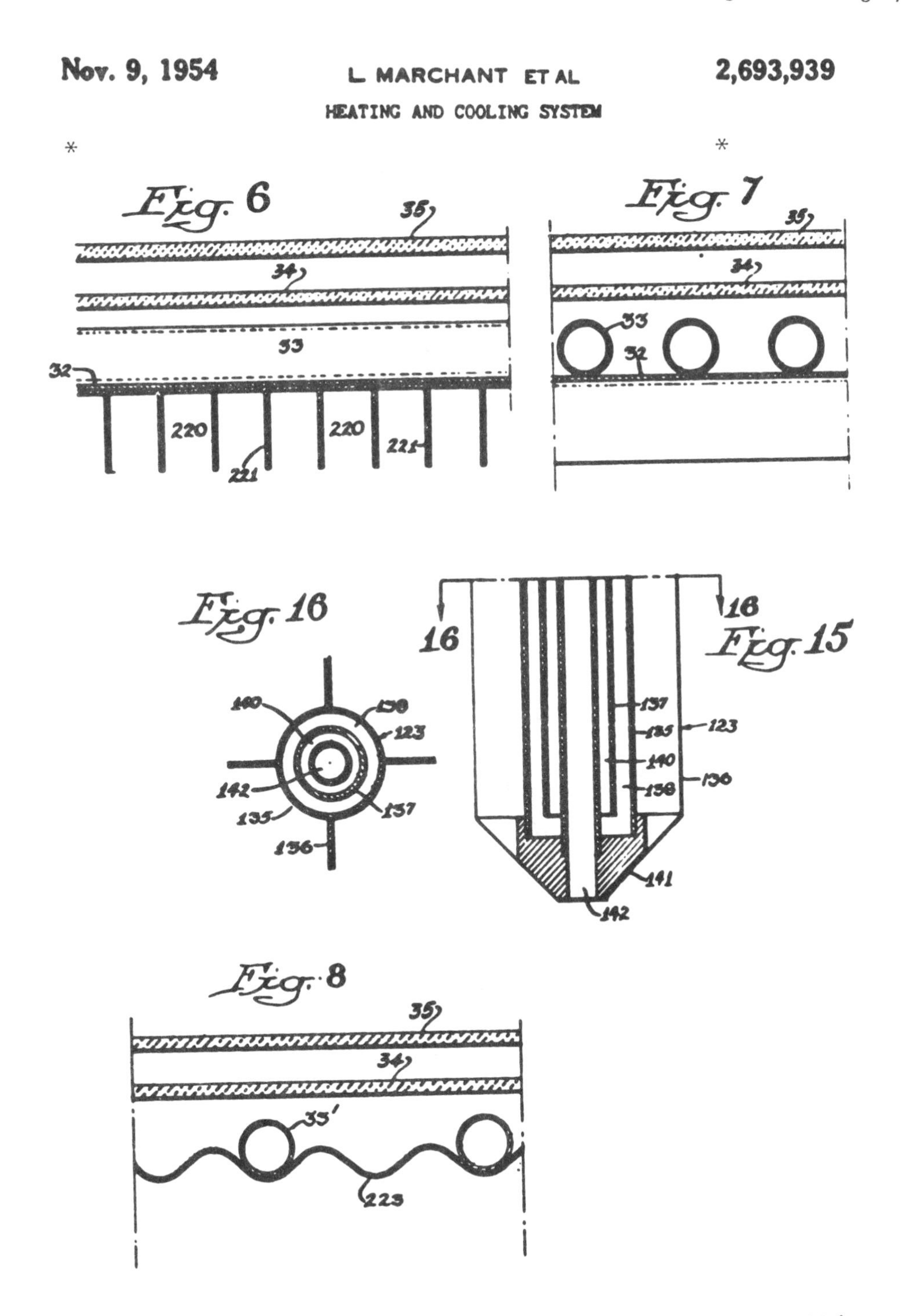
Nov. 9, 1954
L. MARCHANT ET AL
2,693,939
HEATING AND COOLING SYSTEM
Fig. 6
35
34
33
32
220
220
221
221
Fig. 7
35
34
33
32
Fig. 16
140
138
123
142
137
135
136
16
16
Fig. 15
137
135
123
140
138
136
141
142
Fig. 8
35
34
33'
223
INVENTORS
BY
ATTORNEYS

Nov. 9, 1954 L. MARCHANT ET AL **2,693,939**

HEATING AND COOLING SYSTEM

* *

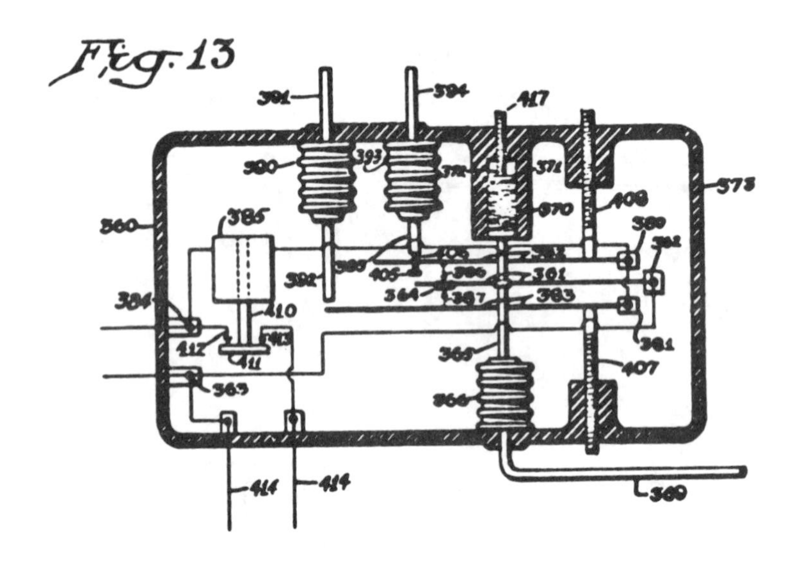

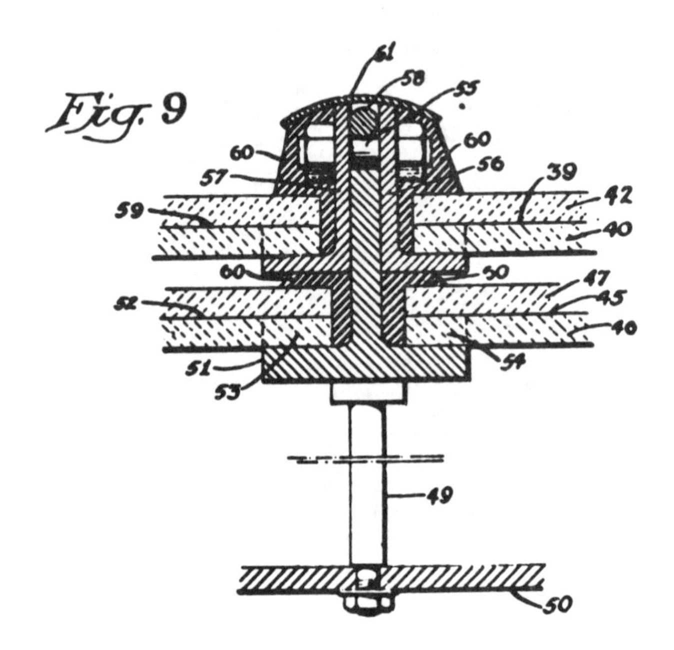

INVENTORS
Edward E. Bratton
Louis Marchant
BY
Wm. Steell, Jackson and Daniels
ATTORNEYS

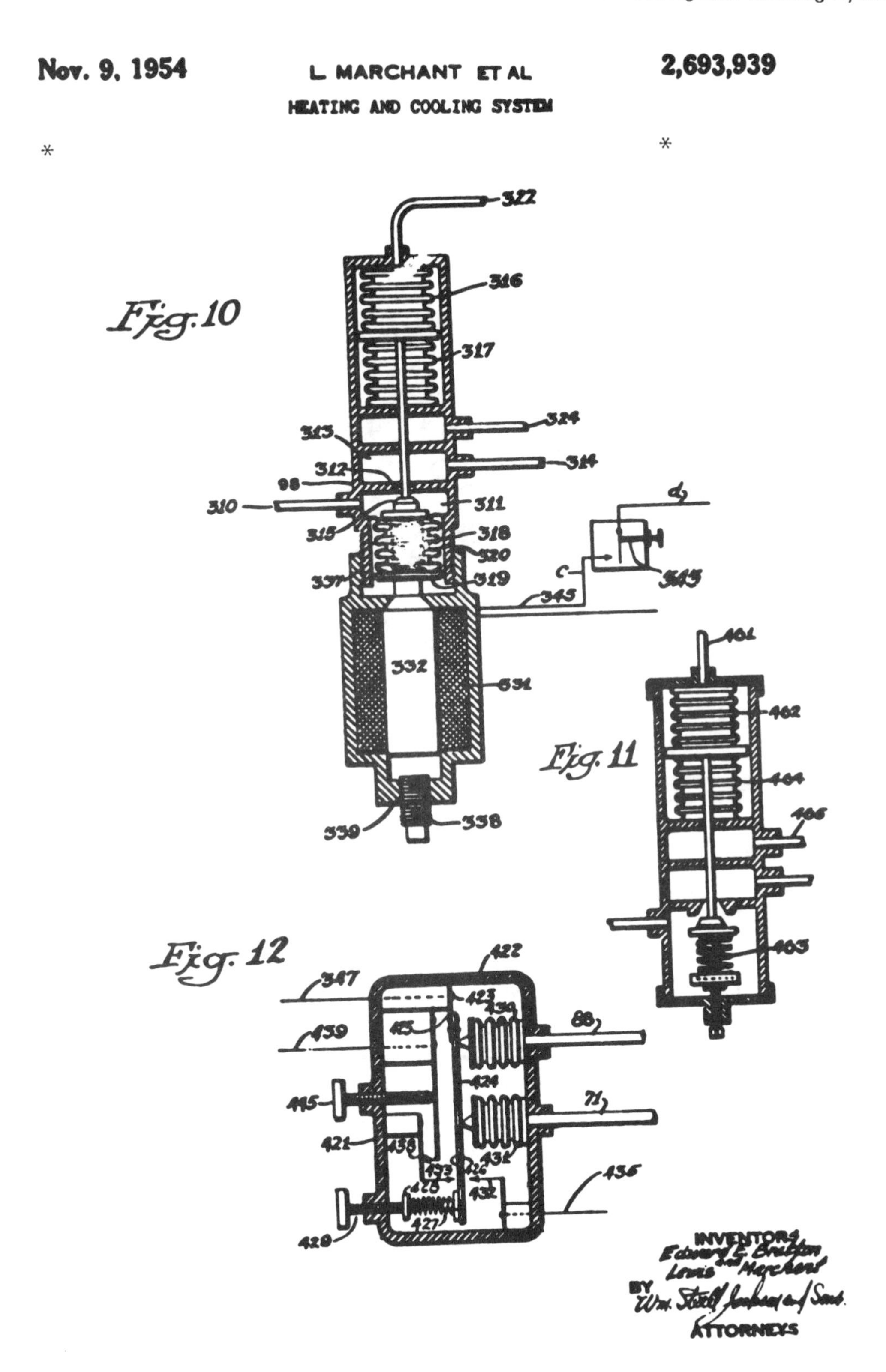
Nov. 9, 1954
L. MARCHANT ET AL
2,693,939
HEATING AND COOLING SYSTEM
Fig. 10
Fig. 11
Fig. 12
INVENTORS
Edward E. Bratton
Louis Marchant
BY
ATTORNEYS

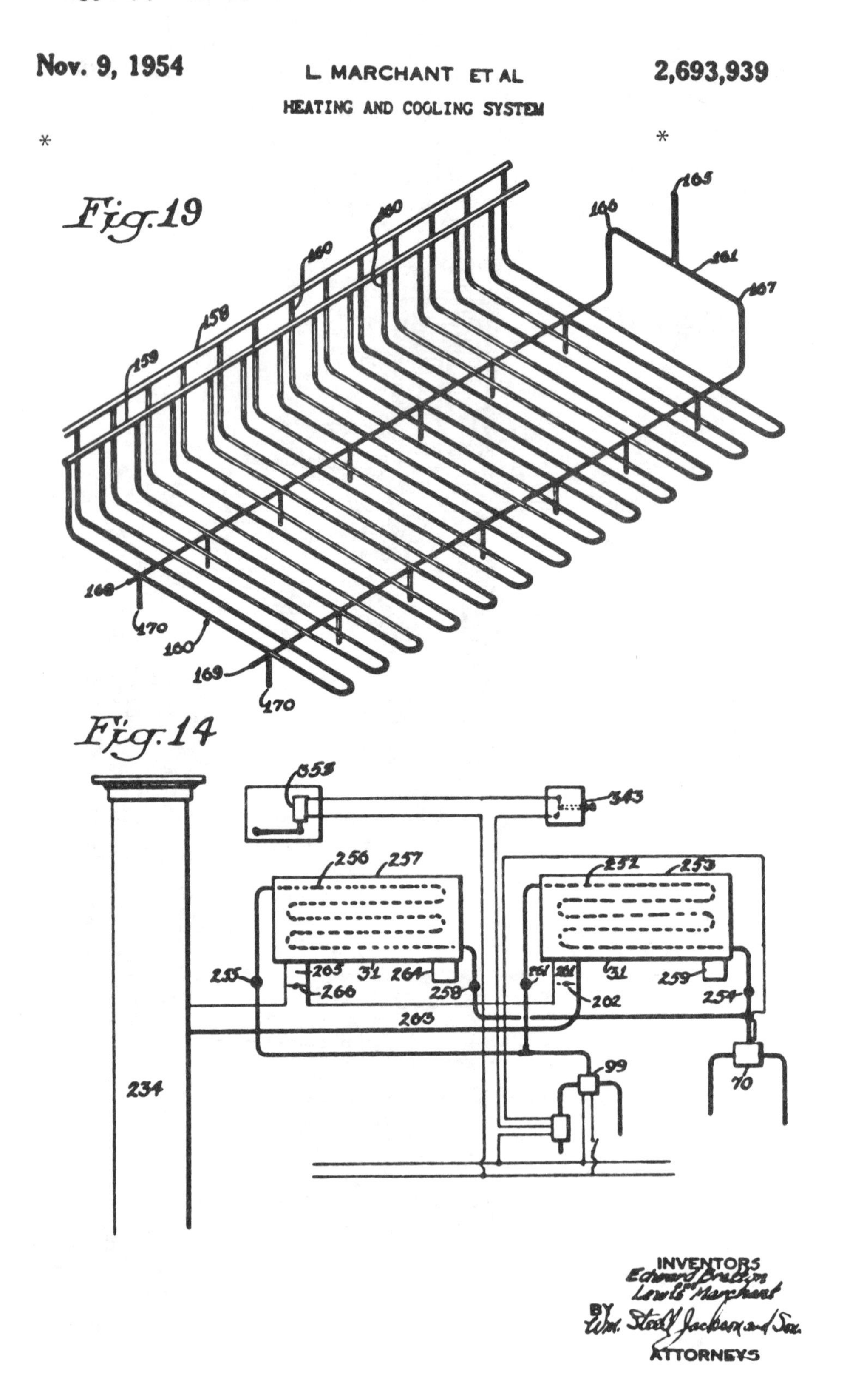
Nov. 9, 1954
L. MARCHANT ET AL
2,693,939
HEATING AND COOLING SYSTEM
Fig. 19
Fig. 14
234
INVENTORS
ATTORNEYS

Nov. 9, 1954 L. MARCHANT ET AL 2,693,939

HEATING AND COOLING SYSTEM

* *

Fig. 17

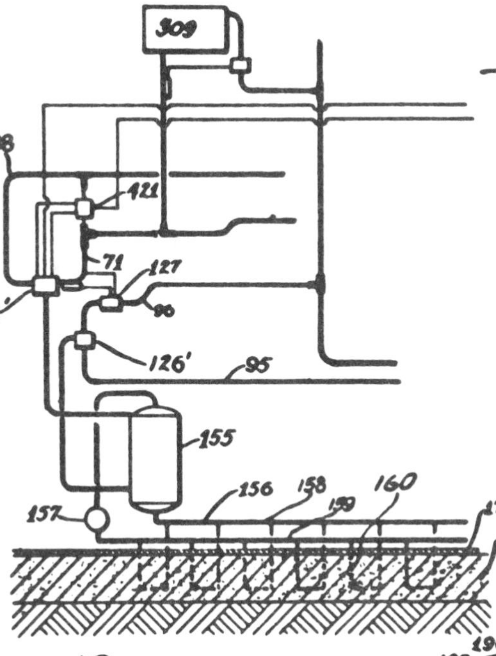

Fig. 18

Fig. 20

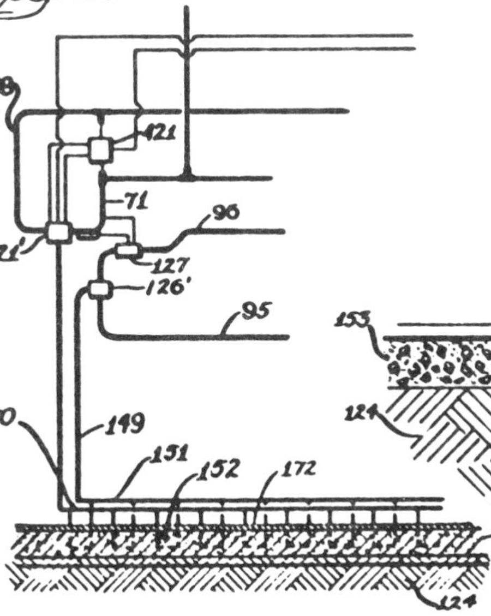

INVENTORS
Edward E. Bratton
and Lewis Marchant
BY
[illegible]
ATTORNEYS

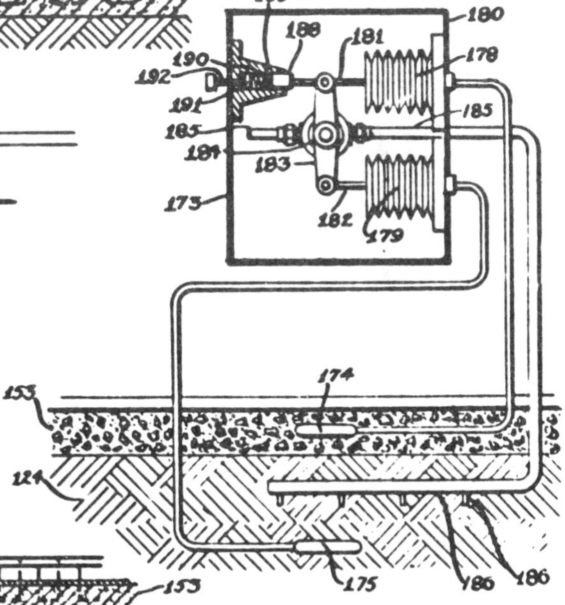

Nov. 9, 1954 L. MARCHANT ET AL **2,693,939**

HEATING AND COOLING SYSTEM

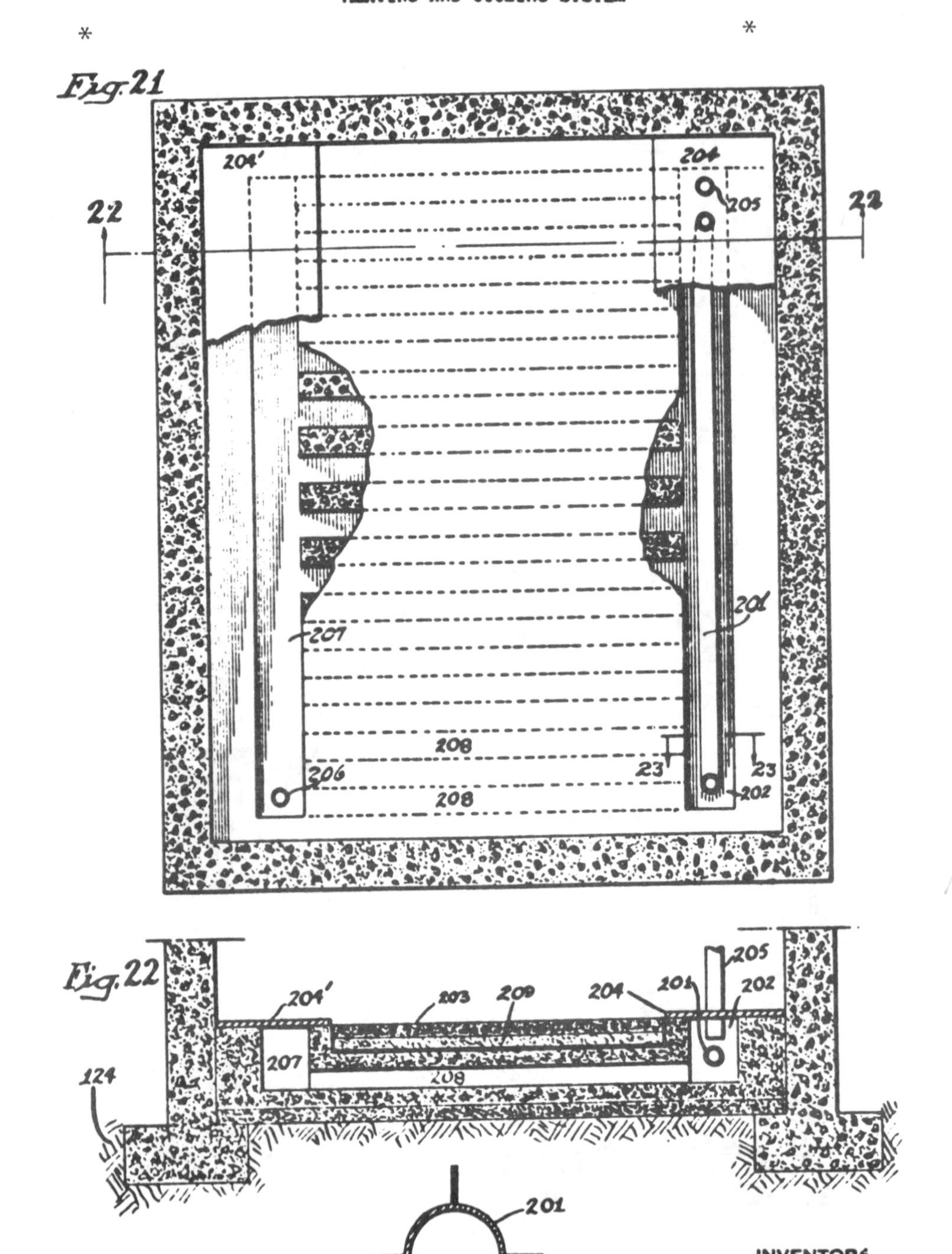

INVENTORS

BY

ATTORNEYS

Nov. 9, 1954 L. MARCHANT ET AL 2,693,939

HEATING AND COOLING SYSTEM

* *

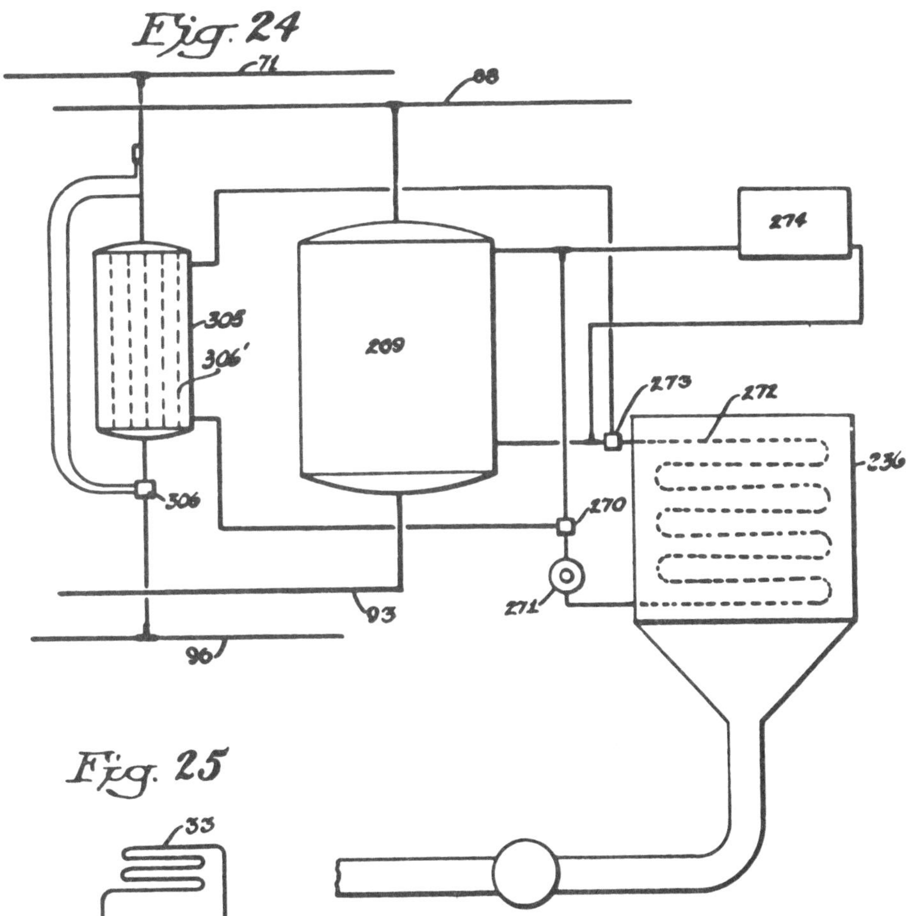

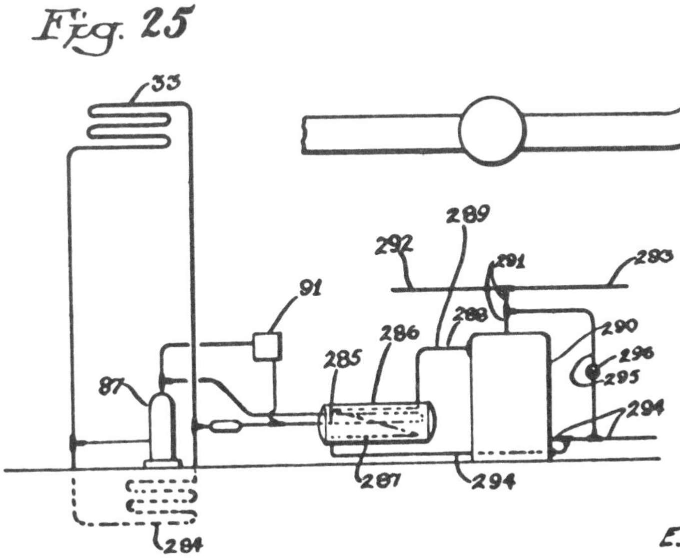

Fig. 24

Fig. 25

INVENTORS
Edward E. Bratton
Lewis Marchant
BY
Wm. Steell Jackson and Sons
ATTORNEYS

Nov. 9, 1954 L. MARCHANT ET AL 2,693,939

HEATING AND COOLING SYSTEM

* *

Fig.26.

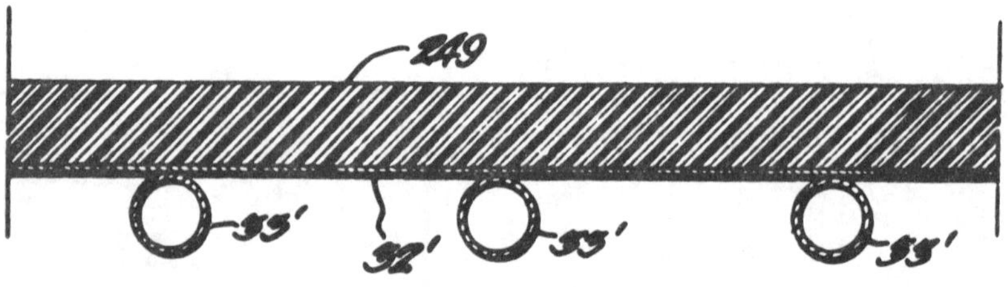

249

35' 32' 35' 35'

INVENTORS
Edward F. Britton
and Lewis Marchant
BY Wm. Steell Jackson and Sons
ATTORNEYS

2,693,939

HEATING AND COOLING SYSTEM

Lewis Marchant, Wildwood Crest, N. J., and Edward R. Bratton, Upper Darby, Pa. *

Our invention relates to systems of and methods for heating, cooling and/or air-conditioning, and components of such systems.

A purpose of our invention is to provide such a system or method having improved efficiency, economy, and convenience.

A further purpose of our invention is to provide a heating system or method which makes a highly effective use of radiation from the sun as a major source of heat.

A further purpose of our invention is to provide a heating system or method which takes heat from solar radiation when available, stores it, and delivers it when needed.

A further purpose of our invention is to provide a heating system or method which can take heat from solar radiation at realtively low temperature during periods of low intensity of such radiation and utilize such heat at higher temperature.

A further purpose of our invention is to provide an improved and efficient ground heat exchanging system having high thermal conductivity, thus permitting the use of the earth as a source of heat when needed, and as a place into which heat can be put for temporary storage, or for gradual discard when necessary.

A further purpose of our invention is to provide an air conditioning system automatically modulated in proportion to requirements for heating or cooling.

A further purpose of our invention is to provide an automatically heated or cooled water supply for household, industrial or other requirements.

A further purpose is to make the adjustment of our system responsive in a predetermined way to conditions of radiation and/or ambient temperatures prevailing at any particular time.

A further purpose is to have a heating, cooling and/or air conditioning system utilizing a powered mechanical refrigeration cycle which needs to operate only during the off-peak periods of the power source.

Other purposes will appear in the remainder of the specification and from the claims.

In the drawings, we have chosen to illustrate some only of the numerous particular embodiments in which our invention may appear, the forms shown being chosen from the standpoints of convenience in illustration, satisfactory operation and clear demonstration of the principles involved.

Figure 1 is a diagrammatic representation of a form of our invention. Figure 2 is a cross section along the line 2—2 in Figure 1 of the heat exchanger there. Figure 3 is a longitudinal section taken somewhat to one side looking toward the center of the refrigerant outlet valve chamber of the hot water heater shown in Figure 1.

Figure 4 is a somewhat diagrammatic cross sectional view, sectioned thru the air intake, of a solar unit in accordance with our invention, shown for the sake of simplicity and clarity without the fins on the back of the solar sheet and without the supporting structure for the glass. Figure 5 is a fragmentary perspective view, broken away, of the unit as shown in Figure 4.

Figure 6 is a sectional view of a part of this unit, including fins, taken longitudinally of the heat transfer fluid tubes. Figure 7 likewise is a sectional view of a part of this unit including fins but taken across the fluid tubes. Figure 8 is a sectional view similar to Figure 7, but of a somewhat different form of unit.

Figure 9 is a fragmentary sectional view of a joint between transparent panels of the unit, together with supporting structure but omitting the solar sheet. It cuts the panels in a plane perpendicular to them along a line perpendicular to the length of the joint.

Figure 10 is a vertical section of a solar coil expansion valve in accordance with our invention.

Figure 11 is a cross sectional view of an expansion valve such as is used elsewhere in our invention.

Figure 12 is a longitudinal section of a differential pressure switch in accordance with our invention.

Figure 13 is a vertical longitudinal section of a temperature modulation controller in accordance with our invention.

Figure 14 is a diagrammatic view of an alternative form of our solar unit and the air duct leading therefrom.

Figure 15 is a vertical section through the lower part of the earth tube shown in Figure 1. Figure 16 is a cross section along the lines 16—16 in Figure 15.

Figure 17 is a diagrammatic fragmentary view of an alternate form of our system.

Figure 18 is a diagrammatic fragmentary view showing a form differing somewhat from that of Figure 17.

Figure 19 is a fragmentary perspective view of the pipes in and near the cellar floor which are shown in Figure 17.

Figure 20 is a sectional diagrammatic view showing the thermostatic control for moistening the ground, which is preferably a part of our invention whether in the form of Figure 1 or of Figure 17 or 18, but is here shown as it would be applied in connection with the form of Figure 17 or 18. For simplicity and clarity of illustration, refrigerant pipes are omitted from this view, and the control box and its elements are exaggerated.

Figure 21 is a horizontal cross section, partly broken away, looking downward, of a somewhat different form of cellar floor heat exchanger. Figure 22 is a vertical section along lines 22—22 on Figure 21.

Figure 23 is a cross section on a larger scale of the refrigerant pipe of Figure 21 showing the detail thereof including fins to facilitate heat exchange.

Figure 24 is a fragmentary diagrammatic view of a somewhat different form of our invention.

Figure 25 is a diagrammatic view, greatly simplified for clarity of illustration, of another somewhat different form of our invention.

Figure 26 is a vertical section corresponding to Figure 7, but showing an alternate form of solar coil, sheet and insulating cover combination.

Describing the invention shown, by way of illustration and not in limitation:

As shown especially in Figures 4, 5, 6 and 7, solar unit 31 has a metal solar-radiation-absorbent sheet 32. Preferably on top of this sheet is solar coil 33, which is intimately attached to the sheet in some fashion such as welding or brazing, so as to allow heat to pass freely from sheet to coil. Another possible arrangement would be to have the coil on the bottom side of the sheet.

Solar coil 33 is a hollow serpentine pipe through which refrigeration-type fluid such as Freon can circulate to absorb heat which the metal has received from radiation, especially from the sun. In this process of heat absorption the refrigerant fluid will preferably be substantially completely evaporated.

It will be understood that the coil could take other forms than that of the serpentine pipe; for example, it could be a grid of pipes.

The sheet and coil are preferably of a metal which is a good heat conductor, such as copper, and it is desirable that they be blackened and roughened on the side toward the sun so as to absorb a maximum of the radiation which falls on them. They should preferably be so positioned as to get a maximum total solar radiation during the colder part of the year, when most of the heating has to be done. Thus, for winter heating of buildings, such as homes, in the northern hemisphere, a very desirable location is on the roof of the building facing south and inclined from the horizontal at an angle which will depend on the latitude. At latitude 40° north this would preferably approximate 45°.

Above sheet 32 and solar coil 33 are covers 34 and 35, one above the other, each made of some material, such as glass, which is transparent to most of the solar radiation. They are spaced from each other and from the coil and sheet, and at their edges they abut on relatively air-tight, heat-insulating surrounding partition 36, with which they form tight joints, details of which are not shown, but which could, for example, involve having the covers rest on a flat ledge of the partition, with suitable sealing material applied over them at the joint. The surrounding partition extends down below the sheet, with which it also forms a tight joint. Thus space 37 between covers and space 38 between cover and sheet are more or less dead air spaces to provide heat insulation for the sheet and the solar coil and thus prevent undue heat loss by conduction or convection to the outdoor atmosphere.

Each transparent cover will preferably consist of a series of panels side by side, each panel being made up of two individual overlapping glass panels which are in contact with each other where they overlap. Thus, in panel 39 of upper cover 35, lower pane 40 extends from lower strip 41 of partition 36 up to an intermediate point of the cover, and upper pane 42 extends down from upper strip 43 of partition 36 to overlap the lower pane 40 at 44. Likewise, in panel 45 of lower cover 34, lower pane 46 and upper pane 47 overlap at 48.

A preferred method of joining these panels is shown in Figure 9. Rods such as 49 are supported in an upright position in any suitable fashion, as for example by passing their reduced ends as bolts through partition 50 of the solar unit below sheet 32 (not shown in that figure) which in such case will have holes for the rods to pass through. Supported on top of the rods is inverted T-rib 51, the horizontal arms of which in turn support both the lower panes of panels 45 and 52 and also, with the help of fillers 53 and 54 lying on top of the arms, the upper panes of those panels.

A plurality of bolts such as 55, each threaded at both ends, rest on top of the shank of the T-rib 51, supporting angles 56 and 57 on opposite sides of that shank. Nuts on opposite ends of the bolts hold the angles tight against the shank, using rod 58 lying between the tops of the angles as a fulcrum. Upper panels 39 and 59 are supported by the angles in the same way as the lower panels are supported by the T-bar. Sealing material 60 helps make a tight joint, and the cap 61 rests on top.

These joints make it possible to open up the solar unit from the top without undue inconvenience whenever cleaning, repair or overhaul of the interior of the unit is desired. Furthermore, a single panel can be removed, as for example to replace the glass, without disturbing the remaining sections.

As shown in Figure 1, solar coil 33 forms part of a heat pump which is adapted to take heat from the solar unit for utilization, as for example in heating a building or in heating water or other media for various purposes, such as domestic uses, or process heating as in the evaporation or concentration of such liquids as milk, juices, dye extracts or brines. In so doing, the heat pump acts on a certain medium of the mechanical refrigeration type, such as the Freon already mentioned, which is capable of acquiring and surrendering heat to transfer heat from the solar unit to a desired location for utilization. In the solar coil the refrigerant undergoes the step in the heat pump cycle in which the input of thermal energy causes large increase of entropy, a step which, as already indicated, preferably causes substantially complete evaporation.

From the vapor end of the solar coil, which is preferably enlarged to form vapor header 68 (Figure 4), the fluid passes through pipe 69, three-way valve 70, and cold vapor pipe system 71 into heat exchanger 73, where it picks up heat from hot refrigerant liquid on the high pressure side of the system. This heat exchanger will preferably be approximately cylindrical, with the refrigerant liquid passing from inlet header 74 through tubes 75 into outlet header 76, while the vapor comes into the central space near the outlet header by way of inlet 77, and leaves near the inlet header by way of outlet 78. As shown in Figure 2, the inlet and outlet are each placed well off center at more or less of a tangent to the periphery of the space and with the one opening into and the other away from the space in the same rotational direction, so that the vapor tends to pass in helical flow through the central space over the tubes, thus increasing the rate of heat exchange.

Any slugs of liquid which may have happened to pass out of the solar coil along with the vapor will be trapped in the bottom part of this heat exchanger tank, and prevented from proceeding further and possibly damaging the compressor. Compressor oil which collects in the heat exchanger can be removed by drain pipe 79 for return to the compressor.

From heat exchanger 73 the refrigerant vapor passes through warm vapor pipe 86 into compressor 87, by whose action it is raised in pressure and temperature.

It leaves the compressor in hot vapor pipe system 88 and from this is supplied through three-way valve 90 to air coil 91. In the air coil, the vapor will condense, giving up heat to air passing through, which air can in turn be used for heating purposes, as in warming a building, for example.

The hot liqiud resulting from condensation of hot vapor in air coil 91 passes through three-way valve 92, hot liquid outlet piping 93, outlet valve unit 94 and hot high pressure liquid pipe system 95 into heat exchanger 73, where, as already indicated, it warms the low pressure vapor which is proceeding toward the compressor. After passing through the heat exchanger, the high pressure liquid, now reduced in temperature, proceeds through cold liquid pipe system 96 and stop valve 97 into expansion valve 98, where its pressure is reduced. From the expansion valve it passes through three-way valve 99 and back into solar coil 33, the inlet end of which preferably forms liquid header 100 (Figure 4). It thus completes its heat pump cycle using the solar coil as evaporator.

Also connected across between hot vapor pipe system 88 and hot liquid outlet piping 93 is hot water supply tank 102, preferably a vertically positioned tank rather similar in construction to an ordinary tube-type heat exchanger. The vapor in this tank passes from inlet header 103 to outlet header 104 through tubes 105, where it condenses, imparting heat to water in the tank surrounding the tubes, and thus furnishes a hot water supply for domestic and other purposes.

It will be noted that as described and shown, there is no valve used between hot vapor pipe system 88 and the hot water supply tank. A valve at this point might of course be put in for convenience in case of repair and overhaul, but during normal operation this connection is preferably kept open at all times. Thus the water will be heated whenever its temperature falls below that of the hot high pressure refrigerant vapor. Furthermore, whenever demands elsewhere tend to cause the hot high pressure refrigerant vapor temperature to fall below the temperature maintained within the hot water heater, refrigerant condensate within that heater will flash into vapor to help maintain the hot high side refrigerant vapor temperature and pressure. Thus the compressor will not be required to function so frequently to maintain hot high side refrigerant vapor temperature and pressure against sudden temporary demands, and the economy of operation of the system will be considerably improved.

Also, with sufficient heat storage capacity in the hot water system relative to the heating needs of the installation, it will be possible also to regulate the system as a whole so that compressor operation can be confined to periods outside of the peak periods of power consumption, thus greatly reducing the cost of electricity to operate the compressor. During periods when the compressor is kept out of operation, the hot water will continually be evaporating refrigerant in the hot water supply tank, which refrigerant will condense in the air coil to heat the air for utilization in heating and will then flow back to replenish the refrigerant liquid in the hot water supply tank. It will be understood that for such replenishment, the system must be made so that such flow will be induced, either by gravity, as in the form shown, or by some pumping means.

In the outlet valve unit 94, as shown in detail in Figure 3, refrigerant coming in from the air coil 91 and hot water supply tank 102 through hot liquid outlet piping 93 causes the liquid level in the valve unit tank 106 to rise bringing up ball 107 until ball lever 108 through the movement of valve connection 109 opens outlet valve 110, releasing refrigerant into pipe system 95 beyond until the liquid level in the valve unit tank has fallen sufficiently to again close the valve. With proper original adjustment, this enables a proper refrigerant level to be maintained in the hot water supply tank, independently of the level at points beyond the valve.

In the preferred form of our heating system, we have provided for use of the earth as a place to store heat during periods in the heating season when more heat is available to the solar radiation heat receiver than is needed for immediate heating purposes, and for later removal of stored heat from the earth, and utilization of it, during periods when insufficient heat is available directly from the solar radiation heat receiver.

To effectuate the heat storage in the earth, hot high-pressure refrigerant vapor pipes system **88** is connected to three-way valve **121**, from which refrigerant pipe **122** leads to earth tube **123**, where the refrigerant condenses, imparting heat to the earth **124** in the immediate neighborhood of the tube. From the earth tube the refrigerant passes through pipe **125** and three-way valve **126** into hot refrigerant liquid pipe system **95**. Thus, with proper setting of the three-way valves, the earth tube can be operated as a condenser to store heat temporarily in the earth.

To remove the heat from the earth for use when needed, cold high pressure refrigerant liquid pipe system **96** is connected to expansion valve **127**, which in turn is connected through pipe **128** to three-way valve **126** on one side of the earth tube, while three-way valve **121** on the other side of the tube is connected to cold refrigerant vapor pipe system **71**. Thus with another setting of the three-way valves, the earth tube can be operated as an evaporator to pick up heat from the earth for ultimate utilization in the same way that heat from the solar coil is directly utilized, through the action of the heat pump circuit, which in turn gives heat to the water in the hot water heating tank **102** and to the air passing through in heat exchange relation with the air coil **91**.

Thus it is possible to take heat from the solar radiation heat receiver and store the excess not used in the building in the earth close to the earth tube, and then to draw on the heat thus temporarily stored at times when insufficient heat is being received in the solar coil.

Because of the relatively high temperature at which this heat can be stored, the coefficient of performance of the system using such heat can be much higher than if the system were forced to rely wholly on the heat normally already in the earth, at the relatively low temperatures which would then prevail, considering especially that withdrawal of heat without replenishment tends to force down the immediately adjacent earth temperatures, having a cumulative effect during the heating season.

The earth tube preferably extends more or less vertically to a distance on the order of 5 to 25 feet into the ground. The detail of its interior is shown in Figures 15 and 16. It consists of three tube walls, one inside another, providing corresponding passageways, the outermost tube wall **135** having vanes **136** to facilitate heat transfer with the earth. Intermediate tube wall **137** does not extend so far down as either of the others, so that there is intercommunication near the bottom between outermost passageway **138** and intermediate passageway **140**, despite the fact that these two passageways are collectively sealed off from the earth by partition **141** at their bottom. Thus refrigerant will pass down intermediate passageway **140**, and then into and up outer passageway **138** or vice versa.

Innermost passageway **142** is connected by pipe **143** (Figure 1) to a water source (not shown). Through its open end in the center of the pointed bottom of the earth tube, moisture can be supplied to the earth. Such water, moistening the earth and preventing it from drying out, will facilitate heat exchange between the earth tube and the earth in contact with it by increasing the rate at which heat passes through the earth nearby in response to temperature gradients imposed by the refrigerant in the earth tube. The efficiency of heat transfer in such earth contacts and thus the efficiency of any system relying on such contacts depends to a great degree on the maintenance of proper moisture in the earth.

Although for the sake of simplicity of illustration only one such earth tube is shown, it will be understood that a number of such earth tubes, connected in parallel, and spaced apart as desired, can (and probably with this form in most cases would) be used, depending upon the thermal requirements of the particular installation involved.

Instead of the earth tube, it may often prove more advantageous to circulate the refrigerant through pipes or passages in exterior contact with, or in, building walls, foundations or floors which are in contact with the earth, for example the cellar floor. This arrangement would under many circumstances be simpler and cheaper to construct. Preferably a wall or floor will be selected that is more heat conductive than the adjacent earth. However, even where the material in the wall or floor is not as heat conductive as the earth, heat exchange with the earth is still likely to be improved. The pipe and the wall or floor can be kept in closer contact than pipe and earth, because the earth tends to lose contact with a pipe due possibly to temporarly freezing of moisture causing separation between them. The area of contact between the wall or floor and the earth is enormously greater than that between pipe and earth.

In the form shown in Figure 18, the refrigerant passes through cellar floor coil system **149** (the end of which is shown broken away) on the way between three-way valves **121'** and **126'**, which correspond in function and in position relative to the rest of the refrigerant system to the previously mentioned valves **121** and **126**, respectively. In the condensing phase, the refrigerant will pass through vapor header **150** and thence to liquid header **151** by way of a plurality of pipe loops **152** connected in parallel across between the two headers. The horizontal parts of these pipe loops are embedded in cellar floor **153**, preferably of concrete of relatively good heat conductivity, so that the refrigerant on condensing gives up heat which passes through the pipe into the floor and thence into the adjacent earth. In the evaporating phase, the flow of refrigerant is reversed.

Instead of having the refrigerant and the earth exchange heat thus by more or less direct conduction, it is advantageous in some ways to use a brine circulation system as an intermediary, as in Figure 17, where the refrigerant runs through heat exchanger **155** between three-way valves **121'** and **126'** and there imparts heat to, or receives heat from, brine circulating system **156** (shown with one end broken away). This circulating system employs pump **157** to circulate the brine between heat exchanger **155** and the place where heat is exchanged with the earth. In the drawing, piping for the heat exchange with the earth is shown as along similar lines to that for the refrigerant in Figure 18, though it would also be possible to employ such a brine intermediary with the brine using an earth tube like that in Figure 1, for example. Figure 19 shows, broken away, the tube skeleton used for the brine in Figure 17, with its two headers **158** and **159** and pipe loops **160**.

Also shown in Figure 19, with one end broken away, is the tube skeleton **161** for use in moistening the ground in the forms of Figures 17 and 18. Water pipe **165** leads to branch pipes **166** and **167**, the lower parts of which, **168** and **169**, respectively, are preferably in, on or under the floor **153** (Figures 17 and 18); and from there the water passes thru moisture nozzles **170** opening into the ground. This permits moistening the ground adjacent the floor to facilitate heat transfer between floor and ground. Above the concrete floor **153** (Figures 17 and 18) may be placed moisture-proof barrier **172** of any suitable material impervious to moisture to keep the ground moisture out of the cellar, but of course allowing passage for the various piping which has already been mentioned.

The supply of moisture to the ground in these devices should preferably be controlled in some manner. While this control may be a simple manual control, it is preferably done automatically by the thermostatic moisture control unit **173** shown in Figure 20. Thermostatic bulb **174** is buried in cellar floor **153**, while thermostatic bulb **175** is buried in the earth at a little distance from the floor, as for example two feet below. Thermostatic bulb **174** is connected by capillary tube to Sylphon bellows **178**; and thermostatic bulb **175**, to Sylphon bellows **179**. The two Sylphon bellows, both of which are enclosed in valve box **180**, have rods **181** and **182**, respectively, connected to opposite ends of valve arm **183**.

which they tend to rotate in opposed directions. To the center of the valve arm is attached the movable part of water valve unit 184 on water supply pipe 185 which furnishes moisture to the ground between the thermostatic bulbs, through the schematically represented pipe-and-nozzle combination 186, which would preferably take the form already described. Rod 181 continues on beyond the end of the valve arm to end in head 188 which in turn is connected to one end of spring 189 in spring well 190. The other end of the spring is connected to spring seat 191, made adjustable by connection to adjustment screw 192.

By providing gas in the respective thermobulbs to give equal gas pressure in the bellows when the temperatures of the two thermobulbs 174 and 175 are equal, so that the two bellows will counterbalance each other, and by adjusting the spring to be in neutral position exerting neither tension nor compression on the rod when the valve is in closed position, the valve will be in closed position when the temperature gradient between the thermobulbs is zero. However, when the temperature gradient between the thermobulbs becomes too great, the imbalance between the forces of the two bellows will be sufficient to push the valve arm around against the tension or compression of the spring to a point where the valve will be open and water will flow to be dispensed in the ground, moistening it by a combination of capillary attraction and gravity flow. The moistening of the ground, by improving conductivity and reducing the temperature gradient, will reduce the imbalance between the two bellows, thus permitting return of the valve to closed position under the force of the spring.

A less desirable alternative would be to simply have the thermobulbs connected to temperature indicators as an aid to intelligent hand regulation.

Automatic moistening control similar to that shown in Figure 20 can be used also on the earth tube (123) in Figure 1, in which case one of the thermobulbs would preferably be in firm and extensive contact with the outside of the tube near its bottom, and the other preferably at a suitable distance away in the ground.

Figures 21 through 23 show a form in which heat exchange between the refrigerant and the earth is effected by running the refrigerant between three-way valves 121 and 126 (not there shown), through heat exchanging tube 201 which is located in trough 202 built into one side of the cellar floor 203 under removable moisture-proof cover 204. Trough 202 is filled with water which is being pumped up through outlet pipe 205, and taken (by a pipe not shown) over to inlet pipe 206 into trough 207 built into the floor on the other side of the cellar, under removable moisture-proof cover 204'. From there it circulates through ducts 208 built into the cellar floor under moisture-proof barrier 209 back to trough 202. Thus heat to be stored in the earth can be taken from the refrigerant tube 201, operating as a condenser, into the water, thence into the cellar floor and from there into the earth. On the other hand, when it is desired to utilize such stored heat it is possible by a different setting of the three-way valves to operate the refrigerant tube 201 as an evaporator to receive heat coming from the earth by way of the floor and water.

In addition to the features of the solar unit (Figures 4 through 8) which have already been described, which enable it efficiently to get heat from radiation, especially solar radiation, and to use such heat for an evaporator in a heat pump, solar unit 31 has provision also for using such heat to heat air in the unit for heating purposes outside the unit, whenever the radiation is sufficient to produce temperatures high enough to make this practicable.

To effectuate this, the solar unit's radiation-absorbing sheet 32 is in direct contact, on the opposite side from the sun, with air in air passageways 220, of which the sheet forms one side. Fins 221 (Figures 6 and 7) preferably of highly heat-conducting metal, intimately attached (as by soldering) to sheet 32, extend downward to form the sides of the air passageways and thus to increase the heated metal surface with which the air can make contact. The bottom of the passageways is formed by partition 50 (Figure 4), preferably of some such material as plywood.

In order to increase heat transfer between metal and air, the passageways may desirably be transversely corrugated on one or more sides in order to cause turbulence in the air flowing through the passageways. An illustration of this is in the alternate form shown in Figure 8, in which the solar-radiation-absorbing sheet 223 which is employed is corrugated for this purpose, the horizontal tubes of solar coil 33' being in the troughs of the corrugated sheet.

The air heated in the passageways under the radiation-absorbing sheet then flows into warm plenum 224, located between walls 225 and 226 which support the higher end of the face of the solar unit on flat roof 227. Insulation 228 in these walls and in those closing off the ends of the plenum, of which only 229 is shown, prevents undue heat loss from this plenum.

From the warm plenum the air passes through outlet opening 230, as indicated by the arrows, into downward air tube 231 (Figure 1) across through fan tube 232 to fan 233, which supplies the motive power to draw the air along this course. In installations in houses which formerly used conventional heating systems, it may prove very convenient and inexpensive to make the bore of the chimney, 234, (Figure 14), serve as all or part of the downward tube, or to run the tube through the bore if for any reason it proves undesirable to use the original wall surfaces of the bore.

From the fan the air is driven through tube 235 and air coil housing 236 from which it emerges to heat the house or other building.

In the form shown in the figures, for simplicity of illustration we have the air which heats the house simply filtering up through the house without use of ducts, more or less in the way that heating is accomplished in the case of the so-called "pipeless heater." Instead of this, it will be understood that our invention could use other modes of using the air for heating purposes, such as a complete set of ducts to introduce the heated air into the individual rooms as in the case of more typical modern air heat, or ducts leading into the walls and floors to furnish radiant heat, or both.

In any event, the system is arranged so that the air eventually reaches intake opening 238 in the solar unit (Figures 4 and 5), from which it passes through passage 239 into cold plenum 240, from which it reaches air passageways 220 again.

The refrigerant system is so arranged that when the heat being received into the air circuit from the radiation-absorbent sheet is more than is needed to heat the building, air coil 91 may be operated evaporating to pick up some of it for temporary storage in the earth. The refrigerant for this purpose is admitted from cold liquid pipe system 96 through expansion valve 242 (Figure 1) into three-way valve 92, from which, when the valve is properly set, the refrigerant reaches air coil 91. There it evaporates, absorbing excess heat from the air, and then passes through three-way valve 90, into the low pressure refrigerant vapor pipe system 71. Once the heat is in the refrigerant in this pipe system, its temporary storage in the earth follows the same process as that for heat which has come in refrigerant from the solar coil.

Damper 244 (Figure 4) makes it possible to shunt the air away from the radiation-absorbent sheet 32 during periods when insufficient radiation is being received by the sheet, or when it is not desired to heat the air. When the damper bottom swings to the opposite side of opening 238, the air is shunted directly into the warm plenum, which it traverses to outlet opening 230, and thence through the duct, fan and air coil and back into the house as before. Thus the air circulation system can continue to be used for ventilation, and for heating by means of the condenser in the air coil, without passing the air next to the radiation-absorbent sheet of the solar coil.

Fresh air as desired for hygienic reasons and to replace leakage losses may be admitted into the air circuit in any of a number of places. In the form shown it is done by opening door 245 directly under air intake opening 238 through which air is constantly being sucked into the solar unit by the operation of the air circulation fan 233. The door gets its fresh air through duct 246. The door may be set manually to admit a more or less constant proportion of fresh air.

In case sufficient snow or ice should be deposited on the solar unit to seriously diminish the access of the heat receiver to radiation, hot vapor pipe system **88** has been connected to three-way valve **70** on the vapor side of the solar coil, and three-way valve **99** on the liquid side of the solar coil has been connected to hot liquid pipe system **95**. This makes it possible by proper setting of the three-way valves, which should be operated in tandem, to run the solar coil as a condenser for the purpose of melting the snow or ice. Electrical connections **247** controlled by manual switch **248** have been provided as a suitable way to change these two three-way valves simultaneously over from evaporating to condensing position when desired.

The solar unit in the form shown provides for a sheet oriented and sloped to provide maximum heat receipt by a given area of solar-radiation-absorbent sheet used in connection with a building having a flat roof. It will be understood that by having a building with a sloping roof of the proper position and slope, a similar result can be achieved by a solar unit whose absorbent sheet is more or less parallel to the roof and can therefore be laid on right above, or built into, the roof. In such case, suitable duct arrangements can take the place of the plenums.

It will be understood that in making a solar unit it may under a particular set of circumstances be advantageous as a practical matter to construct the solar unit so that the solar-radiation-receiving sheet presents an angle toward the sun that is less than optimum, as far as radiation received per unit surface is concerned, so long as the radiation received per unit surface is sufficient for the purpose. Thus, with a particular type and position of roof at a particular latitude, under a particular state of relative costs of the different elements of the solar unit, it may prove economical to have the radiation-receiving sheet parallel to or built into the roof, to save the cost of the walls, even though the particular roof is not positioned and sloped so as to make this optimum from the standpoint of the amount of radiation received per unit surface. Esthetic considerations may also affect this matter.

A variation in the form of solar unit is shown in Figure 26. Instead of having the solar coil on top of the radiation-absorbent sheet and above them the transparent covers separated from each other and from coil and sheet, it has the solar coil 33' in intimate contact with the sheet 32' on its underside, and resting on top of the sheet to cut down convection and conduction losses is a relatively thick slab **249** of transparent heat-resisting and heat-insulating plastic such as a polystyrene solution of an unsaturated polyester or of an alkyd, described for example in the pamphlet "Paraplex for Laminating, Molding, and Casting Applications," issued by Rohm and Haas Company, The Resinous Products Division, Washington Square, Philadelphia, Pennsylvania. Even though such a plastic would have considerably less heat conductivity than the glass which would be likely to be used in the other form, it would be desirable to make the total thickness of plastic here considerably more than that of glass in the other form, to help make up, from the heat insulation standpoint, for the absence of the intermediate air spaces in this form.

Instead of the plastic being directly on top of the metal sheet, it may be advantageous to space it slightly, as for example, one eighth of an inch, by some convenient means, such as the insertion in between them of washers held in position by screws through the plastic, or by bosses on the bottom of the plastic.

Instead of a single solar unit, the system may have two (or more) solar units connected into the air and refrigerant systems in parallel, as shown in Figure 14. Here some of the refrigerant from three-way valve **99** will continue on through stop valve **251**, solar coil **252** in solar unit **253**, and stop valve **254** to three-way valve **70**, while the rest of the refrigerant passes through stop valve **255**, solar coil **256** in solar unit **257**, and stop valve **258** on its way between the three-way valves. Likewise, some of the air goes through inlet **259** into solar unit **253**, then through outlet **261** controlled by damper **262**, and into tube **263**; while the rest of it goes through inlet **264** into solar unit **257** and then on through outlet **265** controlled by damper **266** into tube **263**. With such an arrangement, it is possible by use of the individual stop valves and dampers to take one of the solar units temporarily out of the air and refrigerant circuits for cleaning or repairs while the system continues operating at reduced capacity with the other solar unit.

In Figure 24 we have shown a variation in our heating system in which, instead of running the refrigerant through the air coil from which air is supplied to heat the building, for example, we run it through a large brine tank, which serves as a means of heat exchange and heat storage. High temperature refrigerant vapor from pipe **88** runs in through large brine tank **269**, there condensing and giving up heat to brine, the refrigerant liquid passing out into hot liquid pipe **93**. Using appropriate pipes of which an example is shown, brine is drawn from the tank through three-way valve **270** by pump **271** and driven to circulate through air coil **272** and three-way valve **273** back into the tank, and will also circulate as desired through radiators schematically represented by **274**, for use for heating the building, for example. Use of such a brine tank would permit cutting off the refrigerant system compressor during periods of peak electrical load for the power system and heating the house temporarily by means of the heat stored in the brine tank, thus reducing total electrical charges by taking advantage of reduced rates available for off-peak operation. The brine tank also furnishes a reserve of heat to fall back on in case it should be desirable or necessary for any other reason temporarily to stop running the refrigerant circuit at a time when the direct air circuit is not functioning.

Another variation is shown in Figure 25. Here a heating system which corresponds to that in Figures 1, 17 or 18 is represented schematically by such of its more prominent features as solar coil 33, compressor 87, air coil **91** and earth exchange **284**. In the position in the refrigerant system occupied by the refrigerant part of hot water supply tank **102** in Figure 1, across between the hot refrigerant vapor pipe system **88** and hot refrigerant liquid outlet piping **93**, is connected coil **285** in Glauber's salt tank **286**. Through this tank, which as indicated contains Glauber's salt (sodium sulfate dekahydrate; $Na_2SO_4 \cdot 10H_2O$), also passes water piping **287** in hot water system **288**. From the water piping in the tank, the hot water passes through pipe **289** into hot water tank **290**. This tank through outlet pipe **291** supplies domestic hot water supply pipe **292** and hot water heating pipe **293** which is connected for example with radiators (not shown) for heating purposes. The heating water comes back by return piping **294** leading to both tanks and having cut-off **295** through by-pass valve **296** for mixing purposes into outlet pipe **291** to permit moderation of temperature of the water in that pipe if and as desired.

In this form of heating system, the refrigerant coil in the Glauber's salt tank will usually run as a condenser to impart heat to the Glauber's salt, which in turn will pass it on to the hot water system for utilization for heating purposes. However, whenever, for example in order to reduce electricity costs by keeping shut down during peak periods, or to effect repairs, it is desirable to shut down the compressor for a limited period, during which the refrigerant cannot receive heat in the usual way, the Glauber's salt, with its high heat storage capacity will serve a dual function. It will not only continue to furnish heat to the hot water system, but, after the refrigerant liquid in the coil falls below the Glauber's salt in temperature, it will also evaporate the refrigerant to furnish refrigerant vapor for use in the air coil.

In addition to providing a very effective way of heating, our system and method can, and preferably would, also provide for cooling and would preferably form the basis of a complete air conditioning system, for all year round service.

In the form of Figure 1, to meet cooling requirements for the building, the air coil **91** can be run evaporating, to take heat from the air before it passes through the building. In itself, this involves the same refrigerant connections as when the air coil is run evaporating to take heat for temporary storage in the earth, but will normally take place at a time, such as in the heat of summer, when the solar coil is shut off from the refrigerant circuit and the damper 244 is set to by-pass the passageways under the radiation-absorbent sheet.

In the brine-tank form of Figure 24, cooling can preferably be achieved by having a separate cooling tank 305 cooled by the evaporation of refrigerant passing from cold high-pressure refrigerant liquid pipe system 96 through expansion valve 306 into a cooling coil 306' in the tank and discharging into cold low-pressure refrigerant vapor pipe system 71. With proper setting of the three-way valves 270 and 273, pump 271 will circulate brine which has been cooled in tank 305 through air coil 272 by means of appropriate pipes as shown.

It will be understood that whatever else is desired for the purpose of complete air conditioning, such as an air filter, apparatus for humidification or dehumidification, and apparatus for sterilization, may be placed in a position to perform its function on the air being circulated by the fan before the air debouches into the building interior; it may, for example, be placed within housing 236, where the circulating air also comes into contact with the air coil.

If desired, the refrigerant circuit may also be used for other cooling functions. Thus the refrigerant can be used to operate a low temperature evaporator to cool drinking water for use in the house. As shown in Figure 1, cold high pressure liquid from pipe system 96 is reduced in pressure in expansion valve 307, evaporates within evaporator coil 308 cooling the water in the rest of tank 309 and on leaving enters cold refrigerant vapor pipe system 71.

Our system is preferably automatic in its normal operation. To regulate the system as a whole, we preferably regulate the flow of refrigerant into the solar coil, the operation of the compressor, the setting of the damper, and the setting of the two pairs of three-way valves which determine for the air coil and the earth exchange respectively whether it shall be operated evaporating or condensing or cut off (or, in the case of the air coil of the brine-tank form of Figure 24, the setting of the three-way valves which determine whether it shall receive warm or cool brine). Flow into these latter when operated evaporating, and into the water cooler, is also individually controlled. As already explained, automatic control of the earth moistening system is also considered preferable.

Dual solar coil expansion valve 98, besides throttling the refrigerant down, regulates the flow of refrigerant into the solar coil so that, under the particular conditions of radiation and weather obtaining at the time, proper temperatures will be maintained in the solar coil.

More specifically, in solar coil expansion valve 98, as shown in detail in Figure 10, the liquid will enter by liquid input passage 310 in the side into chamber 311 and then go through valve passage 312 into chamber 313 and out through outlet passage 314 leading toward the solar coil. The supply of refrigerant through the solar coil will be cut off whenever valve member 315 closes passage 312.

The action of this valve member is regulated by the opposition to each other of Sylphon bellows 316 and 317 as affected by compression spring 318, attached to plate 319 which with Sylphon bellows 320 helps close off chamber 311. Sylphon bellows 316 is filled with refrigerant vapor coming from thermostatic bulb 321 (Figure 1) which is in intimate association near the outlet of the solar coil with cold refrigerant vapor piping leading from that coil, communication between bulb and Sylphon bellows being by capillary tube 322. Sylphon bellows 317 is in communication through tube 324 with the interior of the discharge end of the solar coil. Thus Sylphon bellows 316 gets superheat pressure, while Sylphon bellows 317 gets saturated vapor pressure; and sufficient superheating tends to build up the pressure in Sylphon bellows 316 and to make it overcome Sylphon bellows 317 together with spring 318 and open the valve passageway 312 to admit more refrigerant into the solar coil to be heated.

The position of the bottom end of spring 318, and therefore the force the spring exerts at any given position of the valve member, is determined by the action of solenoid 331 on armature 332 which pushes up plate 319. When the solenoid has current running through it, the armature will be brought up into the position shown in the drawing. When the solenoid has no current running through it, the armature will drop, with corresponding effect on the spring compression.

The solar coil expansion valve is readily adjustable. When it is desired to adjust the pressure that spring 318 exerts in its contracted position, this can be done by bringing the solenoidal part of the valve closer to the upper part by means of cooperating screw threads 337 on the two respective parts. This adjustment will also change the spring pressure in its extended position, in which the armature will rest against low temperature adjustment plug 338. Independent adjustment of the extended position of the spring is possible as a result of cooperative screw threads 339 by merely turning plug 338.

Control over whether or not current flows through solenoid 331 in the dual temperature expansion valve, is maintained by solar thermostat 343 and outdoor ambient temperature thermostat 344. When these two thermostats are both in proper position, electric current will flow through circuit 345, including conductors *a*, *b*, *c*, *d* and *e*, between opposite sides 346 and 347 of the line, and thus through the solenoid.

Solar thermostat 343 is subject to approximately the same radiation conditions as radiation-absorbent sheet 32, and also the same conditions as far as heat loss to the outdoors is concerned, but is out of contact both with the sheet and with the solar coil and air passageways so as not to be subject to the same conditions as far as giving up heat for utilization is concerned. The solar thermostat will be set to close its electrical contacts whenever its temperature rises above a certain point, such as for example 90° F., sufficient to heat air flowing under plate 32.

Outdoor ambient temperature thermostat 344 has thermostatic element 348 occupying an intermediate position between contact 349 on dual temperature expansion valve circuit 345, and contact 350 on circuit 351 through stop valve 97. The thermostatic element 348, whose position is adjustable by screw 352, is positioned to close contact 349 on the dual temperature expansion valve circuit when the thermostat falls below a certain temperature, say 70° F.

Forming part of the dual temperature expansion valve circuit 345 is also solenoid 353 which when activated will place damper 244 in the position shown in Figure 4, to allow air to pass through the air passageways 220 under the solar sheet. When it is not activated, the damper will swing into position for the air to by-pass these air passageways. (In the diagrammatic representation of Figure 1, for simplicity of illustration of the electric circuit, solenoid 353 and damper 244 which it actuates are shown away from their actual place with reference to the air circulation system, the actual place of the damper in that system being shown in Figures 4 and 5).

Thus, when the temperature of the solar thermostat is above the temperature set, say 90°, and the outdoor ambient temperature is below that set for its thermostat, say 70°, circuit 345 will be closed. As a result of closure of the circuit, the damper will be set so that air heated by the solar-radiation-absorbent sheet will be circulated for heating purposes, and at the same time the dual temperature expansion valve will be set so that much higher superheat in the solar coil vapor will be required to open the solar coil expansion valve, since the armature will have compressed the opposing spring 318 into relatively contracted position. Thus, under these conditions, heat can be taken from the solar sheet by means of the circulating air, while at the same time heat-receipt by the refrigerant can be largely limited to times when the rate of heat-absorption by the solar sheet is so great that it is more than enough to heat the air to the desired temperature.

On the other hand, if the solar thermostat is below the

particular temperature for which it is set, say 90°, or if the ambient outdoor temperature is above that at which its thermostat will close the circuit, say 70°, the circuit will remain open, and the damper will be set so that the circulating air will by-pass the solar sheet, and the armature of the dual temperature solar coil expansion valve will have fallen so that much smaller superheat will be sufficient to open the valve. Thus as the result of this arrangement, the solar coil will be nearly filled with refrigerant, with less superheating of the vapor, and the solar coil, and therefore the solar sheet, will maintain a much lower temperature, so that by virtue of the lowered rate of heat loss relatively more net heat will be taken in.

When the outdoor ambient temperature rises above a certain temperature, say 75° F., thermostatic element 348 touches contact 350 to close stop valve circuit 351, thus closing stop valve 97 to cut off altogether the flow of refrigerant into the solar coil, regardless of how much superheat there may be in the solar coil.

These various solar unit controls will have approximately this overall effect.

When the outdoor ambient temperature is above a certain point, say 75°, there will be no flow of air and refrigerant through the heating portions of the solar unit; the solar unit will have ceased functioning as a source of heat for the rest of the system. Thus, when hot weather makes cooling the primary requirement of the system, any incidental heating needs, as for domestic hot water, will be supplied from the heat removed in the cooling process, raised in temperature by use of the refrigeration cycle, or, insofar as additional heat may be necessary, it will be supplied from the earth.

When the outdoor ambient temperature is in an intermediate range, say 70°–75°, the air will still not be flowing through the heating portions of the solar coil, but the refrigerant will be flowing at a rate determined by the dual-temperature solar coil expansion valve, thus making heat available from the solar unit for use for such things as domestic hot water supply and for storage for ultimate use at times when solar radiation is not being received in great quantity by the solar sheet.

When the outdoor ambient temperature is below that intermediate range, say below 70°, then we must consider the solar thermostat. If the solar thermostat is above a certain temperature, say 90° F., the solar unit will primarily be heating air to be used for heating purposes, but secondarily may furnish excess heat to the refrigerant in the solar coil for the heat pump system. If the solar thermostat is below that temperature, all the net heat available to the solar unit will go into the heat pump system, and at a reduced temperature which will reduce heat losses from the solar unit.

The solar coil expansion valve and the mode of its operation which we have conceived have the great advantage, when heating is required, of flexibly controlling the temperature of the radiation-absorbent sheet in accord with radiation conditions so that when the radiation is sufficient, a temperature will be maintained at which the highly efficient direct transfer of heat by air can be used, and when the radiation is insufficient for that, nevertheless by maintaining a considerably lower temperature and thus greatly reducing radiant and other heat losses, the radiation-absorbent sheet can during a very considerable proportion of the daytime be used as a relatively efficient source of heat for the heat pump.

The operation of compressor 87 is controlled by temperature modulation controller 360, shown mostly in Figure 13.

The conducting contactor finger 361 is pivoted at end 362, through which it is electrically connected to one side of the line at 363. Intermediately between its end 362 and its contact area 364 it is attached to modulating rod 365 which is pressed upwardly by gas-filled Sylphon bellows 366, which in turn responds to pressure generated in thermostatic bulb 367 (Figure 1), which is outdoors beyond building wall 368 and communicates with the bellows by capillary tube 369. Counterbalancing the bellows in its pressure on the rod is compression spring 370 seated against disc 371 in well 372 in the upper part of controller casing 373. Since thermostatic bulb 367 is exposed to the outdoor air, the position of contactor finger 361 will depend on the outdoor ambient temperature.

Held respectively above and below finger 361 by end holders 380 and 381 are flexible contacting spring fingers 382 and 383, both electrically connected to the other side of the line at 384 through solenoid 385. Contact pointers 386 and 387 extend from the respective spring fingers toward contact area 364 of intermediate finger 361.

Sylphon bellows 390, connected by capillary tube 391 to the hot high pressure refrigerant vapor pipe system 88, has rod 392 extending downward from its end toward lower finger 383. Sylphon bellows 393, connected by capillary tube 394 to the warm low pressure refrigerant vapor pipe system 86, has necked rod 395 extending downward past upper finger 382 so that head 405 below the neck 406 will be in a position to raise the finger on upward movement of the rod. Bellows 390 and 393 are opposed in their action by spring fingers 383 and 382 respectively, whose action can be regulated by means of adjusting screws 407 and 408.

Solenoid 385 has armature 410, on the bottom of which is contact plate 411 so arranged as to bridge the gap between contact points 412 and 413 whenever current is flowing through the solenoid. These contact points are in circuit 414 connecting compressor motor 415 (Figure 1) to the line at 363 and 384.

Besides adjusting screws 407 and 408 for the two end fingers, the device has screw 417, which makes possible the adjustment of the setting of the middle finger for a given pressure in Sylphon bellows 366, by fixing the position of disc 371 which is seated against the lower end of the screw, and thus determining the force exerted by spring 370 at any given position of modulating rod 365.

Flexible fingers 382 and 383 are so positioned that contact pointers 386 and 387 are in contact with intermediate finger 361 whenever they are not held away from contact by rods 392 and 395. When either or both of these contact pointers are in contact, solenoid 385 will close the compressor motor circuit, causing the compressor to operate. If the pressure in the high pressure side is high enough for the end of rod 392 to push the lower finger to a position where its pointer will be out of contact, and at the same time the low pressure side pressure is low enough for head 405 to pull the upper finger sufficiently to break its pointer's contact, the solenoid circuit will be broken and the compressor will cease operation.

Thus, the modulating controller will regulate the high and low side pressures of the heat pump system by keeping the compressor operating as long as the pressure in either side requires it. Thus, refrigerant pressures will be maintained to meet the heating and cooling demands of the building and other demands such as those due to heating or cooling water and to temporary heat storage.

Furthermore, the controller will modulate its regulation in accordance with the outdoor ambient temperature. To meet cold weather, the lower the outdoor ambient temperature is, the lower in position the middle finger of the controller will be, and the higher the high pressure side of the system will be kept by the regulator, thus meeting the increased heating load. At the other extreme, to deal with hot weather, the higher the outdoor ambient temperature is, the higher in position the middle finger of the controller will be, and the lower the low pressure side of the system will be kept by the regulator, thus meeting the increased cooling load. In the intermediate temperatures, where such great capacity is not required, the less extreme the temperature, the less extreme will be the high and low side pressures maintained, and the more efficient will be the operation of the system as a result.

Thus with the less extreme outdoor temperatures, the greater efficiency inherent in smaller pressure differential between the high side pressures and the low side pressures will be secured, while with the more extreme outdoor temperatures, the greater capacity inherent in more extreme pressures will be gotten. We will thus automatically have a highly effective and flexible accommodation of the system to the requirements imposed by the weather.

The specific pressure ranges to be used in such a system will obviously depend upon various factors, including such things as the refrigerant used and the capacity of the system relative to the load expected. Where Freon is used as a refrigerant, a typical high side pressure range would be 200 to 250 pounds gauge pressure, and a typical low side minimum pressure would be 35 pounds gauge pressure.

Needless to say, adequate insulation will be required on those parts of the refrigerant system where loss or gain of heat is undesirable.

To control thermal communication between the refrigerant circuit and the earth, differential switch **421** (Figure 12) is provided. To a projection in casing **422** is pivoted at **423** arm **424** consisting of flexible element **425** near the pivot and of rigid element **426**. Against this arm presses compression spring **427** seated on nut **428**, which in turn rides on screw **429** for purposes of adjustment. In the other direction, pressing against the rigid element of this arm, is Sylphon bellows **430** connected to the high pressure side of the heat pump and Sylphon bellows **431** connected to the low pressure side of the heat pump system. These are so connected as to give Sylphon bellows **430** connected to the high pressure side less leverage than Sylphon bellows **431** connected to the low pressure side, in a proportion to be determined by the exact characteristics desired.

Evaporating circuit contact **432** is placed on the Sylphon bellows side of the rigid element of the arm, and condensing circuit contact **433** is put on the opposite side.

The arm is made of electrically conducting material and is connected at **423** to one side **347** of the line. Evaporating circuit contact **432** is connected by suitable wiring **435** in parallel through the three-way valves **121** and **126** to the opposite side **346** of the line. Condensing circuit contact **433** is connected through intermediate contact **438** and suitable wiring **439** in parallel through the three-way valves **121** and **126** to the side **346** of the line. Each of the three-way valves, which may be of any suitable standard variety, has three positions: a neutral position in which it is closed; and two alternative open positions each interconnecting the earth tube with a selected part of the rest of the refrigerant system as already detailed.

When the arm is in neutral position—that is, when it does not touch either of the two opposite contacts—the fact that the circuits through it are open will cause the three-way valves to be closed, thus shutting off the flow of refrigerant between the rest of the refrigerant circuit and earth tube **123** (using the form of Figure 1 as an illustration). Closing the evaporating or the condensing electric circuit by closing of the corresponding contact against arm **424** will set the three-way valves to permit flow of refrigerant through the earth tube to operate it evaporating or condensing, as the case may be, with the aid of refrigerant connections which have already been described. By having the three-way valves **121** and **126** electrically in parallel and controlled from points in common on the circuits they will operate in tandem, changing their settings simultaneously.

In the forms of Figures 17 to 19 and 21 to 23, of course, such three-way valves would control the refrigerant's access to tank **155** or cellar floor coil system **149**, or refrigerant tube **201**, as the case may be, rather than the earth tube. In Figures 17 and 18 the three-way valves actually shown, **121'** and **126'**, vary slightly from corresponding three-way valves **121** and **126**, respectively, in that **126'** is shown without any electrical connections. In this alternative form, instead of the two valves being made tandem in their operation by electrical means as in the case of **121** and **126**, **126'** would be held in tandem with **121'** in some other way, as by mechanical connections. It will be understood that such a method of keeping them in tandem could equally well be applied to any other pair of three-way valves which are here shown as electrically in tandem.

The differential switch operates as follows, as illustrated with reference to the system of Figure 1: When the weighted average of high and low pressures falls below a certain predetermined point, movement of the arm toward the evaporating circuit contact will complete the circuit to throw three-way valves **121** and **126** into position to make the earth tube an evaporator. Likewise when the weighted average of these pressures goes above a certain point, a circuit will be established through condensing contact **433** and intermediate contact **438** to operate the three-way valves so as to have the earth tube operate as a condenser. Adjustable screw **445** is placed so as to break the contact between condensing contact **433** and intermediate contact **438** when the weighted average of these pressures becomes sufficiently high.

By means of this control, it will be possible automatically to operate the system so that whenever the condition of the system is such that heat should be put into the earth, either for temporary storage, or, as during summer cooling, for gradual ultimate dissipation, the heat exchanger will operate condensing for that purpose, and whenever the system needs heat from the earth, the heat exchanger will operate evaporating so that the system will obtain it. This makes it possible to take heat which is orginally received as radiation by the solar unit at a time when the building does not need it and automatically store it in the earth and then later draw on it for use when needed.

Three-way valves **90** and **92** governing the air coil **91** (Figure 1), or, in the form of Figure 24, three-way valves **270** and **273** governing the air coil **272**, are desirably similar in their makeup to those governing the earth tube, and operated in tandem by similar means. Control over them is secured by indoor thermostat **451** having thermostatic element **453**. Below a certain temperature this thermostatic element will close hot contact **454** closing circuit **455** and thus setting the three-way valves to make the air coil operate as a condenser. Above a certain temperature it will close cold contact **456** closing circuit **457** to set the three-way valves to make the air coil operate as an evaporator. Heat then extracted from the house air is delivered into the earth or used when required for heating water.

The expansion valves (**242** and **127** respectively) used in connection with the air coil and the earth tube or other earth heat exchange when operated evaporating, and expansion valve **307** used with the water cooler, all have individual thermostatic controls. Each of these suitably consists of a thermostatic bulb **460** intimately associated with the outside of the discharge tube of the heat exchanger being used as an evaporator, a capillary tube **461** leading from the bulb back to the expansion valve, where Sylphon bellows **462** (Figure 11) with which it is connected is balanced against both spring **463** and another Sylphon bellows **464** which communicates by tube **465** with the interior of the discharge tube of the evaporator. As the superheat increases, Sylphon bellows **462** overbalances the forces against it and opens the valve to admit more refrigerant liquid into the evaporator; when the superheat diminishes, the valve tends to close, decreasing the flow of refrigerant.

With out repeating the more specific description of the operation of the system, as already treated in connection with the description of the system itself, the following are some of the salient features, in a generalized way, of the operation of our system from an overall standpoint, as used for example in the heating of a building.

During those times when the outdoor temperature makes heating the prime requisite, the way the system operates at any given time will depend on the amount of solar radiation being received.

When a relatively large amount of radiation is being received, heat received by the solar-radiation-absorbent sheet **32** (Figures 4 through 8), will be taken mainly into the air in the passageways **220** beneath it and thence passed into the building to be heated at the relatively minor cost of the forced circulation involved. Insofar as necessary, this will be supplemented by heat conveyed from the solar coil **33** in solar unit **31** by heat pump action at a relatively high coefficient of performance. Excess heat not needed to heat the building will be taken, either directly from the solar coil or from the heated air passing through the air coil into the building, by the heat pump and delivered into the earth beneath or adjacent to the building for temporary storage. The process of storage and of later use is greatly facilitated by the automatic maintenance of proper moisture content in the earth contacting and near these surfaces where heat exchange with the earth takes place.

When the radiation falls off to intermediate values, action of the solar thermostat 343 will result in shutting off the passage of the air through the solar unit and the system will get its heat from the solar coil in the solar unit by the heat pump action. Reduction of the temperature of the solar coil as automatically controlled by the dual temperature solar coil expansion valve 98 and solar thermostat 343, will enable the heat-gathering potentialities of the solar coil relative to the rate of radiation received to be greatly increased, at the expense, somewhat, of a decrease in the coefficient of performance. The coefficient of the system can, however, still be maintained by this means above the actual working coefficient of performance of other heat pump systems using natural heat sources under similar climatic conditions. Any excess heat gathered will be temporarily stored in the earth, as before.

Throughout the above conditions, heat from radiation by way of the heat pump can be used also to meet hot water requirements.

When the net heat received from radiation becomes too small to meet heating needs, heat will be provided by the system itself within the building. The amount of this stored heat may deliberately be made large enough to tide the building over peak electrical power periods without operation of the compressor, as by use of the large brine tank 269 as part of the interior system, or by a large hot water heat accumulator tank, as with a sufficiently large version of tank 102, or by Glauber's salt tank 286.

As further heat becomes needed when radiation is insufficient, the system will draw on the adjacent earth by means of its own heat pump action. The presence of the temporarily stored heat in the earth will enable it to do this at temperatures much increased over what the earth temperature would be if the same earth facilities were used without intermittent heat storage.

Thus the capacity of a given earth installation will be greatly increased. Furthermore, use can thus be made of heat coming from a solar radiation receiver at relatively high temperature and temporarily stored in the earth at a relatively high temperature, in place of heat that would otherwise have to come from the earth at earth temperatures that are at best normal, and very often greatly depressed as a result of the operation of the heat pump. As a result, with proper operation of the system, a considerably increased coefficient of performance is possible.

Along with its capabilities in heating, the system always stands ready, by proper use of its refrigerant circuit, to meet cooling needs such as, more especially, the cooling of the building during warm and hot weather, and also the cooling of drinking water. *

June 8, 1954
G. O. G. LÖF
2,680,565
SOLAR HEATING APPARATUS AND METHOD

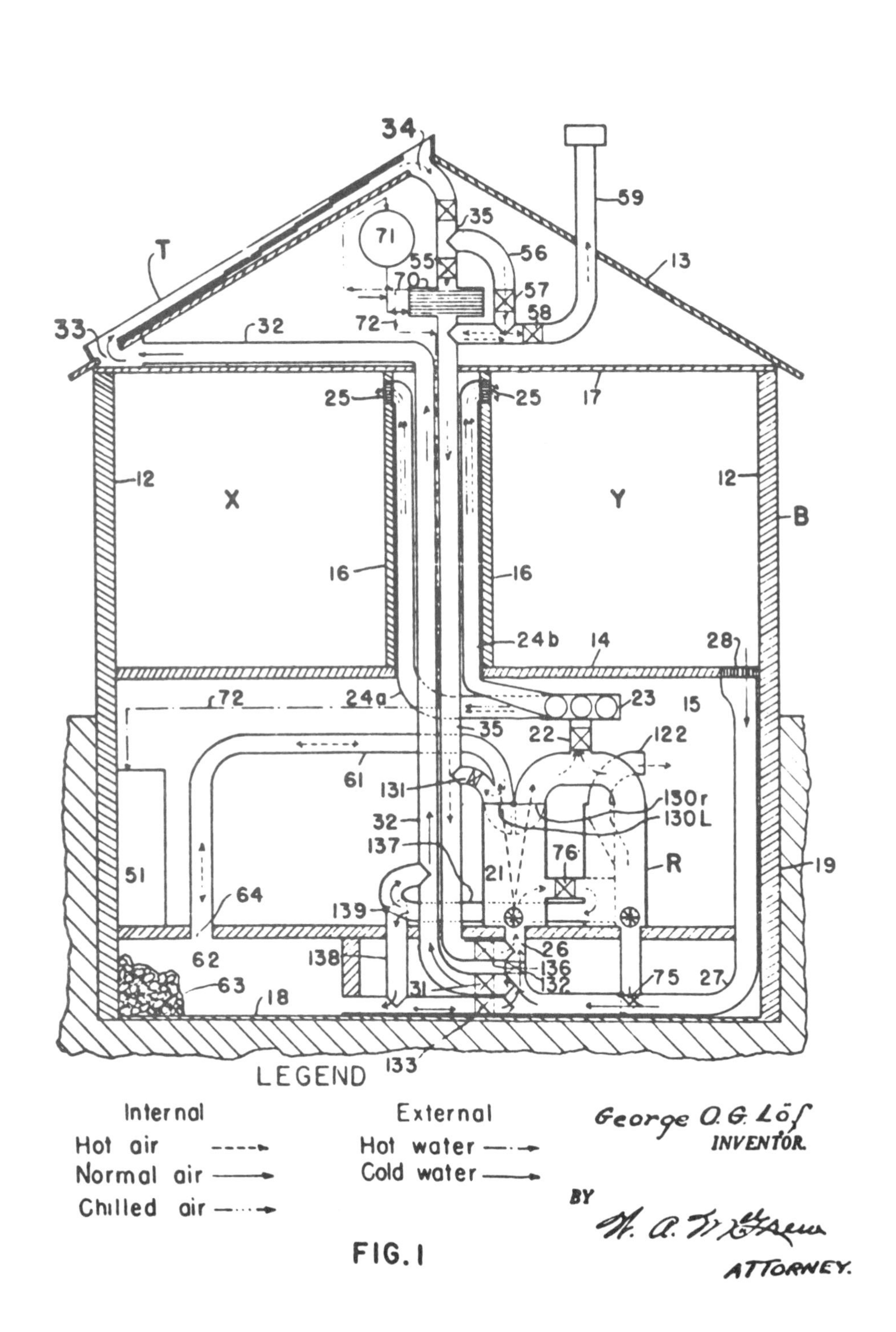
LEGEND
Internal
Hot air
Normal air
Chilled air
External
Hot water
Cold water
George O. G. Löf
INVENTOR
BY
ATTORNEY.
FIG. I

June 8, 1954 G. O. G. LÖF **2,680,565**

SOLAR HEATING APPARATUS AND METHOD

* *

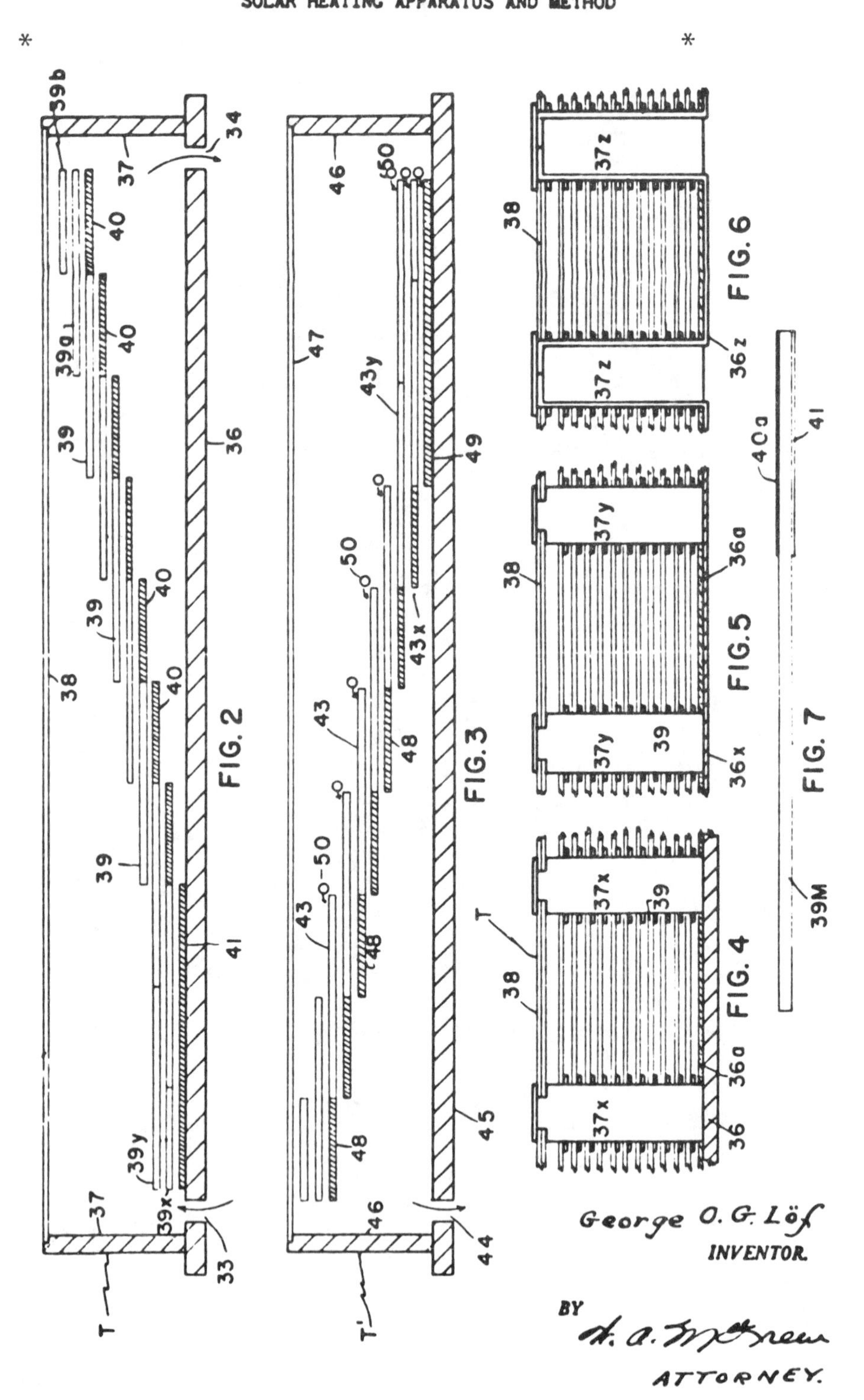

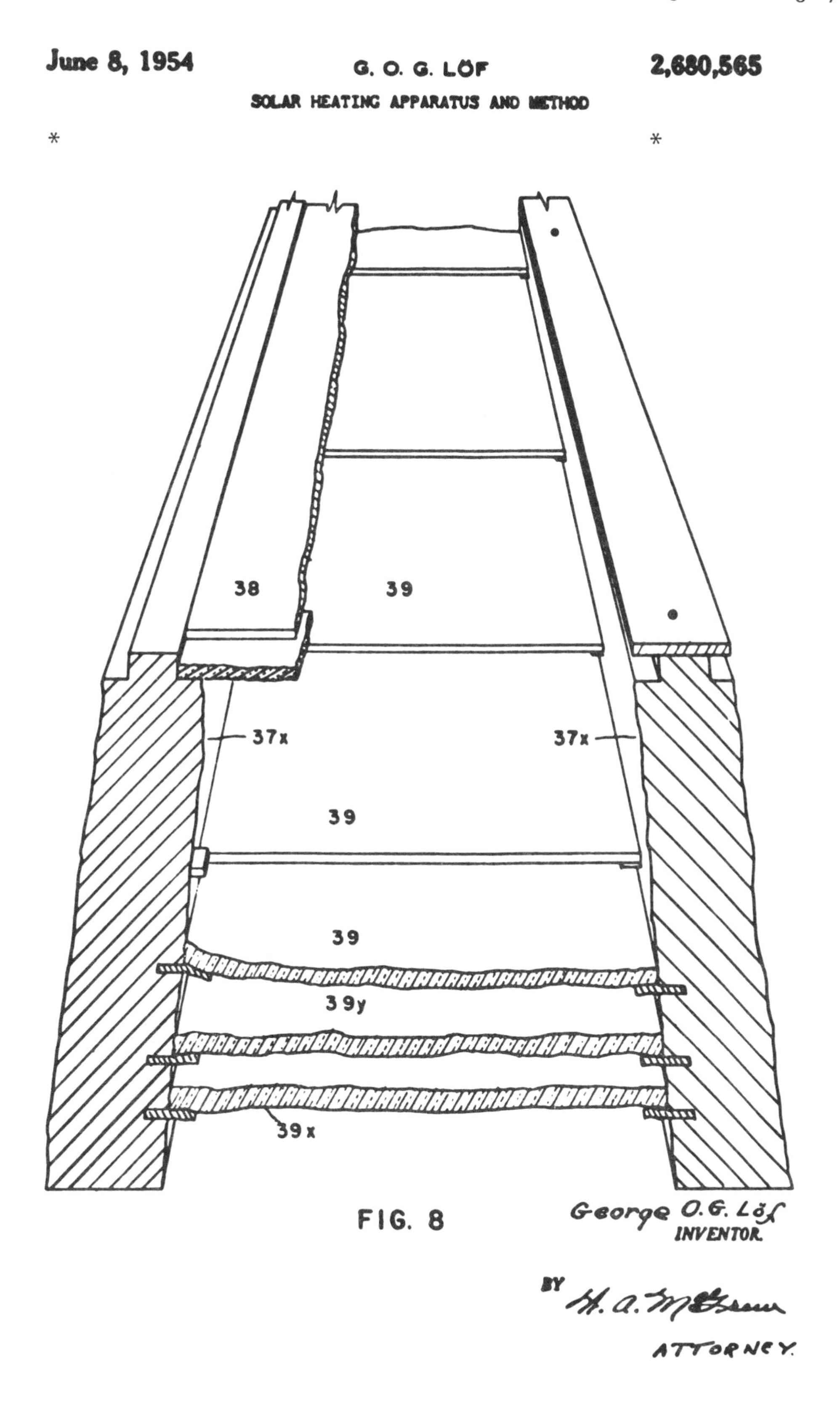
June 8, 1954
G. O. G. LÖF
2,680,565
SOLAR HEATING APPARATUS AND METHOD
*
*
38
39
37x
37x
39
39
39y
39x
George O.G. Löf
INVENTOR
BY
ATTORNEY
FIG. 8

June 8, 1954 G. O. G. LÖF **2,680,565**

SOLAR HEATING APPARATUS AND METHOD

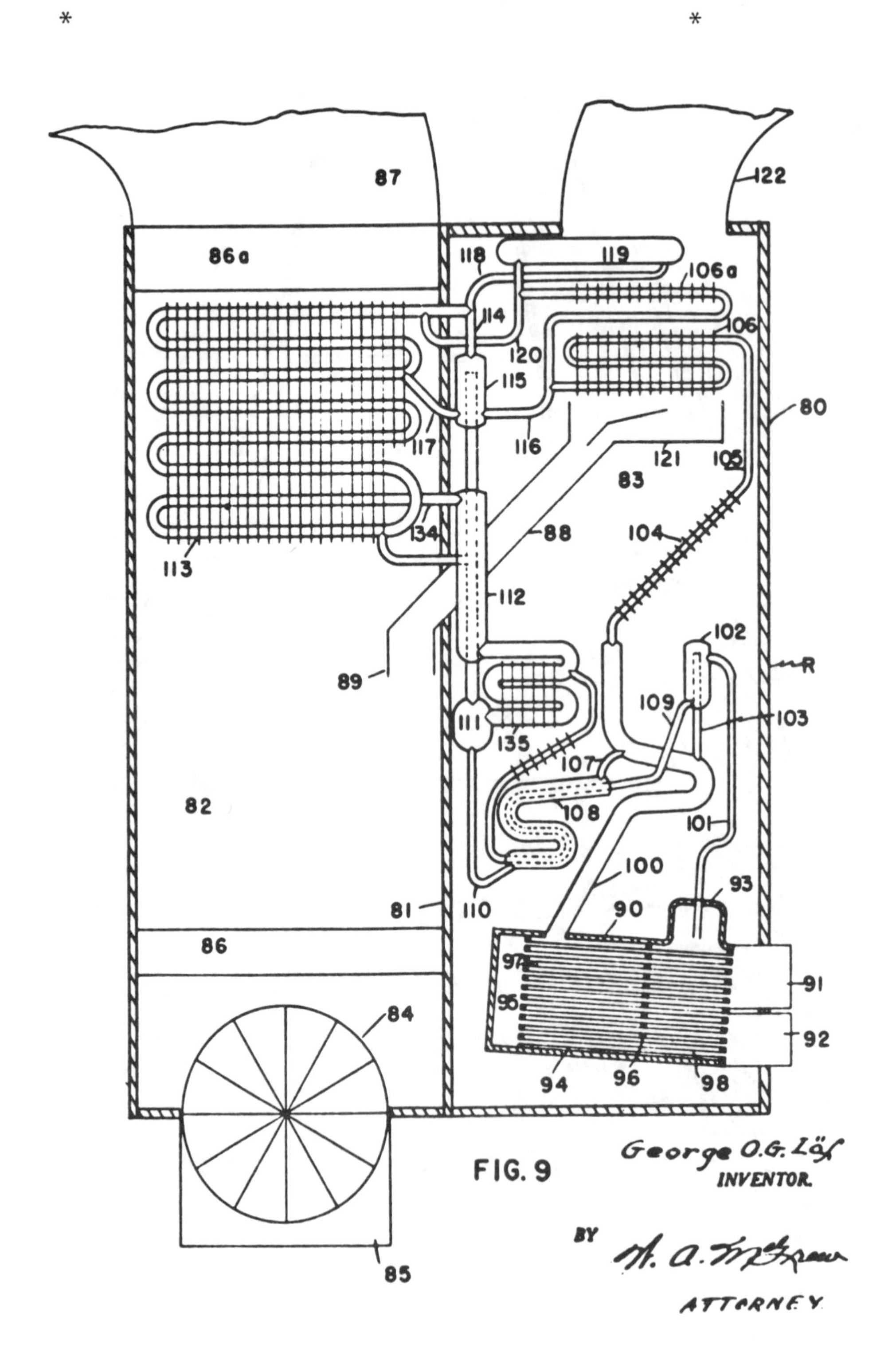

Patented June 8, 1954 2,680,565

UNITED STATES PATENT OFFICE

2,680,565

SOLAR HEATING APPARATUS AND METHOD

George O. G. Löf, Boulder, Colo., assignor to University of Colorado

*

This invention relates to solar heating apparatus and methods and more particularly relates to solar heating systems for household and similar installations.

Solar heating and the use of solar heat traps has been well known and extensively used for such purposes as greenhouse heating and the like, but in the past, little effort has been made to utilize this heating source effectively in household installations. However, in recent years considerable study of the subject has been undertaken and with the changes and innovations being incorporated in present day architecture, solar heating systems are now recognized as a possible adjunct of future home building.

The present invention represents the culmination of a series of investigations undertaken to provide a suitable system for household heating and the like, which is adapted both for installation in existing structures and also for incorporation in new construction.

It is an object of the present invention to provide a simple, efficient and economical method of heating homes or similar structures.

Another object of the invention is to provide a simple, efficient and economical method of conditioning the circulating air of homes or similar structures both as to temperature and moisture content.

A further object of the invention is to provide a simple, durable and economical heating system adapted for installation in homes or similar structures, which is adapted to utilize the maximum effect of solar heating as an energy source in the temperature regulation, water heating, and other appliances of the heating and water supply installations of the structure.

Still another object of the invention is to provide a solar heat trap adapted for installation in existing homes or the like, which may be utilized as a heat exchange medium to heat air, water or other fluids.

Other objects reside in novel combinations and arrangements of parts and in novel steps and treatments, all of which will be described in the course of the following description.

The present invention resides in the discovery that a solar heat trap may be provided in household installations or the like, which contains a plurality of zones or passages, within which heat rays are caused to travel in opposed directions between heat transfer surfaces defining the passages or zones. Within these zones, a fluid, such as air or water, is circulated in contact with the heat transfer surfaces and after heating in this manner, the fluid is circulated to other portions of the structure to be there utilized as a source of heat for the structure or for appliances, the operation of which is essential in the use of the structure. Preferably, there is also incorporated in the system, means for limiting heat radiation within the confined zones and other means for storing excess heat released through said zones.

Having thus described in general the features of the present invention, reference will now be made to the accompanying drawings illustrating typical embodiments and practices of the invention. In the drawings, in the several views of which like parts have been designated similarly.

Fig. 1 is a vertical section through a structure utilizing the features of the present invention;

Fig. 2 is a vertical section through a heat trap unit embodying features of the present invention;

Fig. 3 is a vertical section through another form of heat trap unit also embodying features of the present invention;

Fig. 4 is a fragmentary section through a heat trap installation illustrating a preferred construction for use in existing structures;

Fig. 5 is a similar section illustrating a preferred arrangement for installation in structures under construction;

Fig. 6 is a similar section illustrating a preferred installation built as a prefabricated unit;

Fig. 7 is a side elevation of one of the heat exchange elements utilized in the heat traps of the present invention illustrating a preferred method of surface treatment and drawn to an enlarged scale;

Fig. 8 is an enlarged perspective view partially broken to show interior construction in section of one form of heat trap used in the practice of the present invention; and

Fig. 9 is a schematic assembly view showing arrangement of parts in an air conditioning unit adapted to be operated by a solar heat trap of the type shown in Fig. 1 in a circulating system of the type shown in Fig. 1.

Fig. 1 illustrates an installation in a house or other habitation in which the various forms of solar heat utilization of the present invention have been combined in a single installation. It will be understood that for most purposes, liquid and air room heating installations will not be combined within the same structure, although under certain circumstances, it may be necessary or advisable to do so, for which reason both forms have been described or illustrated in the drawings. The air conditioning circuit illustrated is intended for use independently of or as an adjunct of the household heating system and a typical installation has been shown in Fig. 1. Also, the use of the solar heat source for heating the domestic water supply has been illustrated and this may either be a separate installation or incorporated as an adjunct to the existing household installation.

In Fig. 1, a building designated generally by the reference letter B is intended to illustrate a home or business structure and as shown embodies a two story construction, but which may be any number of stories within the capacity limits of the system to heat. As illustrated, the building has upright walls 12 covered by a roof 13 with a floor 14 partitioning the interior space into a basement 15 and other partitions 16 cooperating with the floor 14 and a ceiling 17 to divide the first floor space into a plurality of rooms designated X and Y. The basement is provided with a floor space 18 of any suitable material, such as concrete, and the foundation structure 19 for the building also may be any suitable material such as concrete.

A section of the roof 13 preferably located so as to have good exposure to the sun in both summer and winter is suitably apertured to receive a heat trap T, the details of which will be described hereinafter. When the heat trap T is to be utilized as a heating source for the building, it may be necessary to have it operating in conjunction with a stand-by heating plant and utilize a common system of conduits, outlets and the like and systems of this type have been illustrated in Fig. 1.

Within the basement 15 or in some other suitable area of building B, a furnace 21, preferably a blower-type circulating air heater, is located to deliver heated air through a valve controlled conduit 22 into a distributor 23 from which a series of conduits 24a and 24b deliver the heated air to room outlets 25. The furnace 21 also has a valve controlled intake 26 preferably supplied by a cold air duct 27 having its inlet opening 28 located as in the floor of room Y to provide a closed circuit air circulating system. However, it should be understood that if desired, an open circuit circulation may be employed, in which case the duct 27 would have its inlet located to receive atmospheric air from a point outside the building B. The furnace 21 may utilize any suitable type of fuel, such as coal, oil or gas and at such times, for example during the night hours, when the system may not utilize solar heating, the furnace is operated as in conventional installations to heat the rooms X and Y through discharge of heated air through outlets 25.

In utilizing the solar heating source in this circuit, at least a portion of the cold air entering through duct 27 is by-passed from the intake 26 through regulation of suitable valves 31 and 132 into a conduit 32 which in turn connects with the lower portion of heat trap T through a suitable opening 33 preferably located at the lower end of said trap. At the upper or opposite end of said trap, another opening 34 connects with a valve controlled conduit 35 which delivers heated air from the trap into furnace intake 26 and thence through the circulatory system as hereinbefore described. With this understanding of the general arrangement of the circulatory system, reference will now be made to the details of construction of the heat trap and its function and operation.

The arrangement shown in Fig. 2 illustrates a preferred construction for installations of the type just described. The unit comprises a framework having a bottom 36 and side walls 37 preferably forming a rectangular enclosure. The bottom and side walls may be formed of any suitable material, such as wood or metal, and preferably are of a dimension not requiring too great an unsupported surface for the glass parts now to be described. The top closure for the heat trap comprises a glass plate 38 supported at its sides and ends by the side walls 37. Although not shown, it will be understood that where it is necessary to protect the cover plate 38, as from hailstones or the like, a suitable wire screen or other protecting means permitting light penetration may be mounted in overhanging relation to plate 38. Within the enclosure thus formed, a series of glass plates 39 are mounted in spaced and substantially parallel relation and preferably staggered lengthwise of the enclosure in the manner shown. Each of said plates except special end plates 39a and 39b are provided at one end with an opaque and essentially non-reflecting area 40 preferably formed as by covering the said surface of the glass with black paint.

The opaque area thus provided preferably will be of a uniform length which is an even division of the total length of the plates 39. As here shown, the length of the opaque area is one third the length of the entire plate except at the lower end where one plate 39x is four times the length of its opaque area and another plate 39y is five times the length of its opaque area. Also at the lower end of trap T, the surface 41 of bottom 36 underlying the transparent portions of plates 39x and 39y is blackened in a manner similar to the plates 39, or a sheet of material, mounted on the bottom will have its upper surface blackened, as shown. Through the arrangement just described, solar heat rays entering through plate 38 are at all times directed against a blackened surface throughout the extent of the plate assembly. Obviously, the length of the opaque areas may be increased or decreased for a given sized plate and as long as the overall effect is similar to that just described, satisfactory results will be obtained.

While the arrangement of the heat trap T thus far described is adequate for most purposes, more satisfactory results will be obtained by providing a reflective medium throughout the opaque area of the glass plates 39. Such an arrangement has been shown in Fig. 7, in which a glass plate 39M having an opaque area provided by applying black paint 40a to its top surface has the portion of its undersurface underlying paint 40a covered with a reflective material such as aluminum foil 41. Through the use of the light reflective medium, a uniform reflective surface or surface effect is obtained which serves to retard heat losses occasioned by temperature differentials between glass plates 39 and bottom 36.

The arrangement of opaque and transparent surfaces just described has the further advantage that as viewed from underneath, the blackened areas provide a uniform reflecting surface. Because of this, the heat emanating from the blackened surfaces by reason of the stoppage of the solar heat rays travels in a reverse direction to said rays with the result that with respect to any given plate, both its top and bottom surfaces are substantially heated. Therefore, when cold air flowing through duct 32 enters the enclosure and passes between the several plates 39, a heat exchange action results which imparts an upward flow to the entering air and aids its travel to a point of escape at opening 34, although the primary air movement is induced by the blower in furnace 21. Due to the aforesaid heat exchange action, a substantial increase in temperature results so that the heated air passing through opening 34 comprises an adequate heating medium for the building. This air travels through conduit 35, enters furnace intake 26 and is then moved by the blower actuation to the distributor 23 and circulated through the rooms in the manner hereinbefore described.

With either type of heat trap as herein described, the parallel arrangement of the glass plates having opaque and transparent areas provides a multiple air film thermal insulation, as well as providing heat transfer surfaces to the air flow between the plates heated by solar radiation. Consequently, the solar heat is transformed to warm air at temperatures high enough to be adequate for house heating purposes even in extremely cold weather, and by providing sufficient capacity through the use of a battery of such heat traps, preferably arranged in adjoining relation, it is possible to generate sufficient heat to function as a heat source for various household appliances, in addition to supplying the required amount of heat for house heating purposes.

For most purposes, the heat trap will be utilized to heat a circulating air stream in the manner just described. However, it is practical to utilize this heat source in heating other fluids, such as water for example. Fig. 3 illustrates such an arrangement in which the trap T' is arranged to have liquid flow between the parallel plates 43 which are generally similar to the plates 39 of Fig. 2 and pass from the enclosure through a lower outlet 44 in the bottom 45 of an enclosure similar to trap T, having side walls 46 and a transparent cover plate 47. As in the other form, the plates have opaque areas 48 preferably covered with black paint and the surface of the bottom 45 underlying the transparent portion of end plates 43x and 43y is covered with black paint as shown at 49.

In this form of assembly, the upright walls 46 and bottom 45 will have to be joined in watertight relation to confine the liquid and prevent leakage into other parts of the structure in which the heat trap is located. As installed, trap T' will be located in an inclined position with the outlet 44 constituting the low point through which the released liquid will flow. The liquid is introduced into trap T' by a series of pipes 50 supplied from one or more headers (not shown) and the conduits have a series of jet or spray outlets from which liquid passes on to the upper ends of the respective plates 43, 43x, 43y and 49.

These plates are heated in the same manner as previously described through the arrangement of transparent and opaque surfaces and the liquid flowing downwardly along the plates is subjected to an intense heat-transfer action with the result that when it collects at the lower end of trap T' and passes through outlet 44, it is at a temperature adequate for the requirements of the household system. Any vapors generated in the heat exchange action will rise in contact with the under-surface of the overhanging plate and thus are subjected to further heat exchange action. Other vapors passing out of the upper ends of the passages between parallel plates and heated air within the enclosure tend to collect in the upper end of the enclosure and act as an additional heat source to assist in the overall heat transfer action of the unit. Moisture condensing at any point in the upper part of the enclosure will ultimately fall on to one of the heat transfer surfaces and then descend along same to reach the outlet 44.

In use, the outlet 44 will be connected with a suitable conduit to deliver the collected contents to a storage receptacle or some other point of ultimate use within the structure. Where the units of this type are to provide the circulating water for a household radiation system, for example, it usually will be necessary to have several of such units arranged as a battery to provide the necessary capacity. When a lesser quantity of heated water is required, as for example in supplying a hot water storage tank, a single unit will provide the required amount of heated water.

From the foregoing description, it will be apparent that the structural arrangements of the present invention may be utilized in heating a variety of fluids of which air and water are typical. Referring again to the arrangement of the circulating system shown in Fig. 1 hereinbefore described, it will be apparent that the various controls of valves, dampers, blower and the like may be automatically controlled as by thermostat regulation, for example.

It will be apparent that in the operation of the system thus far described, the heat trap T on clear days may produce an excess amount of heated air during at least a portion of its operating period. Two satisfactory methods of handling this excess have been shown in Fig. 1. For example, in the roof installation, a valve 55 may be operated to close conduit 35 and cause the heated air passing therethrough to enter a bypass conduit 56. Through suitable regulation of other valves 57 and 58, a portion of the hot air flowing through conduit 56 will pass into a stack outlet 59 while the remainder will flow back into conduit 35 and thence pass to furnace intake 26. If the aforesaid by-pass arrangement is not being utilized in the system, valves 57 and 58 are closed and valve 55 is open to permit the direct flow of air through conduit 35. After delivery into furnace 21, a portion of the heated air may be diverted through suitable damper regulation and passed into a conduit 61 which discharges into a heat storage bin 62.

Preferably, this bin is sealed and insulated from the atmosphere except for the inlet and outlet openings hereinafter to be described and a large portion of the volume of the bin is filled with a heat absorbing and retaining material 63 which preferably is a loose or spaced solid, such as sand, gravel or stacked brick, but which may be a fluid, such as tar, oil, water or the like. Consequently, when the excess of heated air discharged by furnace 21 into conduit 61 is delivered through a suitable opening 64 into bin 62, the bed 63 is gradually heated and functions as a heat storage unit of the system, and the air, after heat extraction, is recirculated to the heat trap through conduit 32. Subsequently, when heated air is no longer supplied to the furnace from heat trap T, warm air flows back through conduit 61 until diverted by a gate 130L and through a branch pipe 131 to pass into furnace 21 and is then distributed through the heat outlets in the manner previously described. The air after passing through rooms such as X and Y then returns to bin 62 via duct 27 with suitable adjustment of valves 75, 132, 31 and 133. Thus, it will be seen that excess heat produced in the operation of the solar heat trap may be utilized in the household system, if desired, or if not, may be wasted to atmosphere to prevent undue heating of building B.

It will also be desirable to provide an arrangement for heating a portion of the domestic water supply of the building at such times as the heat trap is in operation. As shown in Fig. 1, this is accomplished by providing a heat exchange unit 70 mounted about conduit 35 with a portion of the heated air passing therethrough diverted through a system of flues or similar water jacketed passages to heat the contained water of the unit. A portion of the heated water then passes to a storage tank 71, which tank has a cold water return to unit 70. The remainder of the heated water passes through a line 72 which empties into storage heater 51 located in the basement of building B. Suitable draw-off connections may be provided for both tank 71 and storage heater 51 and it will be understood that whenever the heat trap is unable to supply water at the required temperature, the storage unit 51 will be operated in the usual manner to heat the water required in the household supply.

The heat trap T also may be utilized to provide cooled, conditioned air when required for distribution throughout the building. To accomplish this, the furnace operation is stopped and the heated air delivered through conduit 35 is passed from furnace 21 into a refrigerator unit R through the opening of a suitable valve 76. After passing through generator 90 of refrigerator R, the air passes through duct 137 to duct 32 and recirculates to trap T, damper 139 being suitably adjusted for this operation. Air to be circulated by refrigerator R is drawn into same from duct 27 by a suitable blower unit, the course of flow of air through duct 27 having been changed by operation of a suitable valve 75. The air stream passing into refrigerator R after being suitably cooled is delivered to distributor 23 and then circulated through the various conduits 24a and 24b to the room outlets 25 to reduce the room temperature of rooms X and Y.

It will be understood that any suitable refrigerator unit may be used for this purpose and in order to clearly describe the practice of the invention, a suitable air conditioning unit has been illustrated in Fig. 9. This unit comprises a casing 80 having a partition 81 dividing its interior into a cooling chamber 82 and a second compartment 83 in which most of the operating parts are located. The cooling chamber 82 contains a blower 84 preferably having its intake 85 below the casing to receive the returned air flow diverted from duct 27 as previously described. Preferably, compartment 82 will have means for filtering incoming air which may be located at any suitable place, such as the area 86, and a means for humidifying air which may be located at any suitable place, such as the area 86a. An outlet for the air delivered to chamber 82 is provided at its top, as shown at 87, and in the installation shown in Fig. 1, this outlet will deliver the cold air past valve 22 to distributor 23. A conduit 88 having its intake 89 located within compartment 82 extends through partition 81 and discharges its contents within chamber 83 in a manner that will be hereinafter described. The mechanism of this air conditioning unit is of a conventional design of the type used in certain commercial refrigerators except for the generator unit 90 shown in chamber 83, the construction details and operation of which will now be described.

The generator has an air inlet 91 and an air outlet 92 at one of its ends and adjacent thereto a dome 93. The interior of the generator contains a tube section 94 of the general arrangement of conventional boiler construction. The end of the generator opposite inlet 91 contains a space 95 beyond the end of tube section 94 through which the hot air flows to pass into the return passages of tube section 94. A wall 96 divides the tube section into a main heating portion 97 and a secondary heating portion 98, and assists in forming a pressure head in dome 93.

This generator unit is used to vaporize ammonia from an aqueous ammonia solution by a heat transfer action and utilizes hot air supplied from heat trap T in the system shown in Fig. 1. To accomplish this, a conduit 100 delivers aqueous ammonia solution into the enclosure of tube section 94 where it is boiled by the heat transfer action and the resulting vapors rise in the main heating section 97 to pass from the unit through the same conduit 100 through which the solution is delivered to the unit. This counter-current circulation has the further advantage of preheating the solution flowing to generator 90. The gases rising through conduit 100 pass into a rectifier 104 which releases freed ammonia into a line 105 supplying a condenser 106 while the water condensed by rectifier 104 returns to conduit 100.

The gaseous ammonia entering condenser 106 is condensed to the liquid form and passes to evaporator 113 through conduits 116 and 117. Any uncondensed ammonia rises to condenser 106a and the liquid ammonia formed therein passes to the evaporator 113 through conduit 120. The downflowing streams of liquid ammonia meet an upflowing stream of hydrogen gas entering evaporator 113 through conduit 134 hereinafter described, the liquid ammonia being evaporated by said hydrogen accompanied by an extraction of heat from the circulating air in body 82 and thus providing cool air for rooms X and Y. The mixed hydrogen and ammonia vapors then pass from the evaporator through conduit 114, and the inner conduits of 115, and heat exchanger 112, to bulb 111. The gases then pass upward through absorber 135 countercurrent to a downward stream of water hereinafter to be described. The absorber 135 absorbs ammonia from the gases and the remaining hydrogen passes up the outer conduit of heat exchanger 112 to reenter evaporator 113 through conduit 134. The hydrogen reserve tank 110 serves to keep the pressure in the hydrogen system constant during room temperature changes.

When most of the ammonia has been boiled from the aqueous solution in heating section 97 the solution has a higher density and flows to the bottom of the generator 90 and underneath the baffle 96 to the secondary heating section 98 where further evolution of ammonia occurs. The ammonia gas rises into dome 93 creating a pressure which forces the dilute ammonia solution, hereinafter called water, up through conduit 101 into head tank 102. The ammonia vapor accompanying the water continues down conduit

103 to join the main ammonia stream going upward to the condenser from conduit 100. From head tank 102 the water flows by gravity down conduit 109, through the inner conduit of heat exchanger 108, and into the top of absorber 135. The water then flows down the absorber 135 counter-current to the stream of mixed gases flowing upward and absorbs the spent ammonia gases hereinbefore mentioned. The aqueous ammonia solution then flows into bulb 111, down conduit 110, through the annular space in heat exchanger 108, and into conduit 100 through the connecting conduit 107. The aqueous ammonia then flows into the generator 90 to complete the cycle. The flow of aqueous ammonia from the absorber 135 to the generator 90 is actuated by gravity from head tank 102.

The air diverted from chamber 82 which passes through conduit 88 reaches a distributor 121 which directs it across the surfaces of condensers 106 and 106*a* after which it passes into an outlet 122 to be exposed to atmosphere in any suitable manner as through a stack (not shown).

In the operation of an installation such as that shown in Fig. 1, it frequently will be desirable to store heat generated at heat trap T without circulating hot air through the rooms of the building, as for example, when the temperature of the room is sufficiently high through a preceding heating operation and additional heat is passing from the discharge of the heat trap. Under these circumstances, a damper 130*r* in furnace 21 is moved to close the passage through valve 22 to distributor 23 and a damper 130L is opened to allow the gases entering the furnace through intake 26 to pass into conduit 61, the valve in branch conduit 131 being closed. At the same time, damper 75 is moved to shut off the flow of cool air through duct 27 and another valve 132 is closed to block the passage between duct 27 and intake 26 while a valve 133 is open to permit an outward flow of heated air from storage bin 62.

When so arranged, the heated air leaving trap T flows downwardly through conduit 35 and into furnace 21 through intake 26. Having no escape except through conduit 61 hot air passes through duct 61 into storage bin 62. Through the opening of valve 133, a pronounced flow of air through bin 62 is obtained with the air returning therefrom entering conduit 32 past valve 31 which also has been open and thus the air returns to the entrance 33 of heat trap T.

So long as this operation is allowed to continue, the circulating air will be progressively heated, thus raising the temperature of the bed 63 in bin 62 and as this circuit is insulated from other portions and particularly the occupied portions of the building, no appreciable temperature rise occurs in these occupied portions. This circulation will be allowed to continue so long as the solar heat trap is functioning and whenever there is a further demand for heat, either from furnace 21 or air conditioner R or the water heating stages previously described, the circulation can be discontinued and the generated heat made available where required.

When stored heat is to be used for the operation of air conditioning unit R, hot air is drawn through duct 61 from storage bin 62. This hot air proceeds to duct 35 through duct 131 by suitable adjustment of dampers 131 and 130L. The hot air then flows into furnace 21 and into refrigerator R by suitable adjustment of damper 76 and after being used flows through duct 137 and 138 and back into heat storage unit 62 by suitable adjustment of vane 139 and damper 133. It is possible, if desired, to operate the refrigerator R by applying heat from natural or artificial gas or other similar fuel when the heat storage unit is cold and trap T is cold.

In the operation of the system previously described, the location of by-pass conduit 56 provides a convenient arrangement to prevent overheating of the storage water supply which otherwise might occur if heat exchange unit 70 were operated at all times when hot air was flowing through conduit 35. Whenever the temperature of the water in tank 71 reaches an established maximum, the valve 55 may be closed and valve 57 opened to permit the flow of the hot air through branch 56 and thence back to conduit 35 without heating the water in the heat exchange unit 70. Preferably, a thermostat control will be utilized to provide automatic regulation at this stage, although manual or other types of operation may be used, if desired.

In Fig. 1, no attempt has been made to show the insulation of the heat trap, conduit, storage bin and the like. However, it will be understood from the foregoing description that suitable heat insulation may be provided for all of the conductive parts of the system and the insulation to be used for this purpose may be any one of a variety of materials available on the market for such purposes.

Next referring to Fig. 2, it will be understood that if desired this form of construction may be utilized as a water heating unit rather than an air heating unit as described. In order to do so, it will be necessary to make the entire closure, inclusive of bottom 36, side walls 37 and cover plate 38, into a watertight assembly and then pump water in under pressure through the opening 33 to effect its movement across the heat exchange surfaces and its ultimate discharge at outlet 34. As the production of such a unit would involve construction difficulties in providing sufficient structural strength to carry the load and to withstand the pressures required in the pumping action, I prefer to use the form of construction illustrated in Fig. 3 whenever the heat trap is to be used in heating water rather than a gaseous fluid.

In assembling the heat trap in the roof of a structure, various arrangements may be employed. Where the installation is to be made in existing structure, the arrangement shown in Fig. 4 is particularly suitable and comprises upright walls 37*x* which cooperate with end walls 37 (not shown) preferably of similar width and thickness to form a box-like enclosure. The enclosure has a bottom 36 of the type hereinbefore described which preferably comprises the roofing material and the interior space of the enclosure is insulated from the building enclosure by a strip or bed of suitable heat insulating composition 36*a*.

As previously explained, it is necessary to have some suitable transparent cover for the enclosure and this is most conveniently effected by arranging a plurality of glass plates in tiers or layers with a portion of an end surface of one plate overlying another end portion of a second similar plate, a greater portion of which projects beyond the first said plate in a direction lengthwise of the enclosure. When it is necessary to brace the respective plates to support the weight of the cover assembly, suitable straps or bars of wood or metal may be arranged to bridge the space between the members 37x in supporting relation to the cover plate glass.

The arrangement just described will be best understood by reference to Fig. 8 which is a perspective view partially broken away to illustrate an assembly of this character. While the arrangement shown in Fig. 8 is illustrative in general of all the arrangements shown in Figs. 4, 5 and 6, it is more exactly a representation of the construction shown in Fig. 4 and consequently has been given corresponding reference numerals. In the preceding description, the arrangement of transparent and opaque surfaces has been described as being embodied in a plate of glass. While this is a preferred arrangement because of the simplicity of construction and assembly, it will be understood that the opaque black areas may be any suitable material which is non-reflecting, and if desired, may be separate pieces arranged in end to end relation with the transparent plates of glass or other suitable composition.

Where the heat trap units are to be installed in new constructions, it is possible to use the rafters 37y of the roof structure as a part of the trap enclosure, mounting thereon a cover plate 38 in all respects the same as the cover plate 38 shown in Fig. 4 and providing insulation 36a of the type previously described with a bottom portion 36x preferably attached to and in underhanging relation to the rafters 37y. Within the enclosure, the arrangement of transparent and opaque surfaces previously described will be provided.

Still another arrangement has been illustrated in Fig. 6 in which the enclosure is formed to seat upon rafters 37z and has end walls (not shown) similar to those previously described. A bottom piece 36z encloses the space between two adjoining rafters 37z while the usual type of transparent cover plate will be provided at the top of the enclosure. As clearly shown in Fig. 6, the material of the bottom portion 36z is U shaped in section and fits against the top and side surfaces of the rafter 37z. Through this arrangement, it is possible to order any required number of such trap units and mount same on rafters or other upstanding supports with the respective units joined in side by side relation as indicated in Fig. 6.

From the foregoing description, it will be apparent that the solar heating system of the present invention is well suited for incorporation in new constructions or in existing structures, and only a minor amount of the habitable space of the house or other structure is occupied by component parts of the system. When desired, the solar heat trap may be supplemented as a heat source by standard type furnaces, water heaters and refrigerators, although with proper capacity in the heat trap and heat storage units such standby appliances will be unnecessary in many installations. *

Feb. 22, 1966 H. E. THOMASON 3,236,294

BASEMENTLESS SOLAR HOME

* *

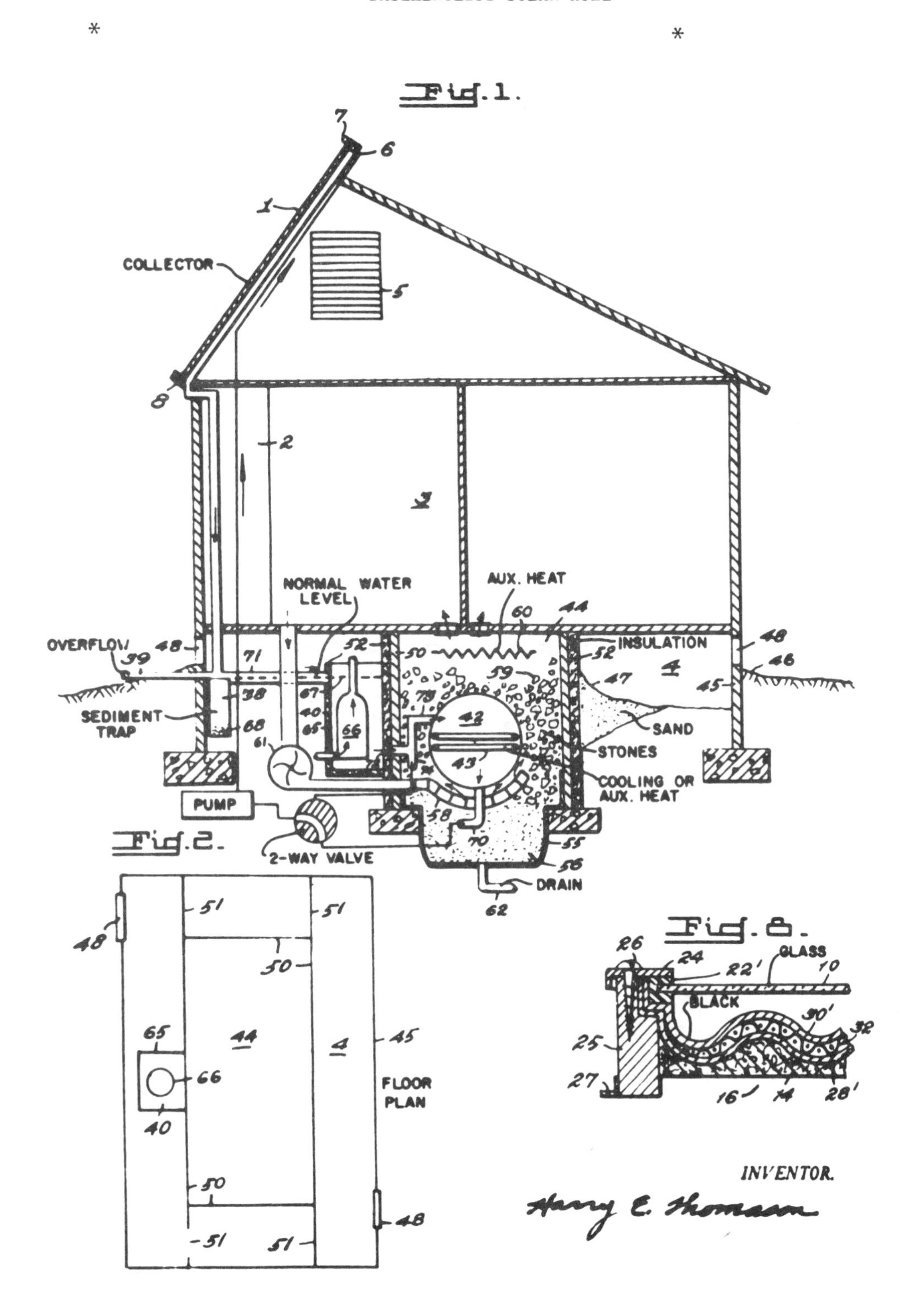

Feb. 22, 1966 H. E. THOMASON **3,236,294**

BASEMENTLESS SOLAR HOME

* *

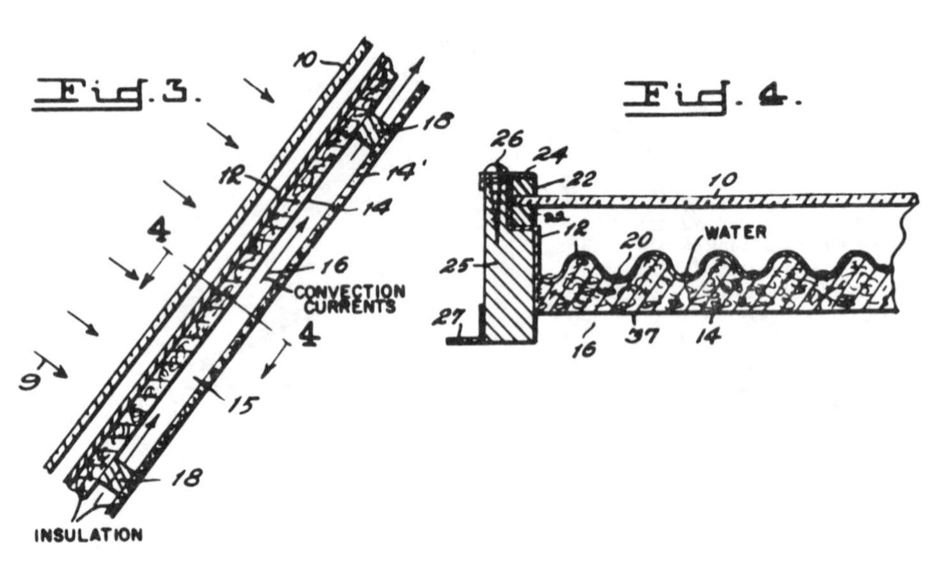

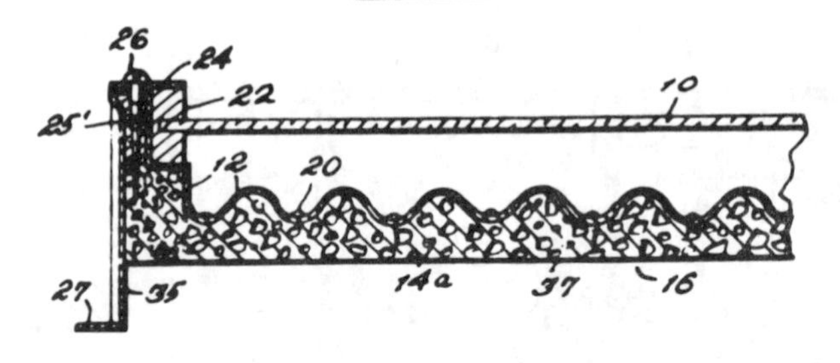

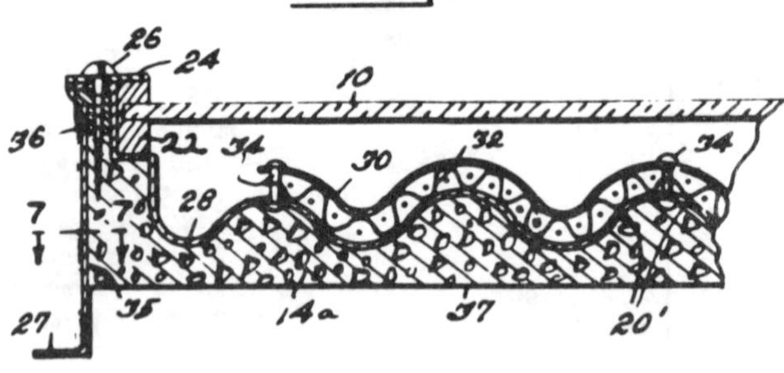

Fig. 7.

INVENTOR.

Harry E. Thomason

3,236,294
BASEMENTLESS SOLAR HOME
Harry E. Thomason, District Heights, Md.
(7354 Walker Mill Road SE., Washington, D.C. 20027)

*

In order to make a solar space heating system worthwhile and acceptable by the public it is necessary that the system be made simple, efficient, long lived and inexpensive to construct, maintain and operate. In many instances it is desirable to have the apparatus reversible for summertime air conditioning and usable to heat domestic water, swimming pool water etc. for the home, motel or other building. Also, the system should have heat storage means for storing heat, for storing "coolness" or for stabilizing home temperatures during variable spring and autumn weather as the ambient air temperatures fluctuate widely. Many homes are being constructed without basements and with only crawl spaces between the floor and the earth. If such type home is to be heated by solar energy, cooled by stored coolness, and the home temperatures are to be stabilized, then simple, low cost, highly effective heat or cold storage apparatus must be devised. The heat collection apparatus must also be simple, inexpensive, highly efficient and long lived.

The present apparatus is intended to meet many of the problems of year-round home comforting at low cost.

In the drawings:

FIG. 1 is a cross section of a solar heated and air conditioned home.

FIG. 2 is a plan view of the heat storage apparatus in relation to the foundation walls of the home.

FIG. 3 is a cross-section of the solar heat collector.

FIG. 4 is a section along line **4—4** of FIG. 3.

FIG. 5 is a modification of the heat collector.

FIG. 6 is another modification of the heat collector.

FIG. 7 is a sectional view along line **7—7** of FIG. 6.

FIG. 8 is a modification of the heat collector.

A solar heated and air conditioned home is illustrated diagrammatically in FIG. 1. Such home has a solar heat collector **1** preferably turned in a southwesterly direction to take advantage of more favorable afternoon solar heat collecting conditions. The home illustrated has closet space at **2** with living quarters at **3** and crawl space **4**. Ventilators are provided at **5** to permit hot air to escape from the attic on hot summer days. The heat collector may have distributor manifolds at **6** and **7** and a collector manifold at **8** for purposes to be more fully described hereinafter.

The solar heat collector is preferably constructed as illustrated in FIGS. 3 and 4. Solar energy comes in as at **9** and passes thru transparency **10** to a darkened collector sheet **12**. Insulation at **14** and further insulation at **14'** provide spaces or chimneys **15** therebetween so that heat escaping through the insulation **14** of the collector on a hot summer day will heat the air in space **15** and cause such air to rise as at **16**. This takes away excess heat automatically and avoids overheating of the space behind the collector, which may be closet space, an attic, or the interior of the home or other building. Spacers **18** support the heat collector spaced from insulation **14'**. The spacer blocks **18** do not extend completely across the collector and therefore the ascending heated air passes therearound. A fluid to be heated is circulated thru the collector, small streams of water **20** flowing down the valleys of a corrugated collector sheet being used for illustrative purposes.

In solar heat collectors temperature extremes from below zero to several hundreds of degrees Fahrenheit may be experienced. Thus, expansion and contraction problems in component parts may be expected. Also, dust, water vapor, condensation, freezing and thawing of water particles, etc. tend to deteriorate the collector. Thus it is desirable to have a collector construction with the edges of the transparent material **10** sandwiched between sealing means, such as long-lived, resilient neoprene sponge material **22**. A cap strip **24** may be simply secured to frame member **25** by screws **26**. Lugs **27**, or other expedients, may be used to secure the collector to a suitable support such as the roof of a building to be heated.

To protect the frame member **25** from damaging effects of water vapor, to seal out dust, and for other advantages, the collector sheet **12** is preferably crimped and made continuous adjacent frame member **25** as illustrated to receive sealing means **22**. Thus, no vapor from inside the collector can get to the frame member and water, dust, etc. from the outside cannot get into the collector.

FIG. 5 illustrates a modification wherein a simple screw securing member **25'** is used to replace frame member **25**. A foam-like insulation material **14*a*** may be used and is foamed into place to rigidify the collecting sheet **12**, to insulate, to simplify construction and to lower construction costs. The collector sheet is preferably made continuous along the collector edge in the crimped fashion illustrated in FIG. 5 (or in FIG. 6) and the base sheet may be corrugated along leg **35**, as shown in FIG. 7, for added strength and rigidity. Thus, the resultant construction has no place for water vapor to escape from the interior to damage frame members, insulation, or such, and water, snow, ice, etc. are similarly sealed out.

The solar heat collector of FIG. 6 preferably includes a corrugated sheet at **28** preferably having bright reflecting upper and lower surfaces, and a second corrugated heat collecting sheet **30** having its outer surface treated to make it absorbent of solar energy and with a low degree of radiation of heat energy, that is, having a "selective black" surface, or having a dull black surface. A liquid or gas to be heated, as at **20'**, is passed down (or up) between the two sheets **28, 30**. In order to spread the fluid and provide better contact between the heated metal and the liquid or gas being heated, a spacer element is provided as at **32**. This spacer element is preferably a mesh-like material. It has been found that corrugated aluminum for sheets **28** and **30** and aluminum screen wire at **32** are good, long-lived and low-cost. The mesh-like (screen) **32** is preferably heat conducting so as to transfer heat readily to the flowing stream of fluid whether it be a gas such as air or a liquid such as water. Means such as rivets **34** may be used to prevent separation of members **28, 30, 32**. Although a gas can be used as the heat transfer fluid, such gas being preferably circulated from the bottom to the top of the collector, a liquid such as water is preferred and the liquid would preferably be circulated from the top to gravitate to the bottom. The spacer **32** tends to spread the liquid and make it contact the portions of the spacer as well as making it contact both of the corrugated sheets to pick up heat from these sheets. Thus, the liquid weaves back-and-forth, in-and-out as it progresses down the canals formed by the corrugated sheets.

Upper sheet **30** is shown as not extending completely to the edge of the collector panel. Thus, if the total amount of fluid introduced at the top will not flow between sheets **28** and **30**, the excess may flow out into the unrestricted channel at the edge. However, the upper sheet may extend completely to the edge if desired, such as in **FIG. 8, thus completely sealing the area in which fluid is flowing.**

If desired a single corrugated sheet may be folded back upon itself as in FIG. 8 to provide both the top sheet **30'** and the bottom sheet **28'**, the resulting folded sheet being approximately one half the width of the original stock material and thus having one edge completely and absolutely sealed without any welding or such. Spacer **32** is similar to that of FIG. 6 and the upper surface of collector sheet **30'** preferably has a black or a selective black coating.

If desired, the original stock material may be tubular in form such that, when it is flattened and crimped along the edges to form the top and bottom sheets, the edges are both completely and absolutely sealed as explained above relative to one edge in FIG. 8.

Although the drawings show corrugated collecting sheets in FIGS. 3–8 the sheets could take other forms such as embossed, planar, V-crimped, etc.

A backing of reflective foil or kraft paper or hardboard or such may be provided at **37** to help retain heat, protect the insulation and to make the collector panel more attractive. Or, corrugated sheet metal similar to sheet **12** may be used for this backing material. The transparency securing screws **26** of FIGS. 5 and 6 may be anchored directly into the sheet itself with sheet metal screws or the screws may screw into captive nuts or into a small strip of wood **25'** in FIG. 5 or **36** in FIG. 6, or into other suitable material. When the plastic foam insulation is foamed into place it adheres tenaciously to the corrugated sheet metal, the box sides **35**, the screw attaching means **25'** or **36** and the backing material **37**. Thus, a long lived, firm, composite, light weight, low cost, highly efficient construction is provided.

The collector construction of FIGS. 6 and 8 minimizes water vapor and heat losses and keeps the outer solar-to-thermal collector surface **30** or **30'** from being exposed to excessive damaging liquid and vapor. Space **15** provides for air circulation to take away excessive heat. Thus collector temperatures are kept from soaring excessively if the apparatus is not in use, and heat passage through the collector into the space behind the insulation **14'** is minimized. As may be seen from FIG. 3 any excessive heat leakage through the collector, such as on hot summer days for example, is carried upwardly under the collector insulation **14** (or **14*a***) and may go into the attic and out through vents **5** by ascending air currents **16** behind the collector. When water is the fluid to be heated this heated water may be collected at the bottom of the collector at **8** (see FIG. 1) to flow into sediment trap **38** and through a domestic water preheater assembly at **40** and on via **72**, **73** to liquid storage drum **42** in the heat or cold storage bin. An overflow pipe to the outside is shown at **39** and cooling or auxiliary heating coils may be provided in drum **42** at **43**. The storage bin **44** is illustrated as constructed in a basementless home in the crawl space **4**, thus avoiding the necessity for an expensive basement construction which many contractors refuse to build and many home purchasers do not want. In some instances the crawl space may be nearly adequate for the heat or cold storage apparatus. If the crawl space is inadequate, a depression in the storage space area may be scooped out and the earth taken from the depression may be banked around the foundation walls **45** as at **46** to help divert rainwater from the foundation walls. Part of the earth may be banked around the storage bin walls as at **47**. However, sand or other granular insulating material is deemed to be a preferable material for this embankment. Due to the low cost, and inasmuch as dry sand is a fair insulator, and inasmuch as dampness tends to dissipate more readily from sand following a dampening thereof, sand is good for the embankment **47**. Windows or ventilators may be provided at **48**.

The storage bin compartment **44** is preferably formed in the crawl space by walls **50**. These walls may support the floor joists to thus save on construction costs for typical steel I beams. These walls may extend beyond the storage bin walls at **51** if desired (see FIG. 2) so as to support the floor joists beyond the storage bin walls. The storage bin is preferably insulated at the top between the floor joists and on the side walls of the storage bin. If desired the insulation may be placed around the outside of the walls as at **52** so that the wall material itself, which may be bricks, blocks or other, will serve to increase heat or cold storage capacity of the bin. Further, when the insulation is placed outside, there is no crushing thereof by the stone or other heat storage apparatus.

The storage bin preferably has a vapor barrier **55** in the bottom thereof and a granular semi-insulating material **56** such as dry sand, thereabove. If desired a second vapor barrier may be provided above the sand. Also, a vapor barrier is preferably provided around bin walls **50** exteriorly of insulation **52**. An air distributor system **58** may be used to distribute air to the area beneath the drum **42** and beneath the stone or other heat storage material **59**. A water cooling element such as a refrigeration evaporator may be inserted in drum **42** as illustrated at **43**. This element cools the drum of water, and stone around the drum, for air conditioning the building during hot weather. Auxiliary heat, for use during long cloudy spells of the winter when solar heat input is insufficient, may be provided by reversing the heat pump operation so as to get auxiliary heat from coils **43**. Or, electric heating element **60**, or a gas or oil burning unit, or a combination of such units, may be used for auxiliary heat. A blower is provided at **61** to circulate air thru the storage apparatus and the building to be héated or cooled.

In the present description main emphasis is on collection by circulating a liquid through the collector and storing hot water in the storage bin **44**. However, it is anticipated that a gas such as air may be circulated through the collector and through the storage bin by a blower whereby to heat the stonelike material **59**, either with or without the drum of water, for storage of the heat. Cooling coils **43** may be used to chill the water in drum **42**, or may be embedded in stone **59** to chill the stone directly for summertime air-conditioning if no water drum is provided.

If desired a drain pipe may be connected in the bottom of the sand space as at **62** so that water could be drained or pumped from the sand in an emergency such as where a local flood, or leaking of drum **42** or of a water line or such would flood the heat bin.

The blower **61** is used to withdraw cold air from the home and introduce in into the heat storage bin through the air distributor system **58**. A very simple, inexpensive air distributor system may be made of building blocks, with holes therein, laid on edge so that the holes align to form air ducts or passages. The blocks are spaced apart slightly to allow air to pass out therefrom at spaced points. The air then spirals back and forth up through the stones and around the drum. Of course bricks or other materials could be used to form perforated ducts to introduce air into the bottom of the bin.

The domestic water preheater assembly **40** has an outer tank **65**, insulated to prevent heat loss, and in inner tank **66** for fresh water under pressure. The fresh water tank is bathed in hot solar-heated water from the solar heat collector and the outer tank need not be under pressure. Normal water level **67** is attained automatically each time it rains, the rainwater falling on the heat collector **1** flowing into collector manifold **8** and down into the automatic rainwater makeup device and sediment trap **38**. When the water has reached the proper level **67**, excess water overflows via **39**. Sediment settles out at **68** to keep the water in the system clean. Thus, the automatic water makeup system requires no expensive valve to possibly fail and cause trouble. If desired, a float-controlled valve can be used to admit makeup water from a public water supply. However, the apparatus herein described makes such arrangement unnecessary for most installations.

For wintertime solar heating, water is withdrawn from the bottom of large drum **42** via outlet **70** and is circulated to distributor manifold **6** at the top of collector **1**. As the water descends it is heated and is collected in collector manifold **8** as hot water. From manifold **8** it flows to sediment trap **38** and via pipe **71** into the outer tank **65** of domestic water preheater **40**. The hot water thus bathes the fresh water tank **66** to heat the water therein and passes on out from outer tank **65** via **72**, **73** into large drum **42** to heat the water in the large drum. The drum of hot water yields up part of its heat load to the surrounding stone or other heat storage material **59** while the water cools back down ready to take on another "load of heat" on its next pass through the heat collector **1**. Air from the home is circulated around the drum of heated water and through the heated stone to warm the air and the home as needed.

For summertime use, water is not drawn out from large drum **42** via outlet **70** but is drawn directly from tank **65** via **72** and **74** and is then recirculated to the heat collector **1** until the domestice water is sufficiently heated. Domestic water heater assembly **40** is insulated from storage bin **44**. During the hot weather the water in large drum **42** may be chilled, preferably at night, by flowing the water over the heat collector via distributor manifold **7**, or by flowing it over the north-sloping roof of the building, or by refrigeration cooling coils **43**, or by a combination of these features. If the water is chilled by flowing it over the north sloping roof, or over the heat collector, it is returned directly to drum **42** by appropriate connections, thus leaving hot water in heater **40** while chilling water in drum **42**. If any water is lost from the heat collector system it is automatically replenished by rainwater. However, if a drought condition occurs, the relatively small reserve of water in the top of the tank **65** may be lost. With the apparatus herein described if the water level in tank **65** drops to a level below the top of large drum **42**, then makeup water from drum **42** will flow automatically into tank **65**, or to outlet **74** while water is being drawn from **74** for circulation to the collector. Thus, a relatively large amount of water is available from drum **42** to automatically replenish water in the domestice water heating system **40** in the event of emergency drought conditions or excessive loss of water from the solar water heating system.

Distributor manifold **7** may be used for many purposes. Water may be circulated to manifold **7** at night to flow down over the outside of the heat collector transparency and to thus cool the water. The water may be collected in trough **8** of the heat collector and passed directly to drum **42** by simple means well-known to an engineer. Or the water may be chilled by circulating it over the north-sloping roof at night. In some climates this method of heat dissipation is adequate for air-conditioning the home. If ice and snow should accumulate on the collector it can be dislodged by flowing water onto the collector transparency by way of distributor **7**. If dust collects excessively and the collector transparency is not washed clean by rainwater, water may be brought onto the collector through distributor manifold **7** to wash the collector. *

PATENTED SEP 3 1974

3,832,992

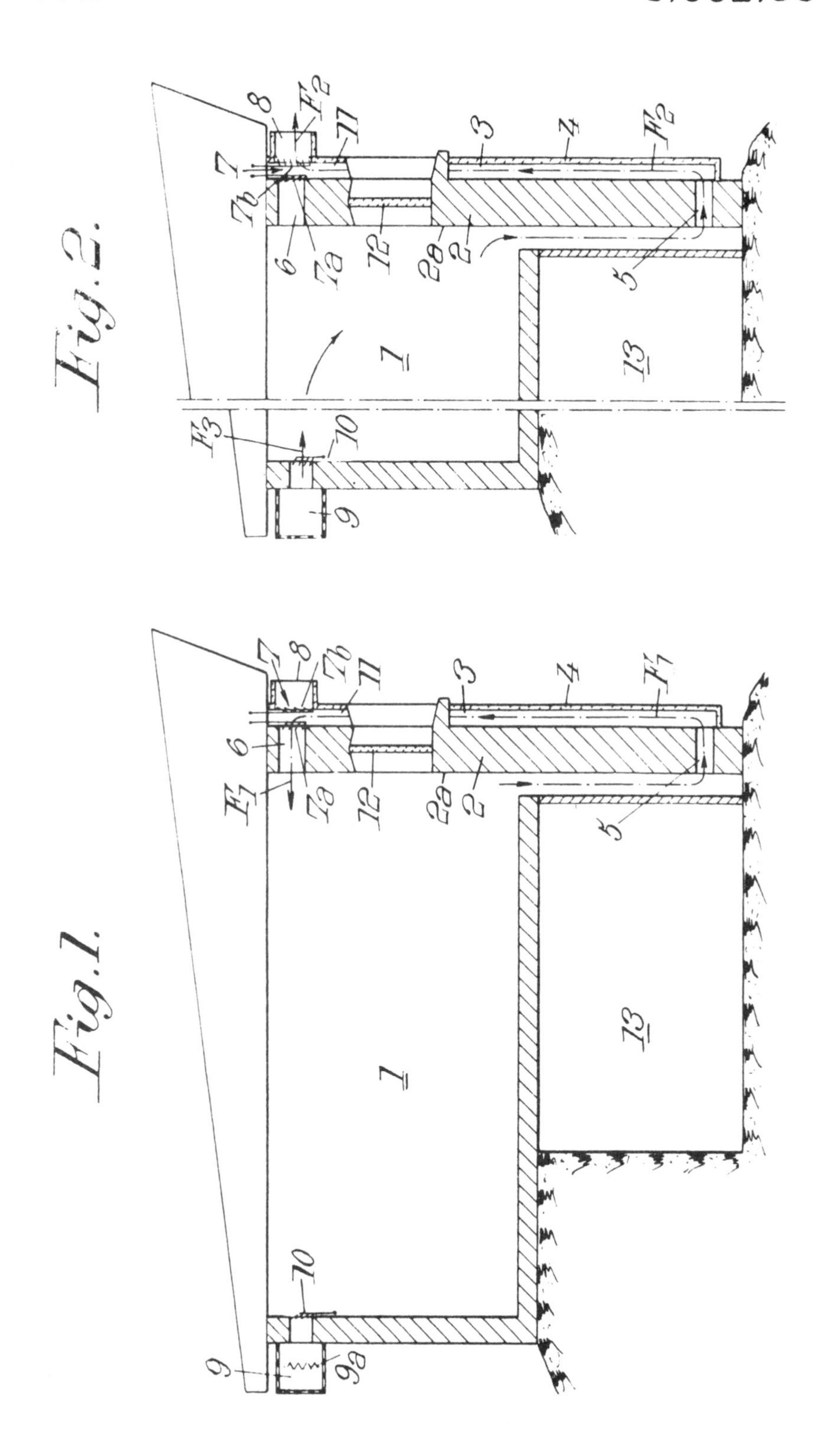

PATENTED SEP 3 1974 3,832,992

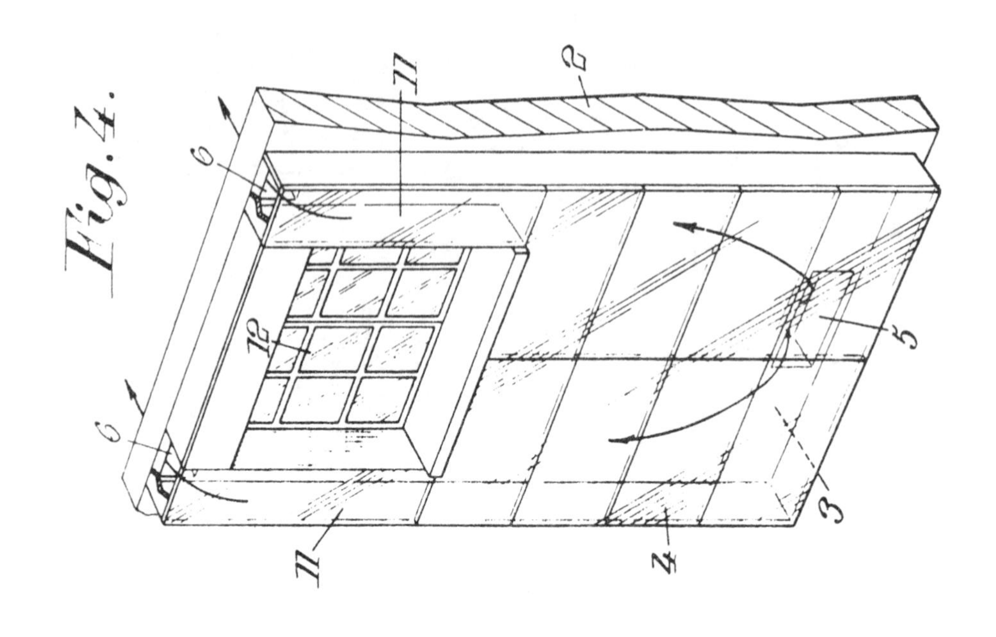

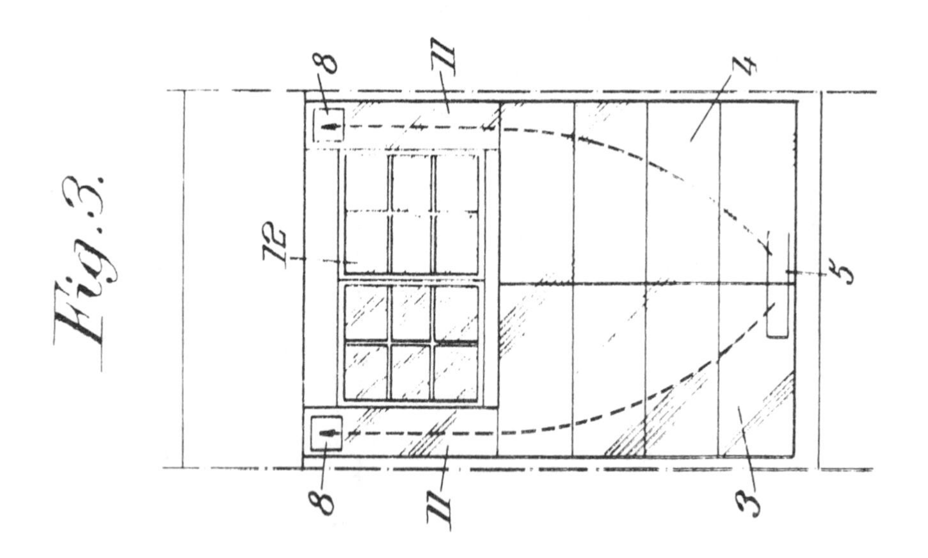

PATENTED SEP 3 1974

3,832,992

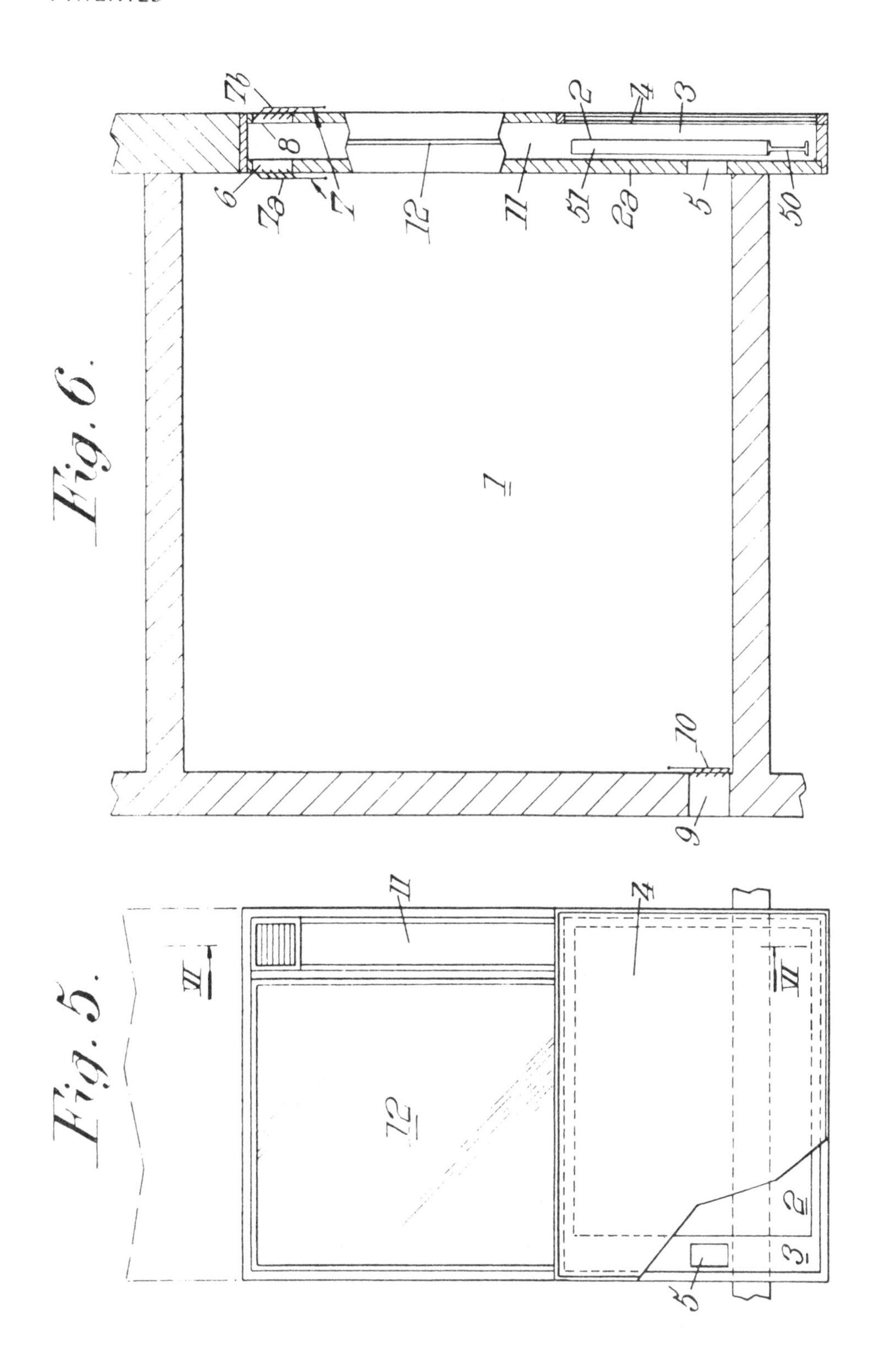

PATENTED SEP 3 1974 3,832,992

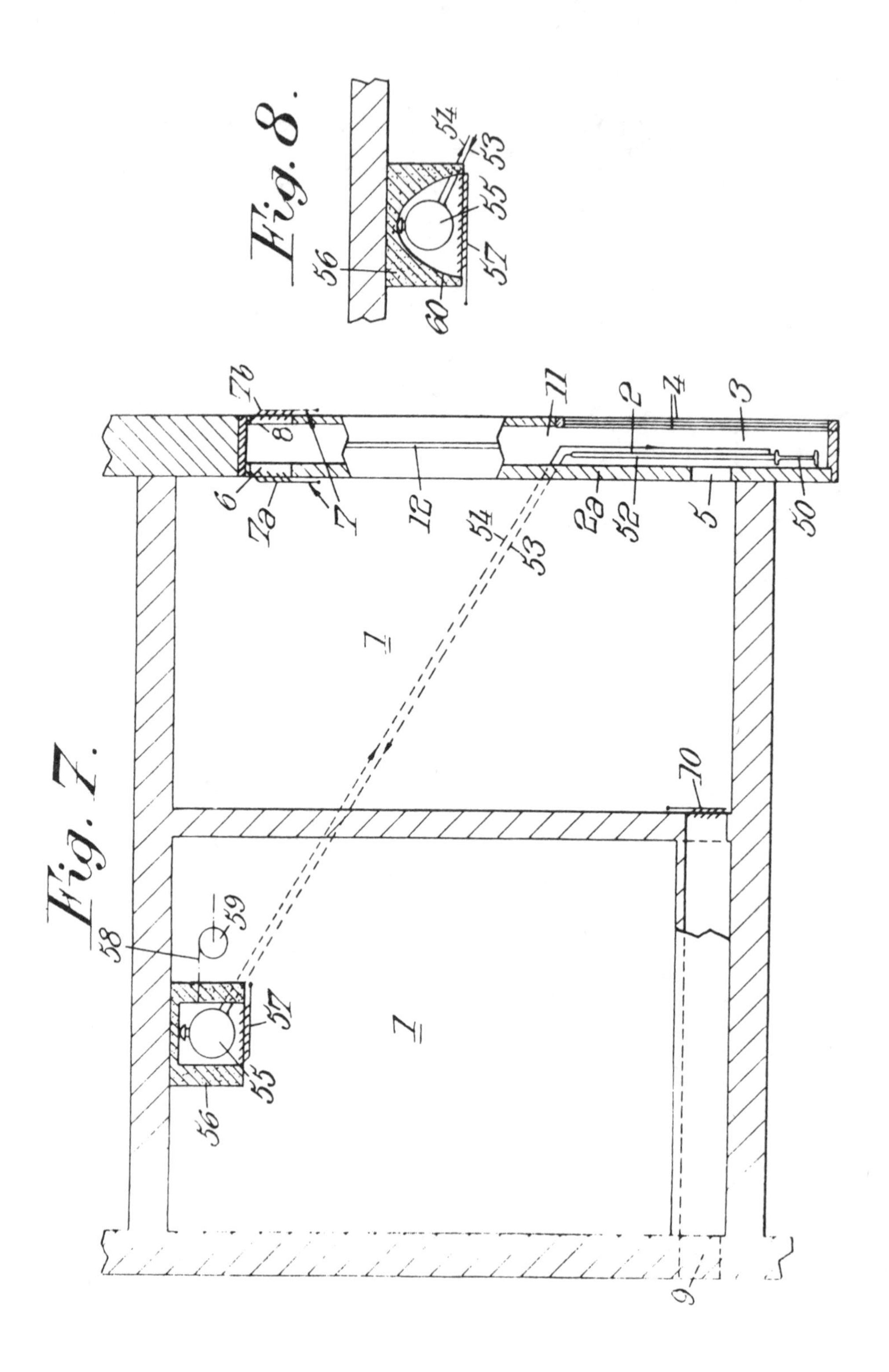

PATENTED SEP 3 1974

3,832,992

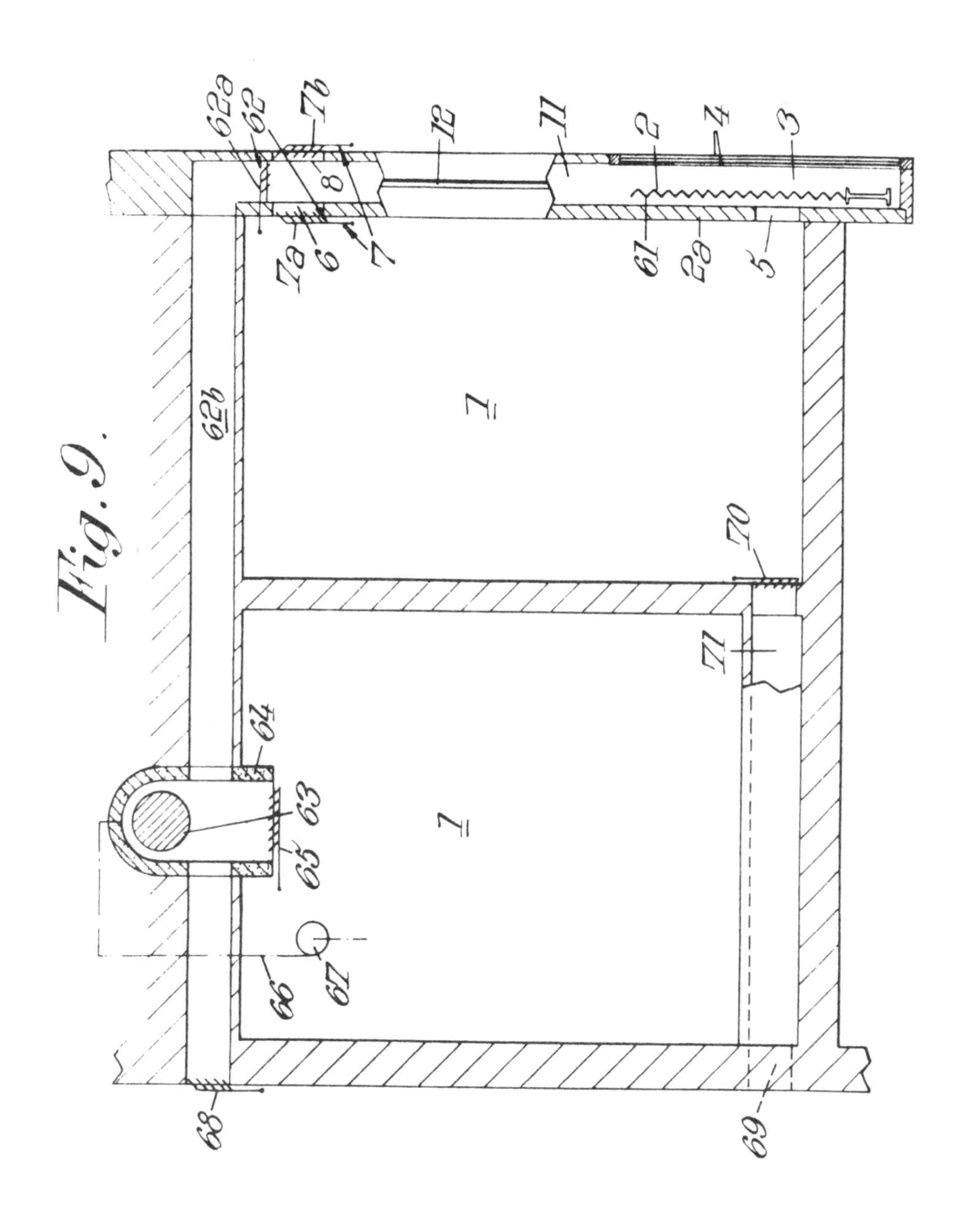

Inventors: **Felix Trombe,** Paris; **Jacques Michel,** Neuilly-sur-Seine, both of France

Assignee: **Agence Nationale De Valorisation De La Recherche (Anvar),** Courdevoie, France

* **ABSTRACT**

The dwelling is equipped with an installation for natural convective air conditioning comprising at least one thermal enclosure bounded by a frontage element of the dwelling exposed to solar radiation and an outer wall transparent to solar radiation and opaque to the far infrared radiation. This outer wall is arranged close to said frontage element, the top and the bottom of this thermal enclosure being able to communicate with the dwelling. The thermal enclosure has at its upper portion, first distributor means arranged to direct hot air into the dwelling or to the outer and the dwelling has a cold air inlet device provided with closure means. *

NATURALLY AIR-CONDITIONED DWELLINGS

The present invention relates to dwellings equipped with natural air conditioning installations, these installations being of the type described in French Patent No. 1,152,129 filed Mar. 1, 1956.

In this patent, there are described air conditioning installations in which the air is heated in at least one thermal enclosure mainly bounded by, on one hand, a frontage element exposed to solar radiation, and on the other hand, an outer wall transparent to solar radiation and opaque to the far infrared radiation, this outer wall being generally arranged parallel to the frontage element and close to said element, the top and the bottom of this thermal enclosure being able to communicate with the dwelling.

The air is heated in this enclosure to be then distributed in the dwelling.

However, it has been observed that in dwellings equipped with such air conditioning installations it was impossible to adjust the efficiency of the air conditioning, which constituted a considerable inconvenience in climates where the temperature differences arising during the three hot seasons (spring, summer and autumn) are large.

In addition, it posed problems due to the necessity for providing, on a same dwelling frontage, frontage elements required for the air conditioning and openings necessary for the comfort and the amenities of the dwelling.

In the absence of special precautions the circulation of air in the dwelling is effected in insufficient manner, which reduced the thermal exchanges.

It also led to habitable rooms whose volume was too large with respect to their floor surface.

It should also be pointed out that hitherto the interception and storage of the energy of solar radiation operated by means of conventional frontage elements constituted, at least to a large extent, by traditional materials, such as concrete or bricks, which led to heavy construction.

In particular many present structures are built from a frame-work in which frontage elements are arranged which cannot be constituted by traditional materials, whose weight would be prohibitive.

The present invention consists of various arrangements which can be applied independently of one another, but which can advantageously be applied in certain of their combinations, these arrangements having the object of overcoming the various above-mentioned drawbacks.

According to a first feature of the invention, on one hand, the thermal enclosure comprises in its upper portion, first distributor means arranged to direct hot air into the dwelling or to the outside, and preferably part into the dwelling, part to the outside, and on the other hand, the dwelling comprises a device for the inlet of cold air provided with closure means.

It will then be seen that when the first distributor means direct all or part of the hot air to the outside, there is produced an aspiration of cold air into the dwelling, by means of the cold air inlet device whose closure means are in a fully or partially open position.

According to a second feature of the invention, the thermal enclosure is associated with at least one reentry passage leading hot air to the top of the frontage, whence it can be distributed into the dwelling **1.**

It will then be seen that it is possible to arrange in the frontage and between the one or more re-entry passages, openings such as windows, whose number and size can be conventional.

Moreover, the circulation of the hot fluid is improved to a considerable extent by the "entraining" effect achieved by the one or more re-entry passages.

According to a third feature of the invention, the frontage element comprises a closed storage space containing a liquid whose mass is sufficient to store the thermal energy resulting from the exposure of said frontage element.

Due to this arrangement there can be formed a frontage element without calling upon traditional materials, which leads, for equal efficiency of interception and of storage to economy of weight in the proportion of at least 5 to 1.

According to a fourth feature of the invention, the frontage element comprises an intercepting space containing a liquid and communicating, preferably through at least one ascending passage and through at least one descending passage, with a reserve space advantageously situated higher than said intercepting space, this reserve space being arranged to restore part at least of the thermal energy accumulated to contribute to the air conditioning of the dwelling, the total mass of the liquid contained in this intercepting space and this reserve space being sufficient to accumulate the thermal energy from the exposure of the abovesaid frontage element.

Due to this feature, not only is a light frontage element produced, but also benefit is derived from rapid heating of the thermal enclosure, and from introduction of thermal energy resulting from this restitution of the thermal energy stored in the reserve space.

According to a fifth feature of the invention, the frontage element comprises a thin and light intercepting panel, and a thermal enclosure comprises, in its upper portion, second distributor means arranged to direct hot air into the dwelling, or to a storage device arranged to store the thermal energy introduced by this air, and to restore part at least of the stored thermal energy to contribute to the air conditioning of the dwelling, these second distributor means being advantageously arranged to direct hot air, in part into the dwelling and in part to the storage device.

By means of this feature there is produced a frontage element which is particularly light and simple, and benefit is derived from rapid heating of the thermal enclosure and from introduction of thermal energy resulting from the restitution of the thermal energy storred in the storage device; moreover the hot air directed to the storage device can, after having yielded a portion of its thermal energy to said storage device, be re-ejected outside the dwelling, and thus create a circulation due to which it is possible to admit fresh air into the said dwelling, coming from the outside and admitted through an opening arranged in a wall of the dwelling not exposed to the solar radiation.

The invention will in any case be well understood with the aid of the complement of description which follows as well as of the accompanying drawings, which complement and drawings relate to preferred embodiments of the invention and do not have, of course, any limiting nature.

In the drawings:

FIG. 1 is a view in diagrammatic section of one embodiment of a dwelling according to the invention, the air conditioning installation being shown in the heating position.

FIG. 2 shows this same dwelling under the same conditions, the air conditioning installation being here shown in the cooling position.

FIG. 3 is a front view, showing the dwelling illustrated in FIGS. 1 and 2.

FIG. 4 is a diagrammatic perspective view of this same dwelling.

FIG. 5 is a partial front view of another embodiment of a collective dwelling according to the invention.

FIG. 6 is a section, with part cut away, along the line VI—VI of FIG. 5.

FIG. 7 is a section, with part cut away, effected in the same place of the dwelling as the section of FIG. 6, but showing another embodiment of the invention.

FIG. 8 is a detailed view illustrating a variation of the embodiment of FIG. 7.

FIG. 9, lastly, is a section, with part cut away, effected in the same place of the dwelling as the section of FIG. 6, but showing again another embodiment according to the invention.

As seen in FIGS. 1 to 7 and 9, the dwelling, denoted by the reference numeral **1**, is naturally air conditioned by an installation in which the air is heated in a thermal enclosure **3**, bounded by:

on one hand, a frontage element **2** constituted, for example, by a wall or a special structure, this frontage element **2** being exposed to solar radiation;

and on the other hand, an outer wall **4** transparent to solar radiation and opaque to the far infrared radiation, this outer wall **4** being arranged parallel to the frontage element **2** and close to said element.

This outer wall **4** can be formed of glass or of plexiglass transparent to radiation of wave lengths less than three microns and opaque to wave lengths greater than three microns. The frontage element **2** can have a surface with a high absorption factor for solar radiation of wave length 0.3 to 3 microns, and high radiation factor in wave lengths of 3 to 50 microns. Of course, this thermal enclosure **3** is completed by connecting walls between the outer wall **4** and the frontage element **2**.

The bottom and the top of this thermal enclosure **3** can be in communication with the dwelling **1**, respectively through a lower passage **5** and an upper passage **6**.

According to the first feature of the invention, assumed applied in FIGS. 1 to 4 and 5 to 9, the thermal enclosure **3** comprises, in its upper portion, first distributor means **7** for directing hot air, into the dwelling **1** through the upper passage **6**, or to the outside by means of an exhaust passage **8**, or again in part into the dwelling **1**, in part to the outside.

The dwelling **1** then comprises an inlet device **9** for cold air provided with closure means **10**.

This cold air inlet means **9** is advantageously situated on a frontage element not exposed to the solar radiation. It can be constituted by a simple air intake or by a cold water trickling cooler **9**a or with any other type of cooler.

These first distributor means **7** can also take a position for which they prevent the circulation of hot air to the upper passage **6** or the exhaust passage **8**. The hot air then remains confined in the thermal enclosure **3**, which enables the obtaining of better thermal storage in the wall element **2**.

To this end, the first distributor means **7** can be constituted by shutter distributors *7a* and *7b* which can, if necessary, both occupy closed positions.

In FIG. 1, the first distributor means **7** are in the "heating" position (distributor with shutters *7a* open, distributor with shutters 7b closed) and the circulation of the hot air is effected along the arrows F_1; the closure means **10** being in the "closed" position.

In FIG. 2, the first distributor means **7** are in the "cooling" position (distributor with shutters *7a* closed, distributor with shutters *7b* open) and the circulation of hot air is effected along the arrows F_2; the closure means **10** are in the "open" position and the circulation of cold air is effected along the arrows F_3.

The frontage element **2** advantageously has, on the side of the interior of the dwelling, thermal insulation *2a*, which enables good operation after exposure to the sun.

According to the second feature of the invention, assumed applied in FIGS. **1** to **4** and **5** to **9** in combination with the first feature, the thermal enclosure **3** is associated with at least one re-entry passage **11** leading hot air to the top of the frontage, whence it is distributed by means of the first distributor means **7** to the upper passage **6** and/or the exhaust passage **8.**

A structure can then advantageously be built, from modules of pre-determined width and, if necessary, height; each module being then able to comprise a thermal enclosure **3** associated with two re-entry passage **11** arranged respectively on each side of an opening **12** situated above the frontage element **2** concerned (FIGS. **3** and **4**); but each module can also comprise a thermal enclosure **3** associated with a re-entry passage **11** arranged laterally with respect to an opening **12** situated above the frontage element **2** concerned (FIG. **5**).

The individual dwelling shown in FIGS. **1** and **2,** comprise a sub floor **13** not comprising any opening on the side of exposure to solar radiation, and the thermal enclosure **3** can be extended below the level of the dwelling.

IF, as shown in FIGS. **5** to **7** and **9,** the structure of which the dwelling **1** forms part is built from a framework, able to comprise supports **50,** such a structure then has a continuous frontage, or "curtain wall," which generally does not include any traditional constructional element (such as concrete or brick) whose weight would be prohibitive.

According to the third feature of the invention, as seen applied in FIGS. **5** and **6,** in combination with the first and second features, the frontage element **2** comprises a storage space **51,** closed, containing a liquid whose mass is sufficient to store the thermal energy resulting from the exposure of the frontage elements **2** thus constituted.

Advantageously this liquid can be constituted by water or by a mixture of water and anti-gel.

According to the fourth feature of the invention, assumed applied in FIG. **7** in combination with the first and second features, the frontage element **2** comprises an intercepting space **52** containing a liquid and communicating through an ascending passage **53** and through a descending passage **54** with a reserve space **55** situated higher than said intercepting space **52.**

This reserve space **55** is arranged to restore part at least of the accumulated thermal energy to contribute to the air conditioning of the dwelling **1,** the total mass of the liquid contained in the intercepting space **52** and in the reserve space **55** being sufficient to accumulate the thermal energy resulting from the exposure of the thus constituted frontage element **2.**

This reserve space **55** can be situated in a room of the dwelling **1** not exposed to solar radiation.

To obtain the restitution of part at least of the thermal energy accumulated in the reserve space **55,** this reserve space **55** can be arranged in a caisson **56** constituted of insulating material and whose lower part is provided with a closure device **57,** for example of the shutter type. During the period when the reserve space **55** stores thermal energy, the closure device **57** is closed, whilst during the period when the said reserve space **55** must restore thermal energy, this closure device **57** is opened.

For the dwelling shown in FIG. **7,** the restitution of thermal energy is obtained by forced circulation of air around the reserve space **55,** this forced air circulation being generated through a circuit **58** including a blower **59.**

However, it is also possible to resort to the modification of FIG. **8** according to which the restitution of energy is obtained by radiation, the inner wall of the caisson **56** being covered with a reflecting material **60,** such as for example aluminium foil; it is then advantageous to give the inner wall of the caisson **56,** a curved shape adapted to reflect to the infrared readiation along a maximum solid angle.

According to the fifth feature of the invention, assumed applied in FIG. **9** in combination with the first and second features, the frontage element **2** comprises a thin and light intercepting panel **51,** such as for example the panel of anodised aluminium or coated with a black absorbant layer.

Under these conditions the thermal enclosure **3** comprises, at its upper part, second distributor means **62** arranged to direct hot air into the dwelling **1** or to a storage device **63** arranged to store the thermal energy introduced by this air, and to restore part at least of the thermal energy accumulated to contribute to the air conditioning of the dwelling **1,** these second distributor means **62** being also able to be arranged to direct hot air, in part into the dwelling **1** and in part to the storage device **63.**

This storage device **63** can be situated in a room of the dwelling **1** not exposed to solar radiation and connected to the second distributor means **62** through a passage **62*b*** opening below said storage device **63.**

This storage device **63** comprises a mass having a high thermal capacity and it can be constituted by a liquid contained in a reservoir or simply by a massive solid element.

To obtain the restoration of part at least of the heat energy accumulated in the storage device **63,** this storage device **63** can be arranged in a caisson **64** constituted of insulating material and of which the part opening in the room concerned is provided with a closure device **65,** for example of the shutter type. During the period when the storage device **63** stores heat energy, the closure device **65** is closed, whilst during the period when the said storage device **63** must restore heat energy, this closure device **65** is open.

For the dwelling shown in FIG. **9,** the restitution of the heat energy is obtained by a forced air circulation around the storage device **63,** this forced air circulation being generated by a circuit **66** including a blower **67.**

However, recourse could be had to a modification, not shown, and according to which the restitution of energy would be obtained by radiation.

According to the second feature of the invention, the hot air directed to the storage device **63** can, after having yielded a part of its heat energy to the said storage device **63**, be re-ejected outside the dwelling **1** through a closable opening **68**, for example of the shutter type.

There is thus created a circulation due to which it is possible to admit the fresh air into the dwelling **1**, said air coming from the outside and admitted through an opening **69** formed in a wall of the dwelling not exposed to solar radiation. This opening **69** is provided with a closure device **70**, for example of the shutter type, and by means of a passage **71** it enables the admission of fresh air into a room of the dwelling to be cooled, such as a room of the dwelling exposed to the solar radiation.

However, there could also, according to a modification of the invention not shown, be introduced air having yielded a portion of its heat energy to the storage device **63** in a room of the dwelling where this air would contribute, due to the residual heat energy, to ensuring a certain amount of heating.

With regard to FIG. **9**, it is pointed out that the first distributor means **7** are advantageously combined with the second distributor means **62**, and the assembly of these distributor means comprises then, at the top of the re-entry passage **11**, shutter distributors **7*a*** and **7*b*** enabling air to be directed respectively to the inside of the dwelling **1** or to the outside, and a shutter distributor **62*a*** which enables air to be directed to the storage device **63**.

It is now convenient, to illustrate better the advantage of the third, fourth and fifth the features of the invention, to give the following indications.

In a temperate zone of the globe, and for an exposure to the south (northern hemisphere) or an exposure to the north (southern hemisphere) it can be considered that at the maximum the heat intake due to solar radiation varies, according to the season, from 5,000 k.cal/m^2/day to 1,300 k.cal/m^2/day.

If a frontage element is regarded as being able to possess an active intercepting surface of 2m^2 (structures formed from modules of 1m80 width and 3m height, like the module illustrated in FIG. **5**) this amounts therefore to from 6,000k cal/day/module to 1,600 k cal/day/module.

If the third feature of the invention is adopted, consisting of making the frontage element **2** comprise a storage space **51** containing water or a mixture of water and anti-gel, it may be considered that this liquid is initially at a temperature of 20°C and reaches, at the end of the period of exposure to solar radiation, 80°C; which is then calculated under these conditions that if the thermal enclosure **3** is closed 100 litres of this liquid are necessary to store these 6,000 k cal/day.

From the constructional point of view, the storage space **51** can therefore have the following dimensions: 150 cm wide, 120 cm high and 60 cm thickness.

A conventional frontage element having the same storage capacity and formed for example of concrete would weight at least 700 kg; by means of the invention therefore an economy in weight is achieved in the ratio of 7 to 1.

If the fourth feature of the invention is adopted, consisting of making the frontage element **2** comprise an intercepting space **52** containing water or a mixture of water and anti-gel, it may be considered, as previously, that this liquid is initially at a temperature of 20°C and rapidly reaches, given the small mass contained in the intercepting space, a temperature of 80° in the course of exposure to solar radiation.

Between the liquid issuing from this intercepting space **52** through the ascending passage **53** and the liquid brought back into this intercepting space **52** through the descending passage **54**, there exists a temperature difference of 60°C which gives a theoretical speed of circulation of the liquid of 60 cm/second, and a practical speed of circulation of the order of 10 cm/second is therefore allowable, taking into account the various pressure losses.

Assuming a dimension of the ascending and descending passages **53** and **54** of the order of 1cm as regards their diameter, it can be calculated that the transport of heat energy is of the order of 2,000 k cal/hour, which is easily sufficient to remove the thermal energy of solar radiation which, for a duration of exposure of 5 hours is at the maximum 600 k cal/m^2/hour, namely 1200 k cal/hour for a dimension of 2m^2 for the intercepting space **52**.

If the fifth feature of the invention is adopted, consisting of making the frontage element **2** comprise an intercepting panel **61**, the air contained in the thermal enclosure **3** is heated in an almost instantaneous manner and it is brought to a temperature level which depends essentially on the value of the solar radiation which it receives, this air being able, as previously indicated, to be directed either into the dwelling **1** or to the storage device **63**.

From the constructional point of view the "curtain wall" according to the third, fourth and fifth features of the invention has a quite normal thickness.

In fact, such a "curtain wall" comprises from the inside to the outside the following components:

An internal insulation **2*a*** whose thickness can be from 6 to 10 cm,

the frontage element **2** formed according to one of the three above-indicated features and which has at maximum a thickness of 6 cm,

the thermal enclosure **3** whose thickness is about 10 cm to permit good air circulation,

and the outer wall **4**, constituted for example of triple glass (Triver), which has, reinforcements included, a thickness of the order of 4cm.

There is thereby produced a "curtain wall" which has a thickness of 26 to 30 cm.

Finally, due to the improvements according to the invention, the dwelling has a certain number of advantages, among which the following may be mentioned:

the hot air can be confined within the thermal enclosure, which enables a better storage of heat energy to be achieved in the frontage element, if the diurnal heating is sufficient, either by reason of the outer ambient temperature, or by the direction intervention of solar radiation penetrating through the openings situated to the south;

when the hot air is removed to the outside, the heat enclosure operates then as an aspirating device and causes an intake of cold air into the one or more rooms of the dwellings;

due to the thermal insulation provided on the inner surface of the frontage element, it is possible to preserve the role of aspirating device of the thermal enclosure well after the end of the exposure to solar radiation, hence after sunset and during the night, the air conditioning by admission of cold air being hence prolongable well beyond this period of exposure to solar radiation;

the positioning of the thermal enclosures and of the frontage elements below openings enables the said openings to be arranged in a quite conventional manner, the visibility to the South being hence entirely preserved;

this feature of the thermal enclosures also enables the height of the rooms of the dwelling to be adjusted to a normal value, which enables the surface occupied by said thermal enclosures to be reduced whilst preserving a favourable ratio between the volume of the dwelling and the surface of the corresponding frontage element, this ratio being able to be equal to 0.16 when said volume is expressed in m^2 and said surface in m^2;

the thermal insulation provided on the inner surface of the frontage element enables the introduction of heat into the dwelling to be avoided during hot periods;

the positioning of the thermal enclosures lends itself to various architectural possibilities amoung which maybe mentioned the production of supporting frontages, frontages extended downwardly for structures on sloping ground, frontages forming a "curtain wall" for storied structures;

the exploitation of the whole height of the storey being profitably applied by means of the re-entry passages forming a chimney, there is obtained a considerable increase in the pressure causing the air circulation;

this circulation is hence increased and the yield of the thermal enclosures is improved;

in a hot period, the volume of the air aspirated into the dwelling, and consequently the volume of cold air admitted into the dwelling, is also increased;

the frontage element ensuring the interception and, if necessary, the storage of the energy of the solar radiation, is particularly light and of little bulk;

the efficiency of storage of the energy of the solar radiation is increased by arranging, inside the dwelling, a reserve space or a storage device of large storage capacity;

the rooms not exposed to solar radiation can be air conditioned.

June 17, 1969 **H. R. HAY** **3,450,192**

PROCESS AND APPARATUS FOR MODULATING THE TEMPERATURE WITHIN ENCLOSURES

* *

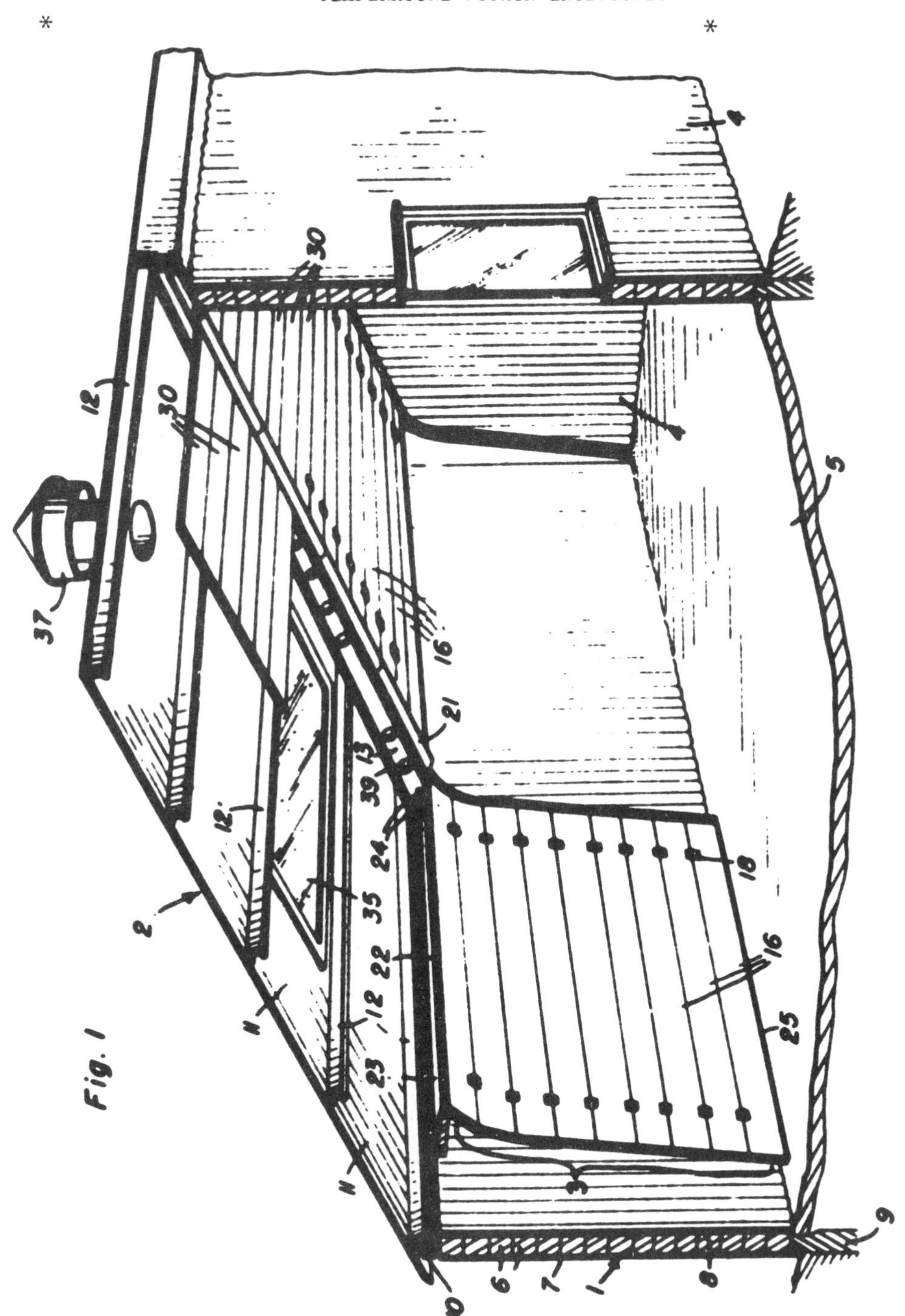

June 17, 1969 H. R. HAY 3,450,192

PROCESS AND APPARATUS FOR MODULATING THE TEMPERATURE WITHIN ENCLOSURES

* *

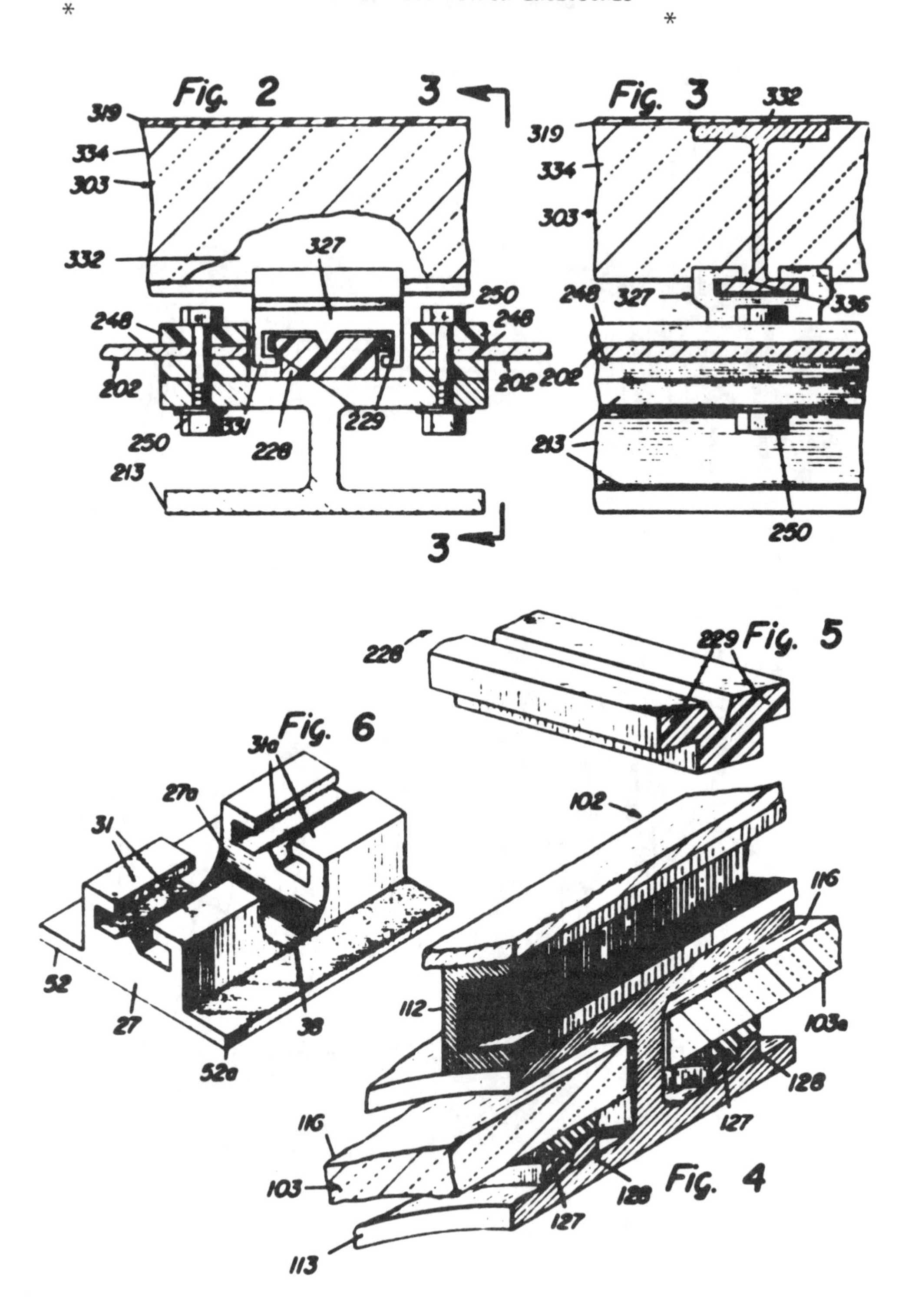

June 17, 1969 H. R. HAY **3,450,192**

PROCESS AND APPARATUS FOR MODULATING THE TEMPERATURE WITHIN ENCLOSURES

* *

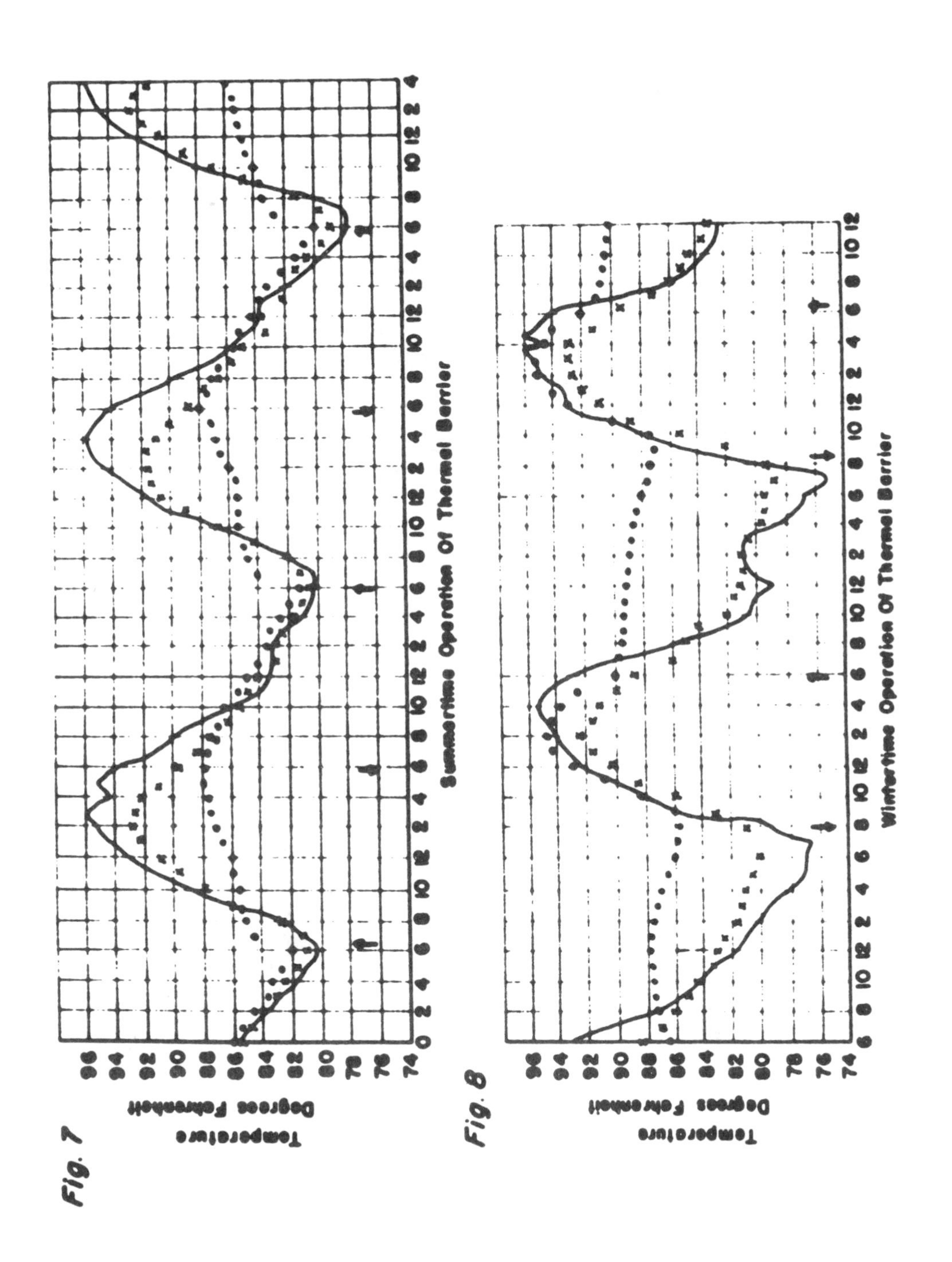

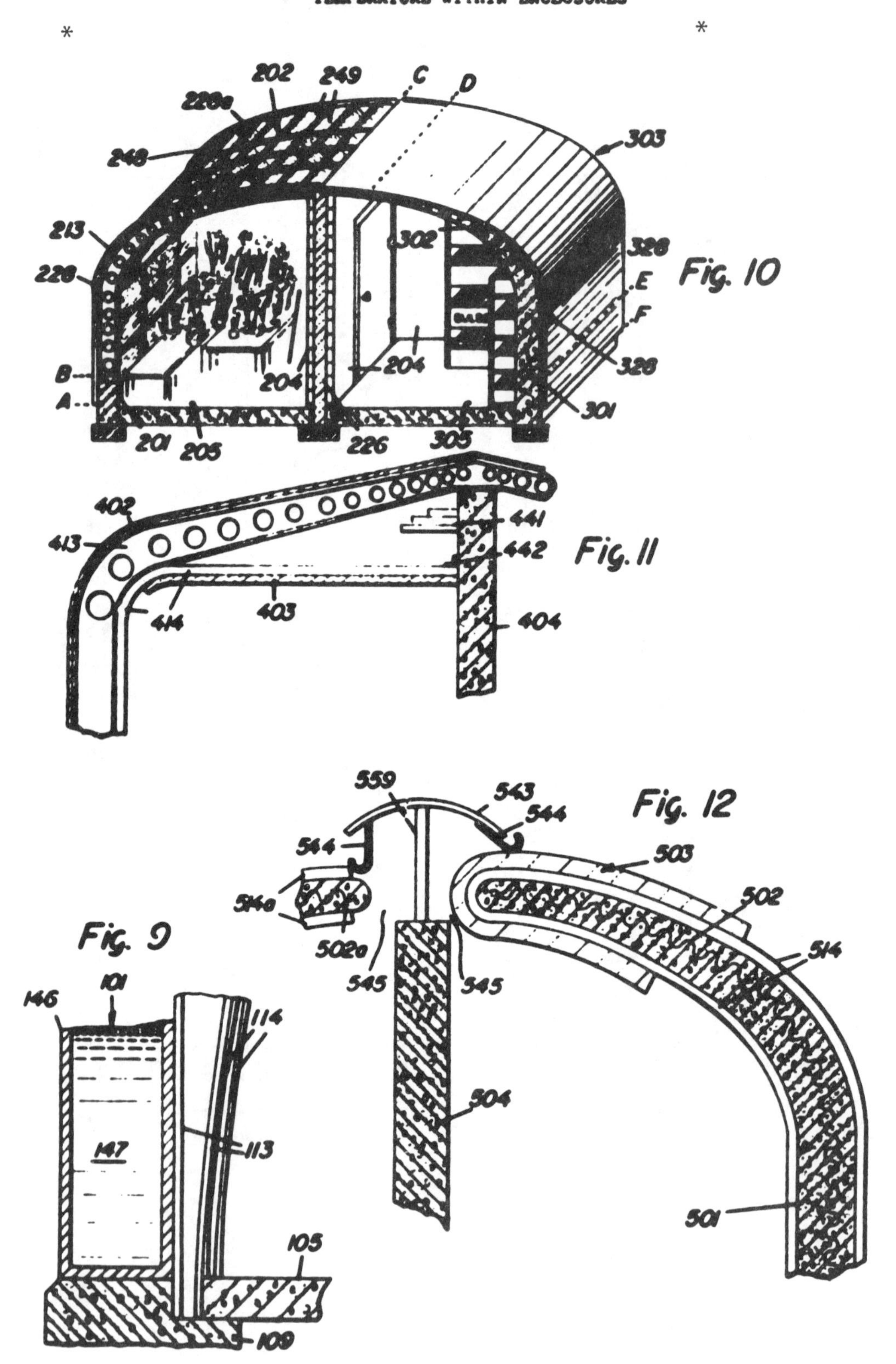

June 17, 1969
H. R. HAY
PROCESS AND APPARATUS FOR MODULATING THE TEMPERATURE WITHIN ENCLOSURES
3,450,192
Fig. 10
Fig. 11
Fig. 12
Fig. 9

June 17, 1969 H. R. HAY 3,450,192

PROCESS AND APPARATUS FOR MODULATING THE TEMPERATURE WITHIN ENCLOSURES

* *

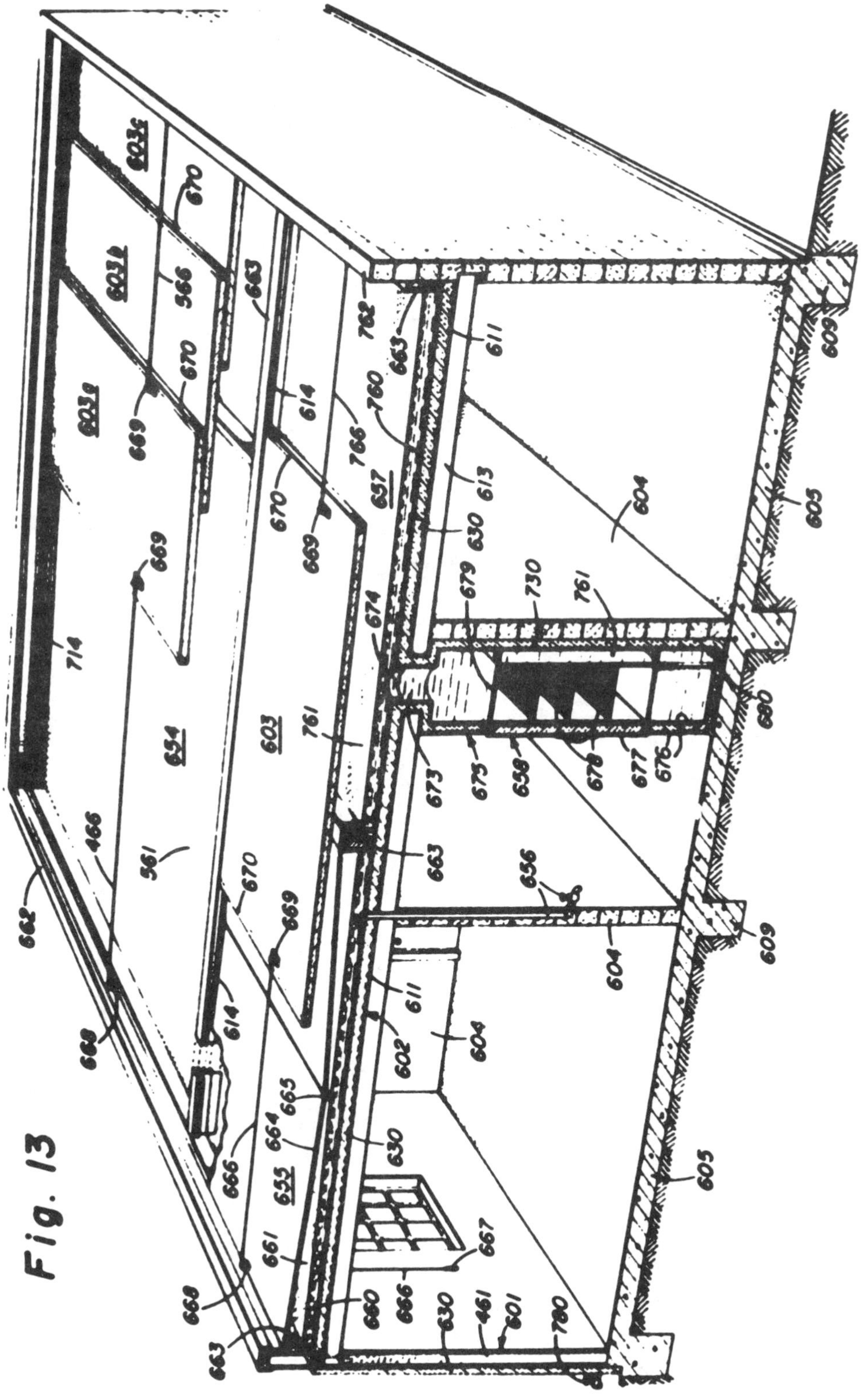

Fig. 13

June 17, 1969 H. R. HAY 3,450,192
PROCESS AND APPARATUS FOR MODULATING THE TEMPERATURE WITHIN ENCLOSURES

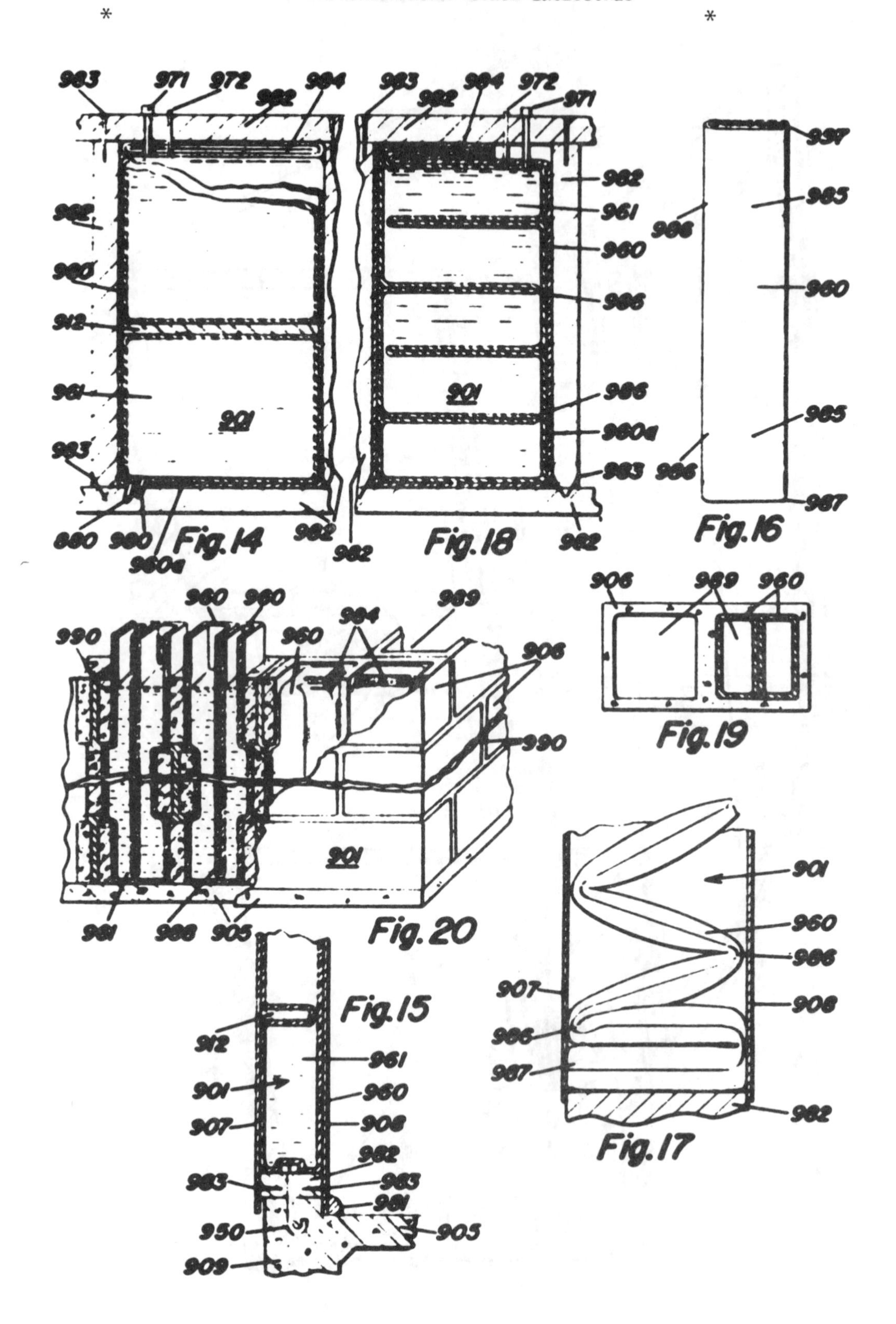

June 17, 1969 H. R. HAY 3,450,192

PROCESS AND APPARATUS FOR MODULATING THE TEMPERATURE WITHIN ENCLOSURES

* *

Fig. 21

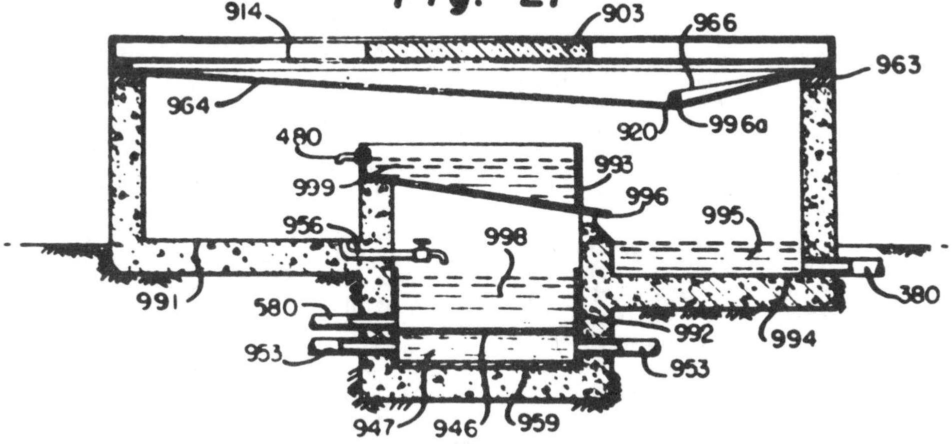

Fig. 22

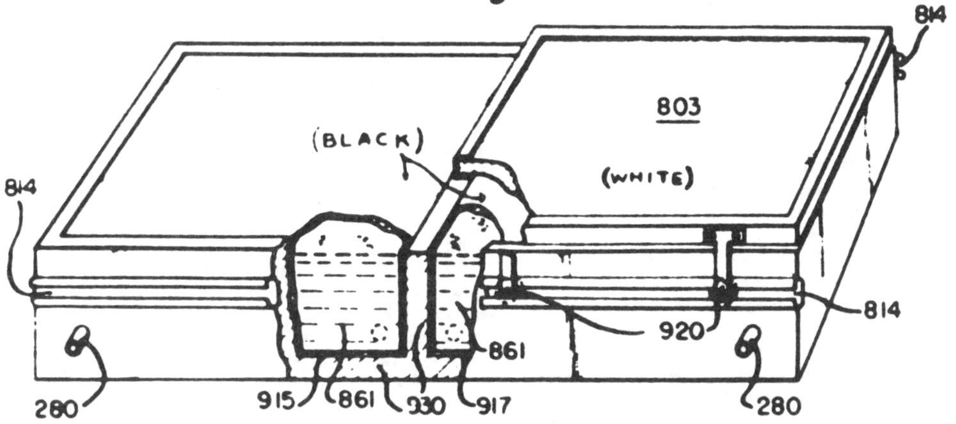

Fig. 23

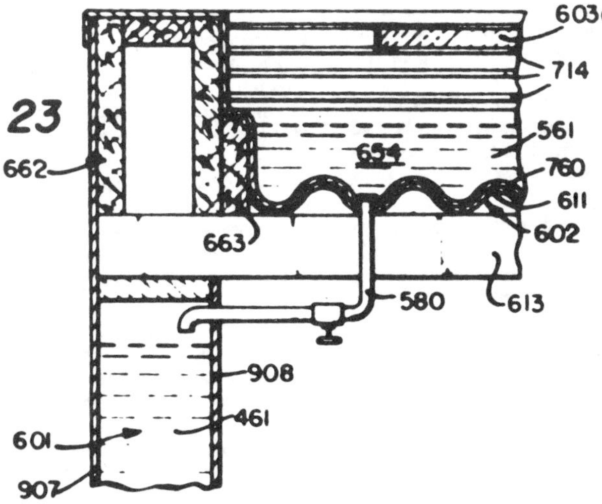

3,450,192
PROCESS AND APPARATUS FOR MODULATING THE TEMPERATURE WITHIN ENCLOSURES

Harold R. Hay, Tempe, Ariz. (795 Roble, Menlo Park, Calif. 94025)

*

ABSTRACT OF THE DISCLOSURE

A process for collecting heat from, and radiating heat to, the sky using insulation moved from a first to a second enclosure or portion of an enclosure. A body of liquid is confined in a horizontal plane and open to the zenith sky. A movable thermal barrier is moved over the liquid in one situation and over another liquid or area during a second condition.

* This invention relates to a process and apparatus for modulating the temperature within enclosures. More particularly this invention relates to a simple manual or automatic manipulation of a thermal valve means to control the temperature within the enclosure as a whole or the temperature of various individual components or contents of the enclosure to suit the objectives for which the enclosure is intended.

In one embodiment, this novel thermal valve means is incorporated into a building and is operated to maintain the internal temperature as closely as possible to the most comfortable of the daily external temperatures.

In another embodiment, the thermal valve means forms part of a greenhouse and may simultaneously modulate temperatures in an adjacent building or room intended for storage of vegetables.

A similar thermal valve means may be incorporated into a solar still, *
wherein it materially influences the distillation of a distilland. Moreover, the thermal valve means may influence evaporation of water from wet materials such as grain and lumber confined within an enclosure designed as a solar drier of which this thermal valve means is a part. Said thermal valve means may be adapted to solar water heaters so as to maintain desirable temperatures therein and it may be used for the cooling and the conservation of food or for the control of processes within enclosures. It is irrelevant in what form of enclosure, or for what purpose, the temperature modulation is achieved by means of my invention.

Before proceeding with descriptions of embodiments of the invention, attention is directed to certain fundamental propositions which will facilitate an understanding of the detailed description hereinafter made.

It has been historic and current practice to build structures from components such as walls, ceilings, roofs and floors which remain permanently fixed in their positional relationship to one another. Thermal comfort within such structures has heretofore been maintained either by a combination of structural design with mechanical energy consuming devices such as fans, heaters and air conditioners or through structural design alone. In hot and dry areas, thermal comfort is obtained with walls 18 or more inches thick to maintain within the structure a temperature approaching the average of the external daily variation. Walls of this type are costly and the average temperature obtained in this manner is not always as comfortable as the more comfortable of the two extremes. It often would be advantageous to maintain internal temperatures near or below the external night temperature in summer and near or above the external day temperature in winter. Hitherto, structural materials used alone have not attained these objectives.

Fireplaces, heaters and air conditioners, and fans may compensate for deficiencies of structural design but are costly in initial investment, in continuing fuel or power requirements and in maintenance. They cannot be afforded by many families in the lower income levels nor can they be used economically where fuel and electric power are not available as in deserts, on mountain tops or in remote areas. In vacation homes such devices may be subject to theft.

Many low density insulation materials have been applied to building structures or other enclosures to obviate the use of massive construction or to reduce the fuel and power consumption of temperature modulating devices. This insulation is fixed in a permanent relation to a structural component such as wall or roof. I have found that there is a disadvantage in having insulation affixed to said components and that a movable thermal barrier of said insulation can be positioned alternately during the day in different locations so as to be useful in relation to components or portions requiring insulation during a portion of the day but which should not be influenced by said insulation during another portion of the day. When this movable thermal barrier is combined with structural portions or components of proper heat storage and heat transfer characteristics, and when these portions or components are oriented properly with respect to the seasonal path of the sun, and when the movable thermal barrier is positioned in concordance with the daily path of the sun, a unique effect is had upon temperature within the enclosure.

In my invention it is usually characteristic that movement of the thermal barrier causes it to be importantly useful in various positionings during portions of the day which are unlike in solar radiation or temperature. The thermal barrier may even act in different capacities during such unlike portions of the day or it may act in the same manner but with relation to different portions or components of the enclosure and it generally serves a beneficial function in a thermal process in each of its possible positionings.

This invention is broadly related to the collection of solar energy, for its storage and for control over its dissipation. While disclosed with particular reference to maintaining temperatures suitable to life or favorable for the preservation of organic materials and with reference to production of potable water from saline or brackish water, to heating or cooling a water supply, or to the drying of grain or lumber, because of the particular utility it is expressly understood that the invention is not restricted thereto.

The primary object of this invention is to provide an improved process for controlling the collection and loss of solar energy characterized by low-cost installation, operation and maintenance.

Another object is to provide an improved process and device for controlling either the collection of solar heat or the loss of heat so as to maintain the interior of an enclosure or the components or portions of the enclosure or of materials or objects within the enclosure nearer the most desirable part of the natural diurnal temperature cycle.

It is an object of this invention to provide a measure of heat control within an enclosure by moving structural components into different positional relationships to other components wherein the components are selectively composed of materials having varying heat storage characteristics and the movement is selectively timed in relation to external temperatures.

Moreover, it is an object of my invention to provide novel solar stills, enclosure walls, and food coolers which may be used in conjunction with a liquid whose temperature is controlled with my thermal valve means to enhance the results obtained therewith, although these novel devices are likewise disclosed as being of value when used independent of said thermal valve means.

It is a further object to provide improved means for heating a water supply for domestic or other use.

An additional object of this invention is to control the temperature of thermally sensitive objects and processes such as evaporation, distillation, heat storage or transfer, and all such processes as are influenced by thermal change within an enclosure. Other objects and advantages of the present invention will become more apparent after reading the following descriptions taken in conjuntcion with the drawings.

The invention is capable of receiving a variety of mechanical expressions illustrated on the accompanying drawings, but it is to be expressly understood that the drawings are for illustration only and are not to be construed as defining the limits of the invention, reference being had to the appended claims for that purpose. For clarity, the description relating to a building structure as illustrated in FIGURES 1 to 12 inclusive will, for the most part, be separated from the description relating to the control of temperatures or processes involving water as a thermal storage and thermal transfer medium although it will be clear that the principles involved and the nature of this invention may be the same in the following discussion of FIGURES 13–23.

FIGURE 1 is a front cut-away perspective view of a building structure in which the novel process is employed;

FIGURE 2 is a sectional and partially cut-away view of a knife-edge runner means for moving a thermal barrier;

FIGURE 3 is a sectional view of FIGURE 2 taken along lines 3—3 of FIGURE 2;

FIGURE 4 is a diagrammatic sectional representation of a means for moving a plurality of movable thermal barriers;

FIGURE 5 is a fragmentary sectional and perspective view of a grooved trackway suitable for use with a knife-edge runer as a means for moving the movable thermal barrier;

FIGURE 6 is a perspective view of a dual knife-edge runner of flexible material suitable, in combination with the grooved trackway of FIGURE 5, for moving the thermal barrier, when connected thereto, and also serving as a hinge for separate panels constituting said thermal barrier;

FIGURES 7 and 8 are temperature variation charts showing effects typically obtained in enclosures fitted with movable insulation;

FIGURE 9 is a diagrammatic sectional view of an embodiment in which a portion of the wall of an enclosure comprises a liquifiable material 147;

FIGURE 10 is a perspective sectional representation of an embodiment in which the movable thermal barrier is moved externally from an area substantially covering a first compartment to an area substantially covering a second compartment;

FIGURE 11 is a fragmentary diagrammatic sectional view of a further embodiment of the invention in which the movable insulation 403 is alternately positioned near the high thermal capacity wall or positioned substantially parallel to the floor at a considerable distance from the roof portion;

FIGURE 12 is a fragmentary diagrammatic sectional view of an embodiment in which the movable thermal barrier 503 is positioned alternately exterior and interior of an enclosure;

FIGURE 13 is a cut-away perspective view of a building structure, a ponded roof, a solar still, and a cold water reservoir and food cooler in which temperatures are controlled;

FIGURE 14 is a fragmentary sectional view diagrammatic of wall framing members confining a fluid within flexible containers between the framing members;

FIGURE 15 is a diagrammatic fragmentary sectional side view of a wall confining a fluid within a flexible container;

FIGURE 16 is a diagrammatic perspective view of a length of tubing partially sealed into interconnecting segments suitable for confining a fluid in spaces between wall members;

FIGURE 17 is a diagrammatic side view of a length of tubing confining a fluid and being placed between wall members;

FIGURE 18 is a diagrammatic sectional view of a wall showing framing and two flexible containers confining a fluid, the innermost container shaped as illustrated in FIGURE 17;

FIGURE 19 is a diagrammatic cross section of a hollow structural block with one cavity containing two portions of flexible tubing for confining a fluid;

FIGURE 20 is a diagrammatic fragmentary partially cutaway perspective view of a wall wherein cavities of hollow blocks are filled by a fluid within a flexible length of tubing;

FIGURE 21 is a diagrammatic cross section of an elongated solar still partially covered by a panel of movable insulation;

FIGURE 22 is a diagrammatic perspective view, partially cut-away, of a combined hot water heater and water cooler;

FIGURE 23 is a diagrammatic fragmentary sectional view of a portion of the roof, roof pond, and wall of FIGURE 13.

A. THERMAL MODULATION IN A BUILDING STRUCTURE

The following description of the invention applies more broadly than to a building structure but is related thereto as one embodiment of an enclosure. Within the meaning of this invention, an enclosure is any structure substantially or usually surrounded by one or more structural elements which confine space or substances in a manner affecting thermal exchange between the confined space or substance and the environment surrounding said enclosure. In the form in which the enclosure is a building structure, this invention usually involves three separate and distinct building elements or components with different heat transfer characteristics. These three elements properly incorporated into the design of a building form a thermal valve means which may be manipulated manually or automatically in relation to the time of day so as to maintain the temperature within the building as close as possible to the more desirable of the daily extremes, to comfort zone temperatures, or to any desired temperature. These three building elements or components are as follows:

(1) *The high thermal capacity wall*

In the embodiment of this invention shown in FIGURE 1, a building structure has at least one substantially vertical wall 1 composed primarily of high thermal capacity material. Said wall should have moderate thermal transfer characteristics and should preferably be oriented toward the equator. Wall 1 may consist of brick, stone, adobe, concrete, or similar materials or mixtures thereof. The interior and exterior surfaces of said wall may be finished with plaster, stucco, paint, or sheathed with metal, plastic, plywood, fiberboard or such materials as do not substantially alter the thermal character of said wall. One might also use a wall consisting of two opposed metal panels, as shown in FIGURE 9, confining a fluid 147 of high thermal capacity such as water or heat storage chemicals of the type of sodium sulfate decahydrate, sodium thiosulfate pentahydrate, etc., in their molten state.

Preferably, high thermal capacity wall 1 should be of such thickness as will provide about a twelve-hour heat lag in attaining maximum or minimum temperature by heat transfer from one face to another. Brick, stone, concrete or earth walls approximately thirteen inches thick have been found suitable, although a thickness range of as wide as three and twenty inches may be satisfactory under varied conditions and in diverse localities.

(II) *The roof*

The building structure of FIGURE 1 has a roof 2 constructed of a material having little resistance to heat transfer and little thermal storage. Thin sheets of metal, glass, asbestos-cement, plastic or similar material may be used. The roof 2 preferably should be low with relationship to the floor to minimize the cubic volume of the room and should slope with substantial equatorial exposure. This type of roof has heretofore been considered undesirable for structures because under former circumstances it produced uncomfortably warm internal temperatures during summertime days and uncomfortably cool temperatures during winter nights.

(III) *Movable thermal barrier*

The building structure of FIGURE 1 has what can aptly be referred to as a thermal valve 3 or otherwise referred to as a movable thermal barrier 3. Said barrier is preferably composed of low density sheets, panels or blocks of insulation having low heat storage and low thermal transfer characteristics. The insulation may be of the rigid type, such as relatively thick sheets of vegetable fiber, cork, foamed glass or expanded polystyrene. The insulation also may be of the semi-rigid type such as batts of wood fiber, mineral wool, fibrous glass, or the foamed products of rubber, polyurethane or other plastic or resin materials.

Movable thermal barrier 3 likewise may be formed from non-rigid materials such as mineral wool, fibrous glass or wood fiber loose-fill insulations held in flexible cloth, paper or other containers, or from aluminum foil or other reflective insulation alone or in combination with other insulators. The combination of rigid and non-rigid materials, some or all of which may be transparent or translucent, is also contemplated.

The above-described material in the movable thermal barrier 3 contrasts with the high thermal capacity wall 1 in having a much lower thermal storage capacity and lower heat transfer characteristics and it contrasts with roof 2 in having a much lower rate of heat transfer. These distinguishing properties of the movable thermal barrier allow it to function effectively as a thermal valve.

In FIGURE 1, the movable thermal barrier is mounted inside the building structure and can be alternatively positioned closely adjacent either the inside of high thermal storage wall 1, which has a partially controlled thermal flow, or of the roof 2, which has an essentially uncontrolled thermal flow. When so mounted the barrier 3 can control the flow of heat into and out of the building structure.

(IV) *Other elements of the structure*

As shown in FIGURE 1, the other three walls of the building structure may be constructed of the same high thermal capacity material as wall 1 or of any other suitable material. It should be realized that the temperature cannot be controlled within the same limits if all walls are not of high thermal capacity. The structure preferably has a poured concrete floor to add its high heat storage although wooden or other flooring can be used. Other elements of the structure should have high heat storage abilities when feasible.

The above description of the various elements of my invention will be clearer after reading the following description taken in conjunction with the drawings:

FIGURE 1 is a cut-away perspective view of a building forming one embodiment of this invention. This structure comprises a substantially vertical high thermal capacity wall 1 constructed of a plurality of stacked bricks or concrete blocks 6. A roof 2 has its lower edge supported by the upper portion of wall 1 while the opposite end of roof 2 slopes upwardly and away from the top of said wall. A movable thermal barrier 3 is disposed within the building structure. Two other walls 4 are shown, which together with a fourth wall (not shown) and a floor 5 complete the enclosure except for doors (not shown) and windows (partially shown).

As shown, the high density wall 1 has outer and inner faces covered by sheath material 7 and 8 which preferably consists of plaster, stucco, tile, or of rather thin elongated sheets of metallic or plastic material joined to the high density wall by bolts, screws, nails, adhesives, etc. The plurality of stacked blocks 6 is supported on a suitable foundation or footing 9.

Near the top of the high thermal capacity wall 1 transverse support means in the form of purlins 12 bearing on I-beam frame 13 can be provided for the roof 2. In FIGURE 1, ventilation eave 10 permits ventilation between the inside and outside of the building. A similar ventilation strip near the upper edge of roof 2 may be used in lieu of roof ventilator 37.

In FIGURE 1, roof 2 consists of a plurality of overlapping metal sheets 11 supported by and fastened to transverse roof members 12. The roof supporting members 12 are supported by I-shaped beams 13. Beams 13 are firmly anchored at their lower extremities in a suitable foundation 9, preferably of concrete. The lower edge of I-beam 13 serves as a base or anchoring point for one or more trackways within which rollers attached to any desired portion of thermal barrier 3 are adapted to travel. If desired, lighting means 21 may be arranged below I-shaped beam 13.

In FIGURE 1, movable thermal barrier 3 is a plurality of elongated and essentially rigid strips of lightweight insulation material or frames of supported non-rigid insulation material 16. The individual insulating panels 16 may be joined by piano-type hinges 18 or panels 16 may be made to adhere to a continuous flexible backing of fabric or metallic material, as for instance sheet aluminum, by use of an adhesive.

The upper horizontal edge of the upper insulation panel 16 preferably has a flexible sealing element 22 to provide, in conjunction with stationary wall seal 23, an effective seal when movable thermal barrier 3 is in its lower position so that air between thermal barrier 3 and wall 1 cannot move into the main portion of the building by leakage or convection. Wall seal 23 is held in position by one or more brackets 24 attached to I-beam 13 or to the walls. A similar sealing means 25 is shown on the lower horizontal edge of the lowest panel member 16. When movable thermal barrier 3 is in its uppermost position essentially parallel to the roof 2, the seal 25 in conjunction with wall seal 23 restricts movement of air between thermal barrier 3 and roof 2 so that this air does not pass into the main portion of the building.

I-beam 13, of FIGURE 1, can be considered as dividing

the building into right-hand and left-hand portions. Movable thermal barrier 3 to the left of beam 13 is in its lowermost position. By examining the area to the left of beam 13 near the point where the beam joins the upper portion of roof 2, it will be seen that a number of permanently positioned insulating panels 30 extend across the building in a generally (but not necessarily) parallel relationship to the upper part of roof 2. The fixed panels 30 form an extension of the thermal barrier between the roof and the interior of the building when the area of movable thermal barrier 3 is not great enough to adequately cover the entire roof area. The manner in which panel 30 and panel 16 cooperate to cover the entire roof area is best seen by observing the area to the right of beam 13. If the roof area is the same as the area of the high thermal capacity wall, stationary panels 30 are not needed.

Panels 30 are shown in FIGURE 1 to be fixed, but they may be movable toward the wall opposite that indicated as wall 1 or panels 30 may be hinged independently but operated as a unit to change from a position approximately parallel to the roof (or floor) to a position approximately parallel to the walls, thus exposing the under portion of roof 2 in the area of panels 30.

FIGURE 1 shows that roof 2 may be constructed of more than one material. The roof may contain, in addition to the metallic sheets, one or more area of glass or transparent or translucent materials such as plastics (e.g. skylights) 35 which permit sunshine to enter the building when movable thermal barrier 3 is in its lowermost position. Also the roof may contain one or more ventilating cowls 37. Alternatively, a ventilation strip of the type of 10 at the eaves may be located at the higher edge of the roof or louvres may be provided in the end walls between roof 2 and the position of fixed panels 30 or thermal barrier 3 in its uppermost position. I-shaped beam 13 contains a number of circular holes 39 which permit cross circulation of air when the movable thermal barriers are in their uppermost positions.

The movable thermal barrier 3 may be either manually or automatically raised and lowered and may be maintained in any raised position by means of counterweights or by inserting a pin, lug or catch into a hole in a portion of the trackway so as to obstruct the downward movement of the roller within the trackway. Said thermal barrier 3 may be raised by either lifting the lowermost panel of the thermal barrier or by pulling a cord, wire or chain attached to the uppermost panel of the thermal barrier, said cord or wire preferably passing over appropriate pulley arrangements located near the top of the roof. Counterweights or spring arrangements and lockable sprockets or other fastening means may be suitably employed. Also, one might employ an entirely different means for moving the thermal barrier from one position to another. For example, the knife-edge runner of FIGURES 2–6 may be employed as described later.

In summertime, the method of using the thermal valve means to obtain internal temperature modulation involves positioning movable thermal barrier 3 near roof 2 during the daytime and adjacent high thermal capacity wall 1 during the nighttime. In this manner, solar heat which penetrates the roof during the daytime is blocked from entering the room by the movable thermal barrier. Also, during the day, the sun's heat will start penetrating high thermal capacity wall 1 but owing to the time lag provided in the wall, the peak heat will not reach the interior surface of the wall until after sunset. At this time the movable barrier is lowered to prevent this heat from passing into the room at night. Simultaneously, lowering the thermal barrier 3 from the overhead position adjacent the roof permits heat radiation from the room through the roof to the cold night sky. Thus the heat of day is excluded from the room while the interior of the room is allowed to cool to night temperatures through internal convection and without the necessity of opening doors, ventilators and windows as is usually practiced with only partial effectiveness if house design, orientation or external wind velocity are not optimum.

The heat stored in the high thermal capacity wall during the daytime is blocked by the presence of the movable thermal barrier at night and dissipates externally to the night sky by radiation. During daytime the interior surface of this wall is cool, exposed and able to absorb from the room a good portion of the infiltrated heat since the movable thermal barrier then is positioned near the roof.

During wintertime, the method of obtaining optimum thermal modulation by means of the movable thermal barrier consists of reversing the relative position of the movable thermal barrier as compared to its position in the summer. Thus during the day the movable thermal barrier would be positioned against the high thermal capacity wall 1 so that heat in the room is not absorbed into this wall which has cooled during the night. Simultaneously, during the day the roof 2 radiates solar heat into the room raising the temperature to or nearer the optimum comfort range. At night the movable thermal barrier is raised to prevent heat loss from the room through the roof and simultaneously the stored heat acting with a twelve-hour heat lag through the high thermal capacity wall enters the room maintaining comfortably warm temperatures throughout the night despite heat loss through leakage at the doors, ventilators and windows.

FIGURES 7 and 8 illustrate the great degree of temperature control achieved by employing the novel thermal valve means of this invention in conjunction with a high thermal capacity wall and other elements of the building structure. FIGURE 7 presents temperature variations achieved during summertime operation of the movable thermal barrier while FIGURE 8 graphically shows the temperature control achieved during wintertime operation of the movable thermal barrier. The solid lines in these graphs represent the official weather bureau shade temperature. The curve defined by *x*'s represents the observed temperature in an adjacent room not provided with a movable thermal barrier. The curves defined by a series of small circles represent the observed temperature in the room provided with a movable thermal barrier.

FIGURE 7 shows that the weather bureau shade temperature, the temperature in an adjacent room and the temperature in the room provided with a movable thermal barrier are all approximately the same at about 6 a.m. Between about 6 a.m. and 8 a.m. the temperature, in the room provided with a movable thermal barrier operated under the conditions indicated, rises somewhat above the other two temperatures, but at about 8 a.m. the temperature in the room provided with the movable thermal barrier begins to level off and does not exceed about 88° while the other two temperatures continuously increase to a maximum of between 92° and 96° at about 2 to 4 p.m. as a result of the uncontrolled effects of the sun. After about 4 p.m. the weather bureau temperature and the temperature in the adjacent room begin to drop and at about 10 p.m. the three temperatures approximate each other again and drop together until about 6 a.m. the next day. Thus, proper placement of the movable thermal barrier can lower the peak interior temperature during the day considerably below the temperature which would exist in the room if there were no movable thermal barrier. The peak with the thermal barrier is approximately one-half that of the outdoor temperature in this example where a 16 to 18 degree diurnal variations was recorded. In cases where a 40 degree variation is common, the benefit of proportionately reducing the peak temperature is of much greater value.

FIGURE 8 illustrates wintertime operation in accordance with this invention. The movable thermal barrier is in a raised position between the hours of about 6 p.m. and 8 a.m. While raised it prevents loss of heat from the interior of the building through the roof and permits heat stored in the wall 1 to flow into the room. Therefore between the hours of 6 p.m. and about 8 a.m. the temperature within a room provided with a thermal barrier is much higher than either the weather bureau shade temperature or the temperature in an adjacent room not provided with a movable thermal barrier. Between the hours of about 8 a.m. and 6 p.m. the movable thermal barrier barrier is in its lowered position to permit solar heat to pass into the building through the roof 2 while at the same time it prevents loss of this heat into the night-cooled wall 1. By using a movable thermal barrier and a high thermal capacity wall one is thereby able to maintain the temperature within a building during the wintertime at a level considerably above that which would otherwise be possible if no thermal barrier means were used. The results shown in FIGURES 7 and 8 were obtained in successive weeks in September when day and night temperature differential was minimal in the area. A much more pronounced effect would be shown when the winter range is 30° to 70° F. and the summer range is 70° to 110° F.

Because the material of the movable thermal barrier and the means for moving it are important aspects of this invention, it is desirable to describe another thermal barrier means which constitutes an alternate to the rigid panels mounted with rollers and trackway. As shown in FIGURES 2, 3 and 10, movable thermal barrier 303 may consist of flexible polyurethane 334 fastened by adhesives to a more weather resistant, flexible backing material 319 and having a plurality of horizontal stiffening I-shaped members 332 attached to said backing strip 319 which transfer the weight of said thermal barrier 303 onto a knife-edge runner 327 a portion of which 336 engages said member 332 while the knife-edge portion is mounted to engage in a grooved trackway 228 suitably mounted on the I-section arched rigid frame 213 of FIGURE 10 which is a part of the enclosure of this invention.

Stiffening members 332, of FIGURES 2 and 3, may be made of aluminum; knife-edge runner 327 may be made of a suitable plastic such as Delrin; grooved trackway 228 may be formed of another plastic such as nylon resin fastened by an adhesive to arched frame 213 which may be made of steel, aluminum, wood, or other appropriate material. FIGURE 2 shows grooved trackway 228 formed with projections 229 partially surrounded by lip member 331 formed as a part of knife-edge runner 327. An enlarged view of continuous grooved trackway 228 with projections 229 is shown in FIGURE 5.

FIGURE 6 shows a dual knife-edge runner 27 and 27*a* having a shape substantially as in FIGURES 2 and 3 except for the portion to be attached to the movable thermal barrier. In FIGURE 6, side projections 52 and 52*a* provide a wide base for fastening knife-edge runners 27 and 27*a* to panels of insulation, such as panels 16 of FIGURE 1, at points suitably oriented to transfer their weight onto structural member 13. The two knife-edge runners 27 and 27*a* of FIGURE 6 are interconnected by a thin flexible section 38, of the same plastic from which said runners are formed, which can serve as a hinge when 27 and 27*a* are fastened to separate abutting panels of FIGURE 1. The lip projections 31 and 31*a* of FIGURE 6 are designed to engage projections 229 of the trackway shown in FIGURE 5 so that knife-edge runners 27 and 27*a* do not become disengaged from said trackway when the latter is mounted onto a vertical portion of a frame member such as 213 of FIGURE 2.

It is apparent that the knife-edge runner of FIGURE 6 could be extended from the dual form illustrated to include any number of knife-edge runners of the type of 27 separated by one less flexible hinge of the type of 38. It is equally obvious that parallel rows of these knife-edge runners could be made with projections 52*a* shared in common by said parallel rows and thus form a single unit comprising a plurality of rows of individual knife-edge runners of the type of 27 and 27*a*.

The advantages to this invention of the use of knife-edge runners and of movable thermal barriers of the types described above are the following: The continuous insulation eliminates forming and mounting a plurality of panels and hinges such as 16 and 18 of FIGURE 1. Likewise, the cost, installation and maintenance expense of the more elaborate trackway and roller moving means are eliminated. Additionally, the movable thermal barrier may now be formed so that the flexible polyurethane 334 constitutes its own sealing means thereby eliminating sealing elements 22 and 25 used in FIGURE 1.

It is obvious that the knife-edge runners will be variously mounted in different embodiments of this invention. FIGURE 4 shows details for mounting two thermal barrier means 103 and 103*a* on a common frame element 113 of the enclosure made by roof 102 supported by purlin 112 fastened to structural frame element 113 to form an enclosure of the type of FIGURE 1. In FIGURE 4, panels 116 bear on knife-edge runners 127 which transfer the load onto grooved trackway 128 suported by said structural member 113. The movable thermal barrier 303 of FIGURES 2 and 3 has been previously described and is supported by structural member 213 so as to be outside of the enclosure made in part by roof 202 composed of transparent material such as glass or suitable plastic affixed to said structural member 213 by bolts 250 which effect a sealing pressure on the plastic or fibrous roof-framing material 248. The exterior mounting of the movable thermal barrier illustrated in FIGURES 2 and 3 can suitably be used for an embodiment of this invention shown in FIGURE 10 which will be described in greater detail.

If the thermal barrier is made in a weather-resistant manner, it may be positioned outside of the high thermal capacity wall and the roof of a building and may be of such size as to cover both simultaneously. FIGURE 10 illustrates this embodiment of the invention in the form of a greenhouse to the left for growing plants and a cold-storage portion to the right for the storage of seeds or bulbs and for retarding the growth of plants kept therein until periods of greater demand.

In this embodiment, thermal barrier 303 is shifted from an equatorially oriented compartment over a ridge at position marked C to the polar side of the biulding. During winter days the equatorial compartment is heated through roof 202 which comprises high heat transfer materials of transparent types also forming a substantial portion of the equatorial wall. During this period 205 and the other walls 204 in addition to the high heat storage wall 201 store heat and all are high heat storage portions of the enclosure and may be considered in common as the high heat storage component of this embodiment. At night, the thermal barrier is moved from the polar side of the building to the equatorial compartment and is disposed externally to insulate both its wall and roof. In addition to preventing heat loss through the equatorially-oriented roof 202 during the nighttime, all of the solar heat stored in wall 201 is directed inwardly at night. In contrast, the earlier embodiment with internal insulation radiates stored heat both inwardly into the room and outwardly to the night sky during the nighttime.

By dividing the building into a plurality of compartments illustrated in FIGURE 10, the novel features of this invention simultaneously produce opposite thermal effects in the compartments. In winter the temperature within the equatorially exposed room is raised during the day and held at an elevated temperature during the night, while the polar-oriented room is prevented by the thermal barrier from increasing greatly in temperature during daytime and is cooled to the sky at night. This dual thermal control provides continuous warmth in the equatorially exposed room for living things and prevents damage therein to materials or goods deleteriously affected by low temperatures while it provides low temperatures corresponding to cold storage in the polar oriented room. If desired, in summer the dual thermal control may be used to lower the temperature in the equatorially oriented room while maintaining an elevated temperature in the polar oriented room. Elevated temperatures in the building structure may be desirable for the drying seeds, fruits, and the like, for forcing faster growth of plants, for the fermentation of fodder in a farm structure or for other purposes.

The movable thermal barrier illustrates in FIGURE 10 may also create desirable temperatures within the compartments by being positioned only a fraction of the day one one or the other of the sides of the building or by being positioned part of the day to insulate only a portion of the roof or wall portions while leaving another portion on the same side unaffected by insulation. This is clear from FIGURE 10 where the length of movable thermal barrier 303 equals the distance between points D–F and leaves an area of roof 302 exposed between limiting points C and D. If, however, the C–D area of said roof should be covered by the thermal barrier, a corresponding section of high heat storage wall 301 between points E and F will be exposed. Similarly, if D–F equals C–B on the structure and the insulation covers roof area 202 between points C–B, the wall portion 201 between points B–A will be exposed, but if the same thermal barrier is moved down to A, a portion of the roof 202 near the ridge at C will be exposed. In this manner it is possible to obtain controlled temperatures ranging substantially from the maximum to the minimum of the daily diurnal variation.

In the embodiment of FIGURE 10, the common wall of the two compartments includes an insulating material 226 to reduce thermal flow between the compartments. The roof 302, walls 304, floor 305 and wall 301 all become the high heat storage portion of this compartment in which the movable thermal barrier is positioned by means of a knife-edge runner assembly 328. Said assembly 328 comprises a knife-edge runner fastened to said thermal barrier by means illustrated in FIGURES 2 and 3 and a trackway such as that shown in FIGURE 5 which in FIGURE 10 is shown as fastened by suitable means directly to the concrete roof and wall portions 302 and 301 respectively. The trackway of knife-edge assembly 328 continues over the ridge C and onto the structural frame member 213 where it is indicated as 228 and a corresponding trackway at the end of the structure is indicated as 228*a*. The roof framing material 248 of roof 202 may be made of plastic, wood or metal and the transparent portions 249 of the roof may be of plastic or it may be of glass.

An alternative arrangement (not shown) with rooms of similar size and shape disposed side by side with identical orientation, permits insulation covering both the sides and the roof of a first room to be laterally shifted on rollers bearing on a foundation common to both rooms so that the insulation covers, during a different portion of the day, the second room.

In the embodiment illustrated in FIGURE 11, showing a portion of the upper part of a building, this invention positions thermal barrier 403 parallel to the floor (not shown) during part of the day and at a considerable angle to and distance from a roof 402 supported by framing member 413. Trackway 414 on which the movable thermal barrier is mounted is parallel to the wall 401 until it reaches a point near roof 402 where it becomes parallel to the floor (not shown) and is fastened at 442 to the other wall 404. The space between roof 402 and thermal barrier 403 of FIGURE 11 tends to build up high temperatures during a summer day. While high temperatures are useful in greenhouses, grain or lumber driers, hot water heaters and solar stills as will be described in section B, the effect is not desirable in houses. Consequently, it is advisable to have louvres 441 or cowls (shown in FIGURE 1) to reduce heat build-up in this enclosed area. The data of FIGURES 7 and 8 were obtained in a house built according to this embodiment of FIGURE 11.

In another embodiment shown in FIGURE 12, insulation 503 is movable on trackway 514 which is continuous over exterior wall 501 and roof 502, passes through aperture 545 in said roof and continues along the interior surface of said roof and said wall to permit thermal barrier 503 to be positioned inside of or outside of the enclosure formed substantially by said roof and said wall. A ridge member 543 and a suitable hinged sealing device 544 is supported adjacent aperture 545 by support 559 mounted at the upper ends of wall 504. The insulation may be positioned totally within the structure during the day in which case the exposed wall 501 and roof 502 store heat which radiates into the room when the movable thermal barrier is put into a nighttime position exterior to said roof and said wall. Instead of thus warming this portion of the enclosure, it can be cooled by the same thermal barrier means by merely reversing the daytime and nighttime positions of said thermal barrier.

In an additional embodiment of the invention which can be made sufficiently clear to those versed in the art by FIGURE 12, one can arrange a switching device (not shown) but similar to those used in railroad tracks, above wall 504 so as to interconnect the trackways both internal and external on the portion of the structure to the right of wall 504 with trackways 514*a* shown broken attached to roof 502*a* to the left of wall 504. By means of such switching mechanism, it is possible to cause movable thermal barrier 503 to pass through aperture 545 to a position either on the interior or on the exterior side of roof 502*a* and of other possible components of a compartment to the left of wall 504, such as a high heat capacity wall (not shown), and thereby provide another means for controlling the temperatures in the two compartments partially indicated to the left and to the right of wall 504 of FIGURE 12.

In another embodiment, not shown, the aperture through which the movable insulation passes is located at the eaves by removing eave ventilator 10 shown in FIGURE 1 and the insulation is caused to take various positional relationships with wall 1 and roof 2. With suitable trackways and apertures at both the eaves and the ridge, the number of positionings increases as does the means for temperature control within the enclosure or within different compartments of the enclosure.

In the preceding embodiments of my invention:

(a) The high heat capacity component of my enclosure may be: a solid wall (1 of FIGURE 1); a wall containing a liquid (101 of FIGURE 9); a wall of both high and low heat storage components (201 with a portion of 202 of FIGURE 10); a wall of high or low heat storage which may be a continuation of the roof materials (202 and 302 of FIGURE 10); or other high heat capacity components of the enclosure and contents thereof;

(b) The thermal barrier may be moved: from wall to roof and back (FIGURE 1); from one compartment to another (FIGURE 10); internally in one compartment (FIGURE 1); externally and over a plurality of compartments (FIGURE 10); alternately from a first position either internal or external to a second position internal or external on the same or on a different compartment (FIGURE 12); and

(c) The roof or cover of my enclosure may be: of thin material of high heat transfer and low heat storage (FIGURE 1); of thick material of moderate heat transfer and high heat storage (FIGURE 12), or of high heat storage materials of varying thickness (302 of FIGURE 10).

It is also evident that while the movable thermal barrier is preferably of low density with low heat capacity and low heat transfer, said barrier could be effective if made of high heat capacity and high thermal storage materials such as thick metal, concrete, confined water, and the like. Movement of such a high heat capacity thermal barrier has obvious limitations in a building structure and costs would be high, but they may be more practical for other enclosures as solar stills. *

In the embodiment of FIGURE 13, my thermal barrier is moved in relation to water in a roof pond 654. Some novel aspects of this embodiment can best be understood after describing some processes and new devices in which my principles have been applied to solar stills and to water heaters and coolers.

B. THERMAL MODULATION OF PROCESS TEMPERATURES

The modulation of temperatures within enclosures inevitably affects thermally sensitive objects and processes within said enclosures. Temperature modulation in a house desirably affects the physiological processes of the occupants even though the enclosure may not always be intact—at times doors and windows may be open. In a greenhouse and for cold storage, this invention was applied in part A to modulate temperatures affecting processes such as growth, blooming and rotting. In all life within the enclosures of part A, thermal modulation affects the heating and evaporation of water constituting a part of that life. My invention can modulate temperatures within enclosures so as to affect processes of evaporation, distillation and drying and it can be applied to heat or cool water for household or industrial uses as will now be described.

In the left foreground portion of roof 602 shown in FIGURE 13, a solar still 655 is illustrated from which water 661 can be drained through pipe connection and faucet assembly 656. In the right foreground portion of roof 602, a water cooling basin 657 is shown which cools a food cabinet 658. Shown partially over the still 655 and partially over the cooling basin 657 is a movable thermal barrier 603 positionable over either said still or said cooling basin to control temperatures in both.

Still 655 is supported on roof 602 with the load transferred by beams 613 to walls 604 and 601. Shown serving as ceiling of the rooms and bottom of the still is a plurality of overlapping sheets 611 of metal, asbestos-cement or plastic shown corrugated. Above sheets 611 is fixed insulation 630, preferably of foamed polyurethane, covered by the still liner 660 which turns upwardly at the wooden framing members 663 which, together with another framing member not shown, form the limits of still 655. Liner 660 is preferably black, relatively thin, sheet plastic such as chlorinated polyethylene, halogenated polyvinyl or polyvinylidene composition, or of polyester. Liner 660 is fastened at its raised edges by adhesives, staples, splined recesses or pressure members (not shown) to framing members 663 to form a distilland basin to contain water 661 preferably one inch or less in depth. The water depth is controlled by an assembly (not shown) consisting of a float valve controlling a distilland inlet. The still cover 664 is shown supported over the distilland basin by framing members 663 and is fastened thereto as described for the liner 660. An elongated weighting means 665, made of plastic or corrosion resistant metal and consisting of an external spline and an internally suspended collecting trough described fully in my co-pending application Ser. No. 482,032, deflects the flexible cover downward causing condensate to converge under weighting means 665 and to be removed from the still through the collecting trough portion of said weighting means. The distilled water may then pass through a connected conduit (not shown) to a point of use.

Distillation in still 655 is best when the distilland has a high temperature in the morning. During the night, therefore, thermal barrier 603 is positioned over still 655 by pulling downward on drawcord 666 at point 667 shown inside the building. Drawcord 666 passes from point 667 through roof 602 over a pulley 668 mounted on framing member 663 and is fastened to the panel of movable insulation 603 by means 669 consisting of an eye-bolt, staple or shackle on said panel or on the framing member 670 thereof.

In the morning, thermal barrier 603 is moved from the position over still 655 by pulling on drawcord 766 fastened to the opposite end of panel 603 from drawcord 666 and passing over a pulley and through roof 602 in the manner described for drawcord 666 to a suitable point in the building. Drawcord 766 may become continuous with drawcord 666 so that a force applied in one direction moves the insulation over the still and applied in the other direction moves the thermal barrier from the position over the still. Thermal barrier 603 moves on trackway 614 by means previously described.

Solar stills of design different from that shown in FIGURE 13 may be employed in this embodiment; as, for example, a roof-type glass-covered still or an air-inflated plastic-covered still. The cover 664 is preferably plastic capable of transmitting solar radiation and wettable on the undersurface. Polyvinyl fluoride film sandblasted to improve wettability is suitable. It is also obvious that water not covered to become part of the solar still can be heated and held at a high temperature by the movable thermal barrier 603 but the temperature would not be so high as under a cover transmitting solar radiation.

In solar distillation, maximum temperatures and distillation rates are reached between 2 p.m. and 4 p.m. Then the distilaltion diminishes rapidly in the 130–100° F. range of domestic hot water supplies and the thermal barrier 603, of this invention, may be advantageously positioned over still 655 to conserve the temperature therein. Thus, the morning temperature of the distilland may be 50° F. higher than it would be if allowed to cool to the night sky as in solar stills of conventional design. Owing to this higher temperature in the morning, the distillation process starts earlier and proceeds longer at the optimum rate of highest possible temperatures, thereby producing a larger yield of distilled water.

Throughout the night, hot water may be drawn off through the pipe connection and faucet assembly 656 interconnected and sealed in a suitable manner with said still. A water storage tank (not shown) may be interposed between the still and the faucet of assembly 656 as may a heat exchanger which transfers heat from the distilland 661 to another water supply, in a manner well-known in the art, when the distilland quality is not adequate for domestic use. Distilland may be kept shallow to obtain maximum distillate and the depth may be increased when it is desired to obtain maximum hot water for domestic or other purposes. Means for varying the depth will be described later. Preferably, water is added to still 655 in the morning when the thermal barrier 603 is moved.

In another embodiment, with a solar still design differing from prior art, and which may be installed on a roof although illustrated in FIGURE 21 as constructed on the ground, the still is constructed in three sections under a common cover 964 with a thermal barrier 903 which may be moved above said cover but not in contact therewith. The first of said sections consists of a wide but shallow distilland basin 991 preferably having a bottom higher than that of a second distilland basin 992 in a second section of the still. Means consisting of conduits and valves 956 are provided to cause distilland to flow from said first to said second basin, and means 580 are provided to drain concentrated distilland (brine) from the second distilland basin. In the second section of the still, under the cover and overlying the second distilland basin, is a third distilland basin 993 the bottom of which is preferably at a higher level than the first distilland basin. Means are provided to permit excess distilland introduced through a distilland feed pipe (not shown) to overflow through a conduit 480 to the first basin; or the first basin may be provided with a separate feed line. Preferably, the first and third basins are shallower than the second basin which, with greater depth, is able to contain all of the distilland from the first basin.

Adjacent to the first or second sections of said still, and preferably with a bottom below that of the third distilland basin 993 to permit collection of condensate by gravity flow from the underside thereof, is a third section of the still comprising a distillate reservoir 994 with an assembly 380 of conduits, valves and, if necessary, a pump for removing distillate 995. Condensate collected on the cover 964, or on the under surface of the third distilland basin, is conducted, by virtue of the shapes thereof or through collecting troughs positioned with conduits in suitable relation thereto, to a point of discharge 996 and 996a into the distillate reservoir. Point of discharge 996a is formed when the cover 964 is deflected downward by a weighting means 920 held in position by tiecord 966 fastened to framing member 963 supporting the cover 964. The materials from which this embodiment are made have been described herein or are well known in the art of solar stills.

In operation, distilland in the first and third basins is distilled during the daytime by solar radiation transmitted through the cover. The vapors are primarily condensed on the cover and are drained into the distillate reservoir 995. When solar radiation and distillation rate have passed their peaks, or at any suitable time, hot distilland 998 from the first basin is drained into the second basin 992 so that it does not lose heat by direct radiation to the sky as does distilland 999 remaining in the third basin 993. Vapors from the hot distilland 998 formerly in the first basin 991 then condense on the cooler under surface of the third basin 993 giving up latent heat to said third basin and causing distilland 999 therein to distill for a longer time than it would if hot distilland from the first basin had not been drained into the underlying second basin 992 to cause multiple effect distillation. The temperature of the distilland in both the second and third basins is higher the following morning than it would be if distilland 998 of the first basin 991 had been allowed to cool to the night sky in said first basin. The warm distilland 998 in the second basin, except for that portion desired to be drained, can be pumped back into the first basin 991 through a suitable conduit 580 and pumping means (not shown) and additional make-up water added to the first and third basins as needed. With warm distilland in both the first and third basins, distillation starts at an earlier hour in the day. This, combined with multiple effect distillation in the second section of the still, substantially increases the daily production of the still. The still may be elongated or circular in shape.

While the foregoing embodiment has been described with reference to a single second basin 992 underlying the third basin 993, it is obvious that distilland 998 from the first basin 991 may be drained into a plurality of basins underlying one another and all underlying what has been referred to as the third basin 993, and all being adapted to drain condensate into a distillate reservoir, and all thus increasing the multiple effect distillation. Moreover, while operable without the movable thermal barrier 903 of the present invention, direct loss of heat by radiation to the night sky from distilland 999 in the third basin 993 may be retarded by movable thermal barrier means 903. By moving said thermal barrier 903 from a first position overlying the distillate reservoir 990 to a second position overlying at least part of the third basin 993, loss of heat from the third basin is retarded. Simultaneously, distillate 995 in the then-exposed distillate reservoir 994 can cool to the night sky. The distillate 995 is maintained at a low temperature during the day when the thermal barrier 903 is returned from the second position to the first position. In a suitably designed still, the cooled distillate 995 serves as a condensor on which at least a portion of the vapors from the first and third distilland basins are condensed. It is obvious that the thermal barrier 903 of this embodiment may be mounted either under or over the cover 964 of the solar still as long as it does not interfere with the distillation process.

In FIGURE 13 is shown the embodiment of my invention in which a domestic hot water supply is drained through a conduit and faucet assembly 656 which may have a storage tank or a heat exchanger interposed between still 655 and the point of use of the hot water. I now describe the heat exchanger being advantageously located within the distilland of the solar still. In the embodiment of my still illustrated in FIGURE 21, in which distilland from a first basin is drained into a second basin underlying a third basin, the bottom of the second basin 992 may be the top of a metal or plastic hot water tank 959 through which water of high quality may be made to pass by suitable means 953. Heat from the distilland 998 in the second basin 992 is then conducted through the wall 946 of the underlying hot water tank 959 to the water 947 therein. By another means, heat exchange is obtained through a closed system of tubes disposed within the second distilland basin 992 in a manner well understood by those versed in the art. In these embodiments, the resulting hot water supply is not necessarily dependent upon the use of a movable thermal barrier 903 since heat is conserved in the underlying storage tank 959 or the tubes (not shown) by the overlying distilland 999 in the third basin 993 and by the distilland 998 which may purposely be left in the second basin. When a tube heat exchanger or a hot water supply tank underlies distilland in stills of prior design, such as 655 of FIGURE 13, the movable thermal barrier becomes essential to conserve heat otherwise lost to the night sky.

In prior design solar water heaters, expensive collectors consisting of sloping black metal absorbers with attached water circulation systems heat water with a thermosiphon action. The heated water at the top of the collector rises through a pipe to an insulated storage tank at an elevated position while colder water returns from the tank to the lower part of the collector through another pipe. This system requires many pressure-tight joints, long pipelines, a storage tank separate from the heat collector and it places concentrated load on roof members on which the tank is mounted. Moreover, the unsightly tank often is camouflaged as a chimney at extra cost. Initial cost and operating and maintenance expenses caused this prior type of water heater to lose the popularity it once held in Florida.

In an embodiment of my invention, illustrated in FIGURE 22, water 861 may be heated in one tank and cooled in another with the movable thermal barrier of my invention. * Two tanks or containers 915 and 917 made of metal or plastic are fastened by suitable means to a roof or other structure preferably orientating the tanks toward the equator. The tanks are mounted adjacently and each has a water inlet (shown as a dotted circle in the breakaway portion of FIGURE 22) and a water outlet 280 which may be insulated by conventional materials. If cylindrical pressure tanks are used, the under half and the ends of each tank are insulated; if rectangular nonpressure tanks 915 and 917 are used, the under surfaces and the sides are protected by suitable insulation 930. The exposed portion (shown black) of each tank capable of receiving solar radiation and of radiating heat to the night sky is preferably blackened by paint or by an electrodeposit or other means.

Along the tops and bottoms of tanks disposed at the same heights, or along the sides of rectangular or cylindrical tanks disposed at different heights, as in FIGURE 22, a trackway 814 is mounted for rollers 920 or for a knife-edge runner assembly identical to those previously described. A panel of insulation 803 generally shaped to parallel and overlie the black surfaces of the tanks, equal in size to the larger of the two tanks, is mounted on the trackway 814 to be moved by means previously described. Sealing means, such as 22, 23, and 25 of FIGURE 1, may be added to reduce heat leakage at the periphery of the insulation panel 803, if needed.

During daytime, the thermal barrier 803 is over the water cooling tank 915 to reduce absorption of heat while permitting water 861 in the heating tank 917 to be heated through its blackened surface. At sunset, the thermal barrier is positioned over the water heating tank 917 to reduce heat loss from this tank to the night sky and to simultaneously expose the water cooling tank 915 to the night sky. In this manner, on a winter day, water above bathing temperature was obtained in the heating tank and preserved at a high temperature throughout the night; during the same diurnal cycle, ice was formed in the cooling tank and was preserved throughout the next day.

In another variation of my heating and cooling system, the black-surfaced water heating tank 917 was caused to underlie a plastic cover capable of transmitting solar radiation and spaced from said tank by suitable means and also underlying a movable thermal barrier. With this embodiment, in summer, water in the heating tank was brought to the boiling point and a high temperature was maintained throughout the night. Because polystyrene insulation does not withstand this high temperature, polyurethane, glass wool, or vegetable fiber insulation 930 should be used.

Lumber driers utilizing solar energy are being developed by the United States Forest Products Laboratory. A fan actuated by electricity, or wind, circulates hot air over a black solar heat absorber and through wet lumber covered by a low-cost plastic film. Grain, fruit, and tobacco driers have been built in a similar manner as have space heaters for animal sheds. In most such installations, heating is indirect and there is considerable loss of heat at night whereas direct absorption and less heat loss at night can result from applying my invention. The movable thermal barrier may be formed from reflective materials shaped to concentrate solar radiation onto the product being dried or onto a solar energy collector of the high thermal capacity type. The movable insulation may be positioned at night to prevent heat loss from the product being dried or from the high thermal capacity collector thus causing the product to dry more at night.

While my movable thermal barrier maintains highest temperatures when used over a transparent cover spaced above a black surface, it cools water better when no such cover overlies the black surfaced cooler, and it maintains the coldest water when mounted over an open pond. Water directly exposed to the night sky apparently loses heat by evaporation and by radiation to the universe. About 6 a.m., the temperature usually reaches a low, approximately equal to the wet-bulb temperature if the pond is less than two and one-half inches deep or a few degrees higher if the pond is six inches deep. In hot-dry climates, the wet-bulb and roof-pond temperatures frequently are 20 to 22° F. colder than the lowest air temperature of night—an effect valuable for modulating temperatures within enclosures.

FIGURE 13 illustrates my invention applied to a roof pond 657 with water 761 contained in the same manner as the distilland 661 in still 655. A cover similar to 664 on still 655 may be used over pond 657 if it is essential to prevent evaporation—it being understood that water temperatures will be a few degrees higher when using a cover. A water inlet assembly (not shown) includes a float valve and an overflow pipe to maintain a predetermined depth of water 761 in pond 657. Movable thermal barrier 603 is positioned either over or away from pond 657 by means previously described with respect to solar still 655.

Roof pond 657 interconnects with food cooler 658 through a hole 673 in pond liner 760—a seal being made by a pressure ring 674 to prevent water leakage. The food cooler 658 consists of a cabinet 675 primarily formed from insulation 730 sandwiched between sheets of metal 676 and having a door 677 opening into a storage space with shelves 678 supported by means usual on a refrigerator. A metal wall 679 suitably sealed to cabinet 675 forms the storage space within food cooler 658 and confines water 761 which surrounds the storage space and interconnects with pond 657. A drain 680 is provided with a valve and conduit assembly (not shown) to remove water 761 from the food cooler 658 and the pond 657.

With a large diameter hole 673 interconnecting pond 657 and food cooler 658, cold water from the pond flows downward to the bottom of the food cabinet by virtue of its density and water warmed by contents on shelves 678 rises to the pond 657 where it can be cooled to the night sky. In another design, two pipes may be used to set up a thermosiphon action to keep the coldest water in the food cabinet. One pipe would connect the food cabinet at a point near drain 680 with pond 657 while the second interconnection would be from the top of cabinet 658 as shown in FIGURE 13 as 673. By these means, using my movable thermal barrier, the temperature within the enclosure comprising the food cabinet 658 may, in a hot-dry region, remain near the freezing point six months of the year and the rest of the year average 16° F. below night air temperature. During periods of high humidity, the pond temperature and that within the food cabinet approximates the 6 a.m. air temperature.

Returning to my process for modulating temperatures in a manner to heat an enclosure in winter and to cool it in summer, I now describe the embodiment of FIGURE 13 in which roof pond 654 covers a portion of the building structure. Pond 654 consists of exposed water 561 confined in the same manner as water 761 in the cooling pond 657 with the important exception that no insulation corresponding to 630 exists between the liner and the corrugated roof sheets which are identical to 760 and 611 respectively. This is better shown in FIGURE 23 in which portions with like numbers correspond with portions in FIGURE 13. With no intervening insulation, heat transfer occurs between air in the rooms under pond 654 and water 561 in said pond. Returning to FIGURE 13, the temperature of pond 654 and the walls 604, the floor 605, and the contents of the rooms underlying pond 654 tend to equalize.

Because of the large area involved, it is frequently desirable to divide my movable thermal barrier into several panels 603*a*, 603*b*, 603*c*, shown in a perspective sectional view, which move, as previously described, on different levels of trackway 714. Interacting projections and seals (not shown) on framing members 670 of panels 603*a*, 603*b*, 603*c* cause 603*b* and 603*c* to move in the same direction as 603*a* is moved by drawcords 466 and 566 operated from within the building. Roof pond 654 is shown existing only over the left and central portions of the building, but not over the portion to the right which may be utility areas such as carport, porch, closets, recreation rooms and the like. Barrier 603*a*–603*b*–603*c* is essentially coextensive with roof pond 654, in this embodiment, when moved toward left parapet 662. Moved toward right parapet 762, the panels 603*a*, 603*b*, and 603*c* assume a stacked relationship exposing all of pond 654 to absorption of solar energy on a winter day, or to loss of heat on a summer night.

The degree of temperature modulation in rooms underlying pond 654 can be controlled either by moving thermal barrier 603*a*–603*b*–603*c* at predetermined hours over pond 654 of constant depth, or by moving it over said pond of variable depth. If the pond is only two inches deep, to much heat may be absorbed in too little water and produce an objectionable high radiation to the head of an occupant or it might equalize the temperature in the room at an excessively high level. The thermal barrier could, in such case, cover pond 654 at an earlier hour in the day than that providing maximum solar radiation, or the depth of pond 654 could be increased to six inches so that the total available solar heat is absorbed but the temperature of pond 659 remains lower than it would were there less depth. Means for varying the depth of a pond are well known and may consist of a sliding sleeve in an overflow drain or a series of drains at different heights, each drain controlled by a different valve. These variable-depth means and the water inlet for pond 654 are not shown in FIGURE 13.

Although roof ponds have been used in prior art to reduce summer heat loads on roofs of air-conditioned buildings, this has proved less satisfactory than the use of thick insulation. In winter, roof ponds have been drained to prevent freezing; and no use has previously been made of them in winter. With my movable thermal barrier, the pond does not freeze but rather becomes a means for heating in winter and it is used for cooling more effectively than prior art in summer. This dual use makes ponding economical and desirable. If available solar energy is inadequate for winter needs when using an open pond, a plastic cover may be applied over the pond, in the manner of solar still 655 of FIGURE 13, to obtain a higher temperature in the pond.

During a full summer day, water evaporation from roof ponds of prior art is high; 1/8 inch of water may evaporate. My pond is exposed in summer only at night and is kept cool and covered during the day; it loses only 1/16 inch of water in a day. Also, my method does not increase the moisture within an enclosure during the cooling operation as does the forced-air evaporative cooler of prior art. High humidities are not only oppressive and tend to be unhealthy, but cause mildew, wood warpage and other damage. If, in hot-dry areas, the humidity should be excessively low when using my thermal barrier method, it is possible to humidify the air within an enclosure by circulating it through the space overlying roof pond 654 and underlying the movable thermal barrier 603*a*–603*b*–603*c*.

Although in most instances the human comfort zone can be maintained within an enclosure using a roof pond and a movable thermal barrier, it is sometimes desirable to have water confined in the walls of the building or enclosure either to supplement or to distribute the heat collected in the roof pond. In FIGURE 13, wall 601 is shown as a water wall, of a type described later, with drain 780 at the bottom of the wall. On the outer surface is shown fixed insulation 630 which restricts heat gain or loss to the inside surface of the wall. Water 461 filling the cavities in wall 601 may be static to add interior heat storage and reduce the range of thermal variation, or it may be connected, through conduit and valve 580 shown in FIGURE 23, with the water 561 in roof pond 654 and drained, through drain 780 shown in FIGURE 13, as desired to fill wall 601 with either hot or cold water from pond 654.

Insulation 630 is most frequently permanently fastened externally on wall 601 of FIGURE 13, although it is possible to mount it in a manner to make it the movable thermal barrier of my invention, and thus heat can be selectively absorbed or dissipated through wall 601. The water confined in a wall, such as 601 with insulation moved to another position, is not cooled to so low a temperature by night sky radiation as is water in an enclosed roof pond which, in turn, does not get so cold as an exposed roof pond. Therefore water walls are primarily of value to supplement thermal modulation with roof ponds.

Like roof ponds, water walls have not been used extensively because advantages contributed to them by my invention have not hitherto been known. To clarify my embodiment using water walls 101 and 601 of FIGURES 9 and 13 respectively, details are shown in FIGURES 14 to 20 which disclose novel types of water walls and methods for forming them. It has been customary in prior art to use rigid elements to directly confine water in the wall. This necessitated costly fabrication of watertight tanks or laborious sealing of panels or other confining elements. By contrast, I have found a simple and effective means to form a low-cost water wall. I have further found a means for controlling thermal convection of water within said water wall. By controlling convection, I equalize the temperature from the top to the bottom of the wall, preventing water from rising any substantial distance as it warms, thus reducing drafts in rooms partially enclosed by such walls.

Wall fragment 901 of FIGURE 14 shows water 961 confined within a flexible plastic liner 960 of low vapor transmission characteristics, such as tubular layflat polyethylene film approximately 6 mils thick, and having a drain 980 in a bottom sealed portion and an inlet 971 with an air vent 972 in the top portion. Inlet 971 is interconnected by a metal or plastic conduit and a suitable valve means (not shown) to roof pond 654 of FIGURE 13, or it may be connected, alternatively, to a domestic water supply. Drain 980 is fitted with a valve (not shown).

While it is unusual for tubular layflat polyethylene to have pinholes which permit water leakage, liner 960 of FIGURE 14 is shown within a second liner 960*a* having a separate drain 880, which removes any water leakage through a pinhole in liner 960. Liner 960*a* is preferably the second wall of a double tubular bag-like enclosure for confining water 961 introduced into the wall cavity after framing is complete—although, in FIGURE 14, framing brace 912 is shown inserted between the two plastic liners. Water inlet 971 and air vent 972 are sealed to inner liner 960 and pass through holes in liner 960a and in a wall framing member 982.

Wall framing members 982 collectively form the framing of wall 901. When said framing members are of wood, they may be fastened by nails 983 or by screws; when of metal, the framing members may be bolted or welded to form a rigid wall. In FIGURE 15, a fragment of wall 901 in cross section shows framing member 982 fastened by bolt 950 embedded in concrete floor slab 905 over footing 909. On the inner and outer face of wall 901 are shown sheathing materials 907 and 908 which may be of pressed fiberboard or aluminum sheets fastened to framing members 982 by nails 983, screws or bolts. A molding strip 981 closes the space between sheathing sheet 908 and floor 905.

In FIGURE 15, water 961 is shown confined in a single flexible liner 960 which conforms to the shape of the cavity formed by framing members 982, as more fully shown in FIGURE 14, and sheathing materials 907 and 908. The significance of my use of a flexible liner such as 960 is threefold. First, the liner is readily fabricated from low-cost plastic tubing available in different compositions and of any reasonable length. It is easily transported in compact rolls and may be sealed by electronic heating means, adhesives, or clamping devices. In FIGURES 14 and 18, plastic liners 960 and 960a are shown folded over and sealed at closure 984. These sealing techniques are far simpler than those of prior art for forming water-tight walls. Secondly, flexible liner 960 conforms to irregular shapes such as the head of bolt 950, or framing brace 912, thereby eliminating concentrated loading which could rupture a more rigid lining placed over such projections. Thirdly, cross braces 912, or other means, can be added to partially divide wall 901 into a series of compartments, as shown in FIGURES 14 and 15, which interconnect but tend to restrict convection currents in water 961. By restricting convection currents, the temperature of water 961 in compartments near the floor remains nearly the same as in compartments near the ceiling instead of being warmer near the ceiling as would result from the tendency of warmed water to rise in an unrestricted water wall. A wall of more uniform temperature does not cause drafts within an enclosure nor radiate heat non-uniformly to occupants therein. My flexible liner for a water wall provides means to minimize these effects.

In FIGURE 16, a section of flexible tubing 960, suitable for a water wall, is shown as being formed into partially closed compartments of predetermined length by seals 985 which leave an unsealed portion 986 to permit water introduced at opening 987 to fill the various compartments of the tubing sealed at the bottom. FIGURE 17 illustrates the manner in which tubing 960 of FIGURE 16 with sealed end 987 tends to fill the cavity in wall 901 when the tubing inserted into the wall cavity is filled with water and when the segment lengths between seals 985 of FIGURE 16 essentially equal the spacing between sheathing members 907 and 908 fastened to framing member 982 of FIGURE 17. Interconnecting channels between segments of the tubing occur at unsealed portions 986.

In wall 901 of FIGURE 17, I have retarded vertical convection of a liquid within tubing 960 to prevent temperature differentials at different heights of a water wall. With sheathing materials 907 and 908 of metal, or other highly conductive and heat-radiating character, vertical temperature differentials caused by conduction exert themselves over no greater distance than the thickness of the wall. The wall 901 of FIGURE 17 is more suited to confine static fluids whereas wall 901 of FIGURE 14 is more suited to use where the confined liquids are to be periodically changed.

Walls 901 of FIGURES 14, 15, and 17 must withstand considerable lateral pressure. For this reason, I prefer metal sheeting as the wall sheathing 907 and 908. Metal sheeting can readily be fastened to framing 982 and is placed in tension by the lateral pressure exerted by fluid in the flexible liner 960. In addition to having great strength in tension, which permits the use of thin sheets, an impact against sheathing 908 would not readily break said sheathing. Rather, sheathing 908 bends inward slightly transferring the force to the fluid in flexible liner 960 which is raised thereby or which in turn distributes the force over a large area of sheathing material 907. After the force of the impact is thus dissipated, sheathing material 908 returns to the shape of its static condition.

FIGURE 18 illustrates the manner in which a partially segmented tubing 960 of FIGURE 16 can fill a cavity wall while enclosed in a second plastic liner 960a not segmented. Unsealed portions 986 of tubing 960 permit water to fill each compartment when added through inlet 971. Air vent 972 and tubing closure 984 are shown as are framing members 982 with fasteners 983.

FIGURES 19 and 20 illustrate the manner in which cavities of a hollow block wall may be filled with a fluid, such as water. Concrete or ceramic blocks, much used, have hitherto not been adaptable to form a water wall because of the porosity of the blocks and leakage at the mortar joints. Irregular shapes occur in the wall cavities owing to misalignment of blocks, to mortar flow into the cavities or to mortar drippage piled up in the cavity at the bottom of the wall. These irregularities preclude using a rigid water-tight liner which could substantially fill the space within the wall cavity.

As shown in the embodiment of FIGURE 20, I may double back, at point 988, a length of flexible tubing 960 open at the ends so that a fluid within said tubing forms two columns within cavities 989 of blocks 906 bonded with mortar 990 to form wall 901 over floor slab 905. The tubing 960 is also shown sealed at closure 984. Although normal irregularities of a hollow block wall partially restrict vertical convection of liquid in wall 901, I prefer, instead of the simple tubing 960 of FIGURE 20, tubing partially sealed in the manner of 985 of FIGURE 16 to form compartments vertically oriented in the cavities of wall 901 of FIGURE 20 rather than laterally oriented as shown in FIGURES 17 and 18.

FIGURE 19 represents a single hollow block 906 used in wall 901 of FIGURE 20. One cavity 989 of block 906 is shown containing the doubled-back tubing 960 of FIGURE 20. It is obvious cavity 989 could be filled by a single column of fluid and that this requires less plastic for tubing 960. This would place more reliance upon a leak-tight seal on tubing 960 at the bottom of the cavity than does doubling back tubing 960 to form two columns of fluid as shown in FIGURE 20.

Many additional embodiments of my invention could be described as combinations with embodiments disclosed. For example, hot water from either pond 654 or pond 655 of FIGURE 13 could be drained into wall 601 constructed in the manner of walls 901 of FIGURES 14, 15, 17, 18, or 20. At a different season, cold water from pond 654 or pond 657 could be drained into said wall. It furthermore may be advantageous for reasons of cost or for protection against contamination and evaporation to have ponds 654, 657, and within solar still 655 either uncovered or covered when the liquid heated or cooled is to be transferred for heat exchange or use in the ways described. Moreover, pond liquid may be transferred into a floor or other component designed in the manner of water walls disclosed.

In addition to preferring a pond horizontally oriented for more efficient solar heating and for cooling to the zenith atmosphere, I prefer that insulation move horizontally over a horizontal pond to a position not over said pond. Hinged insulation panels 30 of FIGURE 1 mounted over the ponds of FIGURE 13 or mounted on a vertical water wall externally are aerodynamically unstable, require frequent adjustment to permit maximum heating and cooling effects as the sun position varies, and are more costly to construct than the sliding panels of my invention. *

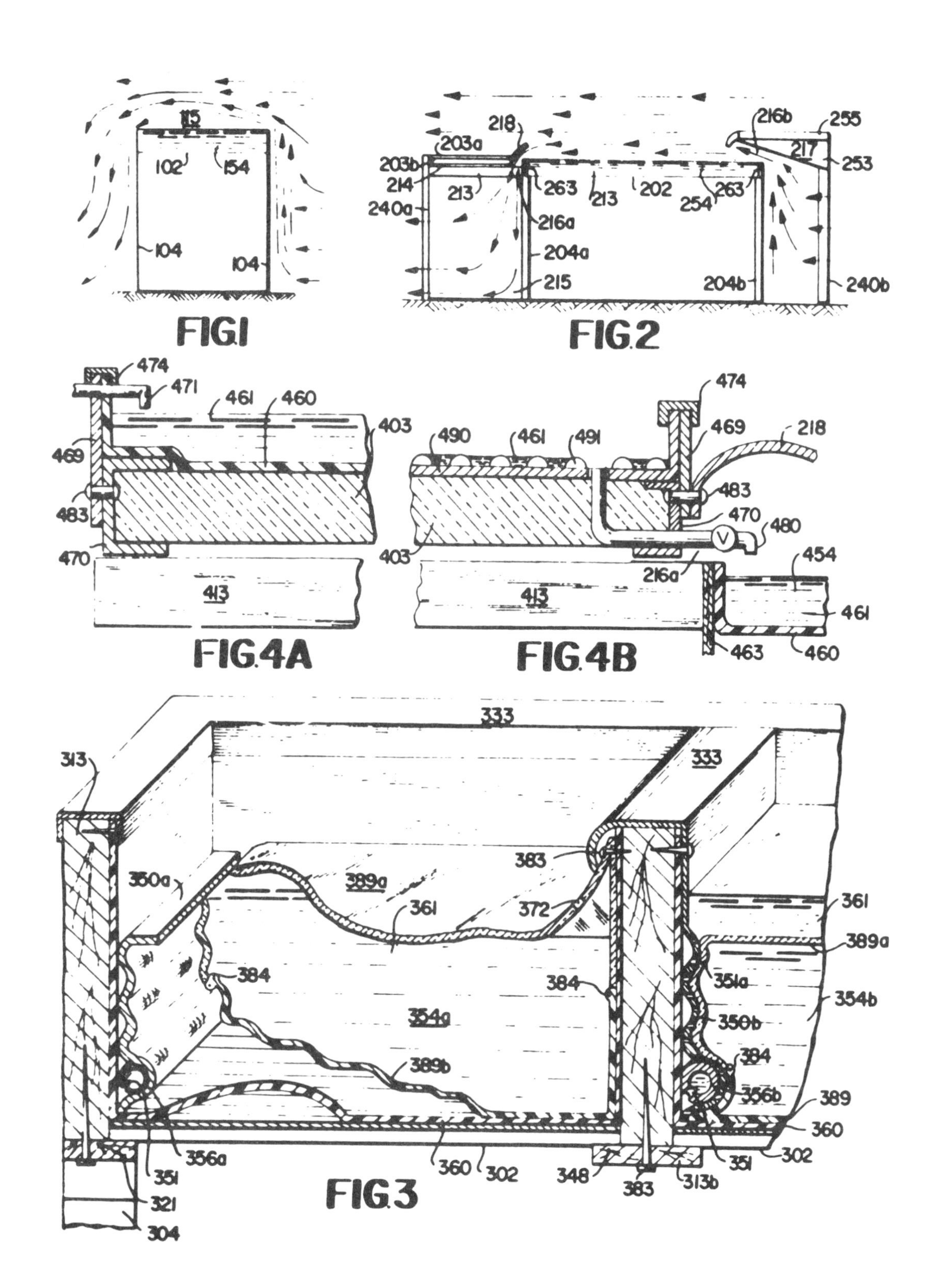
PATENTED FEB 16 1971
HAY, H.R.
3,563,305
SHEET 1 OF 4
FIG1
FIG2
FIG4A
FIG4B
FIG3

PATENTED FEB 16 1971 HAY, H.R. 3,563,305

SHEET 2 OF 4

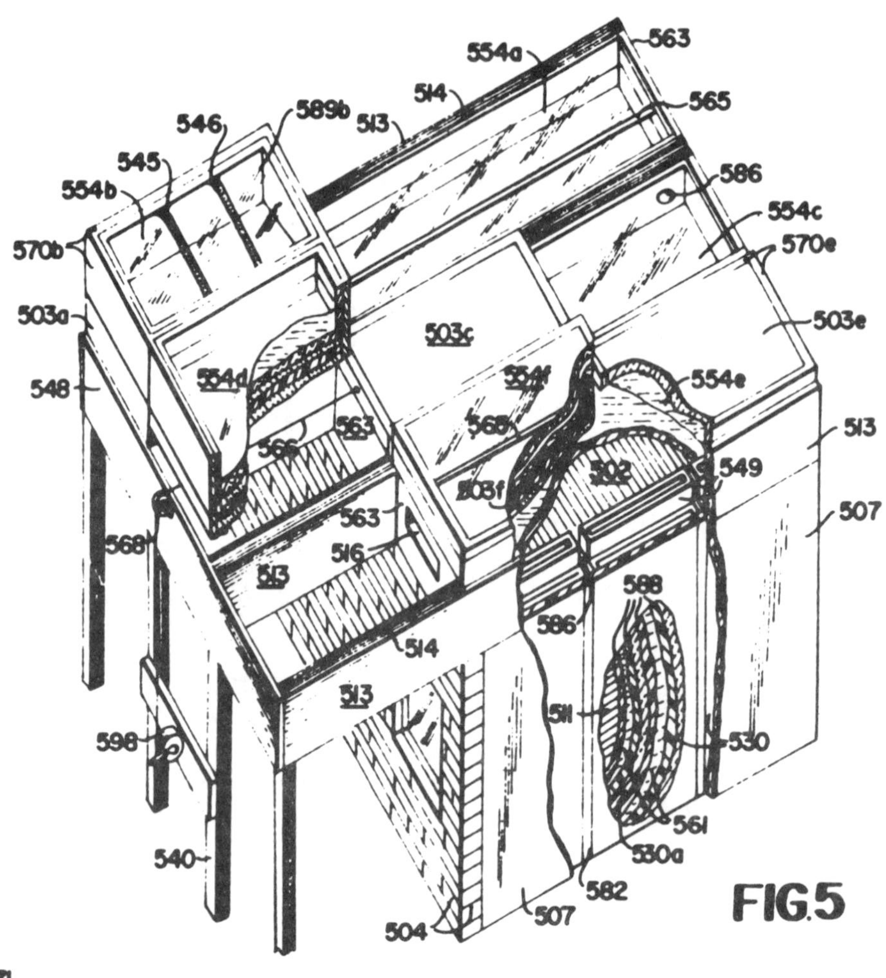

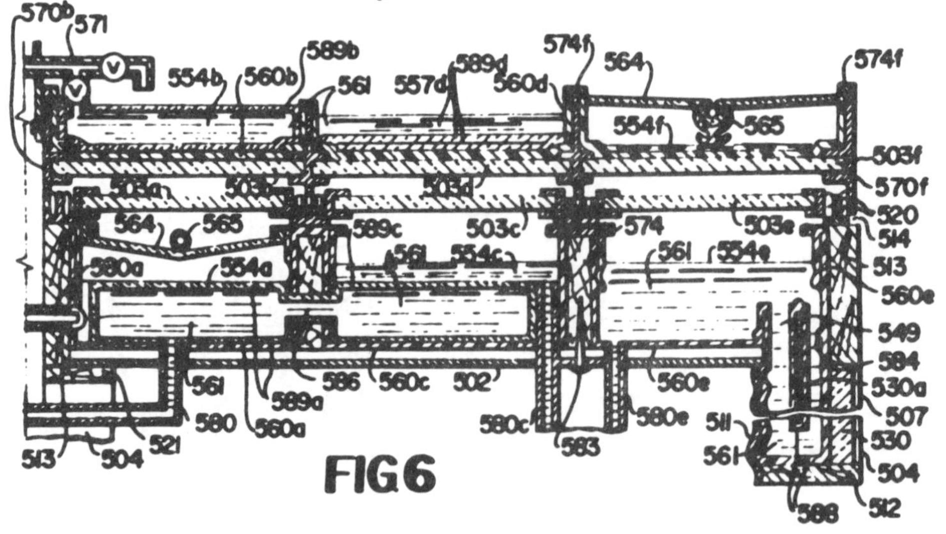

PATENTED FEB 16 1971 HAY, H.R. 3,563,305

SHEET 3 OF 4

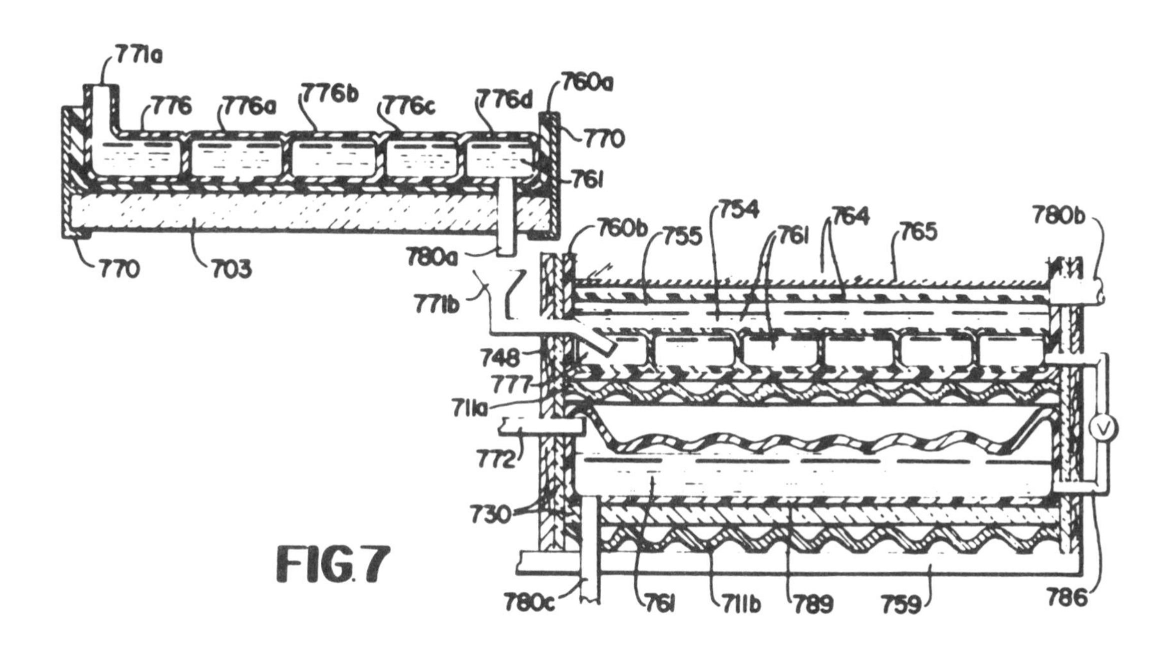

FIG. 7

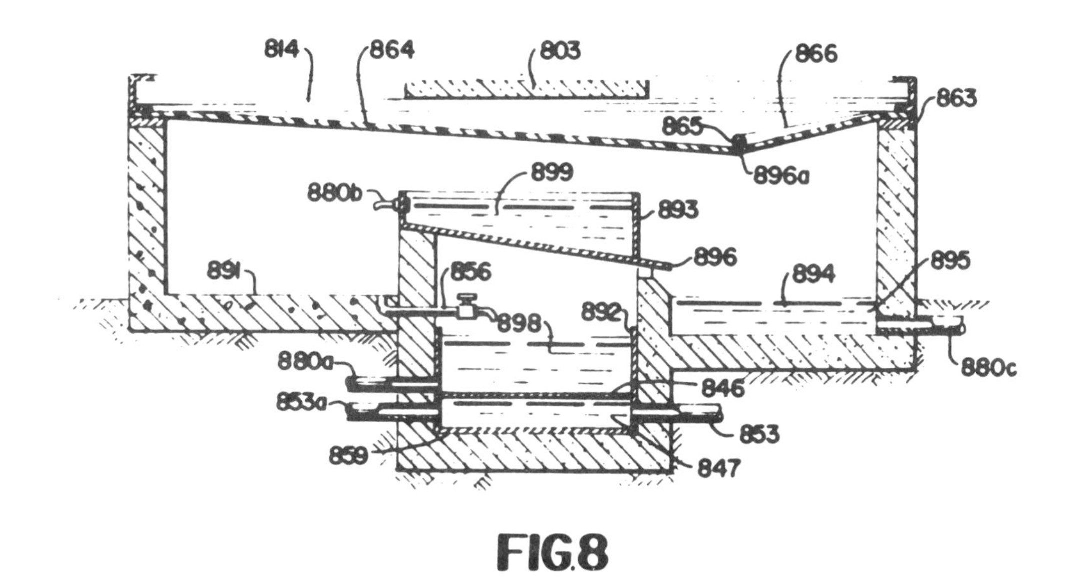

FIG. 8

PATENTED FEB 16 1971 HAY, H.R. 3,563,305

SHEET 4 OF 4

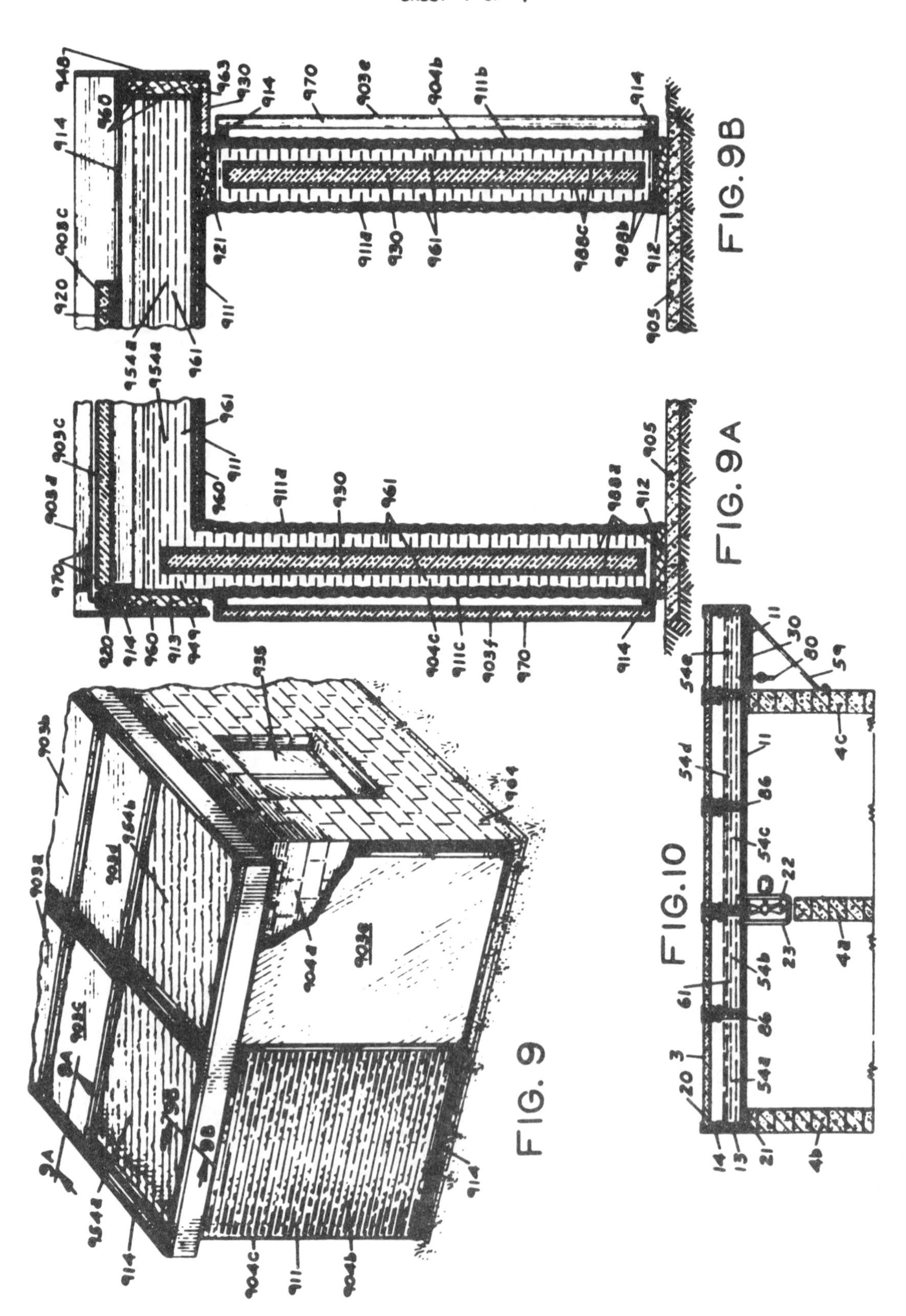

PROCESS AND APPARATUS FOR MODULATING TEMPERATURES WITHIN ENCLOSURES

*

This invention relates to a process and apparatus for controlling the temperatures of substances and enclosures; it primarily involves the collection of solar energy and the dissipation of heat to the night sky or to ambient air. More particularly, the invention relates to the novel design of enclosures and to simple or automatic manipulations of means, in conjunction with or independent of the movable insulation thermal valve means of my prior inventions, to modulate temperatures within an enclosure as a whole, or of its various components or contents. This modulation is accomplished, in some cases, in conjunction with novel means for increasing or retarding evaporation, novel thermosiphon means for heating and cooling, and novel means for thermal transfer and storage though each of the novel means may be used separately or in various combinations.

The novel means, singly or in combination, may be incorporated into a building to maintain internal temperature as closely as possible within a narrow range. In other embodiments, the means may be incorporated into, or onto, other enclosures or devices, as, for example, water heaters or coolers, solar stills, storage containers, etc. It is irrelevant in what form of enclosure, or for what purpose, the temperature modulation is achieved by means of my invention.

The primary object of this invention is to provide an improved process and means for controlling the collection and dissipation of heat characterized by low-cost installation, operation, and maintenance. Another object is to provide an improved process and means to control the collection or the loss of heat so as to maintain the interior of an enclosure, or components or portions of an enclosure, or materials or objects within the enclosure, nearer a desirable temperature.

It is an object of this invention to provide a measure of heat control by moving structural components of an enclosure into different positional relationships to other components wherein the components are selectively composed of materials having different heat storage and heat transfer characteristics and the movement is selectively timed in relation to external temperatures.

Moreover, it is an object to provide a process and means for increasing or decreasing the evaporation of a liquid acting as a heat collector or heat dissipator which may be at least partially confined by a structural member forming an enclosure which may be a building.

It is a further object to provide a process and means for heating or cooling an enclosure by a liquid thermosiphon effect within a heat collector or a heat dissipator, often at least partially formed by a structural member of said enclosure. An additional object of this invention is to provide a process and means for thermal transfer into and form a liquid and to influence heat transfer and loss by means of a movable thermal barrier. It is also an object of this invention to control the collection of heat in a liquid, and dissipation of the heat, to an enclosure the temperature of which is to be affected by said liquid.

It is an added object to provide an improved process and means for heating or cooling a water supply for domestic or other use; and it is an object of this invention to control the temperature of thermally sensitive objects and of processes such as evaporation, distillation, heat storage and transfer, and all such processes as are influenced by thermal change within an enclosure or in a confined volume. Other objects and advantages of the present invention will become more apparent after reading the following descriptions taken in conjunction with the drawings.

The invention is capable of receiving a variety of mechanical expressions illustrated on the accompanying drawings, but it is to be explicitly understood that the drawings are for illustration only and are not to be construed as defining the limits of the invention, reference being had to the appended claims for that purpose.

FIG. 1 is a diagrammatical sectional view of an enclosure obstructing airflow which assumes the general pattern indicated by arrows.

FIG. 2 is a diagrammatic cross section showing means for causing air movement to approximately parallel the upper surface of an enclosure.

FIG. 3 is a fragmentary diagrammatic and partially cutaway view of means for retarding or increasing evaporation of liquid confined above an enclosure.

FIGS. 4A and 4B are fragmentary sectional representations of two means for confining liquid to be cooled by evaporation on top of movable insulation.

FIG. 5 is a diagrammatic perspective and partially cutaway view of an enclosure showing details of roof ponds and wall construction.

FIG. 6 is a diagrammatic sectional view of details of the roof construction and fragmentary details of the wall construction of FIG. 5.

FIG. 7 is a diagrammatic cross-sectional representation of a means for heating or cooling and for storing water.

FIG. 8 is a diagrammatic cross section of a water-heating device with a heat transfer means.

FIGS. 9, 9A, and 9B, respectively, are diagrammatic views of an embodiment of this invention using thermosiphon action to circulate liquid in a wall. FIG. 9 is an exterior, partially cutaway, perspective of a building with movable insulation to control heat gain or loss on a wall. FIG. 9A is a cross section of a wall with a thermosiphon means for thermal control. FIG. 9B is an alternative design for thermosiphon thermal control.

FIG. 10 is a diagrammatic cross section of a building with a fan coil means for transferring roof pond thermal effects to an enclosure.

The following descriptions of various embodiments of my invention will be primarily related to the control of thermal transfer between described components of an enclosure and such natural means for heating as solar irradiation and such means for cooling as night-sky radiation, convection, or dissipation of evaporated liquids to the atmosphere. Within the meaning of this invention, however, the heating and cooling effects may be the result of fuel or other energy and conventional means or devices or by combinations of these effects with natural means. Also within the meaning of this invention, the enclosure may be a container, a building, or any structure having, or capable of having, applied to it the elements of the embodiments to be described. Furthermore, the space to be thermally controlled may underlie or be remote from the novel heating or cooling means but affected thereby; and useful thermal results are obtained if the structure is only partially enclosed.

FIG. 1 shows the effect of a structure with a roof pond on natural wind patterns as determined by smoke tests or wind velocity measurements. Low velocities of 1 to 10 miles per hour cause airflow essentially parallel to the ground until the air impinges an obstructing surface such as one of the outside walls 104 of an enclosure. Then, air passes partially around the obstruction and partially across its top. Airflow over the structure with a flat roof 102 and roof pond 154 produces an air space 115 of little or no air movement. This condition adversely affects water evaporation from ponds 154 and retards cooling the enclosure with which the pond water is capable of thermal exchange.

Wind scoops on ships, and on housetops in Hyderabad, Pakistan, direct airflow to interiors of enclosures for ventilation and for evaporation of water directly from the skin of people. Prior art has also used wind scoops to direct dry air against damp surfaces, such as earthenware jugs, to cool water. Instead of such separate, unsightly, and costly scoops, I use the wall of the structure, and the ground, as major portions of the scoop and add a deflector near the top of the wall at approximately roof pond level. A portion of the deflector may protrude from the wall to trap wind impinging thereon. For this purpose, I may combine the function of the deflector with one or more useful devices, such as a water heater, a solar still, a rain collector, a shading projection, or the movable thermal barrier often a part of my means for controlling temperatures.

FIG. 2 shows an embodiment of my invention in which windflow, indicated as arrow lines, impinging upon wall 204*b* is trapped under member 217 and is caused to flow through a passage 216*b* in a direction approximately parallel to and in close proximity with the water surface of roof pond 254. With properly shaped deflectors, such as those of 217 and 218 of FIG. 2, air velocities at least as high as those prevailing before impingement on wall 204*b* obtain near the surface of pond 254. The significance of this is evident from the fact that when 44 B.t.u. of heat is lost from a square foot of pond surface by evaporation into still air, 75.5 B.t.u. are lost with the air moving only 2 miles per hour. This difference can readily lower pond temperatures and convert a condition of thermal discomfort within an enclosure cooled by the pond to one of comfort.

The embodiment of FIG. 2 comprises space shown partially enclosed by walls 204*a* and 204*b* made of concrete or any material capable of supporting wood or metal roof beams 213, shown extended beyond wall 204*a* to post 240*a*, supporting roof pond 254 confined above metal roof sheets 202 fastened under beams 213 by screws not shown. Roof pond 254 is confined between two beams 213, crossing the enclosure, and end closures 263 between the beams and shown here as above walls 204*a* and 204*b*. The ponds are lined with a suitable material such as black, flexible polyethylene film shown better in FIG. 6 crossing over beams 213 and end closures 263 to provide a weathertight roof above the enclosure. Atop the beams 213 are aluminum trackways 214 of types standard for overhead closet doors in which insulation panels 203*a* and 203*b*, having suitable metal framing with attached wheels (not shown), can be moved with a drawcord passing over pulleys to a winch all as better shown in FIGS. 5 and 6. The insulating panels 203*a* and 203*b*, preferably of rigid polyurethane foam about 2 inches thick and framed in extruded aluminum channels and painted or clad to prevent deterioration by solar irradiation, may be stacked, as better shown in FIG. 5, over the extended beams when roof pond 254 is to be exposed for evaporation cooling and they may completely cover pond 254 when desired.

To the right in FIG. 2, wind-trapping member 217 is supported by posts 240*b* and fastened to beams 213 or to wall 204*b* in a manner (not shown) leaving preferably an elongated opening 216*b*, usually not less than 1 inch nor more than 1 foot in height, between pond closures 263 and the underside of wind-trapping member 217 which may have its extremity near the pond turned down slightly to further cause airflow through passage 216*b* to parallel the water surface of pond 254 and to have high velocity.

Wind-trapping member 217, of FIG. 2, is shown comprising in combination element 255 which may be an elongated water heater or solar still, of types to be later described, and below this an elongated water tank shown as triangular shape 253. The upper surface of member 217 may be provided for rain catchment and the member may shade a walkway between wall 204*b* and posts 240*b*, though, in other instances, no such multiple purpose need be served by member 217.

To the left of FIG. 2, deflector 218 is a piece of elongated metal, plastic, wood, or other suitable material fastened by screws or other means to the framing of top movable insulation panel 203*a* as better shown in FIG. 4B. The space 216*a* between two beams 213 forms a passage for upward-flowing air impinging on wall 204*a* when prevailing winds are from the direction opposite that shown by the arrows. Deflector 218 causes airflow through passage 216*a* to be directed parallel to the surface of the pond after passing over end closure 263.

In operation, cooling of the enclosure is obtained by exposing pond 254 at night by moving insulating panels 203*a* and 203*b* from an extended position overlying pond 254 to a position so far to the left of wall 204*a* as to leave an open passage 216*a* under deflector 218. If prevailing winds are as shown by arrow lines of FIG. 2, air will be deflected by member 217 toward pond surface 254 and travel substantially parallel thereto until at least partially trapped by deflector 218 which causes the air to flow toward the ground and to resume the course it had prior to impinging on wall 204*b*. Air deflected around the enclosure sides, rather than over it, tends to converge again at the left side of FIG. 2 adding to the creation of a partial vacuum near wall 204*a* at ground level which also helps draw air through passage 216*b* and thereby parallel to pond 254 in a manner conducive to create a higher air velocity.

When winds reverse direction from that shown by FIG. 2 arrows, deflector 218 and member 217 still act to increase evaporation and cooling of exposed water in pond 254. When the pond is adequately cooled, or about 1 hour after sunrise, the movable insulation 203*a* and 203*b* is positioned over pond 254 to prevent absorption of solar energy or ambient heat which would warm the pond. Pond water, often cooled several degrees below minimum morning air temperature by nighttime evaporation, can then keep space within a suitably designed enclosure at comfortable temperatures throughout days with 110° F. ambient air. The ponds may absorb heat from this space through a metal ceiling 202 which is the pond support or pond water may be transferred by pump, thermosiphon, or other suitable means to a remote device, such as a fan coil or radiant panel for heat exchange with the space.

Wind deflectors of the type of 218 may be mounted directly to roof beams 213, or to the fascia of buildings, and extend outward from the walls to scoop and direct wind on all sides of a roof to benefit from winds originating from any direction. Moreover, the enclosure walls may be extended beyond the enclosed area to largely eliminate wind deflection around the sides of the building and to increase airflow across the roof pond.

If the novel system for deflecting natural wind across roof ponds does not provide adequate evaporation cooling, forced air may be employed. An electric fan, or blower unit of the standard type, mounted to discharge air across uncovered ponds at night is an effective means for cooling the water. With much greater advantage, I have found that the fan or blower (not shown) can be mounted to force air over the pond while the insulation is positioned above the pond. In FIG. 5, an opening 516 through end closure 563 and above the 554*e* of pond 554*e* can admit unsaturated air which causes evaporation cooling while passing across the pond surface and under insulation panels 503*f* and 503*e* to an outlet not shown. A fan or blower may be used to force the air through opening 516 or natural air currents may be trapped under a suitable deflector, of the type of 218 of FIG. 2, mounted above opening 516 to direct the air through opening 516.

Although the last-mentioned embodiment functions effectively with fixed insulation over ponds, I prefer movable insulation to collect solar energy for heating an enclosure on winter days. The air directed through the plenum formed by the surface of pond 554, the insulation panels 503*f* and 503*e*, and the beams 513 is humidified and may, during periods of very low humidity, pass by the outlet to a duct system discharging into the enclosure. This means for raising the moisture content of air in the enclosure may be controlled by well-known means to provide only the optimum internal humidity. By discharging the cooled and humidified air into a vegetable storage room, the stored produce may be conserved. By passing it downward through wall cavities, such as exist in hollow-block masonry, the cooling effect of the air may be utilized without introducing humidity in the room. The cooled air may also be caused to flow as an air curtain down the outer surface of walls or the enclosure, thereby obtaining a cooling effect on the walls and in the enclosure. Using only the thermal exchange through the pond bottom, forced external air caused adequate cooling of ponded water under movable insulation to maintain room temperatures between 60° and 68° F. when the ambient air entering the blower ranged from 75° to 105° F.

Evaporation of water from roof ponds can be increased by a wicking device whether the ponds are covered or uncovered; and forced air may be introduced under the surface of the roof ponds if desired. In another embodiment, a multistoried building may be cooled without involving insulation movable or fixed. The floor design may include a plenum lined with plastic, metal, or other watertight material to confine water to be evaporated by air forced through the plenum; the cooling effect can then be transferred by conduction or by circulating the water through a fan coil to modulate temperatures of space both above and below the plenum floor. For example, a second-story floor of concrete with downward extending beams closes three sides of a plenum; an acoustical ceiling of metal may be fastened to the underside of the beams to complete the plenum and support an enclosed tray of water about 1 inch deep. A float valve may be used to maintain water level in the tray and an overflow provided for occasional flushing or to drain excess water. Air blown into the plenum may be exhausted through ducts for any purpose earlier mentioned. Both the air and the water will be cooled by water evaporation and will act while within the plenum to cool the room below and the room above.

FIG. 5 shows an embodiment of my invention in which a thermosiphon means within a wall effects heat transfer between space within an enclosure and a roof or plenum pond. This embodiment is of particular value to cool the space when there is inadequate heat exchange through structural elements of the pond; or, it can be used to cool enclosures not underlying the pond. Some elements and materials of the embodiment are described in my patents issued and allowed, of which this is a continuation-in-part, and in other embodiments herein.

As shown in FIGS. 5 and 6, walls 504 and wall plates 521 support beams 513 [illegible] the underside of which are fastened by nails 58[illegible] [illegible]ews, or other means, corrugated metal sheets 502 forming the ceiling of the enclosure and the directly bottom of roof pond 554e having a black plastic liner 560e over which water 561 is preferably maintained about 6 to 7 inches deep when the pond is to be used for winter heating. For clarity, it should be mentioned here that ponds 554a, 554b, 554c, 554d, and 554f do not relate to the thermosiphon action in pond 554e but involve other embodiments of this invention which will be discussed later — though they may coexist on a roof structure and would be similarly affected by the panels of movable insulation. Pond 554e is shown covered by the insulation panels 503e and 503f in their extended position in FIG. 5; the panels are shown in FIG. 6 as if stacked over pond 554e. The insulation of panels 503e and 503f is best shown in FIG. 6 as being framed in an aluminum extrusion 570 to which wheels 520 are fastened to move the panels in trackway 514 atop beams 513. Movement of the panels may be made independent of each other or they may be made to move in an interlocking manner so that a single device such as the winch 598 and drawcord 566 move all insulation panels above the ponds, and to position them over a carport or other suitable area best shown in FIG. 5 where support is provided by extensions of beams 513 and by posts 540.

At least a portion of one wall of the enclosure is formed into a thermosiphon element which contains water 561 in common with roof pond 554e. The thermosiphon wall may be variously constructed; it is shown in FIGS. 5 and 6 as having an inside surface of metal sheets 511 with corrugations horizontally disposed and fastened by lag screws (not shown) to wall studs 582 shown only in FIG. 5. The outer surface of the wall may consist of ⅝-inch thick exterior grade plywood sheathing 507 likewise fastened by lag screws to studs 582. Other parts will be described in relation to the thermosiphon action.

As best shown in FIG. 6, lay-flat action is established through one or more U-shaped lengths of layflat plastic tubing 588 sealed to the roof pond liner 560e at seals 584 with one of the legs doubled and extending upward to form a "chimney" 549 rising somewhat above middepth of pond 554e. Chimneys 549 are shown on both sides of a stud 582 terminating at the level of the bottom of the pond; then, the upper ends of the studs are covered by the liner 560e and a channel 586 is formed between the chimneys. These channels permit cold water at the bottom of the pond 554e to pass around the chimneys 549 and, owing to the higher density of the cold water, to flow down the short leg of the U-shaped siphon tube 588 shown toward the outside of wall 504.

To prevent cold water in the short outer leg from absorbing heat through exterior sheathing 507, a 1.5-inch thick sheet of rigid polyurethane insulation 530 is between them. Also, a 0.5-inch thick sheet of the insulation 530a separates the short and long legs of the thermosiphon tube to retard heat transfer and maintain the temperature differential causing thermosiphon action. Insulation 530a may extend above the bottom of pond 554e to help form the chimney 549 and stops short of the bottom of the wall cavity where the U-shaped thermosiphon rests between the studs on floor plate 512 or on cross bracing, or other suitable support between the studs, at a higher level.

The long leg of the thermosiphon, as shown in FIGS. 5 and 6, starts at the floor plate 512 and ends at the top of chimney 549. Within the wall cavity, it directly contacts corrugated metal sheets 511 forming the inside surface of the wall. Heat from the room readily passes through metal sheets 511 and the thin, 20 mil, flexible plastic and is absorbed by water 561 in the long leg of the thermosiphon where, by virtue of the lower density of warm water, it rises while the colder water from the short leg replaces it in thermosiphon action. It has been found that as little as 0.5° F. differential in the short and long legs is sufficient to initiate thermosiphon action. The warmed water in the long leg flows out chimney 549 and stratifies adequately in the upper portion of pond 554e to permit the more dense colder water at the bottom of the pond to pass down the short leg of the thermosiphon.

The thermosiphon device of FIGS. 5 and 6 is substantially limited to cooling an enclosure having a roof or plenum pond or other high-level reservoir of cold water. Thermosiphon cooling depends, in the embodiments described, upon cooling pond 554e at night by moving the insulation panels 503e and 503f from the daytime position over the ponds to a nighttime position not over the ponds. Used in conjunction with a plenum and forced air evaporation, however, thermosiphon action can be maintained at a more constant temperature level than the cyclic diurnal cooling of an open pond permits. Thermosiphon cooling is inexpensive since corrugated sheets of various thickness to withstand normal head pressures from the water are standard; seamless polyethylene layflat tubing can be used for the U-shaped thermosiphon; and rigid polyurethane is thermally efficient in the thin sheets allowing practical construction.

FIG. 9 is an exterior, partial view of an enclosure having two additional thermosiphon embodiments of this invention disclosed in relation to FIGS. 9A and 9B. Wall **904**, in FIG. 9, is conventional masonry with a window 935. The facing wall, shown with a masonry first portion **904*a*** and a second portion **904*b*** with an exterior of corrugated metal 911 which forms part of my thermosiphon means for controlling space temperatures within the enclosure shown in detail in FIG. 9B. Wall portions **904*a*** and **904*b***, and insulation **903*e***, which is movable on track 914, have areas such that insulation **903*e*** covers at least a portion of wall **904*a*** when exposure of wall portion **904*b*** is desired and covers substantially all of wall **904*b*** when that is advantageous.

Roof ponds **954*a*** and **954*b*** are confined between beams over walls **904** and **904*c*** and center beam 913 on which trackways 914 facilitate positioning insulation panels **903*a***, **903*b***, **903*c***, and **903*d*** to either cover or expose said ponds. Pond **954*b*** is not related to discussion of the embodiments of FIGS. 9A and 9B though it may be interconnected with pond **954*a*** which is a functional element of the embodiment of FIG. 9A but not of that of 9B which it is shown to be overlying in part. Enclosure wall **904*c***, opposite wall **904**, incorporates the embodiment of FIG. 9A and is to be considered as constructed of two portions comparable to **904*a*** and **904*b*** and with an exterior movable insulation panel of the type of **903*e***.

The thermosiphon embodiment of FIG. 9A differs from that of FIGS. 5 and 6 by being effective for solar heating whereas that of FIGS. 5 and 6 is primarily effective for cooling the enclosure and may be mounted in a wall not subject to exposure to solar irradiation. Construction differences are primarily in the exterior portions of the wall and in having the long thermosiphon leg toward the outside of the FIG. 9A embodiment.

In FIG. 9A, pond **954*a*** within liner **960** is confined by corrugated ceiling sheets 911 and beam 913 on which trackway 914 permits positioning insulation **903*a*** and **903*c*** in framing 970 to which wheels **920** are fastened. Wall **904*c*** is constructed of exterior, dark-colored metal sheets **911*c*** and interior metal sheets **911*a*** fastened to floor plate 912 over floor **905** and to studs (not shown) as described in the embodiment of FIGS. 5 and 6. Within the FIG. 9A wall cavity, formed by said studs and metal sheets **911*a*** and **911*c***, a length of layflat tubing **988*a*** is doubled back at floor plate 912 to form two thermosiphon legs sealed at the top to pond liner **960** as described for the embodiment of FIGS. 5 and 6. Water **961** in pond **954*a*** circulates freely under thermosiphon action with water **961** in wall **904*c***. Separating the two thermosiphon legs is insulation **930** extending laterally between two studs (not shown) and vertically from a position about an inch above floor plate 912 to a position approximately middepth of pond **954*a***. The long thermosiphon leg ends in a chimney **949**. Because chimney **949** extends above two studs, channels formed between two adjacent chimneys, similar to the channels **586** of FIG. 5, are preferably blocked by a dam of plastic or eliminated by having the studs extend upward, but covered by pond liner **960**, to the top of insulation **930**.

In operation, insulation **903*f*** is moved on trackway 914 from the nighttime position illustrated in FIG. 9A, to expose metal **911*c*** to solar rays. Heat absorbed by metal **911*c*** is conducted to water **961** in the long thermosiphon leg warming it more than 0.5° F. oF. above the temperature of water **961** in the inner short leg and starting thermosiphon action in the wall cavity. Rising water overflows chimney 949 and stratifies atop pond **954*a*** adequately for cooler water at the bottom of said pond to descend through the short thermosiphon leg for heat exchange with inner metal **911*a*** of wall **904*c*** to modulate temperatures within the enclosure. Insulation **903*f*** is returned to its nighttime position covering exterior metal **911*c*** when adequate heat has been absorbed and to prevent heat loss at night.

The FIG. 9A embodiment is operative for cooling space underlying pond **954*a*** if insulation **903*f*** is positioned away from metal **911*c*** at night to permit radiation of heat from the outer, long, thermosiphon leg to the night sky. When this radiation cooling causes the average density of water in the long leg to be greater than that in the inner, short leg, the direction of thermosiphoning is reversed with warmer water rising into pond **954*a*** through the short leg. More short-circuiting of water across the top of chimney **949** and from one leg to the other occurs when this embodiment is used for cooling than when it is used for heating thus diminishing the value of pond **954*a*** for thermosiphon cooling. Clearly, pond **954*a*** may have its temperature affected by thermosiphon action controlled by movable insulation **903*f*** or without the existence of this movable insulation and without movement of the insulation panels **903*a*** and **903*c*** from a position covering said pond. Or, pond temperature may be affected by proper positioning of all three insulation panels **903*a***, **903*c***, and **903*f*** in a manner to produce optimum heating or cooling of space within the enclosure.

FIG. 9B represents an embodiment in which thermosiphon action is restricted in wall **904*b***. Roof pond **954*a*** is shown confined by plastic liner **960** over metal sheets 911 forming the enclosure ceiling and overhang; the liner **960** also passes over wood end closure **963** and the beams on which trackway 914 is located for moving insulation **903*c*** on wheels **920** for control of temperature in pond **954*a***. The fascia **948** serves as a stop for the movable insulation. Fixed insulation **930**, under the overhang, reduces loss of desirable pond temperatures. Pond **954*a*** need not be present for the thermosiphon means of wall **904*b*** to operate, but if present and having an interconnecting tubing of not much more than one-half inch internal diameter, water **961** from pond **954*a*** will keep the thermosiphon means filled with water without permitting appreciable thermosiphon action between the two bodies of water.

Inner metal sheets **911*a*** and outer metal sheets **911*b*** are fastened by lag screws (not shown) to wood studs (similar to 582 of FIG. 5), to wood roof plate 921 bridging the top of said studs and fastened thereto, and to wood floor plate 912 anchored to concrete floor **905** by bolts (not shown). The thermosiphon element of this embodiment has legs of equal length separated by insulation **930** preferably of closed-cell plastic. The thermosiphon element may be formed by first shaping ½inch thick insulation **930** to a width which causes it to bend slightly when forced between the aforesaid studs and either of a length shorter than the distance between floor plate 912 and roof plate 921 or, if of the same length, holes must be provided through the insulation near floor plate 912 and roof plate 921. The insulation may be coated with asphalt or hermetically sealed in plastic cladding **988*c***. Insulation **930** is then inserted into flexible bag **988*b*** of greater volume than the wall cavity and the bag **988*b*** is sealed with provision made at the top for a suitable water inlet and air outlet means (not shown). The thermosiphon element may then be manually inserted between said studs by pressing to slightly bow the insulation **930**; the bow creates an edge pressure against said studs which holds insulation **930** in place and, later, prevents any appreciable short-circuiting along these edges of water **961** on opposite sides of said insulation. After adjusting the inserted bag **988*b*** loose enough to fill the wall cavity when under a head pressure of water, and after verifying that passageways are open between the two thermosiphon legs above floor plate 912 and under roof plate 921, metal sheets **911*a*** and **911*b*** are affixed to said studs. The thermosiphon element is then filled with water for operation, preferably in conjunction with movable insulation 903e in framing 970 and movable in trackway 914 to a first position covering wall 904b or to another position, such as wall 904a of FIG. 9, thereby exposing at least a portion of wall 904b.

When exterior metal sheets 911b are exposed to solar rays, and their surface temperature exceeds that of interior metal sheets 911a, water 961 in the outer thermosiphon leg attains a higher temperature and lower density than that in the inner leg and rises owing to displacement by cooler and denser water from the inner leg. The warmed water passes over insulation 930, or through holes provided therein, to the top of the inner leg where it gives up heat to the enclosure through metal sheets 911a. The water moves down through the inner leg as it cools below the temperature at a comparable height in the outer leg and passes under, or through, insulation 930 to be reheated by sheets 911b. This embodiment of my invention equally efficient in thermosiphon action for cooling the enclo sure if sheets 911b are exposed at night to allow radiation to a heat sink of temperature lower than that of the enclosed space.

Though the thermosiphon embodiments disclosed are all shown vertically oriented, they tend to operate more efficiently if inclined to a position more favorable for collection of solar heat and greater radiation to zenith sky; this positioning may, however, require additional roof-supporting members. Also, I have found that instead of centering insulation 930 in the cavity of wall 904b, it may be installed offcenter to provide a thinner leg of water to the outside of the thermosiphon and a thicker inner leg. Then, a greater temperature differential is created in the two legs and a more positive thermosiphon effect is created. The volume of water in the thermosiphon system and in any roof or plenum ponds associated therewith, as well as solar radiation intensity or night sky radiation effect, determines the range of temperatures obtained within the thermosiphon system and within the enclosure. Through the previously described effects, movable insulation panels associated with the thermosiphon embodiments provide a useful control means for maintaining desirable temperatures in the thermosiphon system and in the enclosure of which it is a part.

During humid periods, water evaporation is generally required to cool roof ponds adequately to maintain desired enlosure temperatures by control means of this invention. But, in winter, water evaporation from roof ponds causes cooling which offsets solar heating; to retard evaporation then, the roof pond is covered with glass or plastic capable of transmitting solar radiation. If this cover is spaced above the pond, air between the cover acts as an insulator to retard solar heat loss from the pond, but it also forms a solar still which condenses water on the cover and reflects solar radiation causing a heat loss. The embodiments of my invention now to be disclosed provide thermal controls of simple types applicable during differing seasons.

The novel embodiments to control roof pond evaporation are illustrated in FIGS. 5 and 6. Pond 554b atop movable insulation panel 503b is an embodiment enclosing said pond in plastic capable of transmitting solar radiation. As best shown in FIG. 6, layflat tubing 589b retards evaporation or loss of water; the tubing thickness may range from 1 to 10 mils or more and may be of polyethylene, polyvinylchloride, or other suitable material in tubing form and closed at the ends (not shown) by electronic sealing, clamping devices, or by folds maintained by suitable means above the level of enclosed water. Upper panel of movable insulation 503b has framing member 570b with an upward extension around the panel to which may be fastened, by adhesive or clamping means, a black plastic liner 560b in which lays the plastic tubing in the form of a bag 589b. Framing member 570b has a downward extension to which are mounted wheels 520 riding in trackway 514 to facilitate moving the insulation and pond 554b.

An inlet assembly with valves 571, suitably fastened to framing member 570b and connected by flexible hose (not shown) to a water source, is used to add water 561 either into bag 589b to form enclosed pond 554b or over bag 589b and confined by liner 560b. Not shown in conjunction with pond 554b, but similar to 580 and 580a shown for pond 554a of FIG. 6, are provided means for draining water from bag 589b and from liner 560b. An enclosed pond of the type of 554b is useful to supplement heat collection by other roof ponds, such as 554a shown in thermal transfer relationship with the enclosure. Daytime positioning of pond 554b is shown in FIG. 5: ponds 554a and 554b are both exposed to solar irradiation when heating is desired. Water heated in pond 554b may overflow, or be drained by gravity through an interconnecting hose and valve means (not shown), into pond 554a, into a water wall which may not be a thermosiphon-type described earlier, or it may be pumped to another enclosure or place of use. Water remaining in pond 554b at the end of the day may be allowed to cool to the night sky when the supporting insulation 503b, together with insulation 503a is in its nighttime position over pond 554a and reheated the following day, or the water may be drained and replaced on the following day when pond 554a is again exposed to solar irradiation. While this, and other embodiments are illustrated and described as operating in conjunction with a second panel of movable insulation, such as 503a, it is apparent that if the embodiment is supported by movable insulation capable of covering pond 554a alone, there will be no need for the second panel of insulation 503a.

Roof pond 554a, shown in FIG. 6 enclosed as described for pond 554b, has an inlet-outlet 580 partially shown passing through wall 504. A second drain 580a, passing through beam 513 and also fitted with a valve means (not shown), removes water external to the plastic bag 589a when a cover such as 564 is not used. Cover 564, made of polyvinylfluoride film or other strong plastic capable of transmitting solar radiation, is secured to beam 513 by clamping members of wood, metal, or plastic of any convenient type and illustrated as the type of lining fasteners 574 of pond 554e. Cover 564 is held taut by weighting means 565 consisting of an elongated metal or plastic rod or pipe used with the V-cover on solar stills of my prior art. Cover 564 and the air space enclosed above pond 554a result in increased temperatures of pond 554a exposed to solar irradiation and retard heat loss at night, thereby providing advantages sometimes needed for obtaining desired temperatures. With pond 554a enclosed, little or no vapor condensation occurs under cover 564.

Rain water collected over pond 554b, or over cover 564 of pond 554a, causes undesired cooling of ponds when exposed for absorption of solar radiation. Means were previously described for draining water above pond 554b; rain collecting on cover 564 can be drained through perforations (not shown) in pipe 565 of FIG. 6, or through small holes in cover 564 under pipe 565 and thence through drain 580a. It has been found that ties of plastic cord 545 of FIG. 5, passing circumferentially around bag 589b, or folds 546 similarly oriented to triple the thickness of the tubing which forms bag 589b, shape said bag and its enclosed pond for better rain drainage. These ties or folds are not required if pressure from enclosed water adequately rounds upward the top surface of bag 589b.

When ponds used for cooling absorb heat from ambient air or from the cooled enclosure in excess of heat loss by night sky radiation, or when temperatures lower than those produced by radiation alone are desired, water evaporation is an additional cooling means in my embodiment. Roof pond 554c, in FIGS 5 and 6, is similar in construction to pond 554b and basically identical to pond 554a without cover 564. Enclosed pond

554c is shown best in FIG. 6 as being flooded with water 561 exposed to evaporation, usually on summer nights, when insulation panels 503d and 503c are positioned away from over the pond. Cooled by evaporation, water 561 overlying bag 589c absorbs heat from pond 554c which in turn absorbs heat through ceiling 502. Water for flooding pond 554c may come by gravity from a pond at a higher level, such as pond 554d, or may be from a suitable source through an inlet-outlet-and-valve assembly 580c partially shown.

Indirect cooling of pond 554c by evaporation of overlying water has several advantages. An algaecide, added to water in pond 554c, will not be diluted or drained away when salt buildup from evaporated water necessitates flushing with fresh water through inlet-outlet assembly 580c which may include a valve, an overflow, or a siphon set to maintain a suitable water depth over pond 554c. For special purposes a liquid miscible with water, or one which should not be lost by evaporation, may be used as pond 554c; glycerine is an example of a water miscible substance and alcohols or petroleum products of volatile nature are examples of heat-transfer media indirectly cooled by evaporation of water overlying their enclosure in bag 589c. Pond 554c may also consist of a fusible hydrated salt, of the sodium sulfate type used in chemical heat-storage cells, which can be cooled by the indirect evaporation of water without the loss of the chemical or change of its fusion characteristics by contacting the water. Movable insulation 503c and 503d can control exposure of pond 554c and control the evaporation of water overlying said pond. Evaporation for cooling purposes is best accomplished at night when exposed water is used; when an adequate water temperature has been reached, the insulation panels can cover pond 554c and thereby stop evaporation of the water overlying the pond 554c to prevent overcooling of said pond and of the underlying enclosure.

In FIG. 6, plastic bag 589d is shown collapsed as a result of draining water formerly therein through a draining means such as 580 shown with pond 554a. Bag 589d is collapsed when it is desired to evaporate water over insulation panel 503d while minimizing the weight applied thereon. Water 561 added through means such as inlet assembly 571 of pond 554b can then form pond 554d which is provided with an overflow means (not shown) to allow water cooled by evaporation to drain into the water 561 atop pond 554c; or, the cooled water from pond 554d may be transferred to other locations for other use. In daytime, pond 554d may be allowed to remain above bag 589d if the depth is shallow since it would quickly lose heat gained during the day by evaporation at night; moreover, the water would filter out ultraviolet solar rays which deteriorate the cheaper plastics suitable for bag 589d.

The use of open ponds of the type 554e of FIG. 6 has been described in my earlier art and here in reference to thermosiphon walls. Pond 554f, above liner 560f over movable insulation 503f, is shown covered by a transparent plastic film 564 held by clamps 574 and having an elongated weighting means suspended under it in the form of a condensate-collecting trough. Thus pond 554f is enclosed in a solar still with a cover of the type disclosed in more detail in my U.S. Pat. No. 3,314,862. The still of this embodiment consists of pond 554f, cover 564, and condensate collector 565 suitably arranged over movable insulation 503f; it also has conventional means (not shown) for introducing water to be distilled, for removing distill and having a raised salt concentration, and for removing the condensate from collector 565. Pond 554f may be drained in the late afternoon, when distillation yield decreases, and the hot water may be added to pond 554e for space heating of the underlying enclosure, or it may be used for other purposes previously mentioned herein. Pond 554f of the solar still, may also be drained in the morning after radiating its heat to the night sky and the drained water may be used for space cooling; it is then replaced by water of lower salt concentration before solar distillation starts.

Other variations in construction of roof pond embodiments of this invention are shown in FIG. 3 wherein wall 304 and wall plate 321 support corrugated ceiling sheets 302 elsewhere supported by ledge-forming framing member 348 fastened to roof beam 313b by nails 383 or by lag screws. Pond 354a has a black polyethylene liner 360 fastened to beam 313 and capped by coping 333 of plastic or aluminum. Pond 354a is confined in a plastic bag comprising two films united by seals 384. Film 389a is a cover transparent to permit passage of solar rays, while film 389b is preferably black to absorb solar rays to heat pond 354a. To facilitate rain drainage, cover 389a is depressed by drainage member 350a formed of stiff wire mesh or of rigid, perforated plastic and shown corrugated to further ease water drainage to pipe 356a paralleling beam 313 and having holes 351 to allow water to enter pipe 356a for removal by a conduit (not shown). Cover film 389a is shown raised at its right side and fastened to beam 313b by nail 383 to permit escape of air from between the cover 389a and pond 354a through hole 372 in said cover. Venting air through hole 372 is of particular value when adding water to form pond 354a and to minimize bubbles of air between the cover 389a and the surface of pond 354a.

Metal coping 33a crossing over beam 313b serves as flashing and simultaneously forms drainage member 350b with holes 351a which permit water 361 over pond 354b, enclosed by transparent cover 389a and black film 389b, to pass to or from pipe 356b having holes 351 through which water 361 may be introduced or drained through a suitable conduit and valve assembly not shown. Other portions of pond 354b are the same as those of pond 354a. The functions of the enclosed pond 354a and of the flooded water over pond 354b have been previously described in relation to ponds 554b and 554c of FIG. 6, except that here they control temperatures of underlying space without reference to use of movable insulation. If nighttime loss of heat from pond 354a about equals gain during the day, pond 354a fluctuates between a maximum and minimum temperature which may not be much beyond the limits of comfort; then, pond 354a maintains temperatures in the underlying enclosure within an even narrower range owing to the heat capacity effect of the floor, interior walls, room contents, etc. By increasing the depth of pond 354a, the range of maximum and minimum temperatures of said pond can be narrowed; thus pond depth variation is a thermal control means for modulating temperatures in the underlying enclosure.

Pond 354b provides greater cooling than pond 354a and is similarly operable without use of movable insulation. Evaporation of water 361 over pond 354b tends to keep both daytime and nighttime temperatures of pond 354b lower than those of pond 354a and thereby keeps the underlying enclosure cooler.

FIGS. 4A and 4B represent fragmentary sections of a pan of movable insulation with two means for confining water e posed for evaporation and radiant cooling at night or sol heating during daytime. In both FIGS., beam 413 supports movable insulation panel 403 framed by aluminum extrusions 470 to which wheels (not shown) are fastened to travel in a trackway (not shown) to move insulation 403 from a position left of pond 454 of FIG. 4B to a position overlying said pond containing water 461 confined by liner 460. Pond 454 is supported by a ceiling or other means (not shown) which permits thermal exchange with underlying space or transfer of water 461 to serve elsewhere for thermal control.

In FIG. 4A, a metal extension 469 fastened to frame 470 by rivet 483 confines water 461 in liner 460, serves to support water inlet 471, and provides a base to which liner 460 can be fastened by clamping member 474. FIG. 4B represents a similar construction over movable insulation but with a liner 490 having embedded or adhered protrusions 491. Liner 490 may be a felt saturated with asphalt and protrusions 491 may be stone granules embedded in the asphalt; or liner 491 may be an aluminum sheet to which sand or other granular material is adhered by epoxy cement. The function of the protrusions 491 is to distribute water 461 in a thin layer across the top of insulation 403 to allow it to reach higher or lower temperatures than the deeper water 461 of FIG. 4A. In an alternative construction, protrusions 491 may be floc of fibrous nature which not only distributes water but acts by wicking action to increase the surface for evaporation of water.

FIGS. 4A and 4B represent opposite ends of a panel of movable insulation 403. FIG. 4B shows means for discharging overlying water 461 through a conduit and valve assembly 480 into pond 454, or through connections (not shown) to other thermal control means for utilizing the heating or cooling effect of water 461 introduced at inlet 471 of FIG. 4A. The operation of this embodiment is that of pond 554*d* of FIG. 6. Additionally, FIG. 4B shows, attached to extension 469 of framing 470 by rivet 483, the deflector 218 discussed in relation to FIG. 2 as a means 216*a*causing air passing through the passageway 216*a* between beams 413, the bottom of movable insulation 403, and end closure 463, to assume lines of flow more nearly parallel to the surface of pond 454 for purposes of increasing evaporation therefrom.

An embodiment of this invention illustrated in FIG. 7 comprises a means for heating or cooling water and for its storage. Water heating by solar irradiation is best accomplished with a preheating means 776 over a panel of movable insulation 703 having a frame 770 to confine said preheater. Attached to frame 770 are previously described means for moving insulation 703 in trackways on beams (not shown) from the daytime position illustrated to a nighttime position overlying pond 754.

Preheater 776 is an interconnected series of tubular passageways 776*a*, *b*, *c*, and *d*,made in the fashion of an air mattress of black flexible plastic or it may be made of metal interconnecting cells with a blackened upper surface. During a sunny day, water introduced through inlet 771*a* is heated by solar radiation absorbed by the black upper surface and discharges through outlet 780*a* which may be a pipe capable of being raised and held, by means not shown, in a position higher than that illustrated; the high position maintains a desirable depth of water 761 in preheater 776 while the illustrated low position permits complete drainage of said water. Water drains from outlet 780*a* into funnel inlet 771*b* leading into a superheater 777 made in the manner of preheater 776. Above superheater 777 is water pond 754 within plastic liner 760*b* laterally confined by wood or metal sidewalls 748 and fixed insulation 730. Above pond 754 is transparent plastic cover 764 shown here as a solar still cover with an elongated weighting and condensate collecting means 765. Although illustrated as a solar still, this portion of the embodiment alternatively may be a transparent cover in contact with pond 754 thus being a water heater like 554*b* of FIG. 5.

In FIG. 7, draining means 789*b* removes rain from atop cover 764. Connecting assembly 786 conducts water from superheater 777, supported on corrugated sheets of metal or asbestos-cement 711*a*, to a water storage container shown as a plastic bag 789 in space intermediate sheets 711*a* and similar supporting sheets 711*b* which rest on wooden structural members 759 to which are fastened confining sidewalls 748 and similar end walls (not shown). Connecting assembly 786 has a control valve to regulate flow of water 761 from superheater 777 into storage container 789 fitted with outlet 780*c* having a conduit and valve arrangement (not shown) leading to the point of use for the heated water. Breather tube 772 permits air to be displaced from storage container 789 as it is filled with heated water; air displaced above container 789 and under sheet 711*a* escapes at the edges of the relatively loosely constructed 711*a* 748.

In operation, preheater 776 and superheater 777 are filled with water 761 during early morning hours when outlet means 780*a* and connecting means 786 are adjusted to prevent drainage. Any water remaining in superheater overnight will be at a higher temperature than that in preheater 776 owing to the superheater 777 having been covered at night by insulation 703. As solar energy raises the temperature of pond 754 and of water 761 in 777 to a useful range, water in preheater 776 is being warmed. Then cooler water introduced t inlet 771*a* displaces warmed water into superheater 777 where it is further heated before passing into storage container 789. To maintain higher water temperatures in storage container 789 than the average temperature of water in superheater 777, fixed insulation may be inserted between the upper surface of sheet 711*a* and liner 760*b*.

When solar intensity decreases, draining outlet 780*a* is adjusted to remove warmed water from preheater 775 and to displace hot water from superheater 777. Then insulation 703 is positioned over superheater 777 and pond 754 to retard heat loss to the night sky. The functions of pond 754 are several. When available fresh water is limited, its heat storage capacity may be too small to store all of the available solar heat. Then pond 754 can consist of impure water to be distilled to produce more fresh water; or, it may be made deep enough with impure water to store the available solar energy at a useful temperature. Then when warm water is drained from preheater 776 in the evening, the water will be heated in superheater 777 by conduction from pond 754. In addition, water over superheater 777 filters out ultraviolet rays capable of deteriorating an inexpensive plastic which may be used for making superheater 777. If pond 754 is not needed, it may be drained by means not shown; then water 761 in superheater 777 is heated in the manner of pond 554*a* of FIG. 5 and higher temperatures are obtained in superheater 777.

In the embodiment of FIG. 7, the heat exchange relationship between pond 754 and water 761 in superheater 777 is emphasized. As a variation of this heat exchange relationship, the embodiment of FIG. 8 is another form of solar still in heat exchange relationship to provide hot water for domestic purposes or for space heating and may be regarded as a water heater. The embodiment in other form may be installed on a roof though illustrated in FIG. 8 on the ground. It is constructed in three sections under cover 864 with insulation 803 movable above said cover. The first section is preferably a wide but shallow distilland basin 891 having a bottom higher than that of second distilland basin 892 in a second section of the still. Conduit and valve assembly 856 permits distilland to flow from said first to said second basin, and means 880*a* are provided to drain distilland from the second basin 892. Under the cover 864 and overlying basin 892 is a third distilland basin 893 the bottom of which is preferably at a higher level than distilland in basin 891. Means are provided for excess distilland introduced through a feed pipe (not shown) to overflow from basin 893 through conduit 880*b* to basin 891; or basin 891 may have a separate feed. Preferably, basins 891 and 893 are shallower than basin 892 which is able to contain all distilland drained from basin 891.

A third section of the still, preferably with a bottom below that of basin 893 to permit collection of condensate flowing from the underside thereof, comprises a distillate reservoir 894 with a partially shown assembly 880*c* of conduits, valves, and, if necessary, a pump for removing distillate 895. Condensate collected on cover 864, or on the under surface of basin

893, is conducted, by virtue of the shapes thereof, to discharge point 896 or 896*a* and drains into reservoir 894. Discharge point 986*a* is formed when cover 864 is deflected downward by weighting means 865 held in position by tiecord 866 fastened to framing member 863 supporting cover 864. Materials from which this embodiment are made have been described herein or are well known in the solar still art.

In operation, distilland in basins 891 and 893 is distilled by solar radiation transmitted through cover 864; vapors condensed on said cover drain into reservoir 894. When solar intensity and distillation rate have passed their peaks, hot distilland 898 from basin 891 is drained into basin 892 to prevent heat loss by direct radiation to the sky; also, insulation 803 is moved from its daytime position over basin 894 to nighttime position over basin 893 to prevent heat loss by direct radiation to the sky therefrom. Vapors from hot distilland 898 then condense on the cooler under surface of basin 893 giving up latent heat thereto and causing distilland 899 therein to distill longer than it would if distilland 898 had not been drained into basin 892 to cause multiple effect distillation. Distilland in basins 892 and 893 have higher temperatures the following morning than they would have if distilland 898 had been allowed to cool at night in basin 891; then, warm distilland 898, except for that portion desired to be drained, can be pumped back into basin 891 through conduit 880*a* and a pump (not shown) and additional makeup water added to the first and third basins as needed. With warm distilland in basins 891 and 893, distillation starts earlier in the day when insulation 803 is returned over reservoir 894. Thus, the production of the still is substantially increased; the still may be of any convenient shape.

Though this embodiment is described with reference to a single second basin 892 underlying basin 893, obviously distilland 898 from one of more basins such as 891 may be drained into a plurality of basins underlying one another and all underlying basin 893, all adapted to drain condensate into reservoir 894 thus increasing multiple effect distillation. Moreover, this distillation process is improved without the presence of, or movement of, insulation 803; though I prefer using insulation 803 to keep distilland 899 warm at night and to keep distillate 895 cool during the day to serve as a condenser for vapors from basins 891 and 893.

The embodiment of my solar still—water heater shown in FIG. 8 has as the bottom of basin 892 the top of a rigid or semirigid metal or plastic hot water tank 859 through which high quality water passes through inlet and outlet means 853*a* and 835*b*. Heat from distilland 898 in basin 892 passes through wall 846 of tank 859 to water 847 therein. Alternatively, heat exchange is obtained through tubes disposed within basin 892 as well understood by those versed in the art. In these embodiments, a water supply is heated by water transferred from a first location in which it is heated to a location in which heat exchange occurs; and, in my preferred embodiment, movable insulation 803 can be positioned by means of attached wheels (not shown) and trackway 814. The water 847, thus heated, may be used for domestic purposes or for space heating by means previously described.

Optimum use of the heating and cooling means herein described depends, at times, on their use in conjunction with a fan coil in space to be thermally controlled. Air stratification in a room underlying and in direct thermal exchange with a roof pond may cause air at 5-foot height to be 8° warmer in summer than pond temperatures at 8-foot ceiling height. This differential can be reduced to 2° by circulating roof pond water through a fan coil unit which circulates the room air and absorbs heat which is transferred from the fan coil to the roof pond. This use of a fan coil provides novel zone-control means for regulating temperatures in enclosures.

FIG. 10 represents an embodiment of this invention. Two rooms are shown with roof ponds and with a fan coil in the common wall 4*a*. Walls 4*b* and 4*c* are representative of the other walls of the two rooms on which wall plates 12 and wood beams 13 are secured. Corrugated metal sheets 11 supported by the walls or fastened to the beams form a ceiling over the rooms and an exterior overhang which shades wall 4*c*. Wood beams 13 divide the roof into bays with plastic liners (not shown) confining roof ponds 54*a*,*b*,*c*, and *d* shown in thermal exchange with underlying space in the rooms. Roof pond 54*e*, above the overhand, is partially supported by bracket 59 suitably fastened to wall 4*c*. Insulation 30 is affixed to the underside of metal sheets 11 forming the bottom of pond 54*e*. Details of pond construction and of movable insulation 3 mounted with wheels in trackways atop beams 13, are not shown; they may be of different types as shown in FIG. 6.

A fan coil unit of standard type is represented in FIG. 10 by a fan 21 and a bend of metal tubing 23; the water circulating pump is not shown, nor is the conventional system of dampers which control airflow to and from the fan coil. When the fan coil is not in use, rooms constructed as shown are heated or cooled by the static roof ponds. To permit maximum use of a fan coil, the ponds are connected in series; interconnection 86 may be of the bulkhead union type or plastic tubing adequately sealed to the liners of adjacent ponds and preferably positioned to connect all ponds in series to circulate water therein through fan coil tubing 23 suitably connected through pond liners to conduct pumped water from pond 54*b* to pond 54*c*. A conduit and valve means 80 is provided to fill or drain the ponds and to interconnect ponds 54*e* and 54*a* through piping (not shown).

When space of a first room, enclosed by walls 4*a* and 4*b*, is to be preferentially cooled, the fan coil unit is turned on with dampers arranged to circulate through the fan coil only air from said first room. Cooled water 61 from pond 54*b* pumped through coil 23 then absorbs heat from the circulated air and is discharged to pond 54*c* creating a small head pressure of water therein which causes water in pond 54*c* creating a small head pressure of water therein which causes water in pond 54*c* to pass through interconnection 86 to pond 54*d* and eventually, by way of other 54*b*interconnections, to pond 54*b* and to the intake tubing 23 of the fan coil. Effects of this fan coil use are several. Recirculation of air, and extraction of heat from it, causes said first room to have a temperature only a few degrees higher than that of pond water 61 passing through the fan coil. The second room, enclosed by walls 4*a* and 4*c*, will be several degrees warmer partly owing to air stratification and partly because overlying ponds 54*c* and 54*d* are warmer than those over said first room by virtue of the heat extracted from the first room. In preferred operation, the warmest water is discharged from pond 54*d* to pond 54*e* above the overhang. This is beneficial primarily at night when insulation 3 has been moved away from over the ponds; then pond 54*e* will cool considerably by radiation and evaporation before water from it enters ponds 54*a* and 54*b* where it affects the temperature of the first room.

When the second room is to be preferentially cooled, the fan coil dampers are adjusted to recirculate only air of that room through the fan coil. The direction in which the fan coil pump circulates pond water is preferably reversed. The second room then equalizes at a temperature nearer that of the roof ponds than does the temperature of the first room and, at night, pond 54*e* serves to cool the circulating water before it enters ponds 54*d*, 54*c*, and the fan coil thus widening the temperature differential between the rooms. If the first room represents a living room and the second room a bedroom, adjustment of the dampers and reversal of direction of circulation in the roof ponds can assure maximum cooling in the room occupied at the particular time of day— the living room in daytime and the bedroom at nighttime.

The fan coil may be used in several ways to cool rooms in a multistory building. The top story rooms may be directly cooled by thermal exchange with overlying ponds also connected to a fan coil located in lower story rooms cooled by the roof pond water circulated through the fan coil. Alternatively, using forced air evaporation of water in floor plenums as previously described, the fan coil recirculates water cooled in said floor plenums. If one regards movable insulation 3 as the floor of one or more rooms above the rooms of FIG. 10, this floor would rest on beams 13 leaving air spaces above the five ponds shown. A blower at the ends of the ponds forcing unsaturated air across water 61 in the plenum ponds would cause evaporation and directly cool the ponds and also by direct thermal exchange cool rooms above and below the ponds. The additional use of the fan coil to circulate water of the plenum ponds and to circulate air in the underlying, or overlying, room in which it is located would provide additional cooling.

The numerous embodiments of this invention may be used in many combinations with, or without, movable insulation which may be a single panel affecting thermally one or more bodies of a liquid heat-storage material or a plurality of insulation panels affecting thermally one or more bodies of said liquid. FIG. 6 illustrates some combinations including a unified panel 503*b*, 503*d*, and 503*f*, though operation of the separate embodiments shown in FIG. 6 was described as if these three panels were also movable separately.

Useful combinations of embodiments of this invention with conventional heating and cooling means are also encompassed. On sunless days, the roof ponds, or plenum ponds, in direct heat exchange relationship with space above or below may have water added of higher temperature from a gas or electric water heater through a conduit and valve system controlled manually or by a thermostat. The radiant heat from a kitchen stove may also heat overlying ponds and distribute this heat to other areas through conduction in, or circulation of, the water in roof or plenum ponds. For cooling, conventional gas or electric refrigeration unit can be used in rooms underlying those directly cooled by roof or plenum ponds or by fan coils circulating water from such ponds. Air dehumidified by the refrigeration unit can be directed to cool lower rooms and to pass through ducts or stairwells to upper rooms cooled primarily by embodiments of this invention which are not capable of dehumidification. The air from the upper rooms, still partially dehumidified, can then be exhausted, with the aid of a blower if necessary, through roof or plenum ponds to cause more evaporative cooling than more humid exterior air. As previously described, cool air from the ponds can be used to cool other areas directly or indirectly. *

Inventor **Harold R. Hay**
795 Roble, Menlo Park, Calif. 94025

PROCESS AND APPARATUS FOR MODULATING TEMPERATURES WITHIN ENCLOSURES
Patented Feb. 16, 1971

ABSTRACT: Enclosure temperatures are modulated by water heated by solar energy and cooled to ambient air. Control means include moving exterior insulation, enclosing or exposing the water, using forced air, and providing special means for heat storage and transfer. Water ponds horizontally disposed atop the enclosure, or in floor plenums and frequently in direct thermal exchange with underlying space, or water circulating in walls by thermosiphon action may be used separately or in combinations with the control means.

Chapter 7

Swimming Pool Heaters

March 8, 1966 A. J. MEAGHER 3,239,000

SOLAR WATER HEATER AND PROCESS OF FORMING SAME

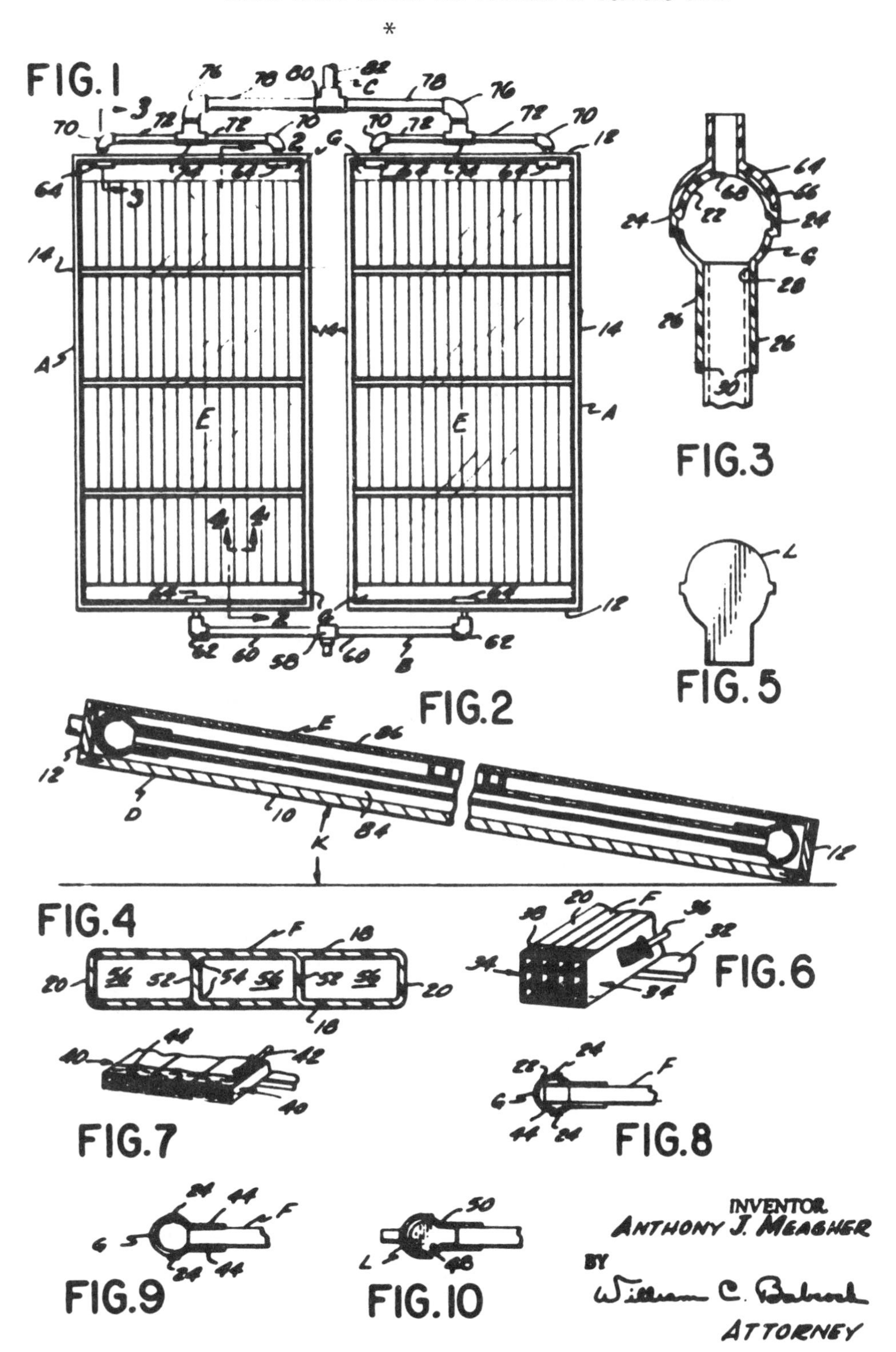

3,239,000
SOLAR WATER HEATER AND PROCESS OF FORMING SAME
Anthony J. Meagher, 3319 Keys Lane, Anaheim, Calif.

The present invention relates generally to the field of solar water heaters, and more particularly to a solar water heater adapted for heating water in a swimming pool, and a process of producing the heater.

During the past few years, the number of residential swimming pools that have been installed has increased tremendously. The majority of these pools have been installed with gas-operated heaters to prolong the period during the year in which the pools can be used comfortably. One disadvantage of such heaters is that they are extremely expensive to operate, whereby many heaters are not used for their intended purpose.

A major object of the present invention is to provide a solar water heater for swimming pools that may be fabricated from preformed plastic components, is simple and easy to install, and due to the character of the material from which it is fabricated, the heater is not subject to corrosion or deterioration after use for a prolonged period of time.

Another object of the invention is to supply a solar water heater that requires little or no maintenance, is automatic in operation, and one that eliminates costly heater bills.

A further object of the invention is to provide a solar water heater that can be produced by a novel process from molded and extruded plastic components without the use of extensive plant facilities, and can, if desired, be sold in a kit form for assembly by the purchaser.

Yet another object of the invention is to furnish a solar water heater which includes a number of tubular sections of substantial width having at least one longitudinally extending partition in each one thereof, which serves the dual function of reinforcing the sections against deformation, and also operates as a heat exchange element to improve the efficiency of the heater.

Still a further object of the invention is to provide a solar water heater that divides the water flowing therethrough into a number of streams of relatively small transverse cross section to obtain optimum heat exchange between the heater and flowing water, which is accomplished without the use of small tubes as has been necessary in previously available solar water heaters.

These and other objects and advantages of the present invention will become apparent from the following description thereof, and from the accompanying drawing illustrating the same, in which:

FIGURE 1 is a top plan view of the solar water heater connected to a water inlet and outlet;

FIGURE 2 is a longitudinal cross-sectional view of the device, taken on the line 2—2 of FIGURE 1;

FIGURE 3 is a fragmentary cross-sectional view of the heater, taken on the line 3—3 of FIGURE 1;

FIGURE 4 is a transverse cross-sectional view of one of the rectangular tubular sections, taken on the line 4—4 of FIGURE 1;

FIGURE 5 is a plan view of one of the inserts used in closing one of the ends of the headers;

FIGURE 6 illustrates a first step in the fabrication of one of the solar water heaters;

FIGURE 7 illustrates a second step in the fabrication of one of the solar water heaters;

FIGURE 8 illustrates a third step in the fabrication of one of the solar water heaters;

FIGURE 9 illustrates a fourth step in the fabrication of one of the solar water heaters; and

FIGURE 10 illustrates a fifth step in the fabrication of one of the solar water heaters.

With continuing reference to the drawing for the general arrangement of the present invention, it will be seen in FIGURE 1 that two of the solar water heaters A are disposed in side-by-side relationship. The heaters A are preferably angularly disposed relative to the horizontal such as being supported on an inclined roof, or the like (not shown), with the degree of angulation being so selected that the heaters are disposed at right angles to the sun's rays during the period of the year when maximum heating of the water passing through the heaters is required.

Water is supplied to the lower ends of the heaters A from a pipe B, with the water flowing upwardly through the heaters to discharge into a pipe C to be returned to the pool (not shown) by the force of gravity. Pipe B is connected to the discharge side of a pump (not shown) that is normally provided to recirculate water from and to a pool. As it is recirculated, the water passes through a filter (not shown) as well as a gas-operated heater. When the solar water heaters A are used, the gas heater (not shown) is bypassed by a conventional piping arrangement, and the gas heater is only used when an auxiliary source of heat is required to bring the temperature up to a desired degree.

Each solar water heater A includes a box D that is defined by a bottom 10, two end walls 12, and two side walls 14. A pane of glass, or other transparent material E preferably covers the top of box D, and is supported on a number of transverse rigid members 16, the ends of which rest on cut-out portions of the side walls 14.

A number of tubular sections F are provided for each of the solar water heaters A, which are preferably formed of a polymerized resin material impregnated with carbon black. The sections F are conveniently formed by extruding the plastic material. One material which has been found satisfactory for this particular purpose is acrylonitrile-butadiene-styrene, which is sold commercially as ABS. Each of the sections F, as can best be seen in FIGURE 4, includes two parallel side walls 18 and end walls 20.

Two headers G are provided for each of the solar water heaters A, which comprise an elongate member formed from a polymerized resin, rubber, or like material, having the transverse cross section shown in FIGURE 3. In transverse cross section the header G includes a circular portion 22 having two diametrically opposed ribs 24 projecting therefrom. Two spaced, parallel flanges 26 project outwardly from portion 22 in a direction normal to ribs 24, with the flanges being in communication with a longitudinally extending opening 28 formed in circular portion 22. The flanges 26 are spaced apart a distance 30, which is substantially the same as the distance between the exterior surfaces of side walls 18.

The process of assembling the sections F and headers G to form a part of a solar water heater A includes the steps of cutting a number of sections of the same length, and placing them in side-by-side abutting contact to rest on a flat surface 32, in the manner shown in FIGURE 6. The sections F are then pressed together in the direction indicated by tthe arrows 34, by clamps or other means (not shown). A brush 36 is thereafter employed to apply an elongate film of waterproof adhesive 38 to the extremities of the end walls 20, as also illustrated in FIGURE 6.

After films of adhesive 38 have been applied to both ends of sections F, as above described, the sections are supported on their side walls 18 on surface 32, as shown in FIGURE 7, and pressure is applied thereto in the direction indicated by arrows 40, whereby portions of the film 38 bond the sections F together and the sections define a panel of substantial width.

A brush 42 (FIGURE 7) is utilized to apply an elongate film 44 of an adhesive to the extremities of the side walls 18. End portions of the sections F are then slidably inserted in the headers G, as shown in FIGURE 8, with the films 44 on the ends of the sections being disposed in the circular portions 22 of the headers G. Headers G and sections F are thereafter moved longitudinally relative to one another to place the films 44 inside the flanges 26. As this relative movement of the headers G and sections F takes place, the film 44 is spread over the interior surfaces of flanges 26. After the adhesive films 44 have set, the headers G and sections F are firmly held together as an integral unit.

In the step of moving the sections F and headers G relative to one another, this movement must be restricted longitudinally to such a degree that the headers and sections will fit within the box D, as shown in FIGURE 2. Sections F must be sufficiently wide that when arranged as panels and engaging headers G (FIGURE 1), spaces 48 will be left at the ends of the headers in which inserts L, as shown in FIGURE 5, can be placed. The inserts L are bonded by a film 50 of waterproof adhesive to the ends of the headers G to close the same. The film 50 also extends to seal the spaces between inserts L and the outer surface portions of the end walls 20 adjacent thereto.

Two transversely spaced, longitudinally extending partitions 52 are formed as an integral part of each section F, as may best be seen in FIGURE 4. The partitions 52 and side walls 18 meet at curved junctions 54 to minimize the possibility of cracking at these localities. The sections F are preferably formed by extruding a plastic or rubber material containing carbon black, which material can be the same as used in forming the headers G. The partitions 52, side wall 18 and end walls 20 cooperatively define a number of longitudinally extending passages 56 through which water flows from the lower pipe B to the upper pipe C (FIGURE 2) to be heated by solar energy.

From experience it has been found that sections F three inches wide and $^5/_{16}$ inch high operate quite satisfactorily when formed from ABS, and the thickness of the walls 18 and 20 and partitions 52 are .051 inch. The partitions 52 serve a two-fold purpose; first to reinforce the sections F against longitudinal deformation when disposed as shown in FIGURE 2, and second, to provide additional surface area from which heat may be transferred to the water flowing through passages 56.

The pipe B (FIGURE 1) includes a T 58 that is connected to the discharge from the pump (not shown), and to two laterals 60 which extend to two L's 62. The L's 62 are connected to two saddles 64, semicircular portions 66 of which are bonded by adhesive, or other means, to the lower headers G, and in alignment with transverse bores 68 formed in the header, as best seen in FIGURE 3.

Two saddles 64 are bonded to each upper header G (FIGURE 1) which are in communication with bores 68 formed therein. Each saddle 64 is connected to an L fitting 70 from which a lateral 72 extends to a T 74. Each T 74 is connected to an L 76 having a second lateral 78 extending to a second T 80. The T 80 is connected to a line 82 which returns the water that has been heated by solar energy to the swimming pool (not shown). Portions of the saddles 64 project through downwardly extending recesses 84 formed in walls 12 of box D, as best seen in FIGURE 2.

The combined transverse cross section of the two bores 68 formed in one of the upper headers G is greater than that of the single bore 68 formed in the header G therebelow. Likewise, the combined transverse cross section of the pipe and fittings leading from the saddles 64 on each of the upper headers G is greater than the transverse cross section of the L 62 and saddle 64 connecting the same to the lower header G. Also, the transverse cross-section of each of the L's 76 and second laterals 78 is greater than the cross section of the bore 68 in one of the lower headers G.

The internal transverse cross section of T 74 and line 82 is at least twice as great as that of one of the second laterals 78. Due to the selection of the internal transverse cross sections just mentioned, water can flow from the two heaters A faster than it is discharged therein through the two laterals 60, whereby the only internal pressure to which the sections F are subjected is that of the hydrostatic head of the water therein.

After the solar water heater has been assembled in the manner described, it is supported at an angle K relative to the horizontal by conventional means (not shown) in a position where it is fully exposed to the sun. The angle K selected is preferably one that most nearly places the upper surfaces of the sections F, when arranged as panels, in a direction normal to that of the sun's rays in the particular geographical area in which the heater is installed during the period of the year when maximum heating of the swimming pool is desired.

In the Los Angeles, California, area, for example, the angle K can vary from 79° relative to the horizontal on June 21st, to 33° relative to the horizontal on December 21st. These angles are for optimum results. In some instances, less than the angle K will be used in an installation to adapt the support of the heaters A to an existing structure. When such an installation is made, it must be realized that the heaters A are not operating at maximum efficiency, and additional area of sections F must be provided to compensate for this lowered efficiency.

The use and operation of the invention is quite simple. After the heater has been installed and pipe in the manner shown in Figures 1 and 2, it is ready for operation. Water is discharged into the lower headers G and rises in the sections F to ultimately flow back to the pool (not shown) through the line 82.

The glass pane E cooperates with the box D to provide a confined space 84 that is filled with air. Rays (not shown) from the sun pass through the pane E to heat the blanket of air that is in contact with the under surfaces of the headers G and sections F, as can best be seen in FIGURE 2, and serves to heat the same.

Upon entering each of the sections F, the water is divided into three upwardly moving columns due to the positioning of the partitions 52 relative to the walls 18 and 20. As water enters the lower ends of the sections F there is a maximum differential in temperature between it and the side walls 18 and end walls 20. The rate of heat transfer from the lower end portions of the sections F and lower header G is at a maximum, and decreases as the water becomes warmer as it rises in the sections.

Partitions 52 form an integral part of each section F, and are heated by the transfer of heat from the side walls 18 thereto. The heated partitions 52 also transfer heat to the water flowing upwardly in the sections in the same manner as the side walls 18 and end walls 20 transfer heat thereto. It will be apparent that the above described operation is continuous, with the upwardly positioned side walls 18 being directly heated by the sun's rays (not shown) from which this heat is transferred to the upwardly moving streams of water in the sections F.

The blanket of air 86 continues to be constantly heated by the sun's rays, and maintained at a substantially constant temperature, even though it is continuously transferring a part of its heat content to those parts of the sections F with which it is in contact. The end walls 20 of the sections F that are in abutting contact serve to transfer heat by conduction to water flowing through the device in the same manner as the partitions 52. *

Jan. 24, 1967 A. W. KOCH **3,299,881**

WATER HEATER

* *

FIG. 1.

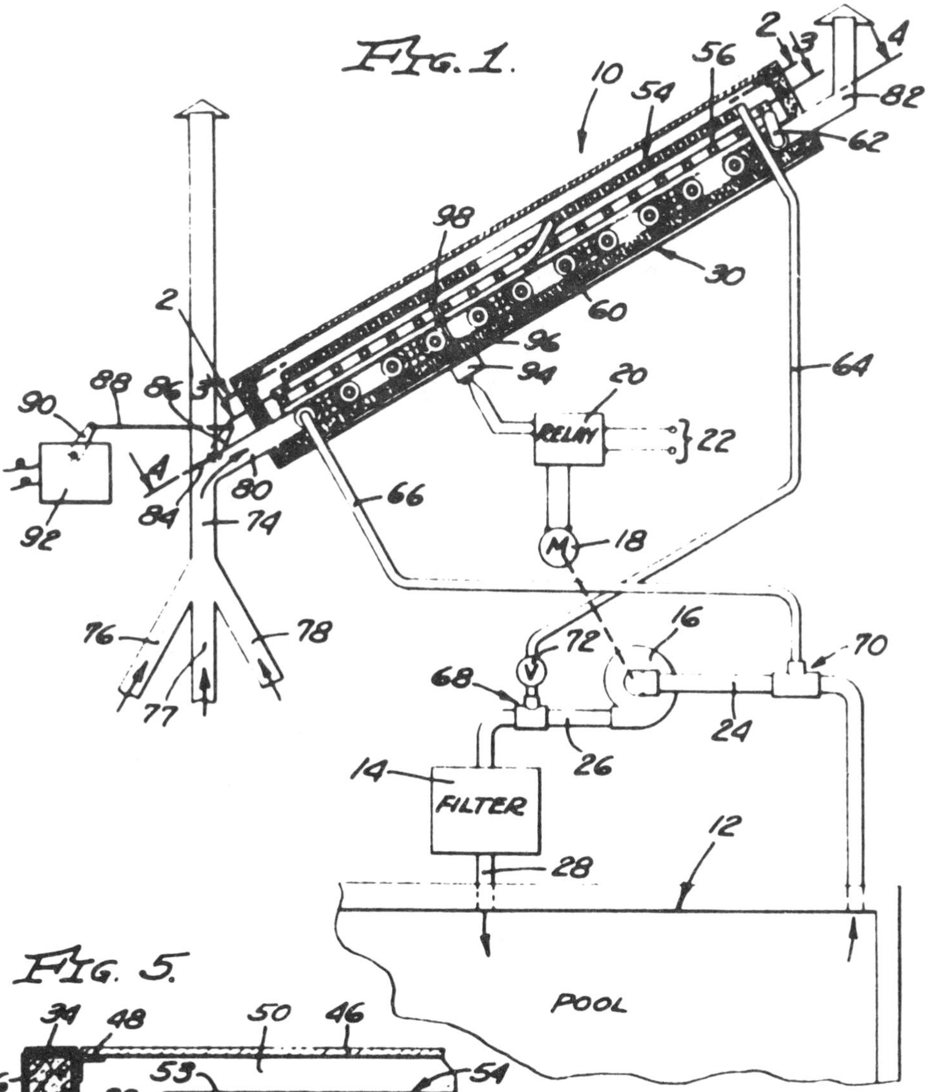

FIG. 5.

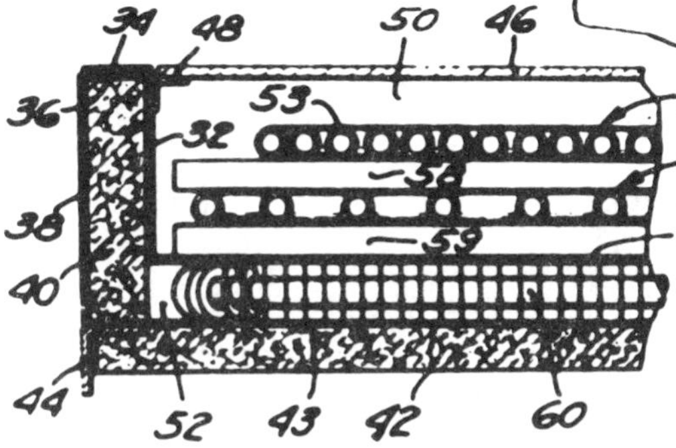

INVENTOR.
ALEXANDER W. KOCH
BY
Herbert E. Kidder
AGENT

Jan. 24, 1967 A. W. KOCH **3,299,881**

WATER HEATER

* *

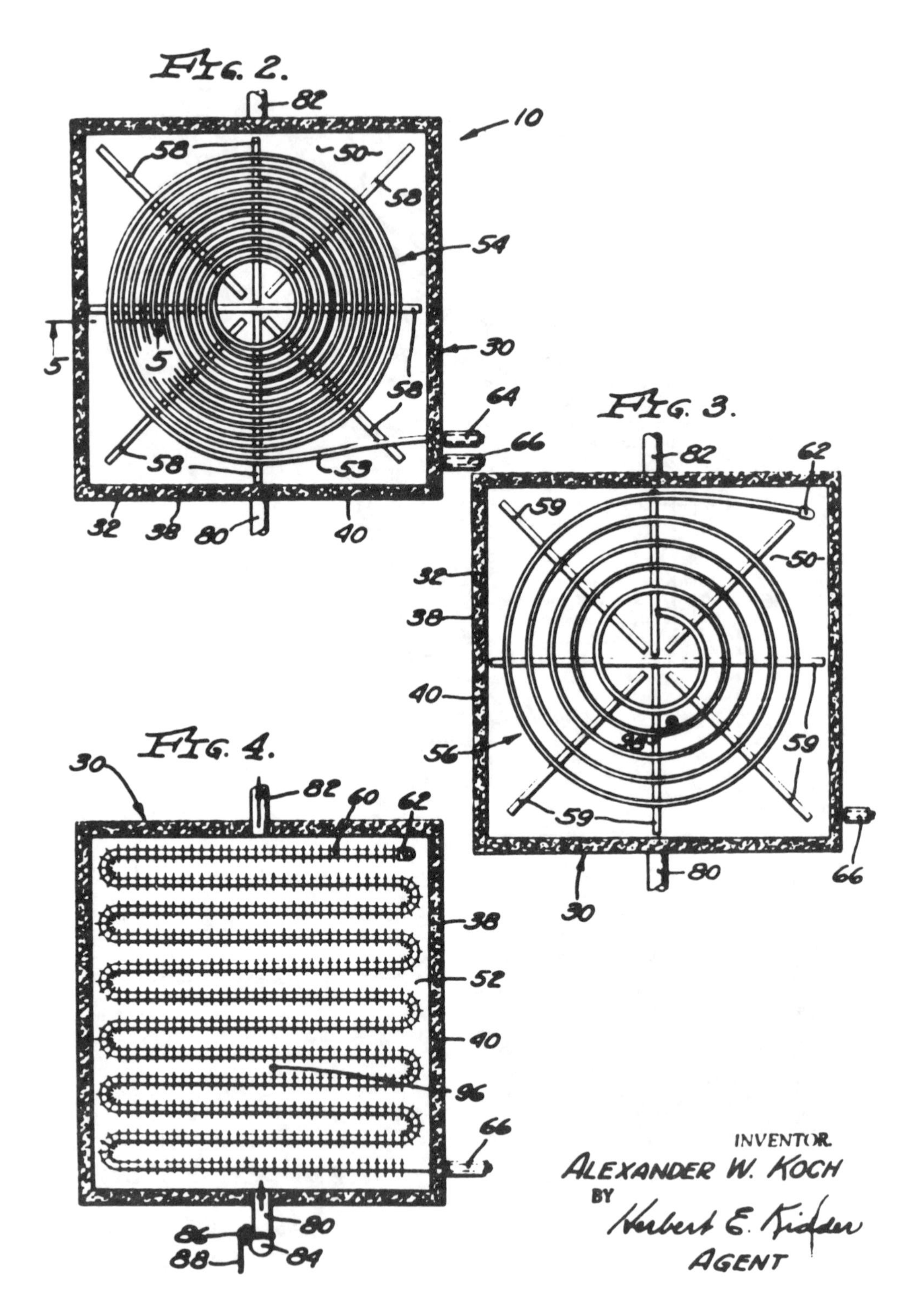

3,299,881
WATER HEATER
Alexander W. Koch, 5677 McKinley Ave.,
San Bernardino, Calif. 92404

*

This invention relates generally to water heaters, and more particularly to a water heater designed primarily for heating a swimming pool, although not limited to that specific use.

Swimming pool heaters are primarily useful for raising the water temperature about 10 degrees above the normal, unheated water temperature, so as to provide greater comfort during the early and late parts of the swimming season, and also to extend the season from about four months to as much as six or eight months, depending upon the weather and air temperature. Both gas-fired and solar water heaters have been used, but each of these has certain drawbacks. The gas-fired heater is a relatively expensive unit to purchase and install, and consumes great quantities of gas. Consequently, the operating cost is so high that many owners, after the first year or so, turn the heater off and use it only for special occasions. The solar heater, on the other hand, costs less to purchase and install, and costs nothing to operate, but it is effective only when the sun is shining. Therefore, at night, or when the sky is overcast, the solar heater is inoperative. Since late Spring and early Fall are frequently seasons of fog and overcast skies, the solar heater is sometimes ineffective at the very times it is most needed.

The primary object of the present invention is to provide a water heater using both solar heat and the waste heat of exhaust gas from gas-burning appliances, whereby the advantages of both gas heat and solar heat are combined in one unit, with none of the disadvantages of either. One very important advantage of the present invention is that it costs nothing to operate, since the gas heat that it uses is waste heat that is being vented to the atmosphere.

Another important object of the present invention is to provide a water heater of the class described, that turns on the water-circulating pump automatically each time that a gas-burning appliance in the home is turned on, or any time that solar heat reaches a predetermined level of intensity. In that way, the thousands of B.t.u. that are lost each day in exhaust gas going up the flue and discharging into the atmosphere, are efficiently utilized by the present invention to warm the water of the swimming pool. At the same time, solar heat is utilized whenever the sun is shining, and this solar heat contributes additional thousands of B.t.u. to the water each hour that the sun is shining.

A further object of the invention is to provide a new and improved arrangement for connecting the water pipes of the heater to the filter pump of the swimming pool so as to obtain a maximum pressure difference between the heater inlet and outlet pipes, without adversely affecting the volume of water delivered to he filter by the pump. This is an important feature, since the long length of pipe in the heater offers considerable resistance to the flow of water, and maximum efficiency of the heater requires high velocity flow of water through the pipes, in order to carry the heat away as rapidly as possible and thereby maintain the maximum temperature difference between the water and the hot air within the box.

Another object of the invention is to provide a water heater of the class described, in which the pipes are virtually free of any tendency to lime up. Liming of the pipes is a serious problem with all gas-fired swimming pool heaters, but in the present invention, there is almost no liming at all, due to the relatively low temperature of the water in the pipes, as compared to the temperature in the usual gas heater.

Still a further object of the invention is to provide a swimming pool heater that is relatively compact, unobtrusively mounted on the house roof where it is out of the way, and simple to install and connect to the existing filter pump system.

These and other objects and advantages of the invention will become apparent to those skilled in the art upon consideration of the following detailed description of the preferred embodiment thereof; reference being had to the accompanying drawings, wherein:

FIGURE 1 is a somewhat schematic representation of a water heater embodying the principles of the invention, the water heater itself being sectioned along a vertical section line extending through the center of the box;

FIGURE 2 is a sectional view through the box, taken at 2—2 in FIGURE 1, showing the top layer of pipe;

FIGURE 3 is a sectional view similar to FIGURE 2, taken at 3—3 in FIGURE 1, and showing the second layer of pipe in the box;

FIGURE 4 is a sectional view taken at 4—4 in FIGURE 1; showing the arrangement of finned copper tubing in the bottom of the box; and

FIGURE 5 is an enlarged, fragmentary sectional view taken at 5—5 in FIGURE 2.

In the drawings, the water heater of the present invention is designated in its entirety by the reference numeral **10**, and in its preferred embodiment, the heater is associated with a swimming pool **12**, having a filter **14**, through which water is circulated by a pump **16**. The pump **16** is driven by an electric motor **18**, which is started and stopped by a relay control box **20**, having the usual timer mechanism. The control box **20** is connected to an electrical outlet **22**. Water is drawn from the pool through a pump intake pipe **24**, and is discharged through a pump output pipe **26** to the filter, from which it returns to the pool through a return pipe **28**.

The water heater **10** comprises an open-top box **30** of relatively shallow depth and considerable area, which is adapted to be mounted on the roof top, preferably on a surface sloping to the south. The dimensions of the box are not critical, but good results have been obtained with a box about 8 feet square and about 8 inches deep. The box **30** is made up of a sheet metal inner box **32** having an outwardly turned flange **34** around its four edges, which overlie inwardly turned flanges **36** of an outer box **38**. The side walls of the inner and outer boxes **32**, **38** are spaced about 2 inches apart from one another, and packed within this space is thermal insulation **40**, which prevents loss of heat from the box. A panel of fiber insulation **42** is attached to the bottom **43** of the outer box **38**, and this prevents loss of heat from the bottom. The box **30** is supported on an angle-iron frame **44**, which may be supported on legs (not shown).

Covering the open top side of the box **30** are panes **46** of glass or transparent plastic, which rest on the horizontal, inwardly projecting flanges of angle irons **48**, which are attached to the sides of the inner box **32** near the top edge thereof. The sides and bottom of the inner box **32**, together with the glass panes **46**, define an upper compartment **50**; while the bottom **51** of the inner box **32** is spaced upwardly from the bottom **43** of the outer box **38** to define a lower compartment **52** between them.

Enclosed within the upper compartment **50** is a considerable length of dark-colored, plastic or neoprene pipe **53**, which is coiled into two vertically spaced horizontal coils **54** and **56**. The pipe **53** can be ½ inch I.D. pipe, and its length should preferably be about 1500 feet for a box measuring 8 feet on a side. The upper coil **54** rests upon a plurality of radially extending, wood strip spacers **58**, which stand on top of the lower layer **56** of pipe, and the lower layer in turn, rests upon spacers **59** which lie on the bottom **51** of the inner box. The coils of pipe in the upper layer **54** are spaced relatively close together, so that they are almost touching one another, whereas the coils in the lower layer 56 are spaced about 2 inches apart to permit convection circulation of hot air through the coils. As best shown in FIGURE 2, the coil of the upper layer 54 starts at the outside, and at the center of the coil, it passes down to the lower layer 56, where the latter coil winds outwardly, terminating finally in a connector 62. Enclosed within the lower compartment 52 is a length, preferably about 100 feet long, of finned copper tubing 60, which winds back and forth from one side of the box to the other, as best shown in FIGURE 4.

The connector 62 joins the end of the pipe 53 in the upper compartment to the adjacent end of the finned copper tubing 60, so that the copper tubing forms a continuation of the pipe 53. The starting end of the pipe 53 in the upper layer 54 is connected to an inlet pipe 64, which passes through one of the side walls of the box 30. The outlet end of the finned copper tubing 60 is connected to an outlet pipe 66 which also passes through the side wall of the box 30. Both the inlet pipe 64 and the outlet pipe 66 are jacketed with insulation to prevent loss of heat to the atmosphere. The other end of the pipe 64 is connected by a T-fitting 68 to the pump output pipe 26, while the heater outlet pipe 66 is connected by a T-fitting 70 to the pump intake pipe 26. A valve 72 in the pipeline 64 permits cutting off the flow of water to the heater 10 during the hottest part of the summer, when the water is naturally warm enough, and any additional heat would be unnecessary.

The heater 10 is preferably located closely adjacent a chimney flue 74, which has collector flues 76, 77 and 78 connected thereto, carrying the hot exhaust gases from the oven, space heater, and water heater, respectively. Thus, the hot exhaust gas from all of the gas-burning appliances in the home are collected and channeled through the chimney flue 74. Connected into the flue 74 is a by-pass pipe 80, which opens into the lower compartment 52 at the bottom end of the sloping box 30. A vent pipe 82 is connected into the lower compartment 52 at the top end of the box, and in this way hot flue gases can circulate freely through the lower compartment 52 from one end to the other.

A by-pass valve 84 is pivoted in the chimney flue 74 at the junction of the by-pass pipe 80, and is swingable between two opposite positions to send the exhaust gases straight up the chimney 74, or off to one side through the by-pass pipe 80 into the compartment 52. In FIGURE 1, the by-pass valve 84 is shown in the position to direct the gases through the heater unit. An arm 86 is attached to the by-pass valve 84, and this is connected by a pushrod 88 to an actuating arm 90 on a motor-driven valve positioner 92. The valve positioner 92 may be remotely controlled, so as to eliminate the necessity of climbing up on the roof to change the valve setting. Alternatively, the by-pass valve 84 could be manually operated, in which case the arm 86 would be swung over to the desired position and secured.

One important feature of the invention is the manner in which the pipes within the heater box 30 are connected to the pipes of the filter circulating system. As shown in FIGURE 1, the heater inlet pipe 64 is connected to the pump output pipe 26, and the heater outlet pipe 66 is connected to the pump intake pipe 24. By virtue of this arrangement, the full pressure drop across the pump is delivered across the inlet pipe 64 and outlet pipe 66 of the heater unit, which makes it possible to drive a greater volume of water through the pipe in the heater box than would be the case if the heater outlet pipe 66 merely discharged into the pool 12 or into the filter 14. The suction pressure within the pump inlet pipe 24 exerts a powerful propelling force on the water flowing through the pipes of the heater box, somewhat analogous to the locomotive at the front end of a string of cars, which pulls the train forwardly, while a pusher locomotive at the rear end exerts a push. In the present instance, the pressure head in the output pipe 26 of the pump corresponds to the "pusher" locomotive, while the suction head of the intake pipe 24 corresponds to the tractor locomotive at the head of the string of cars. A certain small percentage of the heated water that is discharged by the line 66 into the pump intake pipe 24 is picked up by the intake pipe 64 of the heater, but this small amount of recirculated water is of no consequence.

The operation of the invention is believed to be self-evident from the foregoing description. Whenever the temperature within the box 30 rises above 90° F., whether it is from solar heat or from the heat of exhaust gases passing through the lower compartment 52, the thermostat 94 turns the motor 18 on, driving the pump 16. This circulates the water through the coils of pipe 54 and 56 in the upper compartment 50, where the pipe is heated by solar radiation, and the air within the compartment is also heated by direct solar radiation, reflection, and convection. The lower coil 56 absorbs substantial amounts of the heat in the air, thereby exerting an additional cooling effect in the upper compartment.

Upon completing the circuit of the lower layer 56 of pipe, the water is transferred down to the finned copper tubing in the lower compartment 52, where it picks up the heat from any exhaust gas rising through the chimney flue 74, and by-passed through the lower compartment 52. When the temperature within the box 30 drops below 90° F., the thermostat 94 shuts off the motor 18, which may then revert back to a timer-actuated cycle. In addition to directly heating the finned copper tubing 60, the hot exhaust gases passing through the lower compartment 52 also heat up the sheet metal bottom 51 of the inner box 32, and this causes the air within the upper compartment 50 to be heated. Thus, virtually all of the heat in the exhaust gas is dissipated within the box 30, where it is absorbed by the pipe 53 and finned copper tubing 60.

A prototype model of the invention was installed on a residence roof and connected to a swimming pool having approximately 37,000 gallons of water. A careful daily check of the water temperature in the test pool, as compared with the temperatures of unheated water in adjacent neighborhood pools, revealed that the water in the test pool was approximately 10 degrees warmer than in the other pools. As a consequence, the water of the test pool was comfortable for swimming at least a month and a half before the other pools could be used, and the season was extended in the Fall for another month and a half beyond the time that the use of the other pools was discontinued. *

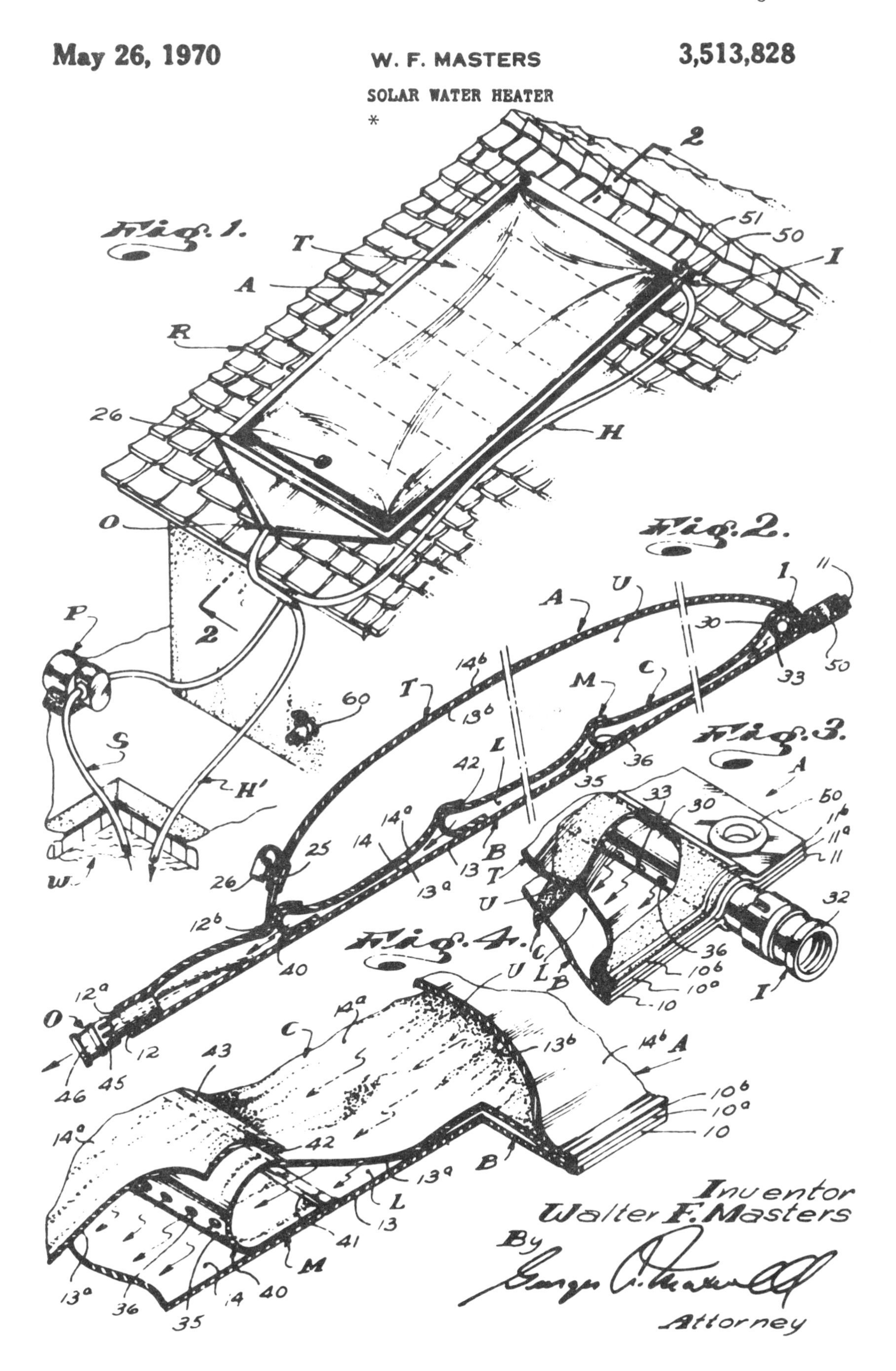
May 26, 1970
W. F. MASTERS
3,513,828
SOLAR WATER HEATER
Fig. 1.
Fig. 2.
Fig. 3.
Fig. 4.
Inventor
Walter F. Masters
By
Attorney

3,513,828
SOLAR WATER HEATER
Walter F. Masters, 3217 Lakeshore Court,
Orlando, Fla. 32803

ABSTRACT OF THE DISCLOSURE

A solar water heater to be engaged on an inclined roof structure and comprising three superimposed sheets, there being an elongate base sheet with a heat reflecting top surface and having upper and lower ends, a black, flexible heat absorbing central sheet, and a transparent solar radiation conducting top sheet, the space between the central and the top sheets being filled with air so the top sheet is spaced from the central sheet, water inlet means connected with a water supply and conducting water between the base and central sheets at the upper end of the structure, irrigating means spaced longitudinally of the structure to maintain water dispersed laterally between the bottom and central sheets as it flows longitudinally therebetween and water discharge means at the lower end of the structure.

This invention has to do with a solar water heater and is more particularly concerned with a novel water heater construction having novel means for distributing water across the surface of a solar heat absorbing and conducting membrane and novel means insulating the heat absorbing and conducting membrane from ambient air or adverse atmospheric conditions.

It is an object and feature of my invention to provide a solar water heater of the character referred to which is particularly adapted for installation on an inclined or pitched roof top and which includes a flat envelope-like structure with a bottom sheet of flexible plastic material, which is related to inclined supporting surfaces such as a roof top, an intermediate heat absorbing sheet of flexible plastic material above the bottom sheet, irrigating means to conduct and direct water between the bottom and intermediate sheets and a top, insulating sheet of clear, flexible, plastic material in spaced relationship above the intermediate sheet.

Another object and feature of this invention is to provide a structure of the general character referred to having upper and lower ends, water inlet and outlet means at said upper and lower ends and a structure wherein said top and intermediate sheets establish an inflatable structure, which defines a body of dead insulating air between the top and intermediate sheets which body of air maintains the top sheet spaced above the intermediate sheet.

Yet another object of my invention is to provide a structure of the character referred to wherein the irrigating means includes a plurality of longitudinally spaced, laterally extending partitions between the bottom and intermediate sheets, which partitions catch waters flowing downwardly between the sheets, distribute the water laterally between the sheets and are provided with laterally spaced apertures through which the water trapped by each partition flows to flow longitudinally downwardly between the sheets downstream of the partitions.

Yet another object of my invention is to provide a heater of the character referred to which is particularly adapted for heating the water in a swimming pool and which includes a pumping means to draw water from the pool and deliver it to the water inlet means at the upper end of the heater and which includes means at the lower discharge end of the heater to conduct heated water back into the pool.

It is an object of this invention to provide a structure of the character referred to wherein the filter pump for the swimming pool can be utilized to supply the water to the heater.

It is another object of my invention to provide a heater of the character referred to which is easy and economical to manufacture, a structure which is easy and convenient to install and operate, and a structure which is highly effective and dependable in operation.

The foregoing and other objects and features of my invention will be fully understood from the following detailed description of a typical preferred form and application of my invention, throughout which description reference is made to the accompanying drawings, in which:

FIG. 1 is a perspective view of my new heater, showing it related to a swimming pool and roof top;

FIG. 2 is an enlarged, detailed sectional view taken substantially as indicated by line 2—2 on FIG. 1;

FIG. 3 is an enlarged perspective view of a portion of my invention with portions broken away to better illustrate details of the construction; and

FIG. 4 is a perspective view of another portion of my invention with portions broken away and in section to better illustrate the details of the construction.

The heater construction A that I provide includes an elongate, flat, substantially rectangular base sheet B of flexible plastic material arranged with its major longitudinal axis on an inclined plane, said base sheet having straight, parallel side edges **10**, a straight, transversely extending top or upper edge **11**, a bottom or lower edge **12**, a flat, substantially downwardly disposed support engaging surface **13** and a flat, substantially upwardly disposed top surface **14**. The bottom or lower edge **12** is preferably V-shaped and has longitudinally outwardly or downwardly convergent edge portions which join at or near the central, longitudinal axis of the sheet.

The construction further includes a central or intermediate sheet C of flexible heat absorbing plastic material, which sheet can be a unitary plastic sheet or can, as illustrated, be fabricated of a multiplicity of pieces of plastic sheeting, as will hereinafter be described.

The sheet C corresponds, generally, in size, shape and disposition with the base sheet B and has side, top and bottom edges $\mathbf{10^a}$, $\mathbf{11^a}$ and $\mathbf{12^a}$. The sheet C is arranged to occur above and overlie the sheet B with its several edges aligned with the several corresponding edges of the sheet B.

The sheet C has a bottom surface $\mathbf{13^a}$ which opposes the top surface **14** of sheet B and has a substantially flat, upwardly disposed top surface $\mathbf{14^a}$.

The construction further includes a top or cover sheet T of clear, transparent, solar radiation conducting, flexible plastic, which sheet can correspond in general size, shape, and disposition with the sheets B and C and has side, top and bottom edges $\mathbf{10^b}$, $\mathbf{11^b}$ and $\mathbf{12^b}$. The sheet T is arranged to occur above and overlie the sheet C with its side and top edges $\mathbf{10^b}$ and $\mathbf{11^b}$ aligned with the corresponding edges $\mathbf{10}$–$\mathbf{10^a}$ and $\mathbf{11}$–$\mathbf{11^a}$ of the sheets B and C.

The bottom edge $\mathbf{12^b}$ of the sheet T is shown as having a straight, transversely extending edge, extending straight across the structure and between the lower ends of the side edges $\mathbf{10^b}$.

The sheet T has substantially flat bottom and top surfaces $\mathbf{13^b}$ and $\mathbf{14^b}$.

The several adjacent side edge portions of the sheets A, B and T are suitably secured and sealed together, as at **20** and **21**, and so that the sheets B and C cooperate to define a lower chamber L and the sheets C and T cooperate to define an upper chamber U.

In practice, the sheets can be fixed and sealed together

by means of a suitable cement, heat sealing or a combination thereof.

The top sheet T is provided with an air conducting stem 25 with a closure 26 removably related to it to facilitate introducing air into the upper chamber U and thereby inflate the construction and to urge and maintain the top sheet T in spaced, insulated relationship from the central sheet C, as clearly illustrated in the drawings.

The sub-assembly made up of the top and central sheets T and C need only be inflated to about 2 or 3 p.s.i. and so that the air within the chamber U is not compressed greatly and so dense as to adversely increase its heat conducting characteristics.

The construction that I provide further includes water inlet means I, irrigating or water dispersing means M and water outlet means O.

The water inlet means I is shown as including an elongate manifold 30 extending transversely across the upper end of the chamber L and having an outer end portion 31 extending laterally outwardly between the sheets B and C and provided with a hose coupling 32 at its outer end.

The manifold 30 is shown as being established by a length of plastic hose or pipe and is provided with a plurality of longitudinally spaced apertures 33, which apertures are disposed longitudinally downwardly relative to the longitudinal axis of the construction and are adapted to dispense and distribute water flowing into and through the manifold substantially uniformly across the lateral extent of the construction and between the sheets B and C.

The sheets B and C are fixed and sealed to and about the portion of the manifold pipe 30 which extends between the edge portions of the said sheets and so that the construction is suitably closed or sealed.

The dispersing or irrigating means M includes a plurality of longitudinally spaced, transversely extending perforated partitions 35 between the sheets B and C, which partitions are adapted to catch and collect water as it flows downwardly between the sheets and to redistribute it laterally and across the plane of the construction as it flows downwardly from each partition.

In the case illustrated, the partitions 35 are provided with a single row of perforations 36.

If the central sheet C is a single sheet of plastic, the partitions 35 can be established of individual perforated strips of sheet plastic arranged between the sheets B and C and having top and bottom edge portions heat sealed or otherwise fixed to the sheets B and C.

In the case illustrated, the central sheet C is made up of a plurality of longitudinally spaced sections and the partitions 35 are established by downwardly and rearwardly turned, perforated lower edge portions 40 on each section, the lower rear edges of which are heat sealed or otherwise fixed to the bottom sheet B as indicated at 41.

The upper, rear, transverse edge 42 of each lower section extends over the downwardly turned partition forming portion of its related upper section and is heat sealed or otherwise fixed to the top of the said related upper section as at 43.

In operation, the central sheet, whether integral or sectional normally lies on the bottom sheet B and is urged downwardly by the air pressure in the upper chamber U. Water introduced into the upper end of the lower chamber L and flowing downwardly between the sheets B and C is normally caused to be pressed and spread out between the sheets by the air pressure in the chamber U acting upon the sheet C.

In spite of the above, there still exists the tendency for the downwardly flowing water to establish channels between the sheets B and C and along or through which the water might rush and flow too rapidly and directly down or longitudinally of the construction.

The portions 35 of the means M serve to prevent channeling of the water in the manner set forth above and assure proper spread and distribution of the water flowing downwardly between the sheets B and C.

The water outlet means includes a short longitudinally extending open ended outlet tube 45 arranged centrally of the construction and extending between the edges of the sheets B and C, with the upper, inner end communicating with the lower end of the chamber L and provided with a hose fitting 46 at its other or outer lower end.

In practice, suitable means are provided to secure the construction to a supporting structure. In the case illustrated, the construction is arranged and supported on a pitched roof R and is shown provided with grommets 50 in its upper edge portion, which grommets are engaged about retaining hooks 51 engaged in the roof structure.

In the case illustrated, the water inlet means I is shown connected with the discharge side of a water recirculating pump P by means of a supply hose H connected with the hose fitting 32. The inlet side of the pump is connected with a suction hose S extending into the water W of a swimming pool.

The hose fitting 46 of the water outlet means is shown connected with a return hose H', which hose extends to the pool or water W.

In practice, when the structure provided is related to a pool construction having a filter and/or heater means, the pump P can be that pump normally provided with such means and the hose H can be connected with a suitable valve controlled T-fitting or the like arranged in the high pressure side of the piping of the filter means (not shown).

Still further, in practice, the hose H can be connected with any suitable water supply, such as a municipal water supply and by means of a hose bib 60, in which case the pump P is not required and the water being heated is fresh water, rather than recirculated water.

In the preferred carrying out of this invention, the central, intermediate, heat-absorbing sheet C is established of black, opaque, flexible, plastic sheeting. The bottom or base sheet B is preferably provided with a white or other highly reflecting top surface 14 and so that heat from the central sheet, moving downwardly through the structure is not absorbed by and conducted downwardly further by the base sheet, but is bounced or reflected back, upwardly toward the central sheet and through the water therebetween.

The ordinary or conventional roof construction with which my new heater is to be related cooperates with related building structure to define an attic or other similar air space. Such air space is in the nature of and serves as a heat sink. Solar radiation absorbed by the roof not only heats the roof, but also heats the air in the noted space below. As a result of the above, the ordinary roof and the air space therebelow defines a large and extensive heat sink which, throughout the daytime, collects many B.t.u.'s of heat energy.

In light of the above, in carrying out this invention, the bottom side 13 of the base sheet B of my heater can be black or some other dark heat absorbing color and such that it will absorb heat collected by the roof structure, on which it is engaged and supported, and such that it will conduct such heat to the water being heated.

While I have described my new heater construction as being engaged and supported by a roof structure and as being employed to heat the water of a swimming pool, it is to be noted and understood and it will be apparent that my heater can be employed to heat other than swimming pool water and that it can be engaged and supported on an inclined supporting surface other than a roof, as desired or as circumstances require and without departing from the spirit of this invention.

From the foregoing, it will be apparent that the heater structure that I provide is extremely easy and economical to manufacture and is highly effective and dependable in operation.

My heater structure is light in weight, neat and compact and is such that it can be easily and conveniently installed and put into service or taken out of service and stored away, without the exercise of any extraordinary or special skill. Finally, my heater is so light in weight and so extensive in plane configuration, that its weight, when in operation, is distributed over so great an area that it can be engaged and supported on most any roof structure without fear of overstressing or otherwise damaging the roof. *

PATENTED JAN 1 4 1975 CRAWFORD, F. R. 3,859,980

SHEET 1 OF 2

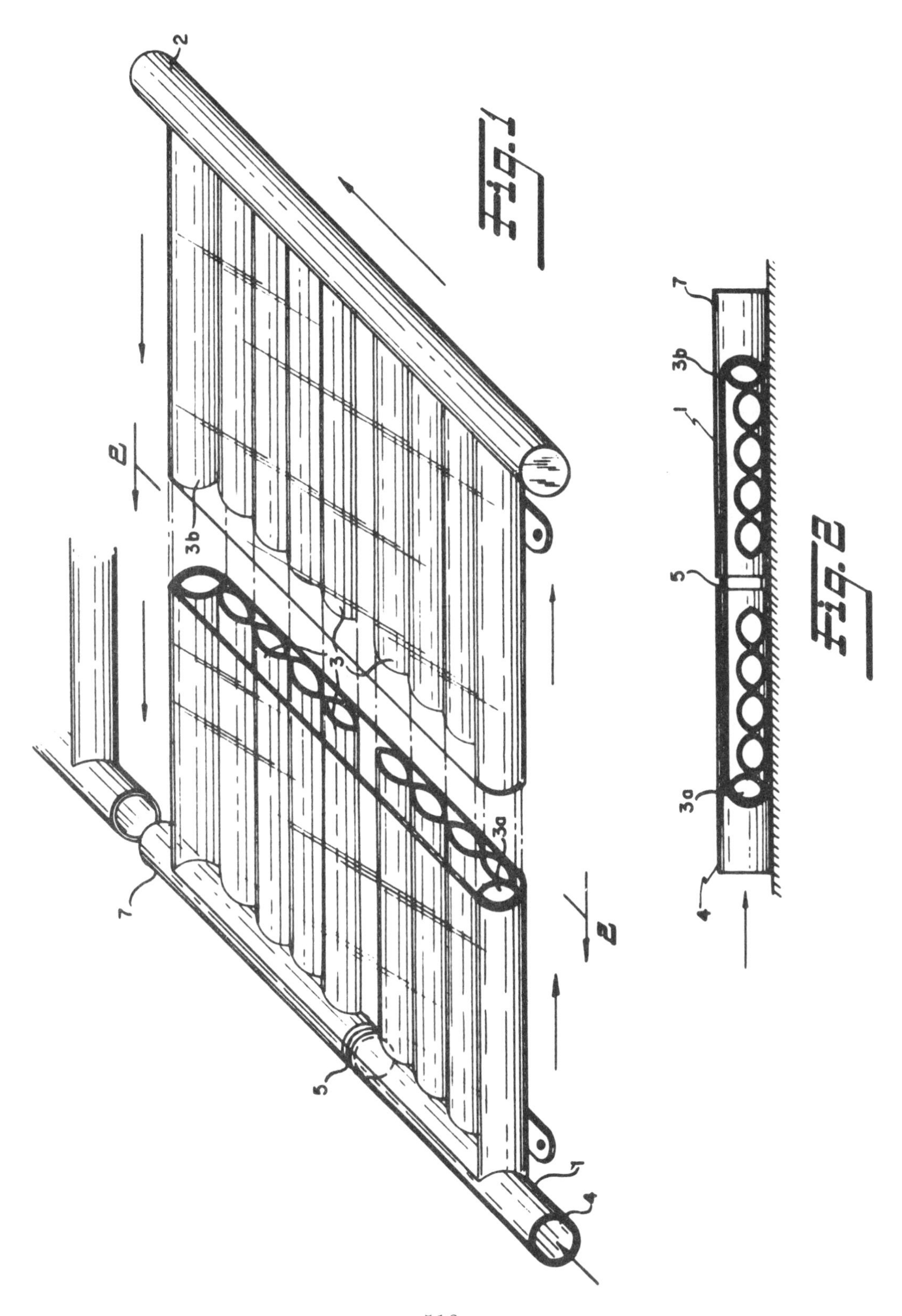

PATENTED JAN 14 1975 CRAWFORD, F. R. 3,859,980

SHEET 2 OF 2

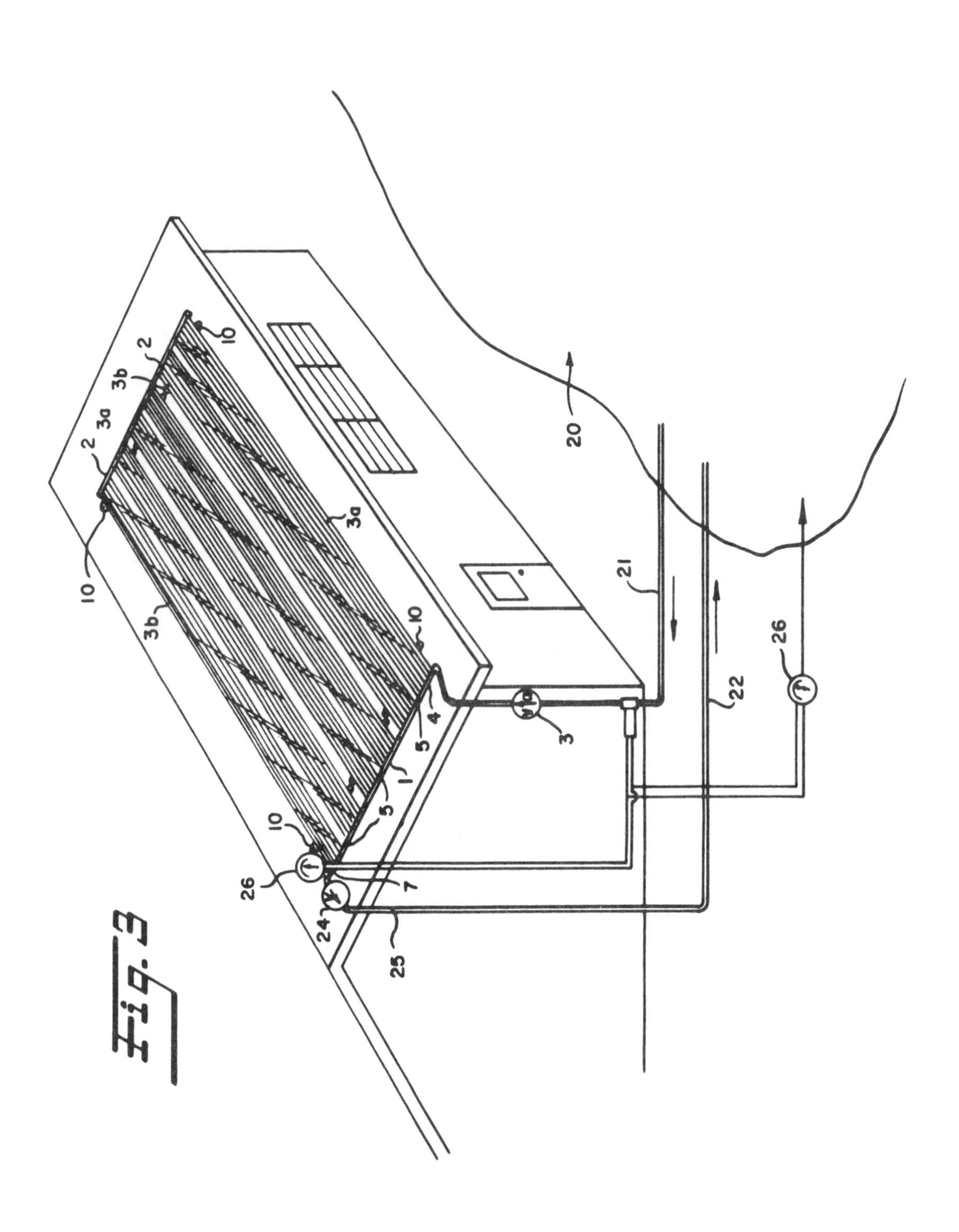

* **ABSTRACT**

This invention provides a solar heating unit constituted of any suitable flexible material, such as plastic, so that when not in use or during transportation it may be rolled into a compact structure easily transported and installed. Further the present solar heating unit consists of a plurality of tubes arranged in parallel relation and connected at their ends to manifolds with the two outermost tubes of the unit and the manifolds having a greater outside vertical diameter than the intermediate tubes, and a transparent envelope enclosing the entire unit and held in spaced relation above and below the surfaces of the tubes between the two outermost tubes, thus providing an insulating pocket of air about the tubes to prevent dissipation of heat by convection into the atmosphere surrounding the unit. The present invention further includes a pump for circulating a fluid at low pressure through the tubes and manifolds together with suitable pressure regulating means and check valve means to prevent reverse flow of fluid from the tubes when the pump is shut down.*

SOLAR HEATER

The prior patent art contains many various types of solar heating units to utilize atmospheric heat to heat water or other fluids, but these devices include rigid structures, such as containing boxes, etc., which render them cumbersome to handle if built up at a point distant to the point at which they are to be used. Many of them require special preparation or a roof, or the like on which they are to be installed, and while they may provide the ultimate result of heating the fluid, as in the present invention, they are more complicated in structure, consequently more expensive to manufacture and far more expensive to install than the present invention which comprises a flexible heating unit utilizing solar energy which unit may be rolled or folded into a compact structure of comparatively light weight and may be easily placed upon a roof or other suitable place of use and unfolded into its operative position.

Another object of this invention is to provide a comparatively flexible and simple solar heating unit which will utilize maximum solar energy and will prevent the convection of heat from its structure by the surrounding atmosphere or by wind.

More specifically the present invention consists of a pair of spaced manifolds and a plurality of tubes connected to and extending between the manifolds, these tubes may be oval in cross section rather than circular and the two outermost tubes of the unit are placed with their maximum diameters at right angles to the maximum diameters of the intermediate tubes, thus the intermediate tubes present a maximum surface to be acted on by the solar energy or heat for heating fluid flowing through them. An envelope of clear material, preferably plastic, encloses the entire unit and the two outermost tubes hold this plastic envelope in spaced relation to provide air insulating spaces both above and below the intermediate tubes in the unit, thus preventing escape of heat from the tubes into the surrounding atmosphere.

However the tubes may be other than oval in shape and in such instances the two outermost tubes and the manifolds will have greater vertical diameters than the intermediate tubes so as to provide the air space between the intermediate tubes and the enclosing envelope.

With these and other objects in view, as may appear from the accompanying specification, the invention consists of various features of construction and combination of parts, which will be first described in connection with the accompanying drawings, showing a solar heater of a preferred form embodying the invention and the features forming the invention will be specifically pointed out in the claims.

In the drawings:

FIG. 1 is a perspective view of the solar heating unit.

FIG. 2 is a fragmentary view in perspective of the unit taken on the lines 2—2 of FIG. 1 and clearly showing the oval diameter of the tubes and enclosing envelope in section.

FIG. 3 is a view showing a solar heating unit connected for heating the water in a swimming pool.

Referring more particularly to the drawings the solar heating unit as shown in FIG. 1 comprises an inlet and outlet manifold 1 and a circulating manifold 2. Tubes 3 are connected to and connect the two manifolds in a fluid circulating system which enters the inlet manifold 1 at its inlet 4 and is directed through substantially one-half of the tubes connecting the manifolds 1 and 2 to cause the fluid to flow through the tubes into the manifold 2 and then return through the remaining tubes to the manifold 1. A partition 5 (shown in dotted lines in FIG. 1) is placed at the manifold 1 substantially equidistant from its ends to cause the above flow of fluid through the unit.

The tubes 3 are oval in diameter as clearly shown in FIG. 2 and the tubes *3a* and *3b* at the outer edges of the group of tubes are placed with their maximum diameters perpendicularly while the tubes intermediate these two tubes are placed with their maximum diameters horizontal. In other words, the maximum diameters of the two edged tubes are placed at right angles to the maximum diameters of the intermediate tubes for the purpose hereinafter specified.

The intermediate tubes having their maximum diameters positioned as above specified present a maximum surface to be acted upon by the sun or solar heat. All of the tubes may be made of black material or painted black to prevent reflection of heat from shiny surfaces and to absorb the solar heat for transmission to the fluid flowing through the tubes.

The tubes and the manifolds may be made of any suitable flexible material, such as sheet plastic so that they may be folded or rolled into a compact form for transportation and for facilitating installation.

The entire unit is enclosed in a clear flexible envelope clearly shown in cross section in fragmentary FIG. 2 and this envelope is held spaced from the intermediate tubes 3 of the unit by the two outside tubes *3a* and *3b* to provide a space both above and below the intermediate tubes and the envelope. This space provides a sheet of air insulation which prevents the convection of heat from the tubes into the surface on which the unit is mounted and also into the atmosphere above and surrounding the unit and protecting the unit from the cooling effect of winds.

The intake manifold 1 has an inlet at one end which

is connected to the source of supply of the fluid to be heated and an outlet 7 at its opposite end through which the heated fluid flows from the unit. In use the outlet 7 may be connected directly to the desired point of use of the heated water or it may be connected to the inlet of a second identical solar heating unit if one unit is unable to provide the desired heating of the fluid flowing therethrough.

It is necessary to provide sufficient force or pressure to the fluid flowing through the unit and to do this an ordinary fluid pump (not shown) together with suitable pressure regulating means (not shown) and both of which are well known and in abundant supply on the open market.

The solar heating unit may be used to heat fluid, such as water or any other suitable fluid which will not chemically react with the plastic tubes.

Due to its flexibility the solar heater unit may be used or placed in any suitable place, such as on the roof of a building, on a driveway or on the ground and it has fasteners 10 attached thereto to hold it in place when installed and prevent displacement by wind, gravity, or circulation of the fluid.

The solar heating unit may be used for, but its use is not specifically restricted to, heating water for swimming pools, heating water for residential heating systems, or for pre-heating water for domestic electric, gas, or oil fired domestic hot water heaters, or the fluid may be heated in the solar unit and delivered to an insulated cistern or container so that heated fluid may be stored up during sunshine for use on cool cloudy days or at night when the heating of the fluid in the heater will not be of suficient degree to provide the desired heat at the point of use of the heated fluid.

FIG. 3 of the drawings illustrates the use of the solar heater above described for heating water in a swimming pool 20. The swimming pool is both the source of supply for water to the heater and the recipient of the heated water. A suitable pump (not shown) is provided to pump water from the swimming pool through the inlet pipe 21 to and through the heater and out of the heater through its outlet and through pipe 22 back to the pool. A check valve 23 is installed in the cool water inlet pipe 21 to prevent cool water from flowing back into the pool from the heating system when the pump is shut off and a pressure valve 24 is installed in the heated water outlet pipe 25 to maintain the desired low pressure of fluid in the heater and to prevent syphoning off water when the circulating pump is shut off.

A thermostat 26 is installed at the top of the solar heater and this thermostat may be set to turn on the circulating pump whenever the temperature reaches a predetermined reading and a second thermostat is placed in the pool and set to turn off the circulating pump whenever the temperature of the water in the pool reaches a predetermined desirable degree.

The system just disclosed for use in connection with the heating of water in a swimming pool may be used in any other system where heated water is desired, such as heating a dwelling or building to supply initially heated water to a fuel operated water heater unit or for storage in an insulated container as hereinabove referred to.

The flexible nature of the plastic material used in the construction of the heater prevents damage by freezing.

From the foregoing description and the accompanying drawings it will be apparent that a solar heating unit is provided which is simple and relatively inexpensive in construction, is flexible when free of fluid and may be folded or rolled into compact form thus facilitating shipment and installation and wherein when in use the shape and function of the heater is maintained by pressure of the fluid exerted within the tubes and manifolds. The envelope forming the insulating air space is kept taut in position by the arrangement of tubes *3a* and *3b* in the vertical position. Thus, no glass or other rigid transparent cover over the device is required.

Fabrication of the entire device from plastic sheeting permits the heater to be rolled up or folded when empty. This greatly reduces shipping and handling costs when the device is marketed. No structural changes or modifications need to be made to a building on which the heater is placed. In addition, the heater may be readily disconnected and stored when not in use, for example, during winter months in northern climates. *

PATENTED MAR 4 1975 KONOPKA, E.J. 3,868,945

*

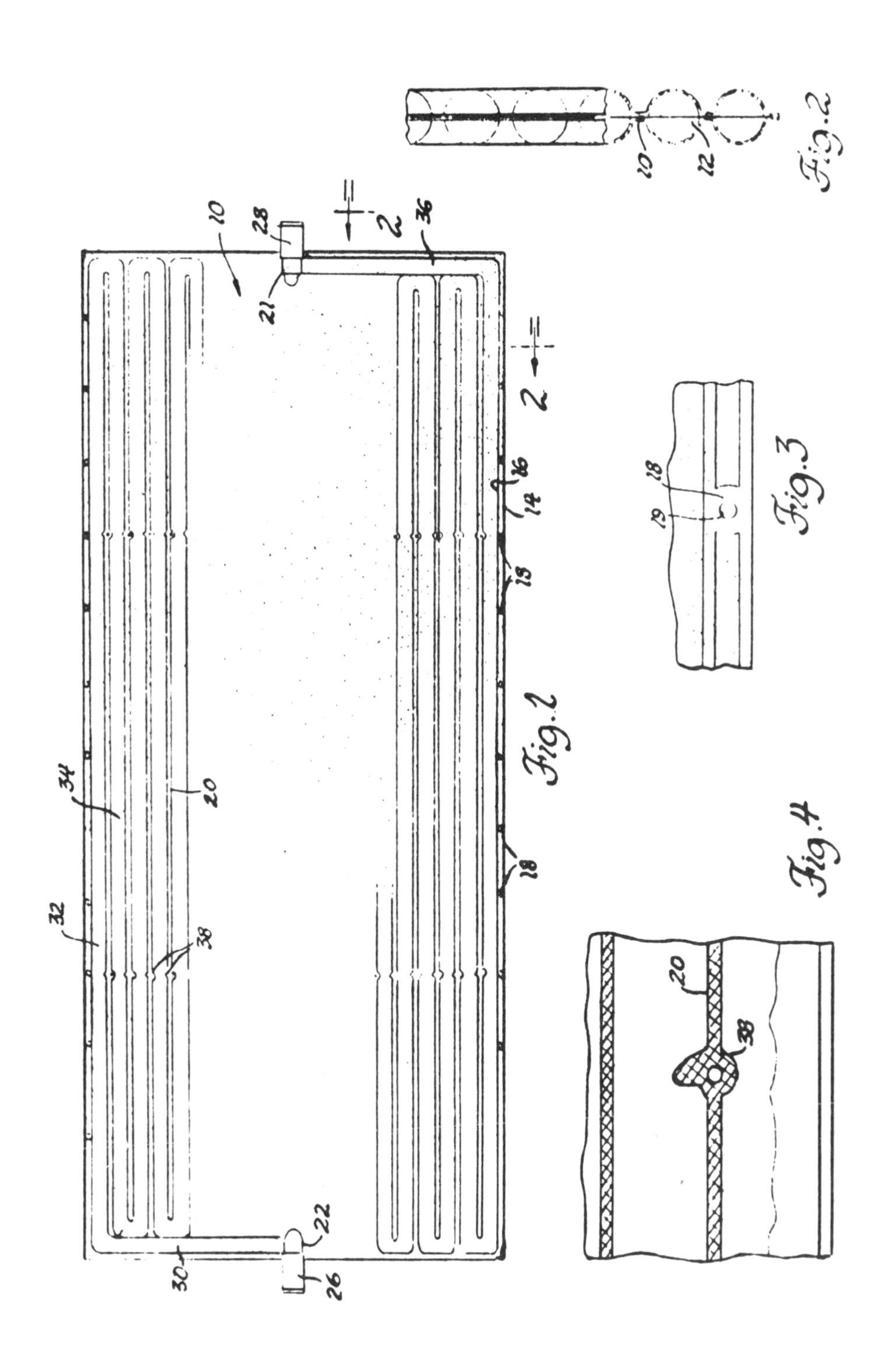

PATENTED MAR 4 1975 KONOPKA, E.J. 3,868,945

*

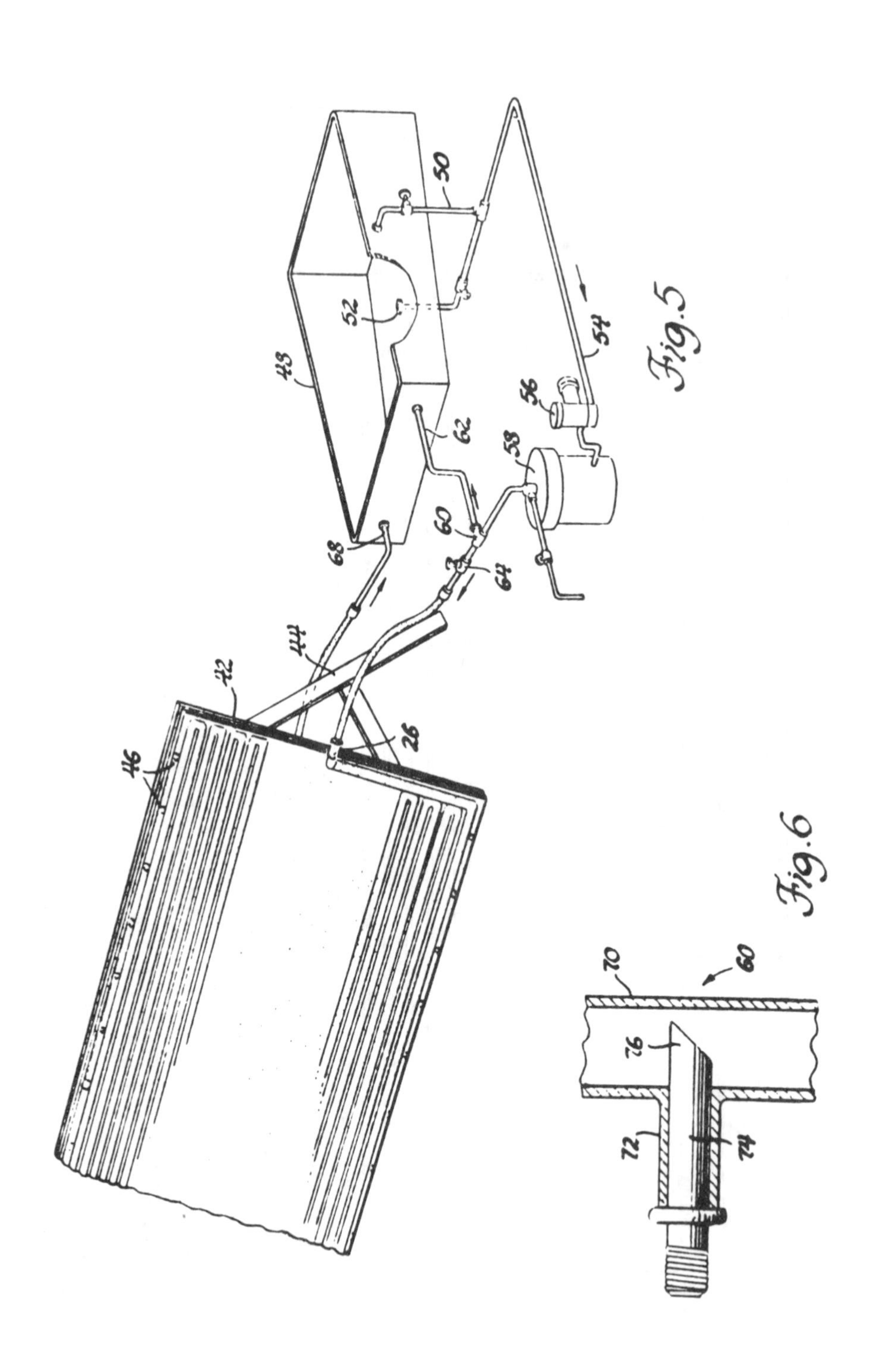

* **ABSTRACT**

A heat exchanger for warming the water in a swimming pool during the day by means of solar heat and for cooling the water at night consisting of a pair of rectangular sheets of black matte finish flexible film plastic sealed together so as to form a closed perimeter having an inlet passage and an outlet passage, and a sinuous flow path consisting of a plurality of straight parallel elongated flow channels formed between the inlet and the outlet. At a plurality of points along each straight flow channel the two plastic sections are heat sealed together to form obstacles to the straight flow path creating zones of turbulance which enhance the efficiency of the heat exchange. A pump removes pool water from a drain, passes it through a filter and divides the filter output between one flow path back to the pool inlet and another flow path to the heat exchanger using an adjustable flow diverter consisting of a T-section having a movable tube extending up from the leg of the T into the arm. *

SOLAR HEATER FOR SWIMMING POOLS

FIELD OF THE INVENTION

This invention relates to heat transfer devices for heating swimming pool water through solar energy and for cooling that water through radiation to a cooler atmosphere and more particularly to such a device which is formed from a pair of sheets of heat sealed plastic film.

BACKGROUND OF THE INVENTION

It has previously been recognized that solar heaters provide a low cost and efficient solution to the problem of maintaining the water in swimming pools at a comfortable temperature. These heaters are simply inserted in the flow path which is necessary to filter the pool water. Then they can warm the water temperature as a result of absorption of solar radiation during the day and they may be used at night to cool the water by exchanging heat with the cooler atmosphere.

One particularly low cost and effective form of such pool water heat exchanger takes the form of a blanket formed of two layers of plastic film heat sealed to one another so as to form a closed tortuous flow path for pool water. Heat exchangers of this type are disclosed for example in U.S. Pat. Nos. 3,022,781 to Andrassy and 3,513,828 to Masters.

SUMMARY OF THE PRESENT INVENTION

The present invention contemplates a heat exchanger for use with swimming pools of the film plastic type incorporating several unique features which increase the efficiency and flexibility of the heat exchanger without appreciably increasing its cost.

Heat exchangers formed in accordance with the present invention employ a pair of rectangular sheets of black matte, opaque film plastic heat sealed together along a plurality of lines to form a single continuous sinuous flow path consisting of a plurality of straight line sections extending the length of the rectangle and joined to one another at their ends. At regular intervals along the heat sealed lines which form the side walls of the straight flow paths the sheets are heat sealed together to create projections extending transversely into the flow paths and forming obstacles which interrupt the laminar flow occurring along these paths. Downstream of these heat sealed obstacles the flow is highly turbulent. This has been found to substantially increase the heat transfer efficiency of the apparatus.

Another novel aspect of the present invention involves the provision of heat sealed grommets around the perimeter of the transfer apparatus. These are simply formed by providing double marginal seams about the perimeter of the sheets and sealing the sheets solidly between these borders at regular intervals to provide solid sections in which holes may be formed for support purposes. These grommets allow the heat exchanger to be supported on an adjustable inclined surface to present the optimum configuration for the reception of solar radiation.

Still another novel aspect of the present invention consists of a device employed to divert a portion of the flow from the pool's filter to the heat exchanger. In a typical installation with a large in-ground pool the heater will operate most efficiently if only a portion of the filter flow is passed through it. The portion of the flow that should be passed through the heater to obtain the optimum results is a variable depending upon such factors as the solar radiation intensity. The present invention provides a low cost, adjustable flow separator in the form of a T-section wherein the input is from one side of the arms of the T. A tubing section extends into the arm from the leg of the T and diverts a portion of the flow into the leg. The portion of the flow diverted is dependent upon the exact projection of the tube into the arm and the angle of attack of flow toward the diverter section.

Other objectives, advantages and applications of the present invention will be made apparent by the following detailed description of the preferred embodiment of the invention. The description makes reference to the accompanying drawings in which:

FIG. 1 is a plan view of a heat exchanger forming a preferred embodiment of the invention, with portions broken away to show specific details of construction;

FIG. 2 is a cross sectional view of the heat exchanger taken along the line 2—2 of FIG. 1;

FIG. 3 is a detailed sectional view of one of the edge grommets formed in the heat exchanger;

FIG. 4 is a detailed sectional view of one of the protuberances in the heat sealed channel walls which create turbulence in the flow channels;

FIG. 5 is a perspective view of a heat transfer system incorporating the present invention; and

FIG. 6 is a detailed sectional view through a flow separator used in connection with the present invention.

Referring to the drawings, a preferred embodiment of the heat transfer unit is formed from a pair of rectangular sheets of polyvinyl chloride film **10** and **12.** Both sheets preferably are black in color. While their dimensions are not critical to the invention a typical heat exchanger will employ sheets of approximately four feet by seven feet. Polyvinyl chloride film of 0.010 inches or more in thickness is suitable for the practice of the invention.

The plastic sheets preferably have a matte or other form of non-reflective surface rather than a polished, reflective surface. We have found that use of a non-reflective surface substantially enhances the heat transfer properties of the unit.

The two sheets are laid adjacent to one another and are joined together along a plurality of lines by heat sealing or dielectric sealing. A pair of border lines **14** and **16**, one inside the other, are formed adjacent to the edges of the sheet. These lines may be separated from one another by approximately one inch, and may extend around the full perimeter of the device. At regular intervals of approximately six inches the areas between border lines **14** and **16** are heat sealed together in an annular configuration **18** having a central hole **20**. The hole **20** is later removed to form grommets which may be employed to support the heat exchanger on appropriate hangers.

The areas of the sheets **10** and **12** intermediate the border lines **14** and **16** are joined together along a plurality of lines **20** so as to form a single sinuous flow path extending from an inlet point **22** to an output point **21**. The inlet and outlet points are passages through the border areas **14** and **16** in which cylindrical plastic hose connectors **26** and **28** are inserted.

The inlet connector **26** joins to a first passage **30** which extends along one short edge of the sheets. This channel extends to one of the long ends where it connects to a flow passage **32** that runs the full length of the sheet. The flow is then directed to the next longitudinal path **34** and continues in this manner for the total width of the heat exchanger until it is returned to the outlet passage **21** via a flow section **36**.

The flow channels are defined with heat sealed lines approximately ⅛ inch in thickness. In order to prevent the flow from becoming highly laminar, which would decrease the heat transfer efficiency of the device, the sealing area is widened in accordance with a predetermined pattern at regular intervals along each flow path as at **38**. These protuberances extend into a pair of flow paths on the adjacent sides of the heated sealed edge. A typical flow protuberance is illustrated in FIG. **4**, and simply consists of a smooth-edged projection which diminishes and diverts the flow area so as to create turbulence in the area of the projection.

When a fluid flow is introduced to the heat exchanger through the inlet connector **26**, in a manner which will be subsequently described, the flow causes the non-sealed sections of the sheets **10** and **12** to separate to form a plurality of closed flow channels as is best seen in FIG. **2**. The fluid first passes through the flow channel **30** into the flow channel **32** and from there into the flow channel **34** and continues to flow the length of the heat exchanger in a zig-zag manner until it reaches the flow channel **36** and then passes out of the heat exchanger through the outlet connector **28**. The protuberances **38** tend to break up the laminar flow, as do the broad transitions in flow path which occur at the end of the channel, to provide a turbulent condition which enhances the heat transfer characteristics of the unit.

FIG. **5** illustrates the manner in which the heat exchanger of FIG. **1** may be supported and connected to a pool. As illustrated therein, an inclined board **42** having an area slightly in excess of the heat exchanger is supported above the ground with appropriate brackets **44**. The angle of inclination of the surface of the board is chosen to be such as to extend normally to the sun's rays. The exact angle differs with various locations, seasons and times of day. The support **44** is preferably adjustable so that the angle of inclination of the board **42** may be modified.

The heat exchanger is supported on the board by slipping the grommets **18** along one edge of the heat exchanger over hooks or screws **46** arrayed along the top edge of the board so that the heat exchanger lies along the board. FIG. **5** also illustrates the manner in which the heat exchanger may be connected to a swimming pool **48** of the in-the-ground variety. The swimming pool is equipped with a first drain **50** located in a sidewall and a second drain **52** located in its bottom. Both of these drains are connected to a line **54** which conveys the fluid to the intake of a suitable pump **56**, preferably of the centrifugal variety. The pump forces water through a normal swimming pool filter **58** of the diatomaceous earth or other standard variety. The outlet of the filter **58** is divided into two sections by an adjustable flow diverter valve **60** which will be subsequently disclosed in detail. One portion of the flow is directed back to the pool through an inlet **62** and the balance is provided to the inlet **26** of the heat exchanger through a line which may include a shut-off valve **64**. The outlet of the heat exchanger is provided to another pool inlet **68** from the output connector **28**.

As is illustrated in FIG. **6**, the flow diverter valve comprises a plastic T-section incorporating an arm **70** having a leg section **72** joining at right angles. A tubular insert **74** disposed within the leg sections has an open truncated end **76** which projects into the center of the arm **70**. The far extending edge of the end **76** terminates just short of the far wall of the arm **70**. The angle of inclination of the insert **74** and its depth of extension within the leg **72** may be adjusted so as to capture a controlled amount of the flow through the arm **70** into the leg **72**. Assuming the flow through the arm **70** is in an upward direction as viewed in FIG. **6**, if the truncated section **76** is adjusted so as to face downwardly, in the manner shown, an appreciable percentage of flow through the arm will be diverted into the leg. However, if the insert **74** is rotated so that the truncated section does not face the flow, a smaller percentage of the flow through the arm will be diverted into the leg. When the insert has been rotated through 180° so that the truncated section **76** faces upwardly, no appreciable flow from the arm will be diverted into the leg.

The flow diverter valve **60** is employed in the arrangement of FIG. **5** to control the portion of the flow from the filter **58** that is passed through the heat transfer unit in order to control the temperature of the pool and optimize the heat transfer. For example, during daylight hours, when the water in the pool is sufficiently warm, the insert **74** is rotated so that no appreciable flow occurs through the heat exchanger, but rather the flow from the filter is passed directly back to the pool through the inlet **62**. On a sunlit day, when the water in the pool is too cool, most of the flow may be diverted through the heat exchanger; however, the flow may be diminished under these circumstances to achieve an optimum heating since an excess of flow through the heat exchanger will result in a decrease in its efficiency.

The heat exchanger may also be used at night to cool the water of a pool that has been overheated by the sunlight during the day. The accumulation of dew on the surface of the heat exchanger and its resultant condensation, aids in the cooling phenomena.

With simpler pools, such as splash pools, there may be no need for a flow diverter valve and the entire flow may be passed through the heat exchanger. When not in use the heat exchanger can be readily folded into a compact configuration for storage. The exchanger itself is low in cost because of the simple materials used and may be readily added to a pool already having a pump and filter at very slight cost.

It has been found that the use of black matte plastic for both layers of the heat exchanger results in maximum energy retention. This is contradictory to previous teachings which suggest the use of a clear plastic top layer for such heat exchangers and a black plastic bottom layer. *

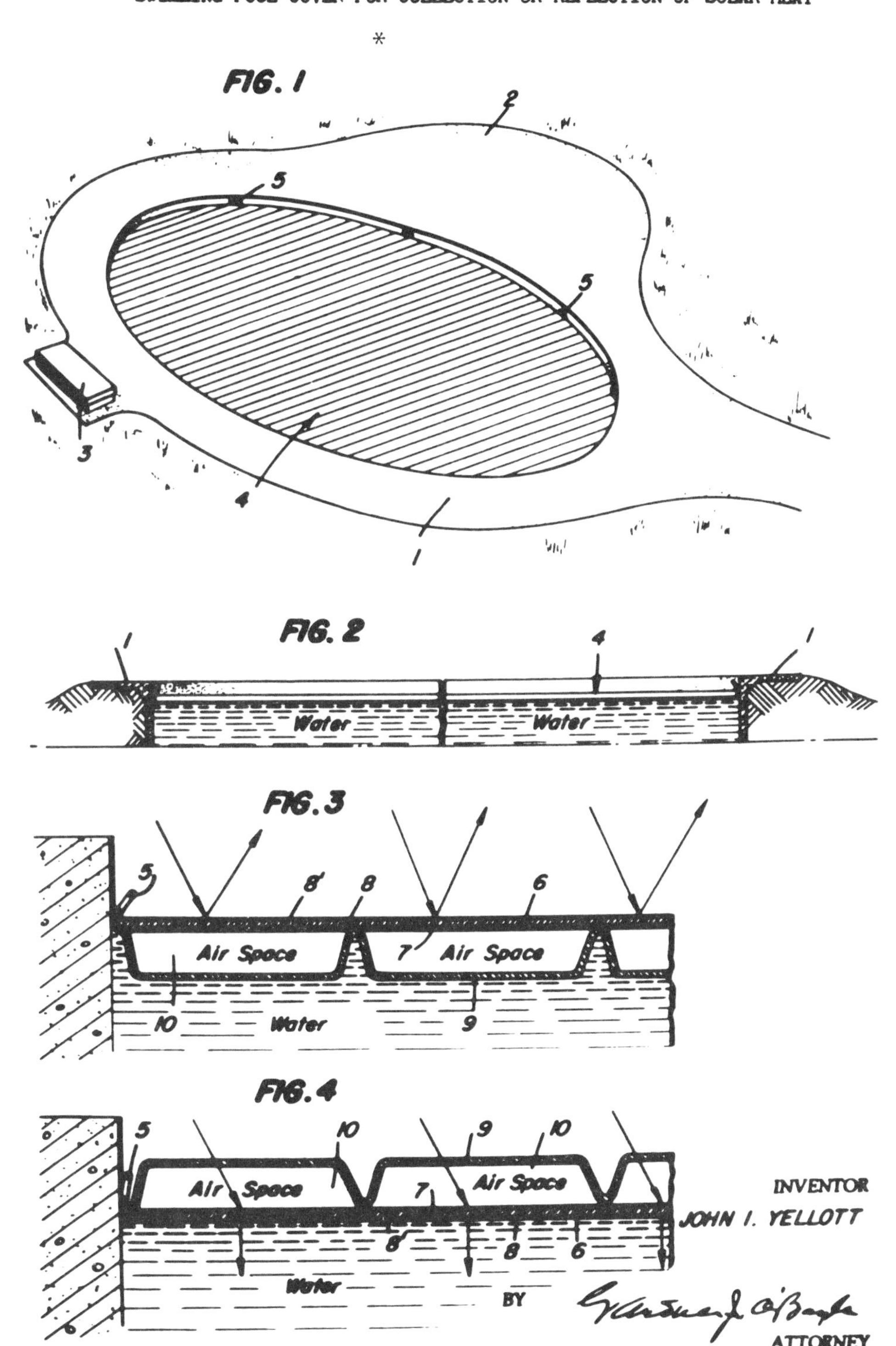
Jan. 15, 1963
J. I. YELLOTT
3,072,920
SWIMMING POOL COVER FOR COLLECTION OR REFLECTION OF SOLAR HEAT
FIG. 1
FIG. 2
Water
FIG. 3
Air Space
Water
FIG. 4
Air Space
Water
INVENTOR
JOHN I. YELLOTT
BY
ATTORNEY

3,072,920
SWIMMING POOL COVER FOR COLLECTION OR REFLECTION OF SOLAR HEAT
John I. Yellott, 901 W. El Caminato, Phoenix, Ariz.

*

This invention relates to covers for relatively small bodies of water, and more particularly to a cover for an outdoor swimming pool.

In accordance with the present invention, the improved cover arrangement is in the form of a pneumatic mattress, of substantially the same area as the surface of the water in the pool, and adapted to float thereon. The mattress comprises, essentially, a sheet of plastic material, particularly adapted to resist deterioration because of weather, and an over-layer of thin transparent plastic attached to one face of the sheet, the over-layer being folded at spaced intervals intermediate of its peripheral edge and heat sealed or otherwise secured to the sheet, whereby to form a plurality of pockets adapted to be filled with air. The exposed surface of the plastic sheet may be covered by a reflective surface, such as a thin layer of aluminum, and the opposite face of the sheet is covered by a dark-colored material, particularly adapted for the absorption of solar energy. The pocketed over-layer is of a thin transparent plastic of the type which is substantially completely transparent to solar rays, but is relatively opaque to the long waves which are radiated by low temperature surfaces.

In the summer, when it is desired to keep the pool both clean and cool, the mattress will be turned so that the dark, absorptive surface is down, facing the water and floating thereon, with the aluminized surface facing the sky, to reflect the sun's radiant energy therefrom, thus keeping the water in the pool relatively cool. Since the reflectance of the aluminized layer is so high that at least 90% of the incident heat is reflected, instead of being absorbed in the pool, and by reason of insulating air space between the upper layer and the water, the cover effectively maintains the temperature of the pool comfortably and pleasantly low.

In the winter, when it is desired to heat the pool, and also prevent dirt, dust and other foreign material from getting into the water, the cover is reversed so that its dark, upper absorptive surface is exposed to the solar energy. The transparent plastic over-layer acts as a heat trap, since the sun's rays pass through the over-layer and are absorbed by the dark surface of the plastic sheet. This surface, when exposed to intense solar radiation, is heated to a temperature which can readily approach 90 to 100 degrees, and the surface then re-radiates, but at a very long wave length. Accordingly, the material constituting the transparent over-layer will be selected so that it is relatively opaque to such rays, and thereby brings about the "green house" effect.

An object of my invention is to provide an improved cover for swimming pools and other bodies of water of relatively small area.

Another object of my invention is to provide an improved swimming pool cover designed for collection or reflection of solar heat.

Yet another object of my invention is to provide an improved cover for outdoor swimming pools adapted to float on the surface of the water in the pool, the cover being constructed and arranged whereby to reflect the sun's radiant energy and thus keep the water relatively cool and dark to prevent the growth of algae, or to heat the water by collecting solar heat.

Still another object of my invention is to provide an improved swimming pool cover adapted to prevent evaporation of water from the surface of the pool.

A still further object of my invention is to provide an improved swimming pool cover adapted for use in conjunction with solar heating apparatus.

Yet a still further object of my invention is to provide an improved swimming pool cover which is strong and rugged in construction, impervious to water, unaffected by the ultra-violet constituent of solar radiation, or by the oxygen of the atmosphere. *

In order to make my invention more clearly understood, I have shown in the accompanying drawings means for carrying the same into practical effect, without limiting the improvements in their useful applications to the particular constructions, which for the purpose of explanation, have been made the subject of illustration.

In the drawings:

FIGURE 1 is a perspective view of a swimming pool, showing a cover floating on the surface of the water in the pool;

FIG. 2 is a cross sectional view of the pool of FIG. 1;

FIG. 3 is an enlarged sectional view along a portion of the major axis of the cover of FIG. 1, showing the reflective surface of the cover exposed to the solar energy; and

FIG. 4 is a view similar to FIG. 3, showing the cover in the inverted positon, with its absorptive surface exposed to solar energy.

Referring to the drawings, and more particularly to FIG. 1, there is shown an oval shaped pool, surrounded by a conventional concrete deck 1, including an apron or extension, designed to accommodate a support for a diving board, deck or lounging chairs, tables and other accessories, normally provided with an outdoor swimming pool. The pool itself is elevated above the surrounding lawn or terrain so that irrigation water will not be able to enter and contaminate the water in the pool, and at one side of the pool there is provided a small box-like structure 3, adapted to house a re-circulating pump, filter, and other equipment needed to keep the pool clean. The cover member of the present invention, designated generally by numeral 4, is of the same general configuration as the pool, and of substantially the same area as the surface of the water upon which it is adapted to float. Suitable handles, comprising flexible loop members 5, are attached to the cover at spaced intervals in the vicinity of the peripheral edge thereof, whereby the cover may be removed from the pool for the purpose of storing the same, or it may be lifted and inverted, for purposes to be described more fully hereinafter.

Referring to FIG. 3, the cover member 4, which is in the nature of a pneumatic mattress, comprises a sheet of plastic material 6, having its bottom surface covered with a layer of dark-colored material 7, particularly adapted for the absorption of solar energy, and having its upper surface covered by a reflective surface 8, such as a very thin layer of aluminum, said reflective surface being protected from the water by means of a laminated overlay 8' of transparent, water and weather resistant, thin plastic film. An over-layer of thin transparent plastic material 9 is attached to the marginal edge of the plastic sheet 6, as by heat sealing, portions of the material 9 being folded at spaced intervals, as shown, and secured along the fold lines to sheet 6 by heat sealing or other means, to form a plurality of air-filled compartments or pockets 10, whereby to increase the buoyancy of the cover.

As indicated hereinbefore, the plastic over-layer 9 is of a type which is almost completely transparent to solar rays, but is relatively opaque to long waves which are radiated by low-temperature surfaces. There are several materials presently available which are completely impervious to water, which is an essential characteristic for the environment in which the material is used, and these materials are also unaffected by the ultraviolet constituent of solar radiation or by the oxygen of the atmosphere, and are inert with respect to the small concentration of chlorine maintained in some swimming pools to prevent the growth of algae. In this connection, the dark surface 7 of the cover, which is adapted for the absorption of solar energy, also insures the shutting off of light from the pool, which in turn will control the growth of algae, which is another important feature of the present invention.

There are several commercially available materials, having the properties referred to above, produced by the Du Pont Company under the trade names "Teslar," a polyvinyl fluoride; and "Mylar," a polyethylene terephthalate. The properties of these materials are described in an article by Frank Edlin of the Du Pont Company, which article appears in the April 1958 issue of Solar Energy, vol. 2, No. 2.

In the summer, the cover is permitted to remain on the pool when the pool is not in use. The aluminized layer reflects the sun's heat, and keeps the water relatively cool. It also prevents evaporation of the water, which is an important feature, for the reason that evaporation brings about or is the cause of a number of undesirable conditions, including (*a*) loss of water, with need for make-up and (*b*) increase of hardness of the water, since the substances dissolved therein, which constitute hardness, do not leave when the surface water evaporates, and thereby build up throughout the summer until it becomes necessary to empty the pool, with the attendant cost and waste of water.

The conventional method of cooling swimming pools in the summer is by spraying some of the water into the air, thus bringing about evaporative cooling. By reason of the high reflectance of the aluminized layer of the cover of the present invention, whereby at least 90% of the incident heat is reflected, rather than being absorbed in the pool, in conjunction with the insulating air space between the upper layer and the water, the cover will maintain the temperature of the pool comfortably low.

In the winter, when it is desired to heat the pool, as well as to keep it covered to prevent dirt or dust from getting into the water, the cover is inverted so that its dark, upper absorptive surface 7 is exposed to the solar energy. The transparent plastic over-layer 9 acts as a heat trap, since the sun's rays pass through the over-layer, to be absorbed by the dark surface.

An important effect accomplished by the cover is the prevention of evaporation from the surface of the pool. In areas where the relative humidity is low, the loss of heat occurs in three ways. About half of the heat is lost by evaporation, another 30% by radiation, and about 20% by convection. The use of the cover will eliminate the evaporation, considerably reduce the radiation, and also, because of the insulating effect of the dead air space between the two layers, loss by convection will be minimized.

While the cover has been described with air spaces or pockets defined by and between the plastic sheets or films, the invention comprehends the use of a suitable absorbent material in each of the pockets. The cover will then be in the form of a quilted black material between the plastic film layers. In this embodiment of the invention, the aluminum foil or coating will be applied to the under surface of sheet 6, instead of on its top surface, as shown in FIG. 4, thus protecting the foil from the water. The bottom and top sheets or films may be of transparent "Teslar" or "Mylar," and the spaces between the films may be filled with black wool such as "Dacron," a polyester fiber.

The operation of the modified cover is the same as the first described embodiment of the invention. For winter operation, the cover will float on the water, and effectively stop evaporation. It will also minimize radiation and convection heat loss, and will reduce the total heat loss to approximately ⅓ of the amount experienced by an uncovered pool. During the day, sunlight will pass through the transparent upper film or sheet, and heat the black filler material. This heat will be transmitted through the lower film, and into the water surface, the normal circulation in the pool being sufficient to mix the water to a point where a reasonably uniform temperature will prevail throughout the pool. For summer use the cover is inverted, so that the foil-clad sheet faces the sun. The aluminum foil reflects a large percentage of the sunlight, thereby minimizing the heat input to the pool. In addition, the insulating filling of "Dacron" will help to reduce the inflow of heat from the surrounding air into the pool.

It is intended that the cover will be used in conjunction with solar heating apparatus, the size of which can be reduced approximately 50% because of the heat-conserving action of the cover. Additionally, it is contemplated that the cover will be used with irrigation canals to prevent evaporation of water.

When the pool is not symmetrical, so that the cover may not simply be reversed or inverted, it may be formed of several segments arranged in such manner that the entire surface of the pool is covered. *

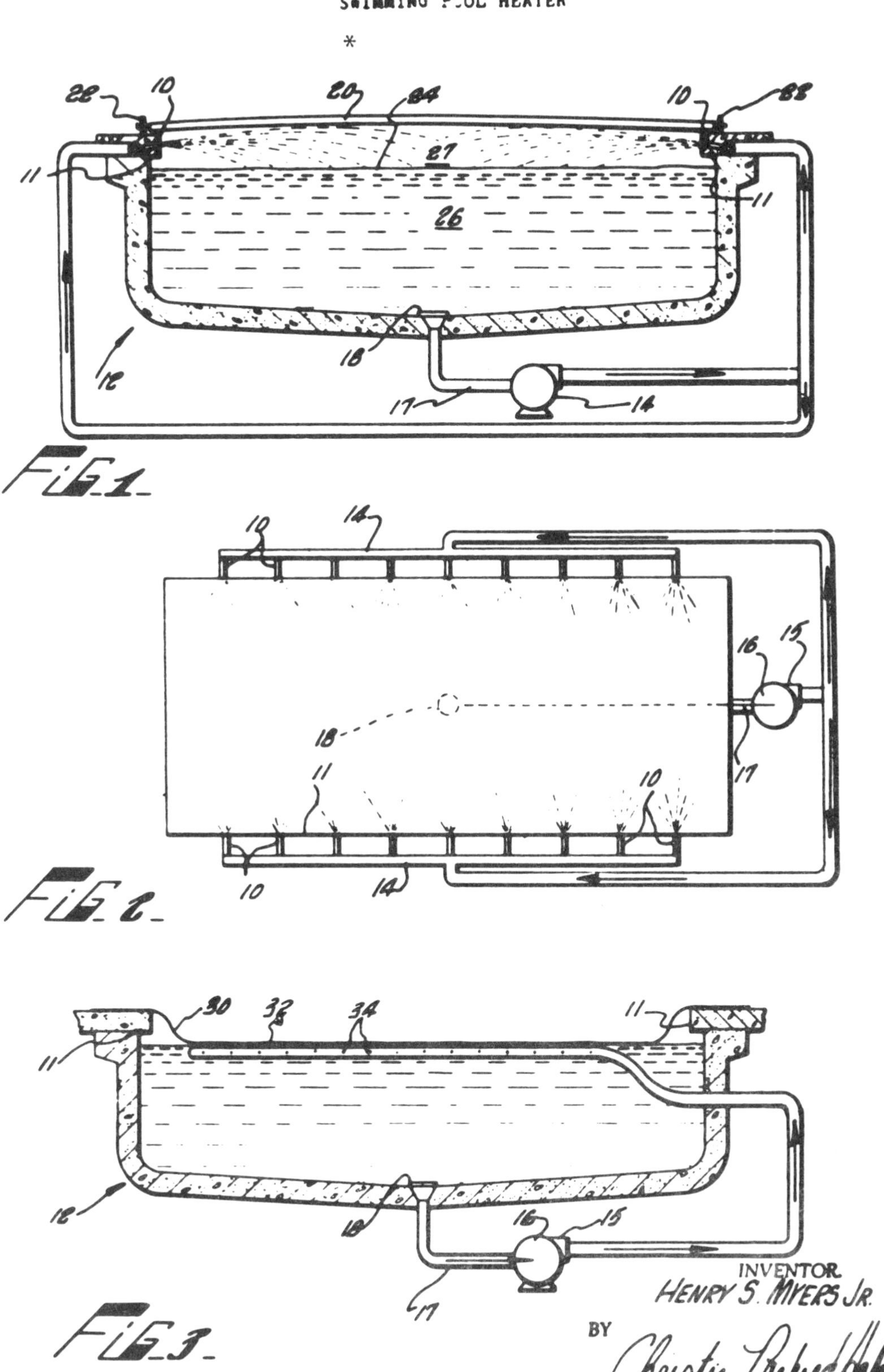
Nov. 19, 1968
H. S MYERS, JR
3,411,163
SWIMMING POOL HEATER
FIG. 1
FIG. 2
FIG. 3
INVENTOR
HENRY S. MYERS JR.
BY
ATTORNEYS

3,411,163
SWIMMING POOL HEATER
Henry S. Myers, Jr., 3695 Denair,
Pasadena, Calif. 91107
*

This invention relates to solar heaters for swimming pools.

Many attempts have been made to heat swimming pools with solar radiation, with varying degrees of success.

A typical solar heater for swimming pools utilizes a number of tubes or ducts normally attached to some type of extended surfaces or fins to form a solar panel. Normally, the solar panel is mounted on a roof, either horizontally or slightly inclined toward the sun. Water from the pool is circulated through the ducts in the solar panel and then returned to the pool.

Several problems have held back the acceptance of solar swimming pool heaters. First, most units have been somewhat unsightly. With many roof designs, it is not possible to hide the unit from view conveniently. In addition, solar heaters of a reasonable size do not have enough capacity to maintain a comfortable water temperature unless the pool is covered at night and in bad weather. Most pool owners do not want to bother with a manual cover, and automatic pool covers have been cumbersome, unsightly, and expensive.

The location of the solar panel some distance from the pool has the disadvantage of adding pressure drop to the circulating system. Moreover, such panels are normally allowed to become relatively hot with the thought that water circulating through them will be hotter and thus warm the pool more when it is returned. This type of heater is inefficient because the high temperature of the panel causes a considerable portion of the solar heat to be lost by radiation and convection to the sky and the surrounding air instead of being absorbed by the water in the pool.

This invention provides a swimming pool solar heater with improved efficiency and appearance.

The heater of this invention uses the swimming pool cover itself as the absorber of solar radiation. For maximum efficiency, the top surface of the cover is black. Water in the pool is circulated against the bottom of the cover to extract heat from it and reduce the temperature of the cover to decrease the loss of heat from the cover.

In one form of the invention, the cover is placed on the pool in contact with the water surface and water in the pool is circulated against the bottom side of the cover. The conventional circulating equipment can be used for this purpose. However, it is preferable to add a perforated distributor hose or conduit near the top of the pool. Water is taken from a lower portion of the pool and circulated through the distributor and the perforations to agitate the layer of water in contact with the bottom of the cover over a substantial surface area. This agitation enhances the heat transfer from the cover to the pool water and keeps the cover relatively cool to minimize the loss of heat from its upper surface.

In the presently-preferred embodiment of the heater, the cover is spaced above the pool and a plurality of nozzles direct a spray of water against the bottom of the cover over a wide area. The water strikes the bottom of the cover, is warmed, and falls into the pool. A pump circulates cooler water from a lower portion of the pool back to the nozzles for contact with the warmer bottom of the pool cover. During the hours of darkness, the water is not circulated against the bottom of the cover to minimize heat transfer from the pool to the cover, which tends to radiate heat to the sky. The advantage of having the cover spaced above the water surface is that it reduces transfer of heat from the water to the cover during the hours of darkness.

The efficiency of the heater of this invention is relatively high because it is operated at a low temperature level to reduce heat loss by radiation and convection. The cover further minimizes heat loss by preventing evaporation of water from the pool.

These and other aspects of the invention will be more fully understood from the following detailed description and the accompanying drawings, in which:

FIG. 1 is a schematic sectional elevation of the presently-preferred embodiment of the heater mounted on a swimming pool;

FIG. 2 is a plan view of the heater shown in FIG. 1; and

FIG. 3 is a schematic sectional elevation of an alternate embodiment of the heater in which the cover is in direct contact with the surface of the water in the pool.

Referring to FIG. 1, a plurality of nozzles **10** mounted along the sides **11** of a swimming pool **12** receive water from a manifold **14** connected to the discharge **15** of a circulating pump **16**. The pump can be of the conventional type normally used with swimming pools, and its suction or inlet **17** is connected to the drain **18** of the swimming pool. The filtering system for the water is normally included at the pump discharge but is not shown because it forms no part of this invention. For certain types of covers, such as hinged rather than rolling designs, or for installations on existing pools, it may be preferable to mount the nozzles integral with the cover rather than in the deck. A swivel or removable connection or a flexible hose to the pump discharge line would then be required.

Each of the nozzles opens toward the center of the pool to direct a spray of water against the bottom of a cover **20** disposed over the pool and supported on rollers **22** adapted to ride along the sides of the pool so the cover can be easily removed when desired. The mechanical means of removing the cover is not important to the invention. Rollers are merely one technique.

As shown best in FIG. 1, the cover is disposed above the surface **24** of a pool of water **26** to leave an air space **27** between the water and the bottom of the cover.

In operating the solar heater shown in FIGS. 1 and 2, the cover is rolled into position over the pool surface, and the circulating pump is turned on to direct a spray of water from the nozzles against the bottom of the cover. Radiation from the sun tends to heat the cover. However, the spray of water directed against the bottom of the cover removes heat almost as fast as it is received from the sun. Consequently, the temperature of the cover is only slightly above that of the water, and, therefore, there is a minimum amount of heat radiated by the cover toward the sky. When the sun is not shining on the cover, the circulating pump is turned off or flow is by-passed around the nozzles and through the normal return line so that no water is sprayed against the bottom side of the cover. The air space between the cover and the surface of the pool acts as an insulator to minimize the heat transfer from the pool to the cover which tends to radiate heat away from the pool. If desired, the bottom surface of the cover is silvered so that it reflects heat from the pool and minimizes heat loss. The cover further decreases heat loss by reducing evaporation of water from the pool.

In the arrangement shown in FIG. 3, a cover **30**, which may be a thin plastic sheet, is supported at its edges on the sides **11** of the swimming pool **12** and rests on a buoyant distributor hose **32** floating on the surface of the water and connected at one end to the outlet **15** of the circulating pump **16**. A plurality of holes **34** along the buoyant hose distribute streams of water over the surface of the pool and agitate the water in contact with the underside of the cover 30. With the heater shown in FIG. 3, water is circulated from the drain, through the circulating pump, into the buoyant hose, out the holes 34, and against the bottom of the cover to remove heat from the cover almost as fast as it is received from the sun. At night, the circulation of water is stopped to minimize heat loss due to radiation from the cover toward the sky. The disadvantage of the apparatus shown in FIG. 3 is that the cover is in direct contact with the water so that there is better heat transfer at night and, consequently, more heat is lost than with the arrangement shown in FIGS. 1 and 2. However, even with an apparatus similar to that shown in FIG. 3, I have found that a normal size residential swimming pool can gain about 100,000 B.t.u.'s per hour on a typical sunny day during the fall in Southern California. A heater of the type shown in FIG. 3 raised the temperature of an unheated pool from the range of 58–63° F. to 77–82° F., or an average temperature increase of about 19° F. *

July 8, 1969 H. M. HEDGES 3,453,666

SOLAR THERMAL BLANKET

*

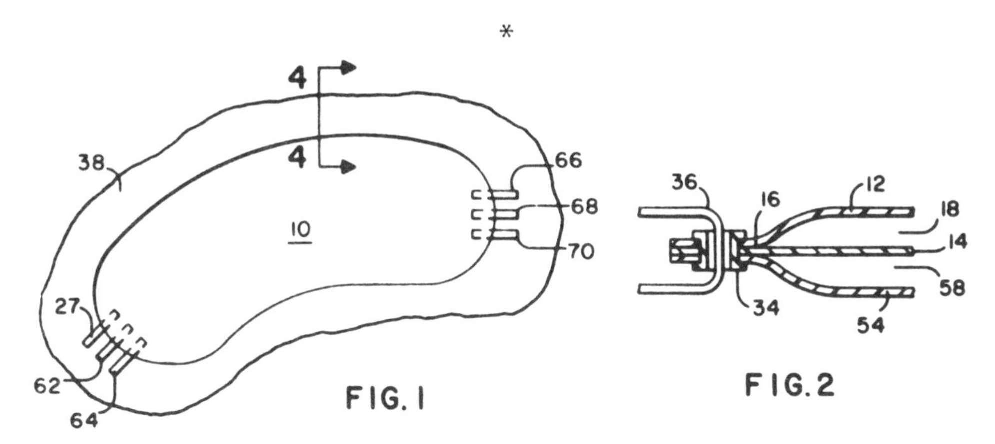

FIG. 1

FIG. 2

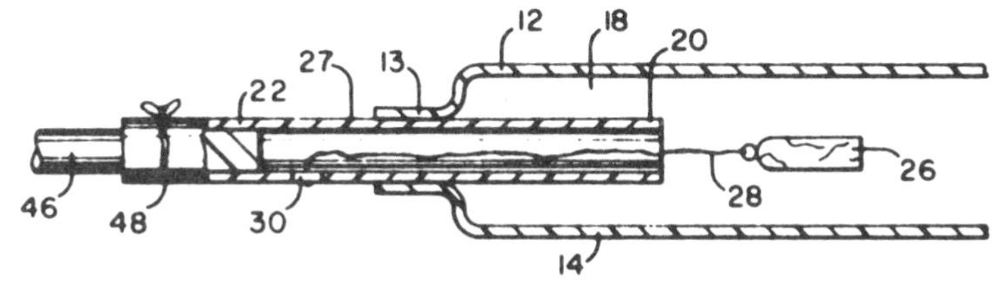

FIG. 3

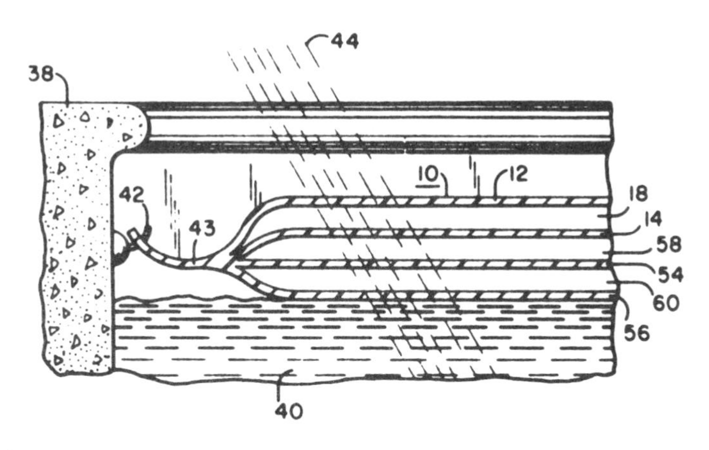

FIG. 4

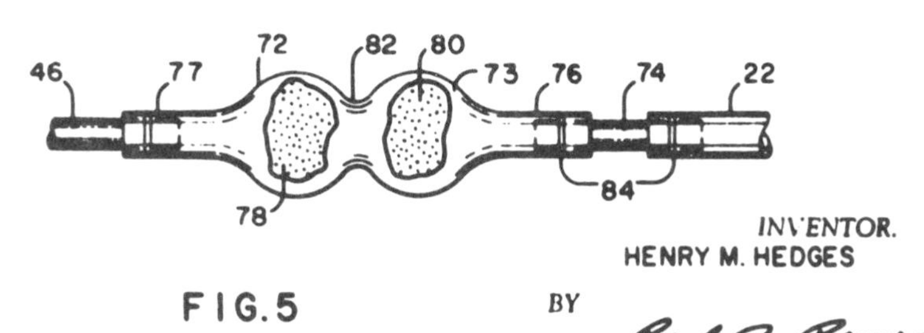

FIG. 5

INVENTOR.
HENRY M. HEDGES

BY

ATTORNEY

3,453,666
SOLAR THERMAL BLANKET
Henry M. Hedges, 1415 Plum St.,
San Diego, Calif. 92106

ABSTRACT OF THE DISCLOSURE

A blanket, useful as a swimming pool cover, formed from a substantially transparent, flexible material, such as a suitable plastic, so that the sun's rays can penetrate the blanket and heat water therebeneath. The blanket includes at least one air chamber having the same width and length as the blanket, which is filled with air to provide an effective insulating quality to the blanket. When the blanket is laid upon the surface of water in a swimming pool, the sun heats the water beneath the blanket and the air-filled blanket restricts transfer of heat from the covered water to the air. Multiple air chambers can be provided one atop another, and the number of such chambers that are inflated controls the amount of heat that escapes from the water to the air.

BACKGROUND OF THE INVENTION

Swimming pools are expensive to heat because of the large volume of water involved and the loss of heat or B.t.u.'s to the air above the water. Yet the use of swimming pools are greatly increased where the water is heated, because many people desire to swim in water having a higher temperature than the water can be heated by the sun considering heat loss to the surrounding air. Even in warmer climates where the sun heats the water to a desirable temperature during the daytime, the water cools during the night to an undesirable temperature when the ambient temperature drops. In colder climates, the temperature of the water is not appreciably increased even during the daytime because of the constant loss of heat to the colder air. Thus conventional heating equipment is required to maintain a suitable water temperature if there is to be optimum use of a pool and such equipment is costly to install and expensive to operate.

SUMMARY OF THE INVENTION

The present invention provides a simple and relatively inexpensive device for effectively heating the water in a swimming pool, without having to install and operate expensive heating systems or where such heating systems have been installed, to reduce the cost of their operation while maintaining a desired water temperature. Also the invention, when installed, protects the pool from dirt, leaves and the like entering the water and protects the pool from unauthorized use.

The preferred embodiments of the present invention take the form of a solar thermal blanket formed completely of transparent, flexible, waterproof material. The blanket contains at least one air chamber with a simple inflating connection that can be readily attached to any source of air such as a vacuum cleaner, hair dryer, etc. The sun's rays penetrate the transparent blanket and heat the water beneath the blanket, and the air filled blanket retains the heat below it.

Therefore it is an object of this invention to provide a new and improved solar thermal blanket formed entirely of a flexible, transparent, water-proof material, adapted to transmit heat from the sun to a body of water therebeneath, the blaanket including at least one air chamber throughout its length and width to serve as a heat conduction insulator.

It is another object of this invention to provide a new and improved solar thermal blanket which includes means to quickly and easily introduce air into the chamber from a variety of air sources, and quickly and easily exhaust air from the chamber, said means being readily stored within the confines of the blanket when the blanket is in use.

It is a further object of the present invention to provide a new and improved solar thermal blanket including a simple structure for easily controlling and varying its heat insulation qualities.

It is another object of the present invention to provide a new and improved solar thermal blanket that functions as a swimming pool cover and which is simple and inexpensive to make and is easy to store and use.

Further objects and advantages of the present invention will readily occur to one skilled in the art to which the invention pertains upon reference to the accompanying detailed description.

FIGURE 1 is a top plan view of a swimming pool with an embodiment of the solar thermal blanket lying in place on the surface of the water.

FIGURE 2 is a fragmentary section of the solar thermal blanket showing the sealed edge of the blanket and a blanket tie.

FIGURE 3 is a fragmentary elevation, partly in section, depicting the blanket air chamber access tube with a dehydrator cartridge affixed to the tube and extending into the internal air chamber.

FIGURE 4 is a cross-sectional view taken along lines 4—4 of FIGURE 1.

FIGURE 5 is a fragmentary eleventon, partly in section, of an embodiment of a dehydrator for use in the invention.

Referring to FIGURES 1 through 4, the embodiment of the invention includes a blanket indicated generally by the number 10. This blanket is used in the present instance as a swimming pool cover that is substantially the same size as the water surface area of the pool with which it is to be used, such as defined by the edge of pool 38. The blanket is formed of a plurality of sheets, see FIGURES 2 and 4, of transparent material such as polyethylene, polyvinyl chloride or other suitable materials. The sheets are sealed along their edge portions 13, 16 and 43 to form one or a plurality of sealed, internal chambers 18, 60 and 58. A satisfactory construction utilizes transparent sheets that are .002 to .005 inch thick and that form internal chambers that may be approximately three-quarters of an inch in height when inflated. The maximum inflated height or width of the chambers will be as desired, however too large a height can permit convection currents within the chamber that reduces its beneficial purpose.

The blanket 10 has a plurality of access inflating and deflating tubes for inflating and deflating the chambers in the blanket. As illustrated in FIGURE 1, tubes 27, 62 and 64 connect at one end to the respective chambers 18, 58 and 60 and tubes 66, 68 and 70 are connected at the other end of the respective chambers 18, 58 and 60. As will be more apparent hereinafter, each chamber need only have one inflating and deflating tube, and a plurality of tubes is merely more convenient. It should also be recognized that the blanket may have one or a plurality of chambers, however it has been found that three chambers provide the optimum conditions for light transmittal therethrough and insulation against heat transfer through the blanket from the water to the ambient air.

Referring to FIGURE 3, there is illustrated a single chamber having sheets 12 and 14 and an access tube 27. The access tube 27 is sealed 13 around its entire circumference between the top sheet 12 and bottom sheet 14 at the edge of the blanket. The access tube 27 is large enough to insert a person's hand therethrough and preferably is approximately six inches wide. It is formed of a similar material as the blanket and extends about two feet outside the blanket to form an external tube portion 22 and about two feet into the chamber 18 to form an internal tube portion 24. The flexible external portion 22 of the access tube 27 is readily attachable to outlets of various air sources for inflating the chamber 18. A vacuum cleaner in blowing condition with a hose outlet 46 in one example. The hose outlet 46 fits inside the end 22, and an air seal is accomplished by tying a line 48 around end 22 or fitting a rubber band over the end 22.

It is desirable to keep the air in chamber 18 dry. In the embodiment of FIGURE 3, this is accomplished by use of a moisture absorbing means such as a cartridge of silica gel 26. The cartridge 26 is secured to one end of line 28. The other end of line 28 is secured to attachment 30 that is secured to the external tube portion 22. Thus the cartridge 26 is inserted into the chamber and left there to absorb moisture from the air in the chamber. The cartridges 26 can be removed as desired by reaching into the access tubes, grasping line 28 and retrieving the cartridge.

OPERATION

The blanket 10, when not in use, is normally deflated and folded into a lightweight compact package for storage. When put to use, the blanket 10 is unfolded and the external tube portions 22 of access tubes 27, 62 and 64 are attached to a suitable source of air such as the vacuum cleaner hose 46 shown in FIGURE 3, and are held in position by the rubber band or elastic cord 48. The blanket is then inflated, and when the chamber 18 contains sufficient air, the external tube portions 22 are removed from the vacuum cleaner hose 46 and closed off by the rubber bands or elastic cords 48. The outer tube portions 22 are then tucked into the inner tube portions 20.

Additionally to prevent the condensing of moisture from the air pumped into the chambers, the air inserted into the chambers can be dried by passing the air through a dehydrator. Referring to FIGURE 5, a container that may be made of plastic or other suitable material has open tube ends 76 and 77 and a pair of enlarged portions 72 and 73 with a reduced diameter or constriction 82 therebetween. Coarse silica gel cartridges may be contained in one of the enlarged portions, as for example 78, and another suitable dehydrating substance 80 may be contained in the other enlarger portion 73. The tube end 77 is connected by a sealed connection to the end 46 of an air source and the other tube end 76 is connected to a more rigid tube 74 to the end 22 of access tube 27. Rubber bands 84, as for example, may be used to seal and hold the connections. In operation the air passes from the air source through hose 46, dehydrating material 78 and 80 and through tube portion 22 to the chamber of the blanket 10.

The inflated blanket is buoyant and floats in position on the surface of the water. Since the blanket is transparent, the usual attractive blue color of the pool water shows through the cover. The blanket 10 is fixed in place by tying the straps 36 to the retainers (not shown) along the pool walkway or by hooking the grommets 34 over the hook members 42. The inflated blanket prevents people, particularly small children, from falling into the water with the resultant possibility of drowning. It also keeps the pool clean because it form a protective covering.

During hours of sunshine, the sun's rays 44 penetrate the completely transparent blanket and heat the water beneath the blanket. Since the air within the blanket is heated, there is also conduction heating of the water which lies adjacent the blanket. The blanket provides a good insulating cover to hold the heat in the water of the pool. Thus, the blanket can be placed over the water surface during the day, and the water will be warm and suitable for swimming. At night the blanket prevents excessive heat loss to the colder ambient air.

When it is desired to remove the blanket from the pool, the straps 36 are loosened from the retainers (not shown) or the grommets are lifted off the hook members 42, and at least a portion of the blanket 10 is moved onto the walkway beside the pool. The external tube portion 22 is removed from the tucked in position and the rubber band or elastic cord 48 is removed. The user's hand is then inserted through the external tube portion 22, and through the internal tube portion 20. The internal tube portion is grasped with the hand and pulled out through the external tube portion 22. The air can now be effectively removed from blanket chambers 18, 58 and 60. If the blanket chambers are moist and the silica gel cartridge 26 is saturated, then the line 28 is pulled out of the access tubes 22 or 62 or 64. The cartridge is removed from the line 28 and dried in a suitable place such as the kitchen oven.

The air may be removed from the blanket in any suitable manner and the access tubes at each end of the blanket facilitate such air removal. However, it should be understood that only one access tube is necessary for inflating or removing inflating air from each chamber. Also the access tube illustrated in FIGURE 3 is the same construction used for all the access tubes 27, 62, 64, 66, 68 and 70.

FIGURE 4 illustrates three chambers 18, 58 and 60 forming one blanket 10. The chambers are disposed one atop another. Separate inflating means, such as the access tubes 27, 62 and 64 are provided for each chamber. This construction provides a greater insulation against heat escaping from the pool water than does two chambers or a single chamber. Further one or more of the chambers can be selectively not inflated or only partially inflated to provide less insulation. This provides a control for maintaining the water at selectively lower temperatures. Thus, a simple means is provided for controlling the heat maintained in the water. *

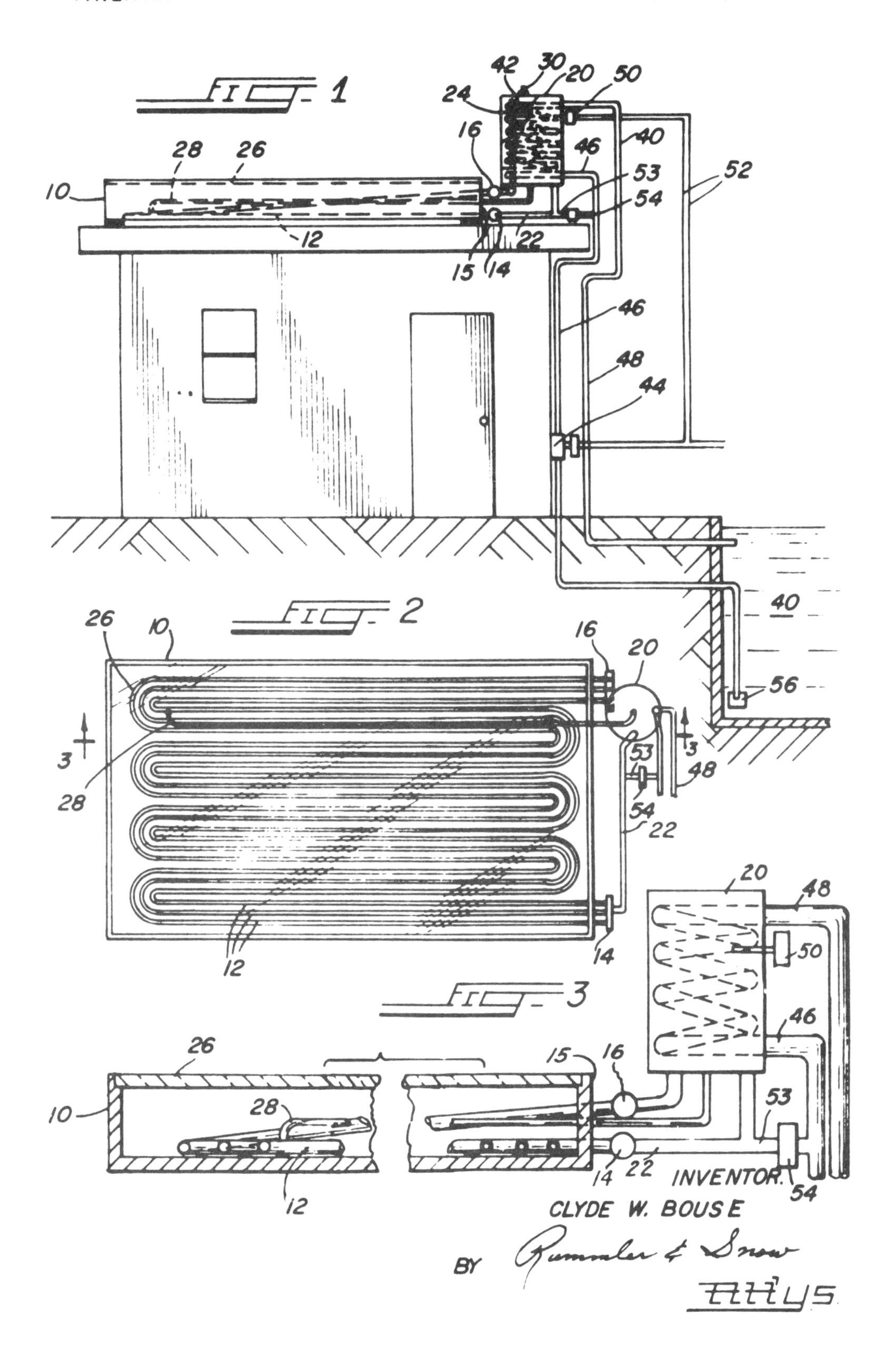
PATENTED AUG 17 1971
3,599,626
FIG. 1
FIG. 2
FIG. 3
INVENTOR.
CLYDE W. BOUSE
BY Rummler & Snow
Attys

*
ABSTRACT: A closed circuit solar water heater in which a sun heated fluid is gravitationally circulated to and from a heat exchanger and control unit in the form of a tanklike receptacle for heating an independent water system circulating through a pipe coil within the said receptacle, the solar heater including coils of copper tubes leading from the bottom of the heat exchanger and control unit and disposed to be heated by sun rays, the said coils receiving the fluid to be heated and then returning the heated fluid into the heat exchanger and control unit near the top thereof for gravitational circulation therethrough, and pump means controlled by the control unit for causing flow of water through the said independent water system and operable only when the temperature of the sun heated fluid in the control unit is above a predetermined level.

SOLAR HEATER FOR SWIM POOLS

BACKGROUND OF THE INVENTION

This invention pertains to solar water heaters and particularly to such devices adapted to supply heat derived from solar energy however, the swim pools and other water reservoir systems wherein an independent and automatically operating heat source may be desired. Many systems have been devised for absorbing the heat of solar radiation and automatically transferring that heat to water or other suitable heat storage fluid and in due to useless the apparatus involved comprises a coil of suitable heat absorbing tubing through which the fluid to be heated by solar radiation is caused to flow in heat exchange relation with the tubing, the tubing being disposed in such a manner as to be heated by both direct and reflected sun rays. Numerous solar heating systems have been proposed and used for heating the water of swim pools and other water storage reservoirs, either as a primary or supplemental heat source. In such systems, however, the pool or reservoir water is positively circulated through the solar heater at a substantially constant rate, regardless of the amount of solar energy available to the heater, with the result that operation of the system is often quite inefficient due to useless pump operation and circulation of unheated water from the heater to the pool or reservoir.

SUMMARY OF THE INVENTION

The present invention seeks to over come the aforesaid difficulty by providing a solar heating system in which the fluid circulating through the solar heater is wholly independent of the water of the pool or storage reservoir and moves in a closed circuit between the sun heated coils and a heat exchanging control unit automatically and continuously as long as the coils are heated by the sun, such circulation being at a rate directly related to the intensity of the sun rays affecting the heater coils. In this system the pool or reservoir water is circulated independently through the heat exchanger control unit by means of a pump which is under automatic control by the control unit to operate only when the temperature of the control unit is above a predetermined figure.

The control unit is a closed hollow receptacle positioned immediately above the solar heater coils and from which the fluid to be sun heated flows gravitationally into the heater coils and thence back to the control unit where it is delivered close to the top of the unit. The water from the pool or storage reservoir passes through the control unit by way of a heat conducting coil entering the control unit near its bottom and leaving adjacent its top. This coil serves as the heat exchanger of transfer means between the sun heated fluid in the control unit and the water of the pool or storage reservoir and thermostatically responsive means is provided in the control unit for controlling the pump and regulating the flow of the water to which the sun heat is to be transferred.

Thus, an essential concept of the present invention is to provide separate and independent flow systems for the solar heated fluid and the water of the main pool or reservoir to which the solar heat is to be delivered and to cause a heat transfer from the one system to the other only when the temperature of the solar heated fluid is above a predetermined level.

BRIEF DESCRIPTION OF THE DRAWINGS

A specific embodiment of this invention is shown in the accompanying drawing in which:

FIG. 1 is an elevational view showing the improved solar heater mounted on the roof of a swim pool equipment house and arranged for heating the pool water;

FIG. 2 is a plan view of the solar heater showing an arrangement of the coils for the fluid to be heated; and

FIG. 3 is an enlarged elevational view of the solar heater as taken on the line 3–3 of FIG. 2.

DESCRIPTION OF THE PREFERRED EMBODIMENT

As shown in the drawings, my improved solar heater, as arranged for heating the water of a swim pool, comprises a flat bottomed pan 10 across which coils of heat conductive tubing 12 are sinuously arranged for direct exposure to sun rays, each coil comprising a single tube running from a delivery manifold 14 at one side of one end 15 of the pan 10 and extending back and forth in serpentine loops over the bottom of the pan to a discharge manifold 16 at the opposite side of the said one end 15 of the pan. In the form shown, three coils are provided and the tubes thereof are disposed side-by-side on the bottom of the pan, to which they are preferably spot soldered, extending substantially the length of the pan in parallel sets connected by 180° bends at alternate ends so that each tube provides an uninterrupted passage from manifold to manifold. All of the tube sets are in a common plane except the last, which terminates at the discharge manifold 16. This last set of three tubes is arranged to rise progressively from the bottom of the pan 10 adjacent one end of the discharge manifold 16 at the opposite end, so that the outlet end of the coils is at a higher level than the inlet end.

The manifolds 14 and 16 are connected directly to a control unit 20 which comprises a closed tanklike receptacle, of about 10 gallon capacity, located directly above the solar heater pan 10, the manifold 14 being connected into the bottom of the control unit by a pipe 22 and the manifold 16 being connected to a riser pipe 24 which enters the control unit at its bottom and extends to within a short distance of its top. Thus the control unit provides a closed circuit for flow of the fluid that the solar heater is intended to handle.

Preferably the interior of the pan 10 and the tubing therein are coated with a flat black paint to provide for maximum absorption of the solar heat and the top of the pan is covered and sealed by a plate glass panel 26 which is suitably secured so as to be water tight. Thus, when the system is filled with a suitable carrying fluid, for example, water, the sun heat will warm the fluid in the tubes 12 and it will be caused to flow upwardly into the control unit 20 and be replaced by cooler fluid from the bottom of the control unit entering the coils by way of the manifold 14.

In order to equalize the pressure in the system and permit a free circulation of heated fluid from the heater coils 12 to the control unit 20 through the riser pipe 24, a relatively small copper tube 28 is connected between the bottom of the control unit 20 and the heater coils at a point close to where the last set of the coil tubes begins to rise toward the manifold 16. Also, to clear the system of air and assure its being filled with heat carrying fluid, a petcock 30 may be provided in the top of the control unit 20.

The control unit 20 of the solar heater system is the means by which the heat collected by the system is efficiently transferred to an associated system, where its presence is desired.

in the present instance a swimming pool 40, and to effect such heat transfer a coil 42, of heat conducting material such as copper, is housed within the control unit 20. Water from the associate system is forced by a pump 44 to circulate through the coil 42 in the control unit, the water entering at the bottom of the coil 42 through the pipe 46 and leaving at the top of the coil 42 through the return pipe 48. As shown, the pump 44 is located in the supply pipe 46.

Operation of the pump 44, and hence flow of the fluid to be heated on the control unit 20, is automatically controlled by an aquastat 50 located near the upper end of the control unit, but below the outlet end of the riser pipe 24 which delivers the sun heated water to the control unit. This aquastat 50, through the leads 52, turns the pump on and off accordingly to changes in temperature of the sun heated fluid flowing through the control unit. Thus the pump is operated only when sun heated water is supplied to the control unit and whenever the temperature drops below a predetermined level the pump is stopped. Thus circulation of water through the coil 42 occurs only when the fluid in the system of the control unit is sufficiently warm and circulation is automatically stopped when solar heat is not sufficiently available.

In most cases, the heat carrying fluid filling the solar heater system will be water and when water is the fluid of the associated system, as in a swimming pool, a connection 53 containing a pressure regular 54 is provided between the supply line 46, from the pool 40, and the supply pipe 22 leading from the bottom of the control unit 20 to the manifold 14 supplying the coils 12. This connection 53 assures the closed circuit of the solar heater system to be filled with water under a suitable pressure at all times. As shown in FIG. 1, a foot valve 56 is installed in the pool end of the pipe 46 so as to keep the pump 44 primed.

In a typical solar heater system for swim pools, the solar heater may be a pan 5 feet wide and 9 feet long, with depth of 7 inches, made from 16 ounce sheet copper and the heating coils 12 may be of ⅝-inch outside-diameter copper tubing. The last set of coil pipes may then have a rise of 5 inches in 8 feet from the pan bottom to reach the manifold 16. The riser 24 leading from the manifold 16 and the connection 22 leading from the control unit to the manifold 14 may each be of ¾-inch inside-diameter copper tubing; and the pressure equalizing line 28 and the connection 52 between the line 46, from the pool, and the line 22 to the heater manifold 14 may be made of ¼-inch inside-diameter copper tubing. The control unit may be a receptacle of about 10 to 15 gallon capacity made of a good heat conductive material.

In such a solar heater the length of each tube would be about 30 feet when arranged in four sets of tubes, as illustrated in FIG. 2. Thus the relatively small diameter of the fluid stream flowing through each tube, in relation to the area of the tube surface subject to the sun heat, and the division of the total fluid volume passing to and from the control unit into a plurality of narrow streams, results in a very rapid heating of the fluid and a relatively fast flow to and from the control unit. Heater efficiency is thereby greatly enchanced and a relatively small heater area is capable of collecting enough sun heat to warm an average home-size swim pool during daylight hours of sunshine and thereby compensate for heat loss from the pool during the nighttime.

It will be understood that other water storage or reservoir systems may be heated automatically by the herein disclosed solar heater system. For example, in insulated storage tank may be connected to the coil within the control unit 20 and the solar heater could then produce hot water for domestic use. ✳

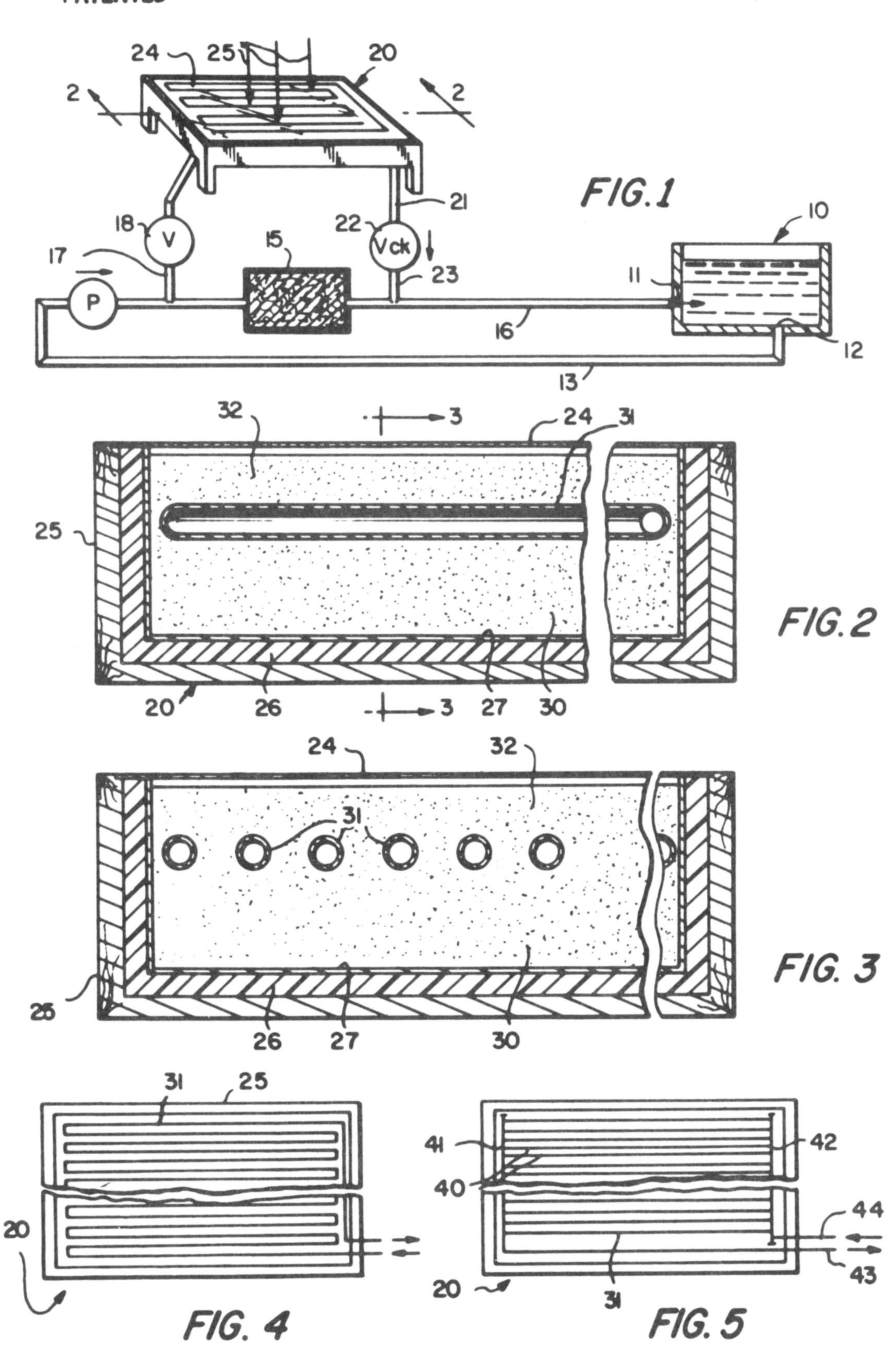
PATENTED JUN 11 1974
3,815,574
FIG.1
FIG.2
FIG. 3
FIG. 4
FIG. 5

SOLAR HEATING SYSTEM

Inventor: George Roy Gaydos, Jr., Rt. 1 P.O. Box 319A, Brandywine, Md. 20613

Appl. No.: 366,148

ABSTRACT

A heating system includes a fluid circuit with a pump and filter for heating water for a pool. A valved bypass circuit includes a heat absorption unit which can be included in the circuit when desired. The heat absorption unit includes a relatively shallow container of thermally nonconductive material such as wood, the interior of which is lined with a layer of foamed polystyrene. The receptacle thus formed is lined on its interior with builder's foil and contains a relatively thick layer of sand in which is buried a continuous array of pipe either in sinuous configuration or, alternatively, a plurality of parallel pipe lengths extending between headers. In either configuration an inlet and outlet connection is provided so that the pump can circulate water through all of the pipe in the absorption unit. The upper exposed surface of the sand in the unit, at least, is covered with a layer of iron oxide. Alternatively, the sand can be omitted and iron oxide can be employed to fill the entire box. Finally, a layer of crystal glass closes the upper surface of the box which is then mounted so as to receive solar radiation.

SOLAR HEATING SYSTEM

This invention relates to an apparatus for efficiently elevating the temperature of water using solar energy.

Man has long recognized that the energy of the Sun represented a vast source of power which, while utilized by many natural processes, has not been effectively harnessed by man for performing mechanical tasks on the surface of the earth. Although several efforts to elevate the temperature of water for evaporation or other purposes have been proposed, none have achieved significant or wide acceptance, possibly because of the relatively low efficiency in the absorption process and the minimal change in water temperature obtainable.

It is an object of the present invention to provide an apparatus capable of elevating the temperature of water to, under proper circumstances, the boiling point, if desired.

Another object is to provide a system including an efficient heat absorption unit for elevating the temperature of water using a solar energy alone.

Yet another object is to provide a system for elevating the temperature of water in a swimming pool.

Briefly described, the system of the present invention includes a body of liquid, the temperature of which is to be elevated, a liquid circulating pump, liquid conducting means for interconnecting the body of liquid and the pump in a closed loop recirculating system, and heat absorption means for receiving the solar radiation, converting it to heat, storing the heat and thereby elevating the temperature of the absorption means and the liquid. The heat absorption means includes a fluid conductor passing through the heat absorption means and coupled to the liquid conducting means to form a part of the recirculating system. The heat absorption means includes a particulate heat absorbing material which substantially surrounds the liquid conductor passing through the heat absorption means, the heat absorbing material having a major surface which is exposed to the solar radiation and which comprises, at least at the major surface, material consisting of black sand which is primarily compounds of iron oxide. The entire body of particulate material can consist of iron oxide, but at least a significant layer at the exposed surface must. The heat absorption means further includes a thermally nonconductive container to support and retain the liquid conductor passing therethrough and the particulate material, and is covered with radiation transparent sheet such as crystal glass which forms a wall of the container adjacent the major surface of the heat absorbing material.

In order that the manner in which the foregoing and other objects are obtained in accordance with the invention can be understood in detail, reference is made to the accompanying drawings, which form a part of this specification, and wherein:

FIG. 1 is a schematic diagram of a typical system according to the invention;

FIG. 2 is a sectional elevation of a heat absorptsion unit, the section being along lines 2—2 of FIG. 1;

FIG. 3 is a section of the heat absorption unit along lines 3—3 of FIG. 2;

FIG. 4 is a foreshortened plan view of a heat absorption unit showing, schematically, a typical serpentine type array; and

FIG. 5 is a foreshortened plan view of a heat absorption unit having a header type array.

Referring now to the drawings in detail, it will be seen that FIG. 1 shows a body of water indicated generally at 10 which can be a swimming pool having a water inlet 11 and an outlet 12, the outlet being connected to a pipe 13 which conducts water away from the pool under the influence of a pump 14 which normally feeds the water to a conventional filter 15 and returns the water to a conventional filter 15 and returns the water to inlet 11 through a pipe 16. This much of the system is conventional in nature, the pump and filter being employed to recirculate and continuously remove undesirable substances from the pool.

Coupled to this system is a heating apparatus including a pipe 27 which is coupled to the circulation system between the pump and filter and is provided with a valve 18 which can be manually or automatically operated but which, when opened, permits liquid to flow through pipe 17 to a heat absorption unit indicated generally at 20. The absorption unit, which will be described hereinafter in greater detail, includes internal piping which conducts the water entering on pipe **17** through the unit and out through pipe **21** which is provided with a check valve **22** which permits fluid flow only in the direction of arrow **23**. Because of the greater resistance to fluid flow presented by filter **15**, majority of the fluid will pass through heat absorption unit **20** when valve **18** is opened. Absorption unit **20** provided with a major surface **24** which is oriented in a direction to receive radiation from the Sun, the direction of solar radiation being indicated by arrows **25**. The water passing through unit **20** is thus heated by this solar energy and it returned to the pool **10**, elevating the temperature thereof.

Heat absorption unit **20** is illustrated in greater detail in FIGS. **2** and **3** which are sectional views to more clearly illustrate the interior construction and materials. As previously mentioned, unit **20** has a major surface **24** disposed to receive radiation, this surface being defined by a pane of glass or other radiation transparent material. The remaining exterior portions of the absorption unit constitute a generally rectangular box **25**, which box can be made of wood as shown or molded from fiberglass or other suitable relatively rigid, thermally nonconductive opaque and durable material. The box is five sided, the remaining side being transparent as previously described, and oriented toward the Sun.

The interior of box **25** is lined on the five opaque sides with a relatively thick layer **26** of a good plastic insulating material such as foamed polystyrene, which material is light and tends not to absorb moisture. Inside insulating layer **26** is a liner **27** of builder's foil which is a double layer of highly reflective metallic foil with a tar or similar layer sandwiched between the two foil layers. This liner prevents damage to or degradation of insulating layer **26** and tends to reflect heat back to the interior of the box.

Contained within the box thus far described is a body of particulate material **30**, most of which can be conventional sand or the like. Resting on or buried in the thick layer of sand is a pipe assembly **31** which includes an array of pipe arranged and disposed to carry the water which flows through the heat absorption unit the water which flows through the heat absorption unit between pipes **17** and **21**, so that the water can absorb heat while passing therethrough. Pipe **31** can be a continuous length of pipe arranged in a serpentine fashion or it can constitute a plurality of parallel pieces of pipe connected at their ends to header members, as will be further described. The pipe can be constructed of copper, but it has been found that the pipe need not be highly thermally conductive material and, in fact, can be plastic pipe, such as commonly used ABS or acrylonitrile butadiene styrene pipe which is less expensive and relatively simple to work. A typical structure includes 25 lengths, or 12½ loops, of ¾ inch ABS pipe, spaced on 3½ inch centers, in a box which is approximately 4 feet by 8 feet in outer dimensions and approximately 6 inches deep. The pipe is covered by about 2 inches of particulate material. The glass pane **24** is 7/16 inch flat crystal glass.

Of particular consequence in the assembly of this structure is the incorporation of a substantial layer **32** of "black sand" or magnetite. For reasons for which are not completely understood, the incorporation of a ferric compound and, specifically, this iron oxide compound as the upper layer of the material beneath the glass in the box vastly improves the heat absorption characteristics thereof and permits maximum utilization of that solar energy which falls upon pane **24**. In fact, material **30** and **32** can all be iron oxide with no added sand, but it is particularly significant that the top one fourth inch of the portion between pipe **31** and window **24** be iron oxide for best effect.

The iron oxide compound which has been utilized primarily and found to be effective is that colloquially referred to as "black sand" and constitutes part of the tailings remaining after a gold placer mining, or gold panning, operation. The material is not truly sand in the sense of being silica compound but, instead, is an iron oxide which is largely magnetite ($F_{e_3}O_4$) with titanium compounds such as ilmenite ($F_e T_i O_3$) or rutile ($T_i O_2$) and other iron compounds, and is a naturally occurring material in for example, the geologic formations in which gold is found. The residue from the placer mining operations has been employed, and has been found to give excellent results, in a structure as above-described.

Further discussions of the black sand, as this term is used herein, can be found in Bureau of Mines Information Circulars 8517 and 7000.

As previously mentioned, the pipe in the box can be arranged in either of at least two ways, these being schematically illustrated in FIGS. **4** and **5**. In FIG. **4**, the pipe is arranged in a serpentine fashion with the pipe being continuously wound back and forth in the box alternatively, it is possible to employ the header approach wherein a plurality of parallel lengths of plastic pipe **40** are connected at one end to a header **41** which is provided with a plurality of equally spaced holes of appropriate diameter. The pipes are connected to each other with a conventional adhesive, commonly used in the assembly of ABS pipe. A second header **42** is connected to pipes **40** at their opposite ends. Inlet and outlet pipes **43** and **44** are connected to headers **41** and **42**, respectively. The assembly can then be placed in the preassembled structure and covered with the iron oxide material. *

US Patent Sept. 23, 1975 3,906,928

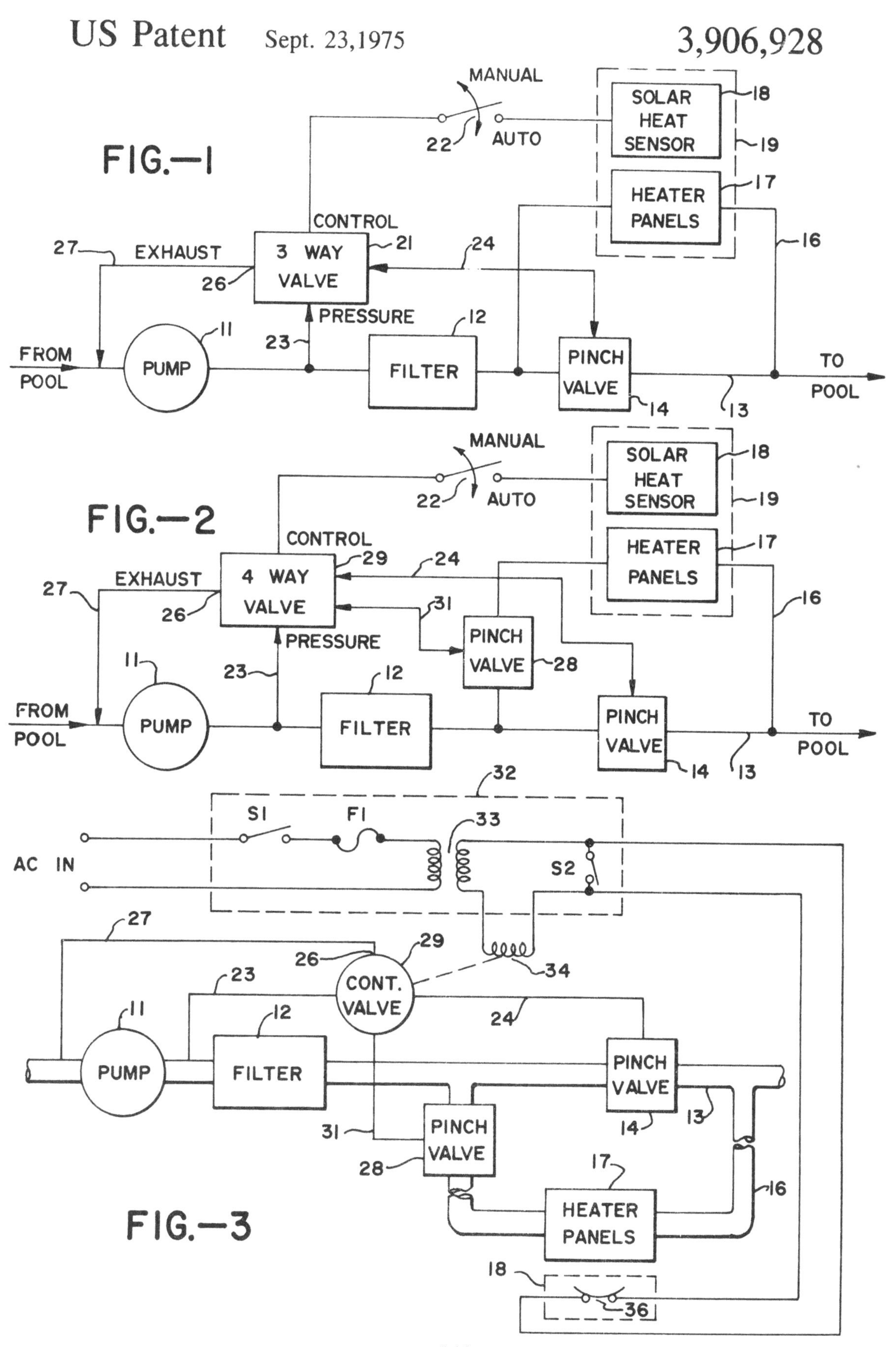

Inventor: **Allen C. Wright,** Moraga, Calif.
Assignee: **Fafco Incorporated,** Redwood City, Calif.

* **ABSTRACT**

A pool water heating system used in conjunction with a pool pump and filter wherein the pool water is directed along one of two paths down stream of the filter. One path directs the filtered water directly back to the pool and the other path directs the filtered water through an array of heater panels for transferring heat generated by solar energy to the water prior to returning it to the pool. A solar heat sensor is positioned to sense the temperature induced by solar energy in the location of the heater panels and to provide an electrical signal which is connected to a control valve. A flow direction valve is positioned in the direct flow path to the pool which is urged to pinch off the flow therethrough by pressure directed to a valve chamber therein. Pressure at the filter inlet is directed to one port on the control valve and an exhaust port on the control valve is connected to the inlet side of the pump. When solar heat is available to heat the pool water the solar heat sensor directs the control valve to communicate the filter inlet pressure with the flow direction valve, causing blockage of direct flow to the pool and flow through the heater panels for heating prior to returning to the pool. When solar heat is not available as determined by the solar heat sensor the exhaust port on the control valve is communicated with the pinch valve to bleed the valve chamber therein and allow filtered water to flow directly therethrough to the pool.

* **3 Drawing Figures**

SOLAR HEATER CONTROL SYSTEM AND METHOD

BACKGROUND OF THE INVENTION

1. Field of the invention

The invention relates to a system for controlling temperature in a confined body of water, and more particularly to a system for automatically heating the water in a swimming pool using solar energy and for cooling the swimming pool water through the use of a manual control.

2. Description of the prior art

Heating systems for confined bodies of water such as swimming pools generally utilize heat energy from burning gas or electric heater elements. Installation, maintenance and operating costs for these types of heater systems are considerable. The water is withdrawn from the pools by a pump associated with a necessary pool water filtering system and is subsequently passed through the heater prior to return to the pool. A heating system for the pool water is needed to either replace or supplement known pool heaters. The replacement or supplementary heater, to be sufficiently attractive, must draw heat energy from a source which will reduce the operating costs normally associated with energy derived from the public utilities.

There is therefore a need for a pool heating system utilizing available solar energy which is relatively inexpensive to install, maintain, and operate.

SUMMARY AND OBJECTS OF THE INVENTION

In general the system disclosed herein is used for controlling the temperature in a confined body of water such as a swimming pool having a pump and a filter associated therewith for removing impurities from the water. Alternate paths exist down stream of the filter, a direct path back to the pool and a path passing through an array of solar heater panels prior to return to the pool. A heat sensor is located to sense the solar energy available for heating at the heater panels. A flow direction valve is positioned in the direct return path to the pool having a control line connected thereto which extends to a control valve. A pressure line extends from a point upstresm of the filter to the control valve. The control valve has an exhaust port which may be connected by an exhaust line to the inlet side of the pump. The heat sensor provides a signal to the control valve which communicates the pressure line to the flow direction valve when solar energy is available at the heater panels sufficient to raise the water temperature above a predetermined temperature. In like manner the heat sensor communicates the exhaust port on the control valve with the flow direction valve when insufficient solar energy is available at the heater panels to raise the water above the predetermined temperature.

In general it is an object of the present invention to provide a system for controlling temperature in a confined body of water which utilizes existing filter system water pressures for controlling the route of water flow through the system.

It is another object of the present invention to provide a system for controlling temperature in a confined body of water which uses only one pressure control valve for blocking a preferred flow path thereby directing the flow through an elevated array of solar heater panels.

Another object of the present invention is to provide a system for controlling temperature in a confined body of water which utilizes water pressure taken from the upstream side of an existing filter for controlling selection of return flow path downstream of the filter to the body of water.

It is another object of the present invention to provide a system for controlling temperature in a confined body of water having pressure controlled flow direction valves in each of two return paths downstream of the filter which are alternately controlled between open and closed position by a control valve receiving control pressure from a point upstream of the filter.

It is another object of the present invention to provide a system for controlling temperature in a confined body of water which may be manually operated to direct flow through an array of solar heater panels to cool the water when the solar energy available is below that required to rise the temperature of the water.

Another object of the present invention is to provide a system for controlling temperature in a confined body of water wherein the pressure controlled flow direction valve is positively opened by control pressure after being in a closed position.

Additional objects and features of the invention will appear from the following description in which the preferred embodiment has been set forth in detail in conjunction with the accompanying drawings.

BRIEF DESCRIPTION OF THE DRAWINGS

FIG. 1 is a block diagram of the system in which the solar heater panels are elevated relative to the direct return path to the pool.

FIG. 2 is a block diagram of the system in which the solar heater panels may occupy any elevation relative to the direct return path to the pool.

FIG. 3 is an electrical and hydraulic schematic of one practical embodiment of the invention.

DESCRIPTION OF THE PREFERRED EMBODIMENTS

The temperature within a confined body of water may be controlled using heating panels which are disposed in the environment surrounding the body of water. One such practical use for a system based on this principle is a system associated with a swimming pool for controlling the temperature of the water in the pool. In the majority of instances it is desired to elevate the temperature of the water in the pool, although there are times when it may be desirable to reduce the temperature of the water in the pool. For either purpose a system associated with a swimming pool such as that shown in FIG. 1 may be used. An inlet from the pool to the system is shown at the left of FIG. 1, through which water is drawn by the action of a pump **11** which provides water pressure to the inlet of a filter **12**. Downstream of filter **12** two return paths may be seen. One path is a direct return path **13** in which a flow direction valve **14** is situated and an alternate path is provided by indirect return path **16** in which is positioned an array of solar heating panels **17**.

A solar heat sensor **18** is positioned so as to sense the availability of solar energy for providing heat to the array of heater panels **17**. It is usual that solar heat sensor **18** is situated proximate to heater panels **17** as indicated by dashed lines **19** so that the actual solar energy available at the location of heater panels **17** is sensed.

Solar heat sensor **18** provides an output signal or control signal which is electrically connected to a control valve **21**. A mode control switch **22** may be provided to interrupt the connection for the control signal from sensor **18**, so that the control valve **21** bay be operated in either an automatic mode or a manual mode. When switch **22** is in the manual position the electrical circuit from solar heat sensor **18** to control valve **21** is open, and actuation of control valve **21** must be by manual means. Control valve **21** has the pressure at the inlet to filter **12** connected thereto through a pressure line **23**. A control line **24** is connected between control valve **21** and flow direction valve **14**. Control valve **21** has an exhaust port **26** to which may be connected an exhaust line **27** extending to the inlet side of pump **11**. It may be seen by reference to FIG. 1 that water leaving solar heater panels **17** or passing flow direction valve **14** continues through the remainder of indirect and direct return paths **16** and **13** respectively to the system outlet to the pool as marked at the right side of FIG. 1.

Ths system of FIG. 1 controls the temperature in a confined body of water, such as that within a swimming pool, in the following fashion in one embodiment. Heater panels **17** and indirect return path **16** are elevated to some degree above direct return path **13**. Flow direction valve **14** may be of the "pinch" type *

flow direction valve **14** contains a valve chamber and a pressure port for communicating pressure to the valve chamber. When pressure is introduced to the valve chamber in flow direction valve **14** a flexible member forming one wall of the valve chamber distends inwardly to block the flow through the valve.

With switch **22** in the automatic position (closed) solar heat sensor **18** is set to provide a control signal at a predetermined solar energy level which initiates flow through heating panels **17** thereby transferring heat to water flowing therethrough. The control signal is connected to control valve **21** which communicates pressure line **23** with control line **24** thereby providing pressure to the pressure port of flow direction valve **14**. Flow direction valve **14** closes, as described above, blocking flow through direct return path **13** thereby causing the flow from filter **12** to be diverted to indirect return path **16** and through heater panels **17**. Heat transferred from heater panels **17** to the water flowing therethrough raises the temperature of the water which is subsequentally returned to the pool through the remainder of indirect return path **16** and the system outlet.

When solar heat sensor **18** detects an insufficient level of solar energy for raising the water in the pool above a predetermined temperature. Control valve **21** is returned to a position whereby control line **24** is placed in communication with exhaust port **26**. Pressure in the valve chamber of flow direction valve **14** is bled off through control line **24** and exhaust port **26**. Means may be provided in the form of exhaust line **27** between exhaust port **26** and the inlet side of pump **11** for positively opening flow direction valve **14** by providing a low pressure to the valve chamber, thereby positively bleeding off the pressure from the valve chamber. Flow direction valve **14** now being in an open condition, the flow from the outlet of filter **12** follows the preferred lower level direct return path **13** to the system outlet to the pool.

In the event it is desired to use the system of FIG. 1 to reduce the temperature of the pool water, switch **22** may be positioned to the manual position. Control valve **21** may now be manually positioned to communicate pressure line **23** with control line **24** closing flow direction vlave **14**. As described above the flow at the output of filter **12** is diverted through indirect path **16** and heater panels 17 whereupon it is returned to the pool. If there is insufficient solar energy available to raise the temperature of the water passing through the panels 17 above the predetermined temperature then heat exchange occurs in the opposite direction and the heater panels 17 remove heat energy form the pool water flowing therethrough and pass it to the surrounding environment. The water returns through indirect return path 16 to the pool at a temperature lower than the temperature at which it was drawn from the pool by pump 11. In this fashion the water in the pool may be reduced in temperature to an equlibrium temperature with the environment surrounding heater panels 17.

Referring to FIG. 2 a block diagram is shown of a system for controlling temperature in a confined body of water, such as that contained in a swimming pool, where the heater panels 17 may not be in a position which is elevated relative to the direct return path 13. Items in FIG. 2 which are direct counterparts of items in FIG. 1 are given identical item numbers. The distinctions in FIG. 2, as compared to that of FIG. 1, lie in the insertion of an additional flow direction valve 28 in indirect return path 16, a four-way control valve 29 which replaces control vlave 21, and an additional control line 31 which extends between additional flow direction valve 28 and four-way control valve 29.

Since the relative elevations of direct return path 13 and indirect return path 16 no longer provide for a preferred return through direct path 13, additional flow direction valve 28 becomes necessary. Four-way control valve 29 is configured to alternately connect exhaust port 26 to control line 24 and pressure line 23 to additional control line 31, and exhaust port 26 to additional control line 31 and pressure line 23 to control line 24. When switch 22 is in the closed or automatic position and solar heat sensor 18 determines that an insufficient level of solar energy is available to raise the pool water above the predetermined temperature, four-way control valve 29 is in the first mentioned position. Thus, flow direction valve 14 is open and additional flow direction valve 28 is closed, whereby filtered water returns to the pool through direct flow path 13. When solar heat sensor 18 detects availability of a sufficient level of solar energy to raise the temperature of the pool water above the predetermined temperature, four-way control valve 29 is urged to the last mentioned position thereby closing flow direction valve 14 and opening additional flow direction vlave 28. Filtered water is then directed through indirect return path 16, through heater panels 17 to receive heat transferred therefrom, and returned to the pool.

FIG. 3 is a practical embodiment of the system shown in FIG. 2 and therefore shows all of the necessary elements for a practical embodiment of the system shown in FIG. 1. In FIG. 3 a control box, shown generally at 32, contains an on-off switch S1 for connecting an AC power input to the system. The circuit is fused by a fuse F1. A transformer 33 is shown for providing power to an actuating coil 34 for four-way control valve 29. Solar heat sensor 18 is shown in one embodiment as a thermal switch 36 located proximate to the array of heater panels 17. Switch S2 in control box 32 performs the function of switch 22 in FIGS. 1 and 2. Switch S2 in the closed condition is equivalent to switch 22 in the open or manual position. Conversely switch S2 in the open condition is equivalent to switch 22 in the closed or automatic position. The operation of the system shown in FIG. 3 involves closing switch S1 to place the system in a ready condition. Depending upon whether manual or automatic operation is desired switch S2 is either closed or opened respectively. The remainder of the operation of the system shown in FIG. 3 is the same as that described for the operation of the system shown in FIG. 2 above.

A method for controlling temperature in a confined body of water such as a swimming pool, involves pumping water from the pool and filtering the water. The method further involves diverting the water downstream of the filter through one of two alternate return paths to the pool. Collecting available solar heat is performed in the heating panels. Sensing of an available solar energy level sufficient to provide heat for transfer to the circulated pool water is performed. The method includes routing the filtered water through the path for receiving heat energy from the environmnet when sufficient solar energy availability is sensed, and routing the filtered water directly back to the pool when insuffient availability of solar energy is sensed. The routing of the filtered flow is obtained by connecting pressure upstream of the filter to an appropriate flow direction valve for blocking or opening the appropriate return path to the pool as determined in the solar energy level determination step. The method also includes positive opening of flow direction valves previously closed by introducing a low pressure from a point upstream of the pump to the previously closed valve.

A system and method has been diclosed for controlling temperature in a confined body of water such as that contained in a swimming pool which may be operated manually or automatically. This system and method includes allowance for elevating the temperature of the water above a predetermined temperature and for lowering the temperature of the water to a temperature of equlibrium with the surrounding environment. The system may be used to supplement a conventional pool heating system by directing the system outlet to the conventional heating system inlet prior to return to the pool. The system provides a replacement or supplementary heating system for conventional pool heating systems and requires comparatively low installation, maintenance and operating costs.

Chapter 8

Solar Activated Dehumidifier

March 1, 1949. E. B. DUNKAK 2,462,952

SOLAR ACTIVATED DEHUMIDIFIER

* *

Fig. 1.

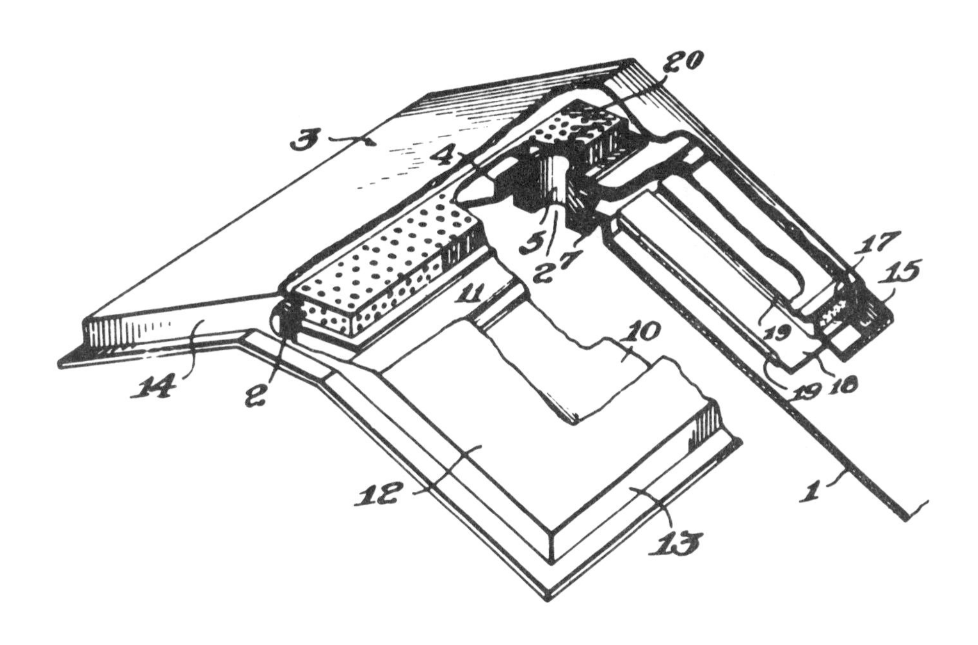

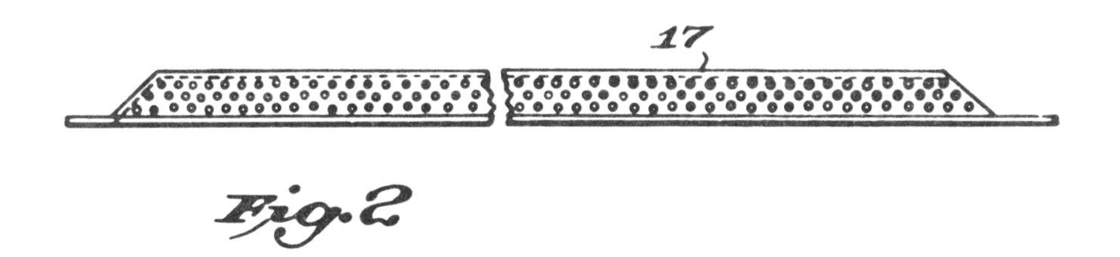

Fig. 2

INVENTOR.
ELMER B. DUNKAK
BY
Semmes, Keegin, Beale & Semmes
Attys

March 1, 1949. E. B. DUNKAK 2,462,952

SOLAR ACTIVATED DEHUMIDIFIER

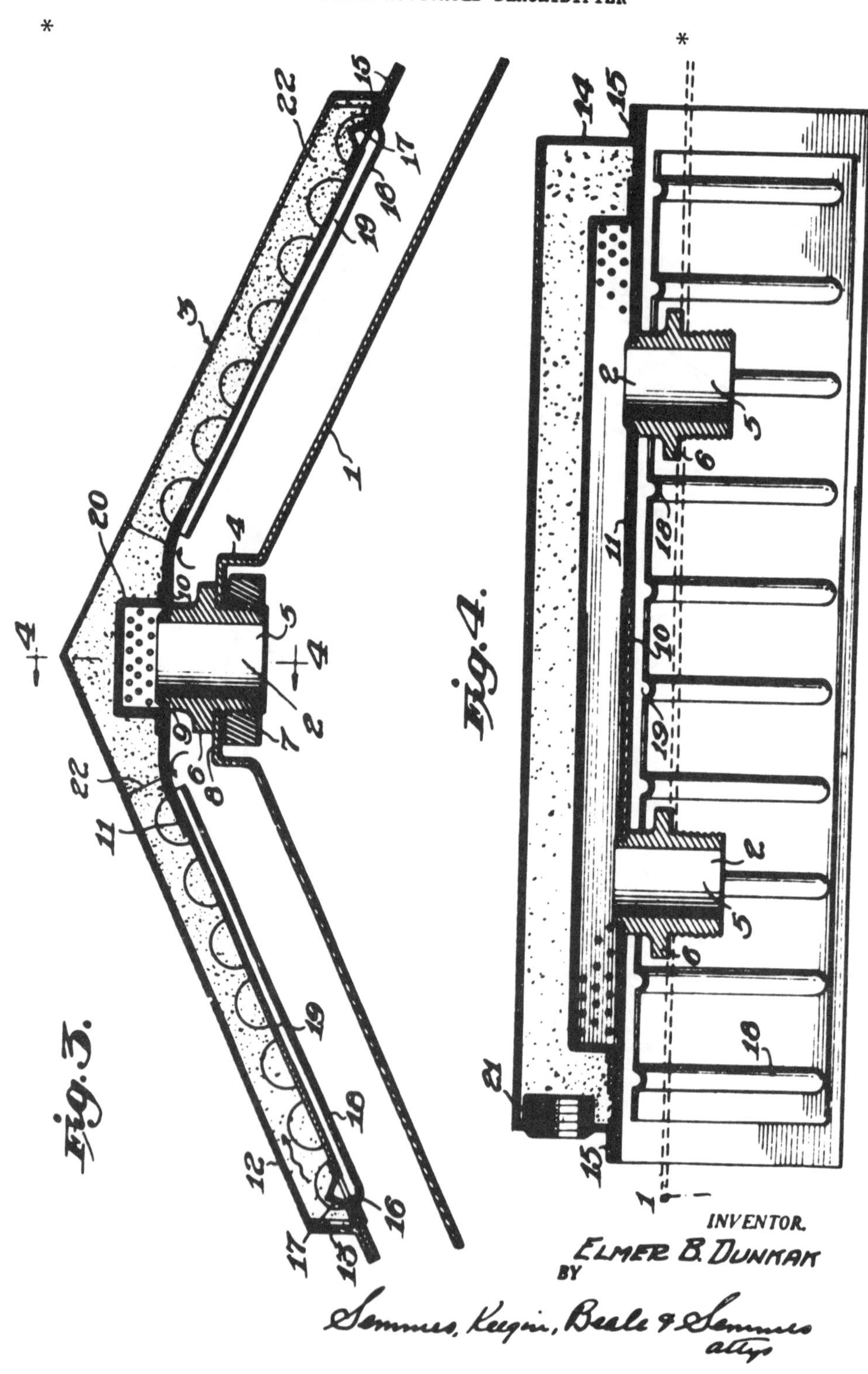

UNITED STATES PATENT OFFICE

2,462,952

SOLAR ACTIVATED DEHUMIDIFIER

Elmer B. Dunkak, Baltimore, Md., assignor to The Davison Chemical Corporation, Baltimore, Md.

*

This invention relates in general to the heat activation of moisture adsorbing material and more particularly has reference to the solar heat activation of silica gel.

Desiccant substances such as silica gel will take up moisture from the surrounding atmosphere until equilibrium of the moisture in the atmosphere and desiccant is reached. When the desiccant has taken up this much moisture it must be replaced or reactivated. Regeneration by activation is generally effected by passing hot gases in contact with the material or by heating the same. Heat for reactivation is generally supplied by burners or electrical heating devices and involves an appreciable financial expenditure. Also the desiccant must be removed from its location of use for purposes of activation. The present invention provides for the activation or reactivation of desiccants such as silica gel by solar radiations.

An object of this invention is to provide an apparatus for the solar activation of a dessiccant such as silica gel.

Another object of this invention is to provide an enclosure breather dehumidifier constructed for the solar activation of the desiccant therein.

With these and other objects in view, the present invention resides in the parts and combinations hereinafter described and shown in the drawings.

In the drawings:

Figure 1 is a perspective view of a breather dehumidifier embodying the features of the present invention.

Figure 2 is a detailed sectional view of the lower screen element of the device of Figure 1.

Figure 3 is a transverse vertical sectional view of the device of Figure 1.

Figure 4 is another vertical sectional view taken on line 4—4 of Figure 3.

The present invention is based upon the concept of utilizing solar heat directly or heat obtained from radiations of the sun for activating or reactivating a desiccant such as silica gel.

Under certain conditions, the direct rays of the sun may be employed for the activation of a desiccant such as silica gel. According to the present invention, it has been found that a desiccant such as silica gel may be activated by spreading the gel in graular form upon a dark, dull, heat absorbing surface in a thin layer and exposing same to the rays of the sun. The rays of the sun can be concentrated upon the gel and dark, dull, heat absorbing surface by lenses or reflectors.

It is also within the concept of the present invention to place the silica gel in a receptacle, the wall or walls of which are formed of material having high thermal conductivity and the exterior surfaces of which are of a dark, dull finish, and then subjecting the receptacle to solar radiations. To facilitate transfer of heat from the walls of the receptacle to the silica gel contained therein, elements of high thermal conductive material may extend inwardly from the walls into the interior space.

The concept of the present invention is particularly applicable to the activation or reactivation of a desiccant in a breather dehydrator.

The air in any enclosure has a varying density when subjected to ambient temperature and pressure conditions such as are encountered in the storage of packages exposed to the elements. In the case of hermetically sealed enclosures the varying density will cause a variable pressure inside the enclosure which is independent of the atmospheric pressure but is proportional to the absolute temperature. If the enclosure is vented, however, a cyclic flow of air into and out of the enclosure will occur due to increments of pressure differential between the enclosed space and the atmosphere. This cyclic flow is termed breathing and its magnitude and rate depend on the range and rate of atmospheric pressure and temperature change.

In order to maintain the air within the vented enclosure at a low relative humidity, a device such as shown in the drawings is associated with the vent opening. As illustrated, the enclosure 1 provided with one or more vents or breather openings 2 has a dehumidifying device indicated generally by reference character 3 mounted thereon. The enclosure may be a tank, a container or housing of any desired type, the contents of which are to have moisture excluded therefrom. Although the enclosure may have any location, in order to render the present invention most effective, it should be exposed so that it can receive the radiations of the sun.

Preferably, the upper portion of the enclosure 1 is provided with a boss 4 surrounding each of the openings 2. Fitted into the openings 2 is a section of pipe or nipple 5 provided with a laterally extending flange 6. The flange 6 is adapted to seat upon the upper portion of the boss 4 and the lower threaded portion of the nipple 5 has a nut 7 mounted thereon which serves to draw the flange 6 against the upper portion of the boss 4. A washer or gasket 8 may be interposed between the nut 7 and the inner surface of the boss 4. Of course, a washer or gasket may also be interposed between flange 6 and the upper portion of the boss 4.

Fitting 5 serves as a mounting for the dehumidifying device indicated generally by reference character 3. As illustrated, the upper portion of the fitting 5 is cut away to form a shoulder 9 which receives a base plate 10 of the dehumidifying device. The cut-away portion of the fitting 5 extends through an opening in the base plate 10, and the plate and fitting are secured together rigidly by welding. In order to reinforce the base plate and to impart rigidity thereto, a reinforcing plate 11 is positioned thereon about the opening which receives the fitting 5.

Mounted upon the base plate 10 is a cover plate 12 which is shaped as illustrated in the drawings to provide a housing between the same and the base plate 10. As shown, the cover plate 12 is provided with side portions 13 and end portions 14, both of which have outwardly extending flanges 15 at the lower extremities thereof. These flanges may be welded or otherwise joined to the coextensive portions of the base plate 10 to form a receptacle for the desiccant. In the base plate 10 adjacent each side thereof there is provided an opening 16 placing the interior of the receptacle formed between the plates 10 and 12 in communication with the atmosphere. Positioned in the receptacle 3 over the openings 16 are screens 17 which are formed of sheet metal provided with a plurality of perforations of a fineness that will permit the free flow of air therethrough while retaining the desiccant in the dehumidifying device 3.

Normally a desiccant such as silica gel in a receptacle such as that indicated by reference character 3 will absorb moisture by infiltration from the surrounding atmosphere even when there is no flow of air from the exterior through the receptacle. It has been found that if the air passage from the atmosphere to the interior of the receptacle containing the silica gel has a length equal to or greater than ten times the diameter or cross section of the passage, the infiltration of moisture from the external air to the interior of the receptacle is minimized to a negligible degree. For this purpose, the opening 16 in the bottom of the plate 10 adjacent each side thereof which is in the form of a slot, is covered by a diffusion plate 18 which is provided with a plurality of semi-cylindrical grooves or embossed portions to provide channels 19 extending from the slot 16 to the inner edge of the plate 18 as illustrated in Figures 1 and 3 of the drawings. The length to cross sectional area of the passages 19 bears the ratio as above pointed out so as to minimize the diffusion of moisture from the external atmosphere to the desiccant in the receptacle 3.

A perforated screen 20 is mounted over the upper ends of the pipe sections or fittings 5 and serves to prevent the flow of the desiccant material into the interior of the enclosure 1 while permitting the free flow of air into and out of said enclosure.

In one end 14 of the cover plate there is provided a fitting 21 internally threaded to receive a plug for the closure thereof. This fitting serves as a means for the introduction and removal of the desiccant in the receptacle 3.

It has been found preferable to construct the receptacle 3 of sheet aluminum or other metal having a high thermal conductivity. The purpose of this is to insure a high rate of heat transfer from the exterior of the receptacle 3 through the walls thereof to the desiccant such as silica gel contained therein. Copper, bronze, steel or any other metal having a high thermal conductivity, may be employed in place of aluminum.

In accordance with the present invention, it has been found that by making the exterior surfaces of the receptacle approach as nearly as possible the surfaces of a black body a considerable amount of heat will be absorbed by the walls of the receptacle when subjected to the radiations of the sun and transmitted to the interior thereof. As a matter of fact, the heat absorbed and transferred through the walls of the receptacle is sufficient to effect activation of a desiccant such as silica gel to remove moisture therefrom. When the receptacle is being subjected to the rays of the sun, the enclosure 1 is likewise being heated. There will be a tendency for the air in the enclosure 1 to move outwardly through vents 5, through the desiccant, to the opening 16 and through channels 19 to exterior atmosphere. This travel of the air from the enclosure 1 through the desiccant tends to carry along the moisture driven from the desiccant by the action of the solar heat transferred to the desiccant through the walls of the receptacle 3.

Upon reduction in temperature of the atmosphere or termination of exposure to the rays of the sun, the air in the enclosure 1 will cool and its pressure will drop. This will cause external air to be drawn through the channels 19 into the receptacle 3, through the activated desiccant silica gel and into the enclosure 1 to bring the pressure therein into equilibrium with the external atmosphere.

The dull black heat absorbing finish on the external surfaces of the plates 10, 12 and 18 may be in the form of a coating compound or in the case of the plates being formed of aluminum the surfaces may be anodized and dyed. If the plates are formed of copper, the oxidized surfaces will become a dull black. It is of course within the concept of the present invention to form the dull black surface of any suitable material and in any manner which will result in a surface having high solar heat absorbing properties. All of the external surfaces of the dehumidifier 3 are finished in dull black to pick up heat from reflected as well as from direct solar radiations.

To increase the transfer of heat from the plates 10 and 12 to the desiccant silica gel when in an activating cycle, a plurality of ribs 22 of metal are positioned between said plates as shown in Figure 3. These ribs may be welded to the plates 10 and 12 to increase the heat transfer. With this construction heat will be more effectively distributed from plates 10 and 12 into the mass of silica gel. Of course, other forms of heat conducting elements may extend inwardly from the walls into the gel bed.

An installation having a gel bed of about 1 inch in thickness and providing a flow path of about 10 inches was found very effective for a particular installation. The flow path and the thickness of the gel bed may of course be varied within wide limits depending upon the size of the enclosure to be vented and the atmospheric conditions.

A construction as shown and described has been found highly effective for maintaining the air in the interior of the enclosure at a low relative humidity and to also maintain the desiccant silica gel in a condition capable of absorbing moisture from external air drawn through the gel bed into the interior of the enclosure. When the device has a high exposure to the sun there will be greater activation of the silica gel. On the other hand, when there is little exposure to the sun, there will be little "breathing" of the air in the enclosure and little use of the silica gel as a desiccant. Thus, in either event, the silica gel will remain in activated condition ready to reduce the humidity of air drawn in from the external atmosphere.

In practice there are three operating conditions under which a breather must function, namely "breathing out," "static condition," and "breathing in."

The first named condition occurs whenever the air inside the enclosure is heated by any means whatsoever and also whenever the atmospheric pressure falls. This condition will be created most often when the enclosure is exposed to the sun's rays. As pointed out above, the receptacle 3 under this condition will heat up and drive out the moisture adsorbed previously and prepare it for the next "breathing in" operation.

The "static condition" exists whenever there is no change in temperature or pressure and therefore no flow of air into or out of the enclosure. The ducts 19 then function to prevent depletion of the silica gel.

The final operating condition "breathing in" is the reverse of the first condition and it occurs whenever the enclosed air is cooled and whenever the atmospheric pressure rises. Under this condition the prime function of the breather comes into use. The air being forced into the enclosure by a pressure differential must pass through the silica gel bed and give up its contained moisture to the gel and then pass into the enclosure as dry air. The moisture given up is held in the silica gel where it can do no damage, until exiting dry air picks it up on the next "breathing out" operation and discharges it to the atmosphere.

Although the physical shape of the dehumidifying device may be varied within wide limits, it has been found that the shape illustrated, i. e. like an open inverted book, is highly satisfactory. This shape provides a top surface most likely to shed rain and snow. Also the air inlet ends of the channels 19 are located at the apex of the underside where they are protected from the entry of wind borne particles of rain, snow and dust.

As before indicated, lenses and/or mirrors may be employed if desired or necessary to increase the heating effect of the sun's rays on the heat absorbing surfaces.

From the foregoing, it will be appreciated that a highly effective arrangement is provided to activate a desiccant such as silica gel by solar radiations and to maintain air in an enclosure at a low relative humidity. *

July 1, 1952 **F. O. ANDEREGG** **2,601,905**

DEHUMIDIFICATION SYSTEM FOR BUILDINGS

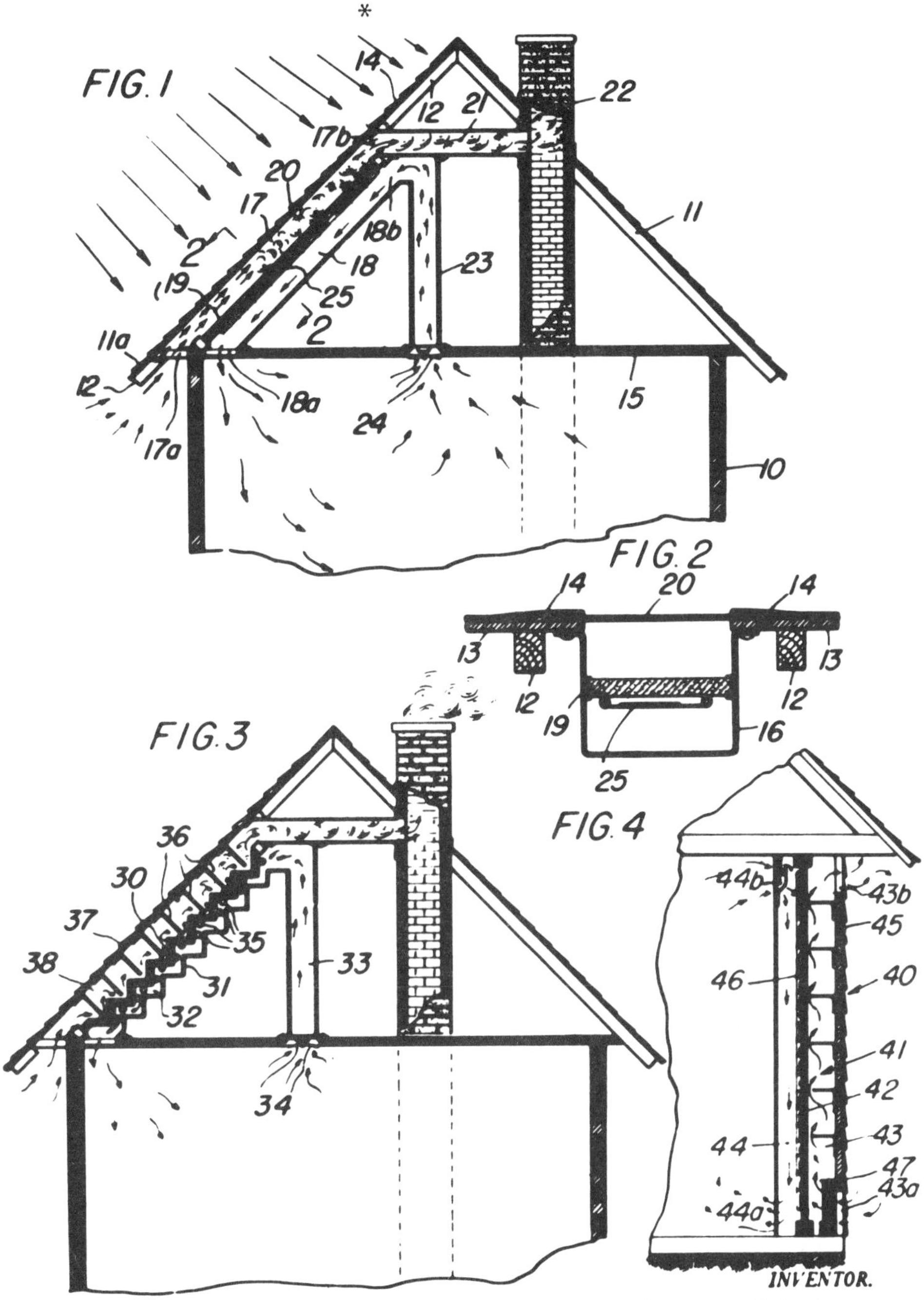

*

FIG. 1

FIG. 2

FIG. 3

FIG. 4

INVENTOR.
Frederick O Anderegg
BY

UNITED STATES PATENT OFFICE

2,601,905

DEHUMIDIFICATION SYSTEM FOR BUILDINGS

Frederick O. Anderegg, Somerville, N. J., assignor to John B. Pierce Foundation, New York, N. Y., a special corporation of New York

*

This invention relates to dehumidying systems, and particularly to those used in buildings for conditioning the interior air thereof.

In my U. S. Letters Patent No. 2,336,456 there is disclosed dehumidifying apparatus utilizing a pervious, porous wall between a flow of air to be dehumidified and a flow of heated air, a cooling coil being disposed at that surface of the pervious, porous wall against which the air to be dehumidified impinges. Thus, the fugacity of the moisture laden air is lowered and the latent heat of vaporization absorbed by the cooling coil. Moisture condenses upon the pervious, porous wall, is passed through the pores to the heated air stream, and is carried away thereby.

In the present system substantially the same dehumidifying principle is employed in a new structural combination which affords rapid and effective dehumidification and conditioning of air within a building.

In its most preferred form, the system of the invention embodies an elongate panel section in the roof or other part of the exterior frame structure of a building, for directing the heat of the sun into one channel of an air-flow conduit of which the said panel section forms the exterior wall. The air-flow conduit is divided longitudinally into exteriorly-disposed and interiorly-disposed channels by a moisture-pervious, porous wall, and opposite ends of the exteriorly-disposed channel are open to the outside atmosphere while opposite ends of the interiorly-disposed channel are open to the inside atmosphere of the building. Forced-circulation means is provided for the interiorly-disposed channel, but heat is relied upon to effect circulation of outside air through the exteriorly-disposed channel. The heat is advantageously derived from the sun by utilizing a heat conductive sheet or plate, preferably blackened sheet copper, for the elongate panel section above mentioned. Cooling means, preferably in the form of a serpentine pipe which circulates cool water, is provided at and along the face of the porous wall within the interiorly-disposed channel.

Generically speaking, the system of the invention may be regarded as embodying an air-flow conduit which extends up and down within the exterior frame structure of a building and which is divided longitudinally into a pair of flow channels by a moisture-pervious, porous wall. Opposite ends of one of the flow channels are open to the outside atmosphere, and opposite ends of the other flow channel are open to the interior of the building.

Among the objects of the invention are:

To provide an efficient and economical dehumidification and air conditioning system for buildings;

To incorporate such a system in the exterior framework of a building in order to utilize otherwise waste space;

To effect adequate dehumidification and comfort cooling of the air within a building while continuously regenerating the dehumidifying material;

To make use of the heat of the sun in the regenerative process.

Additional objects and features of the invention will become apparent from the following detailed description of the preferred embodiments illustrated in the accompanying drawing.

In the drawing:

Fig. 1 is a transverse vertical section taken through a building in which a preferred form of the invention is incorporated, the dehumidifying system appearing in longitudinal vertical section;

Fig. 2 is a fragmentary transverse section taken on the line 2—2, Fig. 1;

Fig. 3 is a view corresponding to that of Fig. 1, but illustrating a somewhat different form of the dehumidifying system; and

Fig. 4 is a vertical section taken through an exterior wall of a building with which another form of the invention is incorporated, the dehumidification system appearing in longitudinal vertical section, and the whole being drawn to a reduced scale as compared with the foregoing figures.

Referring now to the drawing, and particularly to Figs. 1 and 2 thereof, wherein the dehumidification system is incorporated in the roof structure of a building:

The illustrated dwelling house 10 is merely indicative of one type of building to which the invention is applicable. The roof structure 11 thereof is of conventional construction, embodying spaced rafters 12 covered by any desired type of sheathing 13 and external roofing 14, see Fig. 2. A ceiling is shown at 15.

In this embodiment, the dehumidification system of the invention comprises an air-flow conduit 16 divided longitudinally into a pair of flow channels 17 and 18, respectively, by means of a moisture-pervious, porous wall 19. The flow channel 17 is exteriorly disposed, while the air-flow channel 18 is interiorly disposed, the air-flow conduit 16, as such, being built into the external framework of the building, specifically into the framework of the roof structure, as illustrated.

The air-flow conduit 16 is closed exteriorly by blackened sheet copper 20, which provides, in effect, an elongate panel section running up and down the roof structure and exposed to the sunlight.

The exteriorly-disposed flow channel 17 has

open ends 17a and 17b which communicate with the outside atmosphere, the lower open end 17a being disposed under the eaves 11a of the roof, and the open end 17b having its communication with the outside atmosphere by way of a flow channel extension 21 and a flue of a chimney 22.

The interiorly-disposed flow channel has open ends 18a and 18b which communicate with the interior of the building, the lower open end 18a communicating through the ceiling 15 and the upper open end 18b communicating by way of a depending, flow channel extension 23.

A fan 24 is mounted in the flow channel extension 23 for the purpose of forcing circulation of air upwardly therethrough and back downwardly through the main flow channel 18, as illustrated by the appended arrows. Upward circulation of the outside atmosphere through flow channel 17, flow channel extension 21, and the flue of chimney 22 is accomplished by natural draft, and such air is heated by means of the sun's rays caught and transmitted to the flowing air stream by the blackened copper sheet 20.

Disposed at and extending along the face of moisture-pervious, porous wall 19 is a serpentine coil of piping 25, through which cool water is circulated from any suitable source, such as the cold water supply to the building proper.

The interior air to be dehumidified and comfort conditioned is sucked into flow channel extension 23 and is passed downwardly through flow channel 18 by means of the air-circulating fan 24. In passing, it impinges against the cooling coil 25, whereby its fugacity is lowered and any excess moisture which it carries is condensed upon the moisture-pervious, porous wall 19. Thereby relieved of its excess moisture, such circulated air passes back into the interior of the building.

The condensed moisture permeates the moisture-pervious, porous wall 19, passing through the pores thereof to the opposite face, which is constantly scrubbed by the heated outside air passing upwardly through the flow channel 17. As the moisture appears at the said opposite face of the moisture-pervious, porous wall 19, it is taken up and carried away by the flowing stream of outside air. Accordingly, the moisture-pervious, porous wall 19, which is the dehumidifying agency of the combination, is constantly and automatically regenerated. The process is a very simple one, depending entirely upon natural phenomena for performance.

It has been found that a 20° temperature differential between opposite faces of the moisture-pervious, porous wall 19 is the optimum for best results. This can be achieved by regulating the temperature of the cooling medium flowing through the piping 25.

In some instances it is advantageous to provide irregular paths of flow for the air streams, which, as appears from the drawing, are countercurrent. In this way more intimate contact with the moisture-pervious, porous wall can be attained. Thus, as illustrated in Fig. 3, the moisture-pervious, porous wall 30, and the corresponding interior wall 31 of the interiorly-disposed flow channel 32, are correspondingly corrugated transversely of their lengths, and moisture-laden interior air brought to the flow channel 32 by the depending flow channel extension 33 and fan 34 is made to vigorously impinge against the cooling coil 35 and that face of moisture-pervious, porous wall 30 lying within the flow channel 32. Furthermore, a series of baffle plates 36 secured at the inner surface of the exterior wall or panel member 37 of exteriorly-disposed flow channel 38, extends inwardly of such flow channel and into troughs of the moisture-pervious, porous wall 30. These baffle plates serve to force the upwardly-flowing, regenerative air vigorously against the exterior face of moisture-pervious, porous wall 30.

In Fig. 4 is illustrated a somewhat different embodiment of the invention, wherein the dehumidification system is placed within the framework of an exterior wall 40 of the building. The air-flow conduit 41 extends upwardly between spaced studs of the wall framework, and is divided longitudinally by a moisture-pervious, porous wall 42 so as to provide a pair of flow channels 43 and 44. The flow channel 43 has its opposite ends 43a and 43b open to the outside atmosphere through the exterior wall surfacing 45, and the flow channel 44 has its opposite ends 44a and 44b communicating with the interior of the building. As in the foregoing embodiment, a cooling coil 46 is provided at and along the face of the moisture-pervious, porous wall 42 within the flow channel 44, so that the moisture-laden interior air is relieved of its moisture. Also, a fan is provided at the upper open end 44b of the flow channel 44.

While an elongate, exterior panel of blackened copper or other suitable sun-heat concentrating material may be employed in this embodiment, as in the foregoing embodiment, there is here illustrated another manner of heating the outside air flowing through the flow channel 43. An electric heater 47 is disposed at the lower open end 43a of flow channel 43 so as to heat and appreciably dry the exterior air as it enters the flow channel. Any other source of heat, or waste heat, might be utilized for this purpose.

The action of this embodiment of the invention is essentially similar to that of the foregoing embodiments.

While many types of moisture-pervious, porous material may be utilized for the dividing wall in the air-flow conduit of the several embodiments of the invention, is it preferred to employ the material known to the trade as "Microporite," which is fully disclosed in U. S. Patent No. 1,932,971 issued October 31, 1933, to Huttemann et al., entitled "Method of Making Light Weight Block," or the similar specially treated dehydrating material of my U. S. Patent No. 2,005,401, issued September 9, 1941, entitled "Dehydrating Material." These materials in their lightest form give best results. Gypsum, Portland cement and ceramic products having continuous pore systems may also be used.

Obviously suitable cooling means, heating means, and air-circulating means other than those specifically illustrated may be substituted for those shown, and an electric heater or other heating means may be used to supplement the sun-heat panel of the embodiments of Figs. 1 and 3, if desired. *